THE AMATEUR RADIO HANDBOOK

G2MI, Bromley, Kent.

THE AMATEUR RADIO HANDBOOK

THIRD EDITION

RADIO SOCIETY OF GREAT BRITAIN
28 LITTLE RUSSELL STREET, LONDON, W.C.1

Printed in Great Britain for the Radio Society of Great Britain, 28 Little Russell
Street, London, W.C.1, by Loxley Brothers Limited, Letchworth, Hertfordshire

CONTENTS

			Page
	Foreword		7
Chapter 1	FUNDAMENTALS		9
Chapter 2	VALVES		41
Chapter 3	SEMICONDUCTORS		63
Chapter 4	H.F. RECEIVERS		77
Chapter 5	V.H.F./U.H.F. RECEIVERS		121
Chapter 6	H.F. TRANSMITTERS		159
Chapter 7	V.H.F./U.H.F. TRANSMITTERS		210
Chapter 8	KEYING AND BREAK-IN		247
Chapter 9	MODULATION		254
Chapter 10	SINGLE SIDEBAND		293
Chapter 11	FREQUENCY MODULATION		335
Chapter 12	PROPAGATION		342
Chapter 13	H.F. AERIALS		352
Chapter 14	V.H.F. AERIALS		391
Chapter 15	NOISE		408
Chapter 16	MOBILE EQUIPMENT		417
Chapter 17	POWER SUPPLIES		433
Chapter 18	INTERFERENCE..		446
Chapter 19	MEASUREMENTS		461
Chapter 20	OPERATING TECHNIQUE AND STATION LAY-OUT		490
Chapter 21	R.S.G.B. AND THE RADIO AMATEUR ..		496
Chapter 22	GENERAL DATA		500
	Index		535

THE AMATEUR RADIO HANDBOOK
THIRD EDITION

The Radio Society of Great Britain expresses its gratitude to the following who have generously contributed to and advised on the preparation of this edition:

A.E.I. Ltd.
Aerialite Ltd.
W. H. Allen, M.B.E., G2UJ
Avo Ltd.

A. J. Bayliss, B.Sc., G8PD
G. L. Benbow, M.Sc., A.M.I.E.E., G3HB
B.I.C.C. Ltd.
R. S. Biggs, G2FLG
Brimar Ltd.

N. Caws, F.C.A., G3BVG
F. J. H. Charman, B.E.M., G6CJ
B. Christian, B.Sc., Ph.D., G5XD
H. A. M. Clark, B.Sc.(Eng.), M.I.E.E., G6OT
John Clarricoats, O.B.E., G6CL
D. E. Cole
E. S. Cole, C.B., C.B.E., G2EC
D. N. Corfield, D.L.C.(Hons.), A.M.I.E.E., G5CD

Daystrom Ltd.
D. Deacon, G3BCM
Denco (Clacton) Ltd.

C. H. L. Edwards, A.M.I.E.E., A.M.Brit.I.R.E., G8TL
Electronic Tubes Ltd.
K. E. S. Ellis, G5KW

D. A. Findlay, D.F.C., G3BZG
N. A. S. Fitch, G3FPK
G. C. Fox, A.M.I.E.E., G3AEX
D. W. Furby, G3EOH

The General Electric Co. Ltd.
G. G. Gibbs, G3AAZ
W. E. Green, G3FBA

M. Harrington, B.R.S.20249
D. E. A. Harvey, Grad.I.E.E.
J. P. Hawker, G3VA
D. W. Heightman, M.Brit.I.R.E., G6DH
R. C. Hills, B.Sc.(Eng.), A.M.Brit.I.R.E., G3HRH
H. M. Humphreys, GI3EVU

N. G. Hyde, A.M.Brit.I.R.E., G2AIH
E. G. Ingram, GM6IZ
Jason Electronic Designs Ltd.
J-Beam Aerials Ltd.
G. R. Jessop, A.M.Brit.I.R.E., Assoc.I.E.E., G6JP
J. H. Jowett, ex-G3CFR
F. C. Judd, A.Inst.E., G2BCX

J. Douglas Kay, Assoc.Brit.I.R.E., G3AAE
S. Kharbanda, G2PU

J. W. Mathews, G6LL
A. O. Milne, G2MI
L. A. Moxon, B.Sc., A.C.G.I., A.M.I.E.E., G6XN
M-O Valve Co. Ltd.
Mullard Ltd.
A. L. Mynett, B.Sc., G3HBW

National Physical Laboratory
Newmarket Transistors Ltd.
L. E. Newnham, B.Sc., G6NZ
R. D. Nicol, G3ENQ

S. N. Radcliffe, M.A., G3GZB
R.C.A. Great Britain Ltd.

R. G. Shears, B.E.M., A.Brit.I.R.E., G8KW
H. F. Smith, G2DD
R. L. Smith-Rose, C.B.E., D.Sc., Ph.D., F.C.G.I., M.I.E.E.
Standard Telephones and Cables Ltd.
R. F. Stevens, G2BVN
G. M. C. Stone, A.M.I.E.E., A.M.Brit.I.R.E., G3FZL
B. Sykes, G2HCG

Taylor Electrical Instruments Ltd.
D. E. Tomkinson, G3IIE

G. A. C. Wakeling
J. N. Walker, G5JU
H. W. Whalley, M.Sc., G2HW
Woden Transformer Co. Ltd.

E. W. Yeomanson, G3IIR

Acknowledgment is also made to the numerous authors of articles in the R.S.G.B. Bulletin and other journals and of technical books to which reference has been made in the preparation of this edition. The Editor also expresses his thanks to the members of the Council of the R.S.G.B. and to his assistant, Mrs. J. M. Atkinson, of the Headquarters staff.

Editor: JOHN A. ROUSE, G2AHL

FOREWORD

By R. L. SMITH-ROSE, C.B.E., D.Sc., Ph.D., F.C.G.I., M.I.E.E.

President International Scientific Radio Union, Past President Radio Society of Great Britain.

IN the twenty odd years since the previous (1939) edition of this *Handbook* was published, the technique and applications of radio have undergone a major revolution. During the Second World War outstanding advances were made in military applications; and these have had their effect in the civil field since 1945. The impact of these developments on the Amateur Radio world have been the consequence of two major factors. In the first place, many pre-war or older radio amateurs were given a great opportunity of applying the special knowledge and ability they had acquired in the pursuit of their hobby to the benefit of their country in a national emergency. Secondly, radio amateurs obtained a great bonus from the large quantity of surplus military equipment that has come on the market since the cessation of hostilities. Many amateurs returned to their normal civilian professions and activities with a greatly enhanced technical appreciation of their hobby and with experience of varied and complicated apparatus which would have been far beyond their means in normal circumstances.

But first let us look back at the previous edition of this *Handbook* which was published in 1938, and sold to the extent of some 8,000 copies in the first year. Following the outbreak of hostilities in 1939, a tremendous demand arose for assistance in the technical training of recruits to both the communication and radar fields of the armed forces. In this country the most suitable textbook for the use of these recruits was found to be the Society's *Amateur Radio Handbook*, of which a second edition was published in July 1940; in the course of twelve successive printings over 185,000 copies were sold up to 1946.

From a technical standpoint, however, that edition has long since been out-of-date. For example, radar as a technique of the use of radio waves for detecting distant objects was a close military secret in 1938; while today it has widespread applications to all forms of navigation at sea and in the air, and for surveying on land. The knowledge and use of radio waves shorter than about 10 metres was in a very elementary stage: while today, hundreds of millions of people receive their television programmes by much shorter waves; and for special purposes, wavelengths of a few centimetres are in common use, even by amateurs, in this rapidly advancing field.

As will be seen from the list of contents, this new work deals with the whole technical aspects of the power supply and generation of the high frequency electrical oscillations necessary for the transmission of radio waves over a wide range of frequencies. The various types of aerial system suitable for amateur use at different frequencies are treated in some detail, and the methods of modulation and keying transmitters are described.

To enable the amateur to make the best use of the power at his disposal, an understanding is necessary of the manner in which the radio waves are transmitted over the surface of the earth and through its upper and lower atmosphere. Accordingly, a useful chapter has been provided summarizing the great increase in our knowledge of this subject which has taken place in the past quarter of a century.

But by far the largest proportion of amateurs engaged in this hobby are interested in receiving technique; and they find absorbing interest in recording the successful reception of signals from amateur—and perhaps other—transmitters all over the world. It is natural, therefore, to find suitable technical advice, with constructional details, on receivers designed specifically for the various bands of frequencies set aside by international agreement for the use of amateurs.

FOREWORD

One of the important features of radio work, whether on an amateur or professional basis, is the great opportunities it provides for international associations. The ability to make friends in other countries and to co-operate with them in the pursuit of a common hobby, goes a long way to obtaining an understanding of the problems of other nations: such understanding is a great factor in continuing and extending the peace of the world. A recent instance of international co-operation in which amateurs were able to play a part with the professional scientists, is that of the International Geophysical Year of 1957-58, and the follow-on Year of International Co-operation, 1959. During the first of these periods, observers in 66 countries participated in a joint programme carried out at over 1,000 observatories on the physical properties of the earth and its atmosphere, and on the related solar and terrestrial phenomena. This type of research is now being extended to the space surrounding us with the aid of artificial earth satellites; and in a large proportion of this work, radio and electronics techniques are necessary for making many of the observations, and particularly for communicating to the observers on the earth, the results of observations obtained far out in space.

Radio amateurs have their own international body—the International Amateur Radio Union—for joint discussion and co-operation in their experiments. This body is recognised as a participating observer at the more formal meetings of the International Telecommunication Union, on which falls the task of allotting frequencies throughout the radio spectrum, and of determining the conditions of their use on a world-wide basis.

There are many fortunate amateurs who have found that the knowledge and experience in radio matters which they gained in their early life has stood them in good stead in pursuing a professional career in science or engineering. It can be said with confidence that the field for further advancement is just as wide open now as it was in 1938; and none of our younger members engaged in radio work as a hobby need fear that he will not find it of absorbing interest for another generation. Just as for centuries past, the amateur astronomer has been able to contribute to our knowledge of the universe, so will the radio amateur play a part in the continued advances of radio communications and measurements, the possibilities and limitations of which can scarcely be foreseen at the present time.

The Amateur Radio enthusiast has chosen a lively and satisfying hobby; and he will find this *Handbook* an indispensable guide in pursuing whatever field of study and experiment he finds of the greatest interest.

R. L. SMITH-ROSE

CHAPTER I

FUNDAMENTALS

A KNOWLEDGE of the fundamental physical principles underlying radio communication is just as important to the amateur as to the professional radio engineer. It forms the starting point of all design work and is essential for proper maintenance and successful operating.

In the limited space available here it is not possible to discuss these basic principles in great detail, but a number of references are included in the bibliography at the end of the chapter as a guide to those readers who would like to make a further study of any particular part of the subject. Most public libraries will be only too glad to obtain the books listed if they are not already on their shelves.

The pattern of headings follows the syllabus of the Radio Amateurs' Examination very closely, and it is hoped that newcomers will find this chapter a useful introduction to Amateur Radio. More experienced readers may find it useful as a refresher course.

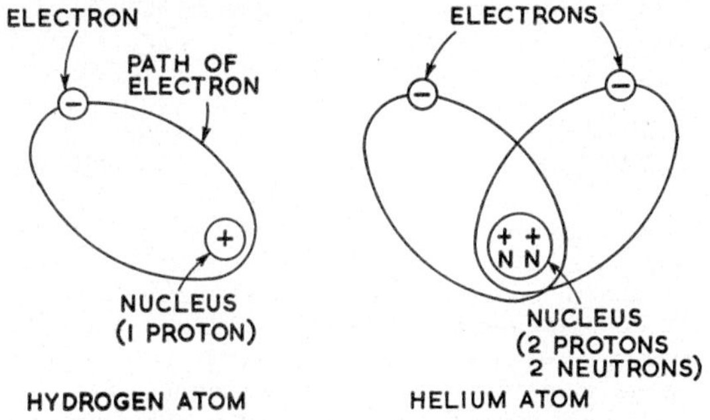

Fig. I. Structure of hydrogen and helium atoms.

ATOMS AND ELECTRONS

All matter is composed of molecules, which is the name given to the smallest part of a substance which can exist and still display the physical and chemical properties of that substance. There are a very great number of different sorts of molecules. Further study of a molecule discloses that it is made up of smaller particles called atoms and it has been found that there are about 102 different types of atoms. All molecules are made up of combinations of atoms selected from this range. Examples of different atoms are hydrogen, oxygen, iron, copper and sulphur, and examples of how atoms are combined to form molecules are (a) two atoms of hydrogen and one of oxygen to form one molecule of water, and (b) two atoms of hydrogen, one of sulphur and four of oxygen to form one molecule of sulphuric acid.

Atoms are so small that they cannot be seen even under the most powerful microscopes. Their behaviour, however, can be studied and from this it has been discovered that atoms are made up of a positively charged relatively heavy core or *nucleus* around which are moving a number of much lighter particles each negatively charged, called *electrons*.

Atoms are normally electrically neutral; that is to say, the amount of positive electricity associated with the nucleus is exactly balanced by the total amount of negative electricity associated with the electrons. One type of atom differs from another in the number of positive and neutral particles (called *protons* and *neutrons*) which make up the nucleus and the number and arrangement of the orbital electrons which are continually moving around the nucleus.

Large atoms, such as those of uranium, are complex, but small atoms, such as those of hydrogen and helium, are relatively simple, as can be seen in **Fig. 1.**

The important fact which emerges from the preceding paragraphs is that all matter is made up of positively and negatively charged particles, which means that electricity is latent in everything around us.

CONDUCTORS AND INSULATORS

The ease with which the electrons in a substance can be detached from their parent atoms varies from substance to substance. In some substances there is a continual movement of electrons in a random manner from one atom to another, and the application of an electrical pressure or voltage (for example from a battery) to the two ends of a piece of wire made of such a substance will cause a drift of electrons along the wire called an *electric current*; electrical conduction is then said to take place. It should be noted that if an electron enters the wire from the battery at one end it will be a different electron which immediately leaves the other end of the wire. By arbitrary convention, the direction of current flow is said to be from positive to negative.

Materials which exhibit this property of electrical conduction are called *conductors*. All metals belong to this

Conductors	Insulators
Silver	Mica
Copper	Quartz
Aluminium	Glass
Brass	Ceramics
Steel	Ebonite
Mercury	Plastics
Carbon	Air
Certain liquids	Oil

class. Materials which do not conduct electricity are called *insulators*, and the table shown above gives a few examples of commonly used conductors and insulators.

SOURCES OF ELECTRICITY

When two dissimilar metals are immersed in certain chemical solutions, or *electrolytes*, an electromotive force (e.m.f.) is created by chemical action within the cell so that if the pieces of metal are joined externally to the cell there will be a continuous flow of electric current. Such a device is called a *simple cell* and such a cell comprising copper and zinc rods immersed in diluted sulphuric acid is shown in **Fig. 2 (A)**. The flow of current is from the copper to the zinc plate in the external circuit; i.e. the copper forms the positive (+) terminal of the cell and the zinc forms the negative (−) terminal.

In a simple cell of this type hydrogen forms on the copper electrode, and this gas film has the effect of increasing the internal resistance of the cell and also setting up within the cell a counter or polarizing e.m.f. which rapidly reduces the effective e.m.f. of the cell as a whole. This polarization effect is overcome in practical cells by the introduction of chemical agents surrounding the anode for the purpose of removing the hydrogen by oxidation as soon as it is formed. Such agents are called *depolarizers*.

Primary Cells. Practical cells in which electricity is produced in this way by direct chemical action are called *primary cells*, of which the commonest type is the dry cell, the construction of which is shown diagrammatically in **Fig. 2 (B)**. The zinc case is the negative electrode and a carbon rod is the positive electrode. The black paste surrounding the carbon rod may contain powdered carbon, manganese oxide, zinc chloride, sal-ammoniac and water, the manganese oxide acting as depolarizer by combining with hydrogen formed at the anode to produce another form of manganese oxide and water. The remainder of the cell is filled with a white paste which may contain plaster of Paris, flour, zinc chloride, sal-ammoniac and water. The cell is sealed with pitch except for a small vent which allows accumulated gas to escape. The e.m.f. developed by a single dry cell is about 1·5 volts and cells may be connected in series (positive terminal to negative terminal and so on) until a battery of cells, usually referred to simply as a *battery*, of the desired voltage is obtained. The symbol used to denote a cell in a circuit diagram is shown in **Fig. 2 (C)**. The long thin stroke represents the positive terminal and the short thick stroke the negative terminal. Several cells joined in series to form a battery are shown; for higher voltages it becomes impracticable to draw all the individual cells involved and it is sufficient to indicate merely the first and last cells with a dotted line between them with perhaps a note added to state the actual voltage. The amount of current which can be derived from a cell depends on its size and the life required and may range from a few milliamperes to an ampere or two.

Secondary Cells. In primary cells some of the various chemicals are used up in producing the electrical energy—a relatively expensive and wasteful process. The maximum current available also is limited. Another type of cell, called a *secondary cell, storage cell* or *accumulator*, offers the advantage of being able to provide a higher current and is capable of being charged by feeding electrical energy into the cell to be stored chemically, and be drawn out or discharged later as electrical energy again. This process of filling and emptying the cell is capable of repetition indefinitely.

The most common type of secondary cell is the lead-acid cell such as that used in motor-car batteries. It consists of two sets of specially prepared lead plates immersed in a solution of sulphuric acid and water. Briefly the action of the cell is as follows: in the discharged state the active material on each plate is lead sulphate. During the charging process the lead sulphate in the positive plate is changed to lead peroxide and sulphuric acid, and the lead sulphate in the negative plate to a form of lead called spongy lead and sulphuric acid. During discharge the reverse action takes place and lead sulphate forms again on both plates. The state of the charge of the cell may be checked by measuring the specific gravity of the electrolyte with a hydrometer since the concentration of sulphuric acid increases during charging and decreases again as the cell is discharged. Typical values of specific gravity are 1·250 for a fully charged cell and 1·175 for a discharged cell. The terminal voltage of a single lead-acid cell when fully charged and left standing is about 2·05 volts. In the discharged condition the voltage falls to about 1·85 volts.

To obtain a long life cells should not be overcharged since this causes flaking and buckling of the plates. Cells should not be left in a discharged state because the lead sulphate may undergo a physical change which it is difficult to break down in the re-charging process and the capacity of the cell will be impaired; cells in this condition are said to be "sulphated," a condition which may sometimes be partially eradicated by prolonged charging at a low current.

Mechanical Generators. Mechanical energy may be converted into electrical energy by moving a coil of wire in a magnetic field. Direct-current or alternating-current generators are available in all sizes but the commonest types likely to be met in amateur radio work are (i) a.c. petrol-driven generators of up to 1 or 2 kW output such as are used for supplying portable equipment and (ii) small motor generators, sometimes called *dynamotors*, which furnish up to about 100 watts of power and comprise a combined low-voltage d.c. electric motor and a d.c. generator

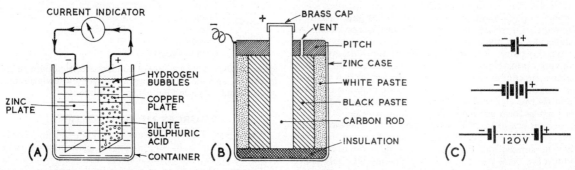

Fig. 2. The electric cell. A number of cells connected in series is called a battery. (a) A simple electric cell consisting of copper and zinc electrodes immersed in dilute sulphuric acid. (b) Sectional drawing showing construction of a dry cell. (c) Symbols used to represent single cells and batteries in circuit diagrams.

so that a high-tension supply may be derived from a 6- or 12-volt car battery.

ELECTRICAL UNITS

(i) Unit of Quantity. Since all electrons, whatever kind of atom they belong to, carry the same charge, the amount of electricity associated with the electron could be used as the unit of quantity of electricity. It is, however, too small for use as a practical unit, and a more convenient unit is called the *coulomb*; this is equivalent to the charge on approximately 6×10^{18} (six million million million) electrons. The analogy here between the molecule of water as a unit of quantity of water and the practical unit, the gallon, is obvious.

A quantity of electricity or number of coulombs is usually denoted by the symbol q.

(ii) Unit of Current Flow. Continuing with the water analogy, whereas a flow of water is spoken of as " x gallons per second " the flow of electricity can be expressed as " x coulombs per second." A current of one coulomb per second is called an *ampere* (abbreviated to *amp.*) and the strength of a current is said to be " x amperes." A current flow is usually denoted by the symbol I. The currents used in radio are

TABLE I

Units and Symbols

Quantity	Symbol used in formulæ	Unit	Abbreviation
Quantity	q	Coulomb	–
Current	I	Ampere	A
Voltage	E or V	Volt	V
Time	t	Second	s
Resistance	R	Ohm	Ω
Capacitance	C	Farad	F
Inductance	L	Henry	H
Mutual Inductance	M	Henry	H
Power	W	Watt	W
Frequency	f	Cycles/second	c/s
Wavelength	λ	Centimetre	cm

The following multiples and sub-multiples of the above units are commonly used:

Microampere	(μA)	=	1 millionth of an ampere
Millampere	(mA)	=	1 thousandth of an ampere
Microvolt	(μV)	=	1 millionth of a volt
Millivolt	(mV)	=	1 thousandth of a volt
Kilovolt	(kV)	=	1,000 volts
Microfarad	(μF)	=	1 millionth of a farad
Micro-microfarad	$(\mu\mu F)$	=	1 million-millionth of a farad
Picofarad	(pF)	=	1 million-millionth of a farad
Microsecond	(μS)	=	1 millionth of a second
Millisecond	(mS)	=	1 thousandth of a second
Megacycle/second	(Mc/s)	=	1,000,000 cycles per second
Kilocycle/second	(kc/s)	=	1000 cycles per second
Microwatt	(μW)	=	1 millionth of a watt
Kilowatt	(kW)	=	1000 watts
Metre	(m)	=	100 centimetres
Kilometre	(km)	=	1000 metres

often very small fractions of an ampere and for convenience the two smaller units *milliampere* (meaning a thousandth of an ampere) and *microampere* (meaning a millionth of an ampere) are used. Thus a current of 0·003 ampere is written as 3 milliamperes. See Table 1 for abbreviations.

The relation between the total quantity of electricity (q) which has passed a point in a wire, the time of flow (t) and the rate of flow (I) is therefore—

$$Quantity \text{ (coulombs)} = Current\ Flow \text{ (amperes)} \times Time \text{ (seconds)}$$

or in symbols—

$$q = I \times t.$$

(iii) Unit of Electric Pressure. In order to make electricity flow continuously through a circuit it is necessary to have some device which can produce a continuous supply of electrons. This may be a battery in which the supply of electrons is produced by chemical action or a dynamo or generator in which mechanical energy is turned into electrical energy. The battery or generator produces an electrical pressure sometimes called an electromotive force or e.m.f. which may be used to force a current through a circuit. The unit of electrical pressure is the *volt*, and voltages are usually denoted in formulae by the symbol E or V.

(iv) Unit of Electrical Resistance. The ease with which an electric current will flow, or can be conducted, through a wire will depend on the dimensions of the wire and the material from which it is made. The opposition of a circuit to the flow of current is called the *resistance* of the circuit and is usually denoted by the symbol R in formulae. The resistance of a circuit is measured in *ohms*, and a circuit is said to have a resistance of 1 ohm if the voltage between its ends is 1 volt when the current flowing is 1 amp. For convenience, because the resistances used in radio equipment may be up to 10 million ohms two larger units called the *kilohm* (meaning 1000 ohms) and the *Megohm* (meaning 1 million ohms) are used. Thus 47,000 ohms may be spoken of as 47 kilohms. See Table 1 for abbreviations.

RESISTANCE AND CONDUCTANCE

Different materials may be compared as conductors by measuring the resistance of samples of the materials of the same size and shape. The resistance (in ohms) of conducting material of one centimetre in length and one square centimetre in cross-sectional area is called the *specific resistance* or *resistivity* of the material. Specific resistance is quoted as x ohms per centimetre cube or more simply as x ohm-cm. If the specific resistance of a material is known, the actual resistance of, say, a piece of wire made from that material can be calculated since the resistance of a wire increases proportionally with its length and inversely with its cross-sectional area.

If the length of a wire is l cm, its cross-sectional area a sq. cm, and its specific resistance S ohm-cm, its actual resistance will be given by the formula—

$$R = \frac{S \times l}{a} \text{ ohms}$$

Approximate specific resistances of typical materials used in radio equipment are given in Table 2. At radio frequencies the resistance of a wire may be very much greater than its direct-current value because radio-frequency currents only travel along the surface shell of the wire and not through the whole body as in the case of direct current. This is called the skin effect and is important in making high-quality radio coils.

Sometimes instead of speaking of the resistance of a circuit the *conductance* of the circuit is referred to: this is simply

TABLE 2
Specific Resistance of Commonly Used Conductors

Silver	$1\cdot6 \times 10^{-6}$ ohm-cm.
Copper	$1\cdot7 \times 10^{-6}$
Aluminium	3×10^{-6}
Brass	7×10^{-6}
Iron	12×10^{-6}
Special high-resistance alloys:	
Manganin	48×10^{-6}
Eureka	49×10^{-6}
Nichrome	108×10^{-6}

the reciprocal of the resistance. The unit of conductance is the *mho*, and conductance is usually denoted in formulae by the symbol G.

The relation between resistance and conductance is therefore—

$$G = \frac{1}{R} \quad \text{or conversely—} \quad R = \frac{1}{G}$$

Thus a resistance of 10 ohms has a conductance of 0.1 mho.

Ohm's Law

Ohm's Law states that the ratio of the voltage applied across a resistance to the current flowing through that resistance is constant. This ratio is equal to the value of the resistance.

Writing this as a formula—

$$\frac{Voltage}{Current} = a\ constant = Resistance$$

or in symbols—

$$\frac{E}{I} = R$$

Note that if E is in volts and I in amperes, then R is in ohms.

It will be seen that this formula relates current, voltage and resistance, so that if two of these quantities are known the third may be calculated by suitably rearranging the formula in the following ways:

$$E = I \times R \text{ (giving } E \text{, knowing } I \text{ and } R) \quad \ldots \text{ (i)}$$

$$I = \frac{E}{R} \text{ (giving } I \text{, knowing } E \text{ and } R) \quad \ldots \text{ (ii)}$$

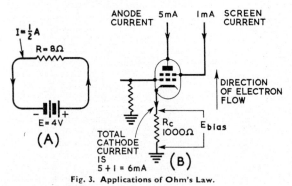

Fig. 3. Applications of Ohm's Law.

$$R = \frac{E}{I} \text{ (giving } R \text{, knowing } E \text{ and } I) \quad \ldots \text{ (iii)}$$

The application of Ohm's Law is illustrated by the following examples.

Example I. *Consider the circuit shown in* **Fig. 3 (A)** *which consists of a battery E of voltage 4 volts and a resistance R of 8 ohms. What is the magnitude of the current in the circuit?*

Here E = 4 volts and R = 8 ohms. Let I be the current flowing in amperes. Then from Ohm's Law (Formula ii)—

$$I = \frac{E}{R} \text{ amperes} = \frac{4}{8} \text{ amperes} = \frac{1}{2} \text{ ampere}$$

It should be noted that in all calculations based on Ohm's Law care must be taken to ensure that I, E and R are in amperes, volts and ohms respectively if errors in the result are to be avoided.

Example II (from a *Radio Amateurs' Examination* paper). *What is the standing bias voltage produced by a cathode bias resistor of 1000 ohms when the characteristics of the valve are such that the anode current is 5 mA and the screen-grid current is 1 mA?*

The circuit is shown in **Fig. 3 (B)** in which the total cathode current is the sum of the anode and screen-grid currents. The cathode current flowing through the cathode resistor will cause a voltage to appear across its terminals which is the required standing bias voltage.

Let E_{bias} = standing bias voltage in volts.

I_c = total cathode current in amperes,

R_c = resistance of the cathode resistor in ohms.

Then from Ohm's Law—

$$E_{bias} = I_c \times R_c \text{ volts}$$

Here I_c = (5 + 1) = 6 milliamperes = 0·006 ampere.

R_c = 1000 ohms.

Substituting in the formula—

$$E_{bias} = 0\cdot006 \times 1000 \text{ volts} = 6 \text{ volts}$$

Electrical Power

When a current of electricity flows through a resistance, e.g. in an electric fire, the resistance gets hot and electrical energy is turned into heat. The actual rise in temperature depends on the amount of power dissipated in the resistance and the shape and size of the resistance. Sometimes the power dissipated is so small that the temperature rise is not very noticeable, but nevertheless whenever an electric current flows through a resistance power is dissipated therein. The unit of electrical power is the *watt*, usually denoted in formulae by the symbol W. The amount of electrical power dissipated in a resistance is equal to the product of the voltage across the resistance and the current flowing through the resistance. Thus—

Power (watts) = *Voltage* (volts) × *Current* (amperes)

or in symbols—

$$W = E \times I \quad \ldots \text{ (i)}$$

Since from Ohm's Law—

$$E = I \times R \text{ and } I = E/R$$

the formula for the power dissipated in a resistance may also be written in two further forms:

$$W = E^2/R \quad \ldots \text{ (ii)}$$

$$W = I^2 \times R \quad \ldots \text{ (iii)}$$

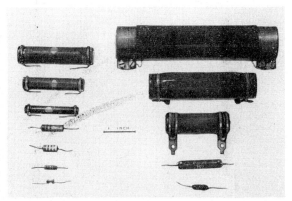

Fig. 4. Typical resistances used in radio equipment. The specimens shown on the left are carbon resistors and those on the right are wire-wound.

These formulae are useful for finding, for example, the power input to a transmitter or the power dissipated in various resistances in an amplifier so that suitably rated resistances can be selected. To take a practical case, consider again the circuit of Fig. 3 (A). The power dissipated in the resistance may be calculated as follows:

Here $E = 4$ volts and $R = 8$ ohms. Let W be the power in watts. Then—

$$W = \frac{E^2}{R} = \frac{4 \times 4}{8} = 2 \text{ watts.}$$

It must be stressed again that the beginner should always see that all values are expressed in terms of volts, amperes and ohms in this type of calculation. Careless use of Megohms or milliamperes, for example, may lead to an answer several orders too large or too small.

Resistances Used in Radio Equipment

As already mentioned, a resistance through which a current is flowing may get hot. It follows therefore that in a piece of radio equipment the resistors of various types and sizes that are needed must be capable of dissipating the power as required without overheating.

Generally speaking, radio resistances (or *resistors* as they are usually called) can be divided roughly into two classes, (a) low power up to 3 watts and (b) above 3 watts. The low-power resistors are usually made of carbon and may be obtained in a wide range of resistance values from about 10 ohms to 10 Megohms and in power ratings of $\frac{1}{10}$ watt to 3 watts. Typical carbon resistors are shown above in Fig. 4. For higher powers, resistors are usually wire-wound on ceramic formers and the very fine wire is protected by a vitreous enamel coating. Typical wire-wound resistors are shown on the right.

Resistances, particularly the small carbon types, are

TABLE 3
The Resistor Colour Code

0 black	5 green	Tolerance colours:
1 brown	6 blue	± 5 per cent .. gold
2 red	7 violet	±10 per cent .. silver
3 orange	8 grey	±20 per cent .. no colour
4 yellow	9 white	

usually colour-coded to indicate the value of the resistance in ohms and sometimes also the tolerance or accuracy of the resistance. The standard colour code is shown in Table 3.

The colours are applied either as *bands* at one end of the resistor as shown in **Fig. 5 (A)**, or as *body*, *tip* and *dot* colours as shown in **Fig. 5 (B)**. As an example, what would be the value of a resistor with the following markings?

(A) COLOUR BANDS—*yellow*   (B) BODY—*blue*
          violet   TIP—*grey*
          orange   DOT—*red*
          silver   (*No tolerance colour on other tip.*)

TYPE A. The yellow first band signifies that the first figure is 4, the violet second band signifies that the second figure is 7, while the orange third band signifies that there are 3 zeros to follow: the silver fourth band indicates a tolerance of ± 10 per cent. The value of the resistor is therefore 47,000 ohms ± 10 per cent.

TYPE B. The blue body gives the first figure as 6, the grey tip gives the second figure as 8, while the red dot signifies that there are 2 zeros to follow: in the absence of any colour on the other tip the tolerance must be taken as ± 20 per cent. The value of the resistor is therefore 6,800 ohms ± 20 per cent.

So far only fixed resistors have been mentioned. Variable

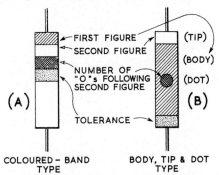

Fig. 5. Standard resistance value markings.

resistors, sometimes called *potentiometers* or *volume controls*, are also used. These are usually panel-mounted by means of a threaded bush through which a $\frac{1}{4}$-in. diameter spindle protrudes and to which the control knob is fitted. Low-power high-value variable resistances use a carbon resistance element and high-power lower resistance types (up to 100,000 ohms) use a wire-wound element.

Resistances in Series and Parallel

Resistances may be joined in series or parallel to obtain some special desired value of resistance. When in series, resistors are connected as shown in **Fig. 6 (A)** and the total resistance of the resistors is equal to the sum of the separate resistances. The parallel connection is shown in **Fig. 6 (B)**, and with this arrangement the reciprocal of the total resistance is equal to the sum of the reciprocals of the separate resistances.

If R is the total resistance, these formulae can be written as follows:

SERIES CONNECTION   PARALLEL CONNECTION

$$R = R_1 + R_2 + R_3 + \text{etc.} \qquad \frac{1}{R} = \frac{1}{R_1} + \frac{1}{R_2} + \frac{1}{R_3} + \text{etc.}$$

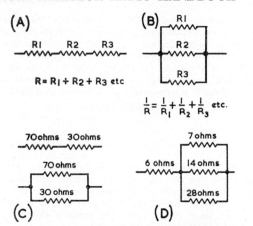

Fig. 6. Resistors in various combinations: (A) series, (B) parallel, (C) (D) series-parallel. The calculation of the resultant resistances in (C) and (D) is explained in the text.

Considering the case of only *two* resistors in parallel—

$$\frac{1}{R} = \frac{1}{R_1} + \frac{1}{R_2} = \frac{R_1 + R_2}{R_1 R_2}$$

which by inverting gives—

$$R = \frac{R_1 R_2}{R_1 + R_2}$$

This is a useful formula, since with it the value of two resistors in parallel can easily be calculated without the use of reciprocals.

To illustrate these rules two examples are given below.

Example I. *Calculate the resistance of 30-ohm and a 70-ohm resistance connected first in series and then in parallel.*

In series connection—

$$R = 30 + 70 = 100 \text{ ohms}$$

In parallel connection, using the special formula for two resistors in parallel—

$$R = \frac{R_1 R_2}{R_1 + R_2}$$

$$= \frac{30 \times 70}{30 + 70} = 21 \text{ ohms}$$

These two calculations are illustrated in **Fig. 6 (C)**.

Example II. *Three resistances of 7, 14 and 28 ohms are connected in parallel. If another resistance of 6 ohms is connected in series with this combination what is the total resistance of the circuit?*

The circuit is shown in **Fig. 6 (D)**. Taking the three resistors in parallel first, these are equivalent to a single resistance of R ohms given by—

$$\frac{1}{R} = \frac{1}{7} + \frac{1}{14} + \frac{1}{28} = \frac{4 + 2 + 1}{28} = \frac{1}{4}$$

Therefore—

$$R = 4 \text{ ohms}$$

This in series with the 6-ohm resistor gives a total resistance of 10 ohms for the whole circuit.

CONDENSERS AND CAPACITANCE

Condensers (or capacitors) have the property of being able to store a charge of electricity. They consist essentially of two conducting plates or strips separated by an insulating medium called a *dielectric*. When a condenser is charged there is a voltage difference between its plates, and the larger the plates and/or the smaller their separation the greater will be the charge that the condenser holds for any given voltage across its plates.

The unit of capacity (or *capacitance*) is called the *farad* and is the capacity of a condenser which holds a charge of one coulomb when the voltage across its plates is one volt. A farad is too large a unit for practical purposes and condensers are usually measured in *microfarads* (μF, one millionth of a farad) and in micro-microfarads ($\mu\mu$F) or *picofarads* (pF, one million-millionth of a farad).

The capacity of a condenser depends on the area of its plates and on the distance by which they are separated and the material between them. When the space between the plates of a condenser is occupied by some other insulating medium than air the capacity of the condenser is increased, the area and spacing being assumed the same in both cases. The factor by which the dielectric increases the capacity compared with air is called the *dielectric constant* of the material. This factor is sometimes called the *permittivity* of the material and denoted by the symbol K. Typical values of K are—air 1, paper 2·5, glass 5, mica 7. Certain ceramics have much higher values of K. If the dielectric is a vacuum, as in the case of the inter-electrode capacity in a valve the same value of K as for air may be assumed. The voltage at which a condenser breaks down depends on the spacing between the plates and type of dielectric used. Condensers are often labelled with the maximum working voltage which they are designed to withstand and this figure should not be exceeded.

Fig. 7 shows an elementary condenser made of two parallel metal plates of area A sq. cm separated by a distance d cm. If the plates are of unequal area, only the smaller one

Fig. 7. Parallel-plate condenser. The capacitance is proportional to the area A and inversely proportional to the spacing d.

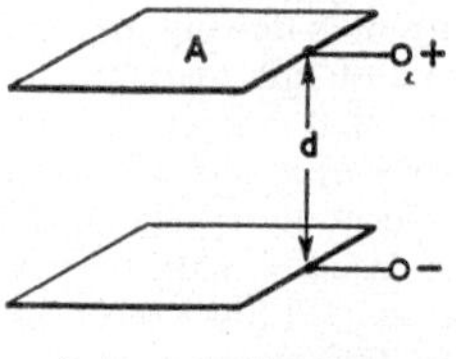

should be taken into account since it is actually the cross-sectional area of the active dielectric which determines the capacity. If the dielectric constant of the material between the plates is K, the capacity of the condenser will be—

$$C = \frac{0 \cdot 0885 \, KA}{d} \text{ pF}$$

where A is in square centimetres and d is in centimetres. If A is in square inches and d is in inches the formula becomes—

$$C = \frac{0 \cdot 224 \, KA}{d} \text{ pF}$$

As an example, suppose two metal plates each 1 square inch in area are spaced 0·004 inch apart in air, the capacity would be—

$$C = \frac{0 \cdot 224 \times 1 \times 1}{0 \cdot 004} \text{ pF} = 56 \text{ pF}$$

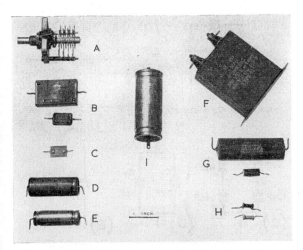

Fig. 8. Typical capacitors used in radio equipment.

A — Air-dielectric variable.   E — Metal-cased tubular paper.
B — Mica.   F — Canned paper.
C — Silvered mica.   G — Tubular metallized paper.
D — Tubular paper.   H— Ceramic
I — Electrolytic.

If mica (for which the value of K is 7) had been used as a dielectric the capacity would be—

$$C = \frac{0 \cdot 224 \times 7 \times 1}{0 \cdot 004} = 392 \text{ pF}.$$

Capacitors used in Radio Equipment

The values of capacitors used in radio equipment extend from about 1 pF to 1000 μF. They are designed for various working voltages and are of many different types of construction. The important varieties are described below.

(i) Air-dielectric Condensers (Capacity range 5–1000 pF max.).

Air-dielectric condensers are usually of the variable type such as are used for tuning transmitters and receivers. High-voltage types for transmitters have relatively large spacings between the plates and the construction of a typical small air-spaced variable condenser is shown at A in **Fig. 8**.

(ii) Mica Condensers (Capacity range 5-10,000 pF).

Stacked-foil type. These are made from alternate thin metal plates and sheets of mica, stacked one above the other, clamped, and usually moulded in Bakelite as shown at B in Fig. 8. They are commonly used as bypass condensers in radio-frequency circuits.

Silvered-mica type. These are made by spraying a coat of silver on each side of a sheet of mica to form the electrodes or plates. Silvered-mica condensers are highly stable in value and are used in r.f. equipment where high frequency stability is required, e.g. in oscillators: an example is shown at C in Fig. 8.

(iii) Paper Condensers (Capacity range 0·001–10 μF).

Paper condensers, shown at D, E and F in Fig. 8, are made from long strips of thin aluminium foil and paper which are wound into a tight roll and then either moulded in Bakelite or sealed in cardboard or metal tubes, or for the larger sizes in rectangular metal cans. Another type of paper capacitor uses metallized paper electrodes in which the foils are replaced by metal sprayed on each side of a strip

of paper. This type is smaller than the foil type for a given capacity and working voltage: see G in Fig. 8.

(iv) Ceramic Condensers (Capacity range 1 pF–0·01 μF).

Ceramic condensers are made by coating two sides of a ceramic disc, tube, or cup, with silver. Ceramic materials having a high dielectric constant are available so that relatively high capacities can be obtained for a small physical size. They are used, for example, as bypass condensers in very high frequency equipment, where small size and low inherent inductance are necessary. They should not be used in oscillators, however, as they usually vary considerably in capacity with temperature changes, the change being positive or negative depending on the type of ceramic material used. Ceramic capacitors are shown at H in Fig. 8.

(v) Electrolytic Condensers (Capacity range 2–2000 μF).

Electrolytic capacitors are made of aluminium-foil plates and have a semi-liquid conducting compound, often in the form of a special impregnated paper, between them. The dielectric is a thin insulating layer which is formed by electro-chemical action on one of the foils when a d.c. polarizing voltage is applied to the condenser. This film is so thin that it is possible to make large-capacity electrolytic capacitors of small physical size. There is an upper limit to the working voltage of electrolytic condensers of about 700 volts and there is also some leakage of current between the plates inside the condenser. An electrolytic condenser is shown at I in Fig. 8. Electrolytic condensers are generally used for smoothing the voltage ripple in power supply units, and also for decoupling purposes. In d.c. circuits the correct polarity of electrolytic condensers must be observed, or permanent damage will result: the condenser may even explode. The maximum working voltage must not be exceeded or similar results may ensue.

(vi) Feed-through Condensers

There is always a small amount of inductance associated with a condenser, partly in the connecting leads and partly in the condenser itself. At very high frequencies (above about 30 Mc/s) it is often difficult to obtain an effective low-reactance path to earth through a bypass condenser because of this stray inductance. Feed-through condensers are

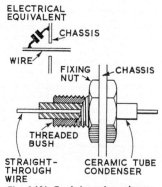

Fig. 9 (A). Feed-through condenser.

specially designed to overcome this difficulty. They consist of a ceramic tube, silvered inside and outside to give the required capacity. The tube is soldered to a bush which may be bolted to a chassis and thereby give a very low inductance path from the outside silvering to earth. The inner silvering is connected to a wire which passes through the tube and protrudes at each end as shown in **Fig. 9 (A)**, the whole device forming a very convenient method of decoupling or filtering supply leads where they enter or leave a screened compartment.

(vii) Split-stator Condenser

A split-stator condenser is a special type of variable

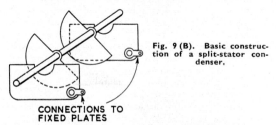

MOVING PLATES

CONNECTIONS TO FIXED PLATES

Fig. 9 (B). Basic construction of a split-stator condenser.

condenser which is used mainly in push-pull radio-frequency amplifier circuits in transmitters. It is made up of two separate sets of moving plates as shown diagrammatically in **Fig. 9 (B)**. The advantages of the push-pull circuit of **Fig. 9 (C)** using a split-stator condenser over that of **Fig. 9 (D)** using an ordinary variable condenser are that the circuit is symmetrically balanced to earth and the shaft

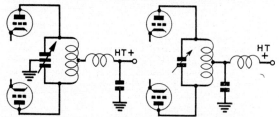

HT+

HT+

Fig. 9 (C). Push-pull circuit using a split stator condenser.

Fig. 9 (D). Push-pull circuit using an ordinary single-section condenser.

is at earth potential. Also in the case of the circuit with the split-stator condenser the balance of the circuit is not so dependant on the position of the tapping point on the coil.

Capacitors in Series and Parallel

Capacitors can be connected in series or parallel, as shown in **Fig. 10**, either to obtain some special capacity value using a standard range of capacitors, or perhaps in the case of series connection to obtain a capacitor capable of withstanding a greater voltage without breakdown than is provided by a single capacitor. When capacitors are connected in parallel, as in Fig. 10 (A), the total capacity of the combination is equal to the sum of the separate capacities. When capacitors are connected in series, as in Fig. 10 (B), the reciprocal of the equivalent capacity is equal to the sum of the reciprocals of the separate capacities.

If C is the total capacity these formulae can be written as follows:

PARALLEL CONNECTION   SERIES CONNECTION

$$C = C_1 + C_2 + C_3 \text{ etc.} \qquad \frac{1}{C} = \frac{1}{C_1} + \frac{1}{C_2} + \frac{1}{C_3} \text{ etc.}$$

Similar to the formula for *resistors in parallel*, a useful equivalent formula for two *capacitors in series* is—

$$C = \frac{C_1 C_2}{C_1 + C_2}$$

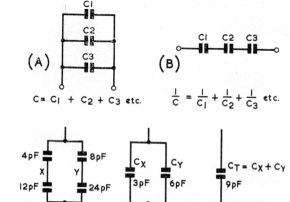

(A)
C1
C2
C3

$C = C_1 + C_2 + C_3$ etc.

(B)
C1 C2 C3

$\frac{1}{C} = \frac{1}{C_1} + \frac{1}{C_2} + \frac{1}{C_3}$ etc.

(C)
4pF   8pF
X   Y
12pF   24pF

(D)
CX   CY
3pF   6pF

(E)
$C_T = C_X + C_Y$
9pF

Fig. 10. Capacitors in various combinations: (A) parallel, (B) series, (C) series-parallel. The calculation of the resultant capacitance of the combination shown in (C) requires first the evaluation of each series arm X and Y as shown in (D): the single equivalent capacitance of the combination is shown in (E).

The use of these formulae is illustrated by an example taken from a Radio Amateurs' Examination paper.

Example. *Two capacitors of 4 and 12 pF are connected in series; two others of 8 and 24 pF are also connected in series. What is the equivalent capacitance if these series combinations are joined in parallel?*

The circuit is shown in Fig. 10 (C). Using the formula for two capacitors in series the two series arms X and Y can be reduced to single equivalent capacities C_X and C_Y as shown in Fig. 10 (D). Thus—

$$C_X = \frac{4 \times 12}{4 + 12} = \frac{4 \times 12}{16} = 3 \text{ pF}$$

$$C_Y = \frac{8 \times 24}{8 + 24} = \frac{8 \times 24}{32} = 6 \text{ pF}$$

These two capacities may now be compounded in parallel to give the total effective capacity represented by the single condenser C_T in Fig. 10 (E).

$$C_T = C_X + C_Y = 3 + 6 = 9 \text{ pF}$$

The total equivalent capacity of the four capacitors connected as described is therefore 9 pF.

MAGNETISM

Permanent Magnets. A magnet will attract pieces of iron towards it by exerting a magnetic force upon them. The field of this magnetic force can be demonstrated by sprinkling

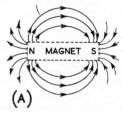

LINES OF MAGNETIC FORCE

N MAGNET S

(A)

Fig. 11 (A). Magnetic field produced by a bar magnet.

iron filings on a piece of thin cardboard under which is placed a bar magnet. The iron filings will map out the magnetic field as sketched in **Fig. 11 (A)**. It will be seen that the field is most intense near the ends of the magnet, the centres of intensity being called the *poles*, and *lines of force* spread out on either side and continue through the material of the magnet from one end to the other.

If such a magnet is suspended so that it can swing freely in a horizontal plane it will always come to rest pointing in the one particular direction, namely towards the earth's magnetic poles, the earth itself acting as a magnet. A compass needle is simply a bar of magnetized steel. One end of the magnet (*N*) is called a *north pole*, which is an abbreviation of "north-seeking pole" and the other end (*S*) a *south pole* or "south-seeking pole." It is an accepted convention that magnetic force acts in the direction from *N* to *S* as indicated by the arrows on the lines of force in Fig. 11 (A).

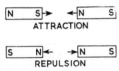

ATTRACTION

REPULSION

Fig. 11 (B). Attraction and repulsion between bar magnets.

If two magnets are arranged so that the north pole of one is near the south pole of another, there will be a force of attraction between them, whereas if similar poles are opposite one another, the magnets will repel one another: see **Fig. 11 (B)**.

Magnets made from certain kinds of iron and nickel alloys retain their magnetism more or less permanently, and find many uses in radio equipment, such as in loud-speakers, polarized relays, headphones, cathode-ray tube focusing arrangements and magnetron oscillators.

Other types of iron and nickel alloys, e.g. soft iron, are not capable of retaining magnetism, and therefore cannot be used for making "permanent" magnets. They are effective in transmitting magnetic force, however, and are used as cores in electromagnets and transformers.

Electromagnets. A current of electricity flowing through a straight wire exhibits a magnetic field, the lines of force of which are in a plane perpendicular to the wire and concentric with the wire. If a piece of cardboard is sprinkled with iron filings, as shown in **Fig. 11 (C)**, they will arrange themselves in rings round the wire, thus illustrating the magnetic field associated with the flow of current in the wire. Observation of a small compass needle placed near the wire

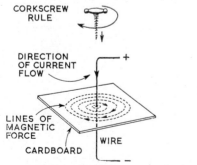

Fig. 11 (C). Magnetic field produced by current flowing in a straight wire.

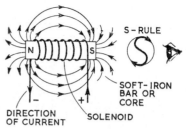

Fig. 11 (D). The "S" rule for determining the polarity of an electromagnet.

would indicate that for a current flow in the direction illustrated the magnetic force acts clockwise round the wire. A reversal of current would reverse the direction of the magnetic field.

The "corkscrew rule" enables the direction of the magnetic field round a wire to be found. Imagine a "right-handed" corkscrew being driven into the wire so that it progresses in the direction of current flow; the direction of the magnetic field around the wire will then be in the direction of rotation of the corkscrew.

The magnetic field surrounding such a straight wire is relatively weak, but a strong magnetic field can be produced by a current if instead of a straight wire a coil of wire or *solenoid* is used: moreover the field can be greatly strengthened if a piece of soft iron, called a *core*, is placed inside the coil. The extent by which the strength of the solenoid magnet is increased by the introduction of the core is called the *permeability* of the core (*cf.* dielectric constant). **Fig. 11 (D)** shows the magnetic field produced by a solenoid, which it will be seen is very similar to that of a bar magnet as shown in Fig. 11 (A). A north pole is produced at one end of the coil and a south pole at the other. Reversal of the current will reverse the polarity of the electromagnet. The polarity of a solenoid can be deduced from the "*S*" rule, which states that the pole which faces an observer looking at the end of a solenoid is a south pole if to him the current is flowing (i.e. from positive to negative) in a clockwise direction; see Fig. 11 (D).

The strength of a magnetic field produced by a current is directly proportional to the current, a fact made use of in moving-coil meters, etc. It also depends on the number of turns of wire, the area of the coil, and the permeability of the core.

Interaction of Magnetic Fields. Similar to the attraction and repulsion of permanent magnets, there can be interaction between the fields of electromagnets or between a permanent magnet and an electromagnet, and in just the same way the interaction is manifest as a force causing relative motion between the two. This interaction forms the basis of several types of electromechanical devices which are used in radio such as loudspeakers, earphones, and moving-coil meters.

The principle of the loudspeaker is shown in **Fig. 12 (A)**. A strong permanent magnet *A* forms part of a soft-iron magnetic circuit *BCD* which has a narrow annular gap between the circular pole-pieces *C* and *D*: a strong radial magnetic field is thereby produced in this gap. Speech-frequency currents are passed through the coil *E* which is free to move in the annular gap and is fixed to a cone *F*. Interaction between the magnetic field in the gap and that due to the current flowing in the coil causes the coil to move

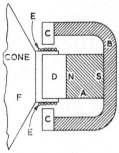

Fig. 12 (A). The principle of the moving coil loudspeaker.

backwards or forwards according to the strength and polarity of the speech signal: the cone therefore vibrates in sympathy with the speech currents and causes sound waves to be produced.

The principle of the earphone is shown in **Fig. 12 (B).** A permanent magnet *M* is situated close to a circular diaphragm *Z* made of magnetic material. The permanent magnet's field holds the diaphragm in a state of stress. Around the arms of the U-shaped magnet are two coils wound with many turns of fine wire and through which speech currents are passed. The magnetic field due to the speech current flowing in the coils adds to or subtracts from

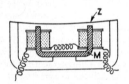

Fig. 12 (B). The principle of the earphone.

the field holding the diaphragm in a state of stress causing it to vibrate in sympathy with the speech signal and emit corresponding sound waves.

The principle of the moving-coil meter is discussed in Chapter 19 (*Measurements*).

ELECTROMAGNETIC INDUCTION

If a bar magnet is plunged into the solenoid coil as indicated in **Fig. 13 (A)** the moving-coil microammeter connected across the coil will show a deflection. The explanation of this phenomenon, known as *electromagnetic induction*, is that the movement of the magnet's lines of force past the turns of the coil causes a voltage to be induced in the coil which in turn causes a current to flow through the meter. The magnitude of the effect depends on the strength and rate of movement of the magnet and the size of the coil. Withdrawal of the magnet causes a reversal of the current. No current flows unless the lines of force are moving relatively to the coil. The same effect is obtained if a coil of wire is arranged to move relatively to a fixed magnetic field. Dynamos and generators depend for their operation on the principle of electromagnetic induction.

If a pair of coils of wire are arranged as shown in **Fig. 13 (B),** when the switch *K* is open there is no magnetic field from the coil *P* linking the turns of the coil *S*, and the current through *S* is zero. Closing *K* will cause a magnetic field to appear due to the current in the coil *P*. This field, as it builds up from zero, will induce a voltage in *S* and cause a current to flow through the meter for a short time

until the field due to *P* has reached a steady value when the current through *S* falls to zero again. The effect is only momentary and is completed in a small fraction of a second. The change in current in the circuit *P* is said to have induced a current in the circuit *S*. The fact that a changing current in one circuit can induce a current in another circuit is the principle underlying the operation of transformers.

Self-Inductance

If a steady current is flowing through a coil there will be a steady magnetic field due to that current. A current change will tend to alter the strength of the field which in turn will induce in the coil a voltage tending to oppose the change being made. This process is called *self-induction*. A coil is said to have *self-inductance*, usually abbreviated to *inductance*. It will have a value of one *henry* (H) if, when the current through the coil changes at a rate of one ampere per second, the voltage appearing across its terminals is one volt. Inductance is usually denoted by the symbol *L* in formulae. As the inductance values used in radio equipment may be only a very small fraction of a henry the units *millihenry* (mH) and *microhenry* (μH) meaning one thousandth and one millionth of a henry respectively are commonly used.

The inductance of a coil depends on the number of turns and on the area of the coil and the permeability of the core material on which the coil is wound. The inductance of a coil of a certain physical size and number of turns can be calculated to a fair degree of accuracy from formulae or they can be derived from coil charts. (See Chapter 22).

Mutual Inductance

A changing current in one circuit can induce a current in a second circuit: see Fig. 13 (B). The strength of the current induced in the second circuit *S* depends on the closeness or " tightness " of the magnetic coupling between the circuits; for example, if both coils are wound together on an iron core practically all the lines of force or magnetic flux from the first circuit will link with the turns of the second circuit. Such coils would be said to be *tightly coupled* whereas if the coils were both air-cored and spaced some distance apart they would be *loosely coupled*.

The mutual inductance between two coils is measured in henrys, and two coils are said to have a *mutual inductance of*

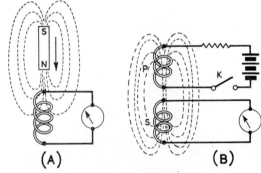

Fig. 13. Electromagnetic induction: (A) Relative movement of a magnet and a coil causes a current to be induced in the coil; (B) when the current in one of a pair of coupled coils changes in value, a current is induced in the second coil.

one henry if when the current in the primary coil changes at a rate of one ampere per second the voltage across the secondary is one volt. Mutual inductance is denoted in formulae by the symbol M.

The mutual inductance between two coils may be measured by joining the coils in series (a) so that the sense of their windings is the same and (b) so that they are reversed. The total inductance is then measured in each case.

If L_a and L_b are the total measured inductances, and L_1 and L_2 are the separate inductances of the two coils and M is the mutual inductance—

$$L_a = L_1 + L_2 + 2M$$
$$L_b = L_1 + L_2 - 2M$$
$$\therefore \quad L_a - L_b = 4M$$
$$\text{i.e.} \quad M = \frac{L_a - L_b}{4}$$

The mutual inductance is therefore equal to one-quarter of the difference between the series-aiding and series-opposing readings.

Inductances Used in Radio Equipment

Inductances are used in radio equipment wherever a circuit is required whose output or performance must be frequency-dependent. For instance they are used in conjunction with condensers to form tuned circuits which select wanted from unwanted frequencies in receivers and transmitters, and they are also used in the form of *chokes* in filters which remove hum in high-tension power supplies.

The value of inductance used in any circuit depends largely on the frequency at which the circuit is operating; for example, coils might be of many henrys inductance for use as power-supply filter chokes where the frequency is 50 or 100 cycles per second or as small as 0·1 microhenry when used as tuning coils at a frequency of, say, 144 Mc/s.

Broadly speaking, coils can be divided into two classes— (a) low-frequency coils or chokes and (b) radio-frequency coils and chokes. Low-frequency chokes range in inductance from 0·5 to 500 henrys and are wound with many turns of wire on iron cores. In **Fig. 14** the general method of construction of such chokes is shown in A, B and C. The core is made up of thin soft iron or special-alloy stampings or laminations A, insulated from each other so as to reduce the power lost due to eddy currents induced in the core. The coil is wound on a bobbin B, which is then packed with laminations as shown at C. Laminations may be obtained in a wide range of sizes and permeabilities.

Radio-frequency coils are either air-cored or dust iron-cored. Air-cored coils are usually wound on low-loss cylindrical or ribbed formers. In Fig. 14 a plug-in coil such as is often used in amateur short-wave transmitters and receivers is shown at D. For maximum efficiency, coils should be of such dimensions that the length of the winding is not less than half and not greater than the diameter.

A perfect radio-frequency coil would have inductance only and no resistance, and the current through it and the voltage across it would be *in quadrature* (i.e. 90° out-of-phase) and no power would be lost in the coil. In practice, however, coils have an appreciable effective series resistance, which may be many times the d.c. resistance of the coil, and power is wasted in the coil. This power loss shows up in the case of a transmitting coil, where currents are high, in a rise in temperature of the coil and its former. Coils in

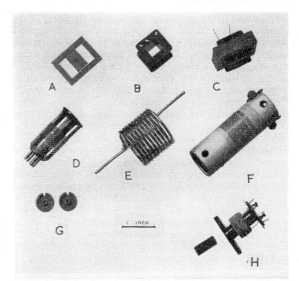

Fig. 14. Typical inductances and magnetic cores. A — Iron laminations (T- and U-type); B — Bobbin; C — Assembled iron-cored inductance; D — Plug-in air-cored coil; E — Low-loss transmitter tank coil; F — High-stability oscillator coil; G — Small ferrite " pot " core; H — Wave-wound coil with adjustable iron core.

which this loss resistance is low are said to be " low-loss " or " high Q." The losses in a coil at radio frequencies are due to (a) eddy currents in surrounding metal objects, including the core if there is one, (b) skin effect (see *Resistance and Conductance*), and (c) dielectric loss in the coil former. For a low-loss coil such as would be used in the output tank circuit of a short-wave transmitter, heavy-gauge wire (e.g. No. 14 s.w.g.) is used, wound as shown at E in Fig. 14 with the minimum of dielectric material inside, the turns of wire being supported by strips of good-quality insulating material which can just be seen cemented to the wires. The coil should be mounted so that there is no part of the metal chassis or screening within a distance at least equal to the diameter of the coil in any direction. For high frequency-stability, such as is needed in a transmitter master-oscillator, coils should be wound under tension on grooved ceramic formers: an example is shown at F in Fig. 14.

For larger inductances, such as would be used in intermediate-frequency amplifiers, the coils are usually fitted with a special kind of iron core (" dust iron ") the permeability of which allows fewer turns of wire to be used for a given inductance; the resistance is thereby decreased and the efficiency of the coil is increased. Solid iron cores cannot be used since the eddy-current losses would more than offset the gain in coil efficiency just mentioned, and a fine iron-alloy powder moulded in an insulating medium is normally used. Rather higher efficiency can be obtained by the use of *ferrites* which are non-metallic magnetic materials of very high resistivity and therefore low eddy-current loss. In Fig. 14, G shows two halves of a ferrite " pot " core. The coil is wave-wound, or simply wound on a bobbin and placed inside the two halves so that it is completely surrounded by the ferrite material.

A typical i.f. coil of wave-wound construction with an adjustable screw-type dust-iron core is shown at H in Fig. 14. The variation of the position of the dust-iron core alters the inductance value. Sometimes an adjustable brass core is used instead of the iron core, but whereas the effect of the iron is to *increase* the inductance because of its high magnetic permeability the effect of the brass is to *reduce* the inductance: the reason for this is that the brass, beside being non-magnetic, has a very low resistance and therefore acts as an efficient short circuited single turn secondary. Although copper would theoretically give a superior performance, brass has a sufficiently high conductivity and is the material normally employed.

The use of magnetic or conductive cores to control the inductance value of a coil is known as *slug tuning*.

For convenience in aerial tuning in a transmitter a tapped coil may be used. If a continuously variable inductance is required the coil can be made to rotate while a variable tapping is made by a sliding pulley following the wire spiral. This type of variable inductance has the disadvantage of relying on three rubbing contacts in series, viz. between the pulley and the wire, between the pulley and the rod on which it moves, and the pivot at the end of the coil. Nevertheless it is capable of giving satisfactory service if properly maintained.

A variable inductance with no rubbing contacts may be made by using two series-connected coils which can be turned relatively to one another through 180° from the series-aiding to series-opposing condition. Such a device depends on the variation of the mutual inductance between the two coils and is called a *variometer*.

Inductances in Series and Parallel

Provided that there is no mutual coupling between inductances when they are connected in series, the total inductance obtained is equal to the sum of the separate inductances. When they are in parallel the reciprocal of the total inductance is equal to the sum of the reciprocals of the separate inductances.

If L is the total inductance (no mutual coupling) the relationships are as follows:

SERIES CONNECTION   PARALLEL CONNECTION

$$L = L_1 + L_2 + L_3 \text{ etc.} \qquad \frac{1}{L} = \frac{1}{L_1} + \frac{1}{L_2} + \frac{1}{L_3} \text{ etc.}$$

For the special case of *two* inductances in parallel—

$$L = \frac{L_1 L_2}{L_1 + L_2}$$

It may be noted that this formula is of the same type as that relating to two *resistors in parallel* or *condensers in series*. The use of these series and parallel inductance formulae is illustrated by the following example taken from a Radio Amateurs' Examination paper:

Example. *Two inductors of 10 and 20 microhenrys are connected in series; two others of 30 and 40 microhenrys are also connected in series. What is the equivalent inductance if these series combinations are connected in parallel? Assume that there is no mutual induction.*

The 10 and 20 μH coils in series are equivalent to $(10 + 20)$ = 30 μH.

The 30 and 40 μH coils in series are equivalent to $(30 + 40)$ = 70 μH.

These two equivalent inductances of 30 μH and 70 μH respectively are in parallel and will therefore be equivalent to one single inductance of—

$$\frac{30 \times 70}{30 + 70} = 21\ \mu\text{H}$$

This is the value of the equivalent inductance of the four coils in this series-parallel arrangement.

ALTERNATING CURRENT

Previous sections have been concerned mainly with current flowing in one direction through a circuit, such a current being produced, for example, by a battery, i.e. *direct current* (usually abbreviated to *d.c.*).

There is another important type of current flow in which current flows backwards and forwards alternately through a circuit. Such currents are called *alternating currents* (*a.c.*).

An alternating current could be obtained by connecting a resistance to a battery through a reversing switch as shown in **Fig. 15 (A)**. On operating the switch *S* backwards and forwards from *a* to *b* the current from the battery would flow in alternate directions through the resistor *R*; the graph in **Fig. 15 (B)** shows how the current would vary with the passage of time and the reversals of the switch. Such a current waveform, in which the current flows at a steady value for equal times in both directions, is called a *square-wave*.

The most common alternating current is that used for the electricity supply mains in which, in Great Britain and most of Europe, the direction of current flow is continuously

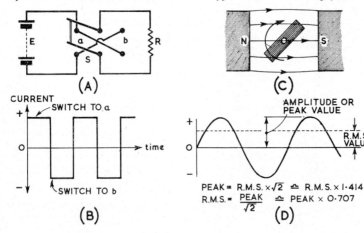

Fig. 15. Alternating current. A simple circuit with a current-reversing switch shown at (A) produces a square-wave current through the resistance R as shown in (B). When a coil is rotated in a magnetic field as in (C) the current induced in the coil has a sinusoidal waveform (D).

PEAK = R.M.S. × $\sqrt{2}$ $\approx$ R.M.S. × 1·414

R.M.S. = $\dfrac{\text{PEAK}}{\sqrt{2}}$ $\approx$ PEAK × 0·707

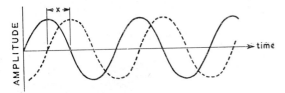

Fig. 16. Phase difference between two alternating currents. Provided that they both have the same frequency the phase difference will remain constant.

changing from positive to negative and back again at a rate of 50 cycles per second. In the U.S.A. and Canada the rate, or frequency, is 60 cycles per second. In each cycle the direction changes twice, but for the purpose of most calculations it is the complete cycle which is more significant than the two half-cycles in opposite directions.

The alternating voltage of the electricity supply does not have a square waveform but fluctuates with a gradual and smooth variation like the swinging of a pendulum. Such a current would be produced by the continuous and steady rotation of a coil in a magnetic field, as indicated in **Fig. 15 (C)**, when the circuit is completed by some device such as a resistance. This is the basic principle used in the *alternator*, a machine for generating alternating current. The waveform of this current has a shape which is defined mathematically as a *sine-wave*, shown in **Fig. 15 (D)**, and the current is said to vary *sinusoidally*.

Alternating currents of much higher frequency are used in radio communication, the frequencies commonly used in short-wave amateur work ranging between 1,800,000 and 30,000,000 cycles per second (1·8–30 Mc/s) and in more advanced work up to 430,000,000 cycles per second (430 Mc/s) or even higher.

Characteristics of Alternating Currents

From the preceding paragraph it can be seen that one feature which distinguishes one alternating current from another is the rate at which the complete cycles of current-reversal take place; this is called the *frequency* of the alternating current and is measured in *cycles per second*.

A second distinguishing feature of an alternating current is its magnitude or *amplitude*, by which is meant the maximum value reached during one cycle or alternation: see Fig. 15 (D).

It is possible to have two alternating currents whose frequency and amplitude are exactly equal but with a time lag, or *phase difference*, between the two so that they are not performing the same part of their cycles at the same instant. This is illustrated in **Fig. 16** in which the solid and dotted sine waves are of the same amplitude and frequency but differ in phase by one-quarter of the time taken for one cycle as indicated by the time x in the diagram.

Thus an alternating current, or indeed an alternating quantity, can be defined by the three properties—frequency, amplitude and phase.

Another term used with reference to alternating current is the *period* of a wave, which is the time taken to perform one cycle. The period of a wave is the reciprocal of the frequency; thus—

$$\text{Frequency} = \frac{1}{Period} \qquad Period = \frac{1}{Frequency}$$

Frequency is usually denoted by the symbol f and period

by the symbol T. As an example, the period of the 50 cycles per second mains is given by—

$$T = \frac{1}{f} = \frac{1}{50} \text{ second}$$

The value of an a.c. voltage or current can be specified by its amplitude. This is often called the *peak* voltage or *peak* current, being the highest value reached during a cycle. Thus the peak value of any a.c. voltage or current is equal to its amplitude (in volts or amperes) as shown in Fig. 15 (D).

The peak value, however, is not the most common way of specifying an alternating voltage or current. The usual value adopted is the *root-mean-square* or *r.m.s.* value which is equal to the d.c. voltage or current which would produce the same amount of power in a resistive load as the alternating voltage or current would produce. The r.m.s. value is less than the peak value, the two being related as follows:

$$\text{r.m.s. value} = \frac{\text{peak value}}{\sqrt{2}} = 0\cdot707 \times \text{peak value}$$

or conversely—

$$\text{peak value} = \text{r.m.s. value} \times \sqrt{2} = 1\cdot414 \times \text{r.m.s. value}$$

Thus an a.c. mains supply of 240 volts r.m.s. has a peak voltage of 240 × 1·414 or approximately 340 volts.

A.C. Circuit containing Resistance Only

Ohm's Law can be used to find the current flowing through a resistance when a certain alternating voltage is applied across its terminals. The current will flow backwards and forwards through the resistance under the influence of the applied voltage and will be in phase with it. The voltage and current waveforms for the resistive circuit of **Fig. 17 (A)** are shown in **Fig. 17 (B)**.

The power dissipated in the resistor can be calculated

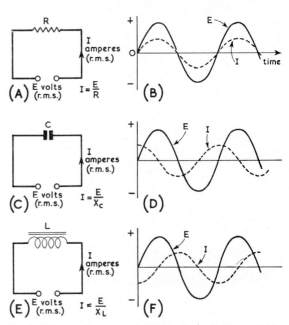

Fig. 17. Voltage and current relationships in a.c. circuits comprising (A) resistance only, (C) capacitance only, (E) inductance only.

direct from the usual power formulae, provided that r.m.s. values for voltage and current are used, viz. :

$$W = EI \qquad W = I^2 R \qquad W = \frac{E^2}{R}$$

If peak values $\hat{E}$ for voltage and $\hat{I}$ for current are used these formulae become—

$$W = \frac{\hat{E}\hat{I}}{2} \qquad W = \frac{\hat{I}^2 R}{2} \qquad W = \frac{\hat{E}^2}{2R}$$

A.C. Circuit containing Capacitance Only: Reactance of Capacitor

When an alternating voltage is applied to a condenser as shown in **Fig. 17 (C)** the condenser will be alternately charged in one direction and then charged in the opposite direction as the supply alternates. At each reversal it becomes momentarily discharged. An observer watching the flow of current in the wires connecting the condenser to the a.c. supply would see an alternating current flowing backwards and forwards through the wires. This current flows in and out of the condenser and not actually through the condenser. A careful study would show that the current is one-quarter period (or 90°) out-of-phase with the voltage, and in advance of it, as shown in **Fig. 17 (D)**. This must be so, for when the condenser is fully charged the voltage is a maximum and the current is zero. No power is dissipated in such a circuit, a current of this type being called a reactive current or *wattless current*.

The magnitude of the current flowing in the circuit depends on the capacity of the condenser and the frequency of the supply, and the condenser therefore exhibits a property of current restriction or opposition somewhat similar to that exhibited by a resistance except that the effect is frequency-dependent and there is a 90° phase difference between the voltage and the current. This property, which is called the *capacitive reactance* of the condenser is measured in ohms and is usually denoted by the symbol X_c; it is given by the formula—

$$X_c = \frac{1}{2\pi f C}$$

where f is the frequency in cycles per second and C is the capacity in farads: the value of π is 3·14.

Sometimes, for convenience, the symbol ω is used to represent $2\pi f$. It is known as the *angular frequency* and is expressed in radians per second.

The following example, taken from a Radio Amateurs' Examination paper, shows how this formula is applied.

Example. *Calculate the reactance offered, at frequencies of 50 c/s and 50 kc/s respectively, of a capacitance of 2 microfarads.*

In the formula for capacitive reactance—

$$X_c = \frac{1}{2\pi f C} \text{ ohms}$$

Before any calculation is made it must be remembered to express f and C in the correct units.
Considering first the frequency of 50 c/s—

$$X_c = \frac{1}{2\pi \times 50 \times 2 \times 10^{-6}} \text{ ohms}$$

$$= \frac{10,000}{2\pi} = 1592 \text{ ohms}$$

Considering next the frequency of 50 kc/s (i.e. 50,000 c/s)—

$$X_c = \frac{1}{2\pi \times 50,000 \times 2 \times 10^{-6}} \text{ ohms}$$

$$= \frac{10}{2\pi} = 1·592 \text{ ohms}$$

It is worth noting that the reactance is inversely proportional to the frequency, so that it would be possible to derive the reactance at 50 kc/s directly from the reactance at 50 c/s simply by dividing by 1,000.

The current flowing " through " a condenser can be calculated by using Ohm's Law, regarding the reactance of the condenser X_c as replacing the more usual resistance R, viz.:

$$I = \frac{E}{X_c} \qquad \left(cf. \ I = \frac{E}{R} \right)$$

A.C. Circuit containing Inductance Only: Reactance of Coil

The opposition of an inductance to alternating current flow is called the *inductive reactance* of the coil: see **Fig. 17 (E)**. It is proportional to the inductance of the coil and also to the frequency and is denoted by the symbol X_L. It may be calculated from the formula—

$$X_L = 2\pi f L$$

As in the case of a condenser, the current in an inductance and the voltage across it are one-quarter period (or 90°) out-of-phase and no power is dissipated in a purely inductive circuit. In an inductive circuit, however, the phase of the current is 90° behind the voltage, i.e. exactly opposite to the case of the capacitive circuit: see **Fig. 17 (F)**.

Example. *Calculate the inductive reactance of a coil of 2 henrys inductance at frequencies of 50 c/s and 50 kc/s respectively.*

The formula for inductive reactance is—

$$X_L = 2\pi f L$$

Since f is 50 c/s and L is 2 henrys—

$$X_L = 2\pi \times 50 \times 2 \text{ ohms}$$

$$= 200 \times 3·14 \text{ ohms}$$

$$= 628 \text{ ohms}$$

Because inductive reactance is directly proportional to frequency, the reactance of the 2H coil at 50 kc/s will be one thousand times its reactance at 50 c/s, namely 628,000 ohms.

The current through an inductance and the voltage across it are connected by the modified Ohm's Law formula—

$$I = \frac{E}{X_L} \qquad \left(cf. \ I = \frac{E}{R} \right)$$

Susceptance

A term sometimes used in calculations is the *susceptance* of a coil or a condenser. Susceptance is simply the reciprocal of reactance in the same way that conductance is the reciprocal of resistance. Susceptance is in general denoted by the symbol Y and is measured in *mhos*.
Thus—

$$Y_L = \frac{1}{X_L} \qquad\qquad Y_c = \frac{1}{X_c}$$

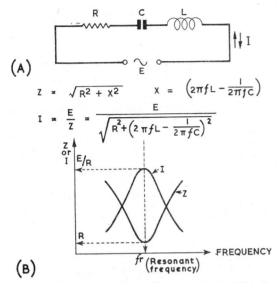

(A)

$$z = \sqrt{R^2 + x^2} \qquad x = \left(2\pi f L - \frac{1}{2\pi f c}\right)$$

$$I = \frac{E}{Z} = \frac{E}{\sqrt{R^2 + \left(2\pi f L - \frac{1}{2\pi f c}\right)^2}}$$

(B)

Fig. 18. The series-resonant circuit. The curves shown at (B) indicate how the impedance and the current vary with frequency in the type of circuit shown at (A).

A.C. Circuit containing L, C and R: Impedance

An a.c. circuit may contain resistance, inductance and capacitance in series, as shown in **Fig. 18 (A)**, each of which opposes the flow of current in a different way as mentioned in the previous sections. The opposition of the composite circuit to alternating current flow is called the *impedance* of the circuit and is denoted by the symbol Z.

The impedance of the whole circuit cannot be found by simply adding the reactances and resistances together, since the relative current and voltage phases associated with each component are not the same. The inductive and capacitive reactance have exactly opposite phase effects and consequently they must first be subtracted from one another to find the total reactance in the circuit, thus—

$$X = (X_L - X_c)$$

The impedance is then found by compounding the total resistance with the reactance of the circuit. This has to be done by taking the square root of the sum of the squares of these two quantities; thus—

$$Z = \sqrt{R^2 + X^2}$$

The current flowing through the circuit may then be found using Ohm's Law but with Z replacing R as follows:

$$I = \frac{E}{Z}$$

If the current in the circuit is known, the voltage across each individual component can be calculated using Ohm's Law with the appropriate value of the resistance or reactance.

Series-Resonant Circuit: Acceptor Circuit

Considering the circuit of Fig. 18 (A), the current flowing may be calculated using the formula $I = E/Z$, where Z is the impedance of the circuit and E is the applied alternating voltage. When Z is written in terms of R, L, C and f, the expression for I becomes—

$$I = \frac{E}{\sqrt{R^2 + \left(2\pi f L - \frac{1}{2\pi f C}\right)^2}}$$

At one particular frequency depending on the exact values of C and L, the capacitive and inductive reactances will be equal and opposite. Under this condition, called *resonance*, the impedance of the circuit will be a minimum, equal to R, and the current will be a maximum. Resonance is a very important phenomenon as it is used to select a desired frequency from other unwanted frequencies. **Fig. 18 (B)** shows how the current and impedance for the circuit of Fig. 18 (A) vary with frequency, the current at resonance being E/R and the impedance at resonance being R.

Series-resonant circuits are sometimes referred to as *acceptor circuits* because at the resonance frequency the impedance is a minimum and they therefore accept maximum current at this frequency.

The frequency at which a certain coil and condenser resonate when connected together can be found by equating the inductive and capacitive reactances; thus—

$$2\pi f L = \frac{1}{2\pi f C}$$

Solving for f—

$$f = \frac{1}{2\pi\sqrt{CL}}$$

If L is in henrys and C is in farads, f will be in cycles per second.

This formula, next to Ohm's Law, is probably the most used of all in radio work as it permits the calculation of the inductance of a coil which will tune to a desired frequency with a given capacity. Its use, together with other formulae relating to the reasonant circuit, is illustrated by the following worked examples taken from various Radio Amateurs' Examination papers.

Example I. *What value of inductance is required in series with a capacitor of 500 pF for the circuit to resonate at a frequency of 400 kc/s? (Assume no resistance.)*

From the resonance formula—

$$f = \frac{1}{2\pi\sqrt{LC}}$$

the inductance is—

$$L = \frac{1}{4\pi^2 f^2 C}$$

Expressing the frequency and the capacitance in the proper units ($f = 400 \times 10^3$ c/s and $C = 500 \times 10^{-12}$F)—

$$L = \frac{1}{4\pi^2 \times (400 \times 10^3)^2 \times (500 \times 10^{-12})}\text{H}$$

Taking $\pi^2 = 10$, this becomes—

$$L = \frac{1}{3200}\text{H}$$

$$= 312 \cdot 5 \text{ microhenrys.}$$

Example II. *If an inductance of 50 microhenrys is in series with a capacitance of 500 picofarads what is the resonant frequency? (π^2 may be taken as 10.)*

At resonance—

$$f = \frac{1}{2\pi\sqrt{LC}}$$

23

$$\text{or } f^2 = \frac{1}{4\pi^2 LC}$$

Expressing the inductance and the capacitance in the proper units ($L = 50 \times 10^{-6}$H and $C = 500 \times 10^{-12}$F)—

$$f^2 = \frac{1}{4 \times 10 \times (50 \times 10^{-6}) \times (500 \times 10^{-12})}$$

$$= 10^{12}$$

Therefore—

$$f = 10^6 \text{ c/s} = 1 \text{ Mc/s.}$$

Example III. *If the effective series inductance and capacity of a vertical aerial are 20 μH and 100 pF respectively and the aerial is connected to a coil of 80 μH inductance what is the approximate resonant frequency?*

In this example the aerial and coil together will resonate at a frequency determined by the capacity and the sum of the aerial effective inductance and the loading coil inductance.

At resonance—

$$= \frac{1}{2\pi\sqrt{LC}}$$

Here the relevant values of inductance and capacity expressed in the proper units are—

$$L = (20 + 80) \times 10^{-6}\text{H}$$

$$C = 100 \times 10^{-12}\text{F}$$

Therefore—

$$f = \frac{1}{2\pi\sqrt{(100 \times 10^{-6}) \times (100 \times 10^{-12})}} \text{ c/s}$$

$$= \frac{1}{2\pi \times 10^{-7}} \text{ c/s}$$

$$= 1 \cdot 6 \text{ Mc/s approximately.}$$

Example IV. *An alternating voltage of 10 volts at a frequency of $5/\pi$ Mc/s is applied to a circuit of the following elements in series: (i) a capacitance of 100 pF, (ii) a non-inductive resistor of 10 ohms.*

(a) What value of inductance in series is required to tune the circuit to resonance?

(b) At resonance, what is the current in the circuit?

(a) For the calculation of the inductance, the resistance can be ignored since it has no effect on the resonant frequency which is given by—

$$= \frac{1}{2\pi\sqrt{LC}}$$

Rearranged, this becomes—

$$L = \frac{1}{4\pi^2 f^2 C}$$

Expressing the frequency and the capacitance in the proper units ($f = 5 \times 10^6/\pi$ cycles per second; $C = 100 \times 10^{-12}$F)—

$$L = \frac{1}{4\pi^2 \times \left(\dfrac{25 \times 10^{12}}{\pi^2}\right) \times (100 \times 10^{-12})} \text{ henrys}$$

$$= \frac{1}{10,000} \text{ H}$$

$$= 100 \text{ microhenrys.}$$

(b) At resonance, the inductive and capacitive reactances cancel out and the circuit will have a purely resistive

impedance of 10 ohms. The current I through the circuit at resonance can then be calculated directly from Ohm's Law: $I = E/R$. Since $E = 10$ volts and $R = 10$ ohms—

$$\text{Current at resonance } I = \frac{10 \text{ volts}}{10 \text{ ohms}}$$

$$= 1 \text{ ampere.}$$

Magnification Factor: Q

At resonance the voltage across the coil (or the condenser) in the circuit of Fig. 18 (A) can be considerably greater than that supplied to the circuit by the generator. The current at resonance is determined by the value of the resistance R whereas the voltage across the coil (or the condenser) is given by the product of the current and the appropriate reactance which may be many times the value of R. The ratio of the voltage across the coil (or the condenser) to that across the resistance is called the *magnification factor* or Q of the circuit. If I is the current at resonance—

$$Q = \frac{IX_L}{IR} = \frac{2\pi fL}{R} = \frac{\omega L}{R}$$

$$\text{or } Q = \frac{IX_C}{IR} = \frac{1}{2\pi fCR} = \frac{1}{\omega CR}$$

where $\omega = 2\pi f$

The Q of a tuned circuit is determined mainly by the coil since good-quality condensers have negligible losses. The Q of a tuned circuit determines its *selectivity*, i.e. its ability to pick out a wanted signal from a number of unwanted signals on adjacent frequencies. A high Q-value corresponds to good selectivity.

Parallel-Resonant Circuit: Rejector Circuit

If a coil and condenser are connected in parallel as in **Fig. 19 (A)** resonance effects appear when the current is of

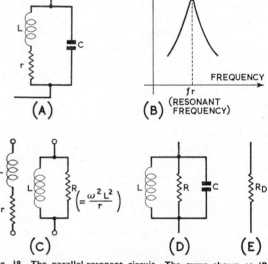

Fig. 19. The parallel-resonant circuit. The curve shown at (B) indicates how the impedance varies with frequency in the type of circuit shown at (A). A series-to-parallel transformation to replace the series resistance by an equivalent parallel resistance can be made as shown at (C). The circuit shown at (A) can therefore be replaced by that shown at (D) in which a perfect coil and condenser are shunted by a parallel resistance. At resonance the impedance of this circuit reduces to a fictitious resistance as shown at (E).

such a frequency that the reactance of the coil and condenser are equal in magnitude and opposite in sign. The resonant frequency of a parallel-tuned circuit is, for practical purposes, given by the same formula as for the series circuit, viz.—

$$f = \frac{1}{2\pi\sqrt{LC}}$$

At resonance the impedance of a parallel-tuned circuit is resistive and is a maximum as shown in **Fig. 19 (B)**. If the coil and condenser were perfect reactive components, the impedance at resonance would be infinite. In practice the condenser can be looked upon as a nearly perfect reactance, but there is always appreciable resistance associated with the coil which limits the resonant impedance of the circuit. The value of the impedance of a parallel-tuned circuit at resonance is called the *dynamic resistance* of the circuit. This is a fictitious resistance and appears to exist only for alternating currents of the resonant frequency; the d.c. resistance of the circuit is, of course, relatively very low.

Parallel-tuned circuits are sometimes called *rejector circuits* because at resonance they have a high impedance and therefore reject current at their resonant frequency.

Dynamic Resistance

There is a series-to-parallel transformation which can be made between the two circuits of **Fig. 19 (C)** in which the series resistance r can be replaced by an equivalent shunt resistance R. Providing the value of r is small compared with the reactance of the coil, as is usually the case in radio circuits, the value of R is given by the formula—

$$R = \frac{X_L^2}{r} = \frac{\omega^2 L^2}{r}$$

where $\omega = 2\pi f$

It follows that the parallel-tuned circuit of Fig. 19 (A) can be replaced by that shown in **Fig. 19 (D)** in which a perfect coil and condenser are shunted by a resistance R. At resonance the capacitive and inductive reactances cancel out and the impedance of the circuit reduces to the fictitious resistance R_D shown in **Fig. 19 (E)**: this is the dynamic resistance of the circuit.

Since at resonance $\omega L = 1/\omega C$, the value of the dynamic resistance of a parallel-tuned circuit is given by—

$$R_D = \frac{L}{Cr}$$

Further, since $Q = \omega L/r$, the dynamic resistance can also be expressed as—

$$R_D = \frac{Q}{\omega C}$$

From this it can be seen that for a high dynamic resistance (which is necessary for high gain in an r.f. amplifier when a parallel-resonant circuit is used as an anode load), the ratio of L to C should be high and r should be small (i.e., the Q should be high). The gain of a pentode radio-frequency or intermediate-frequency amplifier is roughly equal to the dynamic resistance of the tuned-circuit load multiplied by the mutual conductance of the valve: see Chapter 2 (*Valves*).

Resonance Curves and Selectivity

The curves of Figs. 18 (B) and 19 (B) show how tuned

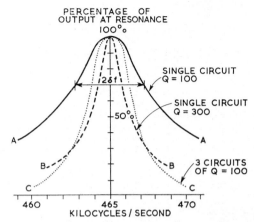

Fig. 20. Selectivity curves of single and cascaded tuned circuits.

circuits are more responsive at their resonant frequency than at neighbouring frequencies. Curves of this nature are called *resonance curves* and show how a tuned circuit can be used to pick out, or select, a wanted signal from a number of unwanted signals on other frequencies. **Fig. 20** shows a resonance curve A for a single parallel-tuned circuit having a resonant frequency of 465 kc/s and a Q of 100. When such a circuit is connected as the anode load in a simple single-stage intermediate-frequency amplifier circuit the curve shows how the gain varies with frequency. For instance, it will be seen that an unwanted signal at 461 kc/s (4 kc/s off tune) would give only 50 per cent of the output of the wanted signal (of equal input amplitude) at 465 kc/s. The dashed curve B is for a similar circuit but with a Q of 300 and shows clearly how a higher Q gives greater selectivity.

There is a practical upper limit to the value of Q which can be obtained with a coil of reasonable size, and since much greater selectivity is required in a receiver than can be obtained with a single-tuned circuit several amplifying stages are commonly used in cascade, each with a resonant circuit as its anode load. The dotted curve C in Fig. 20 shows the response of three circuits in cascade, each with a Q of 100. The response at resonance has been rated at 100 per cent in each case regardless of the additional gain due to the extra valves. It will be seen that the curve is blunter at the peak or " nose " than that of a single circuit with a Q of 300 (a

TABLE 4
Selectivity of Tuned Circuits

Percentage of Output at Resonance	Bandwidth (width across response curve)
95%	$f/3Q$
90%	$f/2Q$
70%	f/Q
45%	$2f/Q$
24%	$4f/Q$
12%	$8f/Q$

(f is the resonant frequency of the circuit.)

desirable feature for telephony reception) and gives more selectivity down the " skirts " than the single circuit.

Another method of obtaining better selectivity than can be provided by a single tuned circuit is to apply *reaction*, or *positive feedback*, a method commonly used in straight receivers: see Chapter 4 (*H.F. Receivers*) The application of reaction artificially increases the Q of the circuit, a value of several thousand being readily obtainable, with a consequent increase in selectivity and sensitivity.

Table 4 is useful for deriving approximate selectivity curves from the Q of the circuit and the operating frequency. Thus as an example, a circuit having a Q of 100 and a resonant frequency of 465 kc/s would have a bandwidth (i.e. width across the resonance curve) of $f/Q = 465/100 = 4.65$ kc/s between points where the output had fallen to 70 per cent of the resonant value on either side of resonance, as marked in Fig. 20. The approximations given in Table 4 may be used with series-tuned circuits or with parallel-tuned circuits whose Q is greater than 10, as is the case in most radio equipment.

Coupled Circuits

For the satisfactory reception of radio telephony it is necessary to amplify equally the carrier frequency and a number of sideband frequencies which occur above and below the carrier frequency and which carry the speech intelligence: see Chapter 9 (*Modulation*). The ideal r.f. response curve would therefore be flat at the peak for a few kilocycles on either side of resonance to pass the sidebands and then fall away rapidly down the " skirts " to provide good adjacent-channel selectivity.

This ideal response characteristic is more nearly obtained by using pairs of mutually-coupled tuned circuits than by the

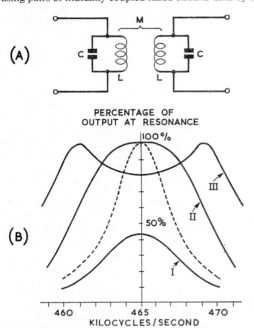

Fig. 21. Inductively-coupled tuned circuits. The curves shown at (B) represent the various frequency response characteristics of the coupled circuit shown at (A) for different degrees of coupling.

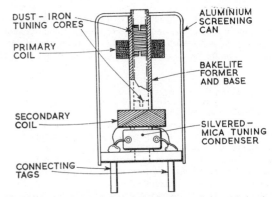

Fig. 22. A practical design for inductively-coupled tuned circuits.

cascaded single-tuned circuits mentioned in the previous section.

The most common type of coupled circuit is that shown in **Fig. 21 (A)** in which inductive coupling is provided by the presence of mutual inductance between the identical primary and secondary circuits. The shape of the response curve of a pair of coupled circuits depends on the degree of coupling between them as well as on the Q of the parallel circuits. If there is little coupling (usually referred to as *loose coupling*) between the circuits, i.e. with the coils spaced far apart, the shape of the response curve is as for two cascaded circuits of the same Q and resonant frequency, but the output voltage would be small. This is shown in **Fig. 21 (B)**, curve I. If the degree of coupling is gradually increased by bringing the coils closer together the output at resonance will increase to a maximum value as shown in curve II. Further increase in coupling is accompanied by a reduction in output at the resonant frequency and the appearance of a double-humped response, curve III.

The degree of coupling corresponding to curve II is called *critical coupling*. For critical coupling the mutual inductance required between the coils is about $1/Q$ of the inductance of either coil.

The dotted curve of Fig. 21 (B) is the overall response curve of two cascaded single circuits of the same Q as those in the coupled pair, and is included to illustrate the broader peak and steeper " skirts " of the latter.

Fig. 22 is a sketch showing a common method of mounting coupled tuned circuits. Two wave-wound coils are mounted on a common cylindrical former which is threaded internally to take a pair of dust-iron cores, one for tuning each coil. Fixed silvered-mica tuning condensers are used and connections are brought out to soldering tags on the base. The whole unit is enclosed in an aluminium screening can. The degree of coupling between the coils is determined by their spacing, the correct coupling being found experimentally rather than by calculation. This is necessary because allowance must be made for a certain amount of unintentional capacitive coupling between the circuits which is additional to that provided by the mutual inductance.

The amount of coupling used in intermediate-frequency transformers in superheterodyne receivers is usually less than the critical value since critically coupled and over-coupled transformers are difficult to tune correctly.

Other methods of coupling tuned circuits are sometimes used. **Fig. 23 (A)** shows a pair of circuits with " top-capacity" coupling. The exact value of the coupling capacity C_c is found experimentally and a good starting value is $1/Q$ of the tuning capacity C, where Q relates to either of the single-tuned circuits. In " bottom-capacity " or " common-capacity " coupling, shown in **Fig. 23 (B)**, the value required will be about Q times the tuning capacity.

Fig. 23 (C) shows another way of employing mutual inductance known as *link coupling* which is useful if the two circuits are separated by an appreciable distance. Current in the primary coil induces a current in the link circuit which in turn induces a current in the secondary coil. The link coils usually have only a few turns of wire and sometimes merely a single turn.

Fig. 23 (D) shows a circuit in which the degree of coupling between primary and secondary may be varied by selecting the number of turns in the primary circuit which are arranged to link with the secondary by means of a switch. The switch is shown in the position of least coupling (narrowest

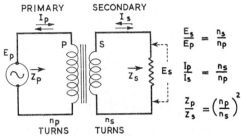

$$\frac{E_s}{E_p} = \frac{n_s}{n_p}$$

$$\frac{I_p}{I_s} = \frac{n_s}{n_p}$$

$$\frac{Z_p}{Z_s} = \left(\frac{n_p}{n_s}\right)^2$$

Fig. 24. The low-frequency transformer.

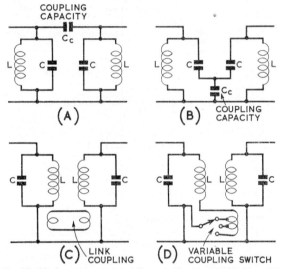

Fig. 23. Various arrangements for coupling tuned circuits : (A) " Top-capacity " coupling, (B) " Bottom-capacity " coupling, (C) link coupling, (D) variable inductive coupling, especially suitable for variable-bandwidth i.f. amplifier transformers.

bandwidth), and this arrangement may be adopted in a variable-bandwidth i.f. amplifier in a superheterodyne receiver.

TRANSFORMERS

The fact that a changing current in one circuit can induce a current in a second circuit, as in Fig. 13 (B), is the basis of transformer action.

Transformers are useful for transferring electrical energy from one circuit to another without direct connection, for example from the anode circuit of one valve to the grid circuit of another valve. In the transfer process it is possible to change the relative voltages and impedances of the primary and secondary circuits, examples being the supply of a low voltage to operate a valve heater from the high-voltage supply mains and the impedance matching of a low-resistance loudspeaker to a valve anode circuit.

The coupled circuits referred to in the discussion on Fig. 21 are examples of transformers with very loose coupling between the primary and secondary windings. In audio-frequency and power-supply transformers, tight coupling is required, and the primary and secondary windings are therefore wound on an iron core with a construction similar to that of the low-frequency choke of Fig. 14 (A-C). The size of core used in the transformer depends on the amount of power to be handled.

Fig. 24 shows a simple transformer with a primary winding P and a secondary winding S. Since both windings are in the same alternating magnetic field, the induced voltages will be in proportion to the number of turns on each coil. Thus if—

Number of turns on the primary	$= n_p$
Number of turns on the secondary	$= n_s$
Voltage across the primary	$= E_p$
Voltage across the secondary	$= E_s$

$$E_s = E_p \frac{n_s}{n_p}$$

The ratio n_s/n_p is called the *turns ratio* and a transformer may step a voltage up or down according to whether n_s/n_p is greater or less than unity.

As an example consider a transformer which supplies valve heaters having 1200 turns in its primary and 32 turns in its secondary. When connected to a 240-volt mains supply the secondary voltage will be—

$$E_s = \frac{240 \times 32}{1200}$$

$$= 6{\cdot}4 \text{ volts.}$$

As long as there is no load connected to a transformer the primary current should be very small. This current is called the *magnetizing current* and can be neglected in most calculations when compared with the primary current due to the secondary load. Since the intensity of the magnetic field set up by the primary and secondary current is the same and since the field intensity is proportional to the number of ampere-turns of each winding it follows that the primary current will be equal to the secondary current multiplied by the turns ratio.

Thus if—

Current in the primary	$= I_p$
Current in the secondary	$= I_s$

$$I_p = I_s \frac{n_s}{n_p}$$

Taking the previous example again, if the heater current is 6 amperes the primary current would be—

$$I_p = \frac{6 \times 32}{1200} \text{ amperes} = 160 \text{ mA.}$$

A transformer has the property of being able to transform impedances. If the impedance offered by the primary of the transformer of Fig. 24 is measured it will be found to be equal to the secondary or load impedance divided by the square of the turns ratio. Thus if—

$$\text{Primary impedance} = Z_p$$
$$\text{Secondary impedance} = Z_s$$

$$Z_p = Z_s \left(\frac{n_p}{n_s}\right)^2$$

It is probably more convenient to remember this result as—

$$\frac{Z_p}{Z_s} = \left(\frac{n_p}{n_s}\right)^2$$

which means that *the impedance ratio is equal to the square of the turns ratio.*

The transformation of impedance is a valuable property and transformers are widely used for matching a load to a source of power, the turns ratio being calculated to give maximum transfer of power to the load.

For example, the load into which an audio-frequency amplifier valve delivers its maximum undistorted output may be 6400 ohms. However, the loudspeaker which it is desired to use with the valve may have an average impedance of only 4 ohms and a matching transformer will therefore be required. The transformer turns ratio can be calculated from the formula just mentioned by taking the square root of the impedance ratio, thus—

$$\frac{n_p}{n_s} = \sqrt{\frac{Z_p}{Z_s}} = \sqrt{\frac{6400}{4}} = \frac{40}{1}$$

This means that a transformer with 40 times as many turns on the primary as on the secondary will give the required impedance match.

Transformers are often referred to by their primary-to-secondary winding turns ratio. Thus a 40-to-1 (or 40 : 1) transformer would have 40 turns on the primary for each turn on the secondary, and would be a "step-down" transformer suitable for matching a primary-to-secondary impedance ratio of $(40)^2 : 1$ or $1600 : 1$. A transformer with a 1 : 2 ratio would have two turns on the secondary for each turn on the primary, and would be a step-up transformer, and match primary-to-secondary impedance ratios of 1 : 4.

THE ELECTROMAGNETIC SPECTRUM

Radio waves are electromagnetic waves forming part of the electromagnetic spectrum which comprises radio, heat, light, ultra-violet, gamma rays, and X-rays: see **Fig. 25.** The various forms of electromagnetic radiation are all in the form of oscillatory waves, but differ from each other in frequency and wavelength. Notwithstanding these differences they all travel through space with the same speed,

APPROXIMATE WAVELENGTHS

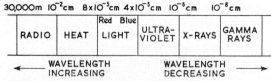

Fig. 25. The electromagnetic spectrum (not drawn to scale) showing the relative position of radio waves.

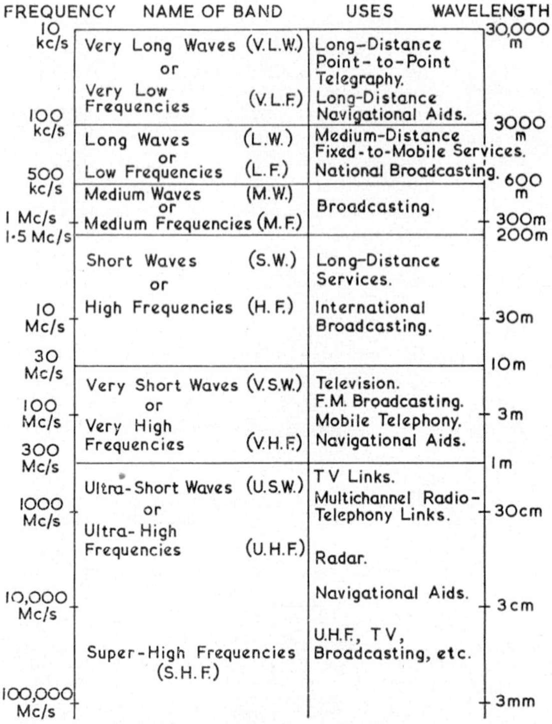

FREQUENCY	NAME OF BAND		USES	WAVELENGTH
10 kc/s	Very Long Waves	(V.L.W.)	Long-Distance Point-to-Point Telegraphy.	30,000 m
	or			
100 kc/s	Very Low Frequencies	(V.L.F.)	Long-Distance Navigational Aids.	3000 m
	Long Waves	(L.W.)	Medium-Distance Fixed-to-Mobile Services.	
500 kc/s	or Low Frequencies	(L.F.)	National Broadcasting.	600 m
1 Mc/s	Medium Waves	(M.W.)	Broadcasting.	300 m
1·5 Mc/s	or Medium Frequencies	(M.F.)		200 m
	Short Waves	(S.W.)	Long-Distance Services.	
	or			
10 Mc/s	High Frequencies	(H.F.)	International Broadcasting.	30 m
30 Mc/s				10 m
100 Mc/s	Very Short Waves	(V.S.W.)	Television. F.M. Broadcasting. Mobile Telephony.	3 m
	or Very High			
300 Mc/s	Frequencies	(V.H.F.)	Navigational Aids.	1 m
1000 Mc/s	Ultra-Short Waves	(U.S.W.)	T V Links. Multichannel Radio-Telephony Links.	30 cm
	or Ultra-High			
	Frequencies	(U.H.F.)	Radar.	
10,000 Mc/s			Navigational Aids.	3 cm
	Super-High Frequencies (S.H.F.)		U.H.F., T V, Broadcasting, etc.	
100,000 Mc/s				3 mm

Fig. 26. The radio-frequency spectrum.

namely, 3×10^{10} cm per second. This is equivalent to about 86,000 miles per second (i.e., once round the world in one-seventh of a second).

Frequency and Wavelength

The distance travelled by a wave in the time taken to complete one cycle of oscillation is called the *wavelength*. It follows that wavelength, frequency and velocity of propagation are related by the formula—

$$Velocity = Frequency \times Wavelength$$

or $c = f\lambda$.

where c = velocity of propagation (3×10^{10} cm/sec.)
f = frequency of oscillation (c/s)
λ = wavelength (cm).

This formula enables the wavelength to be calculated if its frequency is known, and vice versa.

The following example is taken from a Radio Amateurs' Examination paper.

Example. *What are the frequencies corresponding to wavelengths of (i) 150m (ii) 2m and (iii) 75cm.*

From the formula $c = f\lambda$, the frequency is given by—

$$f = \frac{c}{\lambda}$$

Case (i): $\lambda = 150m = 1\cdot5 \times 10^4$ cm
$$c = 3 \times 10^{10} \text{ cm/sec.}$$

$$\text{Therefore } f = \frac{3 \times 10^{10}}{1\cdot5 \times 10^4} = 2 \times 10^6 \text{ c/s}$$

$$= 2\cdot0 \text{ Mc/s}$$

Case (ii): $\lambda = 2\text{m} = 2 \times 10^2 \text{ cm}$

$$\text{Therefore } f = \frac{3 \times 10^{10}}{2 \times 10^2} = 1 \cdot 5 \times 10^8 \text{ c/s}$$

$$= 150 \text{ Mc/s}$$

Case (iii): $\lambda = 75\text{cm}$

$$\text{Therefore } f = \frac{3 \times 10^{10}}{75} = 4 \times 10^8 \text{ c/s}$$

$$= 400 \text{ Mc/s.}$$

Fig. 26 shows how the radio spectrum may be divided up into various bands of frequencies, the properties of each making them suitable for specific purposes. Amateur transmission is permitted on certain frequency bands in the h.f., v.h.f. and u.h.f. ranges. Full details of the frequencies allocated for amateur use will be found in Chapter 22.

AERIALS

An aerial is used to launch electromagnetic waves into space or conversely to pick up energy from such a wave travelling through space. Any wire carrying a high frequency alternating current will radiate electromagnetic waves and conversely an electromagnetic wave will induce a current in a length of wire. The problem in aerial design is to radiate as much transmitter power as possible in the required direction, or in the case of a receiver, to pick up as strong a signal as possible, very often in the presence of local interference.

An aerial may be considered as a tuned circuit consisting of inductance, capacitance and resistance, and for maximum radiation an aerial is usually operated so that it is naturally resonant at the operating frequency, maximum radiation corresponding to maximum high-frequency current flowing in the aerial.

There are two basic types of aerial used by amateurs, (a) the Hertzian aerial, known as a *dipole* or *doublet*, which is self-resonant by virtue of its length in relation to the wavelength of the signal, and (b) the Marconi aerial which may be of any convenient length and relies on an earth connection and is tuned to resonance by means of a coil or condenser. The simple Hertzian aerial is one-half wavelength long and is therefore well suited to the shorter waves (higher frequencies) whereas the Marconi aerial is mainly used at longer wavelengths, e.g., 160m and 80m where it is often impracticable to erect a Hertzian dipole. Full explanations of aerial theory and practical design will be found in Chapters 13 and 14. A typical examination question on the tuning of a Marconi aerial is worked out in Example III on page 24.

PROPAGATION OF RADIO WAVES

Radio waves, on leaving an aerial, travel through space in straight lines with the velocity of light. The waves consist of interdependent electric and magnetic fields which act in directions mutually at right angles and also at right angles to the direction of propagation of the wave.

If the electric field acts in a vertical direction the wave is said to be *vertically polarized* and such waves are launched and best picked up by vertical aerials, **Fig. 27 (A)**. If the electric field is horizontal the waves are said to be *horizontally polarized* and horizontal aerials are then used: see **Fig. 27 (B)**.

Horizontal polarization is most commonly used by

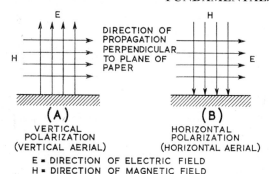

Fig. 27. Diagram illustrating the polarization of electromagnetic waves: (A) represents vertical polarization and (B) represents horizontal polarization, the distinction being in terms of the electric vector rather than the magnetic vector.

amateurs on the short-wave bands for long-distance communication. Vertical polarization is used for mobile work and local work on short waves and very short waves where the " all-round " or omni-directional characteristics of simple vertical aerials are an advantage.

The propagation of short waves to remote parts of the earth depends on reflection of the waves from layers of ionized gas situated between 70 and 200 miles or so above the earth in a region called the *ionosphere*. As the reflecting properties of this region depend on the frequency used and are continually changing with night and day, the time of year, and sunspot activity, it can be imagined that the mechanism of long-distance short-wave propagation is complex and very variable. However, transmission conditions to distant points can be forecast with some accuracy. The propagation of v.h.f. and u.h.f. signals depends not on the conditions in the ionosphere but on meteorological conditions in the lower levels of the atmosphere called the *troposphere*.

The subject of radio-wave propagation is treated in detail in Chapter 12 (*Propagation*).

Fading

It is common for short-wave signals which have arrived at a receiver from a distant transmitter to vary continually in strength. This phenomena is known as *fading* and is caused by the varying relationship between signals arriving at the receiver by different paths whose relative lengths are changing.

The strength of the signal at the receiving aerial terminal is the sum of signals arriving from a transmitter by perhaps two different paths. If the two paths differ in length by an exact number of wavelengths, dependent on the frequency being used, the signals arriving by the two paths will arrive in phase and the total strength of received signal will be a maximum. If, however, the path lengths differ by an odd number of half-wavelengths the two signals will be out of phase and the total received signal strength will be a minimum. Thus if a signal is being received both by ground-wave and sky-wave paths, or by two different sky-wave paths, fading will be experienced when the effective height of the ionized layer which reflects the sky-wave varies since this has the effect of altering the relative path lengths between transmitter and receiver.

Fading may be slow or very rapid: if it is rapid, the fading appears as an audible low-frequency flutter. During fading, the transmitted speech sometimes becomes badly distorted because the carrier and various sideband frequencies do not all fade equally at the same time.

The effect of fading is combated by applying " automatic volume control " (better referred to as *automatic gain control*) to receivers so that the overall gain of the set varies inversely with the strength of the received signal. Other methods used are (*a*) *highly directive aerial systems*, particularly in the vertical plane so as to restrict the possibility of multi-path transmission, and (*b*) *diversity reception* in which two or more spaced aerials or two or more different frequencies are used for a transmission. Diversity reception depends for its operation on the fact that, statistically, fading is unlikely to occur at two different points or on two different frequencies at the same time. Two receivers are used with an automatic change-over arrangement for selecting the stronger of the two signals, a considerable reduction in fading being achieved.

VALVES

The successful development of radio communication has depended overwhelmingly on the thermionic valve. Valves are used as rectifiers for converting alternating currents into direct currents both at power-supply frequency and at radio frequency where the process is more commonly called *detection*. Other common applications are the generation of radio-frequency power in transmitters and the amplification of signals in receivers.

The earliest valves, called *diodes*, had two electrodes enclosed in an evacuated envelope. This is shown diagrammatically in **Fig. 28 (A)**. The filament electrode or *cathode*, was made of tungsten wire and could be heated to incandescence by the passage of a current through it supplied by a low-tension or " A " battery. When incandescent the filament has the property of emitting free electrons which, being negatively charged, may be attracted to the second electrode called an *anode* or *plate* if the voltage of the anode is made positive with respect to the filament by the use of a high-tension (h.t.) battery " B," as shown in **Fig. 28 (B)**.

Reversal of the polarity between anode and cathode, as in **Fig. 28 (C)**, will repel the electrons and prevent the passage of current. The actual flow of current through a valve is in the form of a flow of electrons from filament to anode; nevertheless the conventional flow of current from the positive to the negative battery terminal, i.e., from anode to cathode, is usually assumed.

More efficient emitter materials are now used in valves than the original tungsten filament. For example, thoriated tungsten (a mixture of tungsten and 1–2 per cent of thorium) is up to ten times as efficient as pure tungsten. An even more

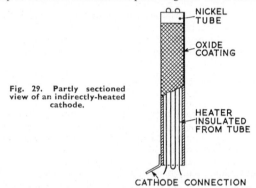

Fig. 29. Partly sectioned view of an indirectly-heated cathode.

efficient emitter very commonly used in valves is the oxide-coated type in which a mixture of barium, strontium and calcium oxides forms a coating on a filament. Such a composite filament gives a copious emission at relatively low temperature.

Valves using a filament as a source of electrons are called *directly-heated* valves. It is an advantage, particularly in equipment operating on a.c. supplies, to use valves of the type having what is called an *indirectly-heated cathode*. An indirectly-heated cathode consists of a nickel tube coated with the rare-earth oxides mentioned above to form the emitting surface which is heated to the required temperature by a filament or heater inside the tube but insulated from it as shown in the sketch in **Fig. 29**.

The introduction of an extra electrode, called a *grid*, between the cathode and anode forms a three-electrode

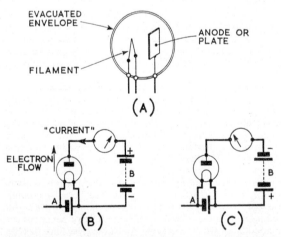

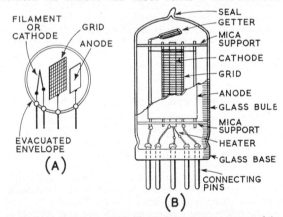

Fig. 28. A simple diode valve: (A) shows the essential construction comprising a filament and an anode: (B) illustrates how current flows through the valve when the anode is made positive with respect to the filament, and (C) shows the cessation of current when the polarity is reversed.

Fig. 30. The triode valve: (A) indicates the basic arrangement of the electrodes, the grid being interposed between the cathode and the anode, and (B) shows the construction of a typical indirectly-heated triode valve.

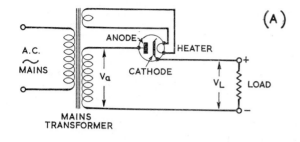

(A)

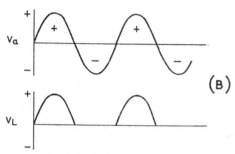

(B)

Fig. 31. The operation of the diode as a rectifier: (A) shows an elementary circuit in which an a.c. supply is rectified, producing uni-directional current pulses in the resistive load, (B) represents the waveform of the a.c. input voltage and the rectified voltage across the load.

valve which is called a *triode* and is shown diagrammatically in **Fig. 30 (A)**. The grid has the property of controlling the flow of electrons from the cathode to the anode, and the more negative the grid voltage is relative to the cathode the smaller the anode current becomes until it is finally cut off altogether. A small change in grid voltage may cause a considerable change in anode current and this effect forms the basis of the valve amplifier.

Fig. 30 (B) shows the construction of an indirectly-heated triode valve. The cathode, grid and anode are mounted between mica supports and are connected to appropriate pins fitted in a glass base. The electrode assembly is surrounded by a glass bulb sealed to the base, and at the top of the bulb is the seal through which the air is exhausted during manufacture. The purpose of the *getter*, which is fired during the evacuation process, is to deposit a gas-absorbing film of barium metal on the inside of the bulb. It remains active after manufacture and maintains a very high vacuum.

More complex valves using more electrodes than the triode are in common use. Detailed information on all types of valve and their applications will be found in Chapter 2 (*Valves*).

Rectification and Detection

The operation of a diode as a rectifier is illustrated in **Fig. 31**. The circuit shows a mains transformer having two secondary windings, one to heat the cathode of the rectifier valve and the other to step the mains voltage up or down according to the output voltage required. The diode will conduct only during the positive half-cycles of the a.c. waveform V_a applied to its anode so that the voltage V_L across the load resistance (and the current through it) will be undirectional as shown. Practical applications of this

circuit to power supplies will be found in Chapter 17 (*Power Supplies*).

The unidirectional conduction of a diode is used in a similar way but at a higher frequency to rectify or " detect " radio-frequency signals, the most common applications being the second detector and the a.g.c. rectifier in superheterodyne receivers.

Amplification and Oscillation

The basic amplifier circuit is shown in **Fig. 32**. The grid is biased slightly negative with respect to the cathode by the

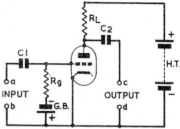

Fig. 32. Basic amplifier circuit (untuned).

bias battery GB in series with the high grid resistance R_g (usually $\frac{1}{2}$–1 Megohm). A steady anode current will flow through the valve and the load resistance R_L.

An a.c. signal applied between the input terminals a and b will be applied through the coupling condenser C_1 to cause the grid-to-cathode voltage to vary above and below its steady biased voltage in sympathy with the a.c. waveform applied. The changing grid-to-cathode voltage will cause a corresponding changing anode current to flow through the load resistance R_L and the anode-to-cathode path in the valve, this variation being superimposed on the steady anode current. The alternating component of the anode current

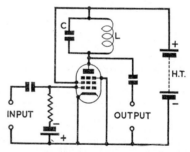

Fig. 33. Basic radio-frequency amplifier circuit (tuned). A pentode is used instead of a triode to simplify the problem of eliminating unwanted feedback.

will produce an amplified replica of the input waveform at the output terminals c and d. It should be noted that the amplified output waveform will be 180° out-of-phase with the input waveform since a positive-going grid voltage causes an increase in anode current which in turn causes a decrease in voltage between the anode and the cathode.

The circuit shown is applicable to audio-frequency amplification. At radio frequencies a frequency-selective amplifier is usually required and selectivity is obtained by using a parallel-tuned circuit, LC, as an anode load instead of the resistance R_L, as shown in **Fig. 33**. Except with special constructional or circuit arrangements triodes are not suitable for use as r.f. amplifiers since the unavoidable capacity between grid and anode inside the valve results in unwanted oscillation. This effect is avoided by the use of a pentode valve, as shown in this circuit. Since the output voltage from such an amplifier is, within limits, proportional to the load impedance it follows that the output voltage will be a maximum at the resonant frequency of the tuned circuit where its impedance is a maximum, falling away on either side of the resonance where the impedance decreases.

The voltage amplification of an r.f. amplifier may be as much as 100 or even higher. If a secondary winding of a few turns is wound round the coil in the anode tuned circuit LC, a voltage will be obtained which can be fed back to the grid circuit as shown in **Fig. 34**. The arrangement then really

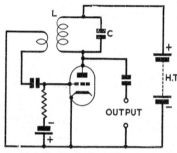

Fig. 34. Basic oscillator.

becomes an amplifier capable of supplying its own input and, provided that the sense of the feedback winding is correct, continuous oscillations will be produced at a resonant frequency determined by the values of L and C. Such a tuned amplifier with suitable feedback from output to input forms the basis of most oscillators used in transmitters and receivers.

Negative Feedback

The type of feedback mentioned in the previous paragraph is called *positive feedback* because the signal fed back from output to input is in phase with the input signal. If an amplifier circuit is arranged so that some of the output is fed back to the input in such a way that it is 180° out of phase with the input signal, *negative feedback* is said to have been applied and a reduction in the overall gain of the amplifier ensues.

At first sight such a reduction of gain appears to be a disadvantage; however, the application of negative feedback yields several advantages which more than offset the reduction in gain. These advantages are—

(*a*) A reduction in harmonic distortion caused in the amplifier.

(*b*) A flattening of the amplifier response curve.

(*c*) A reduction in hum and other amplifier noise.

(*d*) A stabilization of amplifier performance against variations in supply voltages, component values and in valve characteristics.

The way in which negative feedback reduces harmonic distortion may be explained simply as follows. Suppose an amplifier is being fed with an input signal which is a pure tone (i.e. an undistorted sine wave). Due to imperfections in the amplifier, harmonics of the input signal will be

produced which will appear in the output as harmonic distortion. Clearly, by feeding the correct amount of each harmonic, in the correct phase, into the input terminals of the amplifier from some auxiliary source, it would be possible to cancel out the distortion produced in the amplifier. Negative feedback from the output circuit provides just such a type of distortion-cancelling signal and, although complete elimination of distortion cannot be achieved, provided that the gain of the amplifier is high and that a sufficient fraction of the output is fed back, a very worthwhile reduction in distortion may be obtained.

A further reference to negative feedback is to be found in Chapter 9 (*Modulation*).

PIEZOELECTRIC EFFECT

Certain crystalline substances have the property of developing an electric charge on their surfaces when subjected to mechanical strain and, conversely, of exhibiting mechanical strain when their surfaces are electrically charged. This is known as the *piezoelectric effect*.

For radio purposes the most widely applied piezoelectric substance is quartz. This is used in high-stability radio-frequency oscillators and in sharply tuned frequency filters. Another piezoelectric material is Rochelle salt (sodium potassium tartrate): this has somewhat different characteristics from quartz, and is used in crystal microphones and in crystal headphones and loudspeakers. In amateur practice, however, these items seldom if ever require any attention and it is only the quartz crystal that is likely to merit a detailed study.

Quartz Crystals

Apart from the imperfections which normally occur in nature, a crystal of quartz is shaped like a hexagonal prism with a hexagonal pyramid at each end, as shown in **Fig. 35 (A)**. Typical crystals may be an inch or two in diameter and several inches long, and from these a large number of thin slabs or plates having the required electromechanical characteristics can be cut.

If one of these plates is made to vibrate by mechanical means, it will develop an alternating voltage between its opposite faces, and vice versa if an oscillatory voltage is applied to a pair of electrodes on opposite sides of the plate it will vibrate at the same frequency as the applied voltage.

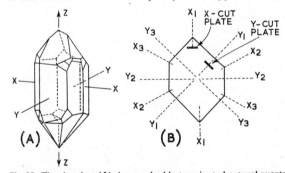

Fig. 35. The sketch at (A) shows a double-terminated natural quartz crystal and indicates the relationship between the X, Y and Z axes. Usually the crystal is found to have one pyramidal termination and one rough end where it has been broken from the parent rock. The sectional drawing (B) shows the various X and Y axes as viewed along a direction parallel to the Z-axis and includes examples of positions of X-cut and Y-cut plates.

If this frequency happens to coincide with a mechanical resonance of the plate, the vibration will reach a considerable amplitude and in extreme cases it may be sufficient to cause the plate to fracture, thereby rendering it permanently worthless. The actual amplitude of vibration is always microscopically small, but the corresponding voltage developed may be of the order of several volts.

The characteristics of such a quartz plate depend on the way in which it has been cut from the natural crystal in relation to the crystallographic axes. These are indicated in **Fig. 35 (B)**. Axes such as XX which bisect the angle between any pair of adjacent faces of the hexagonal section are called the *electric axes*, and those such as YY which are perpendicular to any of the faces of the crystal are called the *mechanical axes*, while the axis ZZ is called the *optical axis*. If a plate is cut so that its faces are perpendicular to an XX-axis or to a YY-axis, it is said to be an X-cut or a Y-cut crystal respectively. Innumerable other cuts can be chosen, simply by tilting the plane of cutting so as to make various angles with the axes, but only a few particular orientations are used in practice and each of these has its own special advantage. An example is the AT-cut crystal: in this type the plane of the cut is rotated 35° from the Z-axis, as shown in **Fig. 36**.

Any quartz plate will have several different mechanical resonances, depending on the mode of vibration. In the

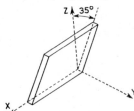

Fig. 36. An AT-cut crystal has its major surfaces at an angle of 35° to the Z-axis. This type of crystal has a low temperature coefficient and is widely used in r.f. oscillators.

ordinary type of crystal used in h.f. transmitters, the most important mode is the thickness vibration, since this gives the highest frequency for a reasonable set of dimensions. Even so, the plate has to be made quite thin to achieve a usefully high frequency. For instance, a crystal designed for 7 Mc/s might have a thickness of only 15 thousandths of an inch. A slight variation in thickness corresponds to a large change in frequency, and therefore to obtain a strong piezoelectric response the plate must be uniformly thick within very fine limits over its entire area.

With this mode of vibration, the main resonant frequency is inversely proportional to the thickness. The precise relationship depends on the angle of cut, as shown in the few examples given here:

Type of Cut	Frequency (kc/s) $\times$ Thickness (mm.)
X	2750
AT	1630
BT	2500

Other factors to be considered include the temperature coefficient of frequency, which is a measure of how much the frequency varies with temperature. This is of great importance in high-precision frequency control, and a discussion of it will be found in Chapter 6 (*H.F. Transmitters*).

Quartz is an exceptionally hard substance and the necessary cutting, grinding and polishing operations are very tedious. The usual materials employed are diamond, carborundum, emery and jeweller's rouge. Great accuracy is essential in the dimensioning and finishing processes, similar to that found in the highest class of optical work.

The grinding of the crystal by these methods results in some damage to the crystalline structure of the surface. Much improved stability and performance can be achieved by using a final etching process, whereby the damaged surface

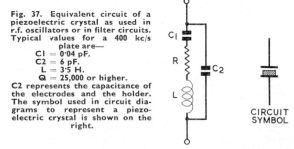

Fig. 37. Equivalent circuit of a piezoelectric crystal as used in r.f. oscillators or in filter circuits. Typical values for a 400 kc/s plate are—
C1 = 0·04 pF.
C2 = 6 pF.
L = 3·5 H.
Q = 25,000 or higher.
C2 represents the capacitance of the electrodes and the holder. The symbol used in circuit diagrams to represent a piezoelectric crystal is shown on the right.

is dissolved away by means of a bath of hydrofluoric acid solution or of ammonium bifluoride. The final adjustment of the crystal to the required frequency is invariably carried out today by this method, which also leaves the crystal perfectly clean.

The acids used for etching are *extremely dangerous* and the method should only be used by those experienced in their handling. In particular, the acid must not be allowed to come in contact with the skin. If it is, medical attention should be obtained *immediately*.

The quartz plate is usually clamped between two flat metal electrodes, and there may or may not be a small air gap adjacent to one of the crystal surfaces. When it is desired to operate with a gap, the plate is clamped at the periphery if it is circular or at the corners if it is rectangular or square, Alternatively, thin film electrodes of gold or silver may be deposited on the faces of the crystal plate and connecting wires can then be soldered to the metallic films at suitable points (the *nodal points*): these wires also serve as supports. The assembly is sometimes enclosed in an evacuated glass envelope to exclude dirt and moisture, both of which have a deleterious effect on the performance of the crystal.

Although such a quartz plate may appear quite similar in constructional features to a small capacitor, its electrical behaviour is very different. Because of the combination of the piezoelectric properties and the mechanical vibration characteristics it behaves as a series-tuned circuit having a very high L/C ratio and a very high Q-value. The internal frictional losses in the crystal are remarkably small and consequently the equivalent resistance is very low. This is of course the effective resistance, considered as part of the equivalent circuit, to r.f. currents: the d.c. resistance is extremely high. **Fig. 37** shows the equivalent circuit of a simple quartz plate: the shunt capacitor C_2 represents the capacitance of the electrodes and the connecting leads.

A circuit of this kind has two resonant frequencies, one corresponding to a high impedance and the other to a low impedance. They are indicated in **Fig. 38** which shows how the r.f. current flowing through a typical crystal changes when the frequency of the applied r.f. voltage is varied. The resonant (or series) frequency corresponds to resonance in the series combination, LC, which behaves as a low-impedance acceptor circuit. The so-called anti-resonant

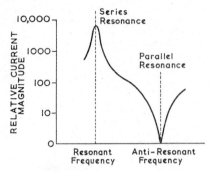

Fig. 38. Typical variation of current through a quartz crystal with frequency. The resonant and anti-resonant frequencies are normally separated by about 0·01 per cent of the frequencies themselves (e.g. a few hundred cycles for a 7 Mc/s crystal).

(or parallel) frequency corresponds to resonance in the high-impedance rejector circuit formed by the LC_1 combination in parallel with C_2.

The difference between the two frequencies is normally a small fraction of one per cent of the nominal frequency. Although there are circuits which have been devised for operating such a crystal on one or other of these frequencies, the majority of circuits used for frequency control in amateur transmitters utilize the parallel or anti-resonant high-impedance condition.

The most important feature with regard to frequency is that for either the resonant or the anti-resonant condition the impedance variation is extremely sharply defined. Thus the impedance may be found to vary by a ratio of more than 10,000 : 1 when the frequency is changed by merely a few hundred cycles. This may be expressed in terms of the equivalent circuit by saying that the Q-value is very high. In fact, a quartz crystal behaves as a tuned circuit with a Q-value many times greater than can be achieved even with the best of inductors and capacitors.

By using a quartz crystal as a substitute for the normal tuned circuit in an ordinary feedback type of r.f. oscillator, the frequency of oscillation is automatically stabilized within very close limits. Such an oscillator is known as a *crystal-controlled oscillator* (or more simply, a *crystal oscillator*), and a typical circuit is shown in **Fig. 39.**

Besides the thin flat plate type of crystal which is preferred for use in r.f. oscillators, a bar type is often used for

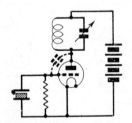

Fig. 39. Basic crystal-controlled oscillator circuit using a quartz crystal. The necessary feedback is provided by the grid-to-anode capacitance (shown dotted).

resonators in filters operating at relatively low frequencies (below about 500 kc/s): an example of this application is the *crystal filter* (sometimes known as a *crystal gate*) in a high-selectivity intermediate-frequency amplifier: see Chapter 4 (*H.F. Receivers*).

Certain crystals have a tendency to operate at unwanted or spurious frequencies, owing to mechanical coupling effects in the crystals themselves, and the circuits in which they are used may have to be designed so as to prevent any possible operation at a frequency other than the wanted frequency.

Where a crystal is required to oscillate at a frequency which is above the normally attainable maximum (usually determined by the minimum practicable thickness), it can be made to vibrate at an overtone frequency if the circuit is arranged to stimulate this action. An overtone is approximately (never exactly) a multiple of the fundamental frequency, and in most cases this type of operation is limited to the odd multiples since the even multiples are associated with modes of vibration which present difficult problems in mounting.

SEMICONDUCTOR DEVICES

Since the Second World War a number of electronic devices using semiconductor materials such as germanium and silicon have been introduced. These devices are bringing about a revolution in communication engineering comparable with that which followed the invention of the thermionic valve at the beginning of the century.

The range of devices includes semiconductor diodes and also semiconductor triodes, known as *transistors*, which have the property of being able to amplify signals. All these

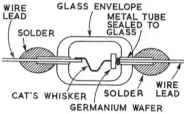

Fig. 40. Point-contact germanium diode.

devices have the important advantage of consuming less power than their thermionic valve counterparts, much of this saving arising from the fact that no cathode-heater power is required in the semiconductor devices. A practical example which illustrates this overall saving in power is a small gramophone amplifier delivering an audio output of two watts. The transistor version consumes $3\frac{1}{2}$ watts representing an efficiency of 60 per cent whereas an equivalent valve amplifier consumes 12 watts corresponding to an efficiency of $16\frac{2}{3}$ per cent. Quite apart from the obvious saving in power consumption, transistors offer the advantage of small size and weight which makes them very suitable for use in portable equipment.

The main disadvantages of transistors, particularly for the radio amateur, is that at present their power-handling capacity and radio-frequency performance still leave much to be desired. There are signs, however, that these disadvantages are gradually being overcome.

The most commonly used semiconductor device is the point-contact *germanium diode*. It consists of a small wafer of germanium, containing a very small but controlled amount of arsenic or antimony, in contact with a " cat's whisker " of wire which may be of phosphor bronze. The general arrangement is shown in **Fig. 40**, the completed diode being sealed against moisture in a glass envelope. Diodes of this type may have a forward resistance of a few

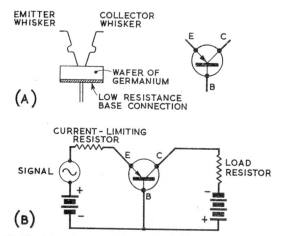

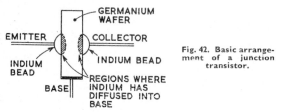

Fig. 41. Point-contact transistor. The basic arrangement of the electrodes is shown at (A): when connected in the circuit (B) it acts as an amplifier giving a current gain.

hundred ohms and a reverse resistance of several hundreds of thousands of ohms and are often used as radio-frequency rectifiers or detectors.

The earliest forms of *transistors* were " point-contact " types comprising a thin wafer of germanium, to one side of which a low-resistance or base connection was made, and a pair of closely spaced "cat's whisker" electrodes pressing on the other side of the wafer and called the *emitter* and *collector* electrodes. The general arrangement of the electrodes is shown in **Fig. 41 (A)**. When connected in the circuit of **Fig. 41 (B)** the point-contact transistor has the property of giving a current gain; i.e., for a certain change in current in the emitter-to-base circuit two to three times that change of current will occur in the collector-to-base circuit. In a typical transistor the emitter circuit may have a resistance of a few hundred ohms whereas the collector circuit may have a resistance of several tens of thousands of ohms, and the overall power gain is therefore considerable.

Point-contact transistors have been superseded by junction transistors on account of their superior characteristics, such as lower noise level, higher efficiency and greater power-handling ability. **Fig. 42** illustrates one method of junction-transistor construction. Two small beads of indium are placed on either side of a thin wafer of germanium and

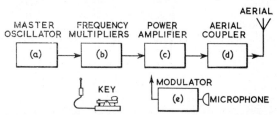

Fig. 42. Basic arrangement of a junction transistor.

then heated sufficiently to cause the indium to diffuse into the germanium as indicated by the shaded areas. This process can be controlled so that there is only a very small gap between the indium-diffused areas. The junctions which form the transistor are (a) between one indium-diffused area and the wafer and (b) between the wafer and the other indium-diffused area. Emitter and collector connections are made to the indium beads and a low-resistance base

connection is made to the germanium wafer. The transistor is then sealed in a metal or glass envelope to prevent ingress of moisture of other contaminants.

Junction transistors exhibit a current gain of slightly less than unity but the power gain available is greater than for the point-contact type since the ratio of output to input resistance is higher. Low-power junction transistors are becoming available which operate at frequencies of tens of megacycles per second. High-power low-frequency types capable of handling powers of several watts are also manufactured. Detailed information on transistors will be found in Chapter 3 (*Semiconductors*).

THE AMATEUR TRANSMITTER

The purpose of the transmitter is to provide radio-frequency energy which can be fed into an aerial for transmission to a distant point on a chosen frequency.

The simplest type of transmitter is one which will send Morse signals in the form of long and short bursts of r.f. energy corresponding to the dashes and dots of the code. A rather more elaborate arrangement is required when the transmission is to be in the form of speech or vision signals. An outline of the function of each stage is given here, but for further details the reader is referred to Chapter 6 (*H.F. Transmitters*).

Modern transmitters are usually made up of several

Fig. 43. Block diagram of a typical amateur transmitter for telegraphy and telephony. A single power supply unit is sometimes relied upon to feed the entire transmitter but there are usually important advantages to be gained by providing separate power supply units especially for the power amplifier and the modulator

distinct circuits or stages consisting of (*a*) a master oscillator, (*b*) one or more frequency-multiplying stages, (*c*) a power amplifier, or output stage, and (*d*) an aerial coupler. For speech or television transmission the necessary modulation is introduced by a further distinct unit, (*e*) a modulator. A typical telegraphy and telephony transmitter system is shown in block diagram form in **Fig. 43**.

The purpose of the master oscillator is to generate a stable high-frequency oscillation which will control the frequency of the emissions from the transmitter. A high degree of frequency stability is required not only to avoid interference with other stations operating on nearby frequencies in the crowded amateur bands but also to ensure that the signal remains within the frequency bandwidth, or pass-band, of modern highly selective receivers and show no tendency to deviate out of it. A high degree of frequency stability is usually obtained by operating the master oscillator at low power to avoid excessive generation of heat and by selecting good-quality components of high electrical and mechanical stability and by using a master-oscillator tuned circuit of high Q.

As the amateur bands are for the main part harmonically related it is common practice to operate the master oscillator in the lowest frequency amateur band and obtain sufficient

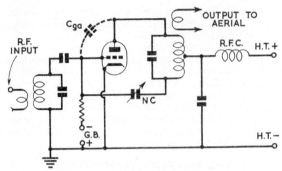

Fig. 44. Triode power amplifier circuit showing the use of a neutralizing condenser NC to balance the grid-to-anode capacitance.

power to drive the power amplifier or output stage from a succession of frequency-multiplying stages For example an oscillator capable of being varied between 1·75 and 2 Mc/s will cover not only the 160m amateur band but also the 80, 40, 20, 15 and 10m bands when multiplied by 2, 4, 8, 12 and 16 respectively. Frequency-multiplier stages use heavily-biased valves which are driven with large input voltages. This has the effect of causing the anode current to flow in short pulses instead of following the sinusoidal waveform of the drive voltage. The pulse-like anode current contains components of frequencies which are multiples of the frequency of the input waveform. A voltage at any one of these frequencies may be developed at the anode by means of a resonant circuit tuned to the required frequency. It is sometimes practicable to select up to the fifth harmonic in one stage; for higher orders of frequency multiplication several stages may be used in cascade.

The power-amplifier stage is driven by a low-power stage at the desired output frequency, a watt or two being sufficient to drive almost any of the pentode or tetrode amplifier valves likely to be used in amateur transmitters. For high-efficiency, a radio-frequency power amplifier is run under class C conditions: see Chapter 2 (*Valves*).

Triode amplifiers are not as often used as tetrodes or pentodes because they require more drive power and need " neutralizing " to avoid self-oscillation. The self-oscillation in a triode amplifier stage occurs as a result of feedback from the anode to the grid circuit through the capacity which exists between grid and anode inside the valve. The feedback may be balanced out, or neutralized, by arranging for an equal feedback voltage of opposite phase to be applied to the grid circuit. This is usually achieved in amateur transmitters by centre-tapping the tuned circuit of the output amplifier as shown in **Fig. 44** to obtain an antiphase neutralizing voltage which is fed back to the grid circuit through the small neutralizing condenser NC.

There are many types of aerial which can be used with a transmitter, and an aerial coupling or tuning unit may be necessary to ensure that the power generated by the amplifier stage is efficiently transferred to the aerial. Generally speaking aerial coupling only becomes a difficult problem if a transmitter has to operate and supply power to an aerial over a wide and continuous range of frequencies; since amateur transmitters operate only on narrow specified bands of frequencies the coupling circuit in practice can often be reduced to merely an inductive link comprising one or two turns of wire wound round the power-amplifier output coil as indicated in the circuit of Fig. 44. A useful

combined aerial coupling and power-amplifier output circuit is the pi-network coupler. It has the advantage of operating over a considerable frequency range and feeding efficiently into a wide range of load impedances and is often used in mobile equipment. It also has the merit of reducing television interference. The circuit is shown in **Fig. 45**. The proper tuning of the aerial and loading of the transmitter output stage is obtained by adjusting the two variable condensers and the tapped coil.

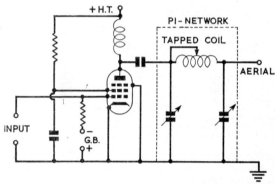

Fig. 45. A pentode power amplifier with a pi-network coupler in the anode circuit.

A radio-frequency power amplifier may be considered as a generator which converts d.c. power taken from the h.t. supply into radio-frequency power to be fed to the aerial. Important factors in connection with an amplifier are—

(*a*) The d.c. power input.
(*b*) The r.f. power output.
(*c*) The efficiency of the amplifier.
(*d*) The anode dissipation.

The d.c. input power W_{in} is equal to the product of the h.t. supply voltage V_a and the anode current I_a of the valve as shown in **Fig. 46** thus—

$$\text{Power input } W_{in} = V_a \times I_a$$

The r.f. output power is often calculated by measuring the r.f. current flowing in a load resistor sometimes called a *dummy load*. This load resistor should be non-inductive and may conveniently be of the high-power carbon type. The output power W_{out} may be calculated by finding the product of the load resistance R and the square of the load current I_{rf}: thus—

$$\text{Power output } W_{out} = R \times I_{rf}^2$$

The efficiency η of the amplifier gives a figure of merit for the stage as a converter of d.c. into r.f. power. The efficiency is calculated by dividing the power output by the

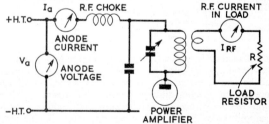

Fig. 46. Diagram showing how the d.c. power input to a radio frequency amplifier and the r.f. power which it produces can be measured.

power input and multiplying by 100 to express the result as a percentage: thus—

$$\text{Efficiency } \eta = \frac{W_{out}}{W_{in}} \times 100 \text{ per cent}$$

It is clear that since no amplifier can be 100 per cent efficient more power is fed into the amplifier than appears at the output as r.f. power. This excess of power is spent or dissipated as heat at the anode of the amplifier valve. The anode dissipation W_{dis}, may be calculated by taking the difference between the input and output power:

$$\text{Anode Dissipation } W_{dis} = W_{in} - W_{out}$$

As an example of the preceding paragraphs consider the case of an 807 valve operating with an h.t. supply of 750 volts and an anode current of 100 mA. If the amplifier is producing a current of 0·71 ampere in a load resistor of 100 ohms calculate (a) the power input, (b) the power output, (c) the efficiency and (d) the anode dissipation of the stage.

(a) Power input $W_{in} = 750 \times 0·1 = 75$ watts.

(b) Power output $W_{out} = 100 \times (0·71)^2 = 50$ watts.

(c) Efficiency $\eta = \frac{50}{75} \times 100 = 66\frac{2}{3}$ per cent.

(d) Anode dissipation $W_{dis} = 75 - 50 = 25$ watts.

As so far described the transmitter is capable of generating a steady radio-frequency signal called a *carrier wave*. This in itself conveys no information and for messages to be transmitted by telegraphy the carrier wave must be broken

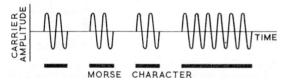

Fig. 47. Morse code signals are produced by breaking the carrier wave into long and short characters. The illustration represents the letter "V."

up into the characters of the Morse code as indicated in **Fig. 47**. This process is called *keying* and various methods which may be adopted are described in Chapter 8 (*Keying & Break-in*).

Telephony transmission is achieved by impressing upon the carrier wave in some way according to the speech waveform which is to be transmitted. This process is called *modulation* and any of the three fundamental characteristics of the carrier wave, namely amplitude, frequency and phase, may be varied in sympathy with an audio signal to produce what are known as *amplitude*, *frequency* and *phase modulation* respectively.

The most commonly used type of modulation is amplitude modulation (a.m.), in which the amplitude of the transmitter output is varied up and down in sympathy with the audio waveform without altering its frequency. The resulting waveform is shown in **Fig. 48**. The amount, or depth, of modulation of the carrier wave will depend on the amplitude of the audio modulation signal, but there is an upper limit of modulation which should never be exceeded if poor-quality transmission and interference with other stations is to be avoided. This limit, corresponding to 100 per cent modulation, occurs when the carrier-wave amplitude is reduced to zero at a peak negative swing of the audio modulating voltage as illustrated at the points P in Fig. 48. Under these conditions the amplitude corresponding to the peak

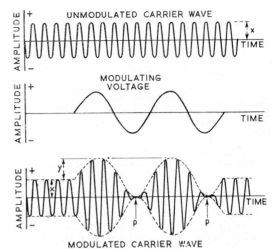

Fig. 48. Amplitude-modulated carrier wave.

positive swing of the modulating voltage is twice that of the unmodulated carrier. Intermediate depths of modulation between zero and this maximum value are usually expressed as a percentage. If x is the unmodulated amplitude of the carrier wave and y is the peak increase (or decrease) in amplitude due to the modulating waveform the depth of modulation is obtained by dividing y by x and multiplying by 100 to express the result as a percentage. Thus the percentage modulation is—

$$M = \frac{y}{x} \times 100 \text{ per cent}$$

An amplitude-modulated wave is equivalent to a carrier wave of constant amplitude together with other frequencies spaced on either side of the carrier called *sidebands*. These sidebands actually carry the audio intelligence and vary in amplitude, with a maximum of half the amplitude of the carrier at 100 per cent modulation, according to the depth of modulation. The frequency spacing between the sidebands and the carrier is equal to the modulating frequency. In **Fig. 49** is shown the frequency spectrum corresponding to

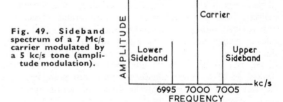

Fig. 49. Sideband spectrum of a 7 Mc/s carrier modulated by a 5 kc/s tone (amplitude modulation).

a 7 Mc/s carrier wave modulated 100 per cent by an audio tone of 5 kc/s. Since at full modulation the amplitude of each of the two sidebands is equal to one-half of the amplitude of the carrier, the power in each sideband is one-quarter of that in the carrier (the power being proportional to the square of the current or of the voltage). The power in the two sidebands taken together is therefore one-half of that of the carrier when it is fully modulated. The sideband concept of an amplitude-modulated signal is important as it indicates that the bandwidth of the circuits in a receiver should be at least twice that of the highest audio

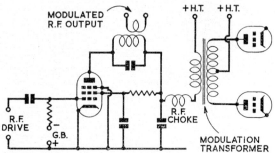

Fig. 50. A popular method of applying amplitude modulation to a radio-frequency power amplifier.

frequency transmitted so that the sidebands may be accepted and distortion be avoided.

The simple a.m. signal just described is wasteful in two ways. First a channel of bandwidth equal to twice the highest frequency of the audio signal used is required, and second at least two-thirds of the radiated power is in the carrier which conveys no actual information and could equally well be omitted and reintroduced at the receiver. Both of these disadvantages are eliminated in the single sideband suppressed carrier method of transmission in which only one set of sideband frequencies and no carrier is transmitted. Full details of this system will be found in Chapter 10 (*Single Sideband Technique*).

Ordinary amplitude modulation is usually obtained by varying the h.t. feed to a class C radio-frequency amplifier, according to the audio waveform to be transmitted, by applying the modulating voltage in series with the h.t. supply through the medium of a modulation transformer as shown in **Fig. 50**. In the method just described, called *plate modulation* or *anode modulation*, the amount of audio power required to modulate the carrier wave fully is equal to one-half of the d.c. power input to the power-amplifier stage. For example, a transmitter power amplifier drawing an anode current of 100 mA from an h.t. supply of 600 volts has an input of 60 watts. A peak audio power of 30 watts is therefore required to modulate this amplifier fully. Further information on methods of amplitude modulation will be found in Chapter 9 (*Modulation*).

In frequency modulation (f.m.) the amplitude of the carrier wave is kept constant but its frequency is varied, or swung to and fro on either side of the nominal value, at a rate corresponding to the modulating frequency and to an extent corresponding to the amplitude of the modulating signal. An f.m. signal has a greater bandwidth than an a.m. signal, but on the other hand an f.m. system offers the advantage of a better signal-to-noise ratio provided that the strength of the received carrier is above a certain threshold value. Frequency modulation is thus well suited for the v.h.f. bands where ample bandwidth is available and a good signal-to-noise ratio is desirable.

Whereas a valve which is used in an amplitude-modulated power amplifier must be run at a reduced input compared with the telegraphy condition to avoid overloading and possible damage, an advantage of frequency modulation is that the power-amplifier stage can be operated at the full telegraphy rating thus allowing a greater output to be obtained from a given valve than under a.m. conditions. Practical details will be found in Chapter 11 (*Frequency Modulation*).

THE AMATEUR RECEIVER

The purpose of a receiver is to select a desired radio signal from amongst the many others that may be receivable and to recover from it the intelligence that it conveys. Usually the power arriving at the aerial terminals is so minute (perhaps only a small fraction of a micro-microwatt) that the receiver also needs to contain an amplifier so that the received signal can be made powerful enough to actuate the headphones or a loudspeaker. A receiver therefore normally has three functions—(i) the selection of the desired signal by a selective tuning circuit, (ii) the conversion of the radio-frequency signals into audio-frequency signals by the process of demodulation or " detection," and (iii) the amplification of the signals to a useful power level. In exceptional circumstances when the incoming signal is very strong, amplification may be unnecessary.

There are two main types of short wave receiver—the straight, or tuned-radio-frequency (t.r.f.) receiver, and the superheterodyne receiver, or " superhet." Of these the more commonly used today is the superheterodyne, on

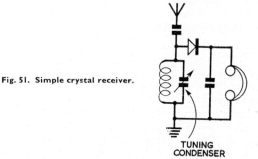

Fig. 51. Simple crystal receiver.

account of its superior selectivity and ease of handling. The t.r.f. receiver offers the advantage of simplicity and cheapness and therefore lends itself more readily to home construction.

The simplest possible receiver comprises a single tuned circuit and a crystal detector, as shown in **Fig. 51**. Such a circuit is not suitable for short-wave work since it lacks both selectivity and sensitivity. A triode (or tetrode or pentode valve) may be used as a detector as shown in **Fig. 52**, the grid and cathode acting as a diode detector and the

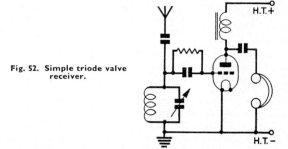

Fig. 52. Simple triode valve receiver.

amplifying properties of the valve providing a certain amount of signal magnification. Although this circuit is more sensitive than that of the crystal set it still lacks selectivity.

Both the sensitivity and selectivity of a valve detector may be increased enormously by applying reaction as shown in

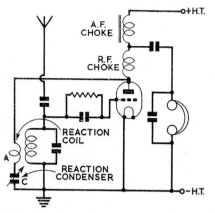

Fig. 53. Simple receiver using a triode valve with reaction.

Fig. 53. Radio-frequency energy in the anode circuit of the valve is fed back to the grid circuit by the reaction coil A. The series condenser C is inserted to control the amount of feedback, or reaction. By increasing the value of C, the reaction is increased and the sensitivity of the detector is increased: eventually a point is reached at which self-oscillation begins. This is marked by an increase in the background noise in the receiver, a characteristic rushing sound, and by the ability of the receiver to produce a heterodyne beat note with a continuous-wave telegraphy signal. For telephony reception this circuit is used with the detector in a condition just short of oscillation.

The amount of audio power available from a single detector stage even with reaction is small, and further audio amplification may be added so that a loudspeaker can be used. This is illustrated in the block diagram **Fig. 54 (A)**.

It is not good practice to connect an aerial directly to a detector valve for two reasons. First, when the detector is oscillating there will be radiation from the aerial which will cause inteference with other neighbouring receivers and, second, the optimum setting of the reaction control, a somewhat critical adjustment, will be adversely influenced by variations in the impedance of the aerial when the receiver is tuned over a band of frequencies. To eliminate these disadvantages it is common practice to use a stage of radio-frequency amplification ahead of the detector as shown in **Fig. 54 (B)**.

A code is sometimes used to describe the make-up of a

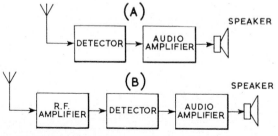

Fig. 54. Methods of providing amplification in a receiver: in A) audio-frequency amplification is applied to the output from the detector: in (B) the radio-frequency signal is amplified before it is fed into the detector and further amplification is provided for the audio-frequency output from the detector

t.r.f. receiver. It takes the form of a numeral representing the number of radio-frequency amplifier stages, followed by the letter V, to represent the detector stage, and this is followed by a further numeral to represent the number of audio amplifier stages after the detector. Thus $1-V-2$ means a t.r.f. receiver with one r.f. stage, a valve detector and two a.f. stages; the receiver shown in Fig. 53 would be designated $0-V-0$.

The best t.r.f. receivers are not really selective enough for use on the higher frequency bands. The superheterodyne

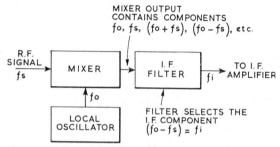

Fig. 55. The principle of frequency-changing.

receiver overcomes this drawback by changing the frequency of incoming signals to a lower fixed frequency called an *intermediate frequency*, usually abbreviated to *i.f.* At this lower fixed frequency, commonly around 465 kc/s, it is easy to obtain high selectivity and high gain with a small number of valves.

A special mixer valve is commonly used for frequency changing. Into it are fed (i) the radio-frequency signal and (ii) a locally-generated oscillator voltage whose frequency is higher than the radio signal frequency by an amount equal to the intermediate frequency. The anode current of the mixer valve contains components at the signal frequency f_s the oscillator frequency f_o and the sum and difference

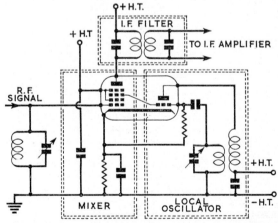

Fig. 56. A typical triode-hexode mixer circuit used for frequency changing in accordance with the principle illustrated in Fig. 55

frequencies $f_o + f_s$ and $f_o - f_s$: it also contains other components, but these are of no importance in the operation of the receiver. The component $f_o - f_s$ is the intermediate frequency and it is selected from the others by an i.f. filter, which usually comprises a pair of coupled tuned circuits tuned to the intermediate frequency, and is then passed on to an i.f. amplifier. The frequency-changing action is illustrated in the form of a block diagram in **Fig. 55** while **Fig. 56** shows a mixer circuit using a triode-hexode valve in which the various parts of the circuit are laid out to correspond with the block diagram.

The block diagram of a complete popular type of superheterodyne receiver is shown in **Fig. 57**. The tuning of the r.f. stage and the mixer and local oscillator stages is usually performed by a three-section ganged variable condenser. A technical difficulty with this arrangement is that the oscillator should ideally always be tuned to a frequency which is equal to the sum of the signal frequency and the intermediate frequency, irrespective of the setting of the tuning condenser. The signal and oscillator circuits are said to " track " cor-

are the frequency of the wanted signal which by design is equal to the *sum* of the oscillator frequency and the intermediate frequency and the so-called second-channel or image frequency which is equal to the oscillator frequency *minus* the intermediate frequency. The second-channel frequency is thus twice the i.f. below the frequency of the wanted signal and unless there is adequate selectivity in the r.f. tuning circuits to exclude signals on the second-channel frequency, both will be received. The degree of r.f. selectivity required is not so high in a superheterodyne as in a straight receiver since it is merely a matter of rejecting a spurious signal differing in frequency from the wanted signal by twice the intermediate frequency instead of a spurious signal only a few kilocycles away.

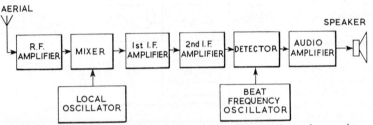

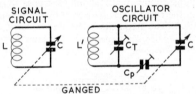

Fig. 57. Block diagram of a typical amateur communications superheterodyne receiver.

rectly if the above requirement is met. In order to obtain correct oscillator tracking it is necessary to modify the inductance of the oscillator coil and add two extra components, a trimmer C_T and a padder C_p as shown in **Fig. 58**. With this arrangement perfect tracking can be obtained at three points with only small errors elsewhere over quite a wide tuning range. Further details will be found in Chapter 4 (*H.F. Receivers*). It should be noted that special tracking circuits can be dispensed with if the frequency range covered by the receiver is small compared with the frequency itself, as for instance in a receiver designed exclusively for the amateur bands.

Since most of the gain and selectivity in a superheterodyne is obtained at the intermediate frequency it may appear unnecessary to use an r.f. amplifier ahead of the mixer. It is, however, desirable for two reasons, first to reduce or eliminate what is called *second-channel* or *image-interference*, and second, to improve the signal-to-noise ratio of the receiver.

Second-channel interference arises from the fact that there are two radio frequencies at which signals, if applied to the mixer, will give rise to an i.f. signal at its output. These

Mixer valves introduce noise and a weak signal applied direct from an aerial to a mixer would be lost in the noisy background. An r.f. amplifier stage is much less noisy than a mixer, and by using such a stage ahead of the mixer an improved signal-to-noise ratio can be obtained.

In many superheterodyne receivers the i.f. amplifier comprises two amplifier stages and three associated i.f. transformers between the mixer and the detector. If greater selectivity is required than can be obtained with high Q coil-and-condenser tuned transformers a crystal filter may be added to the i.f. amplifier, the crystal acting as another tuned circuit of extremely high Q. Such filters are commonly used for telegraphy reception and are described in Chapter 4 (*H.F. Receivers*).

For c.w. telegraphy reception it is necessary to introduce an additional oscillator (known as the *beat-frequency oscillator* or *b.f.o.*) to beat with the i.f. signal in the detector stage and produce an audible tone which can be read as Morse code.

Fig. 58. In the oscillator tuning circuit of a superheterodyne eceiver modifications are necessary to ensure proper tracking with the tuning adjustment of the signal-frequency circuit over a wide frequency range. Where the tuning range is strictly limited such modifications are not necessary.

BIBLIOGRAPHY

1. M. G. Scroggie. *The Foundations of Wireless*, Iliffe (London).
2. F. E. Terman. *Radio Engineers' Handbook*, McGraw-Hill (N.Y.).
3. R. T. Beatty. *Radio Data Charts* (revised by A. L. M. Sowerby), Iliffe (London).
4. F. E. Terman. *Radio Engineering*, McGraw-Hill (N.Y.).
5. *Electrical and Radio Notes for Wireless Operators*, H.M.S.O.
6. *The Admiralty Handbook of Wireless Telegraphy*, H.M.S.O.
7. *The Radio Amateur's Handbook*, A.R.R.L. (U.S.A.).
8. Ladner & Stoner. *Short-Wave Wireless Communication*, Chapman & Hall (London).
9. K. G. Sturley. *Radio Receiver Design*, Volumes I and II, Chapman & Hall (London).

CHAPTER 2

VALVES

THE simplest form of valve is the *diode*, which consists of two electrodes, namely a *cathode* and an *anode*. The two electrodes are contained in an evacuated bulb and connections can be made to them through external pins or contacts. If the cathode is heated, the molecules of which the cathode is composed become increasingly agitated, and if the temperature is high enough some of the atoms composing the molecules will be ejected from the cathode; these atoms have numbers of free electrons associated with them.

Electron Flow

When an electron leaves the parent molecule the latter becomes positively charged because the number of electrons remaining are insufficient to neutralize the positive charge in the molecule. Because the electrons are negatively charged, there is a force tending to pull them back to the cathode. The anode, which is positively charged to a higher potential, is placed near the hot cathode (usually surrounding it more or less completely) in order to attract these electrons. As they travel through the space from the cathode to the anode they may encounter molecules of gas (since the vacuum cannot be a perfect vacuum) and such collisions will impede their progress. Consequently, the amount of gas in the valve must be as small as possible. A valve which has been properly evacuated is described as *hard*. If an appreciable quantity of gas is present, the collision between the electrons and the molecules of gas will ionize the gas and a blue haze will become visible between the electrodes; the valve is then said to be *soft*.

Space Charge

In travelling from the cathode to the anode, the electrons form a cloud in the intervening space, and the electric field or charge associated with this cloud is known as the *space charge*. It tends to repel the electrons leaving the cathode because it is of the same polarity, but if the potential applied to the anode is sufficiently high, the effect of the space charge will be overcome and electrons will travel to it from the cathode: the current flow is completed through the external circuit back to the cathode. This means that there is an external electron flow from anode to cathode. In accordance with established convention, however, that the flow of electric current is " from positive to negative," i.e. in the opposite direction to electron flow, a meter will show a " current " flowing from the positive terminal of the high-tension supply towards the anode.

As the anode potential is increased the electron flow or current will increase up to a point where the space charge is completely neutralized and the total emission of the cathode is reached. The total emission can only be increased by raising the cathode temperature.

Obviously if the anode potential is reduced to zero or is made negative, there will be no electron flow because the space charge remains unneutralized. Hence the valve is able to conduct current in one direction only, and in fact the principal use of a diode is as a rectifier.

Cathodes

A *directly-heated cathode* or *filament* is a metallic conductor in the form of a fine wire or ribbon. It is heated to emitting temperature by its own resistance to the flow of electric current. A single continuous filament may be wound into a helix or folded, or sections may be employed in parallel to provide uniformly distributed emission over a large area. Pure tungsten was used for the filament in early valves and is still used in some very large transmitting valves: such filaments must be heated to a relatively high temperature (white heat) to produce adequate emission, and because of this are termed *bright emitter valves*.

Much higher emission efficiencies can be obtained by using thoriated tungsten filaments which are drawn from tungsten slugs impregnated with thorium oxide. During the valve processing the oxide is converted to pure metallic thorium at the surface, and this has the property of providing copious emission at a relatively low temperature.

Filamentary cathodes may also be made of nickel alloys coated with alkaline-earth oxides which emit electrons freely at an even lower temperature. Such oxides are formed during the processing from barium carbonate or a mixture of barium, calcium and strontium carbonates. This type of filament is usually employed in small receiving valves, and because of the low working temperature they are often known as *dull emitter valves*.

An *indirectly-heated cathode* is a hollow metal tube or sleeve, or in some cases is of thimble shape, having a coating of emissive material on the outer surface. The cathode is heated by radiation from a metal filament, called the *heater*, which is mounted inside the cathode, and the heater is usually electrically insulated from the cathode. The emissive material is generally the same as that employed for filamentary oxide-coated cathodes and operates at about the same temperature. The cathode may be made of pure nickel or copper or of special alloys, depending upon the purpose of the valve: the heater is normally made of tungsten.

Anodes

A valve anode is generally in the form of a hollow cylinder, which surrounds the cathode and other electrodes and is intended to collect as many as possible of the electrons ejected from the cathode. In small valves the anode is made of nickel or nickel-plated steel. When it is necessary to dissipate more heat, the nickel may be carbonized to give a matt black finish and thus improve its thermal radiation. In valves with higher anode dissipations the anode must be made of a material which can operate at high temperatures such as molybdenum, tantalum or zirconium; alternatively, radiating fins are attached to the anode or the anode may form part of the external envelope of the valve and then it can be readily cooled by thermal conduction to a mass of metal forming part of an external circuit or by a circulating-water jacket or an air blast. With the aid of these cooling methods a valve of relatively small physical size can be made to handle very large amounts of power.

Grids

The electron flow from cathode to anode can be controlled in various ways and for various purposes by causing it to pass through one or more *grid* electrodes; in some types of valve there may be as many as four or five grids in succession. A simple system of designation has been generally adopted whereby the generic name given to a valve indicates the total number of electrodes associated with the electron flow, starting from the cathode and ending at the anode: this is shown in the accompanying list.

Number of Grids	Total Number of Electrodes	Generic Name
1	3	*Triode*
2	4	*Tetrode*
3	5	*Pentode*
4	6	*Hexode*
5	7	*Heptode*
6	8	*Octode*

Grids are usually made in the form of a wire helix but are sometimes composed of square-mesh gauze. The wire helix may be of nickel or molybdenum or an alloy wound on support rods of nickel or copper, and it may be circular, oval or rectangular in section. In some v.h.f. valves the grid is made of parallel wires tightly stretched across a hole in a disc or in the form of a squirrel cage. One of the most important requirements in valve design is to prevent the grid from becoming overheated, and for this purpose the grid wire may be carbonized so as to enhance the heat radiation from it and cooling fins are often attached to the support rods: in some types these rods are welded directly to conducting pins in the base which permit the heat to be transferred outside the valve. Many modern high-performance valves employ gold or platinum-plated grids in order to avoid grid primary emission at the unavoidably high operating temperatures.

TYPES OF VALVES

Triodes

The insertion of a grid between the cathode and the anode enables the electron flow to be controlled by applying a relatively small voltage to this third electrode. To distinguish it from other grids serving different purposes in other types of valve, this grid is often referred to as the *control grid* (g_1). The power absorbed in the control-grid circuit is in many cases microscopically small.

By varying the potential of this grid the space charge can be modified in the same way as the anode current in a diode is varied by varying the anode voltage. The grid, because it is an open helix or mesh, does not present any mechanical obstruction to the electron flow, and as long as the potential on it is negative with respect to the cathode (or the negative end of the filament) it will attract no free electrons, but if it becomes positive, electrons will flow to it exactly as if it were

an anode: when this occurs *grid current* will flow. In most valves grid current begins to appear a little before the negative bias reaches zero: this is due partly to the random movement of electrons as they pass the grid on their way to the anode and partly to the contact-potential differences associated with the materials used in the cathode and grid construction.

When it is necessary to ensure that the grid is always negative, the grid circuit must include a source of adequate negative voltage. This voltage, known as the *grid bias*, can be obtained in four ways:

(a) An independent source of fixed voltage.
(b) A resistor in the cathode lead.
(c) Grid current in a grid resistor.
(d) Contact potential.

In (a) the source of voltage may be a battery (usually dry-cells), or in transmitting equipment or high-power audio amplifiers it may be a mains-driven power unit.

In (b) a resistor is connected in the cathode-to-earth lead of an indirectly-heated valve or between the filament-supply centre-tap of a directly-heated valve and earth, and the total cathode current flowing through this resistor causes the cathode to become positive to earth; if the grid return circuit is returned to earth the grid will be negative with respect to the cathode. The resistor is known as the *automatic-bias resistor* and the circuit arrangement as *cathode bias*.

In (c) if the valve is operated at such an amplitude that appreciable grid current flows and if the grid is connected to cathode and earth through a resistor, the flow of grid current will result in the grid becoming negative with respect to cathode. This form of grid bias is employed in oscillators and class C amplifiers and is known as *grid-leak bias*.

In (d) the grid is connected to the cathode through a high-value resistor (usually 1–10 Megohms) and the slight flow of grid current will bias the grid to almost the contact potential. This form of grid bias is suitable only for small valves having very small signal input voltages.

If the grid potential is varied, the anode current will vary in a corresponding manner; further, if a resistance is connected in the anode circuit, the voltage drop across it will vary also in the same way. If this resistance has a suitable value the variation of voltage drop will be of greater amplitude than

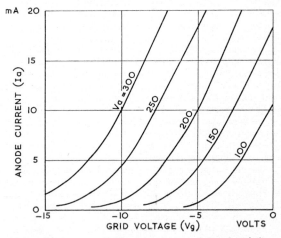

Fig. I. Anode-current/grid-voltage characteristics of a triode.

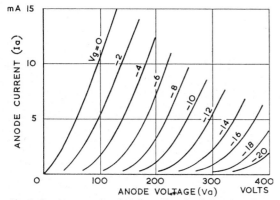

Fig. 2. Anode-current/anode-voltage characteristics of a triode.

the variation of grid voltage; hence the ability of the triode valve to amplify.

If the relationship between the variation in grid voltage and the change in anode current is plotted graphically, the resultant graph is known as a *characteristic curve*. A series of such curves may be plotted with different anode voltages: the set of curves are known as the anode-current/grid-voltage characteristics (I_a/V_g). A second series of curves may be plotted for anode current versus anode voltage for a series of different grid voltages. These are known as the anode-current/anode-voltage characteristics (I_a/V_a). Examples are shown in **Figs. 1** and **2**.

Tetrodes and Screen-grid Valves

A *tetrode* valve is a triode with an additional grid, known as the screen (g_2), interposed between the control grid and the anode. When this screen is maintained at a steady positive voltage, it is found that the amplification factor of the valve, as compared with the triode, is very much higher: the impedance is also greatly increased.

The reason for this improved amplification lies in the fact that the anode current in the tetrode valve is far less dependent on the anode voltage than it is in the triode. In any amplifier circuit, of course, the voltage on the anode must be expected to vary since the varying anode current produces a varying voltage-drop across the load in the anode circuit. A triode amplifier suffers from the disadvantage that when, for instance, the anode current begins to rise due to a positive half-cycle of grid voltage swing, the anode voltage falls (by an amount equal to the voltage developed across the load) and the effect of the reduction in anode voltage is to diminish the amount by which the anode current would otherwise increase. Conversely, when the grid voltage swings negatively the anode current falls and the anode voltage rises: because of this increased anode voltage the anode current is not so low as it would have been if it were independent of anode voltage. This means that the full amplification of the triode cannot be achieved. The introduction of the screen grid, however, almost entirely eliminates the effect of the anode voltage on the anode current, and the amplification obtainable is thus much greater.

A screen is found to function best when its voltage is below the mean value of the anode voltage. Most of the electrons from the cathode are thereby accelerated towards the anode, but some of them are unavoidably caught by the screen: the resulting screen current serves no useful purpose, and if it

becomes excessive it may cause overheating of the screen The total cathode current is equal to the sum of the screen and anode currents.

Another important effect occurs when a screen grid is introduced into a triode: provided that the screen is kept at a constant voltage (not varying with the signal) it reduces the capacitive coupling between the control grid and the anode and therefore helps to eliminate unwanted feedback in amplifier circuits especially at radio frequency. To take full advantage of this feature the screen grid is made with a finer pitch or smaller mesh size than would be necessary merely to obtain greater amplification, and auxiliary electrostatic shields are built into the structure in an attempt to reduce the grid-to-anode capacitance to the lowest practicable value. If the size of the apertures in the screen is made too small the electron flow to the anode will be seriously impeded, but with a reasonable compromise the residual capacitance between control grid and anode can be made 1,000 times smaller. The improved stability in a radio-frequency amplifier depends on the constancy of the screen voltage, and it is for this reason that thorough capacitive by-passing of the screen to earth (i.e. decoupling) is so important.

There is another type of tetrode, known as a *space-charge grid tetrode*, in which a positively charged grid is interposed between the control grid and the cathode. The purpose of this positive grid is to overcome the limiting effect of the negative space charge and thus enable the valve to operate efficiently with very low anode voltage (for example, a 12 volt supply as used for mobile equipment).

The tetrode suffers from the disadvantage that, when the anode voltage swing is so great that on downward peaks it falls below the screen voltage, there is a flow of secondary electrons from the anode to the screen. The effect of this secondary emission is to cause a drop in anode current and a rise in screen current, which in ordinary amplifier circuits results in serious distortion and a reduction in useful power output.

Pentodes

By introducing an additional grid between the screen and the anode and fixing its potential at some low value, usually cathode or earth potential, the flow of secondary electrons can be prevented: the valve can then be operated with much larger anode-voltage swings without distortion and without reduction in power output. This third grid is known as a *suppressor grid* (g_3) and a tetrode which has been modified in this way becomes a *pentode*.

Other methods are also in use for suppressing secondary emission, for example, by increasing the separation between the screen and the anode until the secondary electrons have insufficient energy to reach the screen (as in the " Harries Critical Anode-Distance Valve ") or by introducing small fins projecting inwards from the anode. In another method a pair of deflecting plates are fitted near the anode and connected to cathode or earth. Valves having this form of construction are known as *beam tetrodes* or *kinkless tetrodes*. The term " kinkless " refers to the absence of the kink which appears in the characteristic curve of the simplest type of tetrode due to the flow of secondary emission from anode to screen at low anode voltages.

Beam Tetrodes

A beam tetrode employs principles not found in other types of valves in that the electron stream from the cathode is

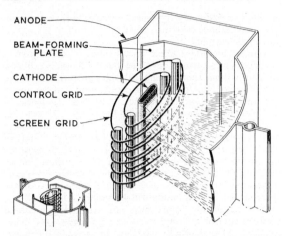

ANODE

BEAM-FORMING
PLATE

CATHODE

CONTROL GRID

SCREEN GRID

Fig. 3. Internal construction of a beam power tetrode valve. The drawing shows the focused streams of electrons between the aligned turns of the control grid and the screen grid, and also the beam-forming or confining plates which shield the anode from the electrons arriving from the regions of the support wires.

focused towards the anode. The control grid and the screen grid are made with the same winding pitch and they are assembled in the valve so that the turns in each grid are in optical alignment: see **Fig. 3.** The effect of the grid and screen turns being in line is to reduce the screen current compared with a non-beam construction. For example, in a pentode of ordinary construction the screen current is about 20 per cent of the anode current, whereas in a beam valve the figure is 5–10 per cent.

The pair of plates for suppressing secondary emission referred to above are bent round so as to shield the anode from any electrons coming from the regions exposed to the influence of the grid support wires at points where the focusing of the electrons is imperfect. These plates are known as *beam-confining* or *beam-forming plates*.

Beam valves were originally developed for use as audio-frequency output valves, but the principle is now applied to many types of radio-frequency pentodes both for receiving

and transmitting. Their superiority over pentodes for a.f. output is due to the fact that the distortion is caused mainly by the second harmonic and only very slightly by the third harmonic, which is the converse of the result obtained with a pentode. Two such valves used in push-pull give a relatively large output with small harmonic distortion because the second harmonic cancels out with push-pull connection. **Fig. 4** shows the characteristic curves of a beam valve and a pentode of equivalent size. The line *AB* is a load line drawn on the curve. It will be seen that the line extends farther to the left before it cuts the zero grid-volts curve than is the case with the pentode; this indicates a greater power output because the power output is proportional to the product of the change in anode voltage between points *A* and *B* on the horizontal axis and the change of anode current between points *A* and B on the vertical axis.

The widespread use of beam power valves as r.f. amplifiers and frequency doublers, etc. is referred to later in this chapter.

Gated Valves

It is convenient for many purposes to be able to control the output of a valve from two different sources. In a pentode valve if sufficient negative voltage is applied to the suppressor grid, the anode current can be cut off, and the effect of cutting off the anode current is to cause a considerable increase in screen current; care must then be taken to avoid exceeding the safe screen dissipation. If the suppressor grid is biased negatively to cut off the anode current and if a positive pulse is then applied to it, an input fed to the control grid will affect the anode current only during the pulse, as if a gate were opened, the pulse being called a *gating pulse*. Because it is difficult to control accurately the magnitude of a pulse, it may happen that the suppressor grid is pulsed positively into the region where it will take current and " rob " the anode. To avoid such a possibility a diode is usually connected between this grid and cathode to act as a low-impedance shunt and thereby prevent a significant positive voltage. In certain valves specially intended for this purpose, a diode is built on the suppressor grid, which is then known as a *dioded suppressor grid*, and the pitch of the turns in the suppressor grid is made finer so that the anode current is cut off by a voltage of the same order as that of the control grid. Instead of a suppressor grid, specially designed beam plates may be employed (as in the beam tetrode) in conjunction with aligned control and screen grids, and the resultant valve is a *gated-beam valve*.

Examples of the use of these valves are television synchronizing circuits, radar, and volume contraction and expansion.

VALVE CHARACTERISTICS

The performance characteristics of all valves as published by the makers are based on the assumption that the cathode is maintained at the proper operating temperature, which in most cases also has an important effect on the useful life of the valve. Under-running may be as detrimental as over-running, particularly in gas-discharge valves such as mercury-vapour rectifiers.

The characteristics are also related to the specified values of anode and grid voltages, and while it is possible and often convenient to operate a valve with anode and screen voltages below the rated values there will generally be a deterioration in performance but the life and reliability will be increased.

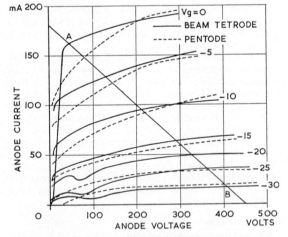

Fig. 4. Comparative characteristic curves of a pentode and a beam tetrode of equivalent sizes. AB is a load line.

generated if an equivalent noise voltage were applied to the grid. For the purposes of comparison with the noise generated by thermal agitation in a resistor (known as *Johnson noise*) it is convenient to express the shot noise generated by a valve also in terms of a resistor: this is an imaginary resistor which if connected in series with the grid would generate the same amount of noise as that produced by the valve and is termed *equivalent noise resistance* (R_{eq}). The value of R_{eq} may be calculated as follows:

For a triode used as an amplifier—

$$R_{eq} = \frac{2 \cdot 5}{g_m} \text{ kilohms}$$

For a pentode used as an amplifier—

$$R_{eg} = \frac{I_a}{I_a + I_{g2}} \left(\frac{2 \cdot 5}{g_m} + \frac{20 \, I_{g2}}{g_m} \right) \text{ kilohms}$$

In these formulae the currents are expressed in milliamperes and the mutual conductance is expressed in milliamperes per volt, all being measured at the operating point.

The noise generated by a multi-grid valve (e.g. a pentode) is much higher than that generated by a triode owing to the partition effect of the anode and screen currents. Although not all of the noise originating at the cathode is developed in the anode circuit (since not all of the cathode current reaches the anode) there is a large partition-noise contribution caused by the element of chance as to whether any given electron goes to the anode and then through the anode circuit or to the screen and *not* through the anode circuit.

Since the value of R_{eq} is determined by the valve characteristics, which do not alter with frequency over its normal working range, it can usually be taken that the equivalent noise resistance is also independent of frequency.

Induced Grid Noise

The random variations in the electron stream as it passes the grid on its way to the anode induce a noise voltage in the grid circuit by reason of the electro-static charges carried by the electrons. This voltage depends on the nature of the impedance in the grid circuit and on the frequency at which the circuit is operating: at low and medium frequencies the effect is negligible because the voltage induced by the electrons approaching the grid is neutralized by that induced by the receding electrons, whereas at very high frequencies the time of transit of the electrons corresponds to an appreciable fraction of a cycle and this leads to a phase difference between the approaching and the receding electrons. The resultant induced grid current has a component which can be more or less taken into account by supposing the connection of an appropriate resistance across the grid circuit. This resistance acts as a generator of thermal noise at an equivalent temperature to that of the valve cathode, i.e. about five times the absolute room temperature; the noise so generated is known as *induced grid noise*. Because it appears as a shunt to the grid circuit this resistance also results in a reduction of the input impedance (see page 46); it is usually expressed as a conductance in micromhos and is known as the *transit-time conductance*, the value increasing approximately as the square of the frequency.

Hiss

The noise generated by a valve when used as the first stage of a high-gain amplifier, usually at audio frequency, is known as *hiss*. This noise includes shot noise and that due to various inter-electrode leakages but it does not include hum. It is generally expressed as an equivalent noise voltage in microvolts applied to the control grid.

Hum

Valve hum is the component of the anode current resulting from modulation of the electron stream due to the use of an a.c. filament or heater supply. When a cathode is heated by a.c. the current generates a magnetic field which can modulate the electron stream, and a modulating voltage is injected into the control grid through the inter-electrode capacities and leakages: additionally there can be emission from the heater in an indirectly-heated valve. The hum is usually expressed as an equivalent voltage (in microvolts) applied to the control grid. Valve hum should not be confused with hum generated in other circuit components.

Primary Emission

In an indirectly-heated valve it is possible for the tungsten heater to become contaminated with emissive material and so emit electrons. This is known as *heater emission*. The emitted electrons will be attracted to any electrode which is positive with respect to the heater, and such an electrode may be the cathode or the screen grid or anode; it can even be the control grid, which although generally negative to the cathode can become sufficiently positive to one end of the heater during at least part of the a.c. cycle of the heater supply. This explains why it is sometimes recommended that the centre-tap of the heater supply should be connected to a positive point in the circuit to reduce hum. The grid can thereby be maintained at a negative potential with respect to the heater.

Grid primary emission is a condition in which a grid commences to emit electrons itself and, figuratively speaking, competes with the cathode. The effect is produced by the heating of the grid which may be caused by an excessive flow of grid current or by the close proximity of the hot cathode or by radiated heat from the anode. The effects are accentuated if the grid becomes contaminated with active cathode material, which can happen if the valve is appreciably over-run even for a relatively short time.

The control grid, the screen and the suppressor grid are all subject to these effects. They are avoided by keeping the grid-cathode resistance low and by avoiding excessive heater, anode or bulb temperature (i.e. by not over-running the valve).

Two examples of the effects of control-grid primary emission can be given:

    (a) In a small output valve the anode current rises steadily accompanied by distortion due to grid current flowing in the high-resistance grid leak in such a direction as to oppose the grid bias.

    (b) In a power amplifier or frequency multiplier in a telegraphy transmitter the drive diminishes when the key is held down, accompanied by rising anode current.

A consequence of primary screen emission in an oscillator or amplifier is that when the screen voltage is removed, for example by keying, the output is maintained often for quite long periods if the valve is already hot.

Anode primary emission is similar to grid emission but occurs when the anode attains a sufficiently high temperature to emit electrons. This effect occurs mostly in rectifiers and causes breakdown between anode and cathode.

Secondary Emission

When an electron which has been accelerated to a high velocity hits an electrode such as a grid or anode, electrons are dislodged and these electrons can be attracted to any other electrode having a higher potential. This effect is termed *secondary emission*. Under controlled conditions one electron can dislodge several secondary electrons, and a series of secondary-emitting " cathodes " will give a considerable gain in electrons. This principle is used in the electron-multiplier type of valve.

Conversion Conductance

The term *conversion conductance* is used in regard to detectors or frequency changers to represent the ratio of the output current of one frequency to the input voltage of another frequency. As applied to the mixer of a superheterodyne receiver, for example, the conversion conductance is the current in the anode circuit at intermediate frequency (measured in microamperes) divided by the input voltage to the grid at signal frequency. The symbol commonly used is g_c and it is generally measured in microamperes per volt.

Conversion or Translation Gain

Conversion or translation gain is the ratio of intermediate-frequency output voltage to radio-frequency input voltage. It can be obtained from the conversion conductance if the dynamic resistance and other parameters of the i.f. transformer used in the mixer anode circuit are known. Both terms are a measure of the efficiency of a mixer but are of course related to the type of i.f. transformer in use.

Cathode-interface Impedance

When a valve is operated for long periods particularly with low cathode current or at complete cut-off, the mutual conductance steadily falls and so also does the available peak emission. This effect is due to the growth of a resistive film, known as the *cathode-interface impedance*, between the metallic cathode and its emissive coating. The film, which may be represented as a resistance in series with the cathode and shunted by a capacitance, acts as an automatic-bias resistor. The falling performance is sometimes colloquially termed *sleepy sickness*. The rate of growth of interface resistance is considerably affected by the material of the cathode and is accelerated by high temperatures resulting from excessive heater voltage. Since the cathode-interface resistance is normally of the order of a few hundred ohms it has a most serious effect on valves having a high slope and a short grid base because the normal likely order of cathode resistor is comparable with this value. The effect of the parallel capacitance is to make a drop in performance less noticeable as the frequency is increased.

Contact Potential

A small potential difference exists between electrodes of dissimilar materials in a valve irrespective of any externally applied potentials. This is known as the *contact potential*. In a simple diode there is a potential difference between the anode and the cathode which causes a current to flow in any external circuit from anode to cathode. The magnitude of this contact potential depends on the cathode material, the type of emissive coating, the anode material and any contaminating film present upon its surface. Its value (anode to cathode) is between $+1$ volt and -0.5 volt, but is most frequently positive; it is affected by cathode temperature and varies throughout the life of the valve. In a triode or any other valve with a control grid a potential difference exists similarly between the control grid and cathode and between other electrodes. All electrodes except the control grid and possibly the suppressor grid can be ignored in practical applications, because the current due to it is small compared with other currents flowing in the circuit. The contact potential is effectively in series with the control grid, with the result that if no external grid bias is applied grid current will flow in the external circuit in the same manner as in a diode. If an increasing external grid bias is applied, a value of negative bias is reached when the grid current ceases and this is a measure of the contact potential for this particular valve. In order to operate the valve satisfactorily it is necessary in most cases to increase the bias still further to a point where the maximum positive signal input does not swing the grid more positive than the contact potential.

USES OF VALVES

The Valve as an Amplifier

When a valve has an impedance connected in series with its anode supply and the voltage on its grid is varied, the resultant change in anode current will cause a voltage change across the impedance. This impedance may be a resistance, an inductance, or in some cases it may behave like a capacity, as for example in a circuit tuned to a frequency above resonance.

Class A Operation

The curve in **Fig. 5** shows graphically the operation of a valve working as an amplifier. This curve, which is known as the *characteristic curve* of the valve, shows how the anode current varies with grid voltage. If the grid bias is fixed at the point A, which corresponds to the centre of the useful straight portion of the curve (i.e. where the grid potential remains negative), any complex alternating voltage applied to the grid will be reproduced as a similar complex current wave of increased amplitude in the anode circuit. Since the travel of the operating condition is up and down the straight portion of the curve, the output wave shape will be exactly similar to that of the input and no distortion will result, but

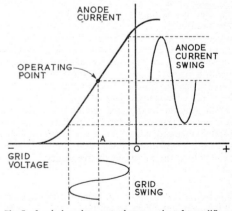

Fig. 5. A triode valve operating as a class A amplifier.

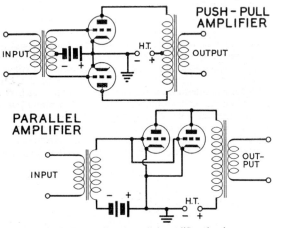

PUSH-PULL AMPLIFIER

PARALLEL AMPLIFIER

Fig. 6. Push-pull and parallel amplifier circuits.

if the bias is adjusted so that the valve operates over a curved portion of the characteristic, there will be a flattening of the corresponding half-cycle and distortion will result. The method of operation where the grid bias is fixed at the centre of the straight portion of the curve is known as *class A operation*.

The amount of distortion produced by a non-linear amplifier is usually expressed in terms of the harmonics which are generated by it. If the input has a complex waveform, the analysis of the distortion is very difficult and it is much more convenient to consider the distortion of a simple sine-wave input. When a sinusoidal input is applied to an amplifier operating over a curved portion of its characteristic, the distorted output is found to contain not only the amplified fundamental but also a number of harmonics (all of which are of course sinusoidal). This can be deduced mathematically by what is known as Fourier's Analysis. The respective amplitude of each harmonic expressed as a percentage of the fundamental is known as the *percentage harmonic content*. Taken collectively the total effect can be calculated by adding together all the individual harmonic components. Since the power represented by the oscillatory wave is a function of the square of the voltage (or the current), the effective *total harmonic content* of the distorted wave will be given not by simple addition but by the square root of the sum of the squares of the voltage (or current) amplitudes of the respective harmonic components.

Distortion of a similar kind occurs when the input signal has a complex waveform. In just the same way as the distorted output of the original sinusoidal signal referred to in the previous paragraph can be resolved into a number of components comprising the fundamental and a series of harmonics, so can a complex input signal itself be resolved into a fundamental and a series of harmonics. If such a complex input signal is fed into a non-linear amplifier each of the sinusoidal components comprised in it will be subject to distortion by the curvature of the characteristic and will appear in the output as a series of harmonically related components. Cross-modulation will also occur and add considerably to the total distortion. The complete analysis of the distortion of a complex wave would need to take into account the relative phases of its harmonic components, but fortunately this is unnecessary in the design of communications equipment.

Push-pull and Parallel Amplifiers

When it is necessary to obtain more output than can be provided by one valve, two or more may be connected in push-pull or in parallel. **Fig. 6** shows the connections for these two methods. The principle used in the push-pull arrangement is that whenever the grid of one valve is positive the other is negative, and in consequence the anode current of one valve is rising as the other is falling; hence the name *push-pull*.

In parallel operation, the grids are connected together and the anodes are connected together with the result that the output is increased in proportion to the number of valves used. In regard to distortion of a sine-wave input, the relative harmonic content is the same as for one valve alone, whereas in the push-pull system all even harmonics (2nd, 4th, 6th etc.) are cancelled out, due to the method of operation. It follows therefore that two valves connected in push-pull will give a considerably greater output for the same degree of distortion than twice that obtained from " single-ended " operation, i.e. from a single valve.

Class AB1 Operation

As mentioned above, when valves are operated in push-pull some of the distortion produced by curvature of the characteristic is cancelled out. This is taken advantage of in *class AB1* operation by employing a negative grid bias slightly greater than that for class A operation and allowing the signal input voltage to swing over the entire curve up to the point where grid current starts. A large part of the distortion which is thereby introduced is automatically cancelled by the push-pull mode of operation.

Class AB2 Operation

If class AB1 operation is carried a stage further and the negative grid bias is increased to a value where the anode current is quite low and if the signal input is allowed to increase so that the grid voltage swings into the positive grid region, the power output is further increased. Class AB2 operation is intermediate between class AB1 and class B and is frequently employed for large a.f. power amplifiers.

Class B Operation

It has already been explained how a valve must be operated over the straight portion of the characteristic if distortion is to be avoided in single-ended operation. The straight portion of a valve curve is only a small part of the whole, and consequently if it were possible to use nearly all of the curve without introducing distortion, much more output would be available. This can be achieved in practice by a method known as *class B* operation, in which the valve is operated at the cut-off point on the curve. This is shown in **Fig. 7**, from which it will be evident that the negative half-cycle is almost completely suppressed. If the valve is used as an r.f. amplifier, this is unimportant since the oscillatory characteristic of the tuned circuit will restore the other half-cycle and remove the harmonic distortion, but for a.f. amplification the method if considered in this simple form is impossible. If, however, two such valves are used in push-pull, each valve will supply the missing half-wave of the other and a normal full-wave will result in the output. Because the mean anode current depends upon the signal voltage, the demand upon the h.t. supply for anode current will fluctuate with the signal amplitude. Hence a power supply with good voltage regulation is

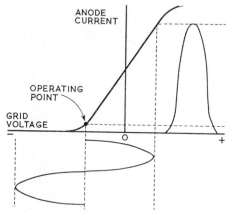

Fig. 7. In a class B amplifier the valve is operated at the cut-off point.

essential. Moreover since the grid is driven positive, appreciable grid current will flow and good regulation in the grid-bias supply is also necessary. Since the grid takes current it consumes power, and this must come from the signal input. The preceding or driver stage must furnish this power adequately without distortion.

Class C Operation

The class B principle is carried a step further in *class C* operation by using the entire valve characteristic. Here the grid is biased to approximately twice the cut-off voltage and is driven far into the positive region in order to reach saturation point, as is shown in **Fig. 8.** Since the grid is driven appreciably positive, considerable grid current flows and the anode is robbed of current at the peak of each cycle, thus causing the anode current pulse to be indented at the top. As the waveform is poor and the distortion very considerable, class C operation is almost entirely restricted to r.f. amplification where high efficiency is very desirable and distortion relatively unimportant. Because of the high values of grid current, considerable driving power is necessary. As in class B, good regulation of the h.t. and grid-bias supplies is essential for class C operation.

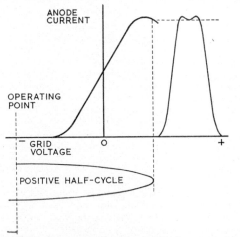

Fig. 8. In class C operation the valve is biased to approximately twice the cut-off voltage.

Ultra-linear Operation

When a pentode or tetrode valve is operated normally the screen grid is decoupled with a capacitor of low reactance to cathode or chassis so that its potential may remain constant at all operating frequencies. If the screen grid were connected to the anode, the valve would perform as a triode: if, however, the screen grid is connected to a part of the output circuit intermediate between anode and h.t., such as a tap on the output transformer, a form of operation intermediate between that of a triode and that of a pentode results. In effect a proportionate amount of negative feedback is applied to the screen grid which lowers the power gain but reduces the distortion. When the screen grids of two pen-

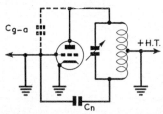

Fig. 9. Output circuit connections in a push-pull ultra-linear amplifier.

todes or tetrodes employed in push-pull class AB1 are connected to taps on the output transformer, the mode of operation is called *ultra-linear;* see **Fig. 9.** The tap positions are usually specified as a percentage of the total number of turns, the figure for optimum performance varying for different valve types.

Neutralized Amplifiers

Earlier mention has been made of the instability of amplifiers resulting from the feedback from the anode of a valve to the grid through the grid-to-anode capacitance and

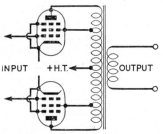

Fig. 10. Neutralizing a grounded-cathode triode amplifier. The circuit is equally suitable for a tetrode or a pentode.

of the possibility of reducing this feedback by using an r.f. type of tetrode or pentode. At high frequencies, particularly if the grid and/or anode circuit has high dynamic resistance, this capacitance may still be too large for complete stability. A solution is to employ a circuit in which there is feedback in opposite phase from the anode circuit to the grid so that the effect of this capacitance is balanced out. The circuit is then said to be *neutralized*.

A typical arrangement is shown in **Fig. 10.** Here the anode coil is centre-tapped in order to produce a voltage at the " free " end which is equal and opposite in phase to that at the anode end. If the free end is connected to the grid by a capacitor (C_n) having a value equal to that of the valve grid-to-anode capacitance (C_{g-a}) shown dotted, any current flowing through C_{g-a} will be exactly balanced by that through C_n. This is an idealized case because the anode tuned circuit is loaded with the valve anode impedance at one end but not at the other; also the power factor of C_n will not necessarily be equal to that of C_{g-a}. The importance of accurate neutralization in transmitter power-amplifier circuits cannot be overstressed.

Grid Driving Power

An important consideration in the design of class B or class C r.f. power amplifiers is the provision of adequate driving power. The driving power dissipated in the grid-cathode circuit and in the resistance of the bias circuit is normally quoted in valve manufacturers' data. These figures frequently do not include the power lost in the valveholder and in components and wiring or the valve losses due to electron transit-time phenomena, internal lead impedances and other factors. Where an overall figure is quoted, it is given as *driver power output*. If this overall figure is not quoted, it can be taken that at frequencies up to about 30 Mc/s the figure given should by multiplied by two, but at higher frequencies electron transit-time losses increase so rapidly that it is often necessary to use a driver stage capable of supplying 3–10 times the driving power shown in the published data. The driving power available for a class C amplifier or frequency multiplier should be sufficient to permit saturation of the driven valve; i.e. a substantial increase or decrease in driving power should produce no appreciable change in the output of the driven stage. This is particularly important when the driven stage is anode-modulated. Care must be exercised, however, to ensure that the maximum grid current or other ratings of the valve are not exceeded.

Grounded Cathode

Most valves are used with the cathode connected to chassis or earth or where a cathode-bias resistor is employed it is shunted with a capacitor of low resistance at the lowest signal frequency used so that the cathode is effectively earthed.

Grounded Grid

Although a triode must be neutralized to avoid instability when it is used as an r.f. amplifier this is not always essential if an r.f. type of tetrode or pentode is employed. However, at very high frequencies (above about 100 Mc/s) a triode gives better performance than a tetrode or pentode, providing that the inherent instability can be overcome. One way of achieving this is to earth the grid instead of the cathode so that the grid acts as an r.f. screen between cathode and anode, the input being applied to the cathode. The capacitance tending to make the circuit unstable is then that between cathode and anode, which is much smaller than the grid-to-anode capacitance.

There is a further advantage in this method of operation in that the phase of the power in the anode circuit is in the same direction as that in the cathode-input circuit, and hence any transfer of power through the cathode-to-anode capacitances (which, however, small, is not negligible at very high fre-

quencies) is added to the output power; i.e. not all the driving power is lost.

Grounded Anode

For some purposes it is desirable to apply the input to the grid and to connect the load in the cathode circuit, the anode being decoupled to chassis or earth through a low-reactance capacitor. Such circuits are often referred to as grounded-anode circuits and are employed in cathode followers and infinite-impedance detectors.

Voltage Amplifiers

When it is desired to use a valve primarily for the purpose of increasing the signal voltage (as in an a.f. or i.f. amplifier) as distinct from increasing the power (as in an a.f. or r.f. output stage), there are four possible methods. These are known as—

    (a) *resistance-capacity coupling*
    (b) *choke-capacity coupling*
    (c) *tuned-anode* (or *tuned-grid*) *coupling*
    (d) *transformer coupling*

In general, the first method is suitable only for audio frequencies unless the gain per stage is very low and the output voltage required fairly small. The second is suitable for audio frequencies and for moderately high radio frequencies, provided that the choke is suitable chosen. The last two may be used up to very high frequencies, the limitation being the shunting capacitances in the tuned circuit or the transformer and in the valve itself.

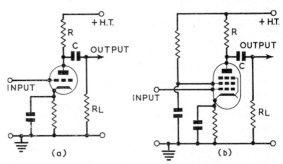

Fig. 11. Basic resistance-capacity coupled amplifier: (a) triode (b) tetrode or pentode.

Resistance-capacity Coupled Amplifier

The basic circuit for a resistance-capacity coupled amplifier is shown in **Fig. 11 (a)** for a triode and in **Fig. 11 (b)** for a tetrode or pentode. Although the essential features are the same, the values of the circuit components will depend on which type of valve is used.

In designing an amplifier using this form of coupling the choice of valve should be determined by (a) the h.t. line voltage available, (b) the required stage gain, (c) the required output voltage of the stage in question, (d) the grid-leak value of the succeeding valve, and (e) the highest frequency to be amplified. The h.t. line voltage will usually be fixed by the design of the remainder of the equipment, but for a.f. amplifiers as a general guide this voltage must not be less than about four times the required r.m.s. output voltage and preferably not less than six times. The actual anode voltage will of course be less than the h.t. line voltage by an amount equal to the voltage-drop in the anode resistor R, and provided that the anode voltage at zero anode current does not exceed the normal maximum rating, all will be in order. The values of the resistor and the mean anode current should be so chosen that the actual anode voltage is about 40 per cent of the h.t. line voltage. The grid bias should be such that with this anode current the valve will operate on the straight portion of its characteristic and will never be driven into grid current; hence the bias must always be greater than about -1 volt.

When a tetrode or pentode is employed the screen voltage will be such as to provide the correct anode current at a suitable grid bias, the voltage being generally about 10 per cent of the h.t. line voltage. A triode provides less stage gain than a pentode but is capable of handling larger input voltages, and the succeeding grid leak R_L into which it delivers its output can be of lower value than in the case of a tetrode or pentode. This may be important because the grid leak is effectively in parallel with the anode resistor as regards the signal and hence it lowers the stage gain. The optimum value of grid leak is dependent on the size and type of valve employed. Output stages should not as a rule have grid leaks higher than 100,000 ohms (unless they are used with automatic bias in which case up to 500,000 ohms may be used), whereas small valves may use a Megohm or higher. The coupling capacitor C to the following valve should have a reactance of not more than one-half to one-quarter of the resistance of the grid leak at the lowest frequency to be used. Similarly the decoupling capacitors for the cathode and screen grid must have a low reactance compared with the associated resistors.

The high-frequency performance depends upon the output capacitance of the valve, the input capacitance of the succeeding valve, the valveholders and wiring capacitance. All of these appear as shunt reactances across the anode resistor (which in effect is itself in parallel with the anode impedance of the valve) and will lower the resultant output load impedance and thereby reduce the gain. For audio frequencies the value of the anode resistor should not exceed 1 Megohm and should preferably be less. The effect of the shunt capacitance is more detrimental when the valve is a pentode than when it is a triode because the anode impedance of a pentode is much higher. In addition the higher output impedance of a pentode makes it unsuitable for driving any output stage that is operated in any other condition than strictly class A. These factors indicate that pentodes (or tetrodes) are more suitable for the early stages of a multi-stage amplifier, but it is well to bear in mind that they are inherently more noisy than triodes.

When a good h.f. response is essential, as in wide-band video amplifiers, it is usual to employ high-slope pentodes with very low values of anode resistor and grid leak, so that the shunting effect of the capacitance is reduced. With low values of anode resistor (for example, 4700 ohms) the anode voltage is nearly equal to the h.t. line voltage and the valve is then operated nearly at the makers' class A ratings. The stage gain and output voltage is small, however, due to the low value of the resistors employed.

Cathode Followers

If a valve is operated with the output load connected to the cathode instead of to the anode, the load is common to both grid and anode circuits and the arrangement is called a *cathode follower*: see **Fig. 12.** Here the input voltage V_{sig} is applied between grid and earth while the output load R_k is connected between cathode and earth, across which the output voltage V_{out} is obtained. If at any instant V_{sig} is made more positive, the grid potential will become more positive and the anode current will increase: hence the cathode current will increase and the increased voltage-drop across R_k will cause V_{out} to increase in a positive direction also. Therefore the output voltage is in the same direction as that of the applied grid voltage: i.e. it " follows " the input voltage.

The amplification of a valve is concerned with the applied voltage between grid and cathode, and in the cathode

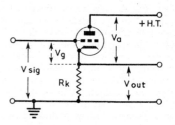

Fig. 12. Cathode follower.

follower this voltage V_g is not V_{sig} but $V_{sig} - V_{out}$. The higher the amplification of the valve the nearer V_{out} approaches V_{sig}. The voltage gain of the stage is—

$$\frac{V_{out}}{V_{sig}} = \frac{\mu R_k}{r_a + R_k (1 + \mu)}$$

where μ is the amplification factor of the valve and r_a is the anode impedance. It is evident that the stage gain must always be less than unity, although when μ is large and R_k is large compared with the anode impedance r_a the gain is nearly unity. Because there is no actual gain in voltage amplitude, the cathode follower can hardly be regarded as an amplifier. However, the circuit has certain advantageous properties, including a low output impedance (from about 50 to several hundred ohms), a high input impedance, low distortion (owing to the high degree of negative feedback through R_k) and negligible phase shift. One of its most important applications is as an impedance transformer where a very wide frequency range is required.

The load in the cathode lead may be a resistor, a tuned circuit or a loaded transformer, but if a tuned circuit or transformer is employed and if it is operated at frequencies off resonance the impedance will fall and the circuit will cease to act as a cathode follower.

For a given valve the optimum load for minimum distortion is the same irrespective of whether the load is connected in the anode or the cathode lead, but in the latter case, i.e. in the cathode follower, the distortion and output impedance are lower than in the former. It is also convenient at times to divide the load so that part of the load is in the anode and part in the cathode circuit: this arrangement gives a greater gain than the true cathode follower and results in less distortion and lower output impedance than the conventional amplifier arrangement.

If a tetrode or a pentode were used as a cathode follower it would behave as a triode because its anode, like the screen, would be at a constant potential. The relevant values of μ and r_a (anode impedance) are therefore those quoted for the valves connected as triodes.

Anode Followers

When a voltage amplifier with a uniform gain over a wide frequency range is required and when the gain is to be independent of changes in supply voltages, valve replacements, etc., it is convenient to use the *anode follower* principle. The anode follower circuit is essentially a single-stage amplifier in which a high degree of negative feedback from the anode to the grid is provided. A typical arrangement is shown in **Fig. 13.** Here a calculated fraction of the output voltage is injected into the grid circuit by a potential divider consisting of the two resistances R_1 and R_2. The effect of this feedback is to reduce the stage gain to a value at which it is almost independent of any variations in the amplification actually produced by the valve. Thus, if the stage gain *without* feedback is A, the effective gain *with* feedback due to R_1 and R_2 is—

$$ n = \frac{R_2}{R_1 + \left(\dfrac{R_1 + R_2}{A} \right)} $$

where the resistances are expressed in ohms. From this formula it is apparent that especially when A is large the gain depends mainly on the ratio R_2/R_1.

In a practical example, if the frequency characteristic of an amplifier *without* feedback were such that the gain fell by, say, 20 dB at either end of the frequency range, this diminution in gain could be reduced to a much smaller amount, e.g. 3·5 dB, by the use of the anode follower principle: at the same time, however, the maximum gain would be lowered from perhaps 200 to something less than 10.

While it is the ratio of R_2 to R_1 that mainly determines the amount of feedback, they should both be reasonably high compared with R_a, the anode load impedance. Ordinarily R_2 may be made equal to R_a.

The two condensers C_1 and C_2 serve as d.c. blocking condensers, but since they are associated with the feedback-determining resistances R_1 and R_2 it is important that the time constants R_1C_1 and R_2C_2 should be made equal so as to maintain a flat frequency response.

Provided that the grid leak R_g is not low compared with R_2 it will not affect the performance. In practice it can be made approximately equal to R_2.

The input impedance of an anode follower is determined

by the value of the series grid impedance represented by R_1. Because in general the input impedance is low, say 50,000 ohms, it is essential that the impedance of the source from which an anode follower is driven is relatively low. This would of course be so if a previous amplifying stage was used because this stage would have to supply an adequate output voltage of low distortion into a load of value R_1: a valve with an impedance of the order of 10 per cent of R_1 would be required.

The output impedance is $1000 (n + 1)/g_m$, where n is the stage gain *with* feedback and g_m is the mutual conductance in milliamperes per volt.

The output load need not be resistive as shown. If desired it could be in the form of a suitable choke or transformer.

Phase Splitters

Where a push-pull type of amplifier is required the simplest arrangement is usually one based on the use of a centre-tapped driver transformer. If it is preferred, however, to use a resistance-capacity coupled driver stage, some ingenuity is needed to produce the two oppositely phased driving voltages from a single valve. Several different circuit arrangements have been devised for this purpose, but only four of them are described here. They are all known as *phase-splitter* circuits.

Paraphase Amplifier. In this arrangement two similar triodes are used, the grid of the second valve being driven from the anode of the first valve to produce the oppositely

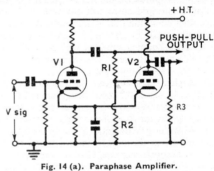

Fig. 14 (a). Paraphase Amplifier.

phased output. The basic circuit is shown in **Fig. 14(a).** Here $V1$ is a normal resistance-capacity coupled voltage amplifier, its output appearing across R_1 and R_2 in series: this supplies one phase of the output. The part of this which appears across R_2 drives the second valve $V2$ which also acts as an r.c. coupled voltage amplifier and supplies the opposite phase. The ratio of R_1 to R_2 is adjusted so that $(R_1 + R_2)/R_2$ is equal to the voltage gain of V_2, and $R_1 + R_2$ is made equal to R_3. Then the output voltages of both valves will be equal and opposite. The operating conditions for each valve are calculated in the same way as for voltage amplifiers but the values of R_1 and R_2 are critical and are chosen to suit the voltage gain. A common cathode resistor can be used and its value should be half that for each valve alone. The by-pass condenser may be omitted with some loss of balance between the two phases at the higher frequencies.

Split-load Phase Inverter. This type uses a single valve having half the load in the anode circuit and half in the cathode circuit as shown in **Fig. 14(b).** The two load resistors are R_1 and R_2. With respect to the load in the anode circuit the valve acts as a normal voltage amplifier, but with respect

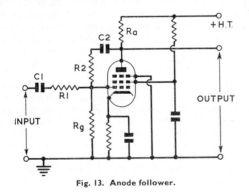

Fig. 13. Anode follower.

to the load in the cathode lead it behaves as a type of cathode follower. Since the current in both loads is the same, the voltages are equal if $R_1 = R_2$ and $R_3 = R_4$, but because of the large negative feedback through R_2 the gain is reduced nearly to unity. Since the ratio of the feedback voltage to

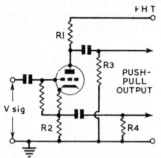

Fig. 14 (b). Split-load phase inverter.

the output voltage is $R_2/(R_1 + R_2)$, and since $R_1 = R_2$ the feedback ratio is 0·5. In other words, an input signal V_{sig} of 1 volt will produce an output of 1 volt across both anode and cathode loads. Because of the feedback developed across R_2, the output impedance in regard to R_1 will be increased while the output impedance in regard to R_2 will be decreased, and the source impedance from which the subsequent push-pull valves are to operate will therefore be unbalanced. Hence this type of phase splitter should not be used if the push-pull stage is driven into grid current at any time or is operated under any other condition than strictly class A. The operating conditions should be determined as if the valve were working as an r.c. coupled amplifier with R_2 omitted and R_1 twice the value actually used. The effective output voltage will be half the value so obtained.

Cathode-coupled Phase Splitter. In this arrangement two similar triodes are used, the input being applied to the grid of one of the triodes while the second valve receives its drive from a coupling resistor R_b in the common cathode lead: see **Fig. 14(c)**. When the grid potential of the first valve V_1 swings positively the current through V_1 increases and the voltage at the point G becomes more negative with respect to earth; i.e. the earth line becomes more negative with respect to the

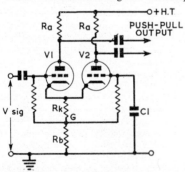

Fig. 14 (c). Cathode-coupled phase splitter.

point G and the grid of V_2 which is coupled to earth through its capacitor C_1 consequently becomes more negative with respect to its cathode. The two grids thus operate in opposite phases. The outputs are taken from the two anodes and are balanced in amplitude and impedance, and the voltage gain is about 25 per cent of that obtainable for each triode

when used as a normal resistance-capacity coupled amplifier. The operating conditions can be determined for each triode by assuming an anode load resistance of $R_a + 2R_b$ and a cathode-bias resistance of $2R_k$. The value of R_b should be approximately $\frac{1}{2}R_a$.

Anode-follower Paraphase Amplifier. If an anode follower is designed to have a high degree of feedback, the gain will be unity and the output will be equal in voltage but opposite in phase to the input. A suitable circuit is shown in **Fig. 14(d)**. As in the anode follower circuit (Fig. 13), if $R_1 = R_2$ and $C_1 = C_2$ and if the voltage gain without feedback is very high, the gain is unity. The outputs have impedances differing to some extent because one output has a value equal to the source impedance of V_{sig} and the other is equal to $2/g_m$. The circuit constants are derived as for an anode follower.

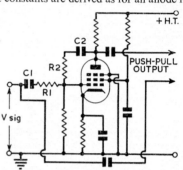

Fig. 14 (d). Anode-follower paraphase amplifier.

Rectifiers

If a diode is connected in series with a resistor across an a.c. supply the diode will conduct current only in one direction and a pulsating d.c. voltage across the resistor will result from each positive half-cycle of the supply to the anode. If a large capacitor is connected across the resistor it will be charged during a d.c. pulse and maintain a voltage (falling somewhat due to discharge through the resistor) until the next pulse occurs a cycle later. Small diodes are used for signal rectification and grid-bias supplies, while larger diodes are used for h.t. supplies.

In a practical power supply the resistor is replaced by the output load, and to obtain the maximum efficiency the voltage-drop or forward resistance of the diode must be small compared with the resistance of the load. A low forward resistance is also essential for good regulation of the output voltage, regulation in this context being the degree to which the output voltage is unaffected by the current load. One way of designing a rectifier valve with a low voltage-drop which is almost independent of current variation is to fill the diode bulb with mercury vapour or xenon. The voltage-drop across a mercury-vapour rectifier is only about 15 volts, which is considerably lower than that of any high-vacuum rectifier.

The cathode of a gas-filled rectifier must be allowed time to attain its proper operating temperature before the anode voltage is applied. This is absolutely essential. Failure to observe this requirement will result in the disintegration of the cathode by ionic bombardment. In some types of equipment, automatically delayed h.t. switching is provided as a safeguard against carelessness of the operator.

The use of diodes as power rectifiers is described in Chapter 17.

Noise Diodes

If a diode is operated in a condition where the emission is temperature-limited, the anode current will contain a component of noise which is readily calculable. The frequency spectrum of the noise would be infinite unless it was limited at the higher frequencies by the shunt capacitance of the valve and its holder and by the electron transit-time between the cathode and the anode.

Temperature-limiting is conveniently achieved by variation of the cathode temperature; hence a directly-heated pure tungsten filament is used and the filament current varied to adjust the anode current and thereby the noise output. An indirectly-heated cathode or a coated or thoriated filament cannot be used since the emissive properties would be destroyed by operation in a temperature-limited condition.

Noise diodes are specially designed for the purpose of noise generation and if required for u.h.f. circuits they are frequently of co-axial construction.

Detectors

In a receiver the detector serves to rectify or demodulate the incoming carrier. If the carrier is modulated with speech or vision signals it must be demodulated in order to extract the modulation signals from it. If the carrier is unmodulated, as in telegraphy, it is necessary to mix with it another carrier of slightly different frequency, usually generated by a local oscillator (known as the *beat-frequency oscillator*), and to rectify the mixture and thus produce an audible beat note or heterodyne in the loudspeaker. A variety of valve circuit arrangements are commonly used for this purpose and some of these are described below. Crystal diodes are also used as signal rectifiers, especially in v.h.f. receivers and in monitoring and measuring equipment.

Diode Detectors. The circuit of a conventional diode detector is shown in **Fig. 15.** An incoming unmodulated carrier V_{sig} produces a steady d.c. voltage across the load R_L, the r.f. component of the rectified carrier being by-passed by the capacitor C_L. When the carrier is modulated the instantaneous voltage across R_L varies in accordance with the amplitude variation of the carrier and at the same frequency as the modulation. Thus, a carrier which is modulated by a 1000 c/s tone will produce a 1000 c/s voltage

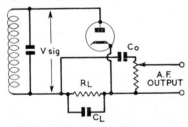

Fig. 15. A conventional diode detector.

across R_L. The shunt capacitor C_L is sufficiently small to have no perceptible effect at audio frequencies. The coupling capacitor C_o is included to prevent any d.c. shunting effect on R_L by any circuit connected to the detector output, such as an a.f. amplifier, and vice versa. To obtain a high degree of efficiency, R_L should be high compared with the impedance of the diode, which in the case of a normal receiving diode varies from about 200 ohms for low-impedance television types to about 10,000 ohms for those incorporated in multiple valves such as double-diode triodes.

A diode detector will not be free from distortion if the signal voltage applied to it is low or if there is an appreciable a.c. shunting effect by the circuit which follows it. In practice the distortion will be negligible if the input voltage is at least 10 volts (peak) and if the a.c. load is at least ten times the d.c. load.

Leaky-grid Detectors. The operation of a leaky-grid detector is somewhat complex but can best be considered as analogous to that of a diode followed by a direct-coupled

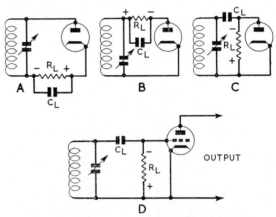

Fig. 16. Derivation of the leaky-grid detector.

amplifier, i.e. one in which the grid of the amplifier is connected directly to the anode of the diode detector. The action can conveniently be illustrated by reference to **Fig. 16.** Here three equivalent arrangements of an ordinary diode detector circuit are shown at **A, B** and **C,** the first being identical with that shown in Fig. 15; in any of them the rectified output can be taken from the opposite ends of the load resistance R_L. If the diode is replaced by the grid and cathode of an ordinary triode, as in **D,** the arrangement becomes a *leaky-grid detector,* the grid now being in effect the diode anode. In this circuit, the load resistance R_L is known as the *grid leak:* if preferred it may be connected across the reservoir capacitor C_L instead of between grid and cathode without affecting the mode of operation. Any d.c. voltage developed across the grid leak by the rectification of a modulated or an unmodulated signal will thus constitute a negative bias for the grid and the anode current in the triode will fall. If the carrier is modulated, this bias will vary in accordance with the modulation signal and so likewise will the anode current vary. An excessively strong signal will tend to bias the valve beyond the cut-off point, and therefore a leaky-grid detector ceases to function satisfactorily when the input voltage is too great. To overcome this limitation, the *power-grid detector* was introduced. This is substantially the same arrangement except that it employs a triode having a lower amplification factor and that it operates with a greater h.t. voltage; the valve thus has a longer grid base and consequently it can accept a larger input while still operating as a direct-coupled amplifier on the linear part of its characteristic. Hence there is less distortion in the " diode " part but generally less sensitivity because of the lower gain.

The r.f. carrier is of course amplified by the normal triode action (since C_L is usually not sufficiently large to eliminate it) and will appear in the anode circuit. By applying some of this energy in the form of positive feedback (i.e. *reaction*) to the resonant circuit connected between the grid and the cathode, a leaky-grid detector can be made to oscillate. In this way it can be used for the reception of c.w. telegraphy. To prevent overloading and other harmful effects in subsequent a.f. amplifier circuits, the r.f. component in the detector anode circuit must be by-passed to earth by a suitable capacitance in combination with a resistor or an r.f. choke.

Tetrodes or pentodes can be substituted for triodes in leaky-grid detector circuits, although some difficulties may be encountered in avoiding *overlap* and *threshold howl* when the self-oscillating condition is required for c.w. reception.

Anode-bend Detectors. This type of detector depends for its action on the curvature in the anode-current/grid-voltage (I_a/V_g) characteristic. If a valve is biased nearly to cut-off and an a.c. input is applied to the grid, the negative half-cycle will drive the grid more negative and only a small change in anode current will occur, whereas the positive half-cycle will drive the grid more positive and cause a considerable increase in anode current. A valve having a short grid base and the sharpest possible bottom bend in its characteristic should be chosen. The valve may be coupled to the next stage by any method applicable to voltage amplifiers.

As in the case of the leaky-grid detector, the output contains an amplified r.f. voltage at the carrier frequency and the circuit can be made to oscillate by feeding back some of this r.f. energy from the anode to the grid circuit, and c.w. reception is thereby made possible without the use of a separate oscillator.

Infinite-impedance Detectors. If an anode-bend detector is rearranged in such a manner that the output load is in the cathode lead of the valve instead of the anode lead, the result is a type of cathode follower. The input impedance is extremely high owing to the 100 per cent negative feedback, and because of this the arrangement is referred to as an infinite-impedance detector. **Fig. 17** shows the essential circuit. The modulated carrier is applied between grid and earth, the output load R_k being in the cathode lead. The load is by-passed by a capacitor C_k which should have a reactance which is low at the carrier frequency but high at the modulation frequency. The anode is also by-passed with a capacitor C_a large enough to have a low reactance at both frequencies. The rectified output is available across the resistance R_k and is supplied to the a.f. amplifier through a filter circuit comprising C_oR_o and C_gR_g. Such a filter is generally necessary because there may be quite an appreciable carrier voltage remaining across R_k despite the effect of C_k. The resistor R_o may be replaced advantageously by an r.f. choke if there is a diminished response at the higher audio frequencies.

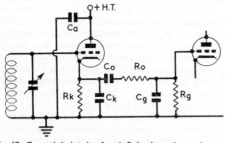

Fig. 17. Essential circuit of an infinite-impedance detector.

56

The resistor R_k should have a high value compared with the reciprocal of the mutual conductance of the valve. Since for most valves this is of the order of 100–1000 ohms, suitable values for R_k will be found in the range 10,000–100,000 ohms.

The gain of such a detector, like that of cathode follower circuits, will be less than unity and of the same order as that of a diode, but owing to the very high input impedance and the much smaller damping effect on the input circuit the actual gain will be appreciably greater than that of a diode. In the simplest case—a detector operating directly from an aerial—a step-up of signal voltage from the aerial into the grid of the same order as that achieved into an r.f. amplifying stage will be obtained.

In practice a detector having a cathode load R_k of 25,000 ohms and an a.c. load of 250,000 ohms with an input of the order of 10 volts r.m.s. will produce a total harmonic distortion not exceeding 3 per cent at 100 per cent modulation. Inputs of less than about 5 volts to such a detector are not advised since the distortion increases at low input levels.

The value of C_k must not be made too small since the valve would then appear as a negative resistance to the tuned circuit, thereby causing instability or at least such an increase in the Q of the coil that the sidebands would be restricted owing to the increased selectivity. A suitable value for C_k, assuming that R_k is about 25,000 ohms, is 250–500 pF for a carrier frequency of 1 Mc/s.

Oscillators

An oscillator is usually a class C amplifier which obtains its grid excitation from its own output circuit and employs either an inductance-capacitance tuned circuit or a quartz crystal as the frequency-determining element.

If the value of the neutralizing capacitor C_n in Fig. 10 is increased to a high value compared with the grid-to-anode capacitance, this circuit will readily oscillate, and in fact it becomes the basic Hartley oscillator circuit. If the amount of feedback through C_n is too small (i.e. if there is insufficient excitation), a small increase in load may tend to throw the circuit out of oscillation, whereas if it is too large the grid current will be excessively high and there will be a wastage of power in the grid circuit.

An important consideration in oscillator design is frequency stability. The principal factors that cause changes in frequency are (a) temperature, (b) anode voltage, (c) loading, and (d) mechanical variations of the tuned-circuit components. Temperature variation will change the valve capacitances by causing expansion or contraction of the electrode assembly and will also alter the inductance and capacitance of the components in the tuned circuit; the resultant change in frequency is called *drift*. A change in anode voltage will change the power level in the circuit, resulting in a change in temperature and also a change in the effective valve capacitance. Many of these effects can be reduced by using a tuned circuit of high efficiency (high Q) and a low L/C ratio (high C), and the circuit should be only lightly loaded.

There are probably more circuit arrangements for oscillators than for any other valve application and these are more appropriately dealt with in the various chapters describing transmitters and receivers.

Frequency Multipliers

Frequency multipliers are designed in the same way as r.f. amplifiers for class C operation but the anode circuit is

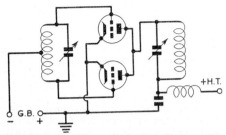

Fig. 18. The push-push frequency multiplier. The circuit produces only even-multiple harmonics: odd-multiple frequencies are automatically cancelled out.

tuned to a harmonic (i.e. a simple multiple) of the grid-circuit frequency. Because of this difference in resonant frequency neutralization is not normally required. The efficiency attainable is hardly ever likely to exceed 50 per cent and it diminishes as the order of harmonic multiplication increases, as shown in the typical figures given here:

Harmonic	..	..	2	3	4	5
Efficiency (%)	..	..	50	40	30	20

If the order of harmonic multiplication required is an even number and if the output obtainable from a single valve is barely adequate, a convenient arrangement is to use two valves connected in push-push. In this method two identical valves have their grids driven in opposite phases (as in the push-pull circuit) but their anodes are joined together and are treated as if they were a single anode: see **Fig. 18.** The anode circuit receives twice as many pulses in a given time as the pulses produced by *either* of the grids, and if it is tuned to twice the frequency of the grid circuit it will develop a voltage of twice the input frequency. A useful output can be obtained at higher even-order harmonics (4, 6, 8 . . .), although of diminishing amplitude. The push-push arrangement is inherently incapable of producing odd harmonics of the input frequency, but of course since its output waveform is not sinusoidal it will generate odd as well as even harmonics of its own nominal output frequency. Thus, if the input to a push-push multiplier were 3·5 Mc/s and the anode circuit were tuned to 7 Mc/s, the output would consist mostly of a 7 Mc/s component but it would also contain relatively weak harmonics of 14, 21, 28, 35 . . . Mc/s. There would be no 10·5 or 17·5 Mc/s components.

Frequency Changers

For a valve to act as a frequency changer it must operate over a non-linear part of its characteristic. This implies that the process is similar to signal detection, and in fact any type of valve that will operate as a detector will operate as a frequency changer. It does not follow from this that any such valves will be efficient. The essential requirement is that an input signal of frequency f_1 is applied together with a heterodyning voltage of frequency f_2 and of such amplitude that it swings over a non-linear part of the characteristic and produces sum and difference frequencies $f_1 + f_2$ and $f_1 - f_2$ in the output circuit. The overall voltage gain of a frequency changer (i.e. the ratio of i.f. voltage output to r.f. signal-voltage input) is known as the *conversion gain*, and the ratio of the beat-frequency component of frequency $f_1 - f_2$ or $f_1 + f_2$ in the output current to the input voltage of frequency f_1 is known as the *conversion conductance* (g_c) and is usually stated in microamperes per volt.

Since the primary purpose of frequency conversion in a communications receiver is to convert the high frequency of the incoming signal carrier to a more convenient lower frequency, it is only the *difference* frequency that is of any interest. To produce a difference frequency, the heterodyne oscillator frequency f_2 can, in principle, be chosen either higher or lower than the signal frequency f_1 and still yield the same result, but for various reasons connected with frequency stability and tuning range it is customary to make f_2 higher than f_1 in h.f. receivers and lower than f_1 in v.h.f. receivers.

Generally the signal voltage should be small compared with the heterodyning voltage: this is usually the case because the frequency changer is necessarily one of the early stages in the receiver circuit.

The voltage gain of a frequency changer is approximately equal to the conversion conductance multiplied by the dynamic resistance of the i.f. transformer primary. Proper allowance must be made in calculating the Q and the selectivity of the i.f. transformer for the anode-cathode impedance of the valve in shunt with the primary. If it is not possible to measure the conversion conductance, the gain of the stage may be calculated as if it were an i.f. amplifier operating at the same point, and as a rough guide the gain as a frequency changer will be about half the i.f. gain.

The basic types of frequency-changer circuit are described below.

Diode Frequency Changers. A diode may be used as a frequency changer, a typical circuit being shown in **Fig. 19.** The three circuits operating at the signal frequency (f_1), the local heterodyne oscillator frequency (f_2) and the output or intermediate frequency ($f_1 - f_2$) respectively are all connected in series with the diode. A resistive load R_k is also connected in series to prevent the diode from acting as a short-circuit to any of the tuned circuits and also to produce a suitable bias for determining the operating point on the characteristic. The impedance presented to any of the three circuits is approximately equal to half the value of R_k. The value of C_k is chosen so that its reactance is low at the three frequencies involved.

Triode Frequency Changers. These are usually of the anode-bend type. The signal is applied to the grid while the oscillator voltage is injected in series with the cathode, and the i.f. transformer is connected in the anode circuit. The anode should be by-passed to earth with a condenser of low reactance at the signal and oscillator frequencies. The capacity

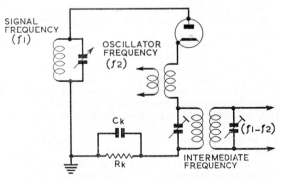

Fig. 19. Typical frequency changer circuit using a diode.

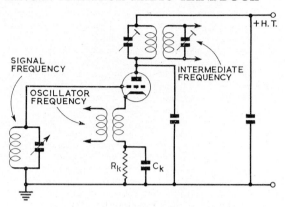

Fig. 20. A triode used as a frequency changer.

used for this purpose will comprise part of the i.f. tuning circuit.

A typical triode frequency changer is shown in **Fig. 20.** The resistor R_k and condenser C_k now provide the automatic bias, the reactance of C_k being low at all three frequencies.

The amplitude of the heterodyne voltage used should be such that the grid voltage swings from beyond cut-off to nearly the point where grid current begins to flow. Triodes are used in this manner where a very high signal-to-noise ratio is essential and where the intermediate frequency is greatly different from the signal frequency. Care should be taken to match the i.f. transformer to the anode impedance.

The value of the conversion conductance g_c will be approximately one quarter of the value of the mutual conductance g_m when the valve is considered as an amplifier.

Pentode Frequency Changers. A pentode valve may be employed as a frequency changer in several different ways. Generally the signal is applied to the control grid and the i.f. output is taken from the anode circuit, while in some arrangements the heterodyne voltage is injected in the control-grid or cathode circuit. In such cases the valve functions in the same way as an anode-bend detector. The same considerations apply as for the triode frequency changer, except that due to the much smaller capacity between the control grid and the anode any interaction between the signal and i.f. circuits when they are not greatly different in frequency is less likely to occur.

Alternatively, the heterodyne voltage may be injected on the screen grid or the suppressor grid, but both of these methods suffer from the disadvantage of requiring a large heterodyne voltage to achieve a reasonably good conversion efficiency.

When suppressor-grid injection is employed, either of the two major bends in the characteristic may be used; if the cut-off bend is chosen, there is a possibility that the maximum safe screen dissipation will be exceeded unless steps are taken to limit the screen current. Because of the large heterodyne voltage that is necessary, it may happen that some of it appears in the control-grid circuit, for instance through the inter-electrode capacities or as a result of poor layout, and this unwanted heterodyne injection will be amplified in the valve (the screen acting as an anode) and it can become comparable in effect to the heterodyne voltage intentionally applied to the suppressor. If it is of opposite phase, demodulation will take place and the conversion efficiency will

be lowered. This effect is particularly troublesome at the higher frequencies.

Multi-grid Frequency Changers. These valves, which are specifically intended for use as frequency changers, are designed to have a reasonably high conversion conductance with as low a value of heterodyne voltage as practicable and a high anode impedance to prevent damping the i.f. transformer unduly. In the design of the receiver the signal frequency can be allowed to approach closely to the intermediate frequency without causing any interaction, and a.g.c. may be used if required. The only disadvantage of multi-grid frequency changers is their limited performance at the higher frequencies.

Some types are designed for use with a separate oscillator to provide the heterodyne voltage and others have a self-contained triode to generate this voltage. In certain types of heptode mixer, a part of the valve is arranged to oscillate as an electron-coupled oscillator, a section of the oscillator coil being included in the cathode circuit. The essential feature of the oscillator is that the voltage which it generates must as far as practicable remain constant over the required frequency range.

A *heptode* (sometimes referred to as a *pentagrid*) has seven electrodes, five of them being grids. Grid No. 1 is the oscillator grid, Nos. 2 and 4 are screen grids, No. 3 the control grid and No. 5 the suppressor grid. In some heptodes, however, the functions of No. 1 and No. 3 grids are interchanged, No. 1 being the control grid. This applies also to *hexode* mixers, which are basically similar to heptodes except that the suppressor is omitted and as a result the anode impedance is somewhat lower.

Some obsolete types of heptode employed grid No. 2 as an oscillator anode, grid No. 3 being the screen grid. This form of construction was frequently called a *pentagrid*, particularly in the U.S.A., and when provided with an additional grid used as a suppressor it was referred to as an *octode*.

It should be borne in mind that multi-grid frequency changers are inherently noisy, having a high equivalent noise resistance. The equivalent noise resistance of a multi-grid mixer is given by—

$$R_{eq} = 20 \times \frac{I_a (I_k - I_a)}{I_k \times g_c^2} \text{ kilohms}$$

where I_a and I_k are the anode and cathode currents respectively (in milliamperes) and g_c is the conversion conductance (in milliamperes per volt).

Multiple Valves

The modern trend is to make radio equipment as compact as possible and it is therefore convenient to take advantage of the special multiple valves which have more than one unit contained in a single envelope but only one multi-pin base. Many such valves are available and they generally contain two units which are associated with each other in a conventional circuit application.

Double-diodes are used for signal rectification and for providing a.g.c. voltages and are often combined with a triode or pentode for a.f. or i.f. amplification. Treble-diode-triodes are used for frequency-modulation discriminators. Double-triodes are used for push-pull amplification, for multivibrators and many other purposes: the two sections may be similar or dissimilar in characteristics. Triodes are combined with r.f. pentodes for use as frequency changers and with a.f. pentodes for audio equipment or as generators for use with cathode-ray tubes. Double-tetrodes and double-pentodes may have certain electrodes commoned to avoid external circulating currents or may have a separate connection to each electrode.

Metal Valves

These valves, which at one time were very popular in the U.S.A., are ordinary valve types assembled in a metal bulb, the lead-out wires being passed through eyelets mounted in the bulb. They are not now fitted in newly manufactured equipment.

Magic-Eye Tuning Indicators

There are two basic types of magic-eye indicator. One type contains a cone-shaped piece of metal, known as the *target*, coated with fluorescent material. Electrons emitted from a cathode impinge on the target and produce a green glow over a part or the whole of its surface. Two or more small rods act as a grid and when the voltage applied to them is altered a shadow of controllable width appears on the target. A small triode may also be mounted within the bulb to amplify the voltage applied to the grid rods and thus improve the sensitivity. The grid of the triode is normally connected to the

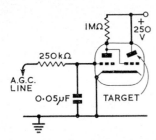

Fig. 21. A " magic eye " used as a tuning indicator.

a.g.c. line in the receiver, the result being that the " eye " opens and closes in accordance with the signal voltage in the receiver.

The other and more recent type has a fluorescent coating on the inside surface of the bulb as in a cathode-ray tube, but the operation is essentially similar.

Certain types give a double indication, one for small voltage variations and one for large variations, and others give a differential indication suitable for the output of f.m. discriminators. **Fig. 21** shows a typical circuit arrangement for a magic-eye indicator in a superheterodyne receiver.

Its applications are by no means limited to tuning adjustments, and in fact magic-eye tubes are often used as voltage indicators in a.f. and r.f. measuring equipment.

Voltage Stabilizers

Two methods are employed for voltage stabilization. The choice depends on the degree of output-voltage control required and the magnitude of the output current. Where all that is needed is a limited range of current and a control within only a few volts, a simple stabilizer of the cold-cathode type is adequate. This comprises an anode and a cathode (not heated) mounted in a bulb filled with an inert gas: when a sufficiently high voltage is applied to the anode the gas

ionizes. The voltage at which this occurs is called the *striking voltage* or *starting voltage*. If the current through the tube is varied it is found that the voltage-drop across the tube is almost constant within a certain range of current variation. The voltage-drop in the centre of the current range is called the *maintaining voltage* and is significantly lower than the striking voltage. The maintaining voltage depends on the

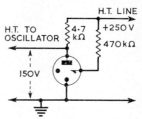

Fig. 22. A cold-cathode stabilizer used to provide a stable voltage of 150 volts from a supply line of 250 volts for the oscillator in a superheterodyne receiver. This eliminates frequency drift caused by mains voltage variations.

nature and pressure of the gas employed and to a limited extent on its temperature.

Some types have an additional electrode like a grid, known as a *trigger*. This electrode is situated close to the cathode, and if a sufficiently high positive voltage is applied to it the gas will ionize in the vicinity of these electrodes so that when the anode voltage rises it strikes at a lower value than it would without the trigger. For this reason the trigger is sometimes known as a *priming electrode*. More elaborate types are provided with a series of anodes and cold cathodes, each pair giving the same voltage-drop and thereby a series of discrete steps of stabilized voltage is made available.

A typical circuit for a trigger type of cold-cathode tube used to stabilize the voltage of the h.t. supply to the oscillator in a superheterodyne receiver is shown in **Fig. 22**.

Where a larger range of current than can be accommodated by a cold-cathode tube or where a closer regulation of voltage is necessary, a triode, tetrode or pentode valve may be used in series with the h.t. supply. A fraction of the output voltage is amplified and applied as grid bias to the stabilizer or regulator valve: this modifies the voltage-drop across the valve and so stabilizes the output voltage at a value depending on the circuit adjustments. Frequently normal amplifier-type valves are used for this purpose but specially designed valves having a lower voltage-drop permit a more economical design.

Voltage-reference Tubes

A voltage-reference tube is a cold-cathode stabilizer designed to pass a very small current but maintain a voltage-drop within exceptionally close tolerances over long periods. Such tubes are used to provide a reference voltage for calibration purposes and they should not be used for heavy current in the manner of a normal stabilizer.

Electron Multipliers

The production of secondary emission by bombardment of a cold electrode is used in an electron multiplier valve to increase the density of the electron current, i.e. to increase the slope of the valve. Since a considerable velocity is essential in the bombarding stream of electrons and since each stage

On the left is a modern equivalent of the popular 807 and on the right a modern version of the 6L6.

(Photo by courtesy of S.T. & C. Ltd.)

of electron multiplication therefore requires a certain minimum voltage, the number of stages that can be operated from a normal h.t. supply is limited.

To prevent the secondary electrons from being attracted back towards an earlier electrode by reason of the relative electrode potentials it is necessary to focus them towards the anode. This is generally achieved by means of beam-forming plates or a construction similar to a cathode-ray tube gun.

Electron multiplier tubes are sometimes used in television receivers and in amateur television transmitters.

TRANSMITTING VALVES

In a transmitter most of the valves employed in the early stages are normal receiving-type valves, but in the final stages valves of higher power-handling capacity are necessary. Such valves fall into two classes, (i) triodes or (ii) tetrodes or pentodes. In general, all valves of more than 25 watts anode dissipation have directly-heated cathodes, and up to the largest sizes used by amateurs the cathodes are of the thoriated-tungsten filament type. Those designed for operation on the higher frequencies are usually provided with special connections on the top or side of the bulb for the anode or grid, or sometimes both, and have special bases or in some types no base at all. This avoids the bunching together of the leads at one end of the valve and thereby lowers the inter-electrode capacitance and reduces the possibility of leakage or breakdown at high voltage.

Triodes. Triode transmitting valves are generally used with grounded-cathode or grounded-grid connections, the former being preferred at frequencies below 150 Mc/s and the latter at higher frequencies. They require more drive than tetrodes or pentodes but are more readily matched into the associated circuits and are often more convenient to modulate: they are seldom satisfactory as frequency multipliers.

Tetrodes and Pentodes. In amateur equipment, tetrodes and pentodes are used because of their high efficiency. Many of the popular tetrodes are in fact beam valves and have pentode-type characteristics. They require little or no neutralization because their inter-electrodes are sufficiently low, but if they are to be anode-modulated it is necessary to modulate the screen voltage as well as the anode voltage and the respective amplitudes must be correctly proportioned.

Some pentodes have a separate connection to the suppressor grid and can be suppressor-grid modulated, though this system is not widely used on account of its low anode efficiency.

Double-tetrodes and Double-pentodes. A range of double valves having anode dissipations in the range 6–50 watts are available and are well suited to amateur requirements. Some have two separate units within one envelope, while others have a common flat cathode, one face being used for one section and the opposite face for the other section. The control grids are " half grids," one on each side of the cathode, and the screen is a common grid surrounding the two control grids and the cathode, while the anodes are flat plates, one on each side. This form of construction avoids circulating

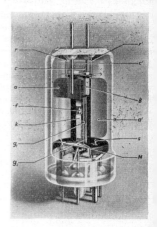

Cut-away view of a v.h.f. double tetrode, the **QQV06-40A.**

r, r'—electrode support rods; c, c'—neutralising capacitors; a, a'—anodes; B—beam plate; M—mica electrode supporting plate; k—cathode; g₁—control grid: g₂—screen grid; S—internal screen.

(Photo by courtesy of Mullard Ltd.)

currents in a common cathode lead or in the screen lead when the two units are used in push-pull and enables a greater efficiency to be obtained at high frequencies. Some types also embody internal neutralization. Satisfactory operation up to about 600 Mc/s can be achieved with some of these double valves, both as class C amplifiers and as frequency multipliers using the third or fifth harmonic.

SPECIAL VALVES

Frame-grid Valves. For certain special purposes valves having a characteristic with a steeper slope and a shorter electron-transit time than are obtainable with normal types of construction are required. These improvements are achieved by locating the grid as close as possible to the cathode. One satisfactory method, shown in Fig. 23, is to wind the grid wire under tension (about half its breaking point) on a stiff rectangular frame to which it is firmly fixed by glazing or gold-brazing. This produces a very rigid grid which can be spaced at distances of the order of only a thousandth of an inch from a suitably flat cathode. Valves with a slope of 15–40 mA/V are made in this way.

Fig. 23. Construction of a frame grid.

Disc-seal Valves. In this type of valve the cathode is in the form of a thimble, while the grid is composed of parallel wires tightly stretched across a hole in a metallic disc and the anode is a plain flat disc, the various parts being spaced by means of glass or ceramic seals. The outer rims of the discs extend beyond the seals for connection to the external circuit which can advantageously be of cylindrical co-axial form to suit the construction of the valve. Such valves are intended for use in grounded-grid circuits and will operate up to frequencies of several thousand megacycles with quite good efficiencies: they are available both as triodes and as tetrodes. The anode is generally cooled by an air blast through radiating fins or by conduction to the external co-axial circuit elements. Valves of this form are also known as *planar, lighthouse, rocket* or *pencil* valves.

A 2C39A disc seal transmitting valve.

(Photo by courtesy of S. T. & C. Ltd.)

In the ceramic stacked triode the electrode discs are sealed directly to accurately machined ceramic washers. The valve can give 15 dB gain at 1000 Mc/s with a noise factor of 8·5 dB.

Nuvistors. This type of valve is intermediary between valves of normal construction and disc-seal or stacked ceramic. The electrodes are of cylindrical shape but smaller than those generally employed and are rigidly supported from one end by a tripod-like structure on a ceramic base. The supports are continuations of the pins which are sealed through the base—no use is made of mica or glass supports

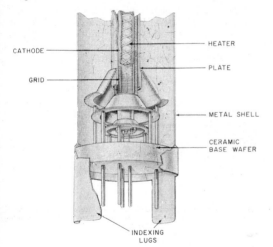

Fig. 24. Cutaway view of a Nuvistor triode showing the cylindrical electrodes and tripod-like supports.

(By courtesy of R.C.A. (Great Britain) Ltd.)

or spacers. This construction produces rugged and efficient valves having low leakage and low microphony. Because the structure is so small the capacitance between electrodes and the lead inductance is low, resulting in a good performance and low noise on v.h.f. A current type coming into wide use is the 6CW4.

Magnetrons. A magnetron is a diode with a cylindrical and concentric cathode and anode, the anode being split into two or more segments or cavities and the whole assembly is placed in a magnetic field parallel to the axis of the electrodes. The magnet may be an integral part of the valve and it is then known as a *package magnetron*. Owing to the axial magnetic field the path of the electrons leaving the cathode is curved, and for a certain field intensity the electrons stop short of the anode and return to the cathode, travelling in circular orbits. The time taken for an electron to complete its orbital journey determines the frequency of oscillation. The energy associated with the moving electrons is given up to the space around the cathode whence it is transferred to the tuned cavities and picked up by a coupling loop.

Klystrons. A *klystron* is a valve containing an electron gun similar to that used in a cathode-ray tube from which a narrow beam of electrons is projected along the axis of the tube and focused through small apertures across which one or more oscillatory circuits are connected; these circuits are in the form of hollow toroidal chambers known as *rhumbatrons*. The beam of electrons is velocity-modulated by the application of an r.f. field, for example by passing the beam through small apertures having an r.f. voltage between them. If this velocity-modulated beam is now passed through a field-free space, known as a *drift space*, the faster-moving electrons will begin to overtake the slower ones so that at some point along the beam alternative regions of high and low electron density will exist. The rhumbatrons are located at points of maximum density. If two rhumbatrons are coupled together by means of a feedback loop, or if a reflector electrode maintained at a slightly negative potential with respect to the cathode is mounted at the end of the tube the energy will be reflected back into a single rhumbatron. The electrons become bunched due to being velocity-modulated, and since the energy is retarded by reason of the distance of travel to the reflector and back again sustained oscillation will take place. Klystrons are employed as oscillators, the reflector type being preferred for low-power work, e.g., as a local oscillator in a superheterodyne receiver.

Travelling-wave Tubes. A *travelling-wave tube* consists of a wire helix supported in a long glass envelope which fits through two wave-guide stubs used as input and output elements. At one end of the tube is a conventional electron-gun assembly which directs an electron beam to the other end: see **Fig. 25.** A voltage pulse or wave travelling along the helix will run round the turns of the helix at roughly its normal velocity but its axial velocity may be only about a tenth of that value, depending on the pitch of the helix. If the electron beam is sent along the centre of the helix and focused by a magnet it will be charge-density modulated by the voltage pulse (i.e. amplitude-modulated) owing to the interaction between the magnetic field of the current in the helix and the electrons. This modulation grows in amplitude along the length of the helix roughly according to the square of the axial distance from the beginning of the helix. By suitable design the output wave-guide coupling can extract more

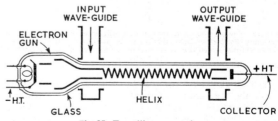

Fig. 25. Travelling-wave tube.

energy than was put in by the input coupling and a considerable power gain can be achieved. For example, a travelling-wave tube amplifier at 4000 Mc/s can produce 5 watts output for an input of only 25 milliwatts, i.e. a gain of 23 dB.

Beam Parametric Amplifiers (Adler Tubes). These tubes utilize a normal electron gun generating a focused electron beam which passes through electrodes to which the input signal is connected (generally coaxially), then through a quadropole of four curved electrodes, which may be cross connected or coupled by inductances to which the pump signal is applied. The quadropole lies in a transverse magnetic field provided by a permanent or electromagnet. The next electrodes are the output electrodes followed by one or more collectors or anodes. The pump frequency, of power only a few milliwatts, is usually at approximately twice the signal frequency. They have so far been made for frequencies between 200 and 4,000 Mc/s and achieve a noise factor of about 2db, a gain of over 20db and a wide bandwidth. Unlike most parametric devices they are inherently stable because the input, pump and output connections are quite separate.

CATHODE-RAY TUBES

In a cathode-ray tube, the electrons emitted from a hot cathode are first accelerated to give them a high velocity and are then formed into a beam and finally allowed to strike a fluorescent screen, thereby causing a spot of light to appear at the point where the beam strikes. The part of the tube which generates the beam of electrons is known as the *gun*. A beam of moving electrons can be deflected laterally by electric or magnetic fields, and since its weight and inertia are negligibly small it can be made to follow almost instantaneously the variations of periodically changing fields even up to very high radio frequencies, producing a visible image of these variations.

In a simple type of tube the gun consists of a heater, cathode, grid and two anodes: see **Fig. 26.** The intensity of the electron beam and therefore the brightness of the trace on the screen is regulated by the grid potential as in a valve. Anode No. 1 has a positive potential with respect to the cathode and accelerates the electrons which have passed through the grid: it is provided with small apertures through

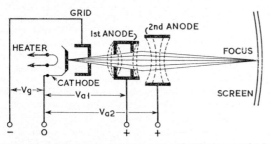

Fig. 26. The electron gun used in one type of cathode-ray tube for focusing the electron beam into a narrow pencil of rays. The electric fields of force act in the manner of lenses for deflecting the paths of the electrons.

which the electron stream passes. The stream, on emerging from the apertures, is formed of electrons travelling in parallel straight-line paths. The electrostatic fields set up by the potentials on anodes Nos. 1 and 2 form an *electron lens*

which causes the electron paths to converge or focus to a point at the fluorescent screen. The focal length of the lens depends on the spacing of these anodes and their respective potentials, and this type of focusing is known as *electrostatic focusing*. The beam can, however. also be focused by a current passing through a coil mounted axially on the neck of the tube or by a permanent magnet. These methods are known as *magnetic focusing*. An electron gun, in its simplest form, can be a triode in which case it must be magnetically focused, but more complicated guns in the form of tetrodes, pentodes and hexodes are commonly used. In general, electrostatic focusing is much more convenient for oscilloscope tubes, but either method is applicable to television or radar tubes.

The focused beam can be deflected electrostatically or electromagnetically. For *electrostatic deflection* two pairs of plates are mounted at right angles to each other, as in **Fig. 27(a).** The beam passes between the plates and is bent upwards and downwards by potentials between the horizontal

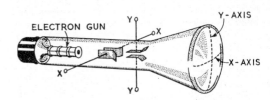

Fig. 27(a). Electrostatic deflection of the electron beam in a cathode-ray tube.

pair of plates (the *Y*-plates) and from side to side by the vertical pair (the *X*-plates). For *magnetic deflection* two pairs of coils are mounted radially on the neck of the tube, as in **Fig. 27(b),** one pair causing vertical deflection (*Y*-axis) and the other pair horizontal deflection (*X*-axis).

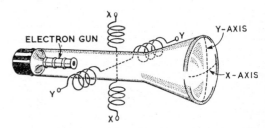

Fig. 27(b). Electromagnetic deflection of the electron beam in a cathode-ray tube. The coils are sometimes provided with magnetic cores.

In the electrostatic-deflection type of tube, the beam can be split into two by a separator plate thus enabling the screen to show two independent traces simultaneously. Such a tube is known as a *double-beam* tube. Two or more beams can also be produced by tubes having multiple gun assemblies mounted within a single neck.

The brightness of the trace on the screen depends on the final anode voltage and on the beam current and the speed at which the spot moves. Care must be taken to avoid too bright a spot since an intense concentration of high-speed electrons will burn the screen, and too great a beam current will shorten the life of the cathode.

CHAPTER 3

SEMICONDUCTORS

SEMICONDUCTOR devices perform similar functions to those performed by thermionic valves in radio equipment and fall broadly into two categories: *crystal diodes* and *transistors*. Unlike their thermionic counterparts semiconductors require no heater voltage and are current operated, as opposed to voltage operated, devices.

Although the crystal diode in its modern form has been accepted readily by radio amateurs as a variant of a device with which they are already familiar, the transistor presents a more difficult problem, and demands an understanding of its characteristics before it can be successfully used. Most texts on the subject are directed towards the specialist in the field and it is the purpose of this chapter therefore to introduce the reader to the fundamentals in particular of semiconductor circuitry without resorting to advanced physics or complex electron flow theory and with particular reference to the requirements of the Amateur Radio enthusiast.

It was not until 1948 that the first practical transistors were made but development has been so intensive since then that a very wide range of types is now available including those suitable for v.h.f. The many readily available transistors justify serious consideration by the radio amateur who is planning the construction of new apparatus. The practical advantages include reduced power consumption, smaller physical size and improved ruggedness.

A possible disadvantage lies in the fact that, unlike the thermionic valve, many of the transistor characteristics are temperature-dependent. However, in most applications the effect can be very largely offset by careful attention to the circuit design and on skilful development of the bias circuits. The requirements are so different from those of thermionic valve circuits that it is advisable to consider the basic electron-flow processes before attempting a full understanding of transistor circuit technique.

THEORY OF SEMICONDUCTORS

The ability of a substance to conduct electricity depends on the readiness with which electrons can become detached from their parent atoms. In the case of pure germanium, which is a crystalline substance, there are very few free electrons at room temperatures, and the material is classed as a *semiconductor*. Each atom has four valence electrons, which are the electrons on which conductive properties depend, and atoms " knit " with their neighbours in a fashion typical of crystalline substances as indicated in **Fig. 1.** The few electrons that may be available as current carriers are those which have been " shaken " free by thermal agitation. The effect of thermal agitation is to cause electrons to break away from their bonds and drift into the orbits of neighbouring atoms. Normally the process is quite random, but when a voltage is applied between two points on the substance the movement of electrons becomes a general drift towards the positive pole of the applied voltage.

Each time an electron breaks away from its atom it leaves a vacancy, or " hole," which remains until it is filled by another electron from a neighbouring atom. Thus the " hole " effectively moves in a direction opposite to that of the electron, and a general flow of electrons in one direction can be looked upon as a flow of " holes " in the reverse direction. Although this may appear to introduce an unnecessary or purely hypothetical concept it undoubtedly simplifies the problem of understanding the way in which crystal diodes and transistors operate.

The conductivity of a germanium crystal may be greatly improved by the addition of a small amount of impurity into the crystal, and two different types of impurities are purposely added in this way—those with five valency electrons and those with only three. Such an impurity is arsenic which is a penta-valent substance. When added to germanium it interrupts the crystal formation because each arsenic atom has one excess electron which prevents it from fitting into the pattern. The surplus electrons are very mobile and are readily available as current carriers when a voltage is applied. Germanium which has been treated in this way in known as *n* type germanium because the current carriers are electrons and therefore negatively charged. If indium is added as an impurity, however, a similar effect occurs but this time each impurity atom introduces a " hole " because indium is a tri-valent element. As explained above,

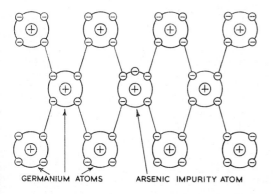

GERMANIUM ATOMS   ARSENIC IMPURITY ATOM

Fig. I. In pure germanium, which is a crystalline substance, the four electrons in the outer orbit of each atom form tight bonds with those in neighbouring atoms and leave few electrons available for carrying electric current. The addition of a small amount of impurity such as arsenic, which has five electrons in the outer orbit, introduces free electrons to the structure and increases the electrical conductivity. Germanium " doped " in this way is known as *n* type.

a " hole " may be mobile and thus improve the conductivity of the crystal. Germanium doped with indium is known as *p* type because conduction is due to positively charged carriers (i.e. " holes ").

The P–N Junction

Fig. 2 shows a germanium crystal, half of which has been doped with arsenic and the other half with indium. One half is therefore *p* type and the other *n* type. If such a crystal is prepared, then at the junction between the two regions, free

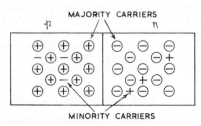

Fig. 2. If an impurity with only three electrons in the outer orbit is added to a germanium crystal, electron deficiencies, or "holes" are introduced and the germanium is known as *p* type. A combination of *p* region and *n* region in a single crystal, as shown in this diagram, is the basis of a junction diode.

electrons will move across from the *n* region and begin to fill up the " holes " in the *p* region. Because the recombination process entails a flow of charge carriers through the junction, a contact potential is developed across the junction of such a polarity as to oppose the flow of carriers and a state of equilibrium is quickly reached. There remains a thin region in the vicinity of the junction which has been cleared of mobile carriers and is known as the *depletion layer*.

In **Fig. 3** the *p-n* junction is shown with an external voltage applied such that the *p* region is made positive and

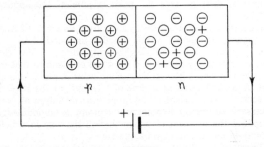

Fig. 3. A *p-n* junction with an external voltage applied as above is said to be forward biased. The relationship between voltage and current is not linear but follows an exponential law.

the *n* region negative. Under these conditions the device behaves as a good conductor because the holes in the *p* region and the electrons in the *n* region are of the correct polarity to support current flow. The magnitude of the current flowing will depend on (among other things) the applied potential, but the relationship between current and voltage is affected by the presence of the depletion layer, and the resultant characteristic takes the form shown in **Fig. 4**. This is the forward characteristic of the *p-n* junction.

If the polarity of the external voltage is now reversed, the available current carriers in the two halves are then of the wrong polarity for conduction and the device behaves rather

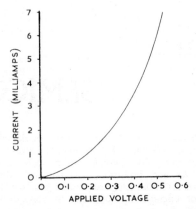

Fig. 4. Forward characteristics of a *p-n* junction diode.

like a very high resistance. The relatively small current that does flow is due to the presence of thermally-generated holes and free electrons. Thus, at room temperature there will always be a few *n* type carriers in the *p* region and, likewise, some *p* type carriers in the *n* region. Such carriers are present in only small proportions and are termed *minority carriers*. Because they are so few in number, the reverse current reaches saturation at a very small applied voltage. **Fig. 5** shows the complete forward and reverse characteristics of a typical *p-n* junction; its suitability as a rectifier can be clearly seen and the device is known as a *junction diode*.

It is important to note that the reverse conduction is entirely dependent on thermally-generated carriers, and it therefore varies markedly with the temperature of the junction. In fact, the relationship in the case of germanium is such that the current approximately doubles for each 8° C. rise in the temperature of the junction. This feature is perhaps the most significant difference between thermionic and crystal diodes.

Many crystal diodes in current use are of the *point-contact* type. These differ from the junction diode in that they

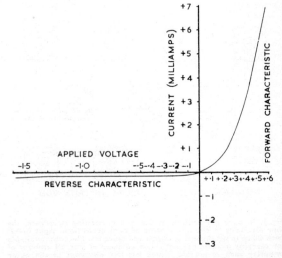

Fig. 5. Complete characteristics of a *p-n* junction diode showing the way in which reverse current saturates at a very low value.

employ a single piece of *n* type germanium with a " cat's whisker " in contact with its surface. Although the underlying principle of operation is based on that of the junction diode, the exact mechanism of the process is not yet completely understood; it is believed, however, that the effect of the " cat's whisker " is to create a small region of *p* type substance in the vicinity of the contact. The particular characteristics of the point-contact diode are high forward resistance and good high frequency performance.

The Transistor

In **Fig. 6** an elaboration of the basic *p-n* junction is shown in which the *n* region is made very thin and a second region of *p* type germanium is added to form a *p-n-p* sandwich. This device can be considered as two *p-n* junctions mounted back to back: each junction is capable of being biased separately and of reproducing the characteristics described previously. If, however, both junctions are biased simultaneously rather special conditions apply. The left-hand junction is biased in the forward direction and therefore presents a low

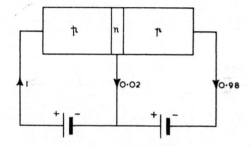

Fig. 6. A *p-n-p* sandwich forms two *p-n* junctions mounted back to back and is the basis of the transistor. The left-hand junction is forward biased but a large proportion of its input current becomes transferred to the right-hand junction, which is reverse biased. Power gain arises because an input current into a low resistance appears in a circuit of much higher resistance.

resistance to the flow of current, while the right-hand junction is biased in the reverse, i.e. high resistance, direction. Because the *n* region is very thin, many of the current carriers flowing into the *n* zone from the forward biased circuit become captured by the *p* region in the reverse biased circuit. For example, if a current of 1 mA flows into the left-hand *p* region, instead of the whole of this current appearing in the connection to the *n* zone, about 98 per cent of it may flow into the right-hand *p* region and thus appear in the normally very high resistance circuit. Only about 2 per cent of the " input " current will then be extracted from the *n* region. This is the basic transistor action, power gain being achieved by virtue of the fact that an input current fed into a low resistance circuit reappears in a circuit of much higher resistance. If the " sandwich " is made *n-p-n* instead of *p-n-p* the same process will occur provided that the polarities of the bias circuits are reversed. Most transistors available at the present time are of the *p-n-p* type and of a construction similar to that shown in **Fig. 7**. Germanium is the most commonly used substance but silicon is also used and has the advantage of being less temperature dependent.

In all transistors the outer electrode of the forward biased junction is termed the *emitter*, the centre electrode the *base*, and the reverse biased electrode the *collector*.

Early transistors were not junction types but were known

as *point-contact transistors*. These employed a method of construction similar to that of the point-contact diode except that two " cat's whiskers " were involved. They tended to be unreliable and inconsistent and have been almost completely superseded by the junction type.

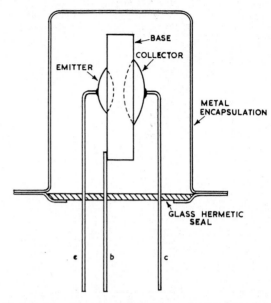

Fig. 7. Construction of a typical *p-n-p* audio frequency or r.f. transistor. This is known as the alloyed junction type in which the junctions are formed by alloying *p* type impurities into opposite faces of a wafer of *n* type germanium. The centre region is known as the base electrode, the forward biased electrode is termed the emitter, and the reverse biased electrode the collector.

BASIC CIRCUIT CONFIGURATIONS

So far in this description the transistor has been considered as operating in such a way that the base connection is common to both the emitter and the collector circuits. This is known as the *common base* configuration and is characterized by a current " gain " of a little less than unity, and by a low input resistance and a very high output resistance. The recognized symbol for the current gain in this arrangement is α (alpha). From **Fig. 8,** which indicates the current distribution when one unit of current is fed into the emitter or input electrode, it can be seen that the ratio of collector current to base

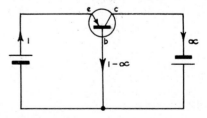

Fig. 8. In this diagram the *p-n-p* transistor is represented by its circuit symbol. The symbol α is used to express the ratio of collector current to emitter current and is typically 0·98. Thus the ratio of collector current to base current is $\frac{\alpha}{1-\alpha}$ and is known as β.

current is $\alpha/(1-\alpha)$: this ratio is given the symbol β (beta). In a typical transistor, β is about 50. Thus, if a common emitter arrangement is adopted, the device becomes capable of providing a worthwhile current gain. The available power gain is very high and, for this reason, the *common emitter* arrangement is by far the most widely used.

Nevertheless when using a transistor at frequencies near the practical limit for its type there may be an advantage in

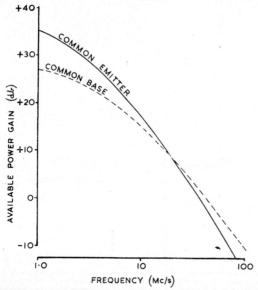

Fig. 9. Because of the finite transit time of the current carriers, the current gain of a transistor falls off as frequency is increased. The frequency at which the common base current gain has fallen by 3 db is known as the alpha cut-off frequency and is given the symbol $f\alpha$. The available power gain falls off at a rather faster rate, as shown in this graph which is plotted for a transistor with an $f\alpha$ of about 10 Mc/s.

using the common-base circuit. This arises because, although the common-emitter arrangement is capable of greater low frequency power gain, the gain falls off at a faster rate with increasing frequency than it does in the common-base arrangement. Typical gain frequency characteristics of a transistor in each of these two configurations are shown in **Fig. 9**.

The third possible configuration is the *common collector* arrangement but this has only specialized application. It is analogous to the cathode follower valve circuit and is characterized by a high input resistance and a fairly low output resistance. The current gain is $\frac{1}{1-\alpha}$, which is equal to $\beta + 1$, and therefore approximately the same as that of the common-emitter circuit. In spite of the high current gain, the power gain is not very great because of the adverse impedance transformation. This arrangement is however well suited for use as an input stage for a crystal microphone or pick-up owing to its high input impedance and low output impedance.

Typical characteristics of a transistor operating in each of of the three configurations are listed in **Fig. 10**.

IMPORTANT TRANSISTOR CHARACTERISTICS

In spite of the fact that the basic operation of the transistor is so different from that of the thermionic valve, there are

Configuration	Input Resistance	Output Resistance	Current Gain	Power Gain
COMMON BASE	40 ohms	I Mohms	0·98	1,000 (30 db)
COMMON EMITTER	2 Kohms	30 K ohms	50	10,000 (40 db)
COMMON COLLECTOR	100Kohms	I K ohms	50	40 (16 db)

Fig. 10. Typical small-signal low frequency characteristics of a junction transistor in each of the three basic configurations are shown in this table.

distinct resemblances between some of their characteristics.

Fig. 11 shows a family of collector characteristics for a typical transistor in the common emitter configuration. The general appearance is very similar to that of the anode characteristics of a pentode valve, but each curve in the

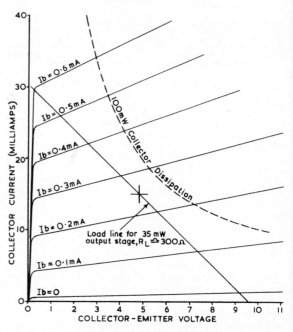

Fig. 11. A typical family of collector characteristics for a transistor in the common emitter configuration. Their general shape is very similar to the anode characteristics of a pentode valve and they can be used in a similar way. To demonstrate this, a load line has been superimposed to represent the working conditions of the class A output stage of Fig. 15. Note the low "knee" voltage which enables very high efficiencies to be obtained in a transistor power stage.

family is plotted for a particular value of input *current* (I_b) to the base electrode in contrast to the input *voltage* applied to the grid of the thermionic valve. This clearly illustrates the importance of regarding the transistor as a current operated device. The lowest curve of the family represents the collector current that will flow even without any input current and is termed the *collector leakage current*. This is the basic temperature dependent parameter and causes the whole family of collector characteristics to move upward with increasing temperature.

When using the collector characteristics for determining the working point and the load impedance for a particular application the procedure is similar to that for a thermionic

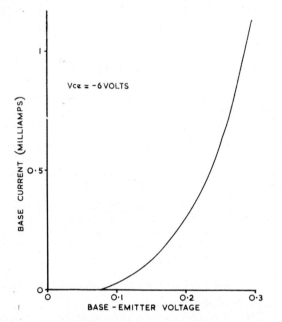

Fig. 12. The input characteristics of a transistor resemble the forward characteristics of a junction diode. The slope of the curve gives the small-signal low frequency input resistance of the transistor and varies with bias level.

valve: see Chapter 2 (*Valves*). As an example, a load line has been drawn across the characteristics to represent a class A power stage operating from a 6 volt supply and delivering a power output of about 35 mW into a transformer coupled 300 ohm load. (This load line represents the conditions in a stage operating from a 6 volt supply but with a voltage drop of 1·2 volts across an emitter stabilising resistor.) Because of the very small " knee " voltage it is possible to achieve very high output circuit efficiency in a transistor stage.

The small signal output resistance of the transistor at any point is given by the slope of the characteristic at that point, while the current gain (β) can be readily deduced by relating the base and collector currents at the same point.

Fig. 12 represents the input characteristics of a typical common emitter connected transistor and is obviously similar to the normal forward characteristic of a junction diode. This curve may be used for determining the input bias conditions when the required collector current has been established. The small signal input resistance is indicated by

the slope of the curve at the working point and, as can be seen, varies quite considerably with the base current. Only one curve is usually shown because the input characteristics are fairly independent of the collector voltage.

The frequency limitation of a transistor is normally expressed by quoting the frequency at which the current gain has fallen to 70 per cent of its low frequency value in the common base arrangement. This is usually known as the frequency of *alpha cut-off* and is denoted by the symbol $f\alpha$. Because of various capacitive effects, the power gain begins to decrease at a much lower frequency and it is not ordinarily practicable to operate a transistor at frequencies greater than $\frac{f\alpha}{2}$, except perhaps as an oscillator.

A very important rating for a transistor is the *maximum collector dissipation*. Most manufacturers quote this for a specified ambient temperature and give a figure which indicates the derating factor to be applied at higher temperatures.

STABILIZATION OF THE WORKING POINT

To give some idea of the importance of good stabilization of the working point, **Fig. 13** shows a curve of collector leakage current plotted against the junction temperature for a typical low power transistor in the common emitter circuit. At room temperature the leakage current is quite insignificant, but at 40° C. (104° F.) it rises to almost 1 mA, which may be considerably greater than the desired working current in a small signal stage. A good bias circuit will reduce the maximum leakage current to an acceptable level over the required working temperature range and also reduce the effects of the variation of characteristics between transistor samples.

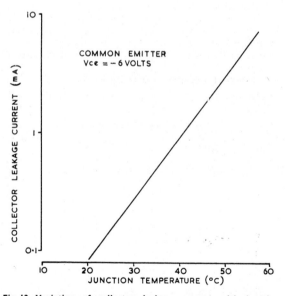

Fig. 13. Variation of collector leakage current with junction temperature for a typical l.f. transistor. Leakage current increases so rapidly with temperature that it is possible for a condition known as " thermal runaway " to occur. This arises when an initial increase of temperature leads to sufficient rise of leakage current to cause a further significant rise of temperature. The process then becomes rapidly cumulative and the transistor is destroyed. A carefully designed bias circuit and a knowledge of the transistor's limitations are the best safeguards against this.

In **Fig. 14** a transistor is shown with a skeleton bias circuit of a form which is applicable to most types of transistor stages used in communications equipment and which uses a single battery to supply the input bias and collector voltage. The base of the transistor is fed from a potentiometer formed by R_1 and R_2, while a third resistor R_3 is inserted in the emitter lead. The amount of bias current I_b fed into the base electrode, and therefore the amount of collector current I_c that will flow, is decided by the difference between the voltages V_b and V_e. If, for any reason, the collector current tries to increase then the voltage drop across R_3 (i.e. V_e) will also increase. This will leave less voltage available for

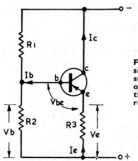

Fig. 14. The basic elements of a single battery bias circuit. Good stability of working point can be obtained with a bias system of this type at the expense of a relatively small extra battery drain.

providing bias, and therefore the bias current will decrease and try to oppose the change in the collector current. The effectiveness depends on (a) the bleed current in the base potentiometer being sufficient to ensure that V_b remains constant, and (b) the value of R_3 being large enough to produce a significant voltage change across it when the collector current changes. A good rule of thumb for small signal stages is to arrange that the bleed current is about one fifth of the desired collector current and to drop about one-fifth of the total battery voltage across the emitter resistor R_3. This is best demonstrated by a worked example.

The Practical Design of a Bias System

Suppose that the transistor has the characteristics

shown in Figs. 11 and 12 and that it is to be used in the 35 mW output stage represented by the load line in Fig. 11. Suppose also that the battery voltage is 6 volts and the required collector current is 15 mA. Following the recommendation above, the bleed current in the base potentiometer is therefore $\frac{1}{5} \times 15 = 3$ mA, and the voltage drop across R_3 is $\frac{1}{5} \times 6 = 1\cdot2$ volts. Ignoring the base current taken by the transistor (which is much smaller than the bleed current) the required total resistance of the

potentiometer is $\dfrac{6V}{3mA} \times 10^3 = 2{,}000$ ohms. As already

explained, the emitter current is approximately equal to the collector current (see Fig. 6) and it is therefore convenient to find the value of R_3 by dividing the voltage drop across it

by the collector current, thus— $\dfrac{1\cdot2V}{15mA} \times 10^3 = 80$ ohms.

From the output characteristics shown in Fig. 11, the required base current I_b is 0·25 mA, and reference to the input characteristics shown in Fig. 12 indicates that the base emitter voltage required to produce this current is 0·19 volt. Adding this voltage to V_e gives $V_b = 1\cdot2 + 0\cdot19 = 1\cdot39$

volts and therefore $R_2 = \dfrac{1\cdot39V}{3mA} \times 10^3 = 464$ ohms. Since

the total potentiometer resistance required has been calculated to be 2,000 ohms, R_1 must be $2{,}000 - 464 = 1{,}536$ ohms.

This output stage is used in the 35 mW amplifier shown in **Fig. 15** and it will be noticed that resistors of the nearest preferred values to those calculated are specified. Decoupling capacitors are used to isolate the bias circuit at signal frequencies.

COUPLING CIRCUITS FOR TRANSISTOR STAGES
Audio Frequency Stages

Because the transistor is a *current* operated device and has a relatively low impedance input circuit compared with the usual thermionic valve arrangement, it is more important to ensure proper impedance matching of the coupling circuits linking small signal transistor stages than in the corresponding valve circuits. The procedure is complicated by the fact that transistor impedances vary with operating conditions and it is necessary to establish the working point before attempting to calculate the coupling requirements. This will normally be chosen on the basis of allowing a sufficiently large quiescent collector current to handle the signal without any clipping of the current waveform.

For audio frequencies, the input and output impedances can then be determined by measuring the slope of the static characteristics at the working point discussed previously or

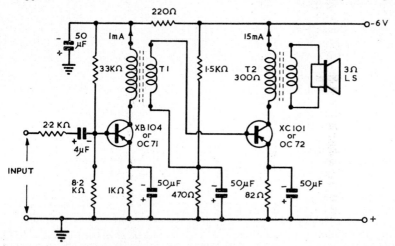

Fig. 15. A class A 35 mW audio output stage and driver. Many "personal" transistorized receivers use an output stage of this type.

of battery supply voltage resulting in a 200 c/s change of frequency. Normal battery drain is about 0·25 mA.

Although there are several methods of coupling the oscillator to a following stage, the method shown is a useful one because it provides fairly good isolation between the oscillator and the output circuit yet enables an output voltage of about 100 mV to be developed across a load of 3 K ohms. If it is desired to couple into a lower load impedance it may be advantageous to wind a coupling link adjacent to the tank coil but care must be taken to avoid excessive damping of the coil or frequency stability will be impaired.

Pre-amplifier for use with Crystal Microphones

When using a crystal microphone in conjunction with a lengthy connecting cable it is very desirable to employ some form of impedance transformation so that a low impedance cable may be used. If the microphone is to feed into a transistor amplifier (which will probably have an input impedance of about 3 K ohms) then impedance transformation becomes essential. The pre-amplifier shown in **Fig. 20** can be built into a unit about the size of a matchbox, complete with batteries, and may be mounted conveniently on

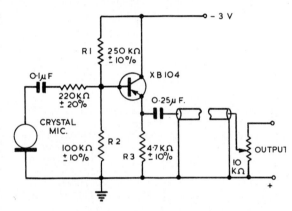

Fig. 20. Pre-amplifier for use with a crystal microphone. It is possible to construct this device in such a small space that it is quite practical to mount it, complete with the battery, in the microphone base and thus obtain the advantage of a low impedance feed to the power amplifier or modulator.

the microphone. Although it does not amplify the voltage output of the microphone, it does provide power gain and will deliver a voltage of about 100 mV into a 3 K ohm load. Battery consumption is almost negligible and the smallest dry cells will be sufficient to power it. An XB104 transistor operates in a common-collector stage and is biased by resistance R_1, R_2 and R_3. R_3 also forms the load resistance.

The device has been particularly designed to feed into the class B push-pull output stage and driver of Fig. 22. Normal working collector current is 120 μA.

Pre-amplifier for use with a Moving Coil Microphone

Small 50 ohm moving coil earpieces operate quite well as microphones and lend themselves admirably for use with transistors. The pre-amplifier of **Fig. 21** is designed to be fed directly from this type of microphone, without a step-up transformer, and will produce adequate output to drive the power amplifier of Fig. 22.

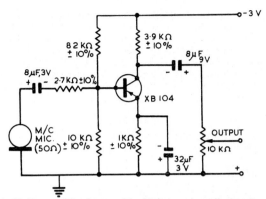

Fig. 21. Pre-amplifier for use with a 50 ohm moving coil microphone. The XB104 used in this circuit and that of Fig. 20 may be replaced by an OC71.

An XB104 transistor is used in common emitter configuration, with a 3·9 K ohm resistive load in the collector circuit. A 3 volt battery is required and, as in the previous circuit, need only be of the pen-light type to supply the very small drain of approximately 250 μA. The 8 μF capacitor coupling the microphone to the XB104 transistor is necessary to avoid shunting the 10 K ohm bias resistor by the microphone coil and thus upsetting the bias conditions. Because of the non-linearity of the input characteristic it is advisable to connect a 2·7 K ohm resistor in series with the microphone in order to ensure that the transistor is current fed. If it is desired to increase sensitivity it is in order to reduce the value of the resistor, the minimum value being set by the degree of distortion tolerated.

Class B 250 mW Push-pull Output Stage and Driver

When considering the design of transistorized power output stages, the class B push-pull configuration appears attractive in that it is capable of high power efficiency. This means that a reasonable power input may be obtained from relatively low power transistors and battery consumption is kept to a minimum. Most current transistorized broadcast receivers employ this form of output stage. A typical example, together with its driver stage, is shown in **Fig. 22** and is ideal for building into amateur mobile equipment. In conjunction with a 8,000—10,000 gauss speaker, adequate output volume is available for use in a car or a fair sized domestic room. It may also be used as a low power modulator provided that the secondary winding of the output transformer is adjusted to suit the input resistance of the stage to be modulated. The input circuit of the driver stage has been arranged so that the amplifier may be fed from either of the two microphone pre-amplifiers shown in Figs. 20 and 21.

In a true class B stage (see *Chapter 2*) the transistors would have zero collector current flowing until signal is applied, but in practice it is necessary to operate with a small quiescent current of about 2 mA in each transistor to reduce cross-over distortion. Such distortion is characterized by a sharp discontinuity in the output waveform at the point where one transistor is taking over from the other, and produces a very objectionable effect on speech and certain musical passages. The bias required to produce the quiescent current is developed by a conventional resistance network but an interesting problem arises here in that it is not practicable to decouple the bias circuit of a stage working in class B because each transistor only handles one half of the waveform, which results in uni-directional signal currents in each of the transistor electrodes. Under these conditions, signal currents would charge the capacitors and cause serious interruption to the bias conditions. The bias resistors must therefore form part of the signal frequency circuit and will consequently dissipate signal power. For instance, in Fig. 22 the emitter

TABLE 2
Transformer details for the circuit of Fig. 22

T1
Ratio, 2 : 1 + 1
Primary resistance, 90 ohms
Primary inductance, 3·5H at 4 mA d.c.
Secondary resistance, 100 ohms (total)
The Fortiphone type A203 may be used although it may not exactly meet this specification.

T2
Ratio, 4·2 + 4·2 : 1
Primary resistance, 7 ohms (total)
Primary inductance, 0·4H
Secondary resistance, 0·2 ohms
The Fortiphone type A204 may be used although it may not exactly meet this specification.

resistor R_4 dissipates approximately 15 per cent of the maximum available output power. If the value of the resistor were reduced in an attempt to increase power output, there would be a danger of damaging the output transistors.

A collector current of 3 mA is required in the driver stage to enable it to drive fully the output transistors and is established by the bias resistors R_1, R_2 and R_3. The driver transformer T_1 has a centre tapped secondary winding to provide the required anti-phase drive voltages for the output pair. Negative feedback is applied from the secondary of

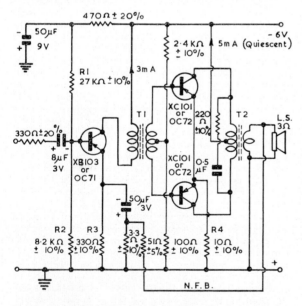

Fig. 22. Class B 250 mW push-pull amplifier. Ample loudspeaker volume and extremely low power consumption are the important features of this unit which may be fed from either of the pre-amplifiers of Figs. 20 and 21.

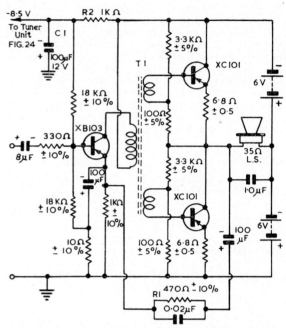

Fig. 23. "Single-ended" 320 mW push-pull amplifier. Modern transistor circuit techniques are represented by this amplifier in which the use of an output transformer is avoided. It is specially suited for use in portable apparatus, and facilities are provided for coupling it to the tuner unit shown in Fig. 24.

the output transformer to the emitter of the driver stage in order to improve the frequency response and further contribute to the suppression of harmonic distortion. Another effect of feedback applied in this way is to increase the input resistance of the driver from its intrinsic value of about 1 K ohms to approximately 3 K ohms with the component values specified. The input voltage required to fully drive the output stage is about 60 mV R.M.S. at 400 c/s which corresponds to a power gain of about 200,000 times (i.e. 53 db).

A "Single-ended" 320 mW Push-pull Amplifier

This amplifier (**Fig. 23**) is similar to the class B output stage and driver just described. There is, however, one very significant difference in that it does not employ an output transformer. All of the available output power is delivered direct to the loudspeaker without suffering the losses inevitably incurred in a practical output transformer. To achieve this, without using a centre-tapped speech coil, the output transistors are arranged in a configuration known as *single-ended push-pull*.

The transistors are connected in series across a 12 volt battery, the speaker connecting the junction of the transistors with a centre tap on the battery supply. Thus each transistor operates from 6 volts and feeds alternate half-cycles of the amplified signal into the 35 ohm speech coil. Two separate bias circuits are required and the driver transformer must have two isolated secondary windings. Normal quiescent collector current for the two output transistors is about 2 mA.

Negative feedback is applied from the speaker to the emitter of the driver stage, the degree of feedback being

TABLE 3

Transformer and loudspeaker details for the circuit of Fig. 23

T1

Ratio 2·5 : 1+1
Maximum primary resistance, 200 ohms (1,720 turns of 43 s.w.g. enamelled wire on the former).
Primary inductance, 3H at 3·8 mA d.c.
Maximum secondary resistance, 60 ohms per winding (688 turns of 39 s.w.g. enamelled wire for each winding The secondaries should be bifilar wound and sandwiched between the two half-primaries).

Loudspeaker

35 ohm speech coil, 10,000 gauss magnet.

controlled by resistance R_1. The recommended value is 470 ohms but this may be adjusted to suit individual requirements bearing in mind that a higher resistance will mean less feedback and consequently more distortion, while a lower resistance will mean better quality reproduction but lower sensitivity. Apart from reducing distortion and extending frequency response, negative feedback increases the input resistance of the driver stage. By returning the bottom half of the driver base potential divider to the 10 ohm emitter resistor across which the feedback voltage is developed, the damping effect of the bias resistor to audio frequencies is much reduced. This makes the amplifier particularly suitable for use with the transistorized 1·8—2 Mc/s tuner unit of Fig. 24 because the a.c. loading on the detector circuit is reduced to a minimum. The decoupled battery line to the left of R_2 (Fig. 23) can be used for feeding the tuner unit, the value of R_2 being chosen to give a voltage

of 8·5 at this point. If the tuner unit is used in exactly the form shown in Fig. 24, R_2 should be 1 K ohms, but if the amplifier is used without the tuner unit R_2 must be increased to 12 K ohms. C_1 can then be reduced to 5 μF.

Superheterodyne Tuner Unit Covering the 1·8-2 Mc/s Band

Fig. 24 shows the circuit of a superheterodyne receiver with a tuning range of 1—3 Mc/s, thus providing coverage of the 160 metre amateur band, together with the trawler band and many medium wave broadcasting stations. Although the selectivity and noise performance may not be up to communications receiver standard, the sensitivity and a.g.c. characteristics are good and the general performance is more than adequate for the majority of Top Band contacts. The receiver is intended to feed into the amplifier of Fig. 23 and, as the total power consumption of the two units is only about 35 mA at 12 volts, the equipment has considerable appeal for mobile or portable enthusiasts. The prototype was built into a box measuring approximately 9 in. × 4 in. × 6 in. and weighed 3 lb., complete with a 7 in. × 4 in. elliptical speaker, but excluding batteries.

Best results are obviously obtained with a good outside aerial for which a 75 ohm input is provided. However, for complete portability an alternative aerial coil can be wound on a 8 in. × ⅜ in. diameter ferrite rod. Performance with this aerial coil is surprisingly good without an additional aerial. In many cases, the directional properties of the ferrite rod aerial are a distinct advantage in reducing the effects of interference.

The receiver is best described on a stage-by-stage basis.

The Frequency Changer

The first stage consists of an XA102 or OC44 transistor working as a self-oscillating frequency changer. Oscillations are maintained by mutual inductance coupling between collector and emitter circuits, and the signal frequency applied to the base. Thus, at heterodyne frequencies, the transistor is effectively operating in common base configuration, but to signal frequencies it appears as a common emitter stage. With an i.f. of 470 kc/s, the maximum heterodyne frequency is 3·5 Mc/s and it is therefore essential to specify a h.f. transistor type for this application. Any undamaged XA102 or OC44 transistor should perform satisfactorily; if it is desired to use some other type of transistor, slight

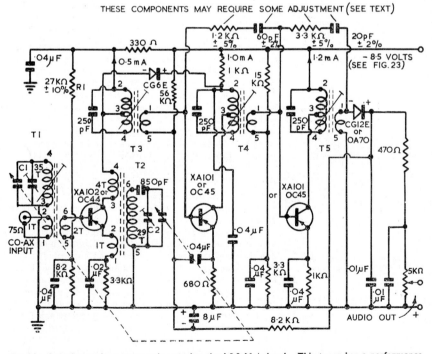

Fig. 24. Superheterodyne tuner unit covering the 1·8-2 Mc/s band. This tuner has a performance adequate for most Top Band work and has considerable appeal for mobile or portable enthusiasts. C1, C2 is 400pF per section twin-gang (Wingrove & Rogers type C78). Coil winding details are given in Table 4. Total battery consumption, including that of the power amplifier of Fig. 23, is about 35 mA at 12 volts.

adjustment of the resistor R_1 may be necessary to obtain satisfactory operation over the band. When operating correctly, the heterodyne voltage appearing across the emitter winding of the oscillator transformer should be about 150–200 mV peak at mid-band, and this should be achieved with a collector current not greater than 1 mA, or noise performance will be impaired.

To obtain a power match from the aerial coil to the transistor, the base of the transistor is fed from a low impedance winding tightly coupled to the aerial coil. Aerial and oscillator tank coils are tuned by a symmetrical two-gang variable capacitor of the type commonly used in broadcast receivers. This enables a wide frequency range to be covered but if this facility is not required a small capacity gang padded with fixed capacitors may be used to produce a bandspread effect.

Frequency changing takes place due to the non-linearity of the transistor input characteristic, the i.f. being selected by a tuned transformer in the collector circuit. It is not practical to apply a.g.c. to a stage of this type because any attempt to reduce gain would introduce the risk of oscillator failure and frequency pulling under certain conditions.

Intermediate Frequency Amplifier (470 kc/s)

Two neutralized common emitter i.f. amplifying stages are specified, each running at a no-signal collector current of about 1 mA. A.g.c. is applied to the first stage only, the signal level at the second stage being too high to permit gain control without introducing excessive distortion. Coupling between stages is by single tuned transformers of a type which are generally available and which provide the required anti-phase voltage for neutralizing purposes. Each coil operates with a working Q factor of approximately 50 at low signal levels.

The quoted values of neutralizing components are correct

TABLE 4

Coil winding details for the circuit of Fig. 24

Aerial Coil (T1)
Wound on Neosid pot core assembly type 10D.
Tuned coil: start at tag 3, wind on 35 turns of 30 s.w.g. s.s.e. distributed between the three sections of the former.
Base coil: start at tag 5, wind on 2 turns of 22 s.w.g. enam. over " earthy " end of tuned coil.
Input coil: start at tag 1, wind on 1 turn of 22 s.w.g. enam. over " earthy " end of tuned coil.
Alternative Rod Aerial
Wound on Neosid 8 in. × $\frac{3}{8}$ in. rod type F 14, Spec.1
Tuned coil: start at tag 3, wind on 27 turns of 30 s.w.g. s.s.e. on $\frac{7}{16}$ in. o.d. × $\frac{3}{8}$ in. i.d. Paxolin former, winding length 1$\frac{1}{2}$ in.
Base coil: start at tag 1, wind on 2 turns of 30 s.w.g. s.s.e. over " earthy " end of tuned coil.

Oscillator Coil (T2)
Wound on Neosid pot core assembly type 10D.
Tuned coil: start at tag 5, wind on 29 turns of 30 s.w.g. s.s.e. distributed between the three sections of the former.
Collector coil: start at tag 3, wind on 4 turns of 30 s.w.g. s.s.e. over " earthy " end of tuned coil.
Emitter coil: start at tag 1, wind on 1 turn of 30 s.w.g. over " earthy " end of tuned coil.

I.f. Transformers
It is difficult to wind these coils without specialized apparatus and it is recommended that commercially available types with the following specifications be used.
T3 and T4: Unloaded Q, 100; Working Q, 50; Ratio of collector winding to secondary winding, 6 : 1.
T5: Unloaded Q, 160; Working Q, 50; Ratio of collector winding to secondary winding, 1·85 : 1.

for the transistor type specified, assuming that the receiver has been carefully laid out and wired. On the subject of layout it is as well to point out that, whereas with valve circuitry instability sometimes arises due to stray capacitive couplings, with transistor circuitry it is stray electro-magnetic couplings which must be studiously avoided. It is particularly important in this receiver that the aerial coil should be placed as far away from the detector and audio stages as is practicable.

If transistors other than those specified are used then it may be necessary to neutralize empirically. It might be found acceptable to replace temporarily the neutralizing components with variable types, considering each i.f. stage individually, and adjust them until the stage ceases to oscillate. By measuring the values of the variables and replacing them with fixed components of equal value, the stage will be approximately neutralized. A far more satisfactory method is to feed a 470 kc/s signal from a signal generator or a test oscillator, backwards through the stage in question and to adjust the values of the neutralizing components until a voltage null is obtained at the input of the transistor. This should be carried out with the receiver switched on but with the preceding and following transistors removed from the circuit. To indicate the null, a sensitive measuring instrument is called for because the process should be carried out at a low signal level. A valve voltmeter or an oscilloscope with an amplifier might be suitable but failing this it is often possible to make use of an existing superheterodyne receiver provided that it has a 470 kc/s i.f. amplifier and that access can be obtained to the input of the frequency changer stage. Neutralizing carried out in this way will be very precise and should ensure a good symmetrical i.f. response.

Detector Stage

A point contact germanium diode is used as a detector in a conventional series rectifying circuit. There is, however, one very significant departure from valve receiver technique in that detection is carried out at a low impedance level. This is done to enable the detector to feed straight into the relatively low input resistance of a transistor audio stage without introducing an adverse ratio of a.c. load to d.c. load for the diode. The d.c. component of the rectified signal is tapped off to provide a.g.c. and care must therefore be taken to ensure that the polarity of the diode is correct.

Automatic Gain Control Circuit

As already stated, it is not practical to control the gain of either the mixer stage or the second i.f. stage. Gain control of the first i.f. stage is effective over a limited range but under high-signal conditions overloading may result. Some additional control before the first i.f. stage is therefore desirable and is provided in this design by a point contact crystal diode operating as a dynamic limiter. The diode is effectively shunted across the primary of the first i.f. transformer but because it is reverse biased it does not damp the circuit significantly under small signal conditions. When the receiver is tuned to a strong station, the rectified signal at the detector is fed back to the gain controlled stage and alters the bias conditions and so reduces the collector current. The mutual conductance of the transistor is thereby reduced and the stage gain decreases. Reduction of collector current also results in a smaller voltage drop across the 1 K ohm resistor in the collector circuit, which tends to put the dynamic-limiter diode into conduction and so damp the first i.f. transformer. A reasonable a.g.c. delay is provided by the fact that the controlled stage does not change gain significantly during the early stages of current reduction. An excellent a.g.c. characteristic is produced and the receiver will comfortably handle any signal strength it is likely to meet.

If an S meter is required it is satisfactory to connect a 0–1 mA meter in the feed to the first i.f. stage collector, preferably between the battery supply line and the 1 K ohm resistor.

Alignment

Once the i.f. stages have been neutralized, alignment procedure is similar to that for a valve receiver. If the tuner is fitted with an S meter, this will form a satisfactory output indicator, but a pair of phones connected to the output feed will do almost as well. First, couple a sufficiently strong i.f. signal into the aerial coil and peak up the i.f. transformers; repeat this several times to determine whether there is any inter-dependance of tuning, which might indicate that neutralizing is not completely satisfactory. If the ferrite rod aerial coil is being used, the signal can be coupled in by placing it about 12 in. away from a coil connected to the signal generator.

When the i.f. stages appear to be satisfactory, feed a signal at 1 Mc/s into the aerial and, with the tuning capacitor fully in, adjust the slug in the oscillator coil for maximum output. Do the same at 3 Mc/s with the gang fully open but this time using the oscillator capacity trimmer. The band limits have now been set and it only remains for the aerial and oscillator circuits to be tracked. Tune to a signal at about 1·3 Mc/s and adjust the aerial coil inductance for maximum signal; for the rod aerial this will mean sliding the coil along the rod. Repeat the procedure at about 2·5 Mc/s but this time adjusting the aerial circuit capacity trimmer. It will be advisable to repeat the tracking procedure two or three times in order to ensure best results. When correctly aligned, the sensitivity on the 1·8 Mc/s band should be such as to give a good output signal with only about 2 μV (30 per cent modulated) of r.f. at the 75 ohm input.

Other applications of semiconductors are described in Chapter 5 (*V.h.f. Receivers*), Chapter 16 (*Mobile Equipment*) Chapter 17 (*Power Supplies*) and Chapter 19 (*Measurements*).

SEMICONDUCTOR DIODES

Power Diodes

Although metal rectifiers of the copper-oxide or selenium type have long been popular as power rectifiers, the problems of heat dissipation and of change of characteristics with time are very troublesome.

As a result of intensive development work carried out on semiconductor materials since the introduction of the transistor it is now practicable to produce *p-n* junctions, using either silicon or germanium, with the ability to handle very large powers. Such devices are available covering applications at all power levels and are even being used in electric traction installations. Samples little larger than a r.f. transistor will handle the power requirements of a domestic television receiver and are ideal for use in radio equipments where space is at a premium.

Temperature rise in such a rectifier is due to working losses which may be divided into two parts: loss during the conducting part of the cycle, where forward resistance causes voltage drop, and loss during the non-conductive part of the cycle due to the finite back resistance of the diode. The difference between losses in a selenium rectifier and those in a silicon diode are best shown by reference to **Fig. 25** where it can be seen that the selenium rectifier has a considerably larger forward voltage drop at a given current, and also has a larger reverse " bleed " current. Germanium diodes are a little better than silicon for forward characteristics but have a much inferior reverse characteristic.

Another important difference between the conventional

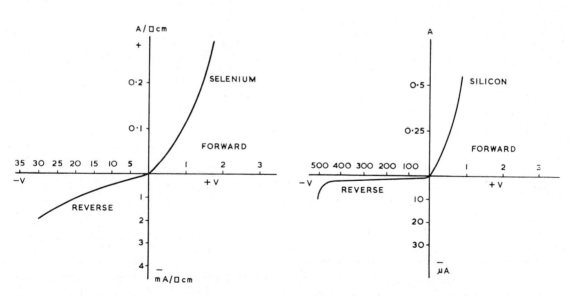

Fig. 25. Typical characteristics of selenium and silicon power diode units.

selenium rectifier and a silicon device lies in the shape of the reverse characteristic. The selenium rectifier has a " soft " turnover occurring at a relatively low voltage, while the silicon diode has a much more definite turnover occurring at a much higher voltage. This voltage is sufficiently high for most applications without having to couple diodes in series, but very great care must be taken to ensure that the peak inverse voltage can never rise to the reverse turnover voltage. Whereas the selenium rectifier can withstand some abuse in this respect, irreparable damage will result if the silicon diode is overloaded.

Zener Diodes

By adjustment of the processing techniques, it is possible to produce p-n junction diodes with very stable and consistent reverse characteristics and with the " turnover " or breakdown voltage occurring at a particular precise voltage level. Such diodes are available covering a range of breakdown voltages and are very useful as voltage stabilizing elements. When reverse-biased at or about the breakdown voltage, the device can handle a wide range of currents with very little change of voltage. Temperature coefficient of breakdown voltage varies with type but, for diodes designed to stabilize at about 6 volts, may be negligible.

Variable-Capacity Diodes

Yet another application for the p-n junction diode is as a voltage-dependent capacitor in radio or electronic circuitry. As was explained earlier in this chapter, when a junction diode is biased in the reverse direction a region at the junction becomes swept clear of current carriers and is known as the *depletion layer*. The thickness of the region increases as the applied voltage is increased and can be considered as an insulator between two electrodes. The capacitor thus formed is therefore voltage-dependent and, in the case of a particular commercial sample, has a capacity

which is approximately proportional to $\dfrac{1}{\sqrt{V}}$, where V is

the reverse bias voltage. Although any p-n junction will exhibit this effect, devices with carefully controlled parameters are produced specifically for this purpose and find application for processes such as automatic frequency control, or for parametric amplification (see Chapter 5).

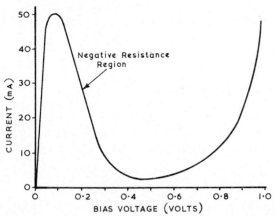

Fig. 26. Static characteristics of typical gallium-arsenide tunnel diode.

The Tunnel Diode

A device which may prove superior to the transistor in certain v.h.f. or u.h.f. applications, and which is undergoing intensive development, is the tunnel diode. This derives its name from the quantum-mechanical tunnelling effect on which its operation depends and promises to be useful at frequencies about 100 times greater than current transistors, yet requiring only a fraction of the power.

Briefly, it consists of a p-n diode made from heavily-doped materials and with an extremely thin junction region. Unlike the transistor it operates largely on the passage of *majority* carriers across the junction, and a signal is thus transmitted through the diode at much the same speed as it would be through a metallic conductor, hence the excellent high-frequency performance.

When biased to a particular part of the characteristic, the device presents an incremental negative resistance, see **Fig. 26,** and thus may be treated as a two-terminal amplifier. At present, a major disadvantage lies in the difficulty of designing coupling circuits for cascaded stages. With a negative resistance characteristic perhaps extending up to a frequency of thousands of megacycles the risk of spurious oscillations occurring can be readily appreciated. The problem is largely tied up with the method of making connection to the diode junction, and the type of encapsulation becomes extremely important.

V.H.F. TRANSISTORS

As the field of transistor applications expands, the need for transistors with better performance at high frequencies is increasingly felt. While it has been practical for many years now to produce laboratory samples with useful performance in the 100 Mc/s range, it is only recently that large-scale production of v.h.f. transistors has become practicable.

The factors which chiefly determine the high frequency performance of the device are first, the finite time taken for current carriers to diffuse across the base region of the transistor, and secondly, the internal feedback path between output and input circuits.

In order to minimise the distance through which current carriers must travel, several involved manufacturing techniques have been developed for reducing the width of the base region, and there are a number of transistor types in which improved high-frequency performance has been achieved solely in this way. As an extension of this process, the " drift " transistor has a base region which is not only very narrow but has a graded impurity concentration across its width. This has the effect of providing an accelerating force to the current carriers, which then traverse the base region more rapidly than if they were merely diffusing through the crystal lattice.

Among various interpretations of this technique, a particularly interesting device is the " alloy-diffused " transistor where a " graded " base region is obtained by a method which allows base widths of only a few microns to be economically achieved. This type seems ideally suited for operation at frequencies up to about 200 Mc/s yet may show worthwhile advantages even at the lower broadcast frequencies, where the low collector-base feedback capacitance of about 2 pF allows good amplification to be obtained without the complication of neutralizing circuits.

CHAPTER 4

H. F. RECEIVERS

RECEIVERS for Amateur Radio purposes vary widely in complexity, from simple two valve designs to sets with up to 20 valves or so, but whether simple or complex, home-constructed or factory-built, are unlikely to prove satisfactory unless careful attention has been paid to the many problems presented by modern two-way h.f. operation.

The radio amateur needs a *communications receiver* which will provide maximum intelligibility from signals having extremely wide variation in strength (incoming signals may easily differ in voltage by 10,000 times and occasionally by up to about 500,000 times) in restricted frequency bands which are often extremely congested. Ideally, each main mode of transmission—telegraphy (c.w.), and telephony by amplitude modulation (a.m.), single sideband (s.s.b.), double sideband (d.s.b.) or narrow band frequency modulation (n.b.f.m.)—requires a receiver having different response characteristics. In practice, however, the amateur usually wishes to use only a single receiver for all purposes, on all amateur bands between 1·8 and 30 Mc/s. Thus all but the most specialized designs are likely to include some measure of compromise in order to provide a reasonable degree of flexibility.

The main requirements for a satisfactory receiver are:

(i) High *sensitivity* and *signal-to-noise ratio*, to permit the reception of weak signals.

(ii) Good *selectivity*, to permit the selection of the required signal from among others—possibly much stronger—on immediately adjacent frequencies. The degree of selectivity should preferably be variable to suit the differing requirements of the various modes of transmission.

(iii) Maximum freedom from *spurious responses*.

(iv) A high order of mechanical and electrical *stability*.

(v) Adequate, preferably calibrated, *bandspread* tuning of the amateur bands, coupled with the ability to reset the receiver accurately and quickly to a desired frequency. The *tuning rate* should be sufficiently low to facilitate the exact tuning of s.s.b., d.s.b. and c.w. signals.

(vi) Internal *beat frequency oscillator* (b.f.o.) for the reception of c.w. and suppressed carrier signals.

(vii) Sturdy and reliable construction and components providing ease of repair, alignment and general maintenance.

BASIC TYPES OF RECEIVERS

Regenerative Detector (" straight ") Receivers. The simplest practical receiver for amateur communication is a regenerative detector followed by one or more stages of a.f. amplification (0–V–1 etc.): see **Fig. 1(a)**. Because of the high gain which can be achieved in a correctly adjusted regenerative detector when set to a point just beyond that at which oscillation begins, this type of receiver can be used on surprisingly weak c.w. signals. Since the gain is much reduced as the regeneration (" reaction ") control is backed off, it will receive only fairly strong telephony stations. Because of regenerative feedback, the effective Q of the single tuned circuit and hence its selectivity, is reasonably good for c.w. reception, provided that the tuned circuit is not heavily damped by the effect of the aerial. The selectivity, however, is much reduced in the presence of strong signals on adjacent frequencies, and even in the most favourable circumstances cannot be made as good as in a modern superhet receiver. A further disadvantage is that the aerial is directly coupled to the oscillatory circuits and so interference may be caused to other receivers. This form of receiver was popular in the early days of short wave work and even now can provide a useful introduction to receiver construction.

Tuned Radio Frequency (T.R.F.) Receivers. Considerable improvement can be obtained in a regenerative detector receiver by including a stage of tuned radio frequency amplification before the detector stage: **Fig. 1(b)**. This provides greater gain, improves selectivity (mainly because the detector tuned circuit can be less heavily damped), and isolates the regenerative detector from the aerial and so much reduces radiation from the receiver.

Although the selectivity of a t.r.f. receiver is deficient by modern standards and it is now rare to find such sets retained for normal amateur operation, it has some advantages for the home constructor: (i) Simplicity of construction with no i.f.

Fig. 1. Block diagram of simple h.f. receivers suitable primarily for Morse reception. (a) Regenerative detector followed by one or more stages of a.f. amplification. (b) The addition of a tuned r.f. amplifier improves selectivity and sensitivity and also reduces radiation from the receiver. (c) Simplest practical superhet receiver. By using triode pentode valves (ECF82/6U8) all stages can be accommodated in a two-valve arrangement. (d) The addition of one or more i.f. amplifiers greatly increases gain and permits the receiver to be used for telephony reception.

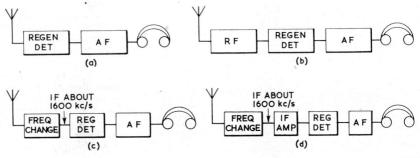

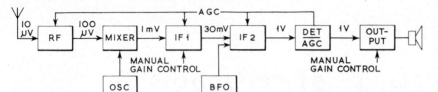

Fig. 2. Block diagram of a typical superhet h.f. communications receiver showing typical pattern of voltage gain. The i.f. is usually of the order of either 470 kc/s or 1600 kc/s.

alignment or oscillator tracking problems; (ii) good signal-to-noise ratio on weak c.w. signals; (iii) complete freedom from spurious responses. Overall gain when the detector is not oscillating is usually insufficient to provide good telephony performance on very weak signals.

Super-regenerative Detector Receivers. The high gain of a regenerative detector can be further increased and utilized for telephony reception by introducing a voltage at a super-sonic frequency in such a way that r.f. oscillation ceases every half cycle of this second frequency, known as the *quench* frequency. This quenching voltage can be generated in a separate valve or, more commonly, in the regenerative detector stage. Although extremely high gain in a single stage is possible, this type of receiver has high interstation noise and poor selectivity while additional complications are necessary to receive c.w. or to avoid the emission of a rough signal capable of causing interference over considerable distances. Super-regenerative receivers are still of interest for simple portable equipment on 28 Mc/s and above but have little application on the lower frequency bands.

Superhet Receivers. By changing the frequency of the incoming signal to a lower fixed *intermediate frequency* in one step (single conversion), two steps (double conversion) or three steps (triple conversion), it becomes possible to build a high gain amplifier of controlled selectivity. Although the mixing process by which the frequency of the incoming signal is changed is inherently more noisy than amplification at the signal frequency, this disadvantage can be overcome by including one or more radio frequency amplifiers ahead of the first mixer. The main practical disadvantages of the superhet are its susceptibility to various forms of spurious response, and the relative complexity of construction and alignment. The superhet principle is now used in the vast majority of amateur communications receivers and this class will receive more detailed treatment in this Chapter than other types of receiver. The simplest forms of superhet are shown in **Fig. 1 (c)** and **(d)**. The block diagram of a typical superhet receiver for amateur communication is shown in **Fig. 2** with the main amplification in the i.f. stages. The importance of achieving high selectivity for Morse reception, permitting the rejection of the audio " image " signal, is illustrated in **Fig. 3.**

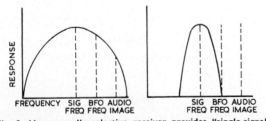

Fig. 3. How a really selective receiver provides "single-signal" reception of Morse signals. The broad selectivity of the response curve on the left is unable to provide substantial rejection at the audio "image" frequency, whereas with the more selective curve on the right the audio image is inaudible.

Selectable Sideband Receivers. As explained elsewhere in this Handbook, conventional a.m. signals radiate sets of sidebands on each side of the carrier frequency, up to plus or minus the highest transmitted audio frequency. Since the two sets of sidebands are mirror images of one another, either set of sidebands can be completely removed without affecting the intelligence of the transmission, though (as explained in Chapter 15) there will be a slight reduction of signal-to-noise ratio. In a crowded band it will be highly advantageous to restrict the receiver bandwidth so that the set responds to the carrier and only one set of sidebands and then to tune to

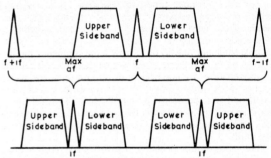

Fig. 4. A local oscillator frequency higher than the signal frequency (i.e. *f + i.f.*) keeps the upper and lower sidebands of the intermediate frequency signals in their original positions. However, when the local oscillator is placed below the signal frequency (*f−i.f.*) the i.f. signals transpose the positions of the sidebands. By incorporating two oscillators, one above, the other below the input signal, sideband selection is facilitated.

whichever is the less affected by interference. Since the interfering stations may change at any moment, it will be clearly beneficial to arrange the set so that it can immediately be switched from one to the other set of sidebands without having to adjust the tuning knob. There are various arrangements which permit this to be done, usually by providing two frequency conversion oscillators, one placed on each side of the signal frequency **(Fig. 4).**

In order to receive without distortion one sideband and carrier of a double sideband a.m. signal the receiver bandpass must conform to certain requirements. For example, if a receiver with a sharply peaked bandpass is tuned to receive one sideband, the selectivity may be sufficient to reject the other sideband but when so tuned the carrier will almost certainly be placed well down the slope of the response curve. In these circumstances the sideband received will be too strong for the carrier; this results in distortion, as though the original signal was greatly overmodulated. If, however, the receiver bandpass approaches that of the ideal flat top shape (say, 2·5 to 3 kc/s wide) with steep sides, the receiver may be tuned so that the carrier is located at the edge of the bandpass or not more than about 5db below maximum response. The carrier and one set of sidebands can then be received without unduly restricting the a.f. response. Since

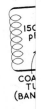

designs.
rate of th
The same
the main
swing fro
capacitor
a combin
often use
the frequ
only. E:
rate will
within e

Cross-r

After
down to
coping
when su
side the
by *cros*
Whe
whose
the rel
and in
will no
amplif
lineari
reduce
strong
Cle
before
teristi
overl
conve
ampl
parti
It
figur
doub
recep
high
beer
awa
an :
like
real

flat-top response curves are difficult to achieve without the aid of effective bandpass crystal or mechanical filters, this form of reception is not always practicable without a fairly complex receiver, though reasonably effective results can often be achieved on receivers having a final i.f. of the order of 85 kc/s.

With an extremely carefully controlled bandpass characteristic it is possible to carry this process a stage further: the receiver can be set to receive either set of sidebands while suppressing both the other set of sidebands and the carrier, thus in effect converting an a.m. signal into an s.s.b. one. It is then necessary to re-insert a carrier as for s.s.b. reception. A great advantage of this form of reception is that it provides for a.m. signals the relative freedom from phase distortion enjoyed by s.s.b. signals.

PERFORMANCE REQUIREMENTS

Before typical circuitry can be discussed, it is necessary to consider certain of the basic performance requirements in some detail.

Sensitivity

Weak signals need to be amplified much more than strong ones in order to provide a satisfactory output level to headphones or loudspeaker. There are, however, definite limits to this process, and simply adding more amplifying stages will not provide a solution, the limitation being the noise generated both externally and within the receiver (principally in the early stages), which may mask any very weak signals present. This noise, which is described in detail in Chapter 15 (*Noise*), arises partly from sources within the early stages of the receiver (and is thus to a certain extent under the control of the designer) and partly from external sources. The weakest signal which can be satisfactorily used for communication purposes is therefore not governed ultimately by how much overall amplification is available from a receiver but by how weak a signal can be heard above the general noise level. This characteristic of an h.f. receiver is normally defined by stating the minimum signal voltage at the aerial terminals required to produce a specified output with a certain ratio of signal above the noise level at a specified setting of the selectivity control: this is known as the *signal-to-noise* ratio (or more strictly as the *signal-plus-noise-to-noise* ratio).

To give an idea of practical performance, a receiver with a 10db signal-to-noise ratio (at normal selectivity) with an input of 1 to 3μV is in the high quality class while a receiver which will provide this ratio for a 5μV signal will not miss many worthwhile signals. In most locations, the weakest c.w. signal readable on a high class receiver will be about 0.5μV.

A receiver's sensitivity performance could thus be quoted in the following manner: (i) *telegraphy*: 1μV c.w. signal across the input sockets to give better than 10db signal-to-noise ratio with a passband of 1.5 kc/s; or (ii) *telephony*: 3μV signals modulated 30 per cent to give better than 10db signal-to-noise ratio with a passband of 6 kc/s. For accurate assessment of a receiver's performance, all the factors quoted above must be specified since variation of any one will affect the others. The sensitivity of a receiver is increased by reducing the bandwidth to the limits imposed by the type of transmission: the effect on receiver noise of reducing the i.f. band-

width is discussed in detail in Chapter 15 to which the reader should refer. Since individual operators possess to differing degrees the ability to copy a weak signal well down in the noise, it would not mean that the quoted signals would be the weakest that it would be possible to copy, but nevertheless form a very useful guide when comparing receiver specifications. Unfortunately few amateurs have available the test apparatus required to test manufacturers' figures. A simple but quite effective (and severe) test of sensitivity which can be applied to any well screened receiver is to remove the aerial and replace it by resistor equal to the receiver's input impedance: if the receiver noise then peaks up when the first r.f. circuit is tuned through resonance (often possible by means of a panel-mounted aerial trimmer) on the highest frequency bands it is reasonably certain that the receiver possesses high sensitivity.

Selectivity

The ability of a receiver to separate stations on closely adjacent frequencies is determined by its *selectivity*. Chapter 1 (*Fundamentals*) explains why it is necessary to use a superhet receiver with a low intermediate frequency to obtain a very high degree of selectivity.

The ultimate limits to practical selectivity are governed by the *bandwidth* of the type of transmission which is to be received. For high fidelity broadcast reception the response of a receiver needs to extend to some 15 kc/s on either side of the carrier frequency, equivalent to a bandwidth of 30 kc/s; for average broadcast reception this figure can be reduced to about 10 kc/s; for communications-quality telephony in the amateur bands 6 kc/s for the reception of both sidebands or 3 kc/s for the reception of one sideband will suffice; for telegraphy at manual keying speeds the total bandwidth could be reduced to less than 100 c/s, although to accommodate transmitter and/or receiver instability a 300 c/s bandwidth is generally regarded as more practical. These ideal receiver characteristics are indicated in **Fig. 5.**

To compare the selectivity of different receivers or the same receiver in different positions of its selectivity control, curves of the type shown in **Fig. 6** can be used. There are two ways in which these curves must be considered: the first is the *nose* figure which represents the bandwidth in kilocycles over which a signal will be heard with relatively little loss of strength; the other figure—regarded by many amateurs as the more important—is the bandwidth over which a really powerful signal is still audible (often taken as a reduction of 1,000 times on the strength of the signal when correctly tuned in) and this is often termed the *skirt* performance. These two sets of figures are related by what is

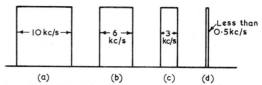

Fig. 5. The ideal characteristics of the overall bandpass of a receiver are determined by the type of signals to be received. (a) This would be suitable for normal broadcast reception (a.f. response to 5 kc/s); (b) suitable for a.m. communications (a.f. to 3 kc/s); (c) the bandpass can be halved for single sideband reception without affecting the a.f. response (still 3 kc/s); (d) extremely narrow channels (about 100 c/s) are occupied by manually keyed Morse signals, but some allowance must be made for receiver and transmitter instability—by adjustment of the b.f.o. any desired a.f. beat note can be produced.

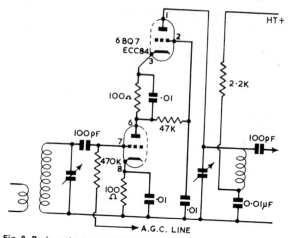

Fig. 9. Basic series-cascode r.f. amplifier. Although formerly used mainly for v.h.f. receivers, this arrangement is now commonly found in h.f. receivers.

more high gain r.f. pentodes (valve types such as 6BA6, EF85, EF183/6EH7, EF95/6AK5, EF93, 6BZ6, 6SG7, 6CB6, EF91 and 6DC6 are suitable) with a tuned input circuit between grid and cathode and with the valve operating into an inductive load which may be either the primary winding of an interstage r.f. transformer or a tuned circuit. A typical circuit is shown in **Fig. 8.** However, this is not the only possible arrangement: of increasing popularity is the series-cascode circuit, while the grounded-grid amplifier is suitable for use with a triode mixer or other applications where high gain is not required.

In the matter of optimum signal-to-noise ratio and overall stage gain, there is little to choose—for frequencies below 30 Mc/s—between a correctly designed r.f. pentode and the double-triode cascode. However, the cascode is sometimes less susceptible to cross-modulation and some constructors consider it less critical in adjustment and operation. A typical series-cascode circuit is shown in **Fig. 9.** Suitable valves include the ECC84 and 6BQ7.

The correct matching of the aerial to the valve input impedance is of great importance in securing optimum signal-to-noise ratio: the voltage gain obtained from the step-up ratio of the input circuit is not degraded by valve noise. General coverage receivers are often designed with a medium impedance input (300–600 ohms) with loose aerial coupling to the grid circuit, the aerial coil having a fair number of turns. For amateur-bands-only receivers it is usual to reduce the input impedance to 75 ohms, with the few turns of the aerial input coil overwound on the earthy end of the grid coil to provide very tight coupling. This system is to be recommended as it enables the maximum voltage step-up to be obtained. With tight coupling it is advisable to include a panel controlled aerial trimmer across the tuned grid circuit. When low impedance input circuits are to be used in conjunction with end-fed and similar aerials having a range of impedances, it is highly desirable to fit an external aerial matching unit: often that used for the transmitter can be employed by means of a co-axial change-over relay.

The first tuned circuit in a receiver is of especial importance in determining the sensitivity of the receiver and it should be noted that the alignment of this circuit to that of the mixer

presents particular problems owing to the effects produced when coupling different types of aerial to the receiver. If the aerial is reactive its connection will usually cause detuning of the input circuit. A satisfactory method of overcoming this difficulty is to fit a panel control aerial trimmer to allow the circuit to be readily brought into accurate adjustment by the user when changing bands or aerials. If a receiver is designed solely for use with a non-reactive feeder of known impedance, this control would be unnecessary.

A short-base r.f. pentode will usually have a lower noise contribution than a variable-mu pentode, but in practice this is likely to be noticeable only above 21 Mc/s; a variable-mu type is often used for convenience of a.g.c. action, and the reduction of cross modulation. Of the present range of pentode valves, the 6CB6 and EF91 provide low noise but may prove susceptible to cross-modulation effects; the American-manufactured 6DC6 is better in this respect. Where a high slope, short-base r.f. pentode is used in an a.g.c.-controlled stage, the screen feed resistor should be of fairly high value (33 K to 47 K ohms) to lengthen the grid base, and so continue to give linear though reduced amplification as the negative bias is increased.

Controlled regenerative feedback in an r.f. amplifier can be of material assistance in increasing stage gain and in giving greater protection against image response. As explained in Chapter 15, this will be at some cost in signal-to-noise ratio. Thus although regeneration is sometimes useful for smaller receivers, it is to be avoided in high-performance designs. Optimum signal-to-noise ratios cannot be obtained from an r.f. amplifier unless all forms of positive feedback due to stray capacitances, inefficient screen decoupling and the effect of common cathode lead inductance are reduced to the lowest possible figure. Coupling between input and output circuits must be kept extremely low (see page 100); one form of coupling which is sometimes overlooked is that due to the common rotor spindle of a ganged tuning capacitor being slightly above earth potential. Some r.f. valves have two cathode pins (one for input connections, the other for output connections) to overcome the inductive coupling of a common cathode lead.

Where a low noise mixer is used, the r.f. gain can be appreciably reduced without loss of signal-to-noise ratio and with benefit to cross-modulation characteristics; with a

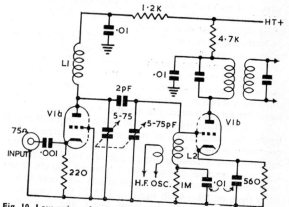

Fig. 10. Low noise r.f. amplifier-mixer using ECC85 double triode valve. The first triode section functions as a grounded-grid amplifier with untuned input; the second triode forms the mixer inductively coupled to the h.f oscillator.

flat-top response curves are difficult to achieve without the aid of effective bandpass crystal or mechanical filters, this form of reception is not always practicable without a fairly complex receiver, though reasonably effective results can often be achieved on receivers having a final i.f. of the order of 85 kc/s.

With an extremely carefully controlled bandpass characteristic it is possible to carry this process a stage further: the receiver can be set to receive either set of sidebands while suppressing both the other set of sidebands and the carrier, thus in effect converting an a.m. signal into an s.s.b. one. It is then necessary to re-insert a carrier as for s.s.b. reception. A great advantage of this form of reception is that it provides for a.m. signals the relative freedom from phase distortion enjoyed by s.s.b. signals.

PERFORMANCE REQUIREMENTS

Before typical circuitry can be discussed, it is necessary to consider certain of the basic performance requirements in some detail.

Sensitivity

Weak signals need to be amplified much more than strong ones in order to provide a satisfactory output level to head-phones or loudspeaker. There are, however, definite limits to this process, and simply adding more amplifying stages will not provide a solution, the limitation being the noise generated both externally and within the receiver (principally in the early stages), which may mask any very weak signals present. This noise, which is described in detail in Chapter 15 (*Noise*), arises partly from sources within the early stages of the receiver (and is thus to a certain extent under the control of the designer) and partly from external sources. The weakest signal which can be satisfactorily used for com-munication purposes is therefore not governed ultimately by how much overall amplification is available from a receiver but by how weak a signal can be heard above the general noise level. This characteristic of an h.f. receiver is normally defined by stating the minimum signal voltage at the aerial terminals required to produce a specified output with a certain ratio of signal above the noise level at a specified setting of the selectivity control: this is known as the *signal-to-noise* ratio (or more strictly as the *signal-plus-noise-to-noise* ratio).

To give an idea of practical performance, a receiver with a 10db signal-to-noise ratio (at normal selectivity) with an input of 1 to 3μV is in the high quality class while a receiver which will provide this ratio for a 5μV signal will not miss many worthwhile signals. In most locations, the weakest c.w. signal readable on a high class receiver will be about 0.5μV.

A receiver's sensitivity performance could thus be quoted in the following manner: (i) *telegraphy*: 1μV c.w. signal across the input sockets to give better than 10db signal-to-noise ratio with a passband of 1·5 kc/s; or (ii) *telephony*: 3μV signals modulated 30 per cent to give better than 10db signal-to-noise ratio with a passband of 6 kc/s. For accurate assessment of a receiver's performance, all the factors quoted above must be specified since variation of any one will affect the others. The sensitivity of a receiver is increased by reduc-ing the bandwidth to the limits imposed by the type of trans-mission: the effect on receiver noise of reducing the i.f. band-

width is discussed in detail in Chapter 15 to which the reader should refer. Since individual operators possess to differing degrees the ability to copy a weak signal well down in the noise, it would not mean that the quoted signals would be the weakest that it would be possible to copy, but never-theless form a very useful guide when comparing receiver specifications. Unfortunately few amateurs have available the test apparatus required to test manufacturers' figures. A simple but quite effective (and severe) test of sensitivity which can be applied to any well screened receiver is to remove the aerial and replace it by resistor equal to the receiver's input impedance: if the receiver noise then peaks up when the first r.f. circuit is tuned through resonance (often possible by means of a panel-mounted aerial trimmer) on the highest frequency bands it is reasonably certain that the receiver possesses high sensitivity.

Selectivity

The ability of a receiver to separate stations on closely adjacent frequencies is determined by its *selectivity*. Chapter 1 (*Fundamentals*) explains why it is necessary to use a super-het receiver with a low intermediate frequency to obtain a very high degree of selectivity.

The ultimate limits to practical selectivity are governed by the *bandwidth* of the type of transmission which is to be received. For high fidelity broadcast reception the response of a receiver needs to extend to some 15 kc/s on either side of the carrier frequency, equivalent to a bandwidth of 30 kc/s; for average broadcast reception this figure can be reduced to about 10 kc/s; for communications-quality telephony in the amateur bands 6 kc/s for the reception of both sidebands or 3 kc/s for the reception of one sideband will suffice; for telegraphy at manual keying speeds the total bandwidth could be reduced to less than 100 c/s, although to accommodate transmitter and/or receiver instability a 300 c/s bandwidth is generally regarded as more practical. These ideal receiver characteristics are indicated in **Fig. 5.**

To compare the selectivity of different receivers or the same receiver in different positions of its selectivity control, curves of the type shown in **Fig. 6** can be used. There are two ways in which these curves must be considered: the first is the *nose* figure which represents the bandwidth in kilocycles over which a signal will be heard with relatively little loss of strength; the other figure—regarded by many amateurs as the more important—is the bandwidth over which a really powerful signal is still audible (often taken as a reduction of 1,000 times on the strength of the signal when correctly tuned in) and this is often termed the *skirt* per-formance. These two sets of figures are related by what is

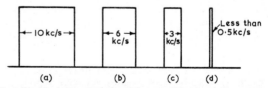

Fig. 5. The ideal characteristics of the overall bandpass of a receiver are determined by the type of signals to be received. (a) This would be suitable for normal broadcast reception (a.f. response to 5 kc/s); (b) suitable for a.m. communications (a.f. to 3 kc/s); (c) the bandpass can be halved for single sideband reception without affecting the a.f. response (still 3 kc/s); (d) extremely narrow channels (about 100 c/s) are occupied by manually keyed Morse signals, but some allow-ance must be made for receiver and transmitter instability—by adjustment of the b.f.o. any desired a.f. beat note can be produced.

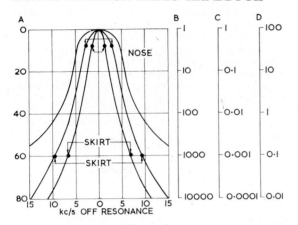

Fig. 6. The ideal vertical sides of Fig. 5 cannot be achieved in practice. The curves shown here are typical. These three curves represent the overall selectivity of receivers varying from the "just adequate" broadcast curve of a superhet receiver having about four tuned i.f. circuits on 470 kc/s to those of a moderately good communications receiver. A, B, C and D indicate four different scales often used to indicate similar results: A is a scale based on the attenuation in decibels from maximum response; B represents the relative signal inputs for a constant output; C is the output voltage compared with that at maximum response; D is the response expressed as a percentage.

termed the *shape factor* of the receiver, found by dividing the bandwidth at the skirt by that at the nose. The ideal receiver would have a shape factor of one on each position of selectivity; such a receiver would in practice be impossible to design at the present state of the art. Even the very best modern receiver is unlikely to achieve a shape factor much less than 1·5, and most good receivers range from about 2·5 to 5·5. A receiver which has a skirt bandwidth, at −60db, of less than 10–15 kc/s can be considered to have fairly good selectivity characteristics.

Spurious Responses

One of the major defects of simple superhet receivers is that the same station can usually be received at more than one position of the tuning dial, or alternatively that the various oscillators within the set provide signals which can be tuned in at various points on the dial as though they were external carriers. This means, in practice, that strong commercial stations are often heard as though they were operating within the amateur bands, while searching for weak stations is made more difficult by tuning through the carriers generated within the receiver, often referred to as *birdies*.

The most important causes of spurious responses are (i) the reception of signals on the image frequency of the receiver; and (ii) the reception of harmonics of the various oscillators in a receiver. These are considered in more detail later in the chapter.

All superhet receivers suffer from image response (see Chapter 1) which becomes progressively more important as the signal frequency increases. In practice the effect may be reduced to a very low figure by raising the intermediate frequency. In general terms, the image response of a given receiver compared with its response on its correct frequency needs to be reduced by at least 32 times (30db) at the highest frequency to which the set tunes (usually about 30 Mc/s). A

full specification should give the receiver's response to image signals at various frequencies: that at the highest frequency to which the set tunes is the most important.

In a single conversion superhet, birdies can be caused by harmonics of the beat frequency oscillator, but in practice this seldom happens. On the other hand, with double- and triple-conversion receivers (and with single-conversion receivers operated in conjunction with a converter), the elimination, or at least reduction, of birdies becomes a major design problem. It is seldom possible in a wide coverage multi-conversion receiver to avoid birdies altogether, and the problem then resolves itself to ensuring that they do not fall in frequently used portions of the amateur bands. The ideal specification would be in the form " internally generated spurious responses are below the noise level in all cases."

Spurious responses are discussed in more detail on page 103.

Stability

The ability of a receiver to remain tuned to a particular frequency depends upon both electrical and mechanical stability of the tuned circuits, more especially those in the local oscillator(s). The primary cause of electrical instability in an oscillator (see Chapter 6) is the effect of heat on the tuned circuit and valve electrodes. Even in the best designs, there will usually be a steady variation appearing as drift in the first 10–15 minutes after switching on a cold set; but in good designs it should then settle down and little further significant change occur.

After undergoing a number of heat cycles, some components do not return precisely to their original values. This makes it very difficult to maintain accurate calibration of a bandspread dial over a long period. Many receivers therefore include a crystal controlled oscillator of high stability providing 100 kc/s or 1000 kc/s marker signals on which the calibration can be regularly checked and adjusted. A calibration marker of this type is also extremely useful where the set has both a coarse (bandset) tuning knob and a fine (bandspread) tuning knob as it enables the main dial to be re-set accurately when changing bands.

Mechanical instability, which usually appears as a definite shift in frequency when the receiver is subjected to any form of mechanical shock or vibration, cannot easily be defined in the form of a performance specification. Sturdy construction, a heavy chassis and suitable mounting of components are required to reduce this form of instability. Receiver drift can be specified in terms of maximum drift in cycles per second over given periods of time, usually quoting a separate figure to cover the warming up period.

Tuning Rate

To tune accurately and rapidly to a suppressed carrier type of transmission (see Chapter 10), it is desirable to be able to set the receiver to within about 25 c/s or so of a particular frequency. Such accuracy of tuning, which is also most beneficial for c.w. reception, is unlikely to be achieved unless each complete revolution of the tuning knob represents only a moderate shift in the frequency of the receiver. Typical figure for a modern high grade receiver would be 5 kc/s or so per revolution, but equally important would be a tuning mechanism with a smooth action, free from backlash. The trend to very low tuning rates is a feature of the most modern

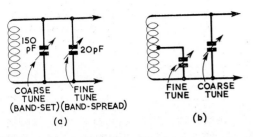

Fig. 7. Two common methods of providing bandspread tuning. (a) Small value capacitor connected in parallel across the main tuning capacitor. (b) Tapped coil permits different degrees of band-spreading to suit the various amateur bands, but can result in unwanted resonances.

designs. The use of step down gears to reduce the tuning rate of the control knob is termed *mechanical bandspreading*. The same effect can be achieved electrically by placing across the main tuning capacitors (which may vary in capacitance swing from 150 to about 500 pF) much smaller value variable capacitors of the order of 20 pF swing: see **Fig. 7**. In practice a combination of mechanical and *electrical bandspreading* is often used, while there is an increasing tendency to restrict the frequency coverage of receivers to the amateur bands only. Except for receivers having a tunable i.f. the tuning rate will usually vary on each waveband, and sometimes also within each band.

Cross-modulation and Blocking

After a receiver has been made highly selective, preferably down to the −60db level, there may remain the problem of coping with extremely strong local or distant signals. Even when such a station is transmitting on a frequency well outside the i.f. pass band of the receiver, it may affect reception by *cross modulation* or *blocking*.

When a very strong signal reaches the input of a receiver whose gain control is set for the reception of weak signals, the relatively poor selectivity of the early signal frequency and intermediate frequency circuits (prior to selective filters) will not be sufficient to prevent the strong signal from being amplified, so that one of the stages may be driven into non-linearity. This results in the required weak signal being either reduced in strength (blocking) or becoming modulated by the strong signal (cross modulation).

Clearly, the more amplifying stages there are in a receiver before the circuits which determine its selectivity characteristics, the greater are the chances that one of them will be overloaded. From this it follows that in a double (or triple) conversion receiver—where there will at least be one r.f. amplifier and two mixer stages before the selective circuits—particular care is necessary to avoid overloading.

It is difficult for the amateur to assess in terms of actual figures the performance of receivers in this respect. Undoubtedly in many sets a really powerful signal can affect reception over a considerable portion of a band. Even on a high grade receiver costing several hundred pounds, it has been shown that cross-modulation effects can occur 50 kc/s away from an S9 +60db signal and 15–20 kc/s away from an S9 +40db one. At the lower levels, the stage most likely to produce these effects is the second mixer, but for really strong signals (S9 +50db or more) the first mixer can

be the prime source of this interference. Many double-conversion receivers will have a cross-modulation performance much inferior to the example quoted.

The susceptibility of a particular design to this form of interference depends on a number of factors: notably the pattern of gain distribution through the receiver and how this is modified by the action of a.g.c. or the manual gain control (some sets have a dual track potentiometer to provide differing gain tapers on r.f. and i.f. valves), as well as the types of valves used. One method of reducing the amount of r.f. gain needed to override the noise of the first mixer is to use a triode mixer, calling for a fairly high first i.f., and requiring a greater proportion of the receiver gain to be provided by the i.f. stages.

FRONT-END CIRCUITS

R.f. Amplifier

In a superhet receiver, amplification at the signal frequency is highly desirable in order to overcome the noise contributed by the mixer. Also important is the protection provided by the additional tuned circuit against second channel (image) and certain other forms of spurious response. Excessive r.f. amplification, however, increases the likelihood of the receiver suffering from blocking or cross modulation.

The design of the r.f. amplifier stage(s) is governed by the type of mixer and the intermediate frequency of the receiver. With a conventional hexode or heptode mixer, the gain required from the r.f. amplifier will be of the order of 20db at the highest frequency (say 30 Mc/s) to ensure that the optimum signal-to-noise ratio is achieved. This can be obtained from a single good pentode amplifier. If the receiver uses a triode mixer, which has a much lower noise contribution, the gain of the r.f. amplifier becomes less important, but the stage is still useful in reducing spurious responses.

For a single-conversion superhet having an i.f. of the order of 470 kc/s (or for a double-conversion model in which the higher i.f. is of this order), two tuned r.f. amplifiers are needed to reduce image response to negligible proportions on frequencies above about 10 Mc/s, though as noted already, one stage is sufficient to secure optimum signal-to-noise ratio. If the intermediate frequency is increased to about 1·5 Mc/s, then a single r.f. stage should be able to provide good image rejection up to 30 Mc/s.

In practice, the r.f. amplifier usually consists of one or

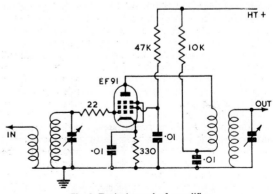

Fig. 8. Typical tuned r.f. amplifier.

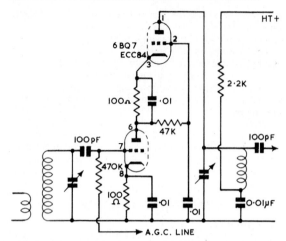

Fig. 9. Basic series-cascode r.f. amplifier. Although formerly used mainly for v.h.f. receivers, this arrangement is now commonly found in h.f. receivers.

more high gain r.f. pentodes (valve types such as 6BA6, EF85, EF183/6EH7, EF95/6AK5, EF93, 6BZ6, 6SG7, 6CB6, EF91 and 6DC6 are suitable) with a tuned input circuit between grid and cathode and with the valve operating into an inductive load which may be either the primary winding of an interstage r.f. transformer or a tuned circuit. A typical circuit is shown in **Fig. 8.** However, this is not the only possible arrangement: of increasing popularity is the series-cascode circuit, while the grounded-grid amplifier is suitable for use with a triode mixer or other applications where high gain is not required.

In the matter of optimum signal-to-noise ratio and overall stage gain, there is little to choose—for frequencies below 30 Mc/s—between a correctly designed r.f. pentode and the double-triode cascode. However, the cascode is sometimes less susceptible to cross-modulation and some constructors consider it less critical in adjustment and operation. A typical series-cascode circuit is shown in **Fig. 9.** Suitable valves include the ECC84 and 6BQ7.

The correct matching of the aerial to the valve input impedance is of great importance in securing optimum signal-to-noise ratio: the voltage gain obtained from the step-up ratio of the input circuit is not degraded by valve noise. General coverage receivers are often designed with a medium impedance input (300–600 ohms) with loose aerial coupling to the grid circuit, the aerial coil having a fair number of turns. For amateur-bands-only receivers it is usual to reduce the input impedance to 75 ohms, with the few turns of the aerial input coil overwound on the earthy end of the grid coil to provide very tight coupling. This system is to be recommended as it enables the maximum voltage step-up to be obtained. With tight coupling it is advisable to include a panel controlled aerial trimmer across the tuned grid circuit. When low impedance input circuits are to be used in conjunction with end-fed and similar aerials having a range of impedances, it is highly desirable to fit an external aerial matching unit: often that used for the transmitter can be employed by means of a co-axial change-over relay.

The first tuned circuit in a receiver is of especial importance in determining the sensitivity of the receiver and it should be noted that the alignment of this circuit to that of the mixer

presents particular problems owing to the effects produced when coupling different types of aerial to the receiver. If the aerial is reactive its connection will usually cause detuning of the input circuit. A satisfactory method of overcoming this difficulty is to fit a panel control aerial trimmer to allow the circuit to be readily brought into accurate adjustment by the user when changing bands or aerials. If a receiver is designed solely for use with a non-reactive feeder of known impedance, this control would be unnecessary.

A short-base r.f. pentode will usually have a lower noise contribution than a variable-mu pentode, but in practice this is likely to be noticeable only above 21 Mc/s; a variable-mu type is often used for convenience of a.g.c. action, and the reduction of cross modulation. Of the present range of pentode valves, the 6CB6 and EF91 provide low noise but may prove susceptible to cross-modulation effects; the American-manufactured 6DC6 is better in this respect. Where a high slope, short-base r.f. pentode is used in an a.g.c.-controlled stage, the screen feed resistor should be of fairly high value (33 K to 47 K ohms) to lengthen the grid base, and so continue to give linear though reduced amplification as the negative bias is increased.

Controlled regenerative feedback in an r.f. amplifier can be of material assistance in increasing stage gain and in giving greater protection against image response. As explained in Chapter 15, this will be at some cost in signal-to-noise ratio. Thus although regeneration is sometimes useful for smaller receivers, it is to be avoided in high-performance designs. Optimum signal-to-noise ratios cannot be obtained from an r.f. amplifier unless all forms of positive feedback due to stray capacitances, inefficient screen decoupling and the effect of common cathode lead inductance are reduced to the lowest possible figure. Coupling between input and output circuits must be kept extremely low (see page 100); one form of coupling which is sometimes overlooked is that due to the common rotor spindle of a ganged tuning capacitor being slightly above earth potential. Some r.f. valves have two cathode pins (one for input connections, the other for output connections) to overcome the inductive coupling of a common cathode lead.

Where a low noise mixer is used, the r.f. gain can be appreciably reduced without loss of signal-to-noise ratio and with benefit to cross-modulation characteristics; with a

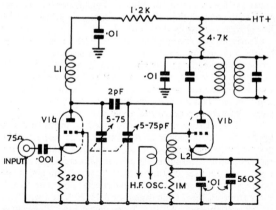

Fig. 10. Low noise r.f. amplifier-mixer using ECC85 double triode valve. The first triode section functions as a grounded-grid amplifier with untuned input; the second triode forms the mixer inductively coupled to the h.f oscillator.

triode mixer a single grounded-grid triode r.f. amplifier may suffice, particularly on 14 Mc/s and above. When fed from a low-impedance aerial transmission line, the valve input circuit need not be tuned. An arrangement of this type is shown in **Fig. 10.**

Mixer

In Chapter 1 it has been shown that any non-linear circuit element will act as a mixer, that is to say if frequencies f_1, f_2 are combined in the element, frequencies f_1, f_2, $f_1 + f_2$ and $f_1 - f_2$ will be present in the output. Thus almost any valve, crystal diode or transistor can function as a frequency converter. In h.f. receiver practice, however, the multi-grid valves, specially designed for the purpose (6BE6, EK90, ECF82/6U8, ECH81/6AJ8 or the older and much noisier 6SA7 and 6K8), are generally used because of the appreciable conversion gain which they provide and their relative freedom from interaction between the signal tuned

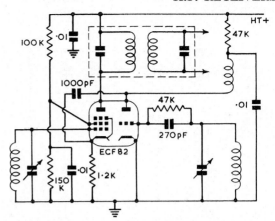

Fig. 12. One multiple valve that can be effectively used as a combined mixer/oscillator is the ECF82/6U8 triode-pentode in which the two sections are isolated by means of internal screening.

To improve oscillator stability both in combined mixer/ oscillator valves and where a separate oscillator valve is used, the d.c. potentials applied to the grid and screen grid of the mixer should remain reasonably constant. It is inadvisable in a high performance receiver to apply a.g.c. to the mixer stage. Also for this reason, and because the screen voltage of a mixer is fairly critical for optimum conversion, the screen supply for the mixer should be derived either from a relatively low impedance source such as a potential divider network not containing high value resistors or from a regulated supply with no high value series feed resistors.

The cathode, screen and anode by-pass capacitors of the mixer have all to be effective at signal, oscillator and intermediate frequencies: a ceramic type of $0.01\,\mu\text{F}$ capacitance will usually prove suitable. Typical mixer circuits are shown in **Figs. 10–14.**

The H.F. Oscillator

The frequency to which a superhet receiver responds is governed not by the signal frequency circuits but by the setting of the local oscillator. Any frequency variations of the

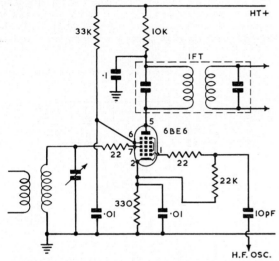

Fig. 11. Although heptode frequency-changer valves such as the 6BE6 (EK90, X727) can be used as a combined mixer/oscillator, their use as a mixer with a separate h.f. oscillator is preferred for high performance receivers.

circuits and the oscillator section. Occasionally the triode mixer is used because of its low noise contribution, but tends to be a little more tricky in operation and provides much lower output; it is subject to oscillator " pulling " unless the intermediate frequency is high, but can be usefully employed in double conversion receivers with a high first i.f. as a means of reducing cross-modulation effects.

It is sometimes difficult with conventional mixer circuits to maintain constant conversion gain over the full tuning range of a receiver. This is partly because of the varying effect of inter-electrode and stray wiring capacitance and partly because of the difficulty of providing a constant oscillator injection voltage as the frequency is varied. A higher and more constant oscillator voltage can generally be obtained by using a separate valve for the oscillator in place of the oscillator section of the normal frequency changer valve. An exception is the ECF82/6U8 triode pentode which can provide efficient conversion in a single valve envelope, particularly at the higher frequencies. A suitable pentode mixer for use with a separate oscillator is the 6AU6.

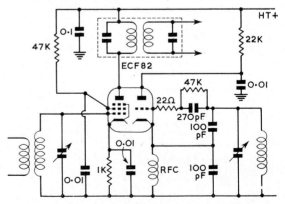

Fig. 13. A Colpitts oscillator for the ECF82/6U8 frequency changer. This requires only a two-terminal coil and is most suitable for use with independent oscillator-signal tuning, as tracking problems do not then arise.

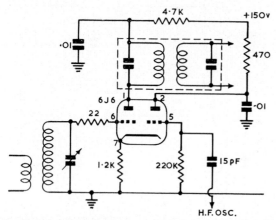

Fig. 14. A double-triode valve used as a low noise mixer with the second section functioning as a cathode-follower to provide isolation between mixer and h.f. oscillator.

oscillator are reflected in apparent variation of the received signal. The overall stability of a single-conversion receiver is determined largely by the design of the h.f. (local) oscillator: that of a double-conversion set by that of both local oscillators, but as oscillator stability is more difficult to obtain with increasing frequency, the first local oscillator (which normally functions on a higher frequency than the second local oscillator) will usually be the determining factor.

The prime requirements therefore of an h.f. oscillator are freedom from frequency changes resulting from mechanical vibration or temperature changes; sufficient but not excessive fundamental output for maximum conversion efficiency; low harmonic output to minimize spurious responses (particularly important in double- and triple-conversion receivers); and no undue variation of output voltage throughout the tuning range. For optimum and constant conversion gain, the oscillator injection voltage to the mixer is fairly critical (usually in the region of 9–10 volts).

Fig. 56 in Chapter 1 shows a typical combined mixer/oscillator frequency changer using a triode hexode or triode heptode valve. Modern multiple valves designed for frequency conversion are capable of good performance, but a separate h.f. oscillator is still preferred for high performance receivers. Apart from the advantages already given, this permits the use of a valve having high mutual conductance so that the amount of positive feed-back required for oscillation is less, resulting in a more constant output

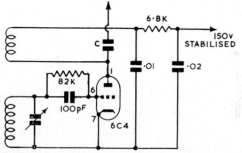

Fig. 15. Typical h.f. oscillator using power triode valve. Alternatively a pentode, such as the 6AU6 or 6BA6, may be used. The value of the coupling capacitor (C) will depend upon the type of injection used.

voltage and better stability. The use of a separate valve also allows the injection coupling to the mixer to be more accurately controlled and reduces interaction effects between signal frequency and oscillator tuned circuits. With double-conversion receivers, the second local oscillator, when operating on a fixed frequency, is often combined with the mixer.

High-slope r.f. pentodes, sometimes triode connected, are commonly used (e.g., 6AU6). To reduce spurious responses the harmonic content of the oscillator output should be kept as low as possible, and for this reason a high-slope power triode valve, such as the 6C4, is often used. Basically, any of the standard forms of oscillator are suitable provided that the harmonic output is low. The most common arrangement, shown in Fig. 15, is the tuned grid circuit with anode positive feedback winding. The Colpitts oscillator shown in Fig. 13 is also popular as the coil has only a single winding.

The stability requirements of an h.f. oscillator are akin to those for a variable frequency oscillator (see Chapter 6) but with the added disadvantage that the oscillator operates on its fundamental frequency to above 30 Mc/s. With the growing interest in single sideband reception, it has become

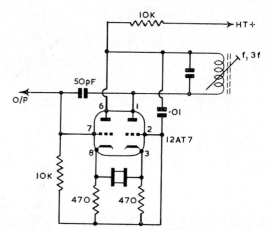

Fig. 16. Crystal oscillator circuit suitable for providing output on the series-resonant fundamental frequency of the crystal or on the third overtone frequency (approximately three times fundamental frequency) depending on the frequency of the tuned circuit.

even more important to ensure a very high order of oscillator stability; one result is a growing tendency to use a crystal-controlled h.f. oscillator: a typical circuit is shown in Fig. 16. Where the tunable h.f. oscillator is retained, many of the techniques of the v.f.o. have been introduced; for example the inclusion of an isolating stage between the oscillator and the mixer; see Fig. 17.

Most oscillators vary in frequency with a change in applied voltages. Since some variation in h.t. is likely when the gain of a receiver is changed, it is highly desirable to stabilize the oscillator h.t. supply by means of a voltage regulator tube. Some factory-built receivers also stabilize the heater current by means of a barretter valve.

Oscillator drift is caused primarily by the effects of rising temperature on the valve capacitances, the coils and the tuning capacitor. Drift can thus be minimized by such measures as adequate ventilation to keep operating temperatures low; swamping of small capacitance changes by a large

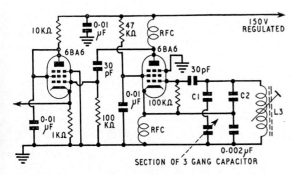

Fig. 17. A cathode follower isolating stage connected between a variable frequency oscillator and the mixer (as used in the receiver described on page 115).

fixed capacitance across the tuning capacitor (part of this swamping capacitance can usefully take the form of a capacitor having a high negative-temperature coefficient); placing of heat sensitive components as far as possible from the main sources of heat; careful choice of tuning capacitor and of the coil formers and winding technique; and rigid, vibration-free construction. Considerable improvement can be obtained by using components which react in opposite directions to heat, thus providing a degree of automatic compensation.

The vanes of the oscillator tuning capacitor must be rigid enough to eliminate the vibration effects (*microphony*) which can otherwise occur when this component is near the loudspeaker. Appreciable r.f. current flows through the oscillator tuning capacitor and a poor rotor contact of varying resistance will cause noise and *twitter* (slight discontinuities and jumps in tuning). The type of wiper contacts generally fitted on gang capacitors can give trouble, and some designers prefer to use a separate variable capacitor mechanically linked to the gang capacitor used for the mixer and r.f. tuned circuits. For maximum stability, a really well-made capacitor, with stout, well-spaced vanes, and double bearings should be selected.

Hum in the oscillator stage results in the appearance of hum modulation, noticeable only when a station is tuned in. To reduce hum in the oscillator stage, it is recommended that the cathode should be connected directly to the earth line and a bypass capacitor should always be connected directly across the heater pins on the valve socket.

A circuit which is finding increasing favour both as a

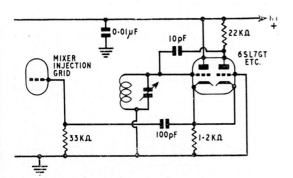

Fig. 18. The cathode-coupled oscillator is suitable for either first or second conversion oscillators.

tunable h.f. oscillator and as a fixed or variable second conversion oscillator, is the cathode-coupled oscillator using a double-triode valve: see **Fig. 18.** This circuit offers the advantage of a two-terminal coil, is capable of good stability and has low harmonic output. The circuit is also most tolerant of high *C* operation, a useful feature where a stable or wide-range oscillator is required.

Under certain conditions the circuit may " squegg," particularly if the grid coupling capacitor is increased much beyond the suggested 10 pF. This can be overcome by fitting a small non-inductive resistor of between 10 and 50 ohms immediately at the grid pin of the first triode section. If a multi-band oscillator with switched grid circuit is required, it is advisable to set up the circuit first with a 3–30 pF trimmer in place of the fixed 10 pF capacitor and to experiment with different settings and/or different series grid resistors on the highest and lowest frequencies required, replacing the trimmer with a fixed capacitor when a suitable value has been

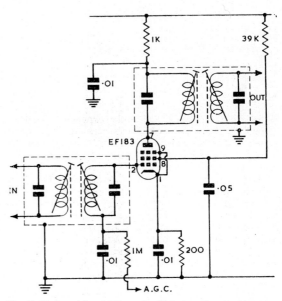

Fig. 19. Modern i.f. amplifier using high-slope frame-grid vari-mu pentode.

found—it is unlikely that this will prove critical. The h.t. bypass capacitor should be connected directly between the anode of the first triode section and the earthing point of the oscillator to ensure low harmonic output. For harmonic suppression, the series inductance of the bypass capacitor is more important than its actual value and it may prove worth trying several types to achieve optimum harmonic suppression, or to use a combination of different types.

I.F. AMPLIFICATION

The i.f. amplifier is the heart of a superhet receiver, for it is here that the main voltage gain occurs (usually of the order of 80db) and the overall selectivity response is shaped.

Fig. 19 shows a typical pentode i.f. amplifier stage, very similar basically to those found in normal broadcast receivers. I.f. transformers comprising pairs of mutually-coupled tuned circuits are used to couple the valve to the preceding and succeeding stages. To permit the gain of the stage to be controlled by an automatic gain control system, the valve usually has variable-mu characteristics. Typical types are EF85, 6BA6, EF93, W727,. 6BZ6, EF183, or the older octal-based types 6K7, 6SG7, 6SK7 and EF39.

The gain obtained in an i.f. stage depends upon the mutual conductance (g_m) of the valve, the Q and the L/C ratio of the resonant circuits in the i.f. transformers and the coupling (k) between the transformer windings. For a specified frequency, the gain will be maximum with the highest possible L/C ratio but if this is increased too much, it becomes increasingly difficult to maintain good stability and long term accuracy of alignment; this may also be affected by variations of the input resistance of the following stage with a.g.c. action.

Gain will be maximum when the product kQ is equal to one. I.f. transformers designed for this condition are said

protection afforded against image (second channel) interference and the " pulling " of the h.f. oscillator by strong signals. These two basic considerations are directly opposed; the i.f. of a single-conversion superhet must therefore always be a matter of compromise. In practice, it will be governed by such considerations as the number of tuned signal frequency circuits before the mixer, the degree of selectivity required, the number of i.f. stages, the absence of strong signals on or about the i.f., and the availability of suitable i.f. transformers. By international usage, frequencies for single-conversion receivers are usually within the band 455–470 kc/s or around 1·6 Mc/s.

In a receiver having no (or only one) tuned r.f. stage, an i.f. of 1·6 Mc/s or above is required to reduce image response to a satisfactory figure at 30 Mc/s. With an i.f. of about 460 kc/s, three tuned circuits (two r.f. stages) are necessary to

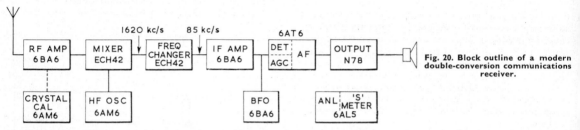

Fig. 20. Block outline of a modern double-conversion communications receiver.

to be critically coupled. When the coupling is increased beyond this point (over-coupled) the maximum gain occurs at two frequencies equally spaced about the resonant frequency and there is a slight reduction in gain at exact resonance: this condition may be used in broadcast receivers to increase the bandwidth for good quality reception. If the coupling factor is lowered (under-coupled), the stage gain falls but the response curve is sharpened (see Chapter 1) and this may be useful in communication receivers. In the past some designs used mechanical methods of varying the coupling by actually moving the coils, but this is difficult to arrange. Alternative and more practical methods of varying selectivity are discussed later in this section.

Further information on i.f. transformer design is given in Chapters 1 and 3.

Choice of I.F.

Choice of intermediate frequency is a most important consideration for the designer. The lower the frequency the easier it will be to obtain high gain and good selectivity. Conversely, the higher the frequency, the greater will be the difference between the frequencies of the signal and the h.f. oscillator, from which it follows that the greater will be the

reduce the image to negligible proportions above about 15 Mc/s.

Two stages of 460 kc/s amplification (six tuned circuits) can provide a fair degree of selectivity without any additional measures such as those described later: typical bandwidths are 6 kc/s nose, 20–30 kc/s skirt. This would be passable for a.m. telephony, though only fair for c.w. reception, and adjacent channel interference would almost certainly be a major problem on crowded bands.

With an i.f. of 1·6 Mc/s, selectivity of the order necessary for modern amateur requirements would be extremely difficult to achieve without the use of crystal filters; though for simple sets selectivity can be considerably improved by using regeneration. A low i.f. of 85–100 kc/s can give with four tuned circuits (two i.f. transformers) a peaked nose bandwidth of the order of 3 kc/s and a skirt bandwidth better than 15 kc/s at −60db.

Double-conversion Receiver

The conflicting requirement of a low i.f. for good selectivity and a high i.f. for good image protection has led to the

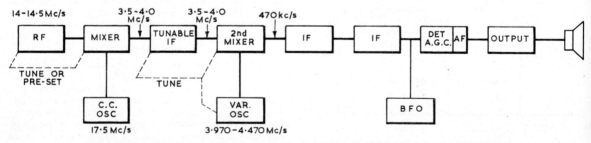

Fig. 21. Outline of double-conversion receiver with crystal-controlled h.f. oscillator and variable first i.f.

development of receivers having two or even three changes of frequency. In the double-conversion set, the incoming signals are first converted to a fairly high intermediate frequency, of the order of 1·6–5 Mc/s, making possible a reduction of image response to negligible proportions with only one r.f. stage, and so avoiding the complications with the ganged tuning of more than three circuits. Then in turn these i.f. signals are changed, usually with the aid of a fixed tuned local oscillator, to a lower i.f. where it is possible to obtain a high degree of selectivity. This second i.f. is often within the range 50–100 kc/s, but may be in the standard i.f. range of 455–470 kc/s. It is at the second i.f. that the main amplification is achieved and the main shaping of the response curve occurs. A block diagram of a representative arrangement is shown in **Fig. 20**. Thus a double conversion receiver can offer both good image protection and high selectivity, but at the cost of added complexity in design and construction. Great care is necessary to avoid the reception of spurious signals resulting from harmonics of one or more of the local oscillators; there is also the risk that the full benefits of the high selectivity may be lost owing to cross modulation resulting from the overloading of one of the early stages, since selectivity is not achieved until fairly late in the receiver.

There is one particularly interesting form of double-conversion receiver used in some of the more elaborate sets and now finding increasing favour with experienced amateurs. In this system the frequency of the first local oscillator is fixed for each band, usually by a crystal, and the output from the first frequency changer represents a band of frequencies which remains constant. The first i.f. section is then made tunable over a definite band, for example from 3·5 to 4 Mc/s, being converted to a lower intermediate frequency by means of a variable local oscillator: see **Fig. 21**. The entire receiver thus can be considered as a series of converters, one for each band, ahead of a single wave-range superhet receiver which, because of the absence of wave-change switching and with the local oscillator always working on a relatively low fixed h.f. range, can be made extremely stable and retain accurate calibration over a long period. A very wide amateur band, such as 28–30 Mc/s, would be split into two or more sections. This principle is also widely used for h.f. or v.h.f. reception in front of a lower frequency receiver: the converter is fixed tuned, with the actual tuning done on the main receiver: see **Fig. 22**.

In the conventional form of double-conversion receiver with fixed first and second intermediate frequencies, the second oscillator is normally fixed tuned, but an effective form of fine bandspread tuning is possible by making the second oscillator variable, by means of a panel control, over a range of about 5 kc/s: the bandwidth of the first i.f. section is usually more than adequate to permit this form of fine tuning without loss of gain.

Careful attention must be given to the screening and decoupling of the second oscillator if birdies and other spurious responses are to be avoided. Often the second frequency-changer (a combined mixer-oscillator such as the 6BE6 is suitable) can be

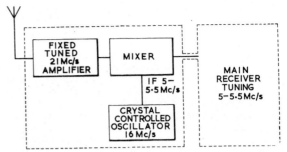

Fig. 22. How a fixed tuned converter is often used ahead of a communications receiver. All tuning is done on the main receiver.

totally enclosed in a metal screening box and all leads emerging from the box decoupled to earth. The second oscillator must be designed for high stability although, as it will normally be working on a moderately low frequency, this is usually not so difficult a problem as the design of the first h.f. oscillator. So that the second oscillator does not operate on a frequency covered in the tuning range of the receiver, it is usual for this to be sited on the low frequency side of the first i.f. In more complex receivers, this oscillator may be crystal controlled: sometimes two crystals are provided—one either side of the first i.f.—to permit side-band selection.

Occasionally designers include an amplifier stage at the first i.f. This arrangement, however, tends to increase the susceptibility of the receiver to cross modulation and blocking.

I.F. Selectivity

The degree of selectivity which can be achieved at 450 kc/s or above solely by the use of two or three double-tuned i.f. transformers of conventional design is not likely to prove sufficient for optimum results on both c.w. and telephony in the crowded amateur bands. In some designs, a higher degree of selectivity has been achieved by increasing the number of tuned i.f. circuits to eight or even 12, each of high Q construction and under-coupled. Since the transfer of energy tends to be low because of the low transformer

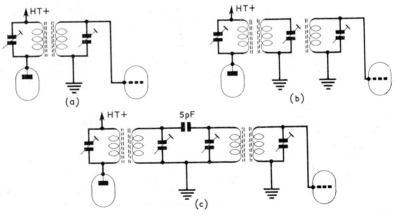

Fig. 23. I.f. inter-valve couplings. (a) The conventional double-tuned i.f. transformer. (b) Special triple tuned i.f. transformers have been used in some designs to provide a useful improvement in skirt selectivity. (c) Two conventional i.f. transformers can be connected in this way to provide four tuned circuits per stage.

coupling factor, more overall valve amplification must be available, and three stages of i.f. amplification may be needed. **Fig. 23** indicates some of the ways in which tuned circuits can be incorporated in the inter-valve couplings.

The selectivity which can be obtained is governed both by the Q of the i.f. transformer and its coupling factor, and good components should be used. Tuned circuits of higher Q than can readily be obtained in the conventional type of i.f. transformer (even when wound with Litz multi-stranded wire) can be obtained by using modern pot cores of high permeability ferrite materials. To provide switched degrees of selectivity, some receivers incorporate i.f. transformers having a low coupling factor but with a small additional primary winding tightly coupled to the secondary and which can be switched into circuit to broaden the response curve. This and the pot core systems are very effective for low frequency second i.f. stages.

Where selective i.f. filters are incorporated, it is most important that stray couplings and signal paths between the stages be kept to a very low figure, or signals will leak round the filter(s) and impair selectivity. Even a relatively small leakage becomes of consequence at −60 and −80db levels. Good layout and effective decoupling of the anode, screen, cathode and heater circuits are of particular importance. Decoupling capacitors should be chosen for low series inductance and with short connecting leads.

I.F. Regeneration

The gain of an i.f. amplifier can be considerably increased by the use of controlled positive feedback up to the point of oscillation. Such feedback also has the effect of providing an apparent increase of Q of the tuned i.f. circuits; this increases the selectivity of the stage. Since the signal-to-noise ratio will have already been largely determined in the early stages, the increase in noise contribution due to regenerative feedback will be of little practical consequence.

Fig. 24 shows a simple method of providing controlled

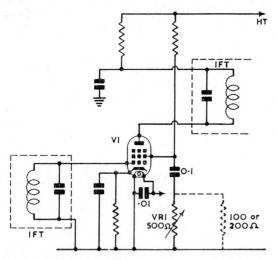

Fig. 24. Controllable regeneration of an i.f. amplifier by varying the efficiency of the screen decoupling. The fixed resistor in parallel with the control may have to be added if the regeneration control is too coarse.

regeneration without additional windings on the i.f. transformer; positive feedback is introduced by varying the effectiveness of the screen decoupling capacitor.

In practice, the use of i.f. regeneration is confined mainly to smaller receivers where the extra gain is of most importance. This is partly because the improvement in selectivity is impaired in the presence of strong signals (where it is most needed) and partly because of the difficulty of maintaining accurate alignment at all positions of the regeneration control.

Crystal Filters

The selectivity of a tuned circuit is governed by its frequency and by its Q (ratio of reactance to resistance). There are practical limits to the Q obtainable in coils and i.f. transformers. In 1929, Dr. J. Robinson, a British scientist, introduced the quartz crystal resonator into radio receivers.

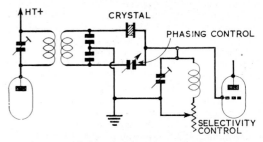

Fig. 25. Variable selectivity crystal filter. Selectivity is greatest when the impedance of the tuned circuit is reduced by bringing the variable resistor fully into circuit. For optimum results there must be adequate screening to prevent stray coupling between the input and output circuits which would permit strong off-resonance signals to leak round the filter.

The advantages of such a device for communication receivers was appreciated by James Lamb of the American Radio Relay League and he developed the i.f. *crystal filter* for amateur operators.

For this application a quartz crystal may be considered as a resonant circuit with a Q of from 10,000 to 100,000 compared with about 300 for a very high grade coil and capacitor tuned circuit. From Chapter 1, it will be noted that the electrical equivalent of a crystal is not a simple series or parallel tuned circuit, but a combination of the two: it has (a) a fixed series resonant frequency (f_s) and (b) a parallel resonant frequency (f_p). The frequency (f_p) is determined partly by the capacitance of the crystal holder and by any added parallel capacitance and can be varied over a small range.

The crystal offers low impedance to signals at its series resonant frequency; a very high impedance to signals at its parallel resonant frequency, and a moderately high impedance to signals on other frequencies, tending to decrease as the frequency increases due to the parallel capacitance.

While there are a number of ways in which this high Q circuit can be incorporated into an i.f. stage, a common method—providing a variable degree of selectivity—is shown in **Fig. 25**. When the series resonant frequency of the crystal coincides with the incoming i.f. signals, it forms a sharply tuned " acceptor " circuit, passing the signals with only slight loss of strength (insertion loss) to the grid of the

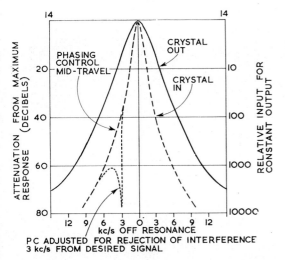

Fig. 26. A graph showing the improvement in selectivity which can be obtained by the use of a crystal filter of the type shown in Fig. 25.

succeeding stage. The exact setting of the associated parallel resonant circuit, at which the crystal will offer an extremely high resistance, is governed by the setting of the *phasing control* which balances out the effect of the holder capacitance. Such a filter can provide a nose selectivity of the order of 1 kc/s bandwidth or less, while the sharp rejection notch which can be shifted by the phasing control through the pass band can be of the order of 45db. **Fig. 26** shows the improvement which can be obtained by switching in a filter of this type in a good communications receiver (a simple method of switching the filter is to arrange the phasing trimmer to short-circuit at one end of its travel). Inspection of the response curve will show that the improvement in the skirt selectivity is not so spectacular as at the nose, and even with a well-designed filter may leave something to be desired in the presence of strong signals.

The degree of selectivity provided by a single crystal depends not only upon the Q of the crystal and the i.f. but also upon the impedance of the input and output circuits.

The lower these impedances are the greater will be the effect of the filter, though this will usually be accompanied by a rise in insertion loss. To broaden the selectivity curve and make the Q of the filter *appear* less, it is only necessary to raise the input or output impedances. In Fig. 25 the input impedance may be lowered by detuning the secondary of the i.f. transformer. The output impedance will depend upon the setting of the variable resistor which forms the selectivity control. With minimum resistance in circuit, the tuned circuit will offer maximum impedance, which can be gradually lowered by bringing more resistance into circuit. Maximum impedance corresponds with minimum selectivity.

A disadvantage of the single crystal filter is that when used in the position of maximum selectivity, it may introduce considerable " ringing," rendering it difficult to copy a weak c.w. signal: this is due to the tendency of a high Q circuit to oscillate for a short period after being stimulated by a signal, producing a bell-like echo on the signal.

Since the minimum nose bandwidth of a single crystal filter working on about 460 kc/s may be as low as 100–200 c/s, it is not possible to receive a.m. telephony signals satisfactorily through the filter unless its efficiency is degraded by operating it into a high impedance. If this is done, such a filter will often prove most useful for telephony reception through bad interference, though at some cost to the quality of reproduction. Even the most simple form of crystal filter, consisting of a crystal in series with the i.f. signal path, without balancing or phasing, can be of use.

Bandpass Crystal Filters

As already noted, the sharply peaked response curve of a single-crystal filter is not ideal, and has by modern standards a relatively poor shape factor: improved results can be achieved with what is termed a *half-lattice* or bandpass filter. Basically, this comprises two crystals chosen so that their series resonant frequencies differ by an amount approximately equal to the bandwidth required; for example about 300 c/s apart for c.w., 3–4 kc/s apart or a.m. telephony or 2 kc/s apart for s.s.b.: see **Fig. 27(b)** .This form of filter, developed in the thirties, has in recent years come into widespread amateur use, aided by the availability of war surplus crystals (for example the FT241 series) at moderate cost. Although this type of filter has a much improved slope over the single crystal filter, in its simplest form there will still be

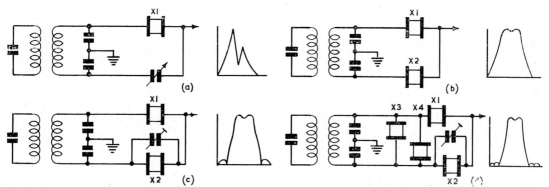

Fig. 27. Half-lattice crystal filters showing the improvement in the shape of the curve which can be obtained when the crystals are correctly balanced or when extra crystals are used to reduce the "humps." Typical crystal frequencies would be X1 464.8 kc/s, X2 466.7 kc/s, X3 463 kc/s, X4 468.5 kc/s.

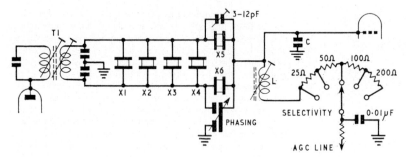

Fig. 28. Up to about six crystals may be used in a single half-lattice filter. Here is a variable selectivity unit for 465 kc/s using FT241 crystals. X1 461.1 kc/s (49); X2 462.9 kc/s (50); X3 468.5 kc/s (53); X4 470.4 kc/s (54); X5 464.8 kc/s (51); X6 466.7 kc/s (52). Numbers in brackets refer to channel numbers for FT241 crystals. T1 and L/C should be tuned to mid-filter frequency.

certain frequencies, just outside the main pass band, at which the attenuation is reduced. Unless a balancing trimmer is connected across the higher frequency crystal the sides of the response curve tend to broaden out towards the bottom of the curve. As the capacitance across the crystal is increased, the sides of the curve steepen, but the side lobes tend to become more pronounced. Capacitance across the lower frequency crystal broadens the response and deepens the trough in the centre of the passband.

To eliminate the " humps " in the response curve additional crystals may be included in the filter, up to about six in number: **Fig. 28.** Examples of bandpass filter response characteristics are shown in Fig. 27. Alternatively, additional filter sections may be incorporated in the i.f. section in cascade. An advantage of using several cascaded filters is that less critical balancing and adjustment are needed. Provided that there is no leakage of i.f. signals around the filter due to stray capacitances or other forms of unwanted coupling (an important consideration with all selective filters), extremely good shape factors of the order of 1·5 can be achieved with about three cascaded filters on about 460 kc/s. This system is used in the receiver described on page 116. There will be an insertion loss of the order of 6db per section.

To provide a sharp variable rejection notch, it is advantageous to incorporate some form of bridged-T filter or Q multiplier (see later) in order to be able to eliminate steady heterodyne interference.

To reduce susceptibility to cross-modulation or blocking, crystal and other selective filters should be placed as near as possible to the front-end of the receiver.

Crystals for Bandpass Filters

For bandpass filters, most amateurs use surplus type FT241 crystals. These are in two groups labelled in frequency and with a channel number. The fundamental frequencies are from 370 to 540 kc/s. The first group are marked in frequencies from 20·0 to 27·9 Mc/s with channel numbers up to 79. The actual crystal frequency may be found by dividing the frequencies marked on the holder by 54. As the channels are spaced 0·1 Mc/s apart, the crystal separations are 1·85 kc/s. The second group of FT241 crystals are marked from 27 to 38·9 Mc/s in 0·1 Mc/s steps, with channel numbers from 270 to 389; the fundamental frequency can be found by dividing the marked frequency by 72. The spacing of this group is about 1·49 kc/s. FT241 crystals of similar channel numbers are likely to show some slight spread of frequencies. Should the precise frequencies required not be available it is possible to raise the frequency of a crystal by edge grinding and to lower it by plating (see Chapter 10).

AN/TRC-1 crystals in similar holders to the FT241 series

are available in fundamental frequencies from 729 to 1040 kc/s and marked in channel numbers from 70·0 to 99·9.

High Frequency Crystal Filters

As the frequency increases, it becomes more difficult to obtain entirely satisfactory characteristics from half-lattice crystal filters. Whereas extremely good results can be achieved on 450–470 kc/s, bandpass crystal filters for intermediate frequencies of 1·6 Mc/s and above may prove less effective when viewed by the highest modern standards, particularly when using the readily available surplus crystals. Since many of the problems associated with superhet design would be solved if sufficient selectivity could fairly easily be obtained with high intermediate frequencies, the development of suitable but inexpensive h.f. crystal filters is a matter of concern to amateurs. Factory-built filters effective to above 10 Mc/s developed for s.s.b. applications are available, but at appreciable cost.

One current line of development of interest to home-constructors is the use of a number of crystals in place of i.f. transformers in an aperiodic (untuned) amplifier. This type of selective amplifier is particularly suited for receivers intended primarily for c.w. reception. A typical circuit of a single filter is shown in **Fig. 29.** In practice at least two filters would be cascaded.

Mechanical Filters

The development in the past decade of mechanical filters has provided the amateur designer with a convenient method of obtaining—at intermediate frequencies between 60 and

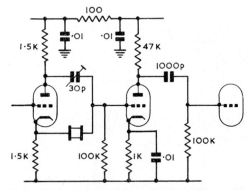

Fig. 29. A crystal may be used in conjunction with an otherwise aperiodic (untuned) amplifier. In practice several similar amplifiers may be cascaded. Typical triode valves would be the ECC85 or the triode-pentode ECF80.

600 kc/s—a bandpass characteristic having almost any desired bandwidth combined with a flat top and steep sides. These filters provide in a compact unit—smaller than the usual i.f. transformer—a stable filter having the characteristics of a multiple crystal network. A functional diagram of a mechanical filter is shown in **Fig. 30.**

The filter consists of three basic elements: (i) two magneto-striction tranducers which convert the i.f. signals into mechanical vibrations and vice versa; (ii) a series of metal discs mechanically resonated to the particular frequency; and (iii) disc coupling rods.

Each disc is equivalent to a series resonant circuit with a high Q (of the order of 5000 or above). Varying the mechanical coupling between the rods—by making them larger or smaller—varies the bandwidth of the filter. The vibration of the discs cannot be observed, and the entire filter is enclosed in a hermetically sealed case. The insertion loss of one of these filters is about 10db, and the only adjustment required is to tune the input and output transducer coils with the appropriate capacitance. Normally, non-critical high impedance circuits are suitable at the input and output ends; for use with transistors, however, the filters can be matched

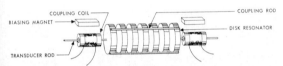

Fig. 30. The Collins mechanical filter. I.f. signals are converted into mechanical vibrations by a magneto-strictive transducer and passed along a series of resonant discs, then finally reconverted to i.f. signals by a second magneto-strictive transducer. Bandwidth of the filter is governed by the number of resonant discs and the design of the coupling rods.—(By courtesy of Collins Radio Co. of England Ltd.)

into low impedance circuits by using a series-resonant termination. To obtain the full benefit of the filter, the input and output circuits must be effectively screened from each other.

Mechanical filters cannot—at least at present—be home-constructed and must be purchased complete. A pair of filters, one for c.w. the other for telephony—adds many pounds to the cost of a receiver, and an amateur can usually construct crystal filter networks at appreciably lower cost.

Ceramic Filters and Transformers

Piezoelectric effects are not confined to the classic materials: quartz crystals and Rochelle salt. In recent years increasing use has been made of certain ceramics, such as barium titanate (for gramophone pickups) and the lead zirconate titanate (PZT) series. Small discs of PZT ceramics which resonate in the radial dimension to the intermediate frequency can be used in bandpass filters in the same way as quartz crystals, though at the present state of development the Q is considerably lower. PZT ceramics can also be used directly to provide an impedance transformation: by providing two sets of electrodes a complete replacement for an i.f. transformer can be obtained, giving improved selectivity characteristics compared with conventional components. To date this type of piezoelectric ceramic i.f. transformer has been used mainly for transistor receivers, as it provides a very convenient means of obtaining the low impedances required for transistor input circuits. While having a good nose

selectivity the skirts tend to be too broad for ceramic filters to be much used in advanced amateur receivers at present.

Q Multipliers

The apparent Q of a coil can be increased by applying regenerative feedback up to the point of oscillation and this means of increasing selectivity has long been made use of in t.r.f. receivers. In recent years it has been applied to a variety of devices generally known as Q *multipliers* of value in superhet practice. Basically, these devices comprise a valve or transistor circuit coupled to an early i.f. stage and arranged to be tunable across the i.f. pass band of the receiver; positive feedback is then advanced near to the threshold of oscillation. Under this condition the effect is that of placing a high Q parallel tuned circuit across the i.f. transformer. At the point of resonance the impedance is high and a signal at that frequency will pass unattenuated: signals on other frequencies will be attenuated by an amount which will depend on the Q of the circuit and the frequency difference compared with the peaked signal. This forms a most useful method of improving the selectivity of a receiver not fitted with a crystal filter; the improvement will be most marked on receivers having no i.f. stage at less than about 455 kc/s. A Q multiplier can be attached to an existing receiver without having to modify the set. Unlike a crystal filter there is little or no insertion loss.

A further feature of the Q multiplier is that by providing negative feedback in a second triode section, the high Q circuit can be switched to a series resonant condition: the unit will then provide a deep, narrow rejection notch tunable across the passband of the receiver, akin to the action of the phasing control of a crystal filter. This application of the Q multiplier is of value even with advanced receivers already having a bandpass crystal or mechanical filter.

Constructional details of a Q multiplier are given later in this chapter.

Bridged-T Filters

A further method of providing a rejection notch which can be used for the elimination of steady heterodyne interference is the *bridged-T* filter.

The basic filter is shown in **Fig. 31** with its associated response curve, which indicates that the filter provides high attenuation at the resonant frequency. This attenuation will be maximum (providing the deepest notch) when the resistor is equal to one-quarter the impedance of the tuned circuit. By providing a variable resistor it thus becomes possible to adjust the notch depth.

Filters of this simple form are to be found mainly in receivers having a low i.f., usually below 100 kc/s. However,

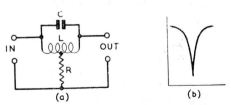

Fig. 31. The basic bridged-T filter circuit (a) and associated response characteristics (b) showing deep notch at resonant frequency. The notch attenuation will be maximum when R is equal to one-quarter of the resonant impedance of LC. In practice two equal capacitors are often used in a capacitive potentiometer instead of a centre-tapped coil.

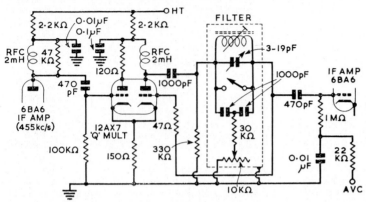

Fig. 32. Bridged-T circuit combined with a Q Multiplier. The notch can be tuned across the receiver bandpass by means of the 3-19 pF trimmer and the depth of the notch adjusted by the 10 K variable resistor.

effective use of this type of filter can be made at 450–470 kc/s by increasing the Q of the filter coil by means of the Q multiplication technique, as indicated in **Fig. 32**. An advantage of the bridged-T filter over the phasing control of a crystal filter is that it causes less distortion of the i.f. response on either side of the deep, narrow notch.

THE DETECTOR

The main types of detector in modern receivers are:
(i) the diode detector, using either a thermionic or crystal diode, found in the vast majority of receivers;
(ii) the regenerative leaky-grid detector, relatively little used in superhets but capable of high gain and good selectivity;
(iii) the infinite impedance detector, offering extremely low loading of the final i.f. transformer;

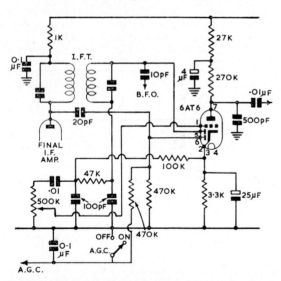

Fig. 33. Typical use of double-diode triode valve for detection, a.g.c. and a.f. amplification. A.g.c. delay is obtained from the cathode bias, but this is not applied to detector diode.

(iv) various forms of heterodyne detector developed primarily for the reception of s.s.b. signals.

Diode Detector

The conventional diode envelope detector functions directly on a.m. signals and in conjunction with a b.f.o. or carrier insertion oscillator on telegraphy and s.s.b. It is an uncomplicated device presenting a stable but rather low impedance load to the final i.f. transformer, and for many years was used almost exclusively. It has the disadvantage that it provides no gain, and may introduce distortion at low signal levels. Because of its relatively low dynamic impedance and consequent a.c. shunting on the final i.f. transformer it is advantageous for the secondary winding of this transformer to have a lower L/C ratio than for the other windings, and to be more tightly coupled than for the earlier transformers; however, in practice, satisfactory results can be obtained using similar

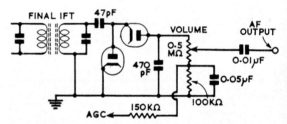

Fig. 34. Diode integrator detector. Either thermionic valves (6AL5, 6H6) or semi-conductor diodes (1N35, OA79, OA81, etc.) can be used.

i.f. transformers throughout a set. To minimize a.f. distortion on weak signals having a high modulation percentage, care should be taken to keep stray capacitance across the diode load as low as possible.

The diode detector is often combined in a single multiple valve with a second diode used as a rectifier to provide a negative a.g.c. bias and also a triode which is generally used for the first stage of a.f. amplification: see **Fig. 33**. This practice can introduce undesirable coupling between the various circuits, but is economical.

Suitable valve types for the detector and a.g.c. diodes would be: EB91, 6AL5, EB34, 6H6 or crystal diodes types OA79, OA81, 1N34. Suitable double-diode and triple-diode triodes include: 6AT6, EBC90, 6AV6, EABC80, 6AK8.

It is possible to use two diodes in a voltage doubler arrangement, offering some advantages for weak signal reception at low distortion: see **Fig. 34**.

Regenerative Detector

The regenerative detector offers the advantages that a high gain can be obtained (permitting its use on weak i.f. signals) and that it can be made to contribute to the selectivity of the receiver. Its main disadvantage is that it is difficult to use in conjunction with an a.g.c. system; furthermore it needs very careful adjustment if full benefit is to be

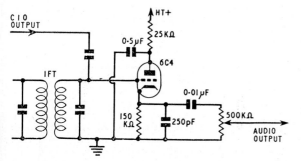

Fig. 35. Infinite impedance detector for use in a communications receiver.

are fed to what is basically a mixer stage: (a) the incoming signal at the intermediate frequency; and (b) a signal from the carrier insertion oscillator (c.i.o.) or beat frequency oscillator (b.f.o.). The difference in frequency represents the a.f. output and, after filtering to remove the components of the original signals, is fed to the a.f. stages. **Fig. 36** shows a typical circuit using a double-triode valve, though alternative arrangements using 6BE6 or ECH81 mixer valves are also commonly used. The reader will appreciate that these detectors can be used both for s.s.b. and c.w. but are unsuitable for the reception of a.m. telephony transmissions, except when the signals are converted to s.s.b. by selective filters.

Another form of heterodyne detector, capable of excellent s.s.b. performance is shown in **Fig. 37**. This uses two germanium crystal diodes in a bridge ring modulator (as for s.s.b. generation) in conjunction with a further single diode

obtained. It is particularly useful for simpler receivers intended primarily for c.w. reception; it dispenses with the need for a separate b.f.o. and can do much to overcome a deficiency of i.f. gain.

I.f. transformers incorporating a feedback coil suitable for this purpose are not readily available. One method is to remove the i.f. transformer from its screening can and to add a feedback winding, finding the correct number of turns for smooth regeneration by trial and error. An alternative method is described on page 112.

Infinite Impedance Detector

The *infinite impedance* detector, **Fig. 35,** has certain advantages though until recently only rarely used in communications receivers. At audio frequencies, there is considerable negative current feedback across the relatively high value cathode resistor, reducing distortion to a very low level. As the triode valve is not driven into grid current, there is little damping of the i.f. transformer, enabling a higher voltage to be developed across the secondary winding than would be possible with a diode detector. Output from the b.f.o. or c.i.o. is fed to the grid of the detector via a small capacitance. It is difficult to use in conjunction with an a.g.c. system unless a separate a.g.c. i.f. amplifier is incorporated.

Product or Heterodyne Detector

For the reception of s.s.b. signals, various forms of mixer or heterodyne detector have been introduced to reduce intermodulation distortion at low signal levels. In the form generally termed the *product detector* two input signals

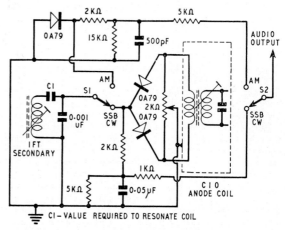

Fig. 37. This arrangement using three germanium diodes provides demodulation for s.s.b., c.w. and a.m. signals and is incorporated in the receiver described on page 115.

which can be switched into circuit for a.m. reception. The resonating capacitance across the secondary of the final i.f. transformer in the receiver comprises two fixed capacitors with a capacitance ratio of approximately 10 : 1 to form an a.c. potentiometer, providing a low impedance load to the diodes. The c.i.o./b.f.o. voltage is fed in push-pull across a balancing potentiometer from a low impedance link winding in the oscillator anode winding. When correctly balanced by means of the 2K ohm potentiometer, there is no output when the c.i.o. voltage is removed. This type of demodulator is used in the advanced amateur receiver shown on page 117.

The Beat Frequency Oscillator

The *beat frequency oscillator* (b.f.o.), termed for s.s.b. reception the *carrier injection oscillator* (c.i.o.), exercises considerable influence on receiver performance on c.w. and s.s.b. signals. Any variation in oscillator frequency will be reflected in variation of the a.f. beat note on a c.w. signal, and will have the effect of detuning the receiver on s.s.b. Since the b.f.o. is tuned to a frequency close to that of the receiver's final i.f., it is an easier matter to obtain the required

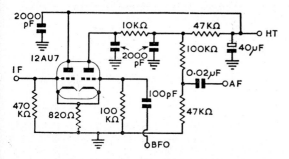

Fig. 36. The product or heterodyne detector is useful for the reception of s.s.b. and c.w. signals but is unsuitable for a.m. telephony signals. Suitable valves include 6SN7, 12AU7 and ECC82.

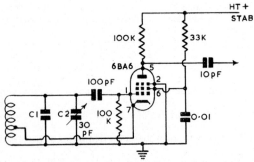

Fig. 38. Typical b.f.o. circuit using electron-coupled oscillator. A high value of C₁ will help stabilize the oscillator. C₂ is the pitch control.

stability with an L/C oscillator than for earlier frequency conversion oscillators. Nevertheless the requirements are fairly stringent, and modern s.s.b. designs tend to favour the use of crystal controlled oscillators.

An output of several volts is required for effective s.s.b. reception, but both harmonic output and stray coupling to receiver circuits other than the detector stage should be low: this calls for effective screening of the oscillator and good de-coupling, including the heater circuit. The stage should be supplied from a stabilized h.t. line. There is some advantage to be gained from providing variable coupling to the detector, though this is rarely found in practice.

Fig. 38 shows a typical circuit. The variable capacitor C_2 provides a control panel variation of about $\pm$ 5 kc/s, the knob often being labelled *pitch control:* the circuit should be carefully adjusted so that at mid-travel of this control, the oscillator frequency corresponds to zero beat of the intermediate frequency. This permits easy change of a.f. beat note on c.w. signals, and provides for simpler adjustment of the b.f.o. when receiving s.s.b. Output from the b.f.o. can be taken from the cathode, a conveniently low impedance point, to minimize pulling of the oscillator by strong signals.

AUTOMATIC GAIN CONTROL

The more r.f. and i.f. stages there are in a superhet receiver, the greater will be the available gain and the greater the possibility of overloading by strong signals unless this gain can be reduced. This may be done manually by altering the bias applied to variable-mu valves by varying a common cathode

bias resistor (there is a tendency in commercially-built receivers to use dual track resistors for this purpose with differing tapers for r.f. and i.f. valves). Since, however, h.f. signals are subject to considerable fading, both slow and rapid, it is advantageous for the gain to be controlled automatically by the strength of the incoming signal. This can be done fairly simply for a.m. telephony signals; the basic circuits can also be adapted with some additional complexity for c.w. and s.s.b. reception. In simple amateur communications receivers, *automatic gain control* (sometimes *automatic volume control* or *a.v.c.*) may be regarded as a luxury rather than an essential, for a poor a.g.c. system is often much worse than no a.g.c. at all.

The basic function of a conventional a.g.c. system is to hold reasonably constant the a.f. output from the detector over wide variations of signal level. This can be done by rectifying a portion of the amplified i.f. signal to obtain a negative d.c. voltage which is then applied as bias to one or more of the earlier stages. An increase in signal at the a.g.c. rectifier causes greater negative bias to be developed and so reduces overall gain; conversely, a fall in signal causes bias to be lowered and gain increases. The application of the a.g.c. voltage should be *delayed* until after the signal has reached a level sufficient to provide a good signal-to-noise ratio.

The greater the number of stages controlled by the *a.g.c. line* and the greater the gain within the control section, the better will be the efficiency of the a.g.c. system—that is to say, the more constant will be the output for wide variations of signal strength.

It is not good practice to apply an a.g.c. potential to the mixer valve(s), although this is often done in simpler receivers: the efficiency of the mixer is reduced and the change in input capacitance with change of operating point can lead to pulling of the oscillator frequency. In receivers with two r.f. stages, the first stage may sometimes be operated under fixed bias conditions to prevent degradation of the signal-to-noise ratio.

A typical a.g.c. system is shown in **Fig. 39**. A portion of the i.f. signal is taken via a capacitor from the anode of the final i.f. amplifier to the a.g.c. rectifier diode and a negative d.c. voltage builds up across the load resistor. As it is important that no signal modulation should appear on the a.g.c. line, the output is fed through one or more sections of resistance-capacitance a.f. filters. The values of these filter components affect the rate at which the a.g.c. system follows

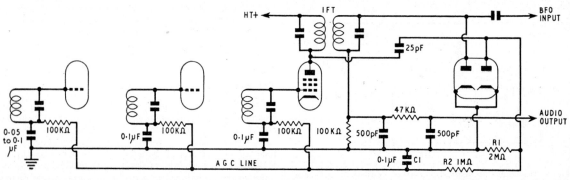

Fig. 39. Typical a.g.c. system and diode demodulator used for a.m. reception. The negative bias is used to control the gain of r.f. and i f amplifying stages.

the variations in signal strength. The larger the time-constant the slower will the a.g.c. respond to signal fluctuations. For a.m. telephony a time-constant of the order of about 0·2 second is commonly employed.

When an i.f. valve is controlled by an a.g.c. line, the screen is usually fed through a fairly high value resistor (about 22K to 47K ohms). This ensures that the screen voltage rises as the negative bias to the valve increases: this provides a longer grid base for the valve and reduces the chances of a valve being driven into non-linear amplification, which would make cross-modulation or blocking more likely.

There are two main reasons why a conventional a.g.c. system, such as that described above, is unsatisfactory on c.w.

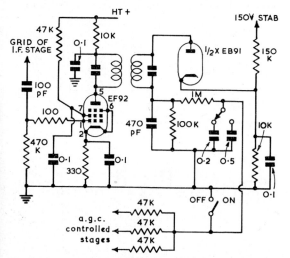

Fig. 40. The use of a separate a.g.c. amplifier and switched time constants enables the a.g.c. system to be used for both a.m. and c.w. reception.

and s.s.b. signals. First, in neither of these modes of transmission is there a continuous carrier on which to base the a.g.c. action. Secondly, the output from the b.f.o. acts on the a.g.c. system as though it were a strong external carrier so reducing the gain of the receiver.

To overcome the absence of a continuous carrier as in telegraphy, the time constant of the a.g.c. system is lengthened so that the gain no longer rises and falls between each Morse symbol. The a.g.c. action is then based on the average signal received over a given period: whereas a discharge time constant of the order of 0·2 seconds is satisfactory for a.m. telephony, a suitable figure for c.w. or s.s.b. is about 0·5–1·0 second. The charge time for the a.g.c. system should preferably be as short as possible, for example 25 milliseconds for a.m., 200 milliseconds for c.w./s.s.b.

To prevent the b.f.o. from reducing gain, it is possible to screen the b.f.o. thoroughly and then arrange a low level injection direct to the signal detector diode but it is difficult to overcome completely the effects of stray coupling. A more practical system is to feed the a.g.c. diode from an entirely separate a.g.c. amplifier, the input of which is in parallel with that of the final i.f. amplifier valve: see **Fig. 40**. With this system the signal for the a.g.c. system is thus taken off before the injection of the b.f.o. In some designs the take-off point is earlier and the selectivity characteristics of the a.g.c. system

are made broader than the main i.f. channel; this permits the reduction of gain by strong adjacent-channel signals which might otherwise cause splatter or cross-modulation.

An alternative automatic *volume* control system which is applicable to all types of transmission consists of rectifying a small portion of the a.f. signal and using the voltage so obtained to control the output of the receiver. The arrangement in its simplest forms tends to be unsatisfactory, however, as it is generally necessary to take the voltage from ,a point after the a.f. gain control.

S METERS

A meter which indicates the approximate strength of the signals applied to the input terminals is a useful adjunct to a communications receiver for comparing the strengths of different stations; for observing the results of tests on receiver or transmitter aerials; for checking the directional characteristics of a rotary aerial; and for use as a tuning indicator.

Many different circuits have been developed for this purpose, but all depend for their operation on the voltage developed across the a.g.c. line of the receiver. Since this bias voltage controls the current flowing in one or more i.f. stages, the simplest *S meter* comprises a meter of about 10 mA f.s.d. connected in the anode circuit of one of the a.g.c. controlled stages. This arrangement, however, provides a reverse-reading meter with minimum current indicating maximum signal strength. To overcome this difficulty a more sensitive meter (usually 1 mA f.s.d.) is often connected in a bridge circuit with zero-setting adjustment, so that a decrease in anode current to one or more a.g.c. controlled stages produces an increase in current flowing through the meter. A simple form of bridge circuit is shown in **Fig. 41** but many variations are found in practice, mainly intended to overcome the difficulty of obtaining a fairly linear calibration of what is essentially a logarithmic scale over a wide voltage range of the order of 100db (voltage ratio of 100,000 times).

There is considerable advantage in employing a separate valve to measure the potential developed across the a.g.c. line, and a recommended circuit using a double-triode valve is shown in **Fig. 42**. This is essentially a valve voltmeter and can be added as a small external unit to almost any existing receiver having an a.g.c. line. R_1 is the zero adjustment to compensate for different levels of receiver noise. The input voltage taken from the receiver a.g.c. line is controlled by R_2.

The calibration scale on a $200\mu A$ f.s.d. meter provides adequate spread for the lower S units but also accommodates readings up to about 20db over S9. Mid-scale reading should

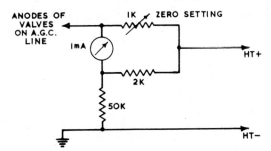

Fig. 41. Basic bridge-circuit for forward reading S meter. In some designs, variation of current to one or more of the screen-grids of the a.g.c. valves is used.

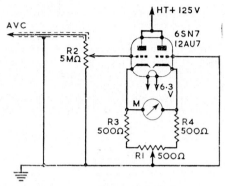

Fig. 42. Valve-voltmeter type of S meter. A suitable meter would be 200 μA full scale deflection. R_3 and R_4 should be 10 per cent tolerance.

be adjusted by R_2 to represent about S8 or S9, and the scale calibrated to suit the receiver concerned. The best relation between S units and decibel ratios has long been a matter of some controversy, and to set up a scale accurately to a pre-determined ratio such as one S point for 6db requires the use of a signal generator having an accurately calibrated attenuator; but unless the gain of the receiver is approximately equal on all bands such calibration will be of limited accuracy. For the average amateur, it is probably best to regard the calibration of an S meter in terms of purely arbitrary units, chosen to suit the actual equipment and the operator's own requirements. For instance, with the unit shown, S1 could be the minimum signal detectable above the noise level and S9 a very strong but non-local signal, with the scale divided evenly for intermediate strengths.

A.F. STAGES

The a.f. output from a diode detector is usually of the order of 0·5–1 volt. A single a.f. amplifier will be adequate for headphone reception, but a further stage of power amplification will be needed to operate a loudspeaker. Since

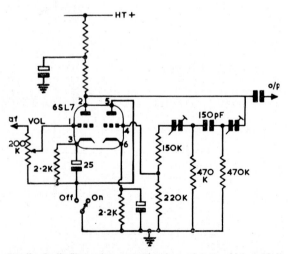

Fig. 43. Audio filter using conventional components which employs negative feedback to attenuate signals except over a narrow band at about 950 c/s.

the signal-to-noise ratio is determined in the early stages of the receiver, there is little point in providing excessive a.f. amplification, though some reserve may be useful to overcome insertion losses if an audio filter (described below) is fitted. In practice, the basic circuit arrangements in this section of the receiver differ little from those found in broadcast receivers, except for provision for the connection of headphones in such a manner that the full output of the receiver is not applied across them, and the loudspeaker muted. For communications purposes there is no point in providing a wide a.f. range, indeed any high modulation frequencies will normally be removed by the selective i.f. stages. It is useful also to restrict bass response, and this can be done by reducing the value of the interstage coupling capacitors from the conventional value of the order of

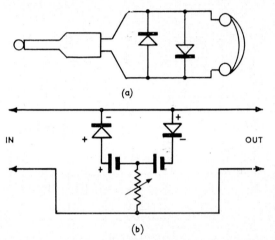

Fig. 44. Simple a.f. peak limiters. (a) Westector metal rectifiers can be used without back biasing potentials to provide suitable limiting for headphone reception. (b) The effectiveness of this limiter with crystal or metal rectifiers is governed by the setting of the variable resistor.

0·01μF to about 0·001μF or less; this will also help remove any traces of mains hum.

A triode-pentode can conveniently be used to provide both a stage of a.f. voltage amplification and power output: one example is the ECL86.

The restriction of a.f. response can be carried to extreme limits for c.w. reception by peaking the response sharply between, say, 800 and 1,000 c/s, the frequency range selected by most operators for telegraphy reception. The design of a filter for a pass band of only 100–200 c/s bandwidth on a.f. signals offers much less difficulty than at intermediate frequencies. An a.f. filter is effective in reducing interference to c.w. reception, but should not be regarded as a substitute for good i.f. selectivity for the following reasons: (i) it is unable to distinguish between the upper and lower sideband beat notes so cannot, in itself, provide true single-signal reception; (ii) being placed so late in the receiver, it does nothing to reduce the susceptibility of the receiver to blocking. A further disadvantage of a sharply peaked a.f. filter is that many operators find it fatiguing to listen for any length of a time to a single-tone note free of harmonics: where a similar degree of selectivity has been achieved in the i.f. stages, a.f. harmonics will usually be reintroduced in subsequent stages so that the peaking is not so noticeable.

An inductance/capacitance tuned circuit can be used as an a.f. filter but the inductor requires a special winding technique if a high Q is to be achieved. Many amateurs use an item of surplus equipment (the type FL8 filter) which is tuned to about 1,000 c/s.

By using frequency selective negative feedback and an extra valve it is possible to construct a sharply tuned filter requiring only preferred values of resistors and capacitors. **Fig. 43** shows one of the many possible arrangements. In the " off " position the first half of the double triode acts as an a.f. amplifier. With the filter " on," the second triode section is switched in series with the cathode of the first section, and provides considerable negative feedback, attenuating all frequencies other than a small band at about 1000 c/s—the precise frequency being determined by the constants of the R/C network between the anode of the first triode and the grid of the second triode.

The fatigue induced by tuned a.f. filters can be avoided by providing a sharp upper cut-off frequency, but with only a gradual attenuation curve for lower frequencies: this can be arranged using a standard choke or a.f. transformer as the inductive element. A typical arrangement is shown in Chapter 16 (*Mobile Equipment*).

In the section on Q multipliers, it was explained that a sharply peaked filter can be used either to provide a narrow response curve or arranged so that it results in a sharp rejection notch. This principle can be applied equally at a.f. and forms the basis of the " selectoject " (select or reject) filter.

Noise Limiters

The h.f. range, particularly above about 15 Mc/s, is susceptible to electrical interference from car ignition systems and electrical appliances using commutation, vibrating contacts or any other mechanism whereby electric sparks, no

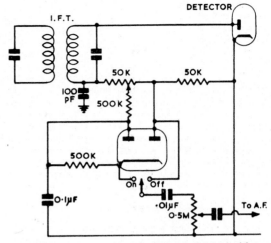

Fig. 46. This type of automatic noise limiter is most suited for a.m. telephony reception. The noise pulses provide fast-acting biasing pulses which cut off signal output during noise peaks.

provide a fast-acting biasing pulse used to reduce momentarily the receiver gain. During the period of the noise pulse, the output of the desired signal will also be reduced but this is of little practical consequence, since the ear is much less disturbed by " holes of silence " than by peaks of noise. A number of effective noise limiters of this type have been developed, and a typical circuit is shown in **Fig. 46.**

Unfortunately, since the noise pulses contain appreciable high-frequency components, the effect of passing these pulses through highly selective i.f. stages will be to distort the pulses, and this will render noise limiting much less effective on communications receivers than on a wideband receiver such as those used for television reception. To overcome this difficulty, noise limiting systems have been developed which derive the cut-off or blanking bias from noise pulses which have not passed through the receiver i.f. stages but are

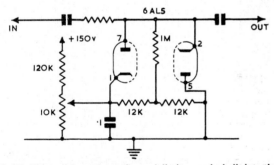

Fig. 45. This positive and negative peak limiter can be built into the receiver. The degree of limiting is determined by the setting of the 10K ohms potentiometer.

matter how minute, are created. The signals radiated—or carried along electric wiring—from such appliances are in the form of high amplitude, short duration pulses covering a wide range of frequencies. In many urban districts, these interference signals set a limit to the usable sensitivity of a receiver.

Because the interference peaks, though high, are of extremely short duration, a considerable improvement can be obtained by clipping or " slicing " all signals which are of appreciably greater amplitude than the desired signal: this can be done by relatively simple a.f. limiters as shown in **Figs. 44-45.** Alternatively the noise pulses can be used to

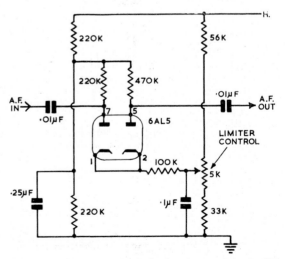

Fig. 47. Variable peak limiter suitable for all types of signals. This is an alternative arrangement of the type of limiter shown in Fig. 45.

97

received on a broad-band fixed tuned receiver: such systems however are fairly complex and to date have been used only in conjunction with elaborate factory-built equipment.

The commonly used series and shunt limiter of the Dickert type, whilst very effective on a.m. signals when following a diode signal detector, is not suitable for use on s.s.b. or c.w. nor to follow a detector of another type.

Separate demodulators are often employed for s.s.b./c.w. and a.m. and it is convenient to place a noise limiter in the audio input to the first a.f. amplifier. An arrangement which will permit the clipping of both negative and positive half cycles is shown in **Fig. 47**. This limiter is not an automatic following type but is manually adjusted by the panel mounted control. Correct operation of this control will be obtained by adjusting the values of the resistors on either side of the potentiometer so that all output is removed at the fully clockwise position.

POWER SUPPLIES

H.f. receivers for use in the home station are normally designed for operation from the supply mains, using a double-wound transformer to provide 6·3 or 12·6 volts a.c. for the valve heaters, and full-wave rectification to give an h.t. line of 200-250 volts. The current ratings will depend on the number of stages and the valves used, and it will be most advantageous to have available reasonable reserves for operation of associated external units such as pre-amplifiers and converters. The rectifier valve and mains transformer should be most generously rated to avoid excessive heating with continuous operation, particularly in the tropics.

Although it is the practice in most commercial designs to accommodate the power pack on the receiver chassis, it represents a major source of heat and can produce stray magnetic fields around the transformer and smoothing choke which can be the cause of hum. The home constructor who may not wish to incorporate accurate thermal compensation of oscillator circuits or magnetic screening will often find it a decided advantage to place the power pack in an entirely separate unit.

Apart from those stages for which closely regulated h.t. supplies are required (oscillators, mixer screen supplies), the actual value of h.t. is not critical. Provided the power pack is run well within its capabilities, sufficient regulation will usually be provided by the load imposed by the receiver. An h.t. rail of 150 or 200 volts, instead of the more common 250 volts can materially reduce heat generated in the receiver.

Heater voltage is more critical; poor performance or short valve life can often be traced to under- or over-running the heaters. Constructors should ensure that the heater voltage—*measured at the valveholders*—is within 5 per cent of the nominal voltage (that is, within the range 6-6·6 volts for a nominal 6·3 volt supply).

The circuits described in this chapter are intended for use with double-wound mains transformers, which completely isolate the chassis from the supply mains, with heaters connected in parallel and operating at 6·3 or 12·6 volts. Some economy is possible by using what is known as a.c./d.c. technique—widely employed in broadcast receivers—in which the mains transformer is omitted and the valve heaters connected in series. This is necessary for operation from d.c. mains, and is sometimes used in competitively-priced,

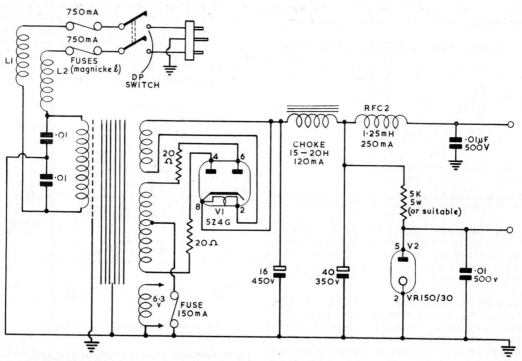

Fig. 48. Typical receiver power unit, incorporating refinements desirable with high-gain communications receivers.

r.f. stage, first mixer and crystal-controlled h.f. oscillator. This system avoids the difficulties of switching h.f. circuits and allows each unit to be designed for optimum performance on the particular band concerned; it is, however, a relatively expensive form of construction, amounting to a single-range receiver with a series of fixed-tuned converters. Some typical designs for the h.f. bands are described in Chapter 16.

Table 1 provides a guide to typical coil windings. For use with ganged circuits, care should be taken to wind coils as similar as possible; coils with adjustable cores permit accurate matching of inductances. Single-layer coils for the h.f. bands can easily be wound by hand; ready-made coils are also available.

Tuning Mechanisms

The tuning drive arrangements can make or mar the performance of a receiver, particularly on s.s.b. and c.w. signals. Points to consider are smooth continuous action and absence of backlash in the reduction gearing. Some operators find a moderately heavy flywheel action of assistance.

Assuming a total bandwidth of the order of 500 kc/s and a 180° tuning span, a reduction ratio of 100 : 1 would be needed to give a tuning rate of about 10 kc/s per revolution. This would generally be considered a good tuning rate, but where the receiver is intended primarily for c.w. or s.s.b. reception it may be advantageous to reduce the tuning rate still further, to around 5 kc/s or even 2·5 kc/s per revolution. With very low tuning rates it will be found advisable to fit a small handle to the tuning knob to facilitate tuning from one end of a band to the other. With receivers having a fairly high tuning rate (on many well-known models this may exceed 100 kc/s per revolution and considerably more on the 28 Mc/s band) it is sometimes possible to fit a further reduction drive on to the existing tuning spindle.

The knob with which tuning is normally done (the bandspread knob on a general coverage receiver) should have a fairly large diameter (at least 2 in.), to facilitate careful setting and should be mounted in the most convenient position for the operator.

A very suitable drive mechanism for incorporation in a home-built receiver is the Eddystone type 898.

Permeability Tuning

While it is the usual practice to tune h.f. circuits with a variable capacitor, it is equally possible to do this by varying the inductance by means of sliding cores. This system, known as permeability tuning, offers considerable advantages in the maintenance of correct L/C ratios and permits closer aerial input coupling. Since the screw principle can be adopted to alter the position of the cores it makes possible almost unlimited mechanical bandspread. Although permeability tuning has been most successfully used for many years by one major American company, the mechanical and electrical complications involved in band-switched receivers have resulted in little progress in this field by amateur constructors. There is considerable scope for further development of permeability tuning systems, particularly for covering single wave ranges, as for example in receivers with fixed tuned front-ends and tunable first i.f. ranges.

TABLE I

Guide to Coil Windings

Figures are given as a guide only and are based on a tuning capacitor with a maximum capacitance of 160 pF. The maximum frequency limit will depend largely on the value of stray capacitances, whilst such factors as closeness of turns, lengths of lead, position of dustcore (where used) will materially affect the frequency coverage. The reaction winding for t.r.f. receivers should be close to the lower end of the main winding. The aerial coupling coil, if of low impedance, should be wound over the earthy end of the main winding. If of medium impedance or for intervalve use, the coupling coil should be spaced a little way from the lower end of the main winding. Where an h.t. potential exists between windings, care should be taken to see that insulation is adequate. Small departures from the quoted wire gauge will not make any substantial difference. Generally, reaction and coupling windings can be moderately fine wire.
   The number of turns for intermediate ranges can be judged from the figures given.

| Diameter of former | Number of turns | | | | S.w.g. (main winding) | Approximate frequency range (Mc/s) | | Remarks |
	Main tuned winding	Low impedance aerial	Medium impedance aerial	Reaction		Minimum	Maximum	
1½ in. ribbed air-core	3	1	2	2	20	13·5	31	Turns spaced two wire diameters
	5	1	2 or 3	2 or 3	20	11·5	23	Turns spaced one wire diameter
	9	2	4	3	22	6·5	14	Slight spacing
	17	3	5	4	24	3·4	6·8	Close wound
	42	6	10	10	30	1·6	3·3	Close wound
⅞ in. Ribbed air-core	8	2	3	3	24	16	30	Close wound
	18	3	5	5	24/26	7	16	Close wound
	40	6	10	10	30	3·5	8	Close wound
⅝ in. dust-iron core	8	2	3	3	26	13·5	31	Close wound
	14	3	5	4	28	7·0	15	Close wound
	26	5	8	6	30	3·2	7	Close wound
	40	6	10	9	32	1·6	3·6	Slightly pile wound

Fixed Capacitors

Several different types of fixed capacitor are found in receivers, and it is important that the constructor should be aware of the uses and limitations of the various types. At one time capacitors fell conveniently into three main categories: paper capacitors for a.f. applications; mica capacitors for r.f. circuits; and electrolytic capacitors for smoothing.

While paper capacitors are still used for almost all a.f. circuits, several different forms of container are now available. The conventional waxed cardboard paper tubulars are still widely used, but should be avoided for any position where a very high insulation resistance is necessary. After a few years' use—and less in the tropics—the d.c. resistance of the cardboard container may amount to no more than about 5 Megohms. If used for inter-valve coupling this may result in a positive bias being applied to the succeeding valve. A low insulation resistance should also be avoided in a.g.c. circuits. To reduce insulation leakage many different types of containers have been introduced, including better forms of waxed-cardboard tubing and metal tubes with insulation seals at the ends.

Quite high a.c. voltage peaks may occur in a.f. stages and capacitors subjected to these voltages should be rated to withstand the peaks plus any direct voltage which may be across them. Capacitors subjected to continuous a.c. stress must always be rated specifically for a.c. working since an a.c. working voltage of 300V is roughly equivalent to a 1,000 volt d.c. rating. For such applications, petroleum jelly or liquid impregnants are better than wax.

When a fixed capacitor is used as part of a tuned circuit, for example to pad the oscillator circuit, it is essential to use a type of capacitor which introduces very little loss. Moulded mica capacitors can be used but the smaller size of silvered mica types have made these the normal choice. The silver coating is attached firmly to each side of the mica plates and the capacitance remains stable over very long periods; it is also possible to obtain this type to close tolerance.

Ceramic capacitors have taken over many of the tasks for which mica capacitors were formerly used, except where a very high order of stability is necessary. The various high-permittivity types are suitable and economical for r.f. or i.f. decoupling and similar purposes. Modern disc type ceramic capacitors are excellent for r.f. bypass applications, combining high capacitance in small space. Because they can often be mounted close to the valveholders or other main components, lead inductance can be kept extremely low.

With low-permittivity ceramic capacitors, use can be made of their sensitivity to temperature variations in order to provide compensation for changes in other component values as the receiver warms up. By using a capacitor with a negative temperature coefficient such as N750 (meaning 750 parts/million/degree Centigrade) to form a small part of the oscillator tuned circuit capacitance, frequency drift can be much reduced. It will usually be necessary to find the correct proportion of the tuned circuit capacitance which should be of the N750 type by experiment. A useful though somewhat expensive component for temperature compensation is the "Tempa-trimmer" which has a variable coefficient but fixed capacity.

Electrolytic capacitors are valuable where high capacitances (above about 1μF) are required. They are relatively inefficient for r.f. applications, and have a limited shelf-life. Care must be taken not to exceed the voltage ratings. Their main use is for ripple reduction in power supplies and for a.f. decoupling.

Where a capacitor forms part of a tuned circuit, close tolerance types—to about 1 per cent—may be needed. For most decoupling and interstage coupling applications, 10 or 20 per cent tolerance types may be fitted.

Resistors

Consideration must always be given to the power which will be dissipated in a resistor, in order that a component of ample wattage rating is fitted. Where little or no current flows through a resistor it is permissible to fit the miniature $\frac{1}{4}$-watt types, though some constructors prefer to keep to a minimum rating of $\frac{1}{2}$ watt. Where appreciable d.c. flows through a resistor (cathode bias, screen feeds, anode load, etc.), the power dissipated should be calculated ($I^2 \times R$, where I is in amperes and R in ohms) but no attempt should be made to fit a resistor likely to run near its wattage rating—always fit a generously rated component for reliable operation. A resistor operating near its wattage limit will run warm and successive heat cycles will tend to cause its resistance gradually to increase. Where the wattage dissipated exceeds about 1 watt it will be advisable to fit wire-wound resistors; otherwise the carbon composition type is generally suitable, though for a few applications where long-term stability is required cracked carbon types—available to tolerances of 1 per cent—may be preferable. Receiver resistors can usually be of 20 per cent tolerance, though for screen feeds and bias resistors it is advisable to fit 10 per cent types.

SUPERHET TRACKING AND ALIGNMENT

The superhet principle, as noted earlier, depends on the provision of a locally generated signal differing from the incoming signal frequency by an amount equal to the intermediate frequency. This local signal may be placed either higher or lower in frequency to the signal, though in practice the oscillator usually operates on the higher frequency side of the signal frequency to avoid difficulties from harmonics.

In simple superhet receivers, the tuning of the signal and local oscillator circuits can be carried out independently using separate variable capacitors. Clearly, this is inconvenient as the operator must continuously adjust two to more knobs when tuning across a waveband. It is usual therefore to fit a ganged variable capacitor with from two to four sections to tune together the oscillator and signal frequency circuits. From this arises the problem of so arranging the tuned circuits that the oscillator and signal frequency circuits *track* together (keep accurately in step) so that for all settings of the control knob the frequency difference between them stays nearly the same. For example, suppose the band 5000–8000 kc/s is to be covered on one waveband with an i.f. of 470 kc/s, the oscillator tracking on the high frequency side of the signal. Then it will be necessary for the oscillator to operate on 5470 kc/s when the set is tuned to 5000 kc/s and 8470 kc/s when tuned to 8000 kc/s. Furthermore the oscillator must track throughout the tuning span; so that, for example, the oscillator is on 6470 kc/s and 7470 kc/s when the set is tuned to 6000 kc/s and 7000 kc/s respectively. Unfortunately, because the resonant frequency of a tuned circuit depends on the square root of the product of the inductance and capacitance, it is not possible simply to reduce one of these factors in order to shift the oscillator tuning span to 5470–8470 kc/s. Both the L and C components must be reduced in the correct proportions. The inductance can be reduced by using fewer turns on the oscillator coil. The capacitance is usually reduced by including in series with the variable tuning capacitor a fixed or variable capacitor known as the *padding* capacitor: if there is no means of adjusting the coil it is usual to make the padding capacitor variable but with a coil having an adjustable core it is more common to use a fixed capacitor of fairly close tolerance. Typical values for padding capacitors in general coverage receivers are given in **Table 2**. With amateur-bands only receivers, it is generally unnecessary to use padders. The padding or coil variation has most influence on the lower frequency end of the tuning span.

To permit ready adjustment of the circuits on the higher frequency end of the tuning range, it is usual to connect small pre-set variable capacitors across the coils, known as *trimmers*. Typical arrangements are shown in Fig. 58 in Chapter 1.

Unfortunately, even with full padding and trimming adjustments, it is not possible to obtain exact tracking of the oscillator with the signal frequency circuits over the entire sweep of a ganged tuning control. The best compromise provides three frequencies—one towards each end of the tuning span and one fairly central position—where the signal frequency circuits will be precisely the i.f. away from the oscillator frequency, with some slight error having to be tolerated at all other positions. For instance, in the above example the circuits would be accurately trimmed at around 7750 kc/s and padded at about 5250 kc/s, and it would then be found that the third point of accurate alignment would be in the region of 6250 kc/s.

These unavoidable alignment errors are small but require some consideration for really high performance receivers. The errors can be minimized by keeping the total tuning span of each waveband as narrow as possible; the situation will be improved if the amateur bands coincide with the accurately tuned portions. Because of this, despite the added complications in the coil assembly, it is preferable that a general coverage receiver should have as many wavebands as possible. In receivers which tune the amateur-bands-only the alignment errors can be kept to a very low figure. Furthermore, it is possible in such sets to overcome the whole problem of tracking by making the signal frequency circuits sufficiently broad-band to provide adequate response at least over the higher frequency bands without retuning; this allows the

entire tuning to be carried out on a single small variable capacitor in the oscillator circuit.

For general coverage receivers, the calculation of the correct coil windings to permit accurate tracking is of some difficulty. This is mainly because the average constructor is seldom able to measure exactly the inductance of hand-wound coils or the various stray wiring capacitances which play an important role in determining the tuning range. Although surprisingly good results can be achieved by intelligent guesswork, there is little doubt that the difficulties encountered in this section of superhet receiver design have been the main reason why so many amateurs use factory-built sets. One solution is the use of the complete tuning units or coil packs, available from a number of manufacturers; another is to follow published designs in which full coil winding data is given. Yet another approach has already been suggested: the construction of amateur-bands-only models with broadly tuned signal frequency circuits or with signal-frequency and oscillator circuits tuned independently (this is much less inconvenient than on a general coverage model, as the adjustment of the signal frequency control can generally be limited to a final touching up on a signal). From almost all viewpoints, the amateur-bands-only approach can be recommended.

A most useful instrument for the preliminary adjustment of the tuned circuits of a receiver is the grid dip oscillator (see Chapter 19) which permits rough checks to be made on the tuned circuits of a receiver during actual construction.

Spurious Responses

One of the most important criteria of a superhet receiver is the presence, or absence, of spurious signals. These spurious responses take three main forms: (i) external signals which cannot be tuned out; (ii) external signals heard on frequencies other than those on which they are operating; (iii) continuous carriers heard in the tuning range of the receiver but which are caused by internal oscillators.

Type (i) is almost invariably due to breakthrough of signals into the i.f. stages, though in a double superhet having a tunable first i.f. such breakthrough will provide tunable signals of type (ii). I.f. breakthrough is generally caused by insufficient pre-mixer selectivity, and in this form is usually troublesome only on receivers having no r.f. stage; it can be reduced by series- or parallel-tuned circuits at the i.f. connected as wave-traps to reject the interfering signals. A more serious form of i.f. breakthrough is direct pick-up of signals in the i.f. stages, and this tends to be more likely with receivers having i.f. of 1600 kc/s or above. More efficient screening of the i.f. stages may be needed, with care taken to minimize stray coupling to external wires such as power leads, aerial, etc. In some cases, where particularly strong local signals are involved, it may be necessary to change the i.f. slightly. Breakthrough of signals can sometimes be difficult to eradicate where a converter is used ahead of a main receiver which picks up signals in the r.f. stages or in the interconnection leads. (Additional advice on preventing breakthrough when using a converter is given in Chapter 5.) It should be noted that signals breaking through need not always be at the i.f.; very strong signals at half the i.f. can occasionally prove troublesome, the non-linearity of the mixer causing spurious signals to appear.

The most common form of type (ii) interference is second channel or image interference, discussed elsewhere. The

TABLE 2

Guide to Values of Padding Capacitors
for General Coverage Receivers

Signal frequency range	Approximate maximum capacity of tuning capacitor	Intermediate frequency	Value of oscillator padder
13 to 30 Mc/s	200 pF	450/465 kc/s	3,000 pF
6 to 13 Mc/s	to		2,000 pF
3 to 6 Mc/s	220 pF		1,425 pF
1·5 to 3 Mc/s			650 pF
10 to 30 Mc/s			3,625 pF
3·5 to 10 Mc/s	360 pF	450/465 kc/s	2,825 pF
1·4 to 4 Mc/s			1,050 pF
12·5 to 32 Mc/s		1600/1620 kc/s	2,100 pF
4·5 to 12·5 Mc/s	360 pF		960 pF
1·7 to 4·5 Mc/s			380 pF

susceptibility of a receiver to this form of interference is a function of the intermediate frequency used and the degree of pre-mixer selectivity. Where less than two r.f. stages are used, an important consideration is to maintain the Q of the input circuits. Image response is, however, only one of the many causes of this type of interference. The harmonics of the h.f. oscillator may beat against strong incoming signals; strong incoming signals may themselves act as the h.f. oscillator and beat against other strong signals. When considering extremely strong signals such as those from a nearby transmitter, there are many possible spurious responses arising from combinations of the fundamental and harmonics of both the local station and the receiver's h.f. oscillator, many with associated image responses. In practice, however, except for the station transmitter, spurious responses of these types can be reduced to insignificance by good pre-mixer selectivity and a high i.f., provided that in so doing cross-modulation effects are not introduced.

Interference of type (iii), generally termed *birdies*, is of great importance in double superhets where unless extreme care is taken harmonics of the second oscillator—or image responses to these—are likely to appear in one or more waveranges of the receiver. For general coverage receivers, the only solution is most careful design and screening of the second oscillator to reduce harmonic generation. With amateur-bands-only receivers, particularly those using a tunable first i.f., careful analysis of possible harmonic interference can be useful in determining a suitable first i.f.

Harmonics of the b.f.o./c.i.o. can cause similar spurious responses, but because of the lower frequencies involved, these can usually be reduced to an insignificant level by screening.

Because of the difficulty of eliminating all spurious responses in double- and triple-conversion receivers, some designers believe that the ideal amateur receiver would be a single-conversion superhet with a high intermediate frequency—but this would depend upon the development of high i.f. filters with a degree of selectivity at present available only in receivers having a low i.f.

Smooth Regeneration

To obtain maximum benefit from regenerative detectors both for superhets and for " straight " receivers, it is essential to obtain smooth control as the stage goes in and out of oscillation. In some cases it may be found that the valve tends to plop in and out of oscillation, and the control cannot be advanced right up to the threshold of oscillation. The following are among the main causes of " ploppy " regeneration: too many turns on the feedback coil (this should have the minimum possible number of turns coupled tightly to the earthy end of the grid coil); the value of grid leak resistor may be incorrect (try the effect of different values, usually in a higher value direction); the anode and/or screen voltages may be too high, or derived from too high an impedance source (since the valve current conditions change during oscillation, screen voltages should be derived from a potentiometer network and high series feed resistors avoided); with straight receivers having the detector stage coupled directly to the aerial, it may be necessary to reduce aerial coupling by means of a series trimmer to avoid heavy loading at aerial resonances.

Another effect, known as *squegging*, can cause poor control of regeneration; this is due to too-violent oscillation and attention to the above points will usually cure this condition also. Poor decoupling of r.f. circuits can produce what is known as *threshold howl* denoted by an a.f. howl just as the valve goes into oscillation; the remedy here is to improve the decoupling—this effect is unlikely to occur with resistance-coupled stages.

In all regenerative circuits depending on positive feedback by induction, the correct " sense " of connection of the grid and feedback windings must be observed: the sense of the windings should be the same for " grid to earth " as " h.t. to anode."

OPERATING THE RECEIVER

To obtain the optimum performance from a communications receiver, whether simple or complex, requires practice and a regard to fundamental technical principles. No two receivers are exactly the same, but some operating hints are generally applicable. Typical controls are shown in **Fig. 52.**

Unless the receiver has an extremely slow tuning rate it will be necessary to develop a delicate touch when tuning weak signals on the higher frequency bands. This will be greatly aided by a smooth-acting slow motion drive having a large reduction ratio. Particularly on c.w., it is important to tune signals carefully, when first heard, for maximum strength and minimum interference, to forestall the sudden appearance of an interfering signal. Maximum use should be made of any crystal filter, as described later.

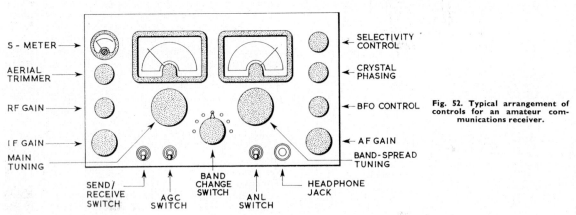

Fig. 52. Typical arrangement of controls for an amateur communications receiver.

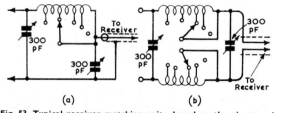

Fig. 53. Typical receiver matching units, based on the pi-network. (a) unbalanced; (b) balanced. Since the impedance transformation is not usually as great as in transmitter output networks, capacitor values can generally be 150 - 300 pF. Suggested winding details for the coils: 25 turns of 28 s.w.g. enamelled copper wire wound on 1 in. diameter, former to occupy a space of approximately 1 in. and tapped at 2, 5, 8, 12 and 19 turns.

If the receiver has separate controls for a.f., i.f. and r.f. gain (often a single control—sometimes with differing tapers —is used for i.f. and r.f. gain), the relative settings of these controls influence the apparent signal-to-noise ratio of the weaker signals. Clearly, if the r.f. gain control is near minimum setting while the other controls are well advanced, most of the gain of the receiver will be after the first frequency changer and there will be almost maximum amplification of the unavoidable noise produced in this stage. On the other hand, if the r.f. gain is always kept at a maximum, the signal-to-noise ratio will be optimum, but there is a greater risk of cross-modulation effects on the stronger signals. Generally therefore the a.f. gain control should be set at about half-travel, the r.f. gain fairly well advanced, and the level of signal or inter-station noise when searching kept under constant control by means of the i.f. gain. In the neighbourhood of strong signals the r.f. gain should be reduced. On c.w. and s.s.b. signals it may be desirable to keep r.f./i.f. gain fairly low to increase the effectiveness of the b.f.o. but when listening to telephony stations with the a.g.c. switched on, the r.f. and i.f. gains should be well advanced, and the a.f. control suitably adjusted.

The receiver noise should always be peaked with the aerial trimmer when first switching to a band. It should not be necessary to re-adjust this trimmer on individual stations.

Consideration should always be given to ensuring a reasonably good match between the aerial input circuit and the aerial or transmission line. Most factory-built receivers are designed for use with an input impedance of about 400 ohms or alternatively low-impedance 80 ohm coaxial cable. If the actual aerial impedance differs appreciably from the design figure, a worth-while improvement in signal-to-noise ratio can be obtained by the use of an aerial matching unit (see **Fig. 53**), using the principles described in the section on h.f. aerials. It should always be remembered that any additional gain which can be achieved in the aerial input circuit is free of valve noise.

On most receivers, the a.g.c. (a.v.c.) switch must be turned off for c.w. and s.s.b. reception to prevent the sensitivity being reduced by the action of the b.f.o.

C.W. Reception with a Single Crystal Filter

Although amateurs played an important role in the development and application of crystal filters their use is not always popular, especially among operators who have not grasped fully the technical principles involved. Such operators complain that when interference occurs, they switch in the crystal filter only to lose the required station because of a considerable reduction of strength. A correctly adjusted filter should not reduce the strength of the signal by any large amount but rather should result in considerable improvement of the signal-to-noise ratio. The reason why some users complain of serious loss of strength is almost always because the b.f.o. control has not been correctly set in advance; this has meant that the station is not accurately tuned in when the crystal is switched into circuit; the loss of strength in such circumstances is really an indication that the crystal is doing its intended job of narrowing the pass band of the receiver.

It is essential with a filter using a single crystal that the b.f.o. pitch control should not be used—as described for s.s.b. reception—as a form of fine tuning control, but should be set in advance to a frequency some 500 or 1000 c/s higher or lower than the crystal frequency. It should then be varied only when a change in the output note is required.

The importance of this stems from the following: suppose the b.f.o. has been set, say, 5000 c/s from the crystal or intermediate frequency but a signal is then tuned in to provide a convenient listening beat note of 1000 c/s. This means that the incoming carrier is either 4000 or 6000 c/s off the frequency to which the set is actually tuned. This may not be of great consequence with the receiver operating in a position of minimum selectivity, but immediately the pass band is narrowed by switching in the crystal, the signal will be greatly attenuated: in order to tune it in correctly it would be necessary to readjust *both* the tuning and the pitch control; in practice the signal is often lost altogether.

Compare this with what happens when the b.f.o. has been correctly set in advance 1000 c/s off the nominal i.f. When the set is tuned, even in a position of broad selectivity, to provide a beat note of 1000 c/s, the signal will either be precisely tuned to the centre of the pass band, or to a position 2000 c/s away: switching in the crystal will thus have much less effect on its strength, either it remains exactly tuned, or at worst it will be on the wrong side of the beat note and can be retuned by adjusting only the tuning control.

To set the b.f.o. control, the phasing control should be positioned at about mid-travel, and, with the b.f.o. turned " off," a steady carrier carefully tuned in to give maximum S-meter reading (or maximum noise output if there is no meter). The b.f.o. is then turned " on " and set first to zero beat with the carrier to ensure that this coincides approximately with mid-travel of the pitch control (if this is not possible, the b.f.o. trimmer may need adjustment), and then further adjusted to provide the beat note most acceptable to the particular operator—usually between 500 and 1000 c/s though a few operators prefer a much lower pitched note. This setting of the b.f.o. should be carefully noted, and normally the control not touched again, all signals being carefully tuned by means of the tuning control for maximum output. An interfering heterodyne note appearing in the pass band can be eliminated by adjustment of the phasing control, the effect of which is to move slightly the very sharp rejection notch produced by the parallel resonance of the crystal.

A sharply peaked crystal filter may cause all stable c.w. signals to " ring " slightly and produce a hollow bell-like note which, if too pronounced, can make a signal difficult to read. If a variable selectivity control is fitted, the effect can usually be overcome by reducing the selectivity slightly.

Reception of Suppressed-carrier Signals

Amateur telephony stations using either single- or double-sideband suppressed-carrier modulation systems are regularly active on almost all the h.f. bands. These transmissions when received on a set operated as for normal a.m. telephony are completely unintelligible, producing a noise which has been likened to Donald Duck speaking on an extremely badly adjusted transmitter.

In order to render these signals intelligible it is necessary to re-insert the missing carrier to an accuracy of the order of about 25 c/s or so for distortion-free reception. This can be done on any good communications receiver either by using the beat frequency oscillator to provide the " carrier " or, preferably, by means of a carrier insertion oscillator which is normally crystal-controlled.

The elegant method of receiving s.s.b. signals is to use a high-selectivity receiver (bandwidth 2–3 kc/s), having a good shape factor, with a crystal-controlled c.i.o. carefully pre-adjusted so that an injected carrier of adequate strength is correctly placed at the edge of the receiver pass band, on the appropriate side of the passband for upper or lower sideband reception. In these circumstances, and provided that the receiver has a really slow tuning rate and is highly stable, it is no more difficult to tune s.s.b. stations than normal a.m. signals: when the receiver is tuned for maximum response to the signal the injected carrier will automatically be within a few cycles of the correct frequency, and a slight final adjustment to the tuning control can then be made until the speech sounds natural and with its correct harmonic relationships.

However, many amateurs do not have available receivers fulfilling the above, very stringent, requirements—met only by the best modern receivers—but wish to listen to s.s.b. signals on older or simpler receivers. This is almost always possible, although it may be found that if the stability of the b.f.o. or—more likely—the h.f. oscillator is deficient, the set may have to be frequently adjusted to prevent the signals from becoming distorted. If the b.f.o. injection is weak, the r.f./i.f. gain should be kept low as otherwise the transmission may sound as though it were an over-modulated a.m. signal, the sidebands being too strong for the carrier.

Assuming that the receiver is reasonably stable but that the tuning rate is too great to permit direct tuning of the signal, the following procedure can be adopted:

(i) The receiver a.g.c. should be switched off.

(ii) The receiver should be tuned until the unintelligible sideband modulation is heard at maximum strength.

(iii) The a.f. gain should be advanced to maximum and the r.f./i.f. gain turned down.

(iv) The b.f.o. should then be switched on.

(v) Leaving the tuning unaltered, the b.f.o. control should be carefully rotated until the speech becomes clear. Once the s.s.b. signal has been resolved, the receiver may be used for other signals without further adjustment of the b.f.o.

Until the final adjustment of the b.f.o. the signals will remain unintelligible. When the adjustment is nearly but not quite correct the speech can be understood but will sound either low or high pitched.

The reception of single sideband and double sideband suppressed carrier signals is considered further in Chapter 10.

MAINTENANCE AND FAULT-FINDING

A difficult problem for an amateur operator is knowing whether his receiver is providing the optimum performance of which it is capable. Valve or component deterioration or the gradual drifting out of alignment of the tuned circuits may degrade performance to a marked extent before the user becomes aware of it, poor results being attributed to the vagaries of h.f. propagation conditions. It should be appreciated that, no matter how well constructed, receivers containing up to 20 valves are certain to require occasional servicing attention.

In a multi-valve receiver, the failure of one or two stages to contribute their full quota of gain may remain unnoticed because of the considerable reserve of gain usually available in such sets yet, especially where the fault lies in an early stage, this may result in serious degrading of the signal-to-noise ratio. There is no simple answer to this problem. Few amateurs have available the laboratory-type instruments necessary to measure h.f. receiver performance to the degree of accuracy required to show up only slight deterioration. In practice, it is by no means unusual for a long spell of disappointing activity on the higher frequency bands to be traced finally to an unsuspected receiver or aerial fault. There are almost certainly many receivers in use which could be greatly improved by careful re-alignment, by replacement of leaky decoupling capacitors or by the substitution of new valves, either the same type or one of the newer low-noise types, though the latter should only be undertaken by those with the requisite knowledge.

An operator should always endeavour to memorize the true " feel " of a receiver when it is working well, so that any later deterioration can be more readily noticed. It is useful also to keep under observation the results being achieved by other amateurs (noting the RST reports they give is not always a good basis for this—better to observe how much difficulty they have in copying weak signals). The selectivity characteristics of a receiver can be kept fairly accurately under review by noting its single-signal capabilities on c.w. signals or the degree of ringing on a single crystal filter. A simple test for sensitivity is described on page 79.

Valve deterioration can often be readily checked by direct substitution of known good valves, though this can sometimes be an uncertain guide because of the need in some stages for slight retrimming to compensate for differences in inter-electrode capacitances when changing valves.

An occasional routine check of the voltages applied to the valve sockets of each stage is most useful, not only for locating actual faults but also for bringing to light gradual changes in valve currents and component values. For maximum usefulness such checks should always be carried out on the same testmeter (preferably of at least 1,000 ohms per volt sensitivity or better still 10,000 or 20,000 ohms per volt) to eliminate the effect on the readings of the current drawn by the meter. It is good practice to note the readings each time into an equipment record book. Most receiver manufacturers issue service information listing typical valve voltages to be expected with meters of defined sensitivity, but it is better to prepare a table of measured voltages for the individual receiver, and to check these from time to time. As the valves age, there will inevitably be some slight changes (of the order of 10 per cent) which can be safely disregarded. Watch should be kept for the fairly pronounced changes which would indicate that a valve is becoming " soft," or its emission failing, or it is otherwise reaching the end of its useful life. Measurement of valve voltages will also help pinpoint such common faults as the gradual increase in value of feed resistors carrying d.c., leakage of decoupling capacitors, high-resistance joints and the like.

To trace the more obsure faults—or those of an intermittent nature—may require considerable patience and some knowledge of radio servicing techniques—many of which are basically applied common sense and a knowledge of Ohm's Law. Because an amateur is seldom so concerned with the time factor as a professional service engineer, it is usually possible for him to trace eventually even the most difficult faults, with the aid of only a testmeter and a small supply of substitute components: the amateur with experience of constructional work soon develops the necessary flair for faulttracing.

Re-alignment

The performance of a receiver is governed to a great extent by the accuracy with which the various tuned circuits in the i.f. and r.f. stages are aligned. In all equipment there is the tendency for such circuits to drift gradually off-tune so that in time re-alignment becomes necessary. The first indication of poor i.f. alignment of a communications receiver is usually a marked reduction in the effectiveness of a crystal filter. Fortunately, modern first-grade components—particularly i.f. transformers and air-spaced trimmers—are extremely stable, and in normal circumstances only minor re-alignment is likely to be needed, usually only to take account of variations in valve inter-electrode capacitances when replacing valves. The performance of older receivers, however, can often be substantially improved by regular re-alignment, particularly where the receiver is subjected to vibration or excessive humidity.

There are two approaches to the problem of re-alignment (or three if one includes taking the set to a good service engineer with experience of communications receivers).

Most manufacturers issue detailed instructions on the alignment procedure recommended for the model concerned, listing such important matters as the correct i.f. and r.f. alignment frequencies, order of adjustment and the layout of the various trimmers and cores. To carry out these procedures generally requires access to at least a reasonably good signal generator, output meter and a supply of non-metallic tools for adjustment of trimmers and cores.

The other approach needs only a keen ear, a few trimming tools, and—vitally important—a clear knowledge of what should and should not be attempted. Remarkably good results can be achieved following this empirical method. But injudicious, haphazard or excessive adjustments can quickly and completely desensitize a receiver so that it can only be made to work again by a full re-alignment carried out with proper servicing equipment. The amateur who is capable of benefiting from this technique should need no guidance; those who do should never attempt to use it.

A useful accessory when checking the accuracy of the r.f. alignment of receivers having accessible air-cored coils, without requiring the alteration of trimmers, consists of an insulated non-metallic rod about 6 in. long with a small piece of dust-iron or ferrite core material fastened at one end of the rod and a similar small piece of brass at the other. When the brass end is inserted into an h.f. coil it will lower the effective inductance; whereas inserting the dust-iron end will increase the inductance. This device (often called a *tuning wand*) can be used to check alignment at various points on a waveband by noting the effect on a signal when the rod is gradually inserted. If the r.f. circuit is correctly adjusted, inserting either end of the rod will reduce the signal. On the other hand if the circuit

is slightly off-tune, the signal can be peaked when inserting one or other end of the rod, depending on whether the circuit is tuned to the high or low frequency side of the signal. This device, unfortunately, cannot always be used on modern receivers, as these often have coils with variable cores which prevent the rod from being inserted.

PRACTICAL DESIGNS

For a number of years amateurs have tended to use factory-built h.f. communications receivers, either those designed specifically for amateur or commercial work, or modified ex-Government receivers manufactured during World War 2. Recently, however, there has been a marked revival of interest in home-construction, particularly of receivers of advanced, modern design. One reason for this is economic: the factory production of high-performance receivers to the most stringent modern requirements (and with the wide flexibility needed to cater for the differing interests of a large number of users) is inevitably costly, and the price of such models is often some hundreds of pounds. On the other hand, the experienced constructor who is prepared to spend considerable time and effort can often construct extremely good receivers for a much more modest sum.

The newcomer to receiver construction is advised to gain experience before tackling an advanced, full-specification receiver, unless skilled assistance is readily available. There is no better way of gaining a sound knowledge of receiver theory and practice than by tackling several designs of a relatively simple nature. A straight (t.r.f.) two- or three-valve receiver will teach the builder much about components, wiring and layout, careful adjustment of regeneration and the like. A simple superhet is invaluable for making clear the problems of i.f. and r.f. alignment and the reduction of spurious images. Once basic experience has been gained, much more ambitious receivers can be tackled with every confidence, even by amateurs having available only a minimum of test equipment; this is especially true if the r.f. coil unit is obtained as a complete assembly or alternatively if plug-in coils are used.

Even if a factory-built receiver is used, there is usually no reason why it should not be improved, or made more suitable for the particular interests of the user; for example, ex-Government receivers such as the R1155, R107, CR100, BC342, BC348 and the Command series (BC453/4/5) or the more-esteemed HRO, Super Pro, SX28 and AR88 models. The performance of the simpler models can be improved greatly by fitting an external pre-amplifier, Q multiplier or crystal filter, S meter and calibration oscillator, while even the best receiver can be improved by an efficient aerial matching unit. It is possible to extend the tuning range and improve performance on the higher frequency bands by means of a modern converter. High-performance converters can be built in a few evenings and yet can show the constructor almost as much about the principles and problems of superhet design as a complete receiver.

Many of the older receivers use r.f. and mixer valves which are relatively noisy by modern standards. The sensitivity of such receivers can be greatly improved by the use of a low-noise converter or by modifying the front-end of the receiver.

A set which is deficient in selectivity may be improved by adding an external unit, comprising a second frequency changer followed by an 85–100 kc/s i.f. section (a device often

A rear view of the t.r.f. receiver. The components may be identified by reference to Fig. 55 (b).

generally uses telephony. Those who work mainly on 1·8 and 3·5 Mc/s (where site noise levels are likely to be high) will not worry so much about extreme sensitivity as the 21 or 28 Mc/s enthusiast.

This is not to suggest that one should rush into tampering haphazardly with a complex receiver of modern design; but there is often no reason why new ideas should not be tried—particularly where they take the form of an external unit. Useful devices are regularly described in Amateur Radio magazines. It is important that the amateur should not be content to regard any receiver as a " black box " labelled " NOT TO BE OPENED."

For those who want to build a receiver, but do not wish to spend too much time on shopping for components, complete kits with step-by-step construction manuals are available.

A SIMPLE T.R.F. RECEIVER

The straight 1–V–1 (a traditional way of indicating a receiver having one stage of r.f. amplification, detector, and one stage of a.f. amplification) can still form an effective receiver for the listener and amateur provided that its fundamental limitations are recognized. These include an inherent lack of selectivity which becomes progressively worse with increasing frequency and the inability to resolve weak modulated signals. But, particularly on the lower frequency bands such as 1·8 and 3·5 Mc/s, it can compete with all but the best superhets in the realm of c.w. reception so long as extreme selectivity is not a first requirement.

The circuit of a simple receiver of this type, built by G3NGS to a design by G8TL, is shown in **Fig. 54**.

The circuit has three stages: a variable-mu pentode as r.f. amplifier and two triodes, contained in the same valve envelope, as regenerative detector and a.f. amplifier.

The signal picked up by the aerial is transformer-coupled to the first tuned circuit consisting of the secondary of L_1 and the tuning capacitor C_1 and applied to the control grid of V_1, the r.f. amplifier valve. After amplification the signal is fed via the untuned primary of L_2 and its associated tuned secondary to the coupling capacitor C_7 and so to the grid of

referred to as a Q5'er) using, if desired, the BC453 Command receiver for this purpose or alternatively an outboard i.f. amplifier with a half-lattice crystal filter. A *Q* multiplier can also be used to improve selectivity.

For c.w. reception it may be possible to improve results by fitting an audio filter or selectoject type of arrangement.

The keen amateur never takes the design of even an expensive receiver too much for granted. All receivers turned out on an assembly line are essentially a matter of compromise, whereas the individual amateur tends to specialize in his interests. The c.w. operator will have very different ideas on what constitutes an ideal receiver to the operator who

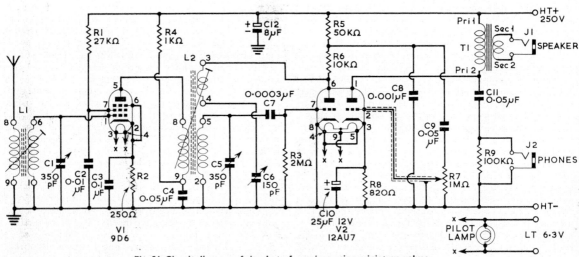

Fig. 54. Circuit diagram of simple t.r.f. receiver using miniature valves.

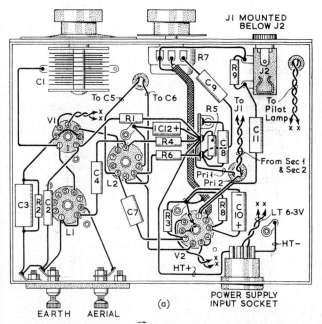

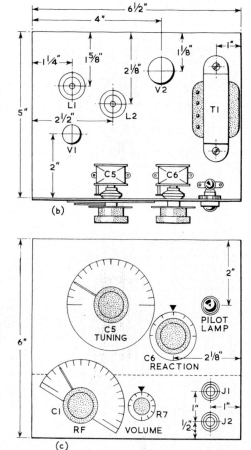

J1 MOUNTED BELOW J2

POWER SUPPLY INPUT SOCKET

EARTH   AERIAL   (a)

(b)

(c)

Fig. 55. Wiring and layout diagrams of the simple t.r.f. receiver. (a) Under-chassis layout of the components showing point-to-point wiring. (b) Above-chassis layout of components. (c) Arrangement of the controls on the front panel.

the detector V_{2a}. It will be observed that a third winding (connections 3 and 4) is included in the L_2 assembly and wired from the anode of V_{2a} via the variable capacitor C_6 to earth. This third winding is closely coupled to the grid coil (connections 5 and 2) to provide regeneration or reaction. Regeneration increases the sensitivity of V_{2a} as a detector and if increased far enough causes the valve to oscillate. The amount of regeneration or reaction is controlled by the variable capacitor C_6. For phone work it is best to set the control just below the point where oscillation begins but for the reception of c.w. (telegraphy) signals C_6 should be advanced to the point where it just begins to oscillate. This point will be marked by a faint " rushing " sound in the headphones or loudspeaker. No advantage will be gained by increasing the amount of regeneration beyond this point. R_6 acts as an r.f. load in the anode circuit of V_{2a} for regeneration.

The audio signal from the detector is built up across the load resistor R_5 and fed via C_9 to the volume (or gain) control R_7. The slider of this control (the centre terminal) is connected to the grid of V_{2b} which functions as an audio amplifier to raise the level of the signal sufficiently to drive a small loudspeaker or headphones. Bias for this valve is developed by the flow of current through R_8 in a similar manner to the bias for V_1. The amplified audio signal is fed to the loudspeaker by transformer T_1 which provides the necessary match for a low impedance (3 ohms) voice coil. The use of headphones is made possible by feeding the audio signal through C_{11} to the jack socket J_2.

The complete receiver, with the exception of the power supply, can be built on an aluminium chassis measuring $6\frac{1}{2}$ in. $\times$ 5 in. $\times$ 2 in. fitted with a front panel 6 in. high, though the dimensions are by no means critical.

Supplies to the valve heaters should be connected with twisted heavy gauge wire to reduce hum and potential drop. One side of the heater line may be earthed at the power input socket or, if hum is prevalent, a " humdinger " should be fitted. This consists of a low-value potentiometer (about 50 ohms) with the outer two contacts connected across the heater line and the centre contact (slider) earthed. The slider should be moved around the centre of its travel until a minimum of hum is found. The potentiometer should then be left at this setting.

Component layout is not critical so long as interstage wiring is short and direct. The radio frequency amplifier (V_1 and its associated components) should be well screened from the following stages to lessen the chance of feedback. For the same reason C_1 should be mounted sub-chassis and C_5 above chassis level. The only other components above the chassis are the speaker transformer T_1 and the reaction control C_6. Miniature slow-motion drives should be fitted to C_5 and C_6 to ease the tuning in of weak signals.

Fig. 55(a) shows the underchassis layout and provides a point-to-point wiring diagram. The placement of parts above chassis is shown in **Fig. 55(b)** and the front panel layout in **Fig. 55(c)**.

The power requirements of the receiver are very small and a power pack giving 6 volts at 1 amp and 250 volts at 30

COMPONENTS TABLE FOR FIG. 54

$C_{1,5}$	350 pF air-spaced variable capacitor (Jackson Bros. (London) Ltd., U-type miniature)
C_2	0·01 μF 350 volt working capacitor (Dubilier)
C_3	0·1 μF 200 volt working capacitor (Dubilier)
$C_{4, 9, 11}$	0·05 μF 350 volt working capacitor (Dubilier)
C_6	160 pF air-spaced variable capacitor (Jackson Bros. (London) Ltd.)
C_7	0·0003 μF silver mica capacitor (Dubilier)
C_8	0·001 μF 350 volt working capacitor (Dubilier)
C_{10}	25 μF 12 volt electrolytic capacitor (Dubilier)
C_{12}	8 μF 350 volt electrolytic capacitor (Dubilier)
L_1	Maxi-Q miniature coil (blue) for range desired (Denco (Clacton) Ltd.). Screening can supplied with coils.
L_2	Maxi-Q miniature coil (green) for range desired (Denco (Clacton) Ltd.). Screening can supplied with coils.
R_1	27 K ohms ½ watt (Dubilier)
R_2	250 ohms ½ watt (Dubilier)
R_3	2 Megohms ¼ watt (Dubilier)
R_4	1 K ohm ½ watt (Dubilier)
R_5	50 K ohms ½ watt (Dubilier)
R_6	10 K ohms ½ watt (Dubilier)
R_7	1 Megohm potentiometer with switch (Dubilier)
R_8	820 ohms 1 watt (Dubilier)
R_9	100 K ohms ¼ watt (Dubilier)

Miscellaneous

T_1	output transformer for speaker
2	Noval valve bases for coils (McMurdo XM9/UC1)
1	dial lamp (Bulgin D170 or similar)
2	phone jacks (Bulgin type J2)
1	9D6 valve (Brimar)
1	12AU7 valve (Brimar)
2	terminals (aerial and earth) (Bulgin)
2	knobs with skirts (Bulgin K401 and K405)
2	knobs (Bulgin K400 and K410)
1	six-way connector (Bulgin P149)
6	solder tags (Bulgin T17)
1	Noval valve base for V_2 with screening can (McMurdo XM9/UC1)
1	B7G valve base for V_1 with screening can (McMurdo XM7/UC1)
2	slow motion epicyclic 6 : 1 drives for C_5 and C_6 (Jackson Cat. No. 4511)

milliamps will be found to be quite adequate. The live side of the mains may be brought into the set via the six-pin plug, taken through the switch on the volume control (R_7), and taken out again to the primary of the mains transformer.

Before switching on for the first time, it is a good practice to check for any short across the h.t. terminals as this can cause serious damage to the power pack. If, on switching on, R_5 and R_6 heat up, check that C_6 is not bent or shorted with metal filings. If the set does not function after ample time for warming up, check that the coils have the same number and are inserted correctly.

A list of components is shown in the accompanying table together with the names of manufacturers of suitable items. There is, however, no reason why electrically equivalent parts of other makes should not be used.

Simple Superhet Receivers

Two and three valve " straight " receivers can still provide acceptable results for c.w. reception on the lower frequency bands, but require most careful adjustment and operation if tolerable selectivity is to be obtained on the higher frequency bands. This is especially true if the receiver is required for two-way working as opposed to general listening where it normally matters less if stations are at times blocked out by adjacent channel interference. For serious operation throughout the h.f. spectrum (or for use in conjunction with a v.h.f. converter), it is practically essential to use a superhet design in which both high gain and good selectivity are obtained at a relatively low radio frequency.

For the home constructor, a first h.f. superhet represents an important milestone. This is not so much because of any inherently greater complexity in its construction; indeed a simple superhet may contain appreciably less components

and require less careful screening than would a good t.r.f. receiver. Rather it is because in the construction of a superhet, the basic assembling and wiring represents only the first parts of the complete work; almost as much effort and as much skill may be required in the adjustment of the tuned circuits and the calibration of the receiver.

With a superhet one may complete the set absolutely correctly and yet be unable to receive any signals at all until a certain stage in the alignment is reached. This presents considerable difficulties to the constructor who does not have access to an adjustable calibrated oscillator of the signal generator or grid dip type and who has therefore to rely on " blind " adjustment of the circuits. It must be stressed that the complete alignment of a complex single or double conversion superhet receiver without an adjustable oscillator can be a difficult operation calling for considerable patience and not a little luck. Where any form of calibrated oscillator covering the i.f. and/or h.f. ranges is available the difficulties are greatly reduced.

TWO VALVE SUPERHET

To gain a working knowledge of superhet principles and to provide a stepping stone for more advanced designs, there is much to be said for constructing a simple superhet, especially if this is designed to offer the minimum alignment problems. **Fig. 56** based on a design by F8JD is typical of the simplest form of what have been termed " super-gainer " receivers. In this type of superhet there is no valve acting as an i.f. amplifier, but this deficiency is largely compensated for by the use of a high gain regenerative detector tuned to the intermediate frequency. The model shown comprises two ECF82 (6U8) triode-pentode valves. The first valve is used as a frequency changer (the pentode section, V_{1a}, as the mixer and the triode section, V_{1b}, as the h.f. oscillator). The pentode section of the second valve, V_{2a}, acts as a regenerative detector while the triode section, V_{2b}, forms an a.f. amplifier capable of providing sufficient output for headphones. Since there is some conversion gain in the first valve, the total gain available is more than in a conventional two-valve straight receiver although somewhat less than in a three-valve t.r.f. receiver.

On all bands, the selectivity of the receiver is governed by that of the regenerative detector operating on about 1·6 Mc/s (the actual frequency is unimportant provided that it is clear of any strong signals). Since so much of the gain comes from the detector stage it is most important to obtain smooth regeneration with a complete absence of any tendency to plop or howl.

To avoid the difficulties of tracking, no ganged capacitors are used: tuning is effected with a low capacitance bandspread capacitor across the oscillator coil. The setting of the tuned circuit in the mixer grid circuit is not critical owing to the damping effect of the aerial and usually needs only rough setting to the band in use, with possibly a little touching up on weak signals. For amateur-bands-only receivers—even advanced ones—independent tuning of the aerial circuit is quite satisfactory, and can provide much better results than poorly aligned ganged tuning.

Since there is no ganged tracking, the two sets of coils, mixer and oscillator, can for convenience be of similar inductance; this means that unmodified plug-in coils of the type used in t.r.f. receivers are suitable. On the lower frequency bands where the oscillator will usually have to be on the high frequency side of the signal frequency, there may be some on which it will be necessary to use the next higher

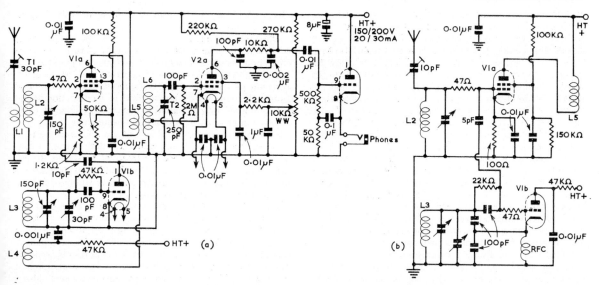

Fig. 56. (a) Circuit diagram of simple superhet receiver using two miniature valves. (b) Alternative frequency changer circuit with "two terminal" coils; this may reduce protection against "image" responses and increase oscillator pulling but makes the construction of the coils easier. V_1 and V_2 are type ECF82/6U8.

frequency range coil in the oscillator position. For those wishing to wind their own coils, the following are the suggested number of turns for a 1 in. diameter former though it must be appreciated that the final inductance will depend not only on the diameter of the former and the number of turns but also on the ratio of the winding length to diameter: range 2–5 Mc/s, L_1 10 turns, L_2, L_3 50 turns, L_4 15 turns; range 4–10 Mc/s, L_1 8 turns, L_2, L_3 24 turns, L_4 10 turns; range 8–20 Mc/s, L_1 5 turns, L_2, L_3 12 turns, L_4 6 turns; range 16–35 Mc/s, L_1 2 turns, L_2, L_3 5 turns, L_4 3 turns. Coils in the *Maxi-Q* range made by Denco (Clacton) Ltd. would also be suitable.

The higher the Q of the mixer coil and the less it is damped by the aerial the greater will be the protection against image interference, while mixer coils adjusted so that there is fairly low C on the amateur bands will increase gain. For complete h.f. coverage using commercially available plug-in coils it may be necessary to fit 300 pF tuning capacitors in the mixer and oscillator circuits in place of the 150 pF suggested.

The "i.f." coil can be conveniently wound on a 1 in. or 1¼ in. paxolin former with some 25 turns for L_5 and about 70 turns for L_6: here again a plug-in type coil designed for 1·8 Mc/s could be used provided the cathode tapping was made. The tap should be as near to the earthy end of the coil as possible, a suggested procedure being to make it at 5 turns reducing this to 3 or 2 turns if oscillation can be maintained. If a 250 pF trimmer is not available a smaller capacity type may be used for T_2 with the remaining value made up by a fixed silver mica capacitor. Here again the higher the Q of the coil the better, and enamelled rather than cotton covered wire should be used.

Alignment. After the set has been wired and subjected to a careful second check proceed as follows.

Plug in V_2 omitting V_1 altogether for the moment. Switch on and check that V_2 is functioning—a touch on the grid of the output triode should produce a gentle hum; a touch on the grid of the pentode section should produce a loud hum or

howl. Try the regeneration control and listen for any slight plop indicating that the valve is going into or out of oscillation. If in any doubt connect an aerial via a small capacitor (say about 10 pF) to the anode side of L_5 and adjust T_2. Since in this condition the set forms a simple 0-V-1 "straight" set it will receive signals operating near the intermediate frequency. Make quite sure that this part of the set is working satisfactorily, remembering that the final results will to a great extent depend upon the smoothness of the regeneration control. If any difficulty is experienced in obtaining a smooth control try in turn the effect of the following: decrease the amount of positive feedback by moving the tap closer to the earthy end of the coil L_6, increase the value of grid leak, alter the voltage on the anode; check the voltage regulation of the power supply.

When satisfied with the operation of V_2, plug-in the 8–20 Mc/s coils and V_1 and connect the aerial to its proper socket. With the mixer tuning capacitor set at roughly mid-travel, try the effect of swinging the main oscillator tuning condenser. If V_{1b} is oscillating, it will almost certainly be possible to hear at least one or two strong whistles, due to

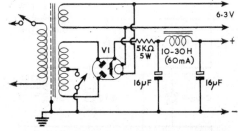

Fig. 57. Typical power pack for small receivers. The 5K resistor should be omitted if the load drawn from the unit exceeds about 25 mA. A typical mains transformer would be 250-0-250 volts h.t. secondary (60 mA rating) and 6.3 volts, 2 amp heater. V1 could be 6X4, EZ90 or U78.

various harmonic beats, etc., between the two oscillators, but it should also be possible to find two not very critical positions on which signals can be heard: these will indicate that at these points the h.f. oscillator is set roughly 1·6 Mc/s (or whatever frequency V_2 is tuned to) above or below the frequency to which L_2 is tuned. If no beats or signals are heard, it is most likely that V_{1b} is not oscillating and this stage should be checked carefully. If beats but no signals are heard, the fault is most likely in the grid circuit of V_{1a}. If signals but also a very large number of spurious beat whistles are heard, this may indicate that there is spurious oscillation in V_{1a} or excessive feedback or incorrect grid leak in V_{1b}.

Once the set is functioning it will still be necessary to calibrate it, so that it may be set rapidly to any desired amateur band. Home wound coils seldom have exactly the same inductance as the originals. This fact, plus differences in stray capacitances, will mean that the frequency ranges obtained in a simple h.f. receiver may vary appreciably from the specified figures. In the absence of a calibrated oscillator, the calibration may require a certain amount of patience but provided that it is always remembered that for any given setting of the oscillator tuning there are two possible frequencies to which the mixer circuit can be set, separated by twice the intermediate frequency, this process is not fundamentally any more difficult than with a straight receiver. The h.f. spectrum, however, usually contains hundreds of strong broadcasting and commercial signals while the amateur bands are narrow and the signals may be relatively weak. One method of locating the amateur bands is first to identify the main broadcasting bands around 14, 16, 19, 25, 31, 41, 49 and 75 metres: four of these (14, 19, 41 and 75) are all fairly close to the high frequency side of the amateur bands on 15, 20, 40 (actually nearer 42) and 80 metres. It will help if an " all-wave " broadcast receiver is available to identify the broadcasting stations.

Variations. Many variations of this basic design are possible without seriously affecting results. For example, the enthusiast with a supply of older valves may find it more economical to fit octal-based types even if this means using three instead of two valves. Such valves as the 6K8, ECH35, 6SA7, etc., can be used for V_1 provided the necessary changes are made to component values; while two separate valves such as the 6SJ7 (or 6J7) and 6C5 (or 6J5) can be used as regenerative detector and a.f. amplifier respectively. If it is wished to keep to two valves only, a twin triode such as the

6SN7 may be used for V_2 provided a different type of regeneration control is fitted.

When building a simple receiver of this type it is advisable to use a fairly large chassis having plenty of room for extra valves and components so that the set may be gradually extended—for example to provide increased gain for the better reception of telephony signals—without having to rebuild completely. One simple but worthwhile modification would be to add a second a.f. amplifier; this could be done by using a 12AT7 in place of V_2 with a 6C4 output valve.

With only the detector working at the i.f., screening is of minor importance, but if eventually it is desired to fit a conventional i.f. stage, it becomes essential to screen the i.f. transformers. Fig. 58 shows one method by which regeneration may be obtained in the detector stage without the need to add an extra feedback winding.

It would be possible to use the simple t.r.f. receiver described earlier as the " i.f. " and a.f. sections of a " super gainer " type of receiver by operating it on about 1·8 Mc/s and placing in front of it a single-valve frequency changer (this could be as V_1 in Fig. 56). Even better results could be obtained by using a more elaborate converter containing an r.f. stage; in this case the receiver would be tuned to about 3 Mc/s or whatever was the ouput frequency of the converter.

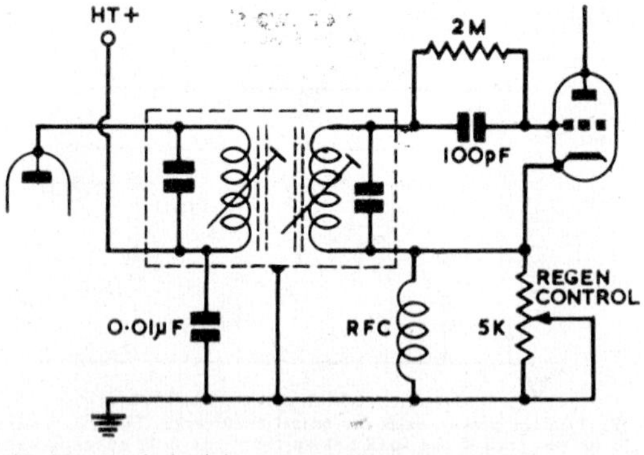

THE Q MULTIPLIER

A useful method of improving the selectivity of receivers not fitted with a crystal filter is the *Q multiplier*. As already explained, this is a tunable filter by which the selectivity characteristics of a conventional i.f. section may be appreciably improved without modification of the receiver itself. When the device is used to peak a signal it may be likened to a high Q parallel tuned circuit placed across the i.f. transformer. At the point of resonance the impedance is high and a signal at that frequency will pass unattenuated: signals on other frequencies will be attenuated by an amount which will depend on the Q of the circuit and the frequency difference to the peaked signal. The improvement will be most marked on receivers having a final or single i.f. of 455 kc/s and below.

Fig. 59 shows a practical circuit developed by G2BVN. L_2 is a high Q coil using ferrite pot construction, its Q being multiplied by the positive feedback of the triode. The effective Q can be made as high as about 4000 which is comparable to that of a crystal filter. Coil and capacitor values for popular intermediate frequencies are given in **Table 3**.

Advantages of this form of filter is that its resonant frequency is varied by C_2 and can thus be tuned across the pass band of the i.f. response of the main receiver, allowing signals to be peaked without critical adjustment of the main receiver tuning. There is no insertion loss. The unit is simple to construct and align and can be installed without altering the receiver wiring. The filter can also be used to reject an unwanted signal by the provision of negative feedback in a second triode. The high Q circuit can then be switched to a series resonant condition and provides a narrow rejection notch similar to that provided by the phasing control of a crystal filter.

The heart of the unit is L_2 which should have an inductance between 120 and 150 microhenries for intermediate frequencies in the range 450 to 470 kc/s. Suitable pot type coils are available from Electroniques (Felixstowe) Ltd. To retain the high Q of this coil it should be mounted at least $1\frac{1}{2}$ in. away from any ferrous metal. C_3 and C_4 should be close tolerance good quality silvered mica types.

Fig. 58. Means of obtaining regeneration when using a standard i.f. transformer and triode detector valve. The choke RFC could conveniently consist of about 100 turns on a $\frac{1}{4}$ in. diameter former.

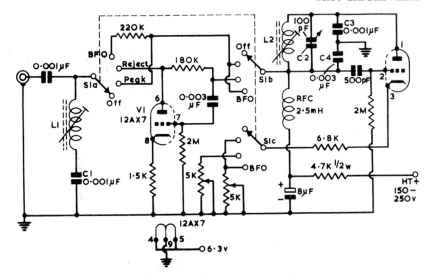

Fig. 59. Circuit diagram of the Q multiplier. The fixed capacitors, with the exception of C_3 and C_4, can be of the disc ceramic type. C_3 and C_4 should be of close tolerance silvered mica type. Resistors, unless otherwise indicated, can be of $\frac{1}{4}$-watt rating. The values of C_3 and C_4 are for an intermediate frequency of 450-470 kc/s. Values for other frequencies are given in Table 3. The function switch is a 3-pole, 4-way Yaxley type.

The coil L_1 is used to tune out the capacitive reactance of the coaxial cable connecting the Q multiplier unit to the receiver i.f. transformer to avoid the need to retrim this circuit. The inductance of L_1 and the capacitance of the cable should tune to the receiver i.f. Assuming the use of not more than 30 in. of good quality semi-airspaced or cellular coaxial cable, L_1 will need to have an inductance of 1·5 to 3 millihenries. L_1, C_1 may be omitted if there is no objection to retrimming the receiver i.f.t. Although the coaxial cable may be connected to any of the i.f. transformers in the receiver, it is advantageous to connect it to the first i.f. transformer as this will reduce the chances of blocking or cross modulation.

With the receiver on and the Q multiplier connected, turn S_1 to OFF and tune in a steady signal, making sure it is correctly centred in the i.f. bandpass. Adjust the core of L_1 for the highest S meter reading or maximum a.f. output. If the coil does not peak then the connecting cable will have to be shortened or lengthened. If the highest signal strength is obtained with the coil fully out this would suggest the cable is too long. Once correctly set this adjustment will not have to be changed.

To adjust L_2 turn S_1 to PEAK, the selectivity control to maximum resistance and C_2 to mid-travel. Adjust L_2 slug until the steady signal is peaked, then slowly rotate the selectivity control, repeaking the slug when necessary. As the control is advanced the signal level should rise and the peak will become sharper until a point is reached where the circuit will break into oscillation. The point of maximum selectivity will be just below this point. With the Q multiplier peaked, the tuning may be varied to boost any signal within the i.f. bandpass and attenuate other frequencies. At maximum selectivity telephony stations should be unintelligible and it will be necessary to back off the control slightly. Should the circuit not go into oscillation, the cathode resistor

(6·8K ohms) should be reduced, but not more than absolutely necessary. Too low a value may indicate that the Q of L_2 is low. The cathode connection of the resistor should be made directly to pin 3 on the valve base.

To obtain best results from the REJECT position, some practice is necessary as the adjustment is critical. A steady carrier should be tuned in and the b.f.o. adjusted to give a beat note of about 100 c/s. C_2 and the reject potentiometer should then be alternately adjusted until the best null is obtained, at which point the tuning should be found to be extremely sharp.

A DOUBLE CONVERSION RECEIVER

The double conversion receiver shown on page 115 was constructed by G3LOK.

The receiver covers all the amateur bands from 1·8 to 30 Mc/s with reasonable bandspread and also provides a continuous coverage of 20 Mc/s in the high frequency range to allow the receiver to be used with converters for the 2m and 70 cm bands, as follows: Band A, 1·8–2 Mc/s; Band B, 3·5–4 Mc/s; Band C, 6·5–7·5 Mc/s; Band D, 12·5–15·5 Mc/s; Band E, 20–27 Mc/s; Band F, 27–40 Mc/s. The circuit diagram, **Fig. 60,** has been simplified by showing only the coils for one waveband, and it should be noted that each setting of S_1 brings into operation a fresh set of tuning coils, with their associated trimmers, for r.f. amplifier, mixer and h.f. oscillator. The tuning scale has a length of 13 in. for each band. The low second i.f. of 85 kc/s provides a nose selectivity of about 2·5 kc/s without the use of a crystal filter.

V_1 (EF80) is a high gain r.f. amplifier with a manual gain control (R_{46}). This stage is inductively coupled to V_2 (6AK5) which forms a pentode mixer. The h.f. oscillator—V_8 (6AM6)—is a modified Hartley arranged so that the actual oscillator uses the grid and screen of V_8 with the output taken from the anode; this enables sufficient injection to be obtained via C_6 with a minimum of " pulling." The first i.f. is approximately 2·1 Mc/s and V_3 (6BA6) provides a stage of amplification at this frequency. IFT_2 couples the output from V_3 to the second frequency changer, V_4 (ECH42), the oscillator frequency being determined by the quartz crystal X_1. By selecting X_1 to be approximately 85 kc/s from the first i.f. (i.e. about 2185 kc/s), the signal is converted to the

TABLE 3

I.F.	L_1	L_2	C_3	C_4
85 kc/s	15 – 60 mH	0·5–2·5 mH	2500 pF	7500 pF
465 kc/s	1·5–3·0 mH	120–150 μH	1000 pF	3000 pF
735 kc/s	750–1000 μH	70–100 μH	750 pF	2250 pF
915 kc/s	250–500 μH	60– 90 μH	500 pF	1500 pF
1600 kc/s	50–120 μH	40– 60 μH	250 pF	750 pF

113

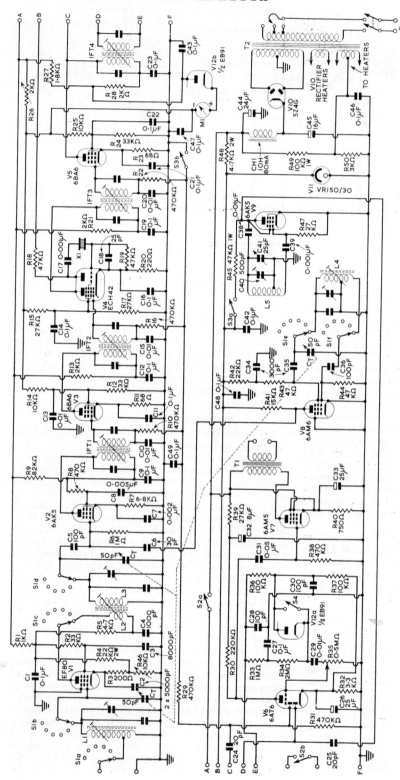

Band	R.f. coil (L1)			Mixer coil (L3)			Coupling coil (L2)	Oscillator coil (L4)			
	Turns	S.w.g.	Tapped at	Adjustable Trimmer	Fixed capacity	Turns	S.w.g.	Tapped at	Adjustable Trimmer	Fixed capacity	Coupling coil (L2)

Fig. 60. Circuit diagram of the double conversion communications receiver. IFT1, 2, 2.1 Mc/s i.f. transformers; IFT1, 2, 85 kc/s i.f. transformers; L1, r.f. coil; L2, r.f. to mixer coupling coil; L3, mixer grid coil; L4, first oscillator coil; L5, b.f.o. coil (for coil winding details see Table); M1, 0·1 mA m.c. meter; T1, output transformer (6000 ohms to 3 ohms); T2, 250-0-250 volts 100 mA, 6·3 volts 3 amp. 5 volts 2 amp.; X1, 2·196 Mc/s crystal. All resistors are ½ watt rating unless otherwise stated. S1a, b, c, d, should short out the coils not in use. The spacing between L2 and L3 is ⅛ in. All coils, except L2 and L3, are ½ in. long. L2 is ¼ in. long, pile wound.

A three-quarter view of the double conversion communications receiver. The controls, from left to right, are: r.f. gain, bandswitch, send/receive switch; tuning; main on/off; a.g.c./b.f.o. switch; b.f.o. tuning; noise limiter on/off; a.f. gain.

second i.f of 85 kc/s. V_5 (6BA6) furnishes a stage of amplification at this frequency and V_6 (6AT6) acts as diode detector, diode a.g.c. rectifier and as a triode a.f. amplifier. V_7 (6AM5) is a conventional output stage; V_9 (a triode-connected 6AK5) is the beat frequency oscillator for c.w. and s.s.b.; V_{11} (VR150/30) stabilizes the h.t. line for all oscillators; V_{10} (5Z4G) is a full-wave rectifier.

One half of the double diode V_{12} (EB91) is used as a noise limiter and its other section is connected in series with the S meter to prevent damage to the movement by reverse current in the event of failure of a decoupling capacitor. The S meter is arranged in a bridge circuit of which the two upper arms are a 1200 ohm fixed resistor and a 200 ohm variable resistor; the lower arms are the cathode-anode resistors of the final i.f. amplifier on one side with the combined parallel resistance of three screen circuits on the other. The screen circuits are arranged with potential dividers which improve the linearity of the meter readings.

The r.f. and oscillator coils are wound on ½ in. diameter low loss formers with adjustable dust cores, each coil having a Philips concentric type trimmer with additional fixed capacity where necessary: see coil table. The tuning capacitors are 50 pF each with double-ended spindles and are ganged together with flexible couplers. Polar type C28-141 or similar are suitable.

A double pole switch brings the b.f.o. into operation at the same time short-circuiting the a.g.c. line to chassis. The send-receive switch cuts the h.t. supply to valves other than the oscillators and the a.f. section. This is to reduce any tendency

for the oscillators to cool off during stand-by periods and permits the a.f. section to be used for monitoring if desired.

ADVANCED RECEIVER WITH TUNABLE FIRST I.F.

The increasing popularity of s.s.b. transmissions has focused attention on the shortcomings of communications receivers which previously would have been considered highly satisfactory. The reception techniques developed for s.s.b. can also be applied with advantage to normal a.m. and c.w. signals. For example, where the receiver is made sufficiently selective it can be tuned to one sideband of a conventional double sideband a.m. signal and reject both the carrier and the second set of sidebands; the signals can then be treated as though they were s.s.b. transmissions. This system can be arranged to provide immediate selection of the upper or lower set of sidebands, permits a significant increase in selectivity to be used without affecting a.f. response as well as reducing phase distortion and selective fading. A receiver having good s.s.b. performance is also likely to provide excellent results on c.w., giving true single signal reception combined with high stability and a low tuning rate.

The requirements of optimum stability and a low, linear tuning rate on all bands call for the use of a crystal-controlled h.f. oscillator in conjunction with a tunable first i.f. section. For a receiver of this type to be free of spurious responses careful selection must be given to the frequency coverage of the tunable section, to screening and to construction generally.

The block diagram of an advanced amateur receiver meeting the above needs, developed by G. R. B. Thornley (G2DAF), is shown in **Fig. 61.** The design considerations will not be dealt with here, but the circuit and performance specifications are given to show in practice the main features of a high-performance receiver of modern design.

The use of a crystal-controlled h.f. oscillator eliminates the problems of tracking front-end oscillator circuits and simplifies construction and final alignment. Nevertheless, it should be appreciated that the construction and alignment of a receiver of this type cannot be undertaken lightly; for the average constructor the work involved is likely to take up to six months or more of spare time.

The receiver has 20 valves (including rectifiers and voltage regulator tube) and covers seven bands, each 500 kc/s wide: *1*, 1·5–2·0 Mc/s; *2*, 3·5–4·0 Mc/s; *3*, 7·0–7·5 Mc/s; *4*, 14·0–14·5 Mc/s; *5*, 21·0–21·5 Mc/s; *6*, 28·0–28·5 Mc/s; *7*, 28·5–29·0 Mc/s. Provision is made for two extra 500 kc/s bands to cover completely the 28·0–29·7 Mc/s band.

Altogether sixteen quartz crystals are incorporated: seven

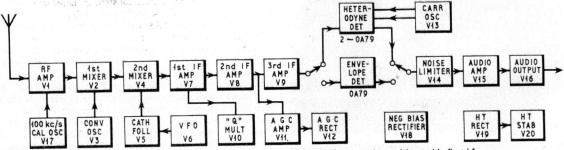

Fig. 61. Block diagram of an advanced amateur communications receiver with tunable first i.f.

for the h.f. oscillator, to provide switched bands; six in three half-lattice bandpass crystal filters centred on 460·8 kc/s with pairs of crystals spaced 2·2 kc/s apart, to provide the main selectivity; two for the carrier insertion oscillator, 1·5 kc/s above and below the centre i.f., to provide selectable sideband reception; and a 100 kc/s calibration oscillator.

For all bands, the tunable i.f. covers 5·0–5·5 Mc/s and the v.f.o., which is the second conversion oscillator, operates on a single, non-switched band of 5460–5960 kc/s; at this frequency high stability can be achieved, particularly as the v.f.o. is isolated from the second mixer by a cathode follower stage. Since the overall stability of the receiver will be determined largely by this oscillator, stability remains closely similar on all bands. A Q multiplication circuit is used to provide a tunable rejection notch.

A photo of the receiver is shown in **Fig. 62** and the full circuit diagram is given in **Fig. 63.**

The aerial input coil on each band provides a match to 75 ohm feeder. As high Q r.f. circuits are required to minimize image response, the r.f. stage is neutralized. A cascode r.f. amplifier (V_1, ECC84) is preferred to a conventional pentode circuit because of its superior cross-modulation characteristics. Signal frequency preselection is by the input coil in the grid circuit and the series fed coil in the anode circuit of V_1. These are selected (together with the aerial input) by three banks of the main bandchange selector switch and pre-tuned for each band with the two ganged 50 pF tuning capacitors. The 160, 80 and 40m anode coils are tapped to provide a reasonably constant stage gain on all bands, with the fourth section of the bandswitch feeding the signal into the grid of the first mixer V_2 (6BE6). The necessary heterodyning frequency is obtained from a crystal controlled harmonic oscillator V_3 (EF80). The required crystal and anode coil are selected by the remaining two banks of

Fig. 62. The advanced amateur bands receiver. The components may be identified by reference to Fig. 64.

the six bank bandchange switch. As suitable types of switch wafers are normally six way the additional 500 kc/s sections of the 10m band are covered by an auxiliary two bank two pole four way Yaxley type switch brought out to a separate panel control. This enables full coverage of the 10m band to be obtained if required.

The tunable i.f. section covering the 5·0 to 5·5 Mc/s range comprises two tuned circuits in the grid of the second mixer V_4 (6BA6) and in the grid of the v.f.o. V_6 (6BA6) arranged as a Colpitts oscillator and tuned by a three gang variable capacitor of 140 pF each section. The v.f.o. output is via a cathode follower V_5 (6BA6) strapped as a triode, with direct injection into the cathode of the second mixer, V_4. Automatic v.f.o. frequency correction when switching sidebands is obtained by a 3–30 pF trimmer capacitor (pre-set to the required value) and a selector switch in the v.f.o. cathode circuit.

The second i.f. output at 460 kc/s is fed into a two half-lattice crystal bandpass filter and to the first i.f. amplifier V_7 (6BA6) and then into a third half-lattice filter section and further amplified by the second and third i.f. stages V_8 and V_9 (6BA6's). A Q multiplier notch filter V_{10} (12AX7) is fed from the anode of V_7. The output of the third i.f. amplifier is switched to the OA79 balanced diode bridge c.w. and s.s.b. demodulator or to a single OA79 diode envelope detector for a.m. reception. The carrier insertion oscillator V_{13} (also type 6BA6) is crystal controlled, the required crystal being selected by S_{12}, the single pole two way SIDE-BAND switch ganged to the v.f.o. correction switch S_{13}.

The required audio output is selected by S_{10} and fed into the negative and positive peak clipping noise limiter V_{14} (6AL5) and the level set by the potentiometer VR_1 (NOISE LIMITER) control. Output is fed via VR_2, the AUDIO GAIN control, to the audio amplifier V_{15} (12AT7) and then to the output valve V_{16} (6BW6). Negative voltage feedback is provided over all audio stages from the secondary of the output transformer. The necessary bias for the output valve is fed via a potential divider from the negative bias supply comprising the transformer T_2 and the rectifier valve V_{18} (6AL5). In the STAND BY position of the operational switch $S_{16,17,18,19}$ the bias is automatically increased and the output valve standing current reduced to approximately 20 mA to lower the loading on the mains transformer T_3.

The i.f. input to the grid of the third i.f. amplifier (V_9) also feeds the a.g.c. amplifier V_{11} (6BA6), the output of which is fed to the shunt rectifier and gate diode V_{12} (6AL5). Resultant current pulses at audio frequency charge the 0·15 μF reservoir capacitor. The charge time constant is fast—of the order of 0·01 second but discharge can only take place via the AVC switch $S_{14,15}$, and either the 500K or 5 Megohm resistors. The discharge time constant is therefore slow—of the order of 0·1 and 1·0 second respectively.

The 10K ohms potentiometer VR_3 is the RF GAIN control and applies bias from the negative supply simultaneously to the a.g.c. line and to the anode of the gate diode. This holds up the decay of the available a.g.c. voltage to a level pre-set by the gain control. Because of Miller effect the varying a.g.c. voltage would affect the grid input capacity of the controlled valves and this would particularly affect the bandpass filter response characteristics and degrade the selectivity and affect the audio frequency response. This effect is overcome in the two associated i.f. amplifier valves V_7 and V_8 by providing negative r.f. feedback with unbypassed 150 ohm cathode resistors. The primaries of the two i.f.

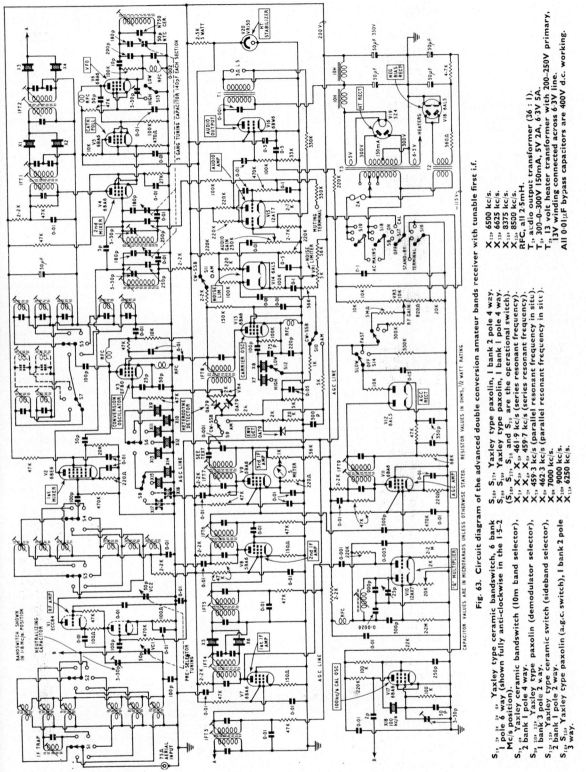

Fig. 63. Circuit diagram of the advanced double conversion amateur bands receiver with tunable first i.f.

S$_1$, S$_2$, S$_3$, S$_4$, Yaxley type ceramic bandswitch, 6 bank.
S$_5$, 1 pole 6 way (shown fully anti-clockwise in the 1·5–2 Mc/s position).
S$_6$, S$_7$, Yaxley ceramic bandswitch (10m band selector), 2 bank 1 pole 4 way.
S$_8$, S$_9$, Yaxley type paxolin (demodulator selector), 1 bank 3 pole 2 way.
S$_{10}$, Yaxley type ceramic switch (sideband selector), 2 bank 1 pole 2 way.
S$_{11}$, S$_{12}$, Yaxley type paxolin (a.g.c. switch), 1 bank 2 pole 3 way.

S$_{16}$, S$_{17}$, Yaxley type paxolin, 1 bank 2 pole 4 way.
S$_{18}$, S$_{19}$, Yaxley type paxolin, 1 bank 1 pole 4 way.
(S$_{16}$, S$_{17}$, S$_{18}$ and S$_{19}$ are the operational switch).
X$_1$, X$_2$, X$_{15}$, 461·9 kc/s (series resonant frequency).
X$_3$, X$_4$, X$_{14}$, 459·7 kc/s (series resonant frequency).
X$_5$, 459·3 kc/s (parallel resonant frequency in situ).
X$_6$, 462·3 kc/s (parallel resonant frequency in situ).
X$_7$, 7000 kc/s.
X$_8$, 9000 kc/s.
X$_9$, 6250 kc/s.

X$_{12}$, 6500 kc/s.
X$_{13}$, 6625 kc/s.
X$_{13}$, 8375 kc/s.
X$_{14}$, 8500 kc/s.
RFC, all 2·5mH.
T$_1$, audio output transformer (36 : 1).
T$_2$, 300–0–300V 150mA, 5V 2A, 6·3V 5A.
T$_3$, 13 volt heater transformer with 200–250V primary, 13V winding connected across 6·3V line.
All 0·01μF bypass capacitors are 400V d.c. working.

CAPACITOR VALUES ARE IN MICROFARADS UNLESS OTHERWISE STATED.   RESISTOR VALUES IN OHMS, ½ WATT RATING

transformers in the anode circuits of V_4 and V_8 are damped with 47K ohm resistors to prevent filter ringing—sufficient damping of V_7 anode circuit is provided by the Q multiplier input loading.

The main h.t. supply is from the mains transformer T_3 and the rectifier valve V_{19} (5Z4), with choke input providing 220 volts to the anode of V_{16}, and the second stage smoothing providing an output of 200 volts to the main h.t. positive rail. A VR150 voltage regulator (V_{20}) provides 150 volts stabilized to feed the v.f.o. and cathode follower and the carrier insertion oscillator (V_{13}).

The calibration oscillator V_{17} (6AM6 or equivalent) provides harmonic output from a 100 kc/s crystal and gives accurate calibration pips every 100 kc/s throughout the receiver range. Operation is controlled by S_{17}, part of the main control switch.

Performance

Automatic Gain Control

Audio rise is 6db for 80db change in signal input above 1μV, and 3db for 60db change in signal input above 10μV.

I.F. Breakthrough Rejection

This is not less than 60db.

Second Channel Rejection

The image rejection to both mixing processes is not less than 60db on all bands.

Selectivity

The selectivity is 2·5 kc/s wide 6db down and 3·7 kc/s wide 60db down. The shape factor of the filter is 1·48.

SIGNAL-TO-NOISE RATIO

Band Mc/s	Aerial input in microvolts for 10db signal-to-noise ratio A3a Reception	Aerial input in microvolts for 20db signal-to-noise ratio A3a Reception
1·5–2·0	0·3	1·2
3·5–4·0	0·28	1·0
7·0–7·5	0·38	1·4
14·0–14·5	0·32	1·2
21·0–21·5	0·32	1·0
28·0–29·0	0·32	1·0

Spurious Responses

On all bands self-generated spurious responses are below a level (throughout the 500 kc/s tuning range) equivalent to a 0.25μV aerial input signal.

Stability

The initial drift from switching on is approximately 500 c/s; the v.f.o. is stable within 10 to 15 minutes (depending on ambient temperature) from cold. Thereafter drift is less than 100 c/s over any one hour period. The measurements were made receiving MSF on 5·0 Mc/s with the open chassis on a bench under normal room temperature conditions. Self-generated heat from the chassis in a poorly ventilated cabinet woud adversely affect these figures and require additional negative temperature coefficient compensation. The necessary value would have to be found experimentally.

Construction

The receiver is built on a 16 s.w.g. aluminium chassis

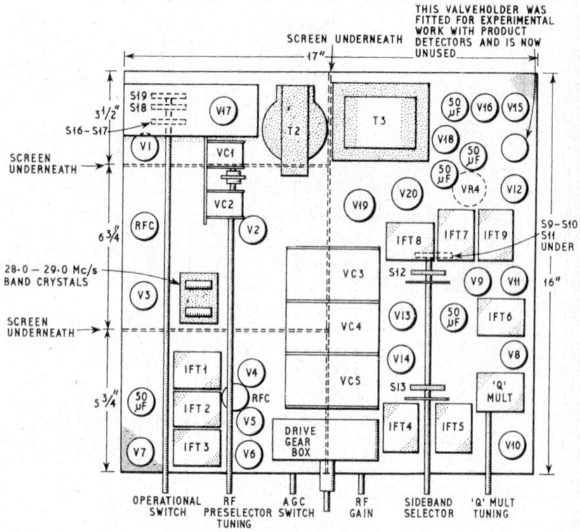

Fig. 64. Above chassis layout in the high performance double conversion amateur bands communication receiver. The dotted lines indicate the screening below the chassis.

measuring 17 in. by 16 in. by $3\frac{1}{2}$ in. deep. The 19 in. by $10\frac{1}{2}$ in. panel is standard rack and panel size. The actual measurements are determined by the physical size of the components used, particularly the i.f. transformers and the three gang tuning capacitor. It is strongly recommended, however, that the chassis is not made smaller than suggested unless this is possible without reducing the signal frequency coil compartments. The Q of the coils and those in the tunable i.f. circuits can be reduced considerably by too close proximity to the cross screens and chassis sides. Close spacing of coils can also lead to undesirable mutual coupling and absorption effects. The chassis layout is shown in **Fig. 64.**

As the r.f. amplifier is neutralized by out of phase feedback from the grid input circuit, the frame of the grid section of the two gang preselection capacitor is above earth. Accordingly this component is made up with two separate 50 pF capacitors mounted on an insulated panel and ganged together with an Eddystone type 529 flexible shaft coupler.

The three i.f. transformers in the bandpass filter require capacitive centre taps. These are provided by removing the original capacitor across the winding and replacing it with two of double the value in series. The junction of the two capacitors is taken out to a separate lead-out wire as the centre tap of the winding. The secondary of IFT_7 feeding the bridge diode c.w. and s.s.b. demodulator must be modified to low impedance series output by replacing the original capacitor with a 1,000 pF unit and whatever value is required to resonate the coil in series as shown in the circuit diagram. Low impedance output is required to feed the c.i.o. output to the OA79 bridge diode demodulator via IFT_8. This is provided by removing one " pie " from a standard i.f.t. and replacing it with a 50 turn scramble winding of 36 s.w.g. enamelled wire tightly coupled to the existing coil.

All variable potentiometers are standard types (wire wound below 100K ohms and carbon above 100K ohms) except for VR_4 in the balanced diode bridge circuit; this is for balancing r.f. and must be non-inductive and therefore carbon.

118

If surplus FT241 crystals are used they are moved to the frequency required by grinding one edge. The crystals for the c.i.o. are positioned at the 20db points. It should be remembered that the actual oscillating frequency *in situ* will be between 100 and 200 c/s lower than the series resonant mode. A small amount of neutralizing capacity—2 pF—was used across two of the filter sections but this would not necessarily give the same response characteristics with some other type of i.f. transformers.

Further advice on lattice filters of the type used in this receiver is given in Chapter 10 (*Single Sideband*).

The conversion oscillator valve (V_3) is a type EF80 and is particularly suitable for this requirement. It must not be replaced with a 6AM6, 6BA6 or similar, because these valves will not give the required r.f. output voltage.

Any suitable moving coil meter of between 500μA and 1·5 mA full scale deflection is suitable for the S meter. The original scale can be covered with glazed drawing paper, hand

COIL WINDING DETAILS

Function	Freq. or band	Winding	Remarks
Signal Frequency V_1 Grid	160m	100T sec. 7T prim 40 s.w.g. enam.	
	80m	55 T sec. 3T prim. 32 s.w.g. enam.	Paxolin former for 160, 80 and 40 metres.
	40m	30T sec. 2T prim. 24 s.w.g. enam.	
	20m	14T sec. 2T prim. 22 s.w.g. enam.	Polystyrene for 20, 15 and 10 metres.
	15m	9T sec. 1·5T prim. 22 s.w.g. enam.	$\frac{3}{8}$ in. diam. 2 in. long, $\frac{3}{8}$ in.
	10m	7T sec. 1T prim. 20 s.w.g. enam. (Spaced 12T per inch) All primaries tightly coupled at cold end of secondary.	diam. with dust core. (Denco Maxi-Q)
Signal Frequency V_1 Anode	160m	100T tap at 50T down, 40 s.w.g. enam.	
	80m	55T tap at 20T down, 32 s.w.g. enam.	
	40m	30T tap at 10T down, 24 s.w.g. enam.	Formers as above.
	20m	14T 22 s.w.g. enam.	
	15m	9T 22 s.w.g. enam.	
	10m	7T 20 s.w.g. enam. (Spaced 12T per inch.)	
Tunable I.F. V_2 Anode & V_4 Grid	5·0–5·5 Mc/s	14T 22 s.w.g. d.s.c. close wound paxolin former as sig. frequency coils.	Cement windings with Denfix polystyrene cement.
V.F.O. V_6 Grid	5·46–5·96 Mc/s	13T 22 s.w.g. d.s.c. close wound paxolin former as sig. frequency coils.	
Conversion Oscillator V_3 Anode	7·0 Mc/s	25T 32 s.w.g. enam. Shunt Cap = 50pF	
	9·0 Mc/s	16T 28 s.w.g. enam. Shunt Cap = 75pF	
	12·5 Mc/s	14T 24 s.w.g. enam. Shunt Cap = 50pF	Former: Aladdin $\frac{3}{8}$ in. diam., 1 in. long, with $\frac{7}{16}$ in. diam. dust core.
	19·5 Mc/s	6T 22 s.w.g. spaced to $\frac{1}{2}$ in. long. Shunt Cap = 40pF	
	26·5 Mc/s	6T 22 s.w.g. spaced to $\frac{1}{2}$ in. long. Shunt Cap = 25pF	
	33·5 Mc/s	5T 22 s.w.g. spaced to $\frac{1}{2}$ in. long. Shunt Cap = 15pF	
	34·0 Mc/s	5T 22 s.w.g. spaced to $\frac{1}{2}$ in. long. Shunt Cap = 10pF	
I.F. Trap	5·3 Mc/s	15T 24 s.w.g. enam. Shunt Cap = 350pF	Former: Aladdin as for conv. osc.
Q Multiplier	460 kc/s	60T approximately 9/42 Litz wire on Maxi-Q pot core $\frac{7}{8}$ in. diam. with adjustable slug (Adjust number of turns as necessary to obtain correct tuning.)	

calibrated and finally removed and marked in with Indian ink.

There is nothing worse than attempting to tune a selective receiver with a " lumpy " drive mechanism or with one that has backlash in the gearing. A really first class reduction drive—preferably with a reduction of at least 100 : 1—is essential. A readily available type is the Eddystone type 898 drive and dial assembly.

All the coils, i.f. transformers and switches for this receiver are available from Electroniques (Felixstowe) Ltd.

Alignment

An ambitious project such as the construction of a double superhet communication receiver will only be undertaken by an experienced amateur with past constructional knowledge. Detailed alignment instructions are not therefore given but the procedure, as in any receiver, is to start from the back and finish at the front. In this case, that means alignment of the carrier insertion oscillator, followed by the tunable i.f. and v.f.o. section, and finally the signal frequency circuits. The 100 kc/s pips from the calibration oscillator in conjunction with the S meter will be found very useful during this process.

The level of the conversion oscillator and v.f.o. inputs to the two mixers V_2 and V_4 is important. There should be sufficient input voltage to obtain correct mixing action but not so much that spurious product generation is increased. A simple way of determining the approximate peak drive voltage to the first mixer without needing a diode probe valve voltmeter is to break the 20K ohm grid resistor connection at the earth end and use a 500μA meter to measure the grid current. This will vary over the six bands because of the different mode of operating the conversion crystals but should be between 100 and 300μA. The cathode drive to the second mixer will have to be measured with a diode probe valve voltmeter and should be approximately 2 volts r.m.s.

The output of the carrier insertion oscillator V_{13}, also measured with a valve voltmeter, should be between 10 and 20 volts r.m.s. at the anode while the r.f. to the two OA79 diodes (either end of the balancing potentiometer) should be about 2·0 volts r.m.s.

Audio negative feedback is provided both as an aid to reduced distortion and also to give control of the total audio amplification. The 330K ohm feedback resistor is adjusted in value so that at full audio gain setting with the a.g.c. operating, the drive to the output valve V_{16} is just less than the point of positive grid excursion.

With the suggested tunable i.f. range (5·0 to 5·5 Mc/s) the receiver can be tuned to MSF on 5·0 Mc/s by setting the bandswitch to the " 3·5–4·0 Mc/s " position and the preselection tuning capacitor to the minimum capacity position. This will peak the signal frequency circuits to 5·0 Mc/s and the first mixer will behave as an amplifier and feed the MSF signal into the tunable i.f. stages. This will provide a standard frequency (correct to five parts in 10^9) for receiver drift measurements and also for adjustment of the 100 kc/s calibration oscillator by means of the pre-set capacitor across the grid circuit of V_{17}, so that the calibration pip on 5·0 Mc/s is zero beat with MSF.

The 56K ohm resistor feeding h.t. to the noise limiter control VR_1 is a nominal value only. It should be adjusted to obtain correct limiter action.

The signal frequency discrimination against i.f. breakthrough is at its worst point when the receiver is in use on those frequencies nearest to the tunable i.f. range. This is at

Band	Harmonic Conversion Oscillator Frequencies					
Mc/s	Re-quired	Crystal used	Second har. of crystal	Third har. of crystal	Fourth har. of crystal	Output
1·5–2·0	7000	7000	14,000	21,000	28,000	Fundamental
3·5–4·0	9000	9000	18,000	27,000	36,000	Fundamental
7·0–7·5	12,500	6250	12,500	18,750	25,000	Second Harmonic
14·0–14·5	19,500	6500	13,000	19,500	26,000	Third Harmonic
21·0–21·5	26,500	6625	13,250	19,875	26,500	Fourth Harmonic
28·0–28·5	33,500	8375	16,750	25,125	33,500	Fourth Harmonic
28·5–29·0	34,000	8500	17,000	25,000	34,000	Fourth Harmonic

the h.f. end of the 80m band. Accordingly, a 5·3 Mc/s i.f. trap is connected in series with the input to the primary of the 80m coil and this gives an additional 20–40db attenuation over the range 3·6 to 3·8 Mc/s. To tune the 5·3 Mc/s i.f. trap, set the main tuning control to 3·7 Mc/s (bandswitch in the 3·5–4·0 Mc/s position) and feed a 100 millivolt signal into the aerial terminal from a signal generator set to 5·3 Mc/s. Adjust the trap dust core for minimum S meter reading.

Muting

Modern practice is to control a transmitter and receiver by means of a relay with either voice (vox) or press-to-talk operation. Breaking h.t. or cathode connections usually causes clicks and thumps and the most satisfactory control method is a source of negative voltage applied to the grids of the controlled valves. In many cases there is already a source of negative voltage provided for the p.a. bias supply and the available potential is usually suitable for muting requirements.

The controlling voltage can be any value from about 30 to 100 volts and is connected to the receiver " muting " terminal. During transmission periods the applied voltage disables the second mixer and the second audio amplifier and so " kills " the receiver. The time constant is fast and the control is free from clicks and thumps. As the controlled r.f. valve (V_4) is not connected to the a.g.c. line the action and the time constant of the receiver a.g.c. system remains unaffected. Obviously there must always be a return path for the controlled grid circuits and if muting is not required the " muting " terminal must be strapped to earth.

The alternative method is to control the receiver from the transmitter send-receive switch. If this is required the receiver can be linked back to the transmitter control switch circuits by means of the STAND BY (SB) position of the receiver operational switch $S_{16, 17, 18, 19}$ and the stand-by terminal provided.

V.H.F./U.H.F. RECEIVERS

IN a v.h.f. receiver it is possible to realize a performance superior in terms of sensitivity and signal-to-noise ratio to that normally obtained on the lower frequencies where, owing to various forms of interference both man-made and natural, a limit is imposed beyond which any attempt to recover signals is fruitless. In v.h.f. reception there is no atmospheric noise except that originating in lightning discharges in the immediate vicinity of the receiver, while the bands are sufficiently wide compared with their occupation that interference between stations is, as yet, not generally a serious problem.

The limiting factor is extra-terrestrial noise and at frequencies up to at least 250 Mc/s, receivers can be designed which will respond to signals only slightly above this level. Interference from the ignition systems of cars is more noticeable on the higher frequencies and in fact becomes objectionable from about 20 Mc/s upwards. Such forms of impulsive interference can be greatly reduced, however, by the use of a noise limiter.

Noise Factor

For these reasons the performance of v.h.f. receivers is usually (and more usefully) specified in terms of *noise factor* which may be defined as

$$\frac{aerial\ noise\ +\ receiver\ noise}{aerial\ noise}$$

and measured as the noise power present at the output of the receiver. With the theoretically perfect receiver, producing no noise in itself, this equation becomes 1/1, i.e. a noise factor of 1 or 0db. The noise factor of a practical receiver that does itself generate unwanted noise is a measure of the amount by which it falls short of perfection.

It is customary to regard each valve stage in the receiver as a noiseless amplifier and to consider the noise that it does in fact generate as originating in a fictitious resistor in its grid circuit. The value of this resistor is such that the noise voltage which would be developed across it is multiplied by the gain of the valve, the result being the real noise present in the valve output circuit. The subject of receiver noise is discussed more fully in Chapter 15 (*Noise*) and the measurement of noise in Chapter 19 (*Measurements*) to which the reader is referred for a more extensive explanation.

Front-end Stages

The requirements of the early stages in a v.h.f. receiver are (i) low noise content, (ii) high power gain, and (iii) ability to develop a signal voltage between grid and cathode.

The first of these requirements implies that noise due to the fictitious resistor in the grid circuit, known as the *equivalent noise resistance*, and that due to *induced grid noise* must be as low as possible: for definitions of these terms see Chapter 2

(*Valves*). Since a pentode has an equivalent noise resistance which may be several times higher than that of a triode owing to the added effect of *partition noise*, triodes are used exclusively for low noise input stages. The second requirement implies that the stage must be capable of developing gain at the desired frequency with the load presented by the input of the following stage. This demands a valve with as high a slope as possible consistent with low capacitances and high input impedance.

In a multi-stage receiver with, say, eight amplifying stages the noise originating in the grid circuit of the first valve will be amplified by eight valves, that in the second by seven, and so on. If the effective noise voltages are denoted by V_1, V_2, $V_3 \ldots V_8$ and the stage gains by G_1, G_2, $G_3 \ldots G_8$, the total noise present at the output of the receiver will be $V_1 (G_1, G_2, G_3 \ldots G_8) + V_2 (G_2, G_3 \ldots G_8) + V_3 (G_3 \ldots G_8)$ and so on. It follows, therefore, that if G_1 is high, say 20 or more, only the noise due to the first stage is of importance, and provided that the remaining stages are reasonably efficient they will contribute little to the overall noise. In cases where the gain of the first stage is low because of an unsuitable type of valve for the frequency concerned or if a considerable bandwidth is required, or when both of these conditions exist, the noise contributed by the second or even the third stage may become important.

If all the noise is not due to the first stage, the noise factor is increased by the noise factor of the second stage. The formula for the overall noise factor $F_{1,\,2}$ of two stages of independent noise factors F_1 and F_2 is

$$F_{1,\,2} = F_1 + \frac{F_2 - 1}{G_1}$$

where G_1 is the available power gain of the first stage. As an example, a mixer has a noise factor of 25 (14db). A triode amplifier preceding such a mixer with a noise factor of 5 (7db) and a power gain of 10 (10db) will cause the receiver to have an overall noise factor of

$$F_{1,\,2} = 5 + \frac{25 - 1}{10} = 7 \cdot 4\ (8 \cdot 7db).$$

From this example it is clear that the mixer noise must be low or the gain of the r.f. stage must be high unless a valve with extremely low noise is used in order to achieve a good overall result.

The third requirement is that the input resistance which appears in the grid circuit due to the transit time of the electrons must be high. Although the noise associated with this resistance (i.e., the induced grid noise) is high because its temperature can be taken as five times the room temperature, the signal voltage applied to the grid will be low unless a step-up in voltage between the aerial (or its feeder) and the grid can be obtained.

When the input circuit is matched to the input impedance

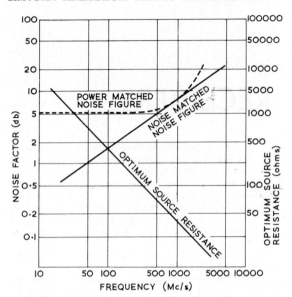

Fig. I. Noise factor and optimum source resistance plotted against frequency for a typical grounded grid criode (type 7077, g_m 9 mA/V, I_a 6·4 mA).

of the valve, an optimum power gain is achieved and the valve is said to be *power-matched*. This condition does not, however, result in the lowest noise. Where the step-up ratio is adjusted for optimum noise factor in contrast to optimum power gain the valve is said to be *noise-matched*.

Fig. 1 shows the variation with frequency of the noise factor and optimum source resistance of a grounded grid stacked-ceramic triode of similar construction to that described on page 61, Chapter 2 (*Valves*). It will be seen that when the valve is power-matched the noise factor is constant at 5·5db up to about 800 Mc/s, whereas below this frequency a higher source resistance (over-coupling) produces considerable improvement in the noise factor. Above this frequency the noise factor does not diminish because the optimum source resistance is then comparable with or may be less than the cathode input resistance ($1/gm$ for this valve is $1000/9 = 110$ ohms).

The noise factor of a valve is affected by the cathode temperature owing to the existence of the space charge in the grid-cathode region. The extent of the space charge is critically dependent on the temperature of the cathode and consequently there will be considerable increase in noise if the heater current is reduced by even a very small amount, e.g. only 5 per cent. It is most important, therefore, to ensure that the correct heater voltage is applied to valves, particularly in the early stages of the receiver. Adjustment of the value of the grid bias in relation to the contact potential of the grid is a means of improving the noise factor. If the grid bias of a valve is steadily reduced below the cut-off point the noise steadily diminishes until the point is reached where grid current begins to flow; beyond this point the noise increases rapidly. **Fig. 2** shows the relation between noise factor and grid bias at a constant anode current for two typical grounded grid triodes. The general shape of the curves is the same but

the minimum noise factors occur at slightly different grid bias values. The optimum bias will vary with the type of valve and different specimens of the same type will also show some variation. It is often worth experimenting to obtain the optimum bias but care should always be taken to keep the anode current constant at the recommended value by means of an adjustable series h.t. dropping resistor.

Circuit Noise

Noise due to circuit components other than valves is produced solely by the resistive component; inductive or capacitive reactances do not produce noise. Coils have negligible resistance in the v.h.f. ranges but the leakage resistance of capacitors and insulators is important and it is therefore imperative to select good quality components, including such items as valveholders and switches. Circuit noise can be regarded as including noise caused by regeneration and although it is common practice to enhance the gain of low frequency circuits by applying regeneration this should be avoided at all costs in v.h.f. receivers because of the additional noise produced. Common causes of regeneration are:

(i) Insufficient decoupling of supply leads and, particularly, heater and cathode circuits. In the range 20–30 Mc/s 0·01 μF non-inductive capacitors are a *minimum* value for this purpose;

(ii) Incomplete neutralizing of triode r.f. amplifiers. An adjustment that merely ensures that the circuit does not actually oscillate is not sufficient. Accurate neutralizing is essential and the appropriate methods are described later in this chapter;

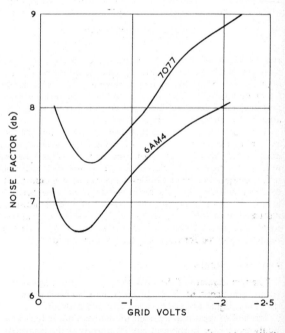

Fig. 2. Noise factor plotted against grid bias for grounded grid triodes, the anode current being held constant (7077 at I_a 6·4 mA at 450 Mc/s; 6AM4 at I_a 10 mA at 250 Mc/s).

(iii) Circulating r.f. currents in the chassis, due to multi-point earthing;

(iv) Poor earth contacts to the chassis. For low noise circuits a brass or copper chassis should be employed; aluminium is not recommended because it is extremely difficult to make a lasting effective connection to it.

Effect of Bandwidth

Before leaving the subject of noise, there is one further point which must be considered. If the noise factor of a receiver is measured with a noise generator it will be found to be independent of receiver bandwidth. This is because the noise from the generator is of the same nature as ordinary noise so that if the bandwidth is doubled the overall noise is also doubled. For the reception of a signal of finite band-width, however, the optimum signal-to-signal ratio is obtained when the bandwidth of the receiver is only just sufficient to accommodate the signal and any further increase in band-width results merely in additional noise. The signal-to-noise ratio at the receiver therefore depends on the power per unit bandwidth of the transmitted signal. To illustrate this point, suppose that the receiver produces 1μV of noise for each 10 kc/s of bandwidth and that an amplitude modulated transmitter radiates a signal 10 kc/s wide and produces 10μV at the receiver. The signal-to-noise ratio is therefore 10, provided that the receiver uses a bandwidth of 10 kc/s. If the bandwidth of the transmission is reduced to 5 kc/s and the radiated power remains the same, the input to the receiver will still be 10μV, but if the bandwidth of the receiver is also reduced to 5 kc/s, only 0.5μV of noise will be accepted and the signal-to-noise ratio will increase to 20. An unstable transmission, requiring a large bandwidth at the receiver, results in a degraded signal-to-noise ratio, so there is clearly a great advantage to be gained by the employment of stable transmitters and receiving equipment having the smallest practicable bandwidth.

CHOICE OF THE FIRST I.F.

Double frequency conversion is usually employed in a receiver for v.h.f. reception and it is convenient to build the r.f. stages and first conversion circuits as a separate unit, known as a *converter*, the output of which is fed into a com-munications receiver with a suitable frequency coverage for the first i.f.

Two methods are possible for tuning over a band when double conversion is employed:

(*a*) The oscillator in the converter may be fixed in frequency and may, therefore, be crystal controlled, tuning being effected by variation of the first i.f. (i.e., by tuning the main receiver) over a band equal in width to that of the v.h.f. band to be covered.

(*b*) The oscillator in the converter may be variable and the main receiver tuning set at the frequency chosen for the first i.f. It has already been shown that the signal-to-noise ratio of a receiver depends upon the bandwidth, and this bandwidth being that of the most selective stage (normally the i.f. ampli-fier in the main receiver) and the amount of noise heard will thus be determined provided no significant noise is contri-buted by the later stages. The use of a bandwidth exceeding 5 kc/s for telephony and considerably less for c.w. reception is therefore undesirable when a good signal-to-noise ratio is the prime consideration.

In any superheterodyne receiver it is possible for two in-coming frequencies to mix with the local oscillator to give the i.f.—the desired signal and the image frequency—and this has an influence on the choice of the i.f. To avoid confusion, the i.f. of the main receiver will in future be referred to in this chapter as the *second i.f.*

One purpose of r.f. amplification ahead of the mixer in a v.h.f. converter is to attenuate signals and noise present at the image frequency and the higher the first i.f. the greater such attenuation will be. Many of the r.f. amplifier circuits em-ployed in v.h.f. receivers have an extremely large bandwidth and if they are so wide that the image ratio is unity (i.e., if the sensitivity of the " second channel " is the same as that for the wanted signal) the noise factor is degraded by 3db. Care should therefore be taken to ensure that the first i.f. is suf-ficiently high. As the first i.f. is raised, however, the per-formance of the main receiver tends to fall off and its contribution of noise may become significant if the overall gain of the converter is insufficient. The value of first i.f. finally decided upon depends on the type of converter to be used and the frequency on which it is to operate.

Two other factors affect the choice of first i.f. First, it is desirable that no harmonic of the local oscillator in the main receiver should fall in the v.h.f. band in use, and second, there should be no breakthrough from stations operating at the frequency selected as the first i.f.

Many communications receivers produce quite strong harmonics in the 70 and 144 Mc/s bands and although these are high-order harmonics and are therefore tuned through quickly they are troublesome inasmuch as they are distracting when searching for signals in the band in question. The problem is more acute when the converter is crystal controlled than when a tunable first oscillator is employed. In the former case freedom from harmonics is required over a tuning range equal to that of the v.h.f. band to be covered whereas in the latter only harmonics from one spot frequency of the local oscillator in the main receiver have to be con-sidered.

The avoidance of breakthrough signals at the frequency selected for the first i.f. is also more difficult when the converter is crystal controlled. Because it is practically impossible to find a band several megacycles wide which is completely unoccupied, other steps have to be taken to avoid breakthrough. Frequencies in the range 20–30 Mc/s are often chosen since fewer strong signals are normally found there than on the lower frequencies, but this condition may well be reversed during periods of high sunspot activity.

Particular attention should be paid to the screening of the main receiver which should be tested by itself with the i.f. stages operating at maximum gain. Signals may be picked up on the aerial terminals and if this occurs they should be replaced by a coaxial socket. Unwanted signals may also enter the receiver along the power supply cable or the loud-speaker leads and these may need to be decoupled or filtered. Other sources of such interference are long earth leads and unearthed control spindles.

When the main receiver is considered satisfactory from this point of view, a further test should be made with the converter connected, preferably by a short length of coaxial cable, but with its local oscillator inoperative. If any signals are heard they will be first i.f. signals and the decoupling or filtering of the power supply leads and any similar connec-tions should be checked again. If difficulty is still experienced,

123

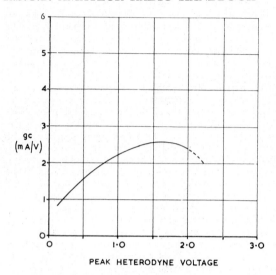

Fig. 3. The relation between conversion conductance and oscillator (heterodyne) voltage in a typical triode mixer (6AM4, V_a 125 volts, R_k 220 ohms).

a stage of i.f. amplification may have to be incorporated in the converter or, if one is already in use, its gain may need to be increased so that the main receiver can be run in a less sensitive condition.

After all abnormal sources of signal pick-up have been eliminated there may still exist a path for i.f. signals through stray capacities in the converter itself. This may be eliminated to a very large extent by connecting a piece of coaxial cable as a quarter wavelength (at signal frequency) shorted stub in parallel with the aerial feeder at the input of the converter. This provides a virtual short circuit to signals at the first i.f. while maintaining a high impedance to the wanted v.h.f. signals. The actual physical length of the stub will depend of course upon the velocity factor of the cable used in its construction.

THE LOCAL OSCILLATOR

It is clear that if the final bandwidth of the complete receiver is to be the same as that used on the lower frequencies the stability of the oscillator in the converter must be as good as the oscillator in the main receiver. For the 70 and 144 Mc/s bands it is possible to build tunable oscillators of good stability and " note " working at frequencies either above or below the signal frequency by the value of the first i.f. On the 420 Mc/s band tunable oscillators are normally designed to operate at one-half or one-third of the required frequency and are followed by suitable frequency multipliers. Crystal controlled local oscillators can be used satisfactorily in any v.h.f. or u.h.f. converter.

The advantages and disadvantages of the two types of oscillator may be summarized as follows.

Tunable Oscillators

(a) Advantages

(i) A directly calibrated dial is possible.

(ii) The cost of a crystal is eliminated.

(iii) Only one valve is required.

(iv) There is less likelihood of harmonic interference from the main receiver.

(v) Only one clear channel is required on the main receiver.

(b) Disadvantages

(i) Long-term oscillator drift makes calibration of the dial unreliable.

(ii) Warm-up drift can be troublesome.

(iii) It is difficult to obtain a better than T8 note (but not impossible).

(iv) Change of oscillator or mixer valve alters the calibration.

(v) Microphony occurs on strong signals due to vibration of the oscillator tuned circuit by acoustic feedback from the loudspeaker.

(vi) They cannot readily be used remotely.

Crystal-controlled Oscillators

(a) Advantages

(i) Accurate vernier logging of stations on the main receiver dial is possible.

(ii) A T9 note is assured.

(iii) Negligible short term or warm-up drift.

(iv) Absence of controls allows remote operation.

(b) Disadvantages

(i) Expensive both in valves (for 420 Mc/s and above) and crystal.

(ii) Possibility of additional self-generated whistles.

(iii) More adjustments and therefore more difficult to align in the first place.

The question of oscillator injection arises irrespective of the type of oscillator it is decided to use. As already stated, if the r.f. stages have high gain and low noise factor, the noise contributed by later stages tends to be less significant, but this assumes reasonable efficiency in the mixer stage. Fig. 3 shows a typical conversion conductance curve for a mixer stage and indicates how the i.f. output varies as the injection voltage is changed, the signal voltage being kept constant: it will be noticed that a considerable loss of gain results if

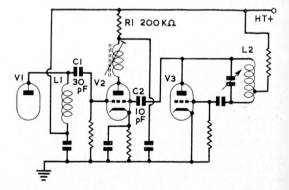

Fig. 4. Typical triode mixer (V_2) and associated oscillator (V_3).

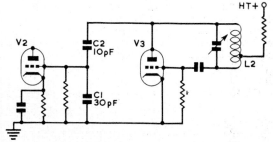

Fig. 5. The triode mixer circuit of Fig. 4 arranged to show the potential divider formed by the oscillator coupling and r.f. to mixer stage coupling capacitors at the injection frequency.

250 K ohms which can be adjusted while listening to a weak signal, it will be found that the optimum value of mixer anode potential is readily obtained. The value of resistance thus determined may weaken strong signals slightly but this is of little consequence in relation to the marked improvement effected in the response to weak signals.

TUNABLE OSCILLATORS

The requirements for a tunable oscillator are similar to those for a variable frequency oscillator designed for transmitter control, i.e. robust construction to guard against vibration, the employment of only the best quality components, including valveholders and insulation, short and rigid wiring and self-supported coils of stout wire. The operating frequency of the oscillator may be either above or below the signal frequency but to ensure the best stability it is usual for it to be on the *low* frequency side of the signal. Where the choice of such a frequency leads to interference with a local television channel, operation on the *high* side of the signal may be necessary although a small change in intermediate frequency sometimes enables the oscillator frequency to be placed to avoid such trouble.

The valve employed will, of course, have considerable influence on the results obtained, and the type chosen should be of robust construction with short leads to the electrodes. Modern all-glass types on either B7G or B9A bases are suitable and some advantage may be obtained by using the " special quality " or " trustworthy " (ruggedized) variety.

There are three main types of circuit for tunable v.h.f. local oscillators: (a) Kalitron push-pull, (b) v.h.f. Colpitts, (c) Hartley.

The Kalitron is particularly applicable to the requirements of the push-pull mixer, while the Colpitts and the Hartley circuits are primarily intended for use with single-ended mixer circuits. Each of the circuits is capable of producing good results if well constructed.

The Kalitron Oscillator

This circuit, shown in **Fig. 6,** is well suited to the 6J6 valve in which the two triodes have a common cathode connection and the cathode lead inductance is therefore cancelled out,

inadequate oscillator voltage is used. The remaining curve on the graph shows that the noise level is at its highest with inadequate injection voltage, and although the noise increases when the injection voltage is too high it is still far less than when it is too low. In the designs presented in this chapter every effort has been made to ensure that adequate injection voltages are attained.

The injection voltage in a triode mixer—the type used by most amateurs at v.h.f.—is found by measuring the current flowing through the mixer grid resistor due to the oscillator injection, i.e., the difference in grid current with and without the oscillator operative. The maximum value of oscillator voltage normally to be expected is about 3 volts peak, and with a grid resistor of, say, 50 K ohms, this corresponds to a grid current of only $60\mu A$, so any lower injection voltage may become difficult to detect. It must not be supposed that a voltage of this magnitude is easy to achieve; to produce such a voltage at the mixer grid is in fact often quite difficult. **Fig. 4** shows a typical triode mixer circuit in which the coil L_1 is tuned to resonance at, say, 70·3 Mc/s and the signal voltage developed across it fed through a 30pF capacitor to the mixer grid. L_2 is carrying oscillations at, say, 50 Mc/s coupled through a 10pF capacitor to the grid of the mixer (V_2). At 50 Mc/s, the inductance L_1 is in effect a short-circuit to earth, and at this frequency the 50 Mc/s oscillations therefore " see " the mixer grid circuit as shown in **Fig. 5**. The 10pF and 30pF capacitors (C_2 and C_1) in the mixer grid circuit become a potential divider such that only one quarter of the original 50 Mc/s voltage at the anode of V_3 appears at the grid of V_2.

An obvious course would be to increase the value of C_2, but signal voltages at the grid of the mixer " see " this capacitor between grid and earth since L_2 appears as a short circuit at signal frequency. Thus only three-quarters of the signal voltage at the anode of V_1 appears at the grid of V_2 with the present capacitor ratio; if C_2 were increased in value even less signal voltage would be available at the mixer grid.

Experimental adjustment of the values of C_1 and C_2 may be made (with appropriate readjustment of L_1 and L_2) to effect the best compromise. Capacities of 30pF and 10pF respectively are of the correct order of magnitude because an r.f. voltage of 10 to 20 is commonly obtained at the anode of V_3 and one quarter of this voltage at the mixer grid is usually adequate.

The required value of oscillator injection voltage depends upon the anode potential of the mixer valve; the lower the anode voltage the lower the required injection voltage and it is this fact that has made the use of relatively high values for R_1 (Fig. 4) commonplace.

If R_1 is replaced temporarily by a variable resistor of about

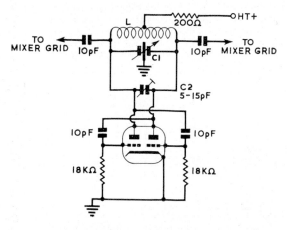

Fig. 6. The Kalitron oscillator. L is 2 turns of 16 s.w.g. $\frac{7}{16}$ in. diameter for 120 Mc/s. C_1 may be 7·5 pF per section.

but other types such as the 12AT7 or 12AU7, which are double triodes with separate cathodes, can be used successfully.

For either 70 or 144 Mc/s converters the oscillator tuning capacitor C_1 may be a small split-stator type with one fixed and one moving plate per section. The wire used for the coil should not be thinner than 16 s.w.g. and the coils should be mounted directly on the soldering lugs fitted to the capacitor. The wires to the anode tags of a high quality (preferably p.t.f.e.) valveholder should be equally stout. Careful proportioning of the parallel capacitance C_2 and the size of the coil will enable the required bandspread to be obtained.

With an h.t. supply of 100 volts the circuit produces about 18 volts peak-to-peak across the anode coil which gives an injection voltage of the correct order to the mixer with 10pF coupling capacitors. The actual value of the injection voltage

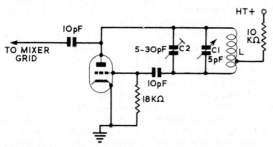

Fig. 7. The v.h.f. Colpitts oscillator circuit. For 120 Mc/s L should be two turns of 16 s.w.g. $\frac{3}{8}$ in. diameter.

will depend upon the relative frequency to which the grid circuit of the mixer is tuned and the oscillator frequency, and for optimum results it is worth trying slightly different values of coupling capacitor. It should be noted that the h.t. supply to the coil is through a low value resistor R; if a choke is used at this point the frequency of oscillation is very likely to be determined by the choke instead of by the tuning inductance.

The V.h.f. Colpitts Oscillator

This circuit, shown in **Fig. 7**, is a very popular one and is readily seen to be a true Colpitts oscillator by referring to **Fig. 8** where the anode-to-cathode and grid-to-cathode capacitances are shown. At lower frequencies these capacitances are not large enough effectively to tap the tuned circuit and therefore external capacitors must be added.

The 6C4 valve is very satisfactory in the circuit as it is free from microphony and gives a fairly high output. A suitable

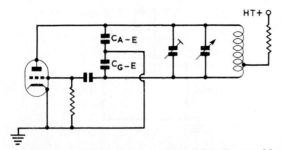

Fig. 8 The circuit of Fig. 7 with the addition of the valve capacities to show the normal Colpitts oscillator circuit.

value for the tuning capacitor C_1 is 5pF with a 5–30pF preset capacitor C_2 in parallel for bandsetting. The required bandspread may be obtained by suitably proportioning the coil and the bandsetting capacitor. As in the Kalitron circuit, the h.t. feed to the tuning inductance is through a

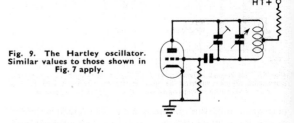

Fig. 9. The Hartley oscillator. Similar values to those shown in Fig. 7 apply.

resistor and not through an r.f. choke in order to avoid the risk of spurious oscillations.

The Hartley Oscillator

The Hartley oscillator circuit shown in **Fig. 9** differs from the v.h.f. Colpitts oscillator arrangement (Fig. 7) only in the position of the h.t. feed to the tuning coil L but it generally gives rather more output than the Colpitts oscillator.

Oscillator Construction

The stability of any of these circuits may be improved by adopting a trough-line construction for the inductance in place of a coil. The following description of a 144 Mc/s

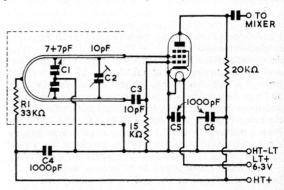

Fig. 10. Hartley oscillator for improved stability. C_1 is a miniature split stator capacitor; C_2, a miniature air spaced trimmer (Wingrove and Rogers); C_3, disc ceramic or silver mica type; C_4, C_5, C_6, hi-K ceramic feedthrough. The valve is a 6AK5. The inductance measures $4\frac{1}{2}$ in. from the open ends to the point where R_1 is connected. The dotted lines represent a copper box surrounding the inductance.

Hartley circuit illustrates the use of such an arrangement. Suitable values for the various components will be found under **Fig. 10**.

The oscillator is built in a copper trough measuring 7 in. × $1\frac{3}{4}$ in. × $1\frac{3}{4}$ in. (see **Fig 11**.). The tuned circuit consists of a hairpin-shaped loop of silver plated copper tube or wire of $\frac{1}{8}$ in. diameter and $4\frac{1}{2}$ in. long held centrally in the box by two transverse strips of polystyrene $\frac{1}{4}$ in. thick secured to the sides by two short 6 B.A. bolts on each side tapped into the strips. The centre-to-centre spacing of the limbs of the hairpin is $\frac{3}{4}$ in. The valveholder is fitted in the side of the box

1¼ in. from one end so that the screen grid pin is immediately adjacent to one end of the hairpin line. The distance between the grid contact and the other side of the line is conveniently bridged by the grid capacitor (C_3). All earthy connections on the valveholder and the earthed end of the grid-leak are taken to a tag under one of the valveholder fixing bolts. The most rigid construction is ensured if the heater and h.t. by-pass capacitors C_5 and C_6 are of the feedthrough type but silvered mica capacitors may be used provided they are securely fixed.

The bandsetting capacitor (C_2) is mounted on a small block of polystyrene ¼ in. thick bolted to the bottom of the box between the two sides of the hairpin loop to bring its contact lugs close to the ends of the line. The split-stator tuning capacitor (C_1) should be of the metal frame type with one moving and two fixed plates in each of its sections. It is mounted across the side members of the box using 6 B.A. bolts, and the width varied slightly to suit the length of the capacitor. The shaft of C_1 is 3¾ in. from the valve end of the box and the connections between the stators and the line are

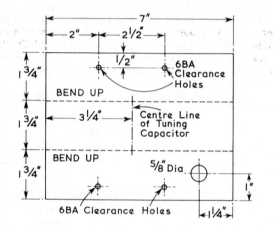

Fig. 11. Details of the 18 s.w.g. copper box for the oscillator of Fig. 10. Two pieces 1¾ in. square are sweated into place to form the ends of the box. No holes in the bottom of the box for outgoing leads are shown.

soldered approximately 1½ in. from the open end of the line. The bandspread available with any given variable capacitor depends on this distance—if necessary the tuning range can be adjusted by altering it slightly.

Screen-grid voltage is fed to the loop end of the line, and the bypass capacitor arrangements should be similar to those for other tunable oscillators. A feedthrough insulator or small length of polystyrene rod drilled to pass the coupling lead from the anode of the valve to the mixer is set in the wall of the box close to the anode tag of the valveholder.

The power requirements of the circuit are very modest, a supply of 25–30 volts at less than 1 mA giving sufficient injection for most mixers, but if this proves insufficient the h.t. may be increased to about 200 volts without causing any serious deterioration in the frequency stability. Under these conditions, however, the anode resistor would of course need to have a higher power rating.

A well regulated h.t. supply is required for best results and a voltage-divider network connected across an 85 or 105 volt

stabilized supply and passing 5–6 mA is quite satisfactory, the actual voltage on the oscillator being varied until the optimum injection to the mixer is obtained.

The frequency stability is such that a c.w. transmission may be held for considerable periods with only slight variations in note while no re-tuning is necessary during quite lengthy 'phone transmissions. A satisfactory degree of oscillator stability is achieved within a few minutes but it is advisable to arrange that the oscillator h.t. supply remains connected during periods of transmission.

CRYSTAL-CONTROLLED OSCILLATORS

In a crystal-controlled oscillator/multiplier chain for a converter it is usually desirable to multiply by not more than five or six times in any one stage. To decide what will be a suitable fundamental frequency a chart such as that shown in **Fig. 12** should be prepared.

As an example, it is found that if the local oscillator in the main receiver covers the range 26·5–28·5 Mc/s, no harmonics from it will fall into the 144 Mc/s band. If the main receiver has an i.f. of 500 kc/s and its oscillator operates above the signal frequency, a first i.f. of 26–28 Mc/s will be satisfactory. Since 26 Mc/s will be the tuning position for a signal on 144 Mc/s, the injection frequency for the converter will be 118 Mc/s (i.e. 144 − 26) and reference to the chart will show how this may be obtained.

It is normal practice to use an overtone oscillator in which the crystal vibrates mechanically at approximately three or five times its fundamental frequency depending upon the adjustment of the circuit. There is no output at the fundamental of the crystal and the harmonics present are related only to the overtone frequency. For example, a 5 Mc/s crystal operating on its third overtone would generate no energy below 15 Mc/s and behave like a crystal of that fundamental frequency.

Crystals specially manufactured for overtone operation are commercially available up to about 100 Mc/s and suitable circuits are supplied by the makers. The cost of such crystals may seem high when compared with surplus fundamental mode types but unless the frequency of operation is very high or the specified tolerance very close (which is unnecessary for most amateur purposes) careful consideration should be given to the purchase of an overtone crystal bearing in mind the greater certainty of trouble-free operation and, in the case of one of the high frequency crystals oscillating at 60 Mc/s or more, whether the greater cost is not offset by the saving in valves and components and the smaller space required for the converter.

In the example under consideration an ideal crystal frequency would be 59 Mc/s, necessitating only a doubler stage to arrive at the required injection frequency of 118 Mc/s.

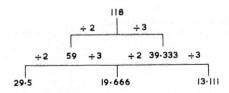

Fig. 12. Type of chart used for determining the fundamental crystal frequency required in an oscillator/multiplier chain.

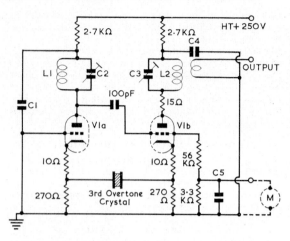

Fig. 13. Butler overtone crystal oscillator circuit. Output may be taken at two, three or four times the frequency of the overtone crystal. L_1, C_2 and L_2, C_3 tune to the overtone and desired output frequencies respectively. C_1, C_4 and C_5 are by-pass capacitors of normal values.

For those who prefer to use the cheaper crystals other choices must be made with the aid of Fig. 12. It would be undesirable to start at 13·111 Mc/s since the second harmonic would fall at 26·222 Mc/s which is within the tuning range of the main receiver and would result in a spurious carrier usually referred to as a *birdie*. A frequency of 29·5 Mc/s appears to be a possibility and a 5·9 Mc/s crystal, provided it would operate on its fifth overtone, would satisfy the requirements. The oscillator unit could then comprise merely one double triode valve, the first section operating as a fifth overtone oscillator and the second section serving as a quadrupler.

Alternatively a start could be made at 19·65 Mc/s, obtained from a 6·55 Mc/s crystal vibrating on its third overtone, the output frequency being doubled or trebled in the second section of a double triode. The multiplier chain could then be completed in one section of a further double triode in which the remaining section served as a mixer stage.

Double triode valves are used extensively as oscillators in v.h.f. converters and among those suitable are the 6J6, 12AT7, 6BQ7A and ECC88. The triode section of the 6U8/ECF82 is also suitable for use as an overtone oscillator. The 6J6 has a cathode common to both sections of the valve and this restricts its use in certain applications. The 6BQ7A and the ECC88 have an internal screen between the two anodes and are therefore particularly suitable for use when one section is to be employed as a mixer.

Several circuits have been described for overtone oscillators, some of which operate the crystal in the parallel (high impedance) mode, while in others the crystal is in the series-resonant mode and therefore has a low impedance. The latter type of circuit is in more general use. A feature which is common to all the series-resonant circuits is that the crystal forms part of the feedback loop so that if it is replaced by a capacitor oscillations will take place at a frequency determined by the coil in the circuit together with its associated capacitances. This can, in fact, happen even with the crystal in circuit as a result of the capacitance between the crystal electrodes and spurious oscillations may be generated unless the circuit is properly adjusted.

The Butler circuit (**Fig. 13**) is particularly useful in receivers and may be employed either as an overtone or as a fundamental oscillator with provision for taking an output at two, three or four times the frequency of the crystal, and, although two stages are required, the arrangement is very satisfactory when good stability is the main criterion. For use as a fundamental oscillator, L_2 is omitted and the anode of V_{1b} bypassed to earth by a suitable capacitor, the output then being taken from a link winding coupled to L_1.

When setting up the oscillator a voltmeter may be connected as shown dotted in the diagram and the tuned circuits adjusted for maximum deflection. For highest stability the coils should both have a low Q value, and if necessary damping resistors may be connected across them for this purpose.

Typical circuits for other overtone oscillators are given in Chapter 7 (*V.H.F. Transmitters*).

R.F. AMPLIFIERS

Although a large number of circuits for r.f. stages have been described from time to time, each with its advantages

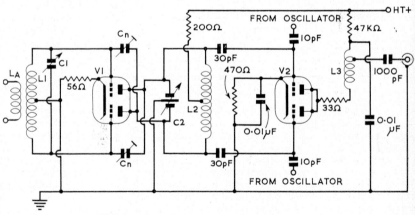

Fig. 14. Push-pull r.f. and mixer stages.

70 Mc/s	144 Mc/s
LA, 3 turns thin p.v.c. covered wire wound round L_1.	LA, 3turns thin p.v.c. wire wound round L_1.
L_1, 9 turns 18 s.w.g. $\frac{1}{2}$ in. diam., $\frac{7}{8}$ in. long.	L_1, 8 turns 20 s.w.g. $\frac{1}{4}$ in. outside diam. spaced one wire diam.
L_2, 11 turns 18 s.w.g. $\frac{1}{2}$ in. diam. self-supporting, $1\frac{1}{8}$ in. long.	L_2, 6 turns 20 s.w.g. $\frac{1}{4}$ in. diam. self-supporting approx. 1 in. long.
L_3, to suit i.f. in use.	L_3, to suit i.f. in use.
C_1, 4·7 pF.	C_1, not used.
C_2, not used.	C_2, 15 + 15 pF split stator.
C_n, 0·5—4 pF.	C_n, 0·5—4 pF.
$V_{1, 2}$, 6J6.	$V_{1, 2}$, 6J6.

and disadvantages, many of them are only slight modifications of the better known arrangements. For simplicity only the three basic types are discussed here: they are all suitable for use on frequencies below about 150 Mc/s. Whichever is built, it is strongly recommended that a copper or brass chassis be used to ensure the best possible connection for earth returns and a consequent reduction in circulating currents in the chassis and therefore better stability and gain.

No over-riding qualities can be claimed for any one of these circuits: each has its attractive features, and indeed improved performance from one circuit is more often the result of a fortuitous combination of layout or choice of optimum component values than a definite technical superiority. So far as the newcomer to v.h.f. work is concerned the simpler the circuit the greater the chance of success.

The choice of push-pull or single-ended input to the converter depends largely on whether a balanced or unbalanced aerial feeder is employed, and although a balanced-to-unbalanced transformer (balun) could be introduced to eliminate losses due to standing waves on the feeder, it may be preferable to avoid this complication by using an input circuit to suit the type of feeder in use.

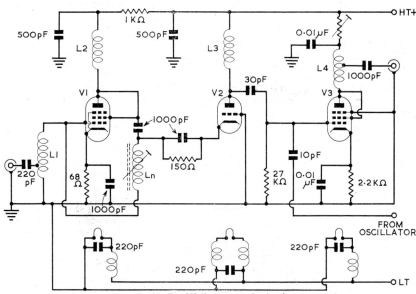

Fig. 15. The Wallman cascode circuit.

70 Mc/s	144 Mc/s

L_1, 10½ turns 18 s.w.g. ½ in. inside diam. ⅞ in. long, tapped 4¼ turns from earthy end.
L_2, 6 turns 20 s.w.g. on ⅜ in. diam. Aladdin former with dust iron core.
L_3, 5½ turns 20 s.w.g. close wound on ⅜ in. diam. Aladdin former with dust iron core.
L_n, 16 turns 26 s.w.g. close wound on ⅜ in. diam. Aladdin former with dust iron core.
Heater chokes, 40 in. 28 s.w.g. enam. close wound on 3/16 in. former.

L_1, 5 turns 16 s.w.g. ⅜ in. inside diam., tapped 3 turns from earthy end.
L_2, 4 turns 16 s.w.g. ⅜ in. inside diam.
L_3, 3½ turns 16 s.w.g. ⅜ in. inside diam.
L_n, 11 turns 26 s.w.g. enam. close wound on ⅞ in. Aladdin former with dust iron core.
Heater chokes, 20 in. 28 s.w.g. enam. close wound on 3/16 in. former.

$V_{1, 3}$, 6AK5; V_2, 6J4, EC91, 6L34 or half 6J6 (these types are not interchangeable). The pre-set variable resistor in the anode circuit of V_3 should be adjusted for best signal-to-noise ratio and a fixed resistor of suitable value substituted. Initially, it may be 100 K ohms.

Push-pull 6J6 R.f. Amplifier

Fig. 14 shows the circuit of the front-end of a converter employing a push-pull circuit arrangement in both the r.f. and mixer stages, the object being to reduce the capacitance across the tuned circuits by effectively putting the input and output capacitances of the valves in series and to cancel out the effect of the cathode lead inductance. Some additional gain is achieved by the step-up in signal voltage between the aerial input and the grids of the r.f. stage.

With the addition of a push-pull oscillator such as the Kalitron arrangement (Fig. 10) this circuit may be used as a complete converter; alternatively the r.f. stage alone may be built as a separate pre-amplifier for use with other converters. If this procedure is adopted an output link winding may conveniently be coupled to the centre of L_2 and the inductance of this coil adjusted to maintain resonance.

The layout of components should match that of the circuit diagram closely and all leads should be of the shortest possible length. To obtain the full advantages from this circuit every effort should be made to achieve complete symmetry in both the electrical and the mechanical features. A copper screen should be fixed across the chassis in such a position that the grid and anode circuits of the r.f. stage are shielded from each other. This screen should fit across the valveholder and be soldered to the centre lug and to the earthed heater pin.

As the amplifier valve is a triode it is necessary to neutralize the feedback between anode and grid circuits, not only to maintain stability but to achieve the optimum signal-to-noise ratio. For the neutralizing capacitors miniature air spaced trimmers of the type made by Wingrove and Rogers and having a capacitance range of 0·5–4·5pF are suitable.

Neutralizing is best accomplished by tuning to a strong signal and disconnecting the h.t. supply to the r.f. stage. The two neutralizing capacitors may then be adjusted in step, keeping the capacitances as nearly equal as possible, until the strength of the signal is reduced to a minimum, L_1 and L_2 being adjusted for maximum signal after each alteration of the neutralizing capacitors. The point of balance is quite sharp and care taken in this task will go far towards obtaining a good signal-to-noise ratio: for best results in this respect, however, a noise generator may be found more satisfactory. A detailed explanation of the use of noise generators is given in Chapter 19 (*Measurements*).

The 0·01μF cathode bypass capacitor in the mixer cathode circuit serves as a short circuit for the i.f. currents and should be of the non-inductive type.

The Cascode R.f. Amplifier

In the circuit shown in **Fig. 15** the first stage, which is a triode-connected 6AK5, operates at approximately unity gain but enables an effective impedance match to be obtained between the signal input circuit and the cathode input circuit of the grounded grid triode stage V_2. Neutralizing is necessary not so much to prevent instability in the first valve as to obtain the best noise factor, and is effected inductively by L_n. Owing to the heavy loading of L_2 by the low input impedance of V_2, the tuning of this circuit is very flat and its adjustment may therefore appear to be unimportant: however, much of the good performance of which the circuit is capable will be lost if care is not taken, preferably with the

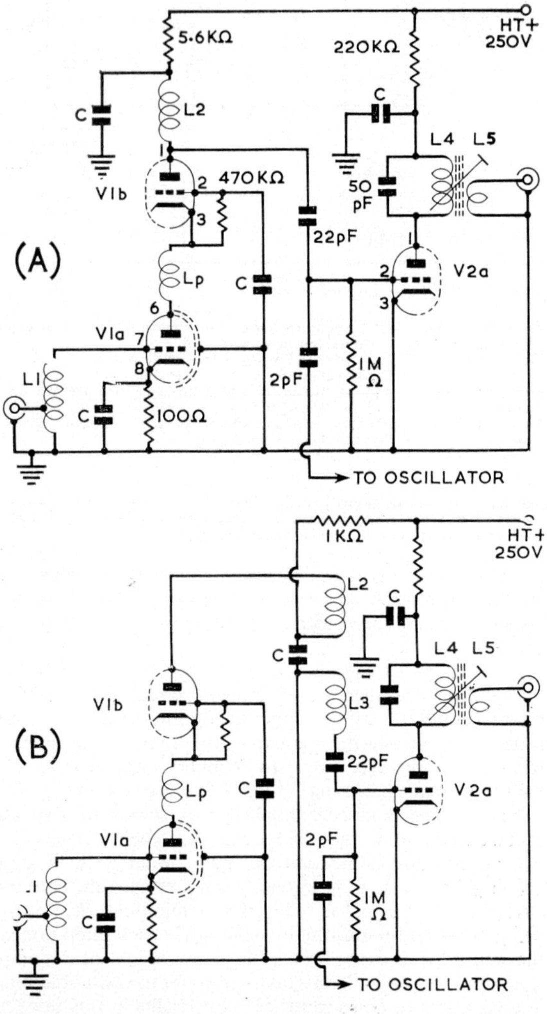

(A)

(B)

Fig. 16. Series cascode or driven grounded grid amplifiers with associated mixer stage. The arrangement in (B) gives appreciably more gain. All values in the two circuits are similar unless otherwise stated. All coils are $\frac{3}{8}$ in. diam. self-supporting and wound with 18 s.w.g L_1, $5\frac{1}{2}$ turns tapped $2\frac{1}{2}$ turns from earthy end; L_2, $3\frac{1}{2}$ turns (circuit(A)), $7\frac{1}{2}$ turns (circuit(B)); L_3 (circuit(B) only), $4\frac{1}{2}$ turns: coupling approximately $\frac{1}{16}$ in. from L_2; L_4, L_5, to suit i.f. in use; L_p, 5-7 turns 28 s.w.g. enam, $\frac{1}{16}$ in. diam. (exact size determined with aid of noise generator); V_1, 6BZ7, 6BQ7A, ECC85 (with reduced h.t.); V_2, 12AT7 (the other section may be used as the local oscillator). All capacitors marked C are 1,000 pF hi-K feedthrough type.

130

aid of a noise generator, to arrive at the optimum adjustment of L_2 and L_p.

The coils L_1 and L_2 should be shielded from one another by a screen mounted across the first valveholder. The neutralizing inductance L_p should be mounted through a hole in this screen with a clearance of approximately $\frac{1}{8}$ in. all round and at right angles to L_1 and L_p.

With h.t. removed from V_1 and a strong incoming signal, neutralization should be carried out by adjusting L_p for minimum response while keeping L_1 and L_2 tuned for maximum signal. Care should be taken to ensure that the anode circuit of V_2 is tuned to the signal frequency and not to the image on the wrong side of the oscillator frequency. If it is tuned to the image frequency any adjustment of L_3 will cause a decrease in signal strength whereas the background noise should rise to a distinct peak when L_3 is tuned to the correct frequency. When the circuit is operating satisfactorily the removal of V_1 from its valveholder should result in a marked drop in the noise level.

The circuit gives slightly more gain than does the push-pull 6J6 arrangement and it is possible to achieve a noise factor of 4db at 145 Mc/s.

Series Cascode or Driven Grounded Grid Circuit

This is one of the simpler types of r.f. amplifier circuit but is nevertheless capable of excellent results. Two versions are shown in **Figs. 16 (a) and (b)**. The latter possesses an additional tuned circuit (L_3) and gives appreciably higher gain but with some reduction in bandwidth although this is still adequate for complete coverage of the 2m band. No screening is necessary and there is no variable tuning, the inductances being adjusted by spreading or closing the turns. A grid dip oscillator is a useful aid although final adjustment should be made on incoming signals or with a noise generator.

As in any v.h.f. circuit, the quality of the bypass capacitors should be excellent and should preferably be of the feedthrough type soldered to the chassis. All r.f. leads should be as short as possible and may, with advantage, be thin strips of copper foil rather than wire in order to reduce the inductance.

The Grounded Grid Amplifier

With any triode r.f. amplifier some means must be adopted to prevent instability due to feedback between the input and output circuits. In the grounded grid configuration it is the grid, rather than the cathode, which is maintained at zero r.f. potential thus providing a screen between the cathode and anode which form the input and output electrodes respectively. Due to the low impedance of the cathode input circuit the grounded grid amplifier is by nature a wideband device and is thus well suited as a 144–146 Mc/s r.f. stage pretuned to the centre of the band.

Fig. 17 shows a two stage grounded grid amplifier employing EC91 (6J4) triodes which are specially designed for this service. The unit is intended to precede a converter which suffers from a poor signal-to-noise ratio and/or lack of gain, and the output arrangement is designed to suit the normal input impedance of a converter. The gain of the two valves in cascade is considerable and may not always be necessary, in which case only the second stage need be constructed and the input circuit of V_1 substituted for that shown for V_2.

The anode circuits are parallel fed and series tuned, the input to V_2 being developed across L_3 while its output appears across L_6. These inductances consist of copper strip cut and

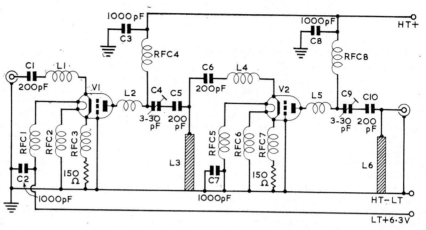

Fig. 17. Two-stage grounded grid triode amplifier. $C_{1, 5, 6, 10}$, 200 pF tubular ceramic or silver mica; $C_{2, 3, 7, 8}$, 1000 pF stand-off or micadisc; $C_{4, 9}$, 3-30 pF Philips trimmers or air-spaced preset capacitors; L_1, 8 turns 20 s.w.g. $\frac{1}{4}$ in. diam. spaced one wire diameter; $L_{2, 5}$, 4 turns 14 s.w.g. $\frac{3}{8}$ in. diam. spaced one wire diameter; L_4, 4 turns 20 s.w.g. $\frac{1}{4}$ in. diam. spaced one wire diameter; $L_{3, 6}$, $RFC_{1, 2, 3, 4, 5, 6, 7, 8}$, see Fig. 18; $V_{1, 2}$, EC91.

shaped as shown in **Fig. 18 (a)** and have an impedance of the order of 80 ohms at the operating frequency. Tuning is effected by the pre-set capacitors C_4 and C_9, and the inductance of L_2 and L_5 should be adjusted by altering the spacing of the turns until resonance occurs with a capacitance of 15–30pF. The input coil, L_1, serves to match the impedance of the 80 ohm input to that of the cathode circuit of V_1 and its adjustment has an important bearing on the noise factor of the circuit.

The two stage amplifier unit may be constructed in a chassis 8 in. $\times$ 2$\frac{1}{2}$ in. deep. Screens cut from thin copper sheet should be fixed across each valveholder and the earthed circuit connections for each stage made to them. The strip inductances L_3 and L_6 should be bolted or soldered to the screen associated with V_2 and to the end of the chassis near to the output socket respectively. Slight adjustments in the shape of L_3 and L_6 may be necessary to fit them neatly into

the layout adopted but they should not be appreciably altered.

The capacitors C_5 and C_{10} serve only to isolate the trimmers C_4 and C_9 from the h.t. and are not strictly necessary provided that the latter are capable of withstanding the voltage.

An important advantage to be gained from this amplifier is the almost complete elimination of i.f. breakthrough due to the special construction of the inductances L_3 and L_6 which allows them to act as very effective short circuits at all frequencies below the pass-band frequency.

In case of instability in this or any other v.h.f. circuit it is always worth trying the effect of an r.f. choke, suitable for the frequency in use, in the heater leads between valves in the signal frequency circuits. Details of such a choke will be found under Fig. 18 (b). Alternatively ferrite beads manufactured by Mullard, Plessey and Radiospares may be threaded on the heater connections in the positions where chokes would be inserted: they have the advantage of causing no voltage drop and of requiring very little space.

Valves for V.h.f. Operation

Valves specially designed for grounded grid service include the 6J4, EC91 and 6L34 on the B7G base and later types capable of operating at frequencies of the order of 900 Mc/s —6AJ4, 6AM4, 6AN4, PCC88 and G.E.C. A.2521 (6CR4), all on the B9A base. The G.E.C. A.2599 (6CT4) and the R.C.A. Nuvistor 6CW4 are excellent valves designed for the grounded cathode configuration.

The input impedance of a grounded grid triode is equal to $1/gm$ and for mutal conductances in the range 6–15 mA/V this implies impedances from 70 to 160 ohms. Such low impedances would tend to damp excessively any tuned circuit and for this reason it is usual to connect the aerial feeder directly to the cathode where the impedances are similar and to insert a small inductance in other cases. No signal voltage step up due to transformer action is possible as is the case when the input is between grid and cathode with the latter electrode at earth potential. The use of a tuned

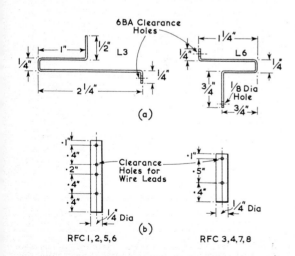

Fig. 18. (a) Detail of L_3 and L_6. Material 16 s.w.g. copper strip $\frac{1}{4}$ in. wide. **(b)** Detail of RFC_{1-8}. Material $\frac{1}{4}$ in. diam. polystyrene rod wound with approximately 20 in. wire. RFC_{1-2} and RFC_{5-6} are twin windings of 24 s.w.g. enam. wire close wound. RFC_{3-4} and RFC_{7-8} are wound with 34 s.w.g. enam. wire spaced to occupy the winding length. All formers are drilled and tapped 6 B.A. at the lower ends.

131

circuit is however, beneficial to reduce i.f. breakthrough or interference from strong local signals such as TV or f.m. broadcasting stations.

TYPICAL TWO AND FOUR METRE DESIGNS
R.S.G.B. CONVERTER CIRCUIT

This converter, using a double triode valve as a combined grounded grid r.f. amplifier and mixer, was designed primarily as a simple circuit for the newcomer to v.h.f. Despite its simplicity it is, however, capable of satisfactory performance and is in use in many stations. The circuit is shown in **Fig. 19.**

One section of a 12AT7 double triode valve (V_1) is connected as a grounded grid triode r.f. stage with the input circuit arranged to couple 80–100 ohm coaxial feeder to the cathode impedance. L_1 serves to match this impedance to the cathode input circuit of V_{1a} which is approximately 150 ohms. The function of the 3–30pF trimmer capacitor C_1 is primarily to prevent short circuiting the bias for V_{1a} when the aerial feeder has d.c. continuity but it also helps to tune out small amounts of reactance due to an imperfectly matched input system.

The coupled inductances L_2 and L_3 form an impedance matching network between the output of the g.g.t. stage and the triode mixer and it is here that sufficient gain is realized to provide adequate sensitivity and a good noise factor. L_2 is resonated at the centre of the band by C_3 and L_3 by its inductance and the input capacity of the mixer. The degree of coupling between these coils determines the bandwidth.

To ensure the best signal-to-noise ratio it is necessary to run V_{1b} at a low anode voltage, hence the high value of R_4.

By so doing, the gain of the stage is reduced to a certain extent, but as the noise falls more rapidly than the signal for reductions down to approximately 45 volts a net gain in the readability of weak signals is obtained.

C_5 forms a bypass for signal and oscillator frequencies present at the mixer anode and as it is part of the tuning capacity for the primary of the i.f. transformer in conjunction with C_6, it is possible to use a relatively large value without fear of bypassing the i.f. signal. To be fully effective in its dual role, C_5 should be of good quality and connected by short leads between the anode tag of the valveholder and the common earthing point of the stage.

The i.f. amplifier (V_2) is a 6AM6 but any r.f. pentode of similar characteristics could be employed in this position. The exact intermediate frequency is not important provided it is above 5 Mc/s; with the transformers described it is 10·2 Mc/s.

A second 12AT7 (V_3) is used as a Hartley oscillator/ doubler, the injection voltage for the mixer being taken from the anode of the doubler section. The injection frequency is on the *low* side of the signal. A split-stator tuning capacitor is used so that, as the rotor is left free, no r.f. current flows through the bearings, a major cause of noise and frequency jumping in v.h.f. oscillators. H.t. voltage to L_4 is fed through R_8 to the centre tap of the coil. It should be noted that this point is *not* bypassed to chassis as doing so is likely to result in instability and a poor note

The grid of the doubler section of the V_3 is driven via C_{16}, bias being produced across the grid leak R_{10}. The anode circuit comprises L_5, series tuned by the 8pF Philips trimmer C_{17}.

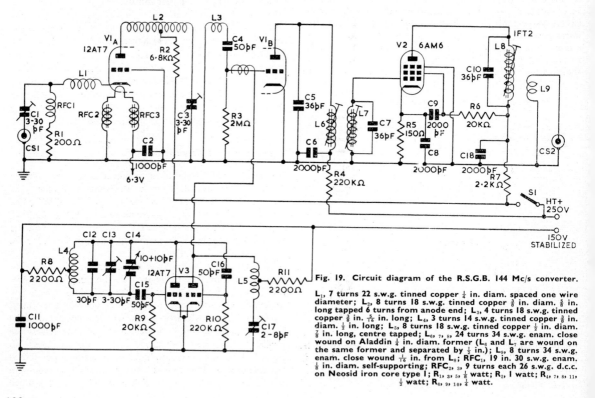

Fig. 19. Circuit diagram of the R.S.G.B. 144 Mc/s converter.

L_1, 7 turns 22 s.w.g. tinned copper $\frac{1}{4}$ in. diam. spaced one wire diameter; L_2, 8 turns 18 s.w.g. tinned copper $\frac{3}{8}$ in. diam. $\frac{5}{8}$ in. long tapped 6 turns from anode end; L_3, 4 turns 18 s.w.g. tinned copper $\frac{3}{8}$ in. $\frac{5}{16}$ in. long; L_4, 3 turns 14 s.w.g. tinned copper $\frac{3}{8}$ in. diam. $\frac{1}{2}$ in. long; L_5, 8 turns 18 s.w.g. tinned copper $\frac{1}{2}$ in. diam. $\frac{7}{8}$ in. long, centre tapped; $L_{6, 7, 8}$, 24 turns 34 s.w.g. enam. close wound on Aladdin $\frac{1}{4}$ in. diam. former (L_6 and L_7 are wound on the same former and separated by $\frac{1}{2}$ in.); L_9, 8 turns 34 s.w.g. enam. close wound $\frac{1}{16}$ in. from L_8; RFC$_1$, 19 in. 30 s.w.g. enam. $\frac{1}{4}$ in. diam. self-supporting; RFC$_{2, 3}$, 9 turns each 26 s.w.g. d.c.c. on Neosid iron core type 1; $R_{1, 3, 5}$, $\frac{1}{4}$ watt; R_2, 1 watt; $R_{4, 7, 8, 11}$, $\frac{1}{2}$ watt; $R_{6, 9, 10}$ $\frac{1}{4}$ watt.

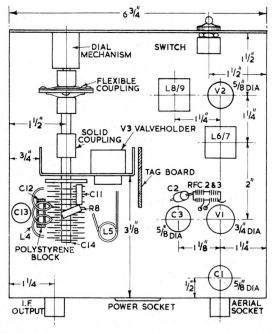

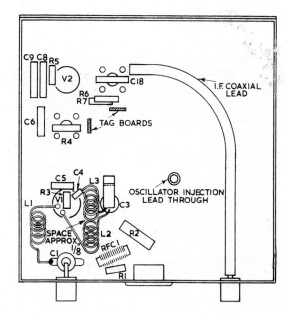

Fig. 20 (Left). Top view of the chassis showing the arrangement of the principal components. **(Right).** Layout of the components below the chassis.

Construction

The layout is shown in **Fig. 20** and is quite straightforward. The 30pF concentric trimmer (C_1) has its spigot bound to the centre conductor of the aerial socket with fine wire and is adjustable through the hole provided in the deck of the chassis. When making this joint care must be taken to avoid overheating, as both components are adversely affected by excessive heat. If the aerial plug is in position during the operation the pin of the socket will remain central, but the use of heat shunts in the form of crocodile clips is recommended.

C_3 is mounted on a small brass bracket and protrudes through the top of the chassis. L_2 is supported at one end by the anode tag of the valveholder (pin no. 1) and at the other is soldered to a lug on the body of C_3. The earthy end of L_3 is soldered to the bracket close to the point where the spigot of C_3 passes through, the two coils being arranged so that their inner faces are about $\frac{1}{8}$ in. apart. The other end of L_3 is attached to the mixer grid capacitor C_4 and no further support is necessary. The oscillator injection lead may be wrapped three times round the grid lead at this point.

The two r.f. chokes ($RFC_{2,3}$) in the heater leads to V_1 are mounted above the chassis and wound side by side on a Neosid iron core, the outer ends of the coils being soldered to the lead-out wires which then serve as supports: one end is connected to a tag placed under a bolt securing the p.t.f.e. valveholder for V_1 and the other to the top of the bypass capacitor C_2.

In the interests of freedom from pick-up of signals at the intermediate frequency, all leads to the i.f. amplifier should be short and the internal connections to the i.f. transformers should be so arranged that the external connections are as direct as possible. The shielding of the coaxial lead from L_9 to the output socket should be connected to

chassis at both ends though its length is unimportant.

All power supplies are taken through an octal plug and socket on the rear drop of the chassis. A switch is provided on the panel which, in its OFF position, removes h.t. from the r.f. and i.f. stages during transmission, leaving the mixer and oscillator operative so that it is possible to monitor a transmitter without overloading either the converter or the associated receiver.

Fig. 21. Rear view of the chassis showing the r.f./mixer valve in right foreground with trimmers C_1 and C_3. The oscillator/doubler assembly is to the left: C_{17} may be seen between the doubler coil L_5 and the chassis.

An underchassis view of the 144 Mc/s converter. L_1 and L_2 are in the right foreground. The co-axial lead feeds the i.f. signal from L_9 to the output socket CS_2 at the top right.

Adjustment

Set the main receiver to approximately 10·2 Mc/s and adjust the cores of L_6, L_7 and L_8 for maximum noise. The exact frequency is not important and some latitude is possible to avoid unwanted signals at the intermediate frequency. The gain from V_2 is such that the r.f./i.f. gain control setting in the main receiver will be quite low, resulting in no background noise being audible when the send/receive switch on the converter is at the SEND position.

The next step is to resonate L_3. With no h.t. on the r.f. stage, the oscillator should be adjusted to give injection at 145 Mc/s. (This may require the temporary removal of C_{12}.) L_5/C_{17} should tune to 145 Mc/s just short of minimum capacity. A meter with a f.s.d. of about 250 volts is then connected between the mixer anode and chassis and L_3 adjusted by opening or closing the turns until the *highest* meter reading is obtained. C_3 should be detuned to avoid inter-action between L_2 and L_3 and care taken that C_{17} maintains resonance in the output circuit of the doubler. C_{13} is then adjusted to set the oscillator to a frequency of $(145 - \text{i.f.})/2$, or 67·4 Mc/s with the i.f. mentioned above. This may be done with the aid of a grid dip oscillator or a closely calibrated absorption wavemeter. In the latter case it will be necessary to monitor the anode current of the oscillator and watch for the " kick " when L_4 passes through resonance.

The doubler anode circuit of V_3 should be set to the required injection frequency, i.e. twice that of the oscillator. If the circuit values are as shown, the only resonance point within the range of C_{17} will be the correct one. This will be indicated by a voltmeter connected between mixer anode and chassis as already described. By adjusting the spacing of L_4 and the capacity of C_{13} the 144–146 Mc/s band may be spread over the entire dial.

H.t. may next be applied to the r.f. and i.f. stages and C_3 tuned to resonance, which will be indicated by a considerable rise in the noise level. It is essential that the aerial be connected to load V_{1a}. It may be necessary to open or compress the turns of L_2 so that resonance occurs at about mid-capacity of C_3. Instability may be produced at low capacity settings of C_3, but if this happens make sure by rotating C_1 that this is not due to incorrect aerial loading.

All preliminary tuning adjustments should be made at mid-scale on C_{14} and if this capacitor is now tuned o'er its range the background noise should vary only slightly over the band. If there is a sharp falling off, tighter coupling between L_2 and L_3 is required, followed by readjustment of C_3 at 145 Mc/s.

C_1 is not a tuning control and no resonance effects should be found when it is adjusted, but at low capacity settings the grounded grid stage will almost certainly go into oscillation. Slight adjustments to the inductance of L_1 may be necessary and, if a noise generator is not available, these should be made for the best readability of a *weak* 'phone signal on approximately 145 Mc/s. With adjustments made as described there should be no difficulty in obtaining really satisfactory performance. The converter must not be connected to a balanced feeder without the addition of a balance-to-unbalance transformer or balun.

With this or any other converter the effects of varying the tuning or coupling adjustments as well as the h.t. voltage applied to the r.f. and mixer stages and the oscillator injection may best be examined with the aid of a noise generator, but although this is advisable to ensure optimum results it is possible to obtain an acceptable performance without this aid. It is most important to ensure that the heater voltage actually applied to the valves is in accordance with the maker's rating.

A LOW NOISE CRYSTAL-CONTROLLED CONVERTER FOR 144 MC/S

The circuit of a 144 Mc/s converter using the A.2599 (6CT4) and A.2521 (6CR4) is shown in **Fig. 22**.

V_1 (type A.2599) is a neutralized input stage, the valve being connected in a capacity bridge which is much simpler to neutralize than the more common inductive configuration. The input to V_2 (type A.2521), the grounded grid second valve of the cascode pair, is tapped down the anode circuit of the first stage, an arrangement which gives better performance compared with that in which the second stage is driven directly from the anode of the first valve. V_3 (type ECC85) is a double triode with an internal screen separating the two systems. The first section is employed as the mixer, while the second is used as a cathode follower to feed the main receiver. The fourth valve, V_4 (also type ECC85) is a crystal controlled oscillator-multiplier using either a 6 or 10 Mc/s crystal, the anode of the first triode being tuned to 30 Mc/s and the second to 120 Mc/s. The oscillator-multiplier is screened from the mixer, to the grid of which it is connected through a 2·5pF capacitor positioned in a clearance hole in the interstage screen.

Construction

The general arrangements above and below chassis are given in **Fig. 24**. The diagrams are drawn to scale so that they may be used for setting out the various components and locating the interstage screening. These screens are made from 18 s.w.g. aluminium sheet suitably bent, their overall height above the chassis plate being 2 in.

All the components including the screening are attached to the lid of a cast alloy box, to the layout shown in the diagrams. If the layout is altered, small adjustments to some of the inductances may be necessary. With the arrangements shown, no instability has been encountered.

The coils and r.f. chokes should be wound as follows:

L_1 (*aerial coupling*): 1 turn of sleeved 20 s.w.g. wire, $\frac{1}{2}$ in. internal diameter, close wound.

L_2 (*input coil*): $6\frac{1}{2}$ turns 16 s.w.g. spaced one wire diameter on $\frac{3}{8}$ in. diameter former, resonated by half dust core similar to that used in L_5.

L_3 (V_1 *anode coil*): $4\frac{3}{4}$ turns 16 s.w.g. spaced $1\frac{1}{2}$ wire diameters, $\frac{3}{8}$ in. internal diameter, tapped $1–1\frac{1}{2}$ turns from anode.

L_4 (V_2 *anode coil*): $3\frac{3}{4}$ turns 18 s.w.g. spaced 2 wire diameters, $\frac{3}{8}$ in. internal diameter, tapped $\frac{3}{4}–1\frac{1}{4}$ turns from anode.

L_5 (*i.f. coil*): 30 turns 26 s.w.g. close wound on $\frac{5}{16}$ in. former (Aladdin type PP5938) with iron dust core.

L_6 (*30 Mc/s oscillator coil*): $16\frac{1}{2}$ turns 18 s.w.g. close wound on $\frac{13}{32}$ in. Aladdin former with iron dust core.

L_7 (*120 Mc/s oscillator-multiplier coil*): $4\frac{1}{2}$ turns 18 s.w.g. $\frac{3}{8}$ in. internal diameter, $\frac{1}{8}$ in. between turns.

RFC$_1$: 26 in. (one-third of a wavelength) 26 s.w.g. enamelled, close wound on $\frac{1}{2}$ watt insulated resistor.

RFC$_2$: 26 in. (one-third of a wavelength) 18 s.w.g. p.v.c. sleeved, close wound, $\frac{1}{4}$ in. inside diameter.

Adjustment

With the various tuned circuits specified it is unlikely that there will be any difficulty in finding the correct oscillator and multiplier frequencies. The 144 Mc/s circuits can be readily tuned up initially with the aid of a grid dip oscillator or a

Fig. 23. Appearance of the low noise converter in its diecast case. The crystal is contained in the evacuated B7G holder to the left of the picture.

strong local signal. With the value of bias resistor specified for V_1 the anode resistor should be adjusted so that not more than 16 mA is drawn by this valve. Adjustment of the tuned circuits to obtain the best noise factor may next be carried using a noise generator as described in Chapter 19 (*Measurements*).

Neutralizing the input stage is quite straightforward. As will be seen from the layout diagrams the variable neutralizing capacitor is adjusted from above the chassis. This component is a 2–8pF concentric trimmer and neutralization occurs with the screw a little more than halfway in (about 5 to 5·5pF).

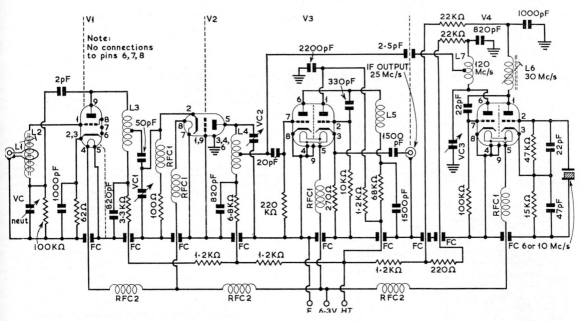

Fig. 22. Circuit diagram of the low noise crystal controlled converter for 144 Mc/s. The feedthrough capacitors are 4700 pF. VC, VC$_{1, 2, 3}$ are 3–9 pF adjustable capacitors (T.C.C. type CC195N or similar); V$_1$, G.E.C. A.2599 or 6CT4; V$_2$, G.E.C. A.2521 or 6CR4; V$_{3, 4}$, ECC85. The h.t. voltage should be 150 volts.

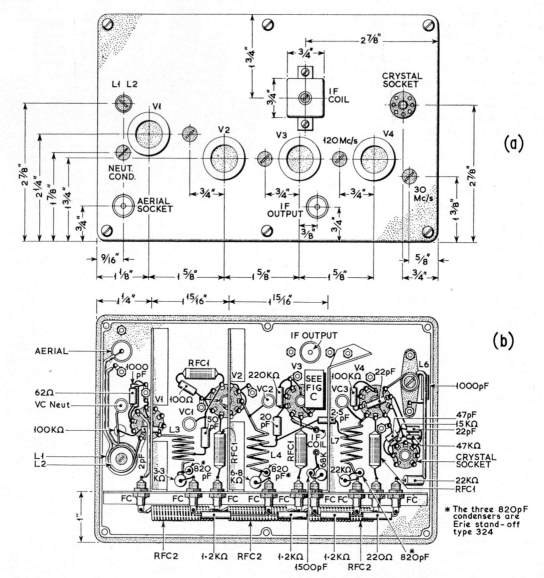

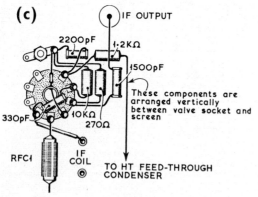

Fig. 24 (a). Above chassis layout showing the positions of the valves, i.f. coil, crystal, input and output sockets. (b) Component positions on the inside of the chassis plate. (c) Detail of the position of the components associated with the second triode (cathode follower) section of V_3. Most of these parts are mounted vertically one above another and cannot be clearly shown in (b).

A CRYSTAL-CONTROLLED CASCODE CONVERTER FOR 144 MC/S

The circuit of an inexpensive crystal controlled converter is shown in **Fig. 25** and comprises an ECC84 double triode (V_1) operating as a d.c. coupled cascode r.f. amplifier, followed by one half of a 12AT7 (V_2) as a grounded grid r.f. amplifier while the second half of the same valve serves as the mixer. Local oscillator injection is provided by one half of V_4 (12AT7) functioning as an overtone oscillator giving output on 21 Mc/s, the second half tripling to 63 Mc/s, followed by a 6C4 triode (V_3) doubling to 126 Mc/s. The

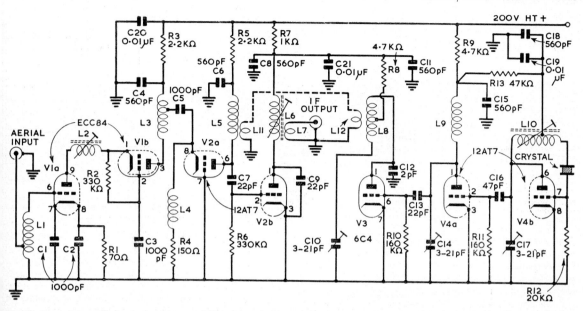

Fig. 25. Crystal controlled cascode converter designed by **VQ4EV.** An internal screen is connected to pin 2 (grid) of the ECC84 and pins I, 2, and 3 must therefore be used for the grounded grid stage. Similarly the two cathode connections (pins 7 and 8) should be used for the first triode.

$C_{1, 2, 3, 5}$, 1000 pF miniature.
$C_{4, 6, 8, 11, 15, 18}$, 560 pF pillar ceramicon.
$C_{7, 9, 13}$, 22 pF ceramicon.
$C_{10, 14}$ (both above chassis), C_{17} (below chassis), 3–21 pF ceramic trimmer.
C_{12} (for i.f.s. above about 12 Mc/s), 2 pF.
C_{16}, 47 pF ceramicon.
$C_{19, 20, 21}$, 0·01μF 500 volt wkg. (T.C.C. Metalmite).
L_1, 6 turns $\frac{3}{8}$ in. i.d. 20 s.w.g. tinned copper, tapped 1$\frac{1}{2}$ turns from earthy end (air spaced.)
L_2, 4 turns 22 s.w.g. enamelled on $\frac{1}{4}$ in. Aladdin polystyrene slug tuned former.
L_3, 7 turns $\frac{3}{8}$ in. 20 s.w.g. tinned copper tapped 3$\frac{1}{4}$ turns from h.t. feed end (air spaced).

L_4, r.f. choke—27 in. 36 s.w.g. enamelled on $\frac{1}{2}$ watt I Megohm resistor.
L_5, 5 turns $\frac{3}{8}$ in. i.d. 20 s.w.g. tinned copper (usually wide spaced turns).
L_6, 24 turns 22 s.w.g. enamelled on $\frac{1}{4}$ in. Aladdin polystyrene slug tuned former (for 18–20 Mc/s i.f.).
L_7, 4 turns 20 s.w.g. P.V.C. covered wound on earthy (h.t.) end of L_6.
L_8, 9 turns $\frac{3}{8}$ in. i.d. 20 s.w.g. tinned copper centre tapped (smaller for lower intermediate frequencies).
L_9, 7 turns $\frac{3}{8}$ in. i.d. 20 s.w.g. tinned copper (smaller for lower intermediate frequencies).
L_{10}, 30 turns 24 s.w.g. enamelled on $\frac{1}{4}$ in.

Aladdin polystyrene slug tuned former, tapped 5 turns from crystal end for h.t. feed.
$L_{11, 12}$, I turn 20 s.w.g. p.v.c. covered self-supporting link coupling coil.
R_1, 70 ohms $\frac{1}{4}$ watt.
$R_{2, 6}$, 330 K ohms, $\frac{1}{4}$ watt.
$R_{3, 5}$, 2·2 K ohms $\frac{1}{4}$ watt.
R_4, 150 ohms $\frac{1}{2}$ watt.
R_7, 1000 ohms $\frac{1}{2}$ watt.
$R_{8, 9}$, 4·7 K ohms $\frac{1}{2}$ watt.
$R_{10, 11}$, 160 K $\frac{1}{4}$ watt.
R_{12}, 20 K ohms $\frac{1}{2}$ watt.
R_{13}, 47 K $\frac{1}{2}$ watt.
Crystal, 21,000 kc/s, Q.C.C. overtone type on B7G base (or 7 Mc/s crystal operating on its third overtone).

anode circuit of V_3 is series tuned and link coupled to the mixer. The i.f. is 18–20 Mc/s.

All signal frequency coils are self-resonant with the interelectrode capacities of the valves and no difficulty should be experienced in peaking the circuits, provided good low inductance v.h.f. bypass capacitors of the ceramicon, disc ceramic or feedthrough types are used.

Construction

To avoid the contact resistance effects experienced with soldering tags when a slightly oxidized aluminium chassis is used, the chassis should be made of light gauge tinplate. Hardly any nuts and screws are needed, as valveholders, coaxial sockets and tags can all be soldered to the chassis. This provides a very efficient connection, is easily carried out with a small iron and reduces the amount of metalwork required. As the oscillator is crystal controlled, the use of a light chassis does not affect the frequency stability of the converter. Additionally, the use of tinplate makes it easy to provide short direct connections to earth points while screening is easy to construct and install. The under-chassis layout is shown in **Fig. 26.**

All h.t. and l.t. supplies are fed along the top of the chassis

passing through holes immediately above the respective h.t. filter resistor or heater pin, at which point they are decoupled to earth. This leaves the various screening compartments free from being cluttered up with h.t. and l.t. wiring and enables the compact construction to be carried out without difficulty. It also reduces the possibility of feedback coupling along these supply wires and the stray capacities of tuned circuits to earth. The careful screening of the oscillator and multiplier stages tends to minimize the danger of swamping the mixer with unwanted injection frequencies, thus main-

A view of the 144 Mc/s converter of Fig. 25.

137

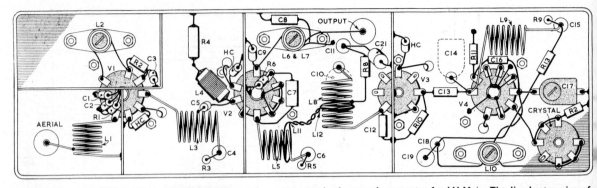

Fig. 26. The sub-chassis layout showing the position of the components in the cascode converter for 144 Mc/s. The live heater pins of each valve (except V_2) are by-passed to earth with 1000 pF miniature capacitors. Incoming h.t. positive and live heater leads are by-passed to chassis with $0.01 \mu F$ 500 volt Metalmite capacitors at the point of connection to the unit.

taining optimum mixer operation. It also reduces spurious responses in other parts of the v.h.f. spectrum. The two variable capacitors used for the oscillator/multiplier chain are mounted above the chassis for ease of access and saving of space within the screening compartments. The i.f. output, cascode and oscillator coil tuning slugs are also adjustable from above the chassis. These coils are wound on miniature $\frac{1}{4}$ in. diameter Aladdin type formers.

The valveholders are made of p.t.f.e. This is especially important for V_1, although poorer v.h.f. insulating materials can be used for the other stage valveholders with no noticeable deterioration in performance.

Adjustment

The crystal oscillator is the first section to be adjusted. If the circuit constants are correct, merely rotating the slug of the oscillator coil L_{10} should produce crystal controlled output on 21 Mc/s. However to allow for circuit discrepancies a small variable capacitor (C_{17}) is also included, so that the actual tuning range of the oscillator is quite broad. This is doubly useful as wide ranges of intermediate frequency can be employed using the same oscillator components. The second stage can be aligned by placing a micro-ammeter in series with the grid leak (R_{10}) to V_3 at the earthy end. The anode circuit of the second half of V_{4a} (L_9/C_{14}) is then adjusted for maximum grid drive into V_3. This can be checked with an absorption wavemeter or grid dip oscillator covering 63 Mc/s. The last oscillator chain circuit (L_8/C_{10}) is finally adjusted for maximum on an incoming signal, but a rough peak can be found when the coil has been resonated as described later.

To tune the i.f. output coil, L_6, the converter is fed into a receiver set to 19 Mc/s (or any other intermediate frequency with a suitable crystal) and an h.f. band aerial temporarily clipped to the mixer grid. This should cause either strong signals to be picked up at the i.f. or the mixer valve to burst into oscillation. In either eventuality this output is peaked at the required i.f. by adjusting the slug in L_6, but more careful adjustment should be made later on with incoming signals. With the i.f. output coil roughly resonant it should be possible to hear a slight, but noticeable, increase in background noise when the anode tuned circuit of V_3 is resonated. The injection output can also be checked by means of an absorption wavemeter covering 126 Mc/s or by using a g.d.o. as in the case of the 63 Mc/s stage.

If no signal generator covering 145 Mc/s is available, a 2m aerial should be connected to the converter and a strong local station tuned in. The signal frequency coils L_1, L_3 and L_5, may then be peaked by altering the spacing of the turns whilst carefully watching the "S" meter on the main receiver. This could also be done by ear with the a.g.c. switched off but a meter provides a more positive indication. The adjustment of the aerial input and mixer grid coils is fairly broad, but the cathode coil (L_3) of the second grounded grid stage will be found somewhat sharper. If strong signals are few, it is advisable to start the signal frequency circuit adjustments with L_3. Properly adjusting this coil to resonance will make weaker stations more easily audible.

When incoming signals are available it is a good plan to re-peak all the oscillator chain circuits by means of their trimmers to give the maximum "S" meter reading and also to re-peak the signal-frequency coils on signals near the centre of the band. By this stage in the alignment procedure car ignition and other unwanted noises should be easily heard and the set-up should sound quite "lively." Adjustment of the cascode peaking coil L_2 is unnecessary for run-of-the-mill work, but for serious v.h.f. operation it is essential to use a noise generator and measure the noise factor of the converter with each half turn of the slug. This may sound tedious, but in actual fact the correct position can usually be found without difficulty. On some models it has been found necessary to reduce the peaking coil by one turn to obtain the best noise figure.

TRANSISTORIZED 144 MC/S CONVERTER

The availability at reasonable prices of transistors suitable for use at frequencies of up to 200 Mc/s makes the construction of transistorized crystal controlled converters a practical proposition for the amateur. The principal advantages of such a converter are compactness, portability and complete independence of mains supplies coupled with very low running costs.

The unit shown in **Fig. 27** has a very good noise factor, while the gain is somewhat higher than a conventional five valve converter although the battery consumption is only 10 mA at 12 volts.

Circuit

The circuit of the complete converter is shown in **Fig. 28.** TR_1 (a 2N1742/T.1832 micro-alloy diffused base type) operates as an earthed emitter neutralized r.f. amplifier, while L_1, C_1 comprise the input tuned circuit. The 72 ohm aerial feeder is tapped down L_1 in order to effect the optimum impedance match to the base of TR_1 to obtain the best noise factor rather than maximum power transfer. (This tapping point may vary with different specimens of transistor.) L_2 is the isolating winding feeding the base of TR_1.

From the standpoint of power transfer there is little advantage to be gained from tuning the base circuit but it does provide some selectivity and a higher impedance across which to connect a protection diode (see Chapter 3—*Semiconductors*). L_3, C_5 provide the collector tuned circuit to TR_1. C_2 and L_{3A} provide neutralization of the collector base capacitance: the adjustment is very critical and can only be carried out with the aid of a noise generator if the lowest noise factor is to be achieved. C_1 and L_2 must be screened from L_3 to prevent instability. When properly neutralized the noise level decreases when the aerial is disconnected.

L_3, C_5 is top end coupled to $L4$, C_7, via a 1pF capacitor, C_6. A screen is placed between L_3 and L_4, an arrangement which increases front-end selectivity and reduces the chances of i.f. breakthrough. L_4, L_5 provide a step-down transformer coupling to the base of TR_2 (a 2N1743/T.1833) which is employed as a mixer in the earthed emitter mode, oscillator injection being in series with the emitter. Potentiometer base biasing is used to provide a standing collector current of about 1 mA. L_6, C_{12} are tuned to the tunable i.f., the output impedance giving sufficient damping to realize a 2 Mc/s bandwidth.

Fig. 27. A transistor 144 Mc/s crystal controlled converter. The crystal is a B7G type at the rear left of the chassis.

A head i.f. amplifier employing a 2N1745/T.1858 (TR_3) as a neutralized grounded emitter is built into the converter and provides more than adequate gain to mask any i.f. breakthrough with all but the most poorly screened receivers used as tunable i.f. strips and is controllable by varying the base bias. It is possible to connect the converter to the main

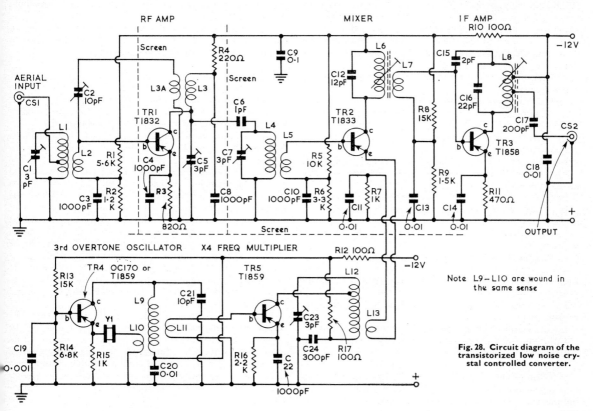

Fig. 28. Circuit diagram of the transistorized low noise crystal controlled converter.

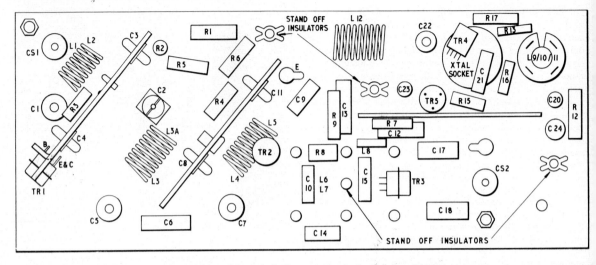

Fig. 29. Under-chassis layout of the principal components in the transistor 144 Mc/s converter.

receiver a.g.c. line so that the mixer stage in the main receiver is not overloaded, a common cause of cross-modulation.

The oscillator chain is crystal controlled and employs two transistors. An OC170 (TR₄) functions as a grounded base overtone oscillator with a potentiometer biasing network adjusted for highest output consistent with reliability. A 10·3583 Mc/s crystal operating on its third overtone controls the frequency at approximately 31·075 Mc/s. The second transistor, a 2N1744/T.1859 (TR₅), is employed as a frequency quadrupler to 124·3 Mc/s. This stage is biased by the drive from TR₄ but a limiting resistor R₁₆ is used in the emitter circuit to ensure that the dissipation is kept below the maximum ratings of the device and to reduce the chance of thermal runaway.

The coils are wound as follows:

L₁: 8 turns 18 s.w.g. $\frac{5}{16}$ in. inside diameter, $\frac{5}{8}$ in. long, tapped 2 turns from earthy end.

L₂: 1 turn 22 s.w.g. covered with sleeving and interwound at earthy end of L₁.

L₃: 9½ turns 18 s.w.g. $\frac{5}{16}$ in. inside diameter, $\frac{3}{4}$ in. long.

L₃ₐ: 1 turn 18 s.w.g., sleeved, and spaced one wire diameter from earthy end of L₃.

L₄: 8 turns 18 s.w.g. $\frac{5}{16}$ in. inside diameter, $\frac{5}{8}$ in. long.

L₅: 1 turn 22 s.w.g. covered with sleeving and interwound at the earthy end of L₄.

L₆: 20 turns 30 s.w.g. close wound on $\frac{1}{4}$ in. former in screening can.

L₇: 2 turns 30 s.w.g. interwound at cold end of L₆.

L₈: 22 turns 30 s.w.g. close wound on a $\frac{1}{4}$ in. diameter former in screening can. The winding is tapped at 16 and 18 turns from the collector end and slug tuned.

L₉: 15 turns 30 s.w.g. close wound on a $\frac{1}{4}$ in. diameter former, slug tuned.

L₁₀, ₁₁: 1 turn 30 s.w.g. interwound at the cold end of L₉.

L₁₂: 9½ turns 18 s.w.g. $\frac{5}{16}$ in. diameter, $\frac{3}{4}$ in. long, tapped 3 turns from C₂₂ end.

L₁₃: 1 turn link interwound at cold end of L₁₂.

It should be appreciated that in view of transistor production spreads the circuit values given are not necessarily the optimum for any particular set of transistors.

The general layout may be seen in **Fig. 29** and follows normal practice, i.e. short leads and in-line layout with the aerial input socket remote from the oscillator stage and the i.f. output socket. The base and collector circuits of the r.f. amplifier are screened from each other and the r.f. amplifier collector and mixer base coils should also be screened from one another in order that all the coupling between them should be via C₆ alone.

The oscillator section should be screened from the i.f. section and L₆/L₇ and L₈ should be in screening cans to minimize magnetic coupling between them.

Adjustment

After the wiring has been carefully checked, 12 volts d.c. may be applied and the total current consumed noted. It should be between 10 and 15 mA. Care should be taken to see that the *correct polarity of the battery* is observed.

The oscillator chain should be aligned first. The slug in the coil assembly L₉/L₁₀/L₁₁ should be carefully adjusted while monitoring the crystal overtone frequency (31·075 Mc/s) until a point is reached where altering the slug causes no appreciable change to the note received. The power should then be switched off and quickly on again to check that the oscillator remains on the same frequency; if it does not, some slight adjustment of the slug in L₉/L₁₀/L₁₁ will be necessary. If the oscillator refuses to oscillate or cannot be locked to the crystal, the biasing of TR₄ should be checked. The next step is to test the multiplier TR₅. It is important that the total current drawn by this stage should not exceed 5 mA; if it does the transistor may be damaged. Reducing the drive from TR₄ or increasing the value of R₁₆ will maintain the dissipation at a safe level.

The current flowing through the mixer transistor TR₂ should be approximately 1 mA initially. C₂₃ should then be adjusted until the current rises to 40 per cent higher. If an absorption wavemeter tuned to the required injection frequency (124·3 Mc/s) is held close to L₁₂ there should be a dip in the mixer current. The use of a g.d.o. is *not* recommended because of the possibility of damage to the transistors.

The battery supply to the r.f. amplifier TR_1 should next be disconnected and the i.f. amplifier coils peaked for maximum noise over the tuning range. The noise level should be flat over the full 2 Mc/s. Peakiness indicates instability which is best overcome by changing the value of the neutralizing capacitor C_{15} which could well be a small 10pF trimmer.

When the i.f. coils have been aligned, the supply to TR_1 can be reconnected and with C_2 set at a low value, C_1, C_5 and C_7 adjusted for maximum noise output. At this stage an aerial can be connected and ignition noises should become apparent.

The various stages can next be peaked up on a strong local signal. C_2 should be adjusted for minimum noise output. Adjustment of the tuning of C_1, L_1 and the aerial tapping point on L_1 may also be needed. The TR_1 collector tapping point on L_3 may also need attention as may the level of oscillator injection and biasing of the mixer stage (TR_2). All these adjustments are best carried out using a noise generator.

A 144 MC/S PRE-AMPLIFIER

A pre-amplifier that will improve the noise factor of all but the very best 144 Mc/s converters (i.e., those using valves such as the 416B, EC57 or A.2599/A.2521 cascode combination) is shown in **Fig. 30**. At the same time, it provides additional signal frequency amplification of about 20db.

The pre-amplifier employs a 6CW4 Nuvistor valve manufactured by R.C.A. for use as a low noise r.f. amplifier in Band V television tuners and similar applications. Its low noise performance is due to its mutual conductance of 12·5 mA/V at an anode current of only 8 mA.

The 6CW4 is employed in the conventional grounded cathode mode (**Fig. 31**) but uses capacity bridge rather than inductive neutralization as the former performs satisfactorily over a wider bandwidth. For this reason the noise factor of the pre-amplifier remains constant to within 0·1db over the range 144–146 Mc/s whilst the overall gain is approximately 20db. The balance of the bridge is upset if VC_2 is detuned to any great extent but the amount is negligible over the 144–146 Mc/s band.

Construction

The pre-amplifier is constructed in a $3\frac{1}{2}$ in. $\times$ $4\frac{1}{2}$ in. $\times$ 2 in.

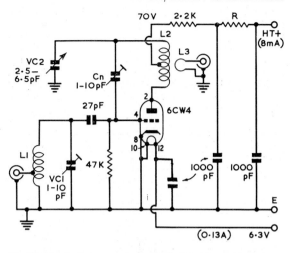

Fig. 31. Circuit diagram of the pre-amplifier shown in Fig. 30. L_1, 5 turns 20 s.w.g. tinned copper, $\frac{1}{4}$ in. inside diameter $\frac{3}{4}$ in. long tapped at $1\frac{3}{4}$ turns from earthy end; L_2, 8 turns 16 s.w.g. enamelled copper, $\frac{7}{16}$ in. inside diameter 1 in. long tapped at $4\frac{1}{2}$ turns from anode end; L_3, 1 turn link of insulated wire around the centre of L_2. It is the minimum value of C_n not the maximum, that is important.

deep Eddystone die-cast box which contains both the circuitry and the valve. A layout diagram is shown in **Fig. 32.** The input coil L_1 is tuned by means of a miniature Wingrove and Rogers 1–10pF air spaced trimmer but if such a trimmer is not available it is possible to adjust the circuit to resonance by compressing or pulling apart the turns of the coil. The anode circuit is tuned by a Wingrove and Rogers 2·5–6·5pF air spaced variable and is fitted with a knob to give the operator the psychological satisfaction of knowing that the r.f. circuit is on the peak of resonance. A small variation is necessary from one end of the 144–146 Mc/s band to the other though, in practice, the variable capacitor can be used to peak the circuit at 145 Mc/s and then left alone. The neutralizing capacitor is also a Wingrove and Rogers 1–10pF miniature air spaced trimmer. It is important that this

Fig. 30. An interior view of the 144 Mc/s pre-amplifier employing a 6CW4 Nuvistor valve.

141

capacitor should have a minimum capacity as low as 1pF and for this reason the concentric type of trimmer is unsatisfactory in this application. If a suitable variable capacitor is not available a piece of flat 80 ohm twin feeder can be used instead, and the length progressively reduced to obtain neutralization. This method has been used effectively in push-pull 6J6 amplifiers for a number of years. The output is taken off by means of one turn loop L_3 wound around the centre of L_2.

The valve is operated in accordance with the maker's recommendation with zero bias and with an h.t. of 70 volts, which is adjusted during the initial tests by selecting a suitable value for R ($8 \cdot 2$ K ohms, 1 watt is satisfactory for a 170 volt supply). Power supplies are fed to the amplifier through 1000 pF feedthrough capacitors.

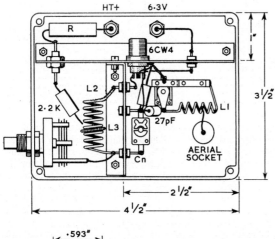

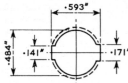

Fig. 32 (Above). Layout diagram. The output socket is mounted immediately below L_2. (Left) Chassis cut-out for the Cinch Nuvistor socket.

The Nuvistor valve requires a special socket (a Cinch type 133–65–10–001) which is soldered by its two fixing lugs to a brass sub-chassis. The dividing partition is also made o brass and on it the anode coil L_2 and neutralizing capacitor C_n are mounted on miniature feedthrough insulators (K.L.G. type or similar).

Adjustment

A strong local signal or signal generator is necessary to adjust the pre-amplifier correctly. A suitable receiver (e.g. converter plus main receiver) should be tuned to a signal around 145 Mc/s and the pre-amplifier without h.t. connected inserted between the aerial and the input of the converter and VC_1 and VC_2 adjusted for maximum signal. C_n should next be adjusted for minimum signal using a non-metallic trimmer screwdriver. This minimum will be found to be very sharp and care is needed to effect the correct adjustment.

H.t. should then be connected to the pre-amplifier when the signal will, of course, be very much stronger. If the neutralizing has been correctly carried out, the pre-amplifier

will be stable and there will be no spurious signals as VC_2 is tuned at either end of the 144–146 Mc/s band. It may be found that instability occurs if VC_2 is grossly mistuned but this is because the capacity bridge has become unbalanced. It does not indicate that the amplifier is unsatisfactory within the range 144–146 Mc/s. Final adjustment should be carried out with the aid of a noise generator (see Chapter 19—*Measurements*) for optimum noise factor.

CONVERTER FOR 70 MC/S

The 70 Mc/s converter described here is quite conventional and is based on well-tried 144 Mc/s techniques. It is divided into two parts: a pre-amplifier and a main converter unit.

The pre-amplifier (**Fig. 33**) employs a grounded grid triode and is built as a self-contained unit. As the input impedance of the grounded grid triode is about 100 ohms with the valve employed, no useful voltage step-up can be achieved between the aerial and the cathode, and therefore the input is connected directly to V_1. The tuned circuit L_1, C_1 is used to tune out circuit reactance and to provide a measure of front-end selectivity, the cathode of V_1 being tapped well down the coil to prevent heavy circuit damping. The anode circuit has a low C, high Q tank circuit from which the output is link coupled.

L_2, L_3 is a bifilar wound self-resonant r.f. choke. However, it would be quite satisfactory to use instead two heater chokes of the type employed in the converter. All the chokes are wound to be self-resonant at $70 \cdot 3$ Mc/s.

The converter (**Fig. 34**) comprises a 6AK5/EC91 (6J4) parallel connected cascode, followed by a 6AK5 triode-connected mixer, a 9002 tunable oscillator operating on the *low* side of the signal frequency and finally a 6AK5 triode-connected cathode follower giving a nominal i.f. output at 7 Mc/s.

The grounded cathode triode of the cascode is neutralized by L_2 resonating with the anode/grid capacity of the valve. This only serves to improve the noise factor of the cascode a little and is unnecessary if the pre-amplifier is employed but is included in case the converter is used alone. It is unnecessary to provide adjustable tuning for L_3 as the circuit bandwidth is large because of the circuit damping caused by the low input impedance of V_2.

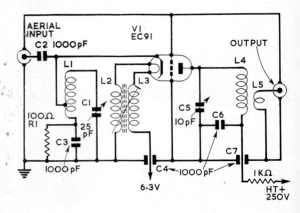

Fig. 33. Circuit of the 70 Mc/s pre-amplifier.

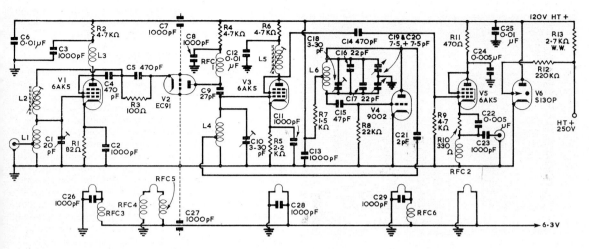

Fig. 34. A converter for 70 Mc/s. Details of the coils are given in Table I.

V_3 operates as an anode bend mixer with the local oscillator injection introduced at a tap on the mixer grid coil L_4. The local oscillator tuned circuit L_6, C_{16}, C_{17}, C_{18}, C_{19} and C_{20}, has a large fixed capacity to swamp valve capacity changes during the warm-up period. The tuning range is restricted so that 180° of the dial represents a tuning range of 70–70·6 Mc/s. The mixer anode circuit is broadly resonant and is capacity coupled into the cathode follower V_5.

Construction

The pre-amplifier is constructed on a $3\frac{3}{4}$ in. × 3 in. × 2 in. deep brass or copper box with an internal partition to separate the anode and cathode circuitry. This screen is made to fit snugly over the suitably orientated B7G valveholder and is soldered to the chassis and to pins 1 and 6 and the spigot of the valveholder. Both tuning capacitors are mounted in one side of the box, and project through the front panel of the complete converter unit.

The converter is built on a copper or brass chassis 8 in. × 2 in. × 2 in. deep **(Fig. 35)**. A partition is soldered in a similar manner to that used in the pre-amplifier over the

valveholder for V_2. The three coils L_1, L_2 and L_3 are mounted on mutually perpendicular axes to prevent interaction between the tuned circuits. Winding details are given in **Table 1**.

The r.f. chokes, with the exception of RFC_2, are made in the following manner. The 24 s.w.g. wire is close wound on to a $\frac{1}{4}$ in. mandrel and then painted with polystyrene cement. When it is dry, the coil is removed. The iron core is made from a standard $\frac{3}{8}$ in. diameter slug filed down until it is a push fit into the coil. The ends are then sealed with polystyrene cement.

Alignment

On completion of the wiring, the simplest method of aligning the r.f. tuned circuits is by means of a grid dip oscillator. If this is not available it is possible to find the band in the following manner. The converter is connected to a suitable power supply and the i.f. output to a receiver tuned to 7 Mc/s. The local oscillator is set to approximately 65 Mc/s using an absorption wavemeter and L_5 and C_{10} are then tuned for maximum noise output. C_1 should next be tuned, resonance being indicated by a pronounced increase in noise (resonance should occur with C_1 approximately half meshed).

Finally, the neutralizing coil L_2 should be adjusted for

TABLE I

Pre-amplifier

$L_{1, 4, 5}$, 16 s.w.g. tinned copper wound on $\frac{3}{8}$ in. diameter mandrel, spacing one wire diameter (L_1, 5 turns, tapped at $1\frac{3}{4}$ turns; L_4, $9\frac{1}{2}$ turns; L_5, 2 turns).
$L_{2, 3}$, Bifilar close-wound, 11 turns each 24 s.w.g. enam. copper. Former $\frac{3}{8}$ in. diam. smooth iron-dust core (see text).

Main Converter

$L_{1, 4, 6}$, 16 s.w.g. tinned copper wound on $\frac{3}{8}$ in. diam. mandrel, spacing one wire diam. (L_1, 7 turns tapped at 3 turns; L_4, 5 turns tapped at $1\frac{1}{2}$ turns; L_6, 3 turns.)
L_3, 11 turns 20 s.w.g. tinned copper wound on $\frac{3}{8}$ in. diam. slug tuned Aladdin former, turns spaced one wire diam.
L_3, 10 turns 20 s.w.g. tinned copper wound on $\frac{3}{8}$ in. diam. mandrel, spaced one wire diam.
L_5, 49 turns 38 s.w.g. enam. copper, close-wound on $\frac{3}{8}$ in. diam. slug tuned Aladdin former.
$RFC_{1, 3, 4, 5, 6}$, 21 turns 24 s.w.g. double silk covered, $\frac{1}{4}$ in. diam. (see text).
RFC_2, 2·5mH.

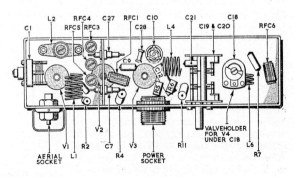

Fig. 35. Under-chassis layout.

A view under the chassis of the 70 Mc/s pre-amplifier. The anode circuit is on the left of the picture.

minimum signal output when tuned to a local signal with the h.t. disconnected from V_1.

In the pre-amplifier, the two turn link L_5 is spaced about $\frac{1}{8}$ in. from the end of the anode coil L_4. With the output coupled to the converter and power applied, C_5 should be tuned for maximum hiss. With the aerial connected C_1 should be adjusted for *minimum* hiss.

U.H.F. RECEIVERS

The 70cm band involves an increase in frequency of three times that used for the 2m band and the 23cm band a further increase of three times. Since the losses in dielectrics, the r.f. skin effects in conductors and valve transit time losses increase rapidly as the frequency is raised, particular care must be exercised in the choice of components, materials and valves for use on the u.h.f. bands if high performance is to be achieved.

Metal parts which form any part of, or are within the field of, a tuned circuit or carry r.f. currents, should be of copper or brass and not of steel or aluminium although these materials may be used if they are silver plated to an adequate thickness for the frequency in use. Where facilities are available, it is best to plate all such parts. They should however not be polished but left matt and protected from tarnish by lacquering. Insulating materials used in or near tuned circuits or in the manufacture of valveholders should be of p.t.f.e. (fluon), polystyrene or polythene. Such materials as Perspex, ceramic, mica or p.v.c. should be employed only with caution; Bakelite and nylon should not be used.

A number of valve types using glass bases require several of the pins to be effectively earthed to achieve stability; short lengths of wire to adjacent tags on the chassis are not sufficient for this purpose. One convenient method is to mount an earthing collar around the valveholder and to bolt it firmly or solder it to the chassis; the appropriate valveholder tags can then be soldered to the collar, as shown in **Fig. 36.** Where valve electrodes require decoupling to earth, feedthrough capacitors should be used. These should be mounted as closely as practi-

cable to the valveholder tag. Those capacitors built into cavities and similar constructions should be made of p.t.f.e. or polythene film clamped between metal surfaces.

TUNED CIRCUITS

As the resonant frequency of a tuned circuit is raised the capacitance and inductance must be reduced until a point is reached at which the necessary inductance becomes so small that it is impracticable to use the ordinary type of coil construction and it assumes the form of a hairpin loop. **Fig. 37** illustrates how progressively high frequencies are attained. **Fig. 37(b)** is frequently employed on 70cm while **Fig. 37(c)** is similar to a butterfly circuit where the capacitor is of the split-stator type. **Fig. 37(d)** represents a multiplication of this structure and in **Fig. 37(e)** there is in effect an infinite number of loops in parallel, i.e. a cylinder closed at both ends with a central rod and known as a *coaxial cavity*. The capacitance element is provided by a threaded rod T, which passes through a threaded end-plate; a disc D_1 is fixed to the lower end of the rod so that it is parallel to a similar disc D_2 attached to a central support. The simple hairpin, shown at Fig. 37(b), is

Fig. 36. Photograph of a B9A valveholder with an earthing collar used to earth the grounded electrodes of a valve. Slots are provided adjacent to tags connected to the external circuit. Leadthrough bypass capacitors are mounted close to the socket.

a very convenient form of construction: it can be made of wide strip rather than wire and is especially suitable for push-pull circuits. It may be tuned by parallel capacitance at the open end P or by series capacitance inserted at the closed end S. In a modification of the hairpin loop, one side can consist of a straight wire or strip while the other side is a sheet of metal which can be part of the chassis, the strip being spaced from the metal; such an arrangement is known as a *strip line*. When very close to the metal sheet but insulated from it by a solid dielectric film, it is known as a *microstrip*.

All of these resonant elements can be either series or parallel tuned. Tuned circuits in the form of hairpin loops or strip lines can be used quite successfully up to about 700 Mc/s; above this frequency butterfly circuits or coaxial

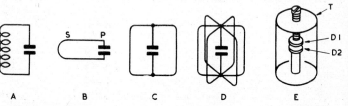

Fig. 37. Progressive development of tuned circuits from a coil to a cavity as the frequency is increased.

cavities must be employed. Because a cylindrical cavity usually requires the use of a lathe for its construction, a simpler type in the form of a trough which can be made with hand tools is frequently used: see **Fig. 38.** The open side may be closed with a well-fitting lid if required: the omission of the lid only reduces the Q slightly. One end of the trough is

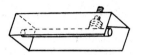

Fig. 38. A trough line tuned circuit.

closed by a plate to which the inner line is secured and the three edges of the plate must make a sound low resistance connection with the trough, preferably by soldering. Tuning may be effected by a disc type capacitor or a small trimmer connected between it and the end of the inner line.

A cavity or trough line must have dimensions for the frequency used and the stray capacitance associated with the valve or crystal connected to it. The dimensions can be calculated from the basic equation

$$l = \frac{\lambda}{2\pi} \, tan^{-1} \frac{1}{2\pi f Z_0 C}$$

where l is the length in the same units as wavelength, f is the frequency in cycles per second, C is the capacitance (total) in Farads, Z_0 is the characteristic impedance in ohms.

The formula may be more conveniently rewritten as

$$l = \frac{30,000}{2\pi f} \, tan^{-1} \frac{10^6}{2\pi f Z_0 C}$$

where l is in centimetres, f is in Megacycles per second, C is in picafarads and Z_0 is in ohms.

The characteristic impedance Z_0 for a coaxial line is evaluated from the formula $Z_0 = 138 \log_{10} \frac{b}{a}$ where b is the inside diameter of the outer tube and a is the outside diameter of the inner tube. For a square trough line the formula is:

$$Z_0 = 138 \log 10^p + 6 \cdot 48 - 2 \cdot 34A - 0 \cdot 48B - 0 \cdot 12C$$

where $p = \dfrac{\text{the inside dimension of the trough}}{\text{the outside diameter of the inner line}}$

$$A = \frac{1 + 0 \cdot 405 p^{-4}}{1 - 0 \cdot 405 p^{-4}}$$

$$B = \frac{1 + 0 \cdot 163 p^{-8}}{1 - 0 \cdot 163 p^{-8}}$$

$$C = \frac{1 + 0 \cdot 067 p^{-12}}{1 - 0 \cdot 067 p^{-12}}$$

It can be seen from the formula for evaluating l that $Z_0 C$ occurs only in one portion of the equation. Quite clearly an infinite number of values of Z_0 and C will give the same multiple. Thus a trough line or cavity with a characteristic impedance Z_0 of 100 ohms and a capacitance of 8pF will be the same length as one for which Z_0 is 200 ohms and C is 4pF if they are both tuned to the same frequency. From this it follows that a graph can be plotted of frequency versus length of inner line for various values of $Z_0 C$, as shown in **Fig. 39.** With its aid a trough line or cavity can be designed or the resonant frequency of an unknown cavity obtained.

The choice of the ratio of outer to inner dimensions is governed by electrical and mechanical considerations and the purpose. The value of the capacitance C is given by the valve capacitance, which may be appreciable, together with any tuning capacitance that may be present. It may prove to be so large that the length required for a high impedance cavity becomes so short as to be unmanageable: in extreme cases it might even be shorter than the valve which is to be mounted inside it.

Cavities are most readily constructed of lengths of standard sized brass or copper tubing and the choice of the ratio of outer to inner dimensions will of course be limited by the range of sizes available. For oscillator or amplifier anode tank circuits, cavities should in general have a low impedance (of the order of 30–40 ohms) whereas for input circuits the impedance may be as much as 100 ohms or higher. Optimum Q for an unloaded cavity occurs when the characteristic impedance Z_0 is 77 ohms. If it appears necessary either for achieving a proper impedance match or for reducing the capacitance loading, the connection from the valve or crystal can be tapped down to a " lower " point on the inner conductor (i.e. nearer the zero potential end). When this is done the value of C is calculated by dividing the valve or crystal capacitance in Farads by the total length of the line in inches, divided by the length from the short circuited end to the tapping point. The tapping point should not, however, be taken too far down the inner conductor otherwise the cavity will probably operate in some other mode than was intended and the resonant frequency will then be quite different from that expected.

Because of the variation in capacitance between various

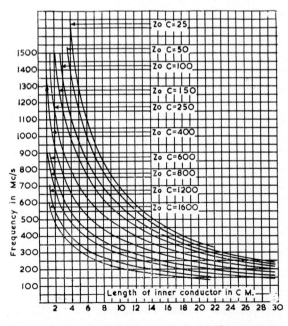

Fig. 39. Chart plotting frequency against length of inner line for various values of the characteristic impedance multiplied by the total capacitance.

samples of the same valve or crystal (usually of the order of 30 per cent) provision should be made for varying the electrical length of a circuit if replacements are likely to be made. This can be achieved by sliding the line or cavity in and out, thus changing the effective length, but since a very high mechanical precision is essential and the sliding surfaces must be plated with non-tarnishable material such as rhodium, it is not recommended for amateur purposes.

A more convenient method is to use a small trimmer capacitance formed of two discs, one mounted on the inner conductor and the other carried on a screwed stem mounted in a threaded bush fitted in the outer conductor. Some means of locking or gripping the thread of the adjustable element is desirable to ensure not only a sound contact but also to prevent any wobbling of the disc as it is adjusted.

A graph relating the diameters and capacitance ranges of disc type capacitors is given in Fig. 7 in Chapter 7 (*V.h.f. Transmitters*).

Input and Output Coupling

Three methods may be used to couple power into or out of a resonant cavity or line: (i) a tapping may be made on to the inner line near the closed end (**Fig. 40(a)**); (ii) a coupling loop may be inserted near the inner line towards the closed end (**Fig. 40(b)**); (iii) a capacity probe may be inserted near the open end of the inner line (**Fig. 40(c)**).

The first method allows no easy means of adjustment and for low impedances the tapping point is often inconveniently near the closed end. The second is more versatile since the

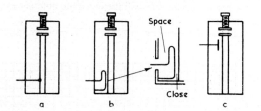

Fig. 40. Three methods of coupling into a line or cavity. (a) Tapping the inner conductor. (b) Boot-shaped coupling loop at low impedance end of inner conductor. (c) Probe at high impedance end of inner conductor.

degree of coupling can be readily adjusted either mechanically by rotating the loop or varying its size, or electrically by tuning the loop with a series or parallel tuning capacitor: when very tight coupling is required the loop should be boot shaped as shown in Fig. 40(b). The third method is generally suitable only for high impedance coupling, the position of the probe varying the coupling, but if required it can be matched to a low impedance circuit, for instance, by inserting a quarter-wave line: details of this technique will be found in Chapter 14 (*V.H.F. Aerials*).

THE MIXER

Two basic types of mixer are used in u.h.f. receivers— triodes (generally connected in a grounded grid circuit) or crystal diodes. In some cases a thermionic diode may be used instead of the crystal type but the performance may be inferior because its capacitance is higher. For the 70cm band either type may be used, but triode valves are more often used than crystals because they are more readily available and have a conversion gain, whereas crystals and thermionic

diodes have a conversion loss. For the 23cm band and below (i.e. frequencies above 1250 Mc/s) the mixer is almost invariably a crystal.

Triode Mixers

A triode valve can be used as a mixer in two essentially different ways. The non-linear characteristic necessary for mixing results from biasing the valve to operate either on the anode bend or on the grid current bend (leaky grid). In the anode bend method the application of the local oscillator voltage will drive the anode current upwards; in the leaky grid method it will drive the anode current downwards. Provided that the recommended oscillator injection voltage applied is correct the resultant anode current will be the same by either method and the conversion gain and the noise factor will be the same. For anode bend operation, valves having indirectly heated cathodes can be provided with automatic bias. Those u.h.f. valves with a common heater and cathode connection, however, will need a separate heater winding. When disc-seal valves mounted in cavities are used the grid disc or ring will have to be insulated from the cavity if they are to be used as leaky grid mixers.

The choice of method will also depend on whether the valve is connected in a grounded grid or grounded cathode circuit. If trouble is experienced with i.f. breakthrough the mixer input electrode (the grid or the cathode as the case may be) should be bypassed to earth with a reactance that is low for the i.f. employed. A typical 70cm mixer is shown as part of Fig. 46 later in this chapter.

The advantages of a triode mixer are the useful power gain that it provides and the reduction in the number of i.f. stages resulting from the fact that it acts as an i.f. amplifier itself. The exact value of oscillator injection is not very critical and a valve is not so readily damaged by accidental pick up of r.f. power from the transmitter as a crystal, but it is of course more expensive and the alternative of including an additional i.f. stage may be considered better value. In a well-designed arrangement the noise factor is of the same order.

Crystal Mixers

As a crystal mixer acts as a diode and operates non-linearly around the bottom bend in the characteristic, the oscillator injection voltage applied must be sufficient to swing the operating point well round the bend. If the voltage is too low the conversion efficiency will be low because the curvature of the working portion of the characteristic will be relatively slight. On the other hand, if the voltage is too high the conversion efficiency is no greater but more noise is produced because the noise output is proportional to the oscillator voltage input. It is clear therefore that the injection voltage employed is fairly critical if optimum noise factor is to be achieved and some means of adjusting its value should be provided in the receiver. Preferably, a meter should be installed permanently in circuit so that the oscillator voltage can be set for the best performance. The meter should be a microammeter connected in series with the crystal, the applied voltage being varied to produce a predetermined current which will vary according to the type of crystal: even different specimens of the same type will produce different current levels. The current is likely to be in the range 0·1–1 mA.

Some crystals require a small negative bias for optimum performance and a suitable bias voltage can be provided by including a resistor of 500–1000 ohms in the circuit, but it

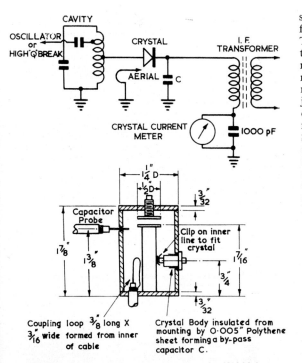

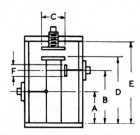

Fig. 41. Typical mixer cavity and circuit for 1296 Mc/s.

should be borne in mind that some microammeters have a resistance of this order and some may even have too high a resistance. The resistor and meter must be adequately by-passed for both r.f. and i.f. currents. A number of crystals suitable for 70cm are available, examples being the GEX66 (CV2290) or U.S.A. CK710, and for 23cm the B.T.H. type CS2A (similar to the CV103).

Fig. 41 shows a typical mixer cavity for 23cm operation.

High Q Break

The local oscillator voltage in a receiver may be generated by a single valve or, as mentioned in the v.h.f. receivers

Fig. 42 (b). Essential dimensions for high Q breaks.

	23 cm	30 cm	70 cm
Inside diameter of outer conductor	43/64 in.	43/64 in.	43/64 in. *
Outside diameter of inner conductor	¼ in.	¼ in.	¼ in.
Dimension A (end to tap on inner)	⁷⁄₁₆ in.	⁷⁄₁₆ in.	⅜ in.
Dimension B (end to coupling probe)	1¼ in.	1¼ in.	5¼ in.
Dimension C (diam. of trimmer)	⅜ in.	⅜ in.	⅜ in.
Dimension D (length of inner conductor)	1⅜ in.	2 in.	6 in.
Dimension E (length of outer conductor)	1¾ in.	2⅜ in.	6½ in.
Dimension F (diam. of probe)	¼ in.	¼ in.	¼ in.

* ¾ in. o.d. tube with 20 s.w.g. wall.

section, at a lower frequency to obtain better stability, and the frequency multiplied by one or more doublers or treblers. The output of an oscillator contains frequencies other than the required one (i.e., harmonics in addition to the fundamental) together with some noise; the output of a chain of multiplier stages includes lower frequencies in addition to the required frequency. Ideally the local oscillator voltage injected into the mixer should be a pure sine wave of the required frequency; other frequencies merely generate more noise in the mixer without contributing at all to the signal. Since a low noise level is an essential requirement in u.h.f. receivers, the voltage injected into the mixer should be at the fundamental only and all other frequencies should be removed by a filter. Such a filter is known as a *high Q break* and usually consists of a coaxial cavity with a coupling loop at the low potential ("cold") end and a probe coupling at the high potential ("hot") end, both being fairly loosely coupled so that a high *Q* value is achieved. Examples of 70cm and 23cm high *Q* breaks are shown in **Fig. 42.** Typical performance of a 70cm filter would be an attenuation of —15db at a frequency 3·5 Mc/s away from the operating frequency. This would ensure that, provided that the original source is higher than 3·5 Mc/s, no other frequency

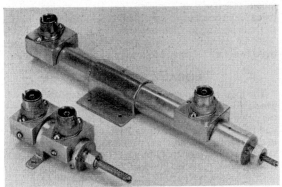

Fig. 42 (a). Two high Q Breaks, the longer for 430 Mc/s, the shorter for 1296 Mc/s.

of sufficient magnitude to matter would be fed into the mixer. Where the last valve in a frequency multiplied oscillator chain is of the disc-seal or coaxial type with a tuned cavity anode circuit, this cavity can readily be made sufficiently selective to operate as a high Q break.

THE INTERMEDIATE FREQUENCY

The same basic considerations apply to the choice of the first intermediate frequency to be used for the u.h.f. bands as for 70 and 144 Mc/s. It should be borne in mind, however, that the frequency ranges to be covered are somewhat wider and therefore it is desirable to adopt a higher first i.f. for a u.h.f. converter. This also helps to improve second channel rejection.

Although interference from second channel signals is almost unknown in the u.h.f. ranges poor second channel ratio will cause a deterioration in the noise performance of the receiver; for example, a 1 : 1 ratio would increase the noise factor by 3db. Trouble may be experienced, however, in the mixer if the i.f. is too high because the signal circuit is then so far removed in frequency from the oscillator injection frequency that it becomes difficult to maintain an adequate mixer heterodyne voltage. A suitable first i.f. for a converter for 70cm will be found between 20–30 Mc/s and for 23cm between 30–40 Mc/s; a 70cm receiver which incorporates a good r.f. stage may use the standard i.f. of 10·7 Mc/s or a lower frequency if preferred.

First I.f. Amplifier

The early stages of the i.f. amplifier following a crystal or thermionic diode mixer must be of the low noise type because this type of mixer has a gain less than unity. Low noise is most readily achieved with a double triode valve such as the E88CC, ECC89, 6BQ7A, or ECC84 used as a cascode; see Fig. 16. After the early stages, an ordinary pentode may be used but one having a low equivalent noise resistance is desirable.

When the mixer is a triode, connected either in a grounded cathode or grounded grid circuit, a pentode type of first i.f. stage is satisfactory because in effect the first i.f. stage is already a triode.

The mixer output impedance must be suitably matched to the input impedance of the first i.f. amplifier valve. This is particularly important if a crystal or thermionic diode is used because in both of these types the impedance is relatively low (about 500 ohms as a mixer). The circuit design and the precautions necessary to avoid i.f. breakthrough are similar to those relating to v.h.f. receivers.

An i.f. amplifier following a crystal mixer should have a noise factor of 2–4db and following a triode mixer, 6–8db.

LOCAL OSCILLATORS

The local oscillator voltage for a u.h.f. converter may be generated either at a frequency near to the signal frequency (i.e., plus or minus the first i.f.) or at a lower frequency and multiplied. These alternatives have been discussed earlier in this chapter in connection with 2 and 4m converters. The same considerations apply to u.h.f. receivers but because of the higher frequencies involved frequency stability is even more important. Receivers for telephony reception on 70cm can be built using a fundamental frequency tunable oscillator but for c.w. the oscillator must be on a lower frequency (for example, 200 Mc/s). All practical receivers for 23cm employ a crystal oscillator and frequency multiplier chain, as do many for 70cm.

Self-excited Oscillators

In addition to the various stable oscillators already described for use in 2 and 4m equipment a type designed by R.C.A. in Switzerland is useful over the frequency range between 420 and 1300 Mc/s. It can be a basis for experimental work as a receiver oscillator and is also invaluable as a signal source and as a form of grid dip oscillator. It is relatively easy to construct and employs a readily available receiving type valve, the 6AF4A.

The basic circuit is shown in **Fig. 43** while **Fig. 44** is a photo of such an oscillator with the end cover removed. The tuned circuit is of the butterfly type (see Fig. 37(c)), but the

TABLE 2
Dimensions of boxes for use with four types of capacitor in the oscillator circuit of Fig. 43.

Capacitor Eddystone Type No.	Capacitance	Inside dimensions of box			Approx. frequency range
		Length	Width	Depth	
551	24 + 24pF	1¾ in.	¾ in.	1¾ in.	800–1150Mc/s
587	10 + 10pF	2¼ in.	1¾ in.	2¾ in.	610–925Mc/s
584	34 + 34pF	2¾ in.	1¾ in.	2¼ in.	420–850Mc/s
1068	40 + 40pF	5 in.	2¾ in.	2½ in.	300–550Mc/s

inductive element is formed by the metal box which contains the oscillator and is tuned by a split-stator capacitor connected across the opposite sides of the box. This results in a rigid construction having the wide tuning range associated with butterfly circuits. Drift due to variations in valve capacitance and loading are reduced by effectively tapping the grid and anode of the valve down the tuned circuit by capacitive potentiometers formed by built-in capacitors and the valve electrode capacitance. The effect of the valve on the circuit can be reduced still further by making these capacitors smaller but the output voltage will fall, the valve ceasing to oscillate if the values are too small; conversely if the values are increased, the output will increase but the drift will also be increased. Typical values are between 2–6pF.

The box is made of about 18 s.w.g. brass or copper sheet and the seams soldered: its height should be just sufficient to accommodate the split-stator capacitor with the valveholder mounted on the end, the valve itself being shielded by a metal chimney or a well fitting cover. If the box is too high the end space will act as a cavity and produce spurious modes of oscillation. The split-stator capacitor should have brass plates soldered across the sides of the fixed vanes and the plates clamped to the sides of the box by a double row of screws. Unless the sides of the box are in intimate contact with the capacitor throughout its length the Q of the circuit will be reduced. The width of the capacitor with the plates in position decides the internal width of the box: the remaining sides of the box should have a dimension of twice the width.

The mid-frequency and tuning range depend on the size of the box and the capacitance swing of the split-stator capacitor. As relatively few suitable capacitors are available the choice is somewhat limited but **Table 2** gives four types

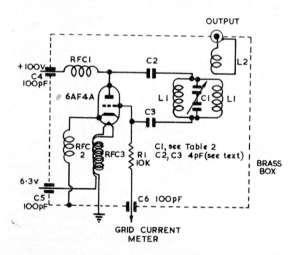

Fig. 43. Circuit of u.h.f. oscillator. C₁, see Table 2; C₂, ₃, approximately 4 pF (see text, value between 2 and 6 pF); C₄, ₅, ₆, 100 pF leadthrough capacitors; L₁, sides of box (see Table 2); L₂, coupling loop; RFC₁, 15 turns 30 s.w.g. enam. ¼ in. i.d. ½ in. long; RFC₂, 8 turns 28 s.w.g. enam. ¼ in. i.d. 7/16 in. long; RFC₃, 15 turns 28 s.w.g. enam. ¼ in. i.d. ½ in. long (two wires wound as a twisted pair).

of Eddystone capacitor, the frequency range for each and other relevant dimensions. The built-in capacitors are formed of two brass plates fixed by small screws (10 B.A.) to the fixed vanes of the tuning capacitor but insulated therefrom by several sheets of thin polythene or p.t.f.e. film (about 0·01 in.). The drilling and tapping must be done with great care.

The two anode tags of the valveholder, which must be made of p.t.f.e., are soldered directly to one plate and the two grid tags to the other. The heater, cathode and anode supplies are filtered with chokes and by-passed to the box with leadthrough capacitors which provide the external connections. A coupling loop is mounted in the box at the end remote from the valve and adjusted so that connection of an external 70 ohm load does not cause the oscillation to cease.

The earthy end of the grid leak is brought out through a leadthrough capacitor and is available to check the grid current. With no anode voltage applied the coupling loop may be connected by a short length of cable to another loop coupled to another oscillator or transmitter, and the tuned box used as an absorption wavemeter, the grid current providing indication. Alternatively, with anode voltage applied, the grid current will kick downwards when an external circuit is tuned through the oscillator frequency, the box acting as a grid dip oscillator. At u.h.f., however, it is not recommended that the oscillator be tuned across the band to find the resonant frequency of an unknown circuit because there are various points at which dips occur due to minor irregularities in the box and coupling loops which make identification difficult.

When the oscillator is used as a source of signal it may be anode modulated with tone by a small a.f. oscillator, or frequency modulated by 50 c/s if the bottom end of the grid leak is connected to the live 6·3 volt heater supply.

Crystal Oscillator Multiplier Chains

The provision of the final oscillator frequency by multiplication from a lower frequency crystal has been referred to already in connection with 2 and 4m receivers. The information generally applies to 70 and 23cm equipment apart from the fact that more multiplying stages are required. Because the injection frequency required is much higher it is however desirable to use a higher frequency crystal in order to keep the number of stages down to a reasonable figure. Whilst lower frequency crystals are cheaper the increased cost of the extra stages must be considered. An additional advantage of the higher frequency crystals is that less difficulty is likely to arise due to self-generated whistles in the receiver and there is less likelihood of interference to other users by spurious radiation. For example, a 70 Mc/s overtone crystal is quite satisfactory for both the 70 and 23cm bands and the frequency is clear of Bands I, II and III television and sound broadcasting. Wherever possible, the crystals chosen should have a low temperature drift. Alternatively, they can be

Fig. 44. The u.h.f. oscillator of Fig. 43 with the valve removed showing the construction.

mounted in a simple oven to give a reasonable control of temperature.

Overtone crystal oscillators tend to give rather lower output than those designed for use with fundamental crystals and this may involve an additional amplifying stage at the crystal frequency. The multiplier stages may be a small pentode for the lower frequencies such as the pentode section of a 6U8 or a 6AK5 and double triodes such as the 6J6 used in push-pull as treblers at the higher frequencies. Small double tetrodes such as the QQV02/6 are very useful as frequency treblers up to 600 Mc/s.

In a 23cm multiplier chain the last doubler from 600–1200 Mc/s presents a problem, and one solution is to use a triode of the planar or disc-seal type in a suitable cavity. Valves

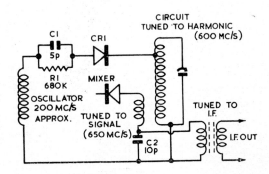

Fig. 45. Circuit of a crystal frequency multiplier from 200 to 600 Mc/s. The resistor-capacitor combination in series with the crystal is to provide automatic bias to the correct operating point for multiplication.

that may be employed are the types DET29, 2C40, 446A, 6BY4 or 7077. It is possible, however, to employ a semiconductor diode as a frequency multiplier, the circuit in **Fig. 45** using a 1N64 crystal multiplying from 200–600 Mc/s. This arrangement will furnish a crystal current of 400μA in a normal crystal mixer. Similar methods can be employed at lower frequencies or at higher frequencies for doubling to 1200 Mc/s although for the latter the crystal would need to be mounted in a cavity similar to that for a crystal mixer. A suitable crystal for multiplier service has a low forward resistance and is capable of passing a high current of the order of 50 mA. The high current is necessary because the harmonic component is only a small percentage of the total current; a low current would result in a very low output. Crystal multipliers must be followed by selective tuned circuits or a high Q break because the output of lower frequencies is considerable and will deteriorate the mixer noise factor.

R.F. AMPLIFIERS

Because mixers of any type are inherently more noisy than amplifiers it is desirable that the mixer in a low noise u.h.f. receiver be preceded by at least one r.f. amplifier stage. Such a stage, because it usually involves additional tuned circuits, improves the second channel ratio and further reduces the noise. For this reason alone it is often worthwhile.

R.f. amplification on the u.h.f. bands can be achieved by using (a) grounded grid triodes, (b) travelling wave tubes, (c) parametric amplifiers, (d) tunnel diodes, and (e) masers. Travelling wave tubes are very expensive and do not effect much improvement on triode valves at frequencies below 1300 Mc/s.

Parametric Amplifiers

Parametric amplifiers are a comparatively recent development in the field of low noise amplification. As the name suggests, they operate by virtue of a varying circuit parameter, in this case, reactance, which is made to store and release signal energy without adding noise. Two basic types have been developed to date: (a) the beam parametric amplifier, or Adler tube, which resembles a travelling wave tube, and (b) the semi-conductor parametric amplifier which uses the property of a semi-conductor that its junction

capacity is proportional to the applied voltage. Both require an external low power " pump " oscillator operating at an integral multiple of the signal frequency, which provides the energy from which the amplified signal is derived. The Adler tube has superior properties and performance to the semi-conductor type, but has the disadvantage that it must be specially made for the frequency band over which it is to amplify, which makes the tube and its associated pump source a somewhat expensive proposition for the amateur. Gains of 20db with noise factors of 1–3db are obtainable at frequencies in the 200–800 Mc/s region.

Tunnel Diodes

The high frequency performance of the tunnel diode has been steadily improved due to better manufacturing technique and in suitable circuitry is capable of low noise amplification up to several hundred megacycles. The tunnel diode is a negative resistance device analogous to a Q multiplier and a typical method of use is to connect the diode across a part of the tuned input circuit of a receiver, so raising the effective Q of the input circuit and increasing the gain from the aerial input to the input of the following r.f. stage. Since the tunnel diode operates at a current of the order of 1 mA, and its major noise contribution is due to shot noise, low noise amplification results. In practice it is desirable to incorporate some form of d.c. stabilization of the operating point, as negative resistance devices are prone to instability unless this precaution is taken. A germanium tunnel diode used in this way is capable of gains of the order of 25db with 3db noise factor at 100 Mc/s.

Masers

The maser (microwave amplification by stimulated emission of radiation) is capable of very low noise amplification in the microwave region and noise factors of 0·1db are theoretically possible when the crystal and associated circuits are cooled to the temperature of liquid helium. The mode of operation is briefly as follows. Certain crystalline materials such as ruby or rutile when doped with traces of chromium exhibit the property of amplifying microwave energy within certain well defined frequency bands because of resonances occurring within the structure of the molecules of the material.

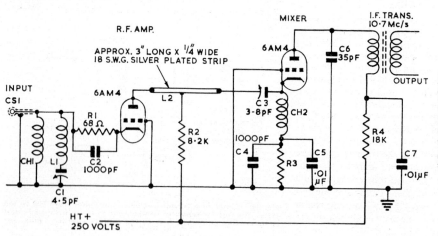

Fig. 46. R.f. amplifier and mixer for 430 Mc/s. C_1, 4·5 pF trimmer (Wingrove and Rogers type C.3201); $C_{2, 4}$, 1000 pF (T.C.C. type CTH310); C_3, 3–8 pF Philips trimmer; $C_{5, 7}$, 0·01μF (T.C.C. type 543); C_6, 35 pF (T.C.C. type SNB101); $CH_{1, 2}$, 24 s.w.g. enam. close wound ¼ in. i.d. 1 in. long; L_1, hairpin loop 1 in. long ₁⁄₁₆ in. wide 18 s.w.g.; L_2, silver plated brass strip 3 in. long ¼ in. wide spaced ⅜ in. from chassis R_3, 220 ohms.

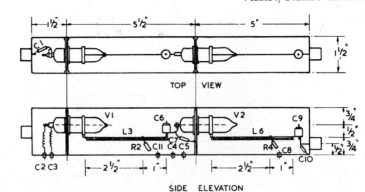

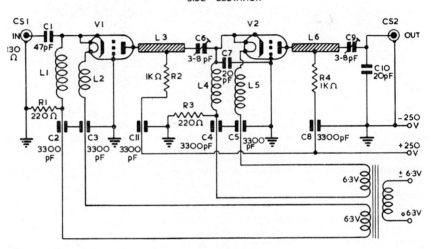

Fig. 47. Two stage 430 Mc/s pre-amplifier using CV354 valves coupled with strip lines in a trough. C_1 47 pF (T.C.C. type SCT1); $C_{2, 3, 4, 5, 8, 11}$, 3300 pF (T.C.C. type CTH315/LT); $C_{6, 9}$, 3-8 pF Philips trimmer; $C_{7, 10}$ 20 pF silvered mica (T.C.C. type SMB101 or SCT11); $L_{1, 2, 4, 5}$, r.f. chokes $\frac{1}{8}$ in. diam. 1 in. long wound with 24 s.w.g. enam.; $L_{3, 6}$, $3\frac{1}{2}$ in. by $\frac{1}{4}$ in. silver plated 18 s.w.g. brass strip; $V_{1, 2}$, DET23 (CV354). CS_1 and CS_2 are Belling & Lee co-ax sockets type L34S.

The maser may take two forms: (a) the crystal is mounted in a cavity and operates as a relatively narrow band two terminal device, or (b) the crystal material may be distributed along a slow wave structure similar to that used in a travelling wave tube when a unilateral four terminal device results with a much greater bandwidth. Current development is directed at improving the travelling wave maser.

Valve U.h.f. Amplifiers

As r.f. amplifiers for u.h.f. tend to be more experimental than the remainder of a receiver it is convenient to construct these stages as separate pre-amplifiers connected between the aerial feeder and the mixer stage. In this way, various types can be tried and modifications easily made without involving a complete reconstruction of the receiver or converter.

A 70cm r.f. amplifier and triode mixer using 6AM4 valves is shown in Fig. 46. The amplifier and mixer are operated in the grounded grid configuration with a strip line as the coupling element between the valves. This line is series tuned at the mixer end with a form of pi network which matches the impedance of the line down to the cathode impedance of the mixer. The aerial feeder is connected directly to the r.f. stage cathode via an isolating capacitor but a tuned input circuit may be included if trouble is experienced from interference from local stations or i.f. breakthrough.

The local oscillator injection may be coupled to the strip line by a loop near the line or coupled directly to the line by a small capacitor (about 1 or 2pF) connected near either end.

Fig. 48. The two stage 430 Mc/s pre-amplifier of Fig. 47. The chassis should be made from 18 s.w.g. copper or brass silver plated.

Fig. 49. Underside view of an experimental 1296 Mc/s pre-amplifier using a 6BY4 or 7077 valve. In the foreground are anode cavities for 23 and 70 cm.

The tuning capacitor of the first i.f. transformer must be wired from the mixer anode pin directly to chassis in order to bypass the signal and oscillator frequencies, and should not be across the coil in the i.f. transformer can. The cathode bypass capacitance comprises two capacitors, one for signal frequencies and one for i.f. The h.t. is connected to the line via a decoupling resistor at a voltage anti-node about half-way along the line, somewhat nearer to the r.f. valve than the centre. This point is found by temporarily connecting the h.t to the centre and by touching the line with a pencil and retuning if necessary until a point is reached where the pencil has no effect. The h.t. should then be permanently connected to this point. This arrangement has a bandwidth at the 3db points of about 6 Mc/s and used with a normal 10·7 Mc/s i.f. has a noise factor of 7–8db.

TABLE 3

R.F. AMPLIFIER VALVES

Type No.	Construction	Mounting	70cm.		23cm.		Slope mA/V
			Gain db	N.F. db	Gain db	N.F. db	
12AT7	Normal miniature	Glass B9A base	10	10	—	—	5.5
6BQ7A	Normal miniature	Glass B9A base	12	9	—	—	6.4
6AM4	Frame grid	Glass B9A base	14	8	—	—	9.8
PC86	Frame grid	Glass B9A base	15	7	—	—	14.0
A.2521/ A.2599	Planar	Glass B9A base	18	7	—	—	15.0
DET29	Disc seal	Coaxial	—	—	13*	11*	14.0
EC56	Disc seal	Coaxial	—	—	—	—	16.0
6299 6280/	Disc seal	Coaxial	17.5	4.5	16	8.5	12.0
416A	Disc seal	Coaxial	20	4.0	—	—	50.0
6BY4	Stacked Ceramic	Coaxial	14	6.0	14	8.5†	6.0
7077	Stacked Ceramic	Coaxial	15	4.5	15	8.0	9.0
6CW4	Nuvistor	Twelvar 5 p.	20	6	—	—	12.5

* at 2300 Mc/s   † at 900 Mc/s.

Note: gain and noise figures are approximate depending on circuit and bandwidth.

Fig. 47 is the circuit of a two stage pre-amplifier for 70cm using two CV354 (DET23 or TD03–5) disc seal valves and shown in **Fig. 48.** This uses a trough line tuned in the same way as the 6AM4 r.f. amplifier. It requires a separate heater transformer with a winding for each valve as the types suggested have a common heater and cathode connection. The bandwidth is about 6 Mc/s, the gain 20db and the noise factor, used in front of a receiver of noise factor 8db, is between 3 and 4db.

The type 12AT7 and 6BQ7A valves may be used in r.f. stages for 70cm and can be conveniently arranged as push-pull grounded grid amplifiers using two parallel lines series tuned at the end remote from the valve, with h.t. fed on to the lines at anti-nodal points. They require neutralizing, however, which can be readily done with two short lengths of wire (about 1 in.) cross-connected from the cathodes and lying near to the opposite anode lines. The 6BQ7A is the slightly better valve. Noise factors of about 10db are obtainable from such a stage.

There are at present few valves suitable for r.f. stages at 23cm and all are of the coaxial disc seal type. Examples are the DET29, EC56, 6299, 6280, 6BY4 and 7077. Abridged data, unfortunately incomplete on these valves and others for 70cm and 23cm, is shown in **Table 3.**

A photo of an experimental pre-amplifier using a 6BY4 or 7077 for 23cm is shown in **Fig. 49.** The underside view shows the mounting of the valve and below the chassis are two anode cavities, the right-hand one for 23cm and the left-hand one for 450–680 Mc/s. The gain with either cavity is 14db with a bandwidth of 6 Mc/s. An amplifier using the 7077 with strip lines as an alternative to a cavity is claimed to have a gain of 15db with a noise factor of 8db at 1200 Mc/s. Whilst this appears a useful gain, the noise factor is little better than that of a good crystal mixer. The r.f. stage will, however, still serve a purpose in improving the image rejection and isolating the feeders from the mixer and oscillator.

Input Matching

In order to achieve maximum efficiency, it is necessary

that the aerial feeders be matched to the receiver input. This is even more important on 23cm because the mismatch is likely to be more severe. An improvement of the order of 3db or more can be obtained by using a matching device. One such device is a two stub tuner, which consists of two adjustable short-circuited stubs of maximum length $\frac{5}{8}$ wavelength spaced $\frac{1}{8}$ wavelength apart, which can be connected by plugs and sockets between the feeder and receiver input. The device should be adjusted on a signal for the best signal-to-noise performance.

TYPICAL U.H.F. CONVERTERS
SIMPLE 420 MC/S CONVERTER

The circuit of a simple but effective 70cm converter designed by G2DD is shown in **Fig. 50.** It can be built on a standard Eddystone die cast box type 650 measuring $4\frac{1}{2}$ in. × $3\frac{1}{2}$ in. × 2 in.

A crystal frequency of about 7740·6 kc/s will produce an i.f. in the 17 Mc/s range but if a higher i.f. is desired a crystal of 7555·5 kc/s would produce an i.f. of 27 Mc/s. The first triode of V_1 together with L_1 is the oscillator circuit and operates on the third overtone of the crystal driving the second triode of V_1 which operates as a tripler giving an output on 69 Mc/s. The second double triode, V_2, doubles to 139 Mc/s in its first half, and triples to 418 Mc/s in the second. The 418 Mc/s output is developed across the strip line circuit, L_4, C_8. Another strip line, L_5, tuned by C_9, comprises the tuned circuit for the mixer crystal, the feeder being tapped on to the strip, the d.c. crystal current being monitored by the meter.

The strip lines L_4 and L_5 are formed from one piece of brass as shown in **Fig. 51.** The output from the crystal oscillator chain is injected into the mixer crystal circuit by mutual coupling between L_4 and L_5. With no feeder connected, a crystal current of about 300μA can be obtained but this value will fall about 25 per cent when the feeder is connected. The optimum value for the mixer crystal specified is between 60–120μA with L_5, C_9 resonated at the signal frequency. The coils L_1, L_2, L_3, L_6 and L_7 are wound on Aladdin moulded formers and tuned by dust cores, which

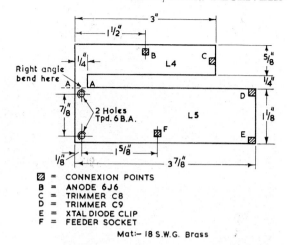

CONNEXION POINTS

▨	=	CONNEXION POINTS
B	=	ANODE 6J6
C	=	TRIMMER C8
D	=	TRIMMER C9
E	=	XTAL DIODE CLIP
F	=	FEEDER SOCKET

Mat:– 18 S.W.G. Brass

Fig. 51. Dimensions of the strip line L_4 and L_5 which is made from a single piece of 16 s.w.g. brass and spaced $\frac{3}{16}$ in. from the chassis. L_4 and L_5 are at right angles as shown in Fig. 52.

should be of the high frequency type (coded yellow). Holes for access for adjustment are drilled in the outside of the box. The i.f. output from the mixer crystal is stepped up in L_6 and amplified by the pentode V_3 and low impedance output to the main receiver obtained from L_8.

The underside of the converter from which the layout can be seen is shown in **Fig. 52.**

If a tunable converter is preferred so that a fixed i.f. can be used or an i.f. selected which is free from breakthrough, the converter can be modified so that the first section of V_2 is used as an oscillator on 104 Mc/s or on 139 Mc/s, the second section acting as a frequency quadrupler or trebler respectively. The oscillator can be bandspread to cover the portion of the 70cm band required. A suitable oscillator coil would comprise 3 turns $\frac{3}{8}$ in. i.d. centre-tapped and tuned by a bandset capacitor of 30pF (Philips trimmer) and bandspread with a 5pF variable. The second section should be loosely coupled to the oscillator by a wire close to the anode lead.

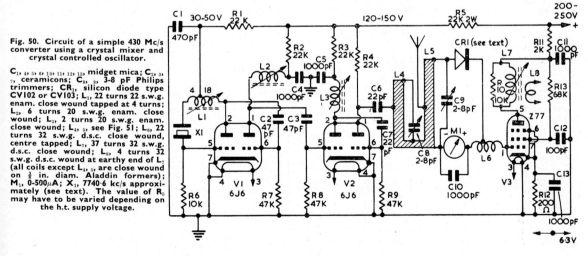

Fig. 50. Circuit of a simple 430 Mc/s converter using a crystal mixer and crystal controlled oscillator.

C_1, $_4$, $_5$, $_6$, $_{10}$, $_{11}$, $_{12}$, $_{13}$, midget mica; C_2, $_3$, $_7$, ceramicons; C_8, $_9$, 3-8 pF Philips trimmers; CR_1, silicon diode type CV102 or CV103; L_1, 22 turns 22 s.w.g. enam. close wound tapped at 4 turns; L_2, 6 turns 20 s.w.g. enam. close wound; L_3, 2 turns 20 s.w.g. enam. close wound; L_4, $_5$, see Fig. 51; L_6, 22 turns 32 s.w.g. d.s.c. close wound, centre tapped; L_7, 37 turns 32 s.w.g. d.s.c. close wound; L_8, 4 turns 32 s.w.g. d.s.c. wound at earthy end of L_7 (all coils except L_4, $_5$, are close wound on $\frac{3}{8}$ in. dia. Aladdin formers); M_1, 0-500μA; X_1, 7740·6 kc/s approximately (see text). The value of R_5 may have to be varied depending on the h.t. supply voltage.

Fig. 52. A view of the underside of the simple 430 Mc/s crystal controlled converter showing the layout and the strip line.

CONVERTER FOR 420 MC/S USING CAVITIES

The circuit diagram of a converter employing cavities is shown in **Fig. 53** from which it will be seen that the local oscillator chain comprises four stages using two type ECC85 double triodes (V_1 and V_2) which provide a total frequency multiplication factor of 20. The first triode section of V_1 operates as a straightforward crystal oscillator with the anode circuit tuned to the crystal frequency of 20·25 Mc/s. The second triode section of V_1 operates as a frequency multiplier having its output on 101·25 Mc/s. Each triode section of the second double triode (V_2) operates as a frequency doubler with outputs on 202·5 Mc/s and 405 Mc/s respectively. The tuned circuits for the first three of these stages use slug-tuned inductances whilst the final stage comprises a shunt-fed coaxial circuit.

The mixer tuning circuit is a relatively large coaxial line to which the aerial is coupled by a hairpin loop. The mixer crystal (a GEX66 or equivalent) is tapped on to the centre line of the cavity. The tuning of this cavity is arranged in the conventional manner by a variable capacity at the " open " end of the line. The local oscillator injection is between the mixer crystal and the i.f. input coil, which is usual practice for post mixer injection.

The i.f. head amplifier consists of a double triode (V_3) operated as a cascode amplifier so that a reasonably low noise performance is obtained. It should be noted that at the frequency of 30 Mc/s it is not necessary to neutralize the

amplifier. It is, however, essential to separate the associated circuits by a screen across the valve socket as shown in **Fig. 54.**

The B.719/ECC85 valves specified are medium impedance high slope double triodes and type 12AT7 can therefore be substituted in so far as V_1 and V_2 are concerned, but some adjustment to inductance values may be necessary.

The power requirements for the converter are 6·3 volts at 1·3 amps and approximately 150 volts at 35 mA.

COIL TABLE FOR FIG. 53

Coil	Turns	Wire	Pitch	Core	Coil former diam.	Frequency Mc/s
L_1	17	24 s.w.g. enam.	Close wound	Dust iron	$\frac{5}{16}$ in.	20·25
L_2	$4\frac{1}{2}$	20 s.w.g. enam.	2 diam.	Dust iron	$\frac{7}{16}$ in.	101·25
L_3	$2\frac{1}{4}$	20 s.w.g. enam.	3 diam.	Copper	$\frac{7}{16}$ in.	202·5
$L_{4,\,5}$	See Fig. 55	—	—	—	—	—
L_6	21	26 s.w.g. enam. centre tapped	Close wound	Brass	$\frac{5}{16}$ in.	30
L_7	27	26 s.w.g. enam.	Close wound	Dust iron	$\frac{5}{16}$ in.	30
L_8	3	22 s.w.g. p.v.c. covered	Close wound on the earthy end of L_7	—		

Construction

The complete assembly is built on to the top plate of a die cast box measuring $7\frac{1}{4}$ in. by $4\frac{1}{2}$ in. by $2\frac{1}{4}$ in. (Eddystone type 845).

The layout is important and attention should be given to the positioning of the various parts, which is shown in Fig. 54. These diagrams are drawn approximately to scale and show the underside and the plan view (outside) respectively, giving a good guide to the lead lengths of the various tuned circuits.

The inductances L_1, L_2 and L_3, which are slug tuned, are wound on standard formers of the moulded type with the winding a tight fit on the former; no other fixing has been found necessary.

Details of the final frequency multiplier circuit L_4 are given in **Fig. 55 (a)**. This circuit is shunt fed by a 2pF capacitor tapped on to the centre line near the " open " end while tuning is accomplished by means of a threaded end cap. It is mounted through the chassis so that the closed end is adjacent to the closed end of the mixer cavity.

The mixer cavity (Fig. 55 (b)) is mounted horizontally and occupies most of the right-hand top half of the box plate. It is fixed to the chassis plate by a horizontal mounting type electrolytic capacitor clip of 2 in. diameter. Tuning is carried out by adjustment of the variable end plate, to which is attached a short length of 0 B.A. studding; in order to ensure a reasonably smooth action a spring made of piano wire is fitted across the screw thread. It is important to see that the fixing clip is the only connection to the chassis and that the rear end is not in contact with the can of the i.f. transformer or the screen for V_3.

The mixer crystal (a GEX66 or equivalent type) is connected to the centre line of the mixer cavity at the point near the closed end by a long screw and sleeve as shown in Fig. 55 (b). The other mixer crystal connection is threaded through the final frequency doubler cavity to form the oscillator injection coupling at point X (as indicated in

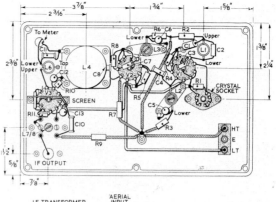

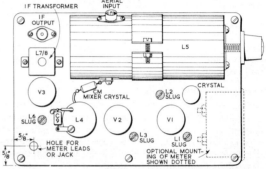

Fig. 54 (Above). Layout of the principal components on the inner side of the diecast box. (Below). Arrangement of the components on the outside of the box.

Fig. 55 (a)) and out to the bypass capacitor C_9 at point Y, where it is connected to the top of the cavity and provides an anchor for the oscillator coupling loop.

The resistors are all of the $\frac{1}{4}$ watt insulated type, while the

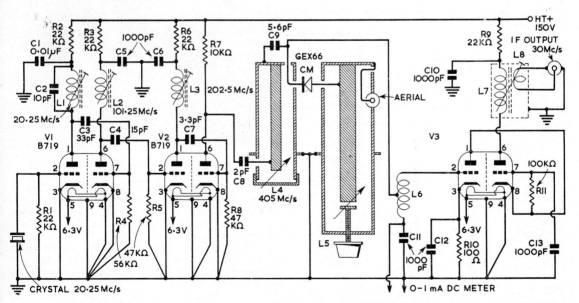

Fig. 53. Circuit diagram of a crystal controlled converter for 430 Mc/s designed by G6JP. V_1, V_2 and V_3 are G.E.C. type B.719/ECC85.

The 420 Mc/s converter showing the mixer cavity.

capacitors should be either disc or tubular ceramic types. In order to obtain optimum performance only new components should be used.

Testing and Adjustments

If the data given in the Coil Table are adhered to, the possibility of resonating the coils to any frequency other than the desired will be slight. The most critical adjustment will be to L_2, but provided there is a similar amount of stray capacity to that in the prototype it is not likely that this coil will resonate on the wrong frequency.

A grid dip oscillator is desirable for circuit adjustment and a simple r.f. pick-up device such as that shown in Fig. 55 (c) will be found to be of considerable assistance. With this it is necessary only to couple the pick-up loop to the coil under adjustment and then tune for maximum reading on the meter. The correct setting of L_4 is indicated by maximum crystal current.

When all connections have been checked, h.t. and l.t. voltages may be applied.

The crystal oscillator valve (V_1) should be inserted first and adjustment made to L_1. The output from the first half of this valve may be checked on a receiver covering 20–25 Mc/s. L_2 should then be adjusted to 101·25 Mc/s. The second frequency doubler valve (V_2) should now be inserted, and the coil L_3 in the anode circuit of the first half of the ECC85 adjusted to 202·5 Mc/s; L_4 can then be tuned to 405 Mc/s as

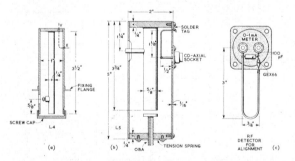

Fig. 55. (a) Details of the final frequency multiplier circuit (L_4 in Fig. 53). (b) The mixer cavity (L_5 in Fig. 53). (c) Simple r.f. pick-up device for use when tuning the crystal oscillator frequency multiplier stages.

mentioned earlier. After the oscillator chain has been satisfactorily adjusted the i.f. amplifier should be aligned at 30 Mc/s.

When this procedure has been completed it will be found that some alteration to the oscillator injection coupling loop will be required in order to obtain a suitable crystal current. This should be between 250–600μA. When the converter is on standby, i.e. with the h.t. removed, the meter will show a small flow of crystal current. The crystal current meter is not built into the converter because apart from the initial setting up and an occasional check, it is not required.

The mixer cavity should be adjusted by (i) screwing the trimmer plate in until it is in contact with the centre line and then, (ii) unscrewing the trimmer until the crystal current falls steeply. At this point the cavity is tuned to the oscillator frequency of 405 Mc/s; the trimmer should then be unscrewed a further half or one turn for the point of maximum noise or signal. Some slight adjustment will be required at the band edges.

In use the performance of the converter has proved to be very satisfactory, and the noise level compares favourably with the majority of converters designed for 144 Mc/s.

CONVERTER FOR 1296 MC/S

The circuit diagram of an experimental 23cm converter employing many of the principles mentioned earlier is shown in **Fig. 56.** The top half of this circuit is the crystal oscillator chain, and the lower half the high Q break, mixer and first i.f. amplifier. A photo of the converter is shown in **Fig. 57.**

The oscillator chain is separated from the remaining circuit so that the output is available for other purposes if required.

Fig. 57. The layout of the 23cm converter.

It uses a third overtone crystal on 70 Mc/s as this reduces the number of stages of multiplication and the possibility of spurious responses (birdies) in the band. There is no reason, however, why a suitably chosen lower frequency crystal with additional multipliers should not be used if desired. Because the output of overtone crystals is rather low, the first section of V_1 is used as an oscillator and the second section as a neutralized amplifier so that adequate drive is available for the first push-pull tripler, V_2.

C_5 is the neutralizing capacitor and can be seen in the photo of the underside of the chassis in **Fig. 58** just above the coil L_1 at the right-hand bottom corner. Neutralization is accomplished by temporarily removing h.t. from the second section of V_1 by disconnecting R_4 and then adjusting C_5 for minimum drive to V_2 as indicated by a meter connected at J_3. As adjustments are made the output should be kept peaked by readjusting C_2 and C_6. The output of V_2 is fed to the double tetrode tripler, V_3, a QQV02-6. This type was used because it is known to be an efficient multiplier to 600 Mc/s. The output circuit of V_3 comprises two parallel

lines, L_4, series tuned by a disc capacitor C_{17}, which can be seen in Fig. 58 at the bottom left-hand side. The output is sufficient to light a small lamp coupled to the circuit.

The final doubler uses a stacked ceramic triode type 6BY4 or 7077 mounted in a tuned cavity, L_6. (The construction of this type of valve is described in Chapter 2—*Valves*.) Other valves may, however, be used in a suitable cavity such as the 446A, DET29 or DET23. The mounting arrangement for the 6BY4 can be seen at the top left in Fig. 58. The cathode

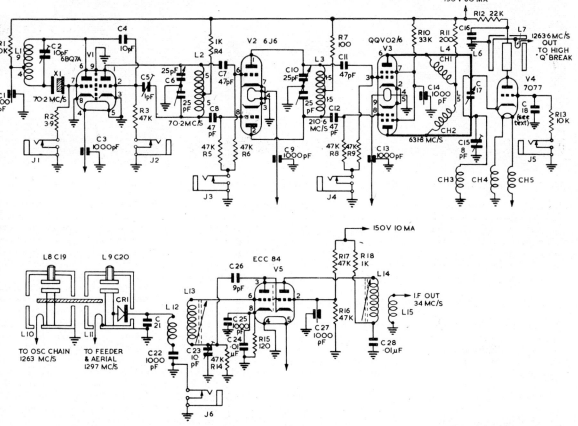

Fig. 56. Circuit of a 23cm converter complete with crystal oscillator chain, high Q break, crystal mixer and cascode first i.f. stage. The live side of J_6 should be connected to the junction of C_{22} and L_{12} in this diagram. The cathode of the second section of V_5 is connected to pin 1 on the valve base.

$C_{1, 3, 9, 13, 14, 27}$, 1000 pF leadthrough (T.C.C. type CTH315/LT).
C_2, 10 pF (Wingrove and Rogers type C3201).
C_4, 10 pF silvered ceramic (T.C.C. type SCT1).
C_5, 3 pF (Wingrove and Rogers type S50-01/1).
$C_{6, 10}$, 25 + 25 pF (Eddystone type 551).
$C_{7, 8, 11, 12}$, 47 pF (T.C.C. type SCT1).
C_{15}, 3-8 pF Philips trimmer.
$C_{16, 18}$, approx. 300 pF built into cavity.
C_{17}, two discs $\frac{3}{8}$ in. diam.
$C_{19, 20}$, two discs $\frac{1}{2}$ in. diameter in cavity.
C_{21}, formed by mounting of crystal diode.
$C_{22, 25}$, 1000 pF (T.C.C. type CTH310).
$C_{24, 28}$, 0·01 μF (T.C.C. type 543).
C_{26}, 3 pF silvered mica (T.C.C. type SMP-101).
$CH_{1, 2, 3, 4, 5}$, r.f. chokes 24 s.w.g., $\frac{1}{8}$ in. i.d. 1 in. long.
CR_1, B.T.H. crystal diode type CS2A.
$J_{1, 2, 3, 4, 5, 6}$, Igranic midget jack.
L_1, 13 turns 18 s.w.g. enam. $\frac{1}{4}$ in. i.d. $\frac{3}{4}$ in.

long, tapped at 4 turns.
L_2, 10 turns 18 s.w.g. enam. $\frac{7}{16}$ in. i.d. $\frac{3}{4}$ in. long, centre tapped.
L_3, 3 turns 18 s.w.g. enam. $\frac{1}{4}$ in. i.d. diam. $\frac{1}{4}$ in. long, centre tapped.
L_4, 2 brass strips $\frac{1}{4}$ in. wide by 18 s.w.g. 2 in. long spaced $\frac{3}{8}$ in.
L_5, coupling loop, 24 s.w.g. covered with sleeving, $1\frac{3}{4}$ in. long, close to L_4.
L_6, cavity—see text.
L_7, coupling loop.
L_8, high Q break cavity, dimensions as mixer cavity L_9 (see Fig. 42).
L_9, mixer cavity (for dimensions see Fig. 42).
$L_{10, 11}$, coupling loops, 1 in. long $\frac{1}{16}$ in. wide, made from inner conductor of co-axial cable.
L_{12}, i.f. transformer primary winding, 20 turns 26 s.w.g. enam.
L_{13}, i.f. transformer secondary winding, 22 turns 26 s.w.g. enam.; interwound with middle 8 turns of primary on Aladdin 19/64 in. former with yellow dust core.

L_{14}, i.f. transformer primary winding, 22 turns 24 s.w.g. enam. close wound on Aladdin 19/64 in. former with yellow dust core.
L_{15}, i.f. transformer secondary winding, 2 turns 24 s.w.g. enam. at earthy end of L_{14}.
$R_{1, 12}$, 10 K ohms $\frac{1}{2}$ watt.
R_2, 3·9 K ohms $\frac{1}{4}$ watt.
$R_{3, 5, 6, 8, 9, 14}$, 47 K ohms $\frac{1}{2}$ watt.
$R_{4, 18}$, 1000 ohms $\frac{1}{4}$ watt.
R_7, 100 ohms $\frac{1}{2}$ watt.
R_{10}, 3·3 K ohms $\frac{1}{2}$ watt.
R_{11}, 200 ohms $\frac{1}{4}$ watt.
R_{13}, 22 K ohms $\frac{1}{2}$ watt.
R_{15}, 120 ohms $\frac{1}{4}$ watt.
$R_{16, 17}$, 100 K ohms $\frac{1}{2}$ watt.
V_1, 6BQ7A.
V_2, 6J6.
V_3, QQV02-6/6939.
V_4, 6BY4 or 7077 (see text).
V_5, ECC84.
X_1, 70·2 Mc/s.

Fig. 58. Underside view of the 23cm converter. The inside chassis dimensions are 10 in. by 4 in. by 1½ in. deep.

spring is on the right and is connected to a series tuned coupling loop L_5. The grid spring is connected to the grid leak R_{13} on the left and is mounted on a circular plate fitted to, but insulated by thin polythene from, the body of the cavity to form the capacitor C_{18}. The two heater chokes and connection springs are at the top. The anode of the valve protrudes into the cavity and is pressed against the centre rod which is mounted on a circular plate similarly insulated by thin polythene from the body of the cavity at the top to form C_{16}. In the interior view of a similar cavity shown in Fig. 49, the small depression in the top of the central rod locates on the anode of the valve. The coupling loop L_7 is also visible. The interior dimensions of the anode cavity are $1\frac{11}{16}$ in. diameter by $\frac{3}{8}$ in. deep, the central rod is $\frac{5}{8}$ in. diameter, the tuning discs $\frac{5}{16}$ in. diameter, and the boot shaped coupling loop, L_7, is $\frac{1}{2}$ in. long by $\frac{1}{4}$ in. wide. The output available from L_7 is of the order of several volts and is adequate for any type of mixer. The coaxial connection provides facilities for connection to other circuits. The high Q break and mixer cavities are similar in size, the dimensions being shown in Figs. 41 and 42.

The top of these cavities seen are at the back of the chassis in Fig. 57. The coaxial cables, which should be of the low loss cellular type, carrying the coupling loops from the oscillator and the feeder respectively, can be seen entering at the bottom of the cavities in Fig. 58. The coupling from the high Q break

into the mixer cavity is by means of a 6 B.A. screwed rod tapped into the centre rod of the break and protruding into the mixer cavity. The amount protruding can be adjusted by inserting a screwdriver through a suitably positioned hole. With a moderate amount of coupling, a crystal diode current of 2 mA is readily obtainable but the optimum current for the crystal mentioned is of the order of $500\mu A$.

The crystal diode is inserted in a tube fixed to the side of the mixer cavity and insulated from it by thin polythene sheet in which it is wrapped, thus forming the capacitor C_{21}, which bypasses the signal and oscillator frequencies, but not the i.f. The crystal mounting is shown in Fig. 57 just behind the near centre valve.

The i.f. output is raised in impedance by L_{12}, L_{13} and amplified by the double triode V_5 (ECC84) connected as a series cascode. A lower noise factor would result if the ECC84 were replaced by an ECC189/6ES8 or an E88CC/6922. The transformer L_{14}, L_{15} provides a low impedance output of 75 ohms for connection to the main receiver.

Typical current measurements at the various test points are as follows: J_1, 1·3 mA; J_2, 0·05 mA; J_3, 1·1 mA; J_4, 0·63 mA; J_5, 0·25 mA; J_6, adjusted between 0·5 and 1 mA.

The input to the crystal mixer should be connected to the aerial feeder via a matching device such as a two stub tuner. Alternatively an r.f. amplifier such as that shown in Fig. 49, may be used between the matching device and the mixer.

CHAPTER 6

H.F. TRANSMITTERS

THE purpose of a transmitter is to convey intelligence from one place to another by the use of keyed or modulated radio-frequency oscillations. This chapter deals with the design, and adjustment of that part of the transmitter which produces the r.f. power, while the methods by which this power may be keyed or modulated are described separately in other chapters. Further, transmitters operating on frequencies below 30 Mc/s only are here discussed; methods of generating r.f. power at frequencies higher than 30 Mc/s are described in Chapter 7 (*V.H.F. Transmitters*).

One of the most important requirements of any transmitter is that the frequency at which transmission takes place shall be stabilized within close limits to allow reception by a selective receiver and to avoid interference with other amateurs using the same frequency band. Another important requirement is that spurious frequency radiations capable of causing interference with television or broadcast reception must be avoided; these problems are considered in detail in Chapter 18 (*Interference*).

The simplest form of transmitter would be a single valve self-oscillator connected directly to an aerial system. Such an elementary arrangement, however, has three serious disadvantages—(i) the limited power obtainable with adequate frequency stability, (ii) the possibility of spurious frequency radiation, and (iii) the difficulty of securing satisfactory modulation or keying characteristics.

The oscillator should therefore be separated from the aerial by a buffer stage or an amplifier. Several amplifier stages may be used in cascade, and by this means a high power output can be obtained with adequate frequency stability.

To cover the amateur bands between 1·8 Mc/s and 30 Mc/s, the oscillator is generally designed to operate on the lowest

frequency band, and for the higher frequencies one or more stages of frequency multiplication are used to achieve the desired output frequency. A further advantage gained by the use of frequency multiplication is that by operating the oscillator at a relatively low frequency it is easier to achieve the necessary frequency stability. A single multiplier stage may produce twice the fundamental frequency (*doubler*), three times (*tripler*), or more; usually, however, the frequency multiplication in one stage is limited to three or four, owing to the rapid diminution in output power as the order of frequency multiplication is increased. It is undesirable to feed the aerial directly from a multiplier stage since other harmonics are produced and may be radiated simultaneously. It may also be undesirable to feed the power amplifier directly from a frequency multiplier. The coupling between one stage and the next may be accomplished in a variety of ways, some of which permit physical separation between the various units—a useful feature in certain designs—while others have the advantages of simplicity, harmonic reduction, and so forth. Methods of coupling are described later.

The power supply for the valve electrodes is obtained from conventional circuits such as are described in Chapter 17 (*Power Supplies*). It is common practice to use separate supply units for the low- and high-power sections of the transmitter, firstly because the voltages used in the two parts often differ greatly, and secondly because interaction effects between the various stages can make the adjustment more difficult when a common supply is used. Unwanted modulation effects may also be introduced.

The basic principles of transmitter circuit arrangement are illustrated by the block diagrams in **Fig. 1**.

THE CRYSTAL OSCILLATOR

The desirable high degree of frequency stability mentioned in the preceding paragraphs can be achieved in the most simple manner by the use of a valve oscillator controlled by a quartz crystal, and in fact such an oscillator when correctly designed and adjusted remains the most frequency-stable device available to the amateur.

The quartz crystal, cut in the form of a suitably dimensioned plate, behaves like a tuned circuit of exceptionally high Q-value and may therefore be connected to the valve oscillator as would a normal frequency-determining tuned circuit. The action of the quartz crystal depends on the piezo electric effect explained in Chapter 1 (*Fundamentals*).

Owing to the natural vibration of a quartz plate when used in such an oscillator circuit, a small but appreciable amount of heat is generated by the internal frictional effects. The temperature rise may cause the otherwise very stable frequency to drift from its nominal value. This frequency drift can be quite serious, especially if the fundamental frequency is multiplied several times in the subsequent stages of the transmitter. Further, if the r.f. current through the crystal

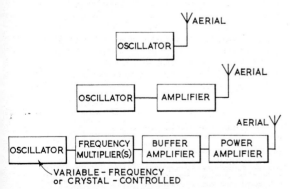

Fig. I. Block diagrams of transmitters showing three possible combinations of oscillators, amplifiers and frequency multipliers. Many other arrangements are in common use, depending on the power output required and the number of frequency bands on which the transmitter is to operate.

159

is allowed to become excessive, the vibrations of the quartz plate may become so large that fracture occurs.

In order to limit the r.f. current and the consequent temperature rise and to reduce the danger of crystal breakage, the power output of an oscillator must be kept at a relatively low value. Certain types of crystal have low temperature coefficients which reduces the amount of frequency drift likely to be encountered, but as these crystals are often somewhat thinner there is an increased possibility of damage. The power output of an oscillator using such a plate is therefore rather less than with other types of crystal. Various crystal cuts may be obtained as described in Chapter 1, some of these) particularly the AT- and BT-cuts, being commonly used for h.f. transmitter control by reason of their low temperature coefficients. The X- and Y-cuts have relatively high coefficients. A few examples of the temperature coefficients for various crystal cuts are given in **Table 1.**

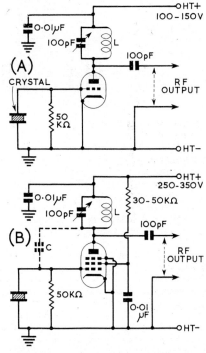

TABLE I
Characteristics of Quartz Crystals

Type of Cut	Normal Frequency Range (Mc/s)	Temperature Coefficient (cycles/Mc/s/° C.)
X	1 — 5	−20
Y	1 — 10	+75
AT	0·5 — 8	0
BC	1 — 20	−20
BT	1 — 20	0
GT	0·1 — 0·5	0

Although, in this table, the temperature coefficients of the AT- and BT-cuts are given as zero, this is true only at certain temperatures and at other temperatures the coefficient may have a small positive or negative value. Only the GT-cut has a true zero temperature coefficient over a wide range of temperature (0–100°C.) but its use is unfortunately restricted to low-frequency applications. For exceptionally high-precision operation over long periods, the crystal may be installed in a thermostatically controlled oven, although in amateur transmitters sufficient frequency stability can almost always be obtained by isolating the crystal from any part of the transmitter which becomes heated in normal operation, such as valves, resistors and power transformers.

The equivalent circuit of a crystal (see page 33) contains a resistance R in series with one of its branches. This represents the mechanical resistance to vibration and is related to the energy which must be supplied to the plate to maintain it in a state of vibration; a low value of resistance implies a high degree of " activity." If this resistance becomes too great, it will be difficult or impossible to maintain oscillation. The crystal is then said to be " sluggish " or inactive, and the fault is occasionally found to be due to the contamination of the crystal surfaces. These surfaces must be kept scrupulously clean and dry and without any traces of grease. Whenever necessary crystals can be cleaned with carbon tetrachloride or even with soap and water.

SIMPLE OSCILLATOR CIRCUITS

Almost any small receiving triode, tetrode or pentode will serve in a crystal oscillator. The use of a small valve is recommended since the power output must be limited in any

Fig. 2. Simple Pierce-Miller crystal oscillator circuits. Suitable values of inductance for the tank coil L are approximately 23 μH for 3·5 Mc/s and 7·5 μH for 7 Mc/s.

case by the dangers of overheating or fracturing the crystal plate. The simplest possible circuits using a triode and a pentode in Pierce-Miller arrangements are shown in **Fig. 2.** In these circuits the reactance of the anode circuit causes feedback though the anode-to-grid capacitance with sufficient amplitude and in the correct phase to maintain the oscillation of the crystal. As the anode tuning capacitance is reduced from its maximum value a point will be reached at which there is a sharp drop in the anode current. This denotes that the conditions for oscillation are being fulfilled and that the crystal is vibrating. At the lowest part of the " dip " the crystal will be vibrating at maximum amplitude. Continuing towards minimum capacitance, the feed current begins to rise again more gradually and the power output drops. When the oscillator is loaded, for example by the input resistance of a following stage, the dip in anode current is less marked than with the unloaded valve. **Fig. 3** shows how the feed current can be expected to vary with the tuning adjustment.

Fig. 3. Variation of feed current with tuning adjustment in a crystal oscillator. When the circuit is not loaded the dip in anode current is very pronounced, but it becomes less marked when a load is applied. For stable operation the tuning should be adjusted to correspond approximately to the point A (or A¹ when loaded).

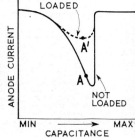

With the triode oscillator shown at (A) in Fig. 2 the h.t. supply should be limited to 100–150 volts for crystals utilizing the BT-cut and similar low temperature-coefficient cuts. The corresponding output powers available are in the region of 0·5–1 watt. A power output of 2–3 watts may be obtained by the use of X-cut crystals and anode voltages up to 250 volts; however, if maximum frequency stability is required the power should be kept as low as possible consistent with adequate drive to the following stages, for reasons previously explained.

With the pentode or tetrode version of the simple crystal oscillator shown at (B) in Fig. 2 the h.t. supply can be increased without risk of damage to the crystal and the corresponding power output can be increased to a possible maximum of 5 watts with a suitable valve. This is because a pentode or tetrode has greater gain, allowing a reduction of the r.f. crystal current for a given output power. A further advantage is that the amplitude of the output can be controlled by varying the screen voltage with a suitable potentiometer. If there is very effective screening between the grid and anode circuits, the small capacitance C of 1–2 pF

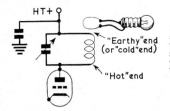

TABLE 2

Typical Harmonic Output Voltages obtainable from a Crystal Oscillator

Harmonic	Fundamental Crystal Frequency			
	3·7 Mc/s	5 Mc/s	11 Mc/s	14 Mc/s
Second	117	142	43	41
Third	58	71	26	25
Fourth	27	21	7	15
Fifth	21	16	2·7	9
Sixth	12	12	2·9	4·3
Seventh	7	7	3·3	—

These voltages were obtained from a Pierce oscillator using a 6AG7 with an anode voltage of 250 volts.

lamp to glow, and its brightness can be used as an indication of the r.f. power that is being developed in the tuned circuit.

In the following pages, some of the more commonly used crystal oscillator circuits are described.

The Pierce-Colpitts Oscillator

In the Pierce-Colpitts oscillator, shown in **Fig. 5**, the crystal operates at a frequency just below the parallel resonance frequency and its equivalent inductance resonates with the anode-to-earth and grid-to-earth capacitances. The simple untuned circuit shown at (A) in Fig. 5 will oscillate with crystals of any frequency and is therefore convenient where widely different frequencies are to be used for various channels. However, if the crystal happens to have a spurious mode of high activity at a frequency differing from the desired frequency, this may be accidentally excited. The arrangement shown at (B) avoids this possibility by the use of a tuned circuit LC to select the desired frequency and at the same time gives appreciably greater output. An electron-coupled circuit based on the untuned Pierce-Colpitts oscillator is shown at (C). Here the screen grid acts as the " anode " of the oscillator and electron coupling takes place through the earthed suppressor grid from the screen to the actual anode. It is dangerous to tune the output tank circuit LC to the crystal frequency, since the crystal current may then be excessive. Any desired harmonic can, however, be selected by suitably tuning the anode circuit. Measurements taken on a 6AG7 valve indicate that harmonics up to the sixth are of useful magnitude and **Table 2** shows typical voltages that can be expected.

Fig.4. A small bulb with a single-turn loop of wire soldered to it will glow brightly when coupled to the coil in a tuned circuit in which r.f. power is present.

may be required to provide sufficient feedback to maintain oscillation.

The r.f. current through an X-cut crystal may be monitored by means of a small low-current lamp in series with it, such as a 60 mA lamp. Alternatively the current may be measured with a suitable thermocouple meter of about 60 mA full-scale deflection. AT-cut and BT-cut crystals are not suitable for such high currents and no convenient method is available to the amateur for current monitoring purposes. Therefore, the most satisfactory technique is to ensure that the condition whereby excessive current is obtained cannot arise by limiting the power input to the stage. A convenient method of quickly checking the power output of an oscillator, in the absence of better test equipment, is to couple a low-power lamp to the anode-circuit inductance (or " tank " circuit) with a single-turn loop of wire: see **Fig. 4**. The loop will absorb sufficient power from the anode coil to cause the

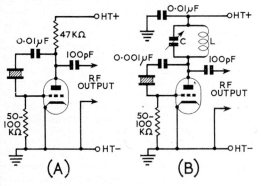

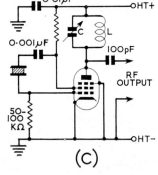

Fig. 5. The Pierce-Colpitts crystal oscillator. (A) shows the simplest form of untuned oscillator. In (B) the resonant circuit enables the fundamental frequency or a harmonic output to be selected. The electron-coupled circuit shown at (C) is especially useful for developing a large harmonic output. The screen resistor can be 47K ohms.

(A)   (B)   (C)

The Tritet Oscillator

The tritet circuit is intended mainly for the production of harmonics of the crystal frequency. A complete practical circuit is shown in **Fig. 6.**

An analysis shows it to be a form of tuned-anode/tuned-

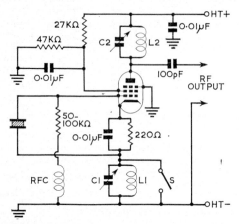

Fig. 6. The tritet oscillator. The oscillator feedback circuit L_1C_1 is tuned to approximately the crystal frequency, while the anode tank circuit L_2C_2 selects the desired harmonic frequency. Care is needed to avoid tuning L_2C_2 to the crystal frequency. If output is required at the fundamental the switch S must be closed so as to short-circuit L_1C_1. Many different types of valve may be used, e.g. 6AG7, 6V6.

grid oscillator, i.e. one in which tuned circuits of the same frequencies are connected in both the grid and the anode circuits. In this case the crystal constitutes the resonant grid circuit and L_1C_1 is the resonant feedback circuit, the effective anode being the screen grid (as in the electron-coupled oscillator): see **Fig. 7.** The interchanging of the positions of the h.t. supply and the tuned circuit as compared with the more usual arrangement and the fact that the circuit is earthed at a different point do not affect the principle

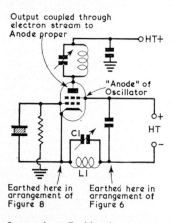

Output coupled through electron stream to Anode proper

"Anode" of Oscillator

Fig. 7. Basic circuit of an electron coupled tritet oscillator showing alternative of the r.f. earth as applied to Figs. 6 and 8.

Earthed here in arrangement of Figure 8

Earthed here in arrangement of Figure 6

of operation. Besides the necessary feedback which occurs in the oscillator section, coupling also takes place from the main anode circuit since current through this circuit passes also through the tank circuit L_1C_1 in the cathode lead. Hence feedback is least when the stage is not loaded.

The circuit is best adjusted by first tuning the cathode

capacitor C_1 from its maximum value downwards; oscillation begins when L_1C_1 is tuned to the fundamental crystal frequency and is indicated by a drop in anode current. The anode circuit L_2C_2 is then tuned for minimum feed current at the chosen harmonic frequency (which should be verified with an absorption wavemeter); at this setting the power output is at its maximum. By increasing C_1 slightly above the setting which gives minimum anode feed current, the crystal current will be reduced and the frequency stability improved.

The value of L_1 is important; it must be so chosen that C_1 is large enough at the required resonance frequency to act as a low-reactance by-pass for the harmonic frequencies which may be generated in the anode tank circuit L_2C_2. A recommended arrangement is a 200 pF variable capacitor in parallel with at least a 100 pF fixed capacitor. The addition of this fixed capacitance has the advantage that it will limit the tuning range and prevent the selection of a harmonic frequency with its associated heavy crystal current and the possibility of overloading caused by oscillation between the two tuned circuits. Output at the fundamental frequency is obtainable by short-circuiting L_1C_1. This can be effected by allowing C_1 to short-circuit at maximum capacitance, thus avoiding the need for a special switch. The circuit is then identical with that shown at (B) in Fig. 2. An important

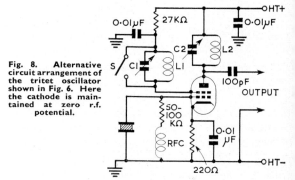

Fig. 8. Alternative circuit arrangement of the tritet oscillator shown in Fig. 6. Here the cathode is maintained at zero r.f. potential.

point to note is that the anode circuit must never be tuned to the fundamental frequency of the crystal without L_1C_1 being short-circuited; otherwise there will be excessive crystal current owing to self-oscillation between the anode and cathode circuits.

In the tritet circuit greater power output can often be obtained by the use of a beam tetrode rather than a pentode. However, if the latter is preferred the suppressor grid should have an independent connection so that it can be directly earthed: a pentode in which the suppressor grid is internally joined to the cathode will not be satisfactory in this type of circuit. Valves with good screening between anode and grid circuits are preferable, although normal a.f. output beam tetrodes such as the 6V6 and 6L6 are often used. With these valves, at an anode voltage of 300 and a screen voltage of 100 V, a second-harmonic output power of about 2 watts is obtainable as well as a fair proportion of other harmonics, although lower voltages are recommended for AT- and BT-cut crystals. If it is inconvenient to allow the cathode of a tritet oscillator to be at a radio-frequency potential with respect to earth, the circuit may be rearranged as shown in **Fig. 8.** The circuit then operates in exactly the same way as before, except that the electron coupling to the true anode is accomplished without permitting the output current to pass through the oscillator tuned circuit L_1C_1 (corresponding to L_1C_1 in Fig. 6). The requirement of low L/C ratio for this circuit is therefore not necessary as it is in the arrangement shown in Fig. 6. The tuned circuit connected to the screen may be short-circuited to allow operation as a normal crystal oscillator at the fundamental frequency. At the harmonic frequencies, since the output current is not passed through the oscillator tuned circuit L_1C_1, slightly greater output can be expected than with the first arrangement. The usual precautions to avoid danger to the crystal should be observed.

Harmonic Crystal Oscillator

The circuit of the " harmonic " crystal oscillator, shown in **Fig. 9,** appears to resemble that of the tritet oscillator. In

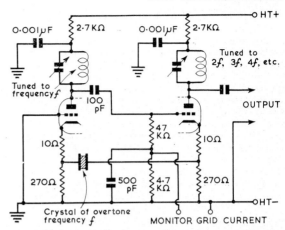

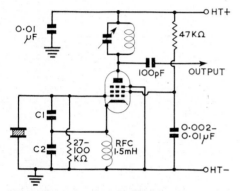

Fig. 9. Harmonic crystal oscillator. Ample power output is available on the fundamental and harmonic frequencies. Recommended valves: 6AG7 ($V_a = 300V$ max.); EF91, EF50, 6V6 ($V_a = 250V$ max.).

Fundamental crystal frequency (Mc/s)	6AG7 EF50/91		6V6	
	C_1	C_2	C_1	C_2
1·5—3	75	250	50	250
3—6	30	100	20	100
6—14	15	100	10	100

Values of C_1 and C_2 are in pF.

fact, however, it is a modification of the Colpitts oscillator described on page 165; the " anode " of the oscillator section proper (i.e. the screen) is at zero r.f. potential and feedback takes place through the capacitors C_1 and C_2. The anode circuit is electron-coupled to the oscillator section, and good power output at either the fundamental or a harmonic frequency can be obtained. No cathode tuning circuit is required, the purpose of the r.f. choke being to provide a d.c. return path for the cathode current while at the same time allowing the cathode to take up the correct r.f. operating potentials.

Overtone Oscillators

The oscillator circuits which have just been described produce vibration of the crystal plate in its fundamental mode. Any required harmonic output is then obtained by the non-linear operation of the valve, the harmonics being selected in the tuned-anode tank circuit. Harmonic output

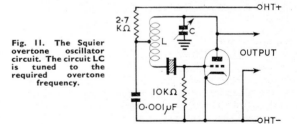

Fig. 10. The Butler overtone oscillator circuit. Many different small triodes are suitable. If more convenient a double-triode such as the 12AT7 may be used.

can alternatively be obtained by making a crystal oscillate at an " overtone " of its fundamental. Theoretically the foregoing circuits could be adjusted to give overtone oscillation of the crystal itself, but it would in general be necessary to inhibit the tendency of the crystal to vibrate at the fundamental frequency; this may be difficult to accomplish with the circuits described.

Usually, circuits which assist the overtone mode of operation cause oscillation at the series-resonance frequency (of the overtone mode) and are typified by the Butler and Squier circuits: these are shown in **Figs. 10** and **11** respectively. Overtone oscillation is more often required for v.h.f. applications where a large frequency-multiplication factor is wanted, and further information on these circuit types is therefore given in Chapter 7 (*V.H.F. Transmitters*). Nevertheless, the possibility of using overtone modes to assist in the avoidance of interference (for example, with television) at certain frequencies is suggested. The separation of the harmonics produced, as compared with operation of the crystal at its

Fig. 11. The Squier overtone oscillator circuit. The circuit LC is tuned to the required overtone frequency.

fundamental frequency, is increased; the harmonics which are produced are multiples of the overtone frequency.

Varying the Crystal Frequency

There are two methods of varying the frequency of a crystal oscillator. One is mechanical and the other is electrical.

The mechanical method requires an alteration of the dimensions of the crystal plate or its mass in some way. This generally involves the grinding of the surface to *increase* its resonant frequency or the loading of the vibrating part to cause a *reduction* of the frequency. Such changes to the plate must of course be regarded in general as permanent and irreversible. Crystal grinding, described in Chapter 1 (*Fundamentals*) requires great care and mistakes made through lack of skill can easily have disastrous results. The limit to the mechanical loading of a crystal is usually set by a gradual decrease of activity as material is added; for this reason a maximum reduction of about 25 kc/s is possible with a 3·5 Mc/s plate. Suitable loading material for a crystal is cold soft solder. It is gently and gradually rubbed into the two surfaces as evenly as possible near the plate centre; the activity should be checked at regular intervals, and in the event of a decrease in activity being noted no further loading should be attempted. Another material found suitable for this purpose is ordinary pencil-lead, which can be removed later if desired through the use of an india-rubber.

In the electrical method a reactance is connected in series with the crystal when the circuit is operated at the series-resonance crystal frequency, or in shunt with it for the parallel mode. The effects of such added reactances are summarized in **Table 3**. This electrical method is often useful for making slight frequency changes such as may be required to avoid temporary interference. The maximum adjustments possible are very small; for instance in the 7 Mc/s band the change will not be more than a few kilocycles. The limits of variation are set either by instability or by a complete lack of oscillation.

TABLE 3

Effect on Crystal Frequency of Adding External Reactances

Reactance Added	Series-resonance Frequency	Parallel-resonance Frequency
Capacitance in series ..	Increased	Unaltered
Capacitance in parallel ..	Unaltered	Lowered
Inductance in series ..	Lowered	Unaltered
Inductance in parallel ..	Unaltered	Increased

Circuit Details

Grid Chokes. The grid resistor which is used in the oscillator circuits shown here constitutes a relatively low-impedance path between grid and earth, and this may cause an appreciable reduction in drive power. An r.f. choke in series with the grid resistor may therefore give a noticeable improvement in performance, more particularly in harmonic-type circuits.

Automatic Bias. Although automatic cathode bias is not essential to the operation of an oscillator, owing to the normal bias produced by the passage of rectified r.f. current through the grid resistor, it may be desirable to protect the valve by inserting a cathode resistor of 100–500 ohms (suitably by-passed with capacitance) to limit the anode current to a safe value if the crystal should fail to oscillate. Examples of automatic bias are shown in the tritet circuits of Figs. 6 and 8.

Screen Potential. It is normally better to feed the screen from a potential divider than from a series dropping resistor

only in order to fix the voltage more closely. The actual screen voltage should be as low as possible consistent with sufficient output being obtained. The power output may be controlled by varying the screen voltage.

Keying. In low-power break-in operation the simplest arrangement for preventing interference in the receiver during " key-up " conditions is undoubtedly to key the oscillator stage. Unfortunately, even crystal oscillators are liable to produce chirp when keyed, particularly when the crystal tends to be inactive. Further, with a sluggish crystal a time lag may be apparent before oscillation starts, with the result that rapid keying is impossible. The remedy occasionally lies in a reduction of the loading on the oscillator or an increase in feedback. With the latter method, care must be exercised to avoid damage through excessive crystal current.

Fig. 12. Basic circuit of grid-bias keying method applied to a crystal-oscillator stage.

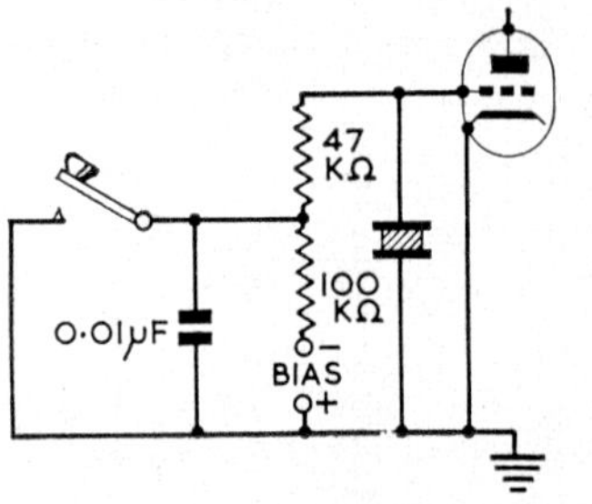

A particularly suitable method of keying any type of oscillator circuit is the use of grid biasing techniques, a skeleton circuit of which is shown in **Fig. 12**. When the key is open, sufficient additional fixed bias is applied to the valve to prevent oscillation. On closing the key this fixed bias is short-circuited and the valve oscillates normally. Details of various keying methods are given in Chapter 8 (*Keying & Break-In*).

VARIABLE FREQUENCY OSCILLATORS

Although the crystal oscillator is the most simple, stable and safe device for providing accurate frequency control, it suffers from the obvious disadvantages of fixed-frequency operation, particularly on congested amateur bands where the operating conditions change from minute to minute. A *variable frequency oscillator* (*v.f.o.*) is now widely regarded as essential for most if not all of the h.f. amateur bands. The frequency-determining circuits of such an oscillator consist of ordinary inductances and capacitances, either or both of which may be variable, but special care is taken to eliminate all possible causes of unwanted frequency variation. A v.f.o. of good design should give a frequency stability comparable with that of a crystal oscillator. Some idea of the stability desirable may be obtained by considering the following example. A sudden frequency variation of 50 c/s when operating in a congested c.w. band can cause the signal to be lost or its intelligibility to be severely reduced if the narrowest receiver pass-band is in use: on the 21 Mc/s band this variation would correspond to only one part in 400,000 of the transmitted frequency.

Basic Types of V.F.O.

Many different v.f.o. arrangements have been developed, but when analysed they are all found to be modifications of one or other of three basic circuits. The modifications are introduced with practical aspects in view; e.g. to allow the earthing of one end of the tuned circuit or to reduce feedback from one part of the circuit to the other. Essentially an oscillator is a tuned amplifier in which some of the output voltage is fed back to the grid 180 degrees out of phase with respect to the anode voltage, and the appropriate feedback

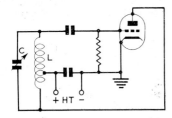

Fig. 13. Basic Hartley oscillator circuit.

may be obtained either by mutual inductance between the anode and grid circuits or by capacitive coupling between parts of the circuit at which the correct phase and voltage relationships exist for positive feedback to occur. Two of the basic circuits referred to above are characterized by these two different forms of feedback, namely inductive feedback in the Hartley oscillator (**Fig. 13**) and capacitive feedback in the Colpitts oscillator (**Fig. 14**).

In either of these basic types of oscillator or in any of their modifications the frequency stability is limited primarily by the stability of the frequency-determining tuned

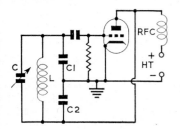

Fig. 14. The Colpitts oscillator circuit. The frequency is determined by the resonant circuit LC, but it must be remembered that in effect C is increased by the presence of the series combination of the feed back capacitors $C_1 C_2$.

circuit and also by the effect of the valve and other components associated with it: other factors such as the operating voltages and currents and the loading of the oscillator are likewise important. All these design problems require close and careful study if satisfactory performance is to be achieved.

Tuned-circuit Stability

To ensure the highest stability over both long and short periods the primary requirement is that the frequency-determining tuned circuit shall be in every way of a high standard. Mechanically, it must be perfectly rigid since any vibration or displacement of the various parts of the tuned-circuit assembly will cause variations in the effective inductance and capacitance and therefore in the oscillator frequency. To overcome these effects, the whole oscillator (in particular the items associated with the tuned circuit) must be made as mechanically rigid as possible. It is preferable to construct the oscillator in a die-cast box, which gives sufficient strength for most amateur purposes and at the

same time screens the v.f.o. from external fields. The wiring should be of stout gauge (16 s.w.g. or thicker).

The tuning capacitor must be of low-loss construction, preferably with ceramic insulation for the stator supports and with bearings for the rotor which prevent any tendency towards wobble or backlash. The electrical connection to the rotor should be made separately through a spring contact in order to avoid the introduction of spurious resistance paths through the bearings. The coil should be wound in such a manner as to make any movement of its turns virtually impossible. Apart from the use of grooves in the former, sufficient rigidity can be achieved by winding the wire under tension. Temperature variations can produce a considerable change in the resonant frequency of a tuned circuit. The effect of a temperature change upon the coil in such a circuit is to cause an expansion or contraction of the former and wire with a consequent change in inductance and resistance values. Both of these values normally increase with the temperature.

The various parts of the tuning capacitor assembly will likewise contract and expand and the amount of the resultant change in capacitance will depend on the type of construction. In general it is found that the resonant frequency of an ordinary tuned circuit comprising a parallel-connected coil and capacitor has an effective negative temperature coefficient of 50–100 parts/million/degree C.

Avoiding Temperature Effects

The most obvious method of avoiding the frequency drift caused by temperature variation is to remove the tuned circuit from all sources of heat. The tuned circuit should be located in a part of the equipment well away from hot valves (which can radiate a large proportion of their wasted power) and high-wattage resistors. It is preferable to place the circuit within its own compartment, and if this is brightly polished on the outside any unavoidable heat will be reflected away from the surface.

The second method, which is in common use owing to the difficulty of preventing all heat from affecting the tuned circuit, is to compensate the frequency variation by means of capacitors having a suitable negative temperature coefficient. When these are connected across the tuned circuit in their correct capacitance proportions, any temperature rise will tend to cause them to increase the resonant frequency, whereas in the remainder of the circuit the effect of the temperature rise is to lower the frequency. The result is that the frequency stays almost constant, i.e. the overall temperature coefficient of frequency is reduced almost to zero. To obtain a required tuning range with a given variable tuning capacitor it is necessary to connect a fixed capacitance of suitable size across the tuned circuit, and a selected proportion of this capacitance may conveniently be of the negative temperature coefficient type.

The compensating capacitors themselves are usually of the tubular wire-ended ceramic type and are available in almost any nominal value of capacitance with several different values of temperature coefficient. Further, if the oscillator is operated at a low power level there will be less difficulty in preventing a temperature rise in the tuning circuit due to heat from the valve. There will also be less heat developed in the tuning circuit itself (arising from r.f. losses), but in any case this is likely to be quite small compared with the amount of heat which reaches it from the valve.

Circuit Q

An important factor in the maintenance of frequency stability is the loaded Q of the frequency controlling circuit, the stability being improved with increase of Q. This is because in a high Q circuit the phase change of the voltage existing during oscillation across the circuit varies with frequency more rapidly than in low Q circuits. Thus, in the high Q case, random phase changes in the oscillator feedback path are cancelled out by smaller changes of frequency than in the low Q case.

The loaded Q value of the tuned circuit may be improved by reducing the losses in its components, the chief loss usually occurring in the coil. Therefore coil formers, which may be ribbed, should be made of low loss material (e.g. p.t.f.e., polystyrene or ceramic) and the wire must be copper, preferably silver plated; Litz wire is useful at frequencies below 1 Mc/s. A specific shape can be found which gives highest *coil Q* (not to be confused with overall loaded *circuit Q*).

The coil should be situated at least 1–1½ coil diameters away from metal screening or other components to prevent loss of energy and subsequent lowering of Q due to induced eddy currents and dielectric losses. Other items associated directly or indirectly with the tuned circuit such as padding capacitors, insulators and so forth must be of high grade material, as any dielectric losses will be reflected in a reduced circuit Q. Capacitors should be of air or mica dielectric except for any necessary temperature compensating ceramic capacitor.

In the practical oscillator the frequency controlling circuit must be coupled to the oscillator valve. The effect of this is to reduce the overall Q of the circuit by an amount depending on the degree of coupling. The coupling should therefore be small. For a given amount of loading, however, the Q of a tuned circuit is proportional to the C/L ratio, which should consequently be as great as possible. In fact the C/L ratio is usually chosen as a compromise between greatest ratio and the ability to tune over the required frequency range using components of convenient value.

Apart from the improvement in loaded Q value obtained through the use of high C/L ratio in the oscillator tuned circuit, the effect of changes in the valve interelectrode capacities due to extraneous influences is considerably reduced, as the ratio of valve capacity to total circuit capacity is very small and as a result is less capable of varying the resonant frequency.

Reduction of oscillator *loading* as a means of improving the circuit Q is exemplified by the Franklin oscillator, which is described in a later paragraph. In this oscillator the two valves are extremely loosely coupled to the tuned circuit through two very small capacitors.

In another type of oscillator the connections from the valve electrodes are tapped down the coil (example: Fig. 19) thus reducing the loading effect of the valve on the circuit and the influence of the interelectrode capacity on the resonant frequency.

Power-supply Variations

Variations in the supply voltages to the oscillator valve can alter its inter-electrode capacitances and other parameters. The obvious method of reducing the effect of these variations is to stabilize the power-supply voltages, and for most purposes a simple stabilizer tube such as the VR150/30 is satisfactory: details of suitable methods are given in Chapter 17 (*Power Supplies*). Small changes in heater voltage generally produce negligible variation of frequency, and their effects may be ignored.

Loading Effects of Following Stages

The loading effect on the oscillator of the amplifier or frequency-multiplying stages which follow it is to cause reactive and resistive components to be reflected into the frequency-determining circuit of the oscillator. The reactive components cause direct frequency variations while the effect of resistance across the resonant circuit is to decrease its Q, thereby reducing the inherent frequency stability.

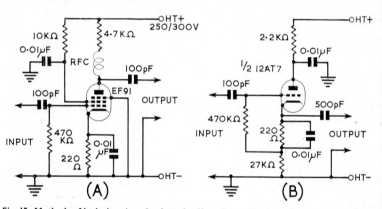

Fig. 15. Methods of isolating the v.f.o. from loading effects. The untuned class A amplifier shown at (A) provides a useful amount of gain besides affording adequate isolation. In the cathode follower (B), the impedance presented to the previous stage is very high while the output impedance is very low (e.g. about 100 ohms): the voltage gain is, however, less than 1. Because of the low output impedance, the cathode follower is well suited for feeding into a coaxial line.

Moreover, r.f. voltages may be fed back from the succeeding stage and these voltages, the amplitudes of which depend upon the power output and the tuning adjustments of other parts of the transmitter, will affect the calibration and the stability of the v.f.o.

For maximum stability the coupling to the following stage must therefore be as loose as possible consistent with the required drive being obtained. It is strongly recommended that the v.f.o. should be followed by an untuned class-A buffer amplifier or a cathode follower, as shown in **Fig. 15**, but where some measure of stability can be sacrificed for the sake of simplicity the v.f.o. can be coupled directly to a class-C buffer or frequency multiplier. Both of the circuits shown in Fig. 15 present a very high impedance to the oscillator stage, and feedback from subsequent stages is at a satisfactorily low level.

The class A amplifier shown at (A) affords a useful amount of gain and is suitable for feeding another stage (provided that the coupling lead from the output capacitor is kept short). The following stage may in most cases be a small tuned class C amplifier.

The cathode-follower circuit shown at (B) has a useful property in that, although the gain is just less than unity, the degree of isolation between input and output circuits is extremely high. Further, the output impedance is quite low (approximately equal to $1/g_m$, where g_m is the mutual conductance in milliamperes per volt at the operating point of the valve used); a typical value is 100 ohms. It is therefore possible to feed the output directly and without serious mismatch into a low-impedance coaxial cable which can then supply the main transmitter at a point remote from the v.f.o. unit.

V.F.O. Design Recommendations

The rules for the avoidance of frequency drift and other variations in a v.f.o. may be summarized as follows:

(a) Ensure complete rigidity and strength of the mechanical structure and wiring.
(b) Protect the tuned circuit from the effect of heat sources such as valves and resistors.
(c) Construct the tuned circuit and associated oscillator components of materials having the lowest r.f. losses.
(d) Operate at the lowest possible power levels.
(e) Provide stabilized h.t. to the valve.
(f) Use a buffer amplifier and/or cathode follower to minimize the loading effect of the subsequent stages.
(g) Screen and decouple all the circuits to prevent the pick-up of r.f. energy from higher-power stages.

Selecting the Frequency

It is usually advantageous to operate a v.f.o. on a relatively low frequency, since firstly the stability is improved as a consequence of the diminished effect of the various factors causing frequency variations, and secondly it can facilitate multi-band operation. Owing to the harmonic relationship between the various amateur bands the output of an oscillator working on a suitable low frequency can be frequency-multiplied to produce the required drive voltage in one or more of the higher-frequency bands. The multiplication is usually effected in separate stages, but often it can be arranged within the v.f.o. unit itself. In many amateur stations a v.f.o. covering the range 1·75–2·0 Mc/s is found to be a very convenient means of providing multi-band frequency control.

Bandspread

It is desirable that the whole of the amateur band to be covered by the oscillator should be spread across the full width of the tuning dial. In this way the operating frequency can be quickly read, adjustment is easier, and the danger of out-of-band operation is reduced. To produce the required bandspread, the tuning capacitance is usually made in the form of fixed (or pre-set) capacitance plus a small variable capacitance just sufficient to vary the frequency over the desired range. The necessary values may be determined by experiment or from simple calculations.

Slow-motion Dials

The most satisfactory type of slow-motion drive for a bandspread tuning capacitor is the friction type with a ratio between 6 : 1 and 9 : 1. Frequency changes can then be made swiftly and the setting accuracy should be adequate, provided that a suitably marked dial is used. The dial may show ordinary scale divisions (0–100 or 0–180) but it is far more convenient to have a dial which has been directly calibrated. The frequency can then be read instantly and the risk of error that is always present in the use of a separate calibration chart is avoided.

Adjusting the V.F.O.

It is important that a v.f.o. should be thoroughly tested before use to ensure that the frequency stability and purity of note expected from it are actually being obtained.

The v.f.o. unit should be connected to its normal power supply and a suitable load applied to the output to simulate the actual operating conditions. If the output is fed into the succeeding stage in the transmitter which is actually going to be used, the grid current of this stage can be measured to observe whether sufficient drive is available. While the v.f.o. is being tested the transmitter should of course not be allowed to radiate. The anode current of the v.f.o. is examined to check whether oscillation is occurring; the current should vary considerably if the grid terminal is touched.

Next, the signal is tuned in on a receiver, a short length of wire from the aerial terminal being placed near the v.f.o. to increase the pick-up if necessary. The most reliable method is to compare the output of the v.f.o. with that of a small crystal oscillator by using a receiver (with its b.f.o. switched off) to examine the beat note produced between the v.f.o. and the crystal oscillator. The amount of frequency drift may be found to vary over the tuning range of the v.f.o. owing to the varying proportion of the fixed and variable capacitances. A harmonic of the crystal oscillator may be used if it is more convenient than the fundamental.

To investigate the keying characteristics it is not normally satisfactory to make the test on the v.f.o. fundamental frequency if the transmitter output is intended to be at some multiple of this frequency. In such cases the v.f.o. output should be fed into a suitable frequency multiplier so that any chirp or other unwanted frequency variation will be magnified to a degree corresponding to the actual output conditions.

Calibration

The calibration of a v.f.o. is best accomplished by the use of an accurate heterodyne frequency meter. Failing this, the v.f.o. may be checked against 10 kc/s and 100 kc/s points from a standard crystal calibrator. It should be remembered that the largest amount of frequency drift is liable to occur during the first few minutes after switching on. For this reason the calibration and testing for frequency variations should not be attempted until a short settling-down period of say 10–30 minutes has elapsed

V.F.O. CIRCUITS

Many different types of circuit are in common use. The power output is invariably low, every feature of their design being determined by the need for the highest possible degree of frequency stability. Any of the arrangements described here will be found satisfactory for use in amateur equipment.

The Electron-coupled Oscillator

In this oscillator a pentode valve is used in such a way that the grid and screen correspond to the normal grid and anode respectively of a triode. The electron flow through the valve

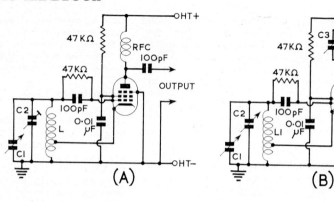

Fig. 16. The electron-coupled oscillator using the Hartley circuit. In (A) the anode load comprises the choke RFC and is therefore untuned. In (B) a resonant anode circuit L_2C_3 enables the fundamental or a harmonic to be selected. For 3·5 Mc/s operation C_1 may be about 500 pF, and the bandspread capacitor C_2 may be 150 pF. The oscillator inductance L_1 will be about 4 μH. Suitable valves are the 6AG7, EF91 and similar small pentodes having an independent connection to the suppressor grid.

is controlled by the action of this " triode " oscillator, and the anode current (i.e. the current in the output circuit) is therefore caused to vary in an oscillatory manner although there is no direct coupling between the output circuit and the oscillator circuit. A marked reduction in the loading effect on the frequency-determining circuit is thus attained.

A popular version of this circuit is shown in **Fig 16**. Here the oscillator portion comprises a Hartley oscillator. The anode circuit may be untuned, as shown at (A), or alternatively the desired output frequency, which may be the fundamental or a harmonic, may be selected by the use of a tuned circuit, as shown at (B). Generally the highest order of harmonic that can be used is the second or third, and since *frequency pulling* (i.e. interaction of the tuning adjustments of the two circuits) is considerably less with harmonic operation than with the output at the fundamental frequency it is desirable to use harmonic output. **Fig. 17** shows the same circuit as Fig. 16 (B) with the triode portion connected as a Colpitts oscillator.

Another valuable property of the e.c.o. circuit is that the frequency variation for a given change in anode voltage is found to be of opposite sign to that caused by a similar change of screen voltage, as shown in **Fig. 18**. If the relative values of these two voltages are carefully chosen, the effect of one electrode can be made to balance that of the other over quite a large range when the two voltages are supplied from a common source.

An important feature to note is that a pentode which has

its suppressor grid internally connected to the cathode is unsuitable for the e.c.o. type of circuit since the cathode is at r.f. potential to earth, and if this same r.f. potential is

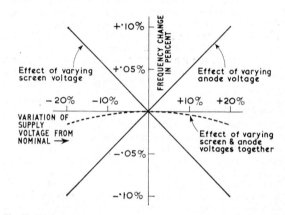

Fig. 18. Variation of frequency of an electron-coupled oscillator with electrode voltages. When the screen and anode voltages are varied simultaneously the effect on the frequency is very much less than that caused by varying either of them alone.

allowed to appear on the suppressor grid direct capacitive coupling between the oscillator section and the output anode circuit will exist. A valve type with a separate connection to the suppressor grid must therefore be chosen so that it can be earthed.

The presence of oscillation is indicated by a rise in the anode current when the grid terminal is touched. When the circuit is oscillating the feed current should be not less than half the non-oscillating value in the case of an untuned anode circuit. It can be altered by varying the grid-leak value and the cathode-tap position. The latter should be placed as near to the earthed end of the coil as possible; usually about one-third of the total number of turns from this end is found to be a suitable position.

When the anode circuit is tuned over a sufficiently wide frequency range, sharp dips in the anode current occur at points corresponding to the various harmonics. The dip is about 25 per cent of the untuned value for the second harmonic and progressively less for higher orders. The anode-current dip becomes less deep and somewhat broader when the load is added and may, for example, be reduced to

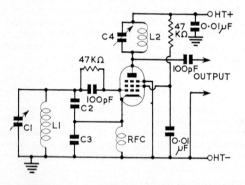

Fig. 17. The Colpitts version of the electron-coupled oscillator. The relative values of C_2 and C_3 determine the degree of excitation: typical values for 3·5 Mc/s are 680 pF for C_2 and 2000 pF for C_3. One advantage over the Hartley type of oscillator is that no tap is required on L_1.

only 20 per cent of the total current. A further refinement for this circuit is to tap the grid connection down the tuning inductance, as shown in **Fig. 19**, thus reducing the loading thereon and improving the Q value.

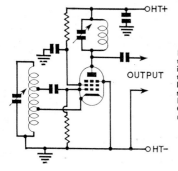

Fig. 19. The Q of the tuned circuit may be increased by tapping the grid connection lower down the coil as shown here in a Hartley-type e.c.o. Component values may be as in Fig. 16.

The electron-coupled oscillator gives probably the highest output of all the v.f.o. circuits, consistent with high stability and good tone quality, and it can therefore be recommended safely to the newcomer to v.f.o. techniques.

The Clapp Oscillator

The circuit of the Clapp oscillator, which was originally devised by G. G. GOURIET of the B.B.C., is shown in **Fig. 20**. It closely resembles that of the Colpitts oscillator. The important difference is that a small capacitor C_1 is inserted in series with the tuning inductance L_1 (which is made correspondingly larger so as to resonate at the required frequency), while the capacitors C_2 and C_3 constitute the feedback system and are of the order of 1,000 pF each. Because they are connected across the valve electrodes, any capacitance

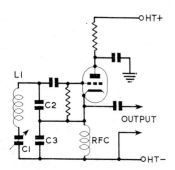

Fig. 20. Basic Clapp oscillator circuit. Very high frequency stability is obtainable with this circuit over a tuning range of about 1·2-to-1.

variations within the valve itself become negligible in comparison. The whole arrangement may be compared with a crystal oscillator, since as previously explained the crystal has an equivalent circuit consisting of a very high inductance in series with a small capacitance in one arm in parallel with a second arm comprising a relatively large capacitance. The inductive reactance of the first arm in combination with the capacitive reactance of the second arm then causes the circuit to oscillate in the parallel-resonant mode. In a Clapp oscillator the first arm of the resonant circuit consists of L_1 and C_1 in series, while the second arm is the series combination of C_2 and C_3.

The tuning control is effected by the small variable capacitor C_1. Satisfactory performance can only be obtained

over a frequency range of about 1·2 : 1 because the power output diminishes rapidly as the series capacitance is reduced. This range is, however, more than enough to cover any of the amateur bands.

A practical circuit for use on the amateur bands is shown in **Fig. 21**. The triode oscillator portion comprises the cathode, grid and screen of a pentode and the output is derived from the tuned circuit connected to the anode proper which is electron-coupled to the oscillator section.

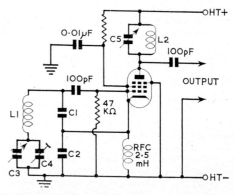

Fig. 21. Clapp type of v.f.o. Suitable values for the 1·8 Mc/s band are as follows: C_1, C_2—2200 pF silvered mica; C_3—50 pF (bandspread); C_4—80 pF (band-set); C_5—200 pF; L_1—70 μH; L_2—11 μH. For the 3·5 Mc/s band these values should be halved, and for the 7 Mc/s band they should be reduced to one quarter. Suitable valves are 6AG7, 5763, EF91, etc. The screen resistor can be 10-47K ohms.

For the highest frequency stability, the valve selected for use in this circuit should have the largest possible ratio between mutual conductance and inter-electrode capacity.

The ratio of the normally equal capacitances C_1 and C_2 to C_3 plus C_4 should be as high as possible consistent with reliable oscillation. If oscillation is not maintained over the desired range, C_1 and C_2 must be reduced in value or the valve should be substituted by one of higher mutual conductance: it may also help to increase the Q of the coil if possible.

The oscillator can be adapted for frequency modulation by connecting a reactance valve to the cathode or across C_3.

The Tesla (Vackar) Oscillator

Whereas the Clapp oscillator is limited in use to a relatively small frequency range, the Tesla oscillator, which is a

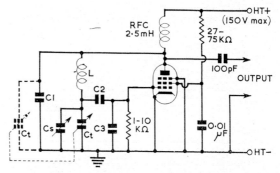

Fig. 22. The Tesla oscillator circuit. Suitable inductance and capacitance values for all bands from 1·8 Mc/s to 28 Mc/s are given in Table 4.

TABLE 4
Inductance and Capacitance Values for the Tesla Oscillator

Frequency Band	Inductance			Single-section C_t					Double-section C_t				
	L (μH)	Number of turns*	Wire size s.w.g. (enamelled)	C_1 (pF)	C_2 (pF)	C_3 (pF)	C_t max. (pF)	C_s max. (pF)	C_1 (pF)	C_2 (pF)	C_3 (pF)	C_t+C max. (pF)	C_s max. (pF)
1·8— 2·0 Mc/s	25·0	46	30	565	4800	470	250	30	500	5000	480	115+115	25
3·5— 3·8 Mc/s	13·0	33	28	285	2600	250	125	20	245	2350	235	70+70	12
7·0— 7·15 Mc/s	7·0	24	24	140	1470	130	11·0	10	134	1250	125	7+7	7
14·0—14·35 Mc/s	3·5	17	22	68	700	68	11·0	5	62	600	58	7+7	3
21·0—21·45 Mc/s	2·3	14	20	44	475	37	5·5	3	41	350	33	5+5	2
28·0—29·7 Mc/s	1·7	12	18	31	300	20	11·5	2	26	210	21	7+7	2

*All coils are wound on a 0·6 in. diameter former.

development of it, provides a fairly constant power output over a much wider range (about 2·5 : 1). It has similar good frequency stability and low harmonic content.

The circuit adapted for amateur use is shown in **Fig. 22.** Operation at the fundamental frequency on all the h.f. bands is practicable. In the simplest arrangement tuning is effected by the variable capacitor C_t in series with the inductance L, but a greatly improved performance is achieved if a split-stator capacitor is used, the other section being connected across C_1. The capacitor C_s serves as a band-setting control. Typical coil and capacitor values are given in Table 4.

As in the Clapp oscillator, maximum frequency stability is obtained by the selection of a valve with the highest possible ratio of mutual conductance to inter-electrode capacitances. A reactance modulator may be added for narrow-band frequency modulation. Cathode keying is found to be satisfactory although screen keying is usually superior.

The Franklin Oscillator

The basic circuit principle of the Franklin oscillator is shown in **Fig. 23.** Here two triodes V_1 and V_2 are connected as a conventional resistance-capacitance coupled amplifier. A rise of potential applied at the grid of V_1 will appear on the grid of V_2 as a fall in potential, and again at the anode of V_2 as a rise in potential though now of course considerably greater than its original magnitude. If sufficient feedback is provided through C_B to the grid of V_1 the whole amplifier will go into oscillation at a frequency determined by the

natural time constant of the circuit which will depend mainly on the values of the resistances and the capacitances C_A and C_B. This is called a multi-vibrator.

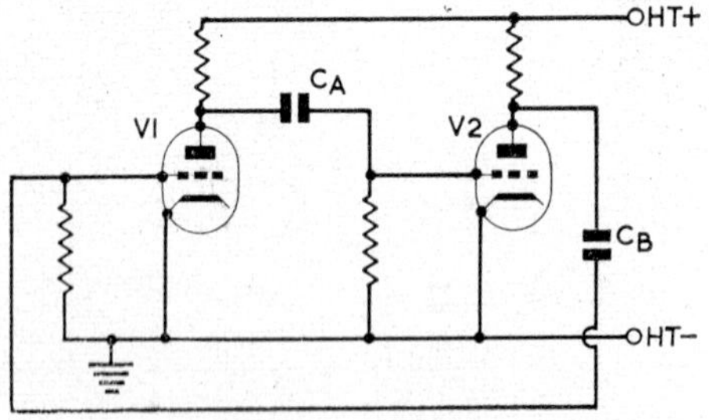

To convert the arrangement into a constant-frequency oscillator of controllable frequency, some means must be provided whereby the feedback or the loop gain is insufficient to maintain oscillation except at the desired frequency. This is done by inserting a parallel resonant

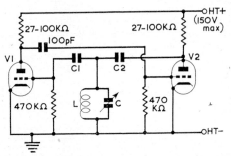

Fig. 24. A practical Franklin oscillator. The tuned circuit LC is coupled to the oscillator (V_1 V_2) through very small capacitances C_1 and C_2 (about 1 pF each). Maximum frequency stability is achieved when these capacitances are reduced to the minimum necessary for reliable oscillation. Suitable valves are 6J6, 12AT7, 12AX7, etc.

circuit LC between the junction of C_1 and C_2 and earth in the feedback path from V_2 to V_1: see **Fig. 24.** This circuit has a low impedance except at its resonant frequency, and at any other frequency the feedback path is virtually short-circuited.

If C_1 and C_2 are reduced to a minimum possible value for maintaining oscillation, the frequency of oscillation will depend almost entirely on the natural frequency of the LC circuit. In practice suitable values are found to be about 1 pf, thus giving a high degree of isolation of the tuned circuit from the remainder of the circuit. Variations in valve capacitance can only slightly affect the tuning ; further, the Q of the tuned circuit can be maintained at a high value since the load presented to it by the valve is small.

No tappings are required on the coil, and the tuned circuit is earthed at one end. Both of these features are of great constructional advantage.

Fig. 23. Basic circuit to explain the operation of the Franklin oscillator. See text.

The circuit may be used also as a crystal-controlled oscillator by substituting a crystal for the LC circuit. Owing to the high amplification available, oscillation is easily obtained with relatively inactive crystals at the frequency of parallel resonance.

The power output obtainable is quite low and extra amplification may be needed to provide adequate drive. Usually this type of oscillator will be found to have poor keying characteristics and the keying should therefore take place in one of the later stages.

To achieve the maximum frequency stability the values of C_1 and C_2 should be reduced as far as possible consistent with stable oscillation. The two capacitors should be varied together so as to be always approximately equal.

Mixer Oscillators

In a mixer type of v.f.o. the output voltage of a crystal oscillator is mixed with the output voltage of a variable-frequency oscillator of much lower frequency in a suitable valve mixer circuit, and the sum or difference of these frequencies which is thereby obtained may be employed to control the transmitter frequency. The degree of frequency stability attainable by this method on any particular band is superior to that normally achieved by the use of the straightforward type of v.f.o. but the additional complexity of the mixer arrangement has prevented it from becoming widely adopted. The principle of its operation is shown in block diagram form in **Fig. 25**.

The reason for the improved stability is explained by considering the following example. Suppose that the crystal frequency (f_2) is 4·0 Mc/s and that the v.f.o. tunes from 200 to 500 kc/s (f_1). By extracting the difference frequency ($f_2 - f_1$) from the mixer by means of a frequency selector the output would cover the amateur band 3·5–3·8 Mc/s. If the v.f.o. is reasonably well designed its frequency should be constant within the limits of $\pm$ 6 c/s at 300 kc/s, which is only one part in 25,000; at the output from the mixer, i.e. in the range 3·5–3·8 Mc/s, this represents a stability of the order of one part in 300,000. For comparison, a typical v.f.o. of straightforward design having an output in the same band would probably have a stability of about one part in 50,000.

In the example just given, the stability multiplication factor is 12. This figure could be increased by using an even lower frequency for the v.f.o. but this would necessitate a crystal frequency nearer to the required output frequency, and a point is eventually reached at which it is difficult to separate them in the succeeding amplifier circuits. Consequently the best compromise must be found. The figures given in the example should prove satisfactory for the 3·5 Mc/s band:

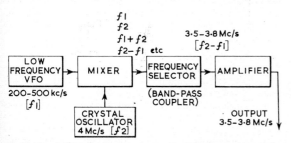

Fig. 25. Block diagram of a mixer-type v.f.o. The frequencies shown would be suitable for producing an output in the 3·5 Mc/s band.

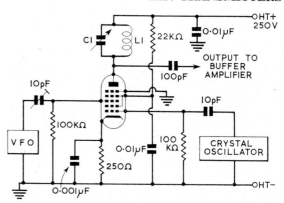

Fig. 26. Low-level mixing circuit for a v.f.o. showing typical values for a 6SA7, 6BE6, etc. The values of L_1 and C_1 are selected as for a normal tank circuit.

a crystal frequency of 7·8 Mc/s in conjunction with a v.f.o. operating over a range of 500–800 kc/s should be satisfactory for the 7 Mc/s band.

A low-level mixer circuit similar to that used in superheterodyne receivers is recommended: either a triode-hexode arrangement or a heptode such as the 6SA7 shown in **Fig. 26** is suitable. The anode circuit L_1C_1 is tuned to the centre of the required frequency band and is coupled to a tuned buffer

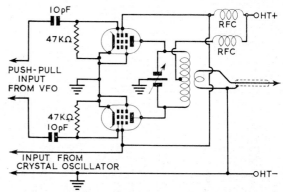

Fig. 27. Push-pull mixing circuit for a v.f.o. using screen injection of the crystal-oscillator voltage. The v.f.o. voltage is applied in push-pull either through a suitably tapped transformer arrangement or from a push-pull oscillator direct. The crystal-oscillator voltage is balanced out in the centre-tapped output tank circuit. Suitable valves are 6AK5, 6BH6, etc.

amplifier. Any of the orthodox coupling methods may be used instead of the capacitive coupling indicated.

In another mixing arrangement the crystal-oscillator voltage is applied in the same phase to the screen grids of a push-pull mixer while the v.f.o. voltage is applied in opposite phases to the control grids, as shown in **Fig. 27**. Alternatively heptode or hexode mixer valves may be used with the v.f.o. voltage applied in push-pull to the control grids and the crystal-oscillator voltage in parallel to the oscillator grids. The crystal-oscillator voltages are then balanced out in the output circuit, leaving only the v.f.o. frequency and the sum and difference frequencies. These are relatively easy to separate in the tuned anode circuit and in the following buffer amplifiers.

Ideal keying characteristics may be more easily obtained with this type of oscillator unit. Neither of the two frequencies initially generated falls within the amateur bands and thus the two oscillators may be left running continuously without fear of causing interference; it is only when mixing takes place that other frequencies are produced. If the mixer itself is suitably keyed, the output in the required band will be interrupted at a low power level and chirp can be avoided, provided of course that the effect of the changing load on the variable-frequency oscillator is negligible.

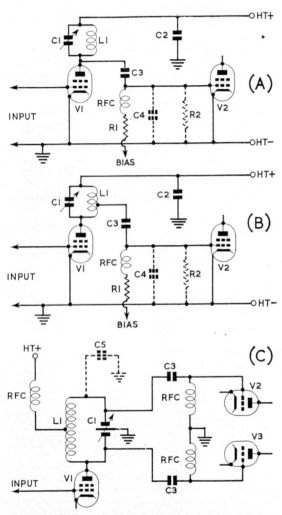

Fig. 28. Typical capacitive coupling arrangements. C_1—tank tuning capacitor; C_2—r.f. by-pass capacitor (about 0·01 μF); C_3—coupling capacitor (about 100 pF); C_4—grid-to-earth capacitance of V_2; R_1—normal grid resistor.

(A) Simplest capacitive coupling circuit.

(B) The grid of V_2 is connected to a tap on the driver tank-circuit inductance L_1, giving improved inter-stage matching. Whether or not this is necessary depends on the operating conditions of either of the stages and the amount of mismatch permissible.

(C) A simple arrangement for coupling a single-ended stage to a push-pull stage. To obtain correct balance of the grid drive to V_2 and V_3 a small capacitor C_5 equal to the anode-to-earth capacitance of the driver valve V_1 should be added.

INTERSTAGE COUPLING METHODS

Correct coupling between two stages is obtained when the input impedance of the driven stage is equal to the output impedance of the driver stage, resulting in the maximum transfer of power. The required condition can be secured in several ways, each of which has its own special advantages that made it more suitable for particular applications.

Capacitive Coupling

Various arrangements of capacitive coupling are shown in **Fig. 28**. In its simplest form, shown in (A), a capacitor C_3 is connected from the anode of the driver valve V_1 to the grid of the next stage V_2 in order to transfer the r.f. voltage from the driver tank circuit L_1C_1. The capacitor C_4, shown dotted, represents the grid-to-earth capacitance of V_2 while R_2 represents the equivalent resistance of the driven grid circuit. Both C_4 and R_2 are effectively in parallel with the driver tank circuit L_1C_1 through the r.f. by-pass capacitance C_2 across the h.t. supply and if the coupling capacitance C_3 is made too great, V_1 may be incorrectly loaded. As the load is increased, the Q of the tank circuit falls and a point is eventually reached at which the efficiency of the driver is lowered; moreover harmonics are produced and may give rise to interference.

The effect of C_4 is likewise to reduce the L/C ratio in the anode tank circuit of V_1 and if it is large it must be allowed for in the design. A method of improving the L/C ratio of the tank circuit is to tap the grid of V_2 into the coil as shown in (B); the Q of the tank circuit is also increased and often the impedance matching between stages can be achieved more accurately with consequent greater power transfer. Besides adding to the mechanical complexity, however, the tapped-coil arrangement shows a tendency to generate parasitic oscillations.

The resistance R_1, which is the d.c. grid return for V_2, is in effect also in parallel with the tank circuit of V_1 and if it were not for the r.f. choke (RFC) in series with it this resistance would present an extra (though small) r.f. load. The r.f. choke reduces the power loss in the resistance by reducing the r.f. current flowing through it, while the d.c. path remains unchanged.

As shown in (C), a single-ended driver valve can be coupled to a push-pull stage V_2 and V_3. In this case, the tank coil of V_1 is centre-tapped and is tuned by the split-stator capacitor C_1. The r.f. voltages at the ends of the coil are equal in amplitude and 180 degrees out-of-phase and are therefore suitable for feeding directly to the grids of V_2 and V_3. The rotor of the split-stator capacitor must be earthed by the shortest route possible, preferably direct on to the chassis. If this is not done, the inductance of the connection may be sufficiently great to prevent harmonics from being adequately by-passed to earth and interference through the inadvertent radiation of these harmonics may result.

Inductive Coupling

Inductive coupling between stages has several distinct advantages as compared with capacitive coupling. The basic circuit arrangement is shown in **Fig. 29**.

To understand these advantages, consider the two tuned circuits L_1C_1 (primary) and L_2C_2 (secondary), loosely coupled by a small degree of mutual induction between the coils, and suppose that each of the circuits resonates separately at a frequency f. If an r.f. voltage of variable frequency is applied to the primary of this arrangement and the resulting output voltage across the secondary is measured, the variation of output voltage with the frequency of the applied voltage will be in the form shown in **Fig. 30**, curve A: i.e. the circuit would possess considerable selectivity with a single peak at the frequency f. If the coils are now brought closer together, thus increasing the coupling between windings, the curve obtained on repeating the measurement will become flatter and the output voltage at the peak will be slightly higher, as depicted in curve B. Further tightening of the coupling causes the response to become still flatter until, after a certain critical value of the coupling has been reached (curve C), two peaks separated by equal amounts of opposite sides of the central frequency appear, with a pronounced dip at the centre (curve D). The value

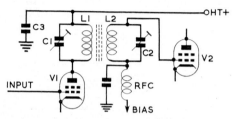

Fig. 29. Inductive coupling. A band-pass effect can be obtained by suitably close coupling between L₁ and L₂. L₁C₁—anode tank circuit of driver stage; L₂C₂—grid tank circuit of driven stage; C₃—r.f. by-pass capacitor.

of coupling just below that which causes the appearance of the two peaks is known as the *critical coupling*. When the circuits are in this condition, it is found that the output voltage remains virtually constant over quite a wide frequency range, often as much as 5 per cent of the central frequency, and also that on either side of the flat top of the curve the voltage falls away somewhat more rapidly than in the single-peaked curve obtained with looser coupling

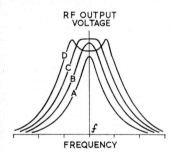

Fig. 30. Variation of output voltage with frequency for the inductively coupled circuits shown in Fig. 29. The curve C indicates the condition known as "critical coupling," the output voltage being constant over approximately a 5 per cent variation in frequency.

(such as curve A or curve B). A pair of resonant circuits having critical coupling, and therefore exhibiting a flat-topped characteristic, are referred to as a *bandpass* or *wide-band* coupling.

The bandwidth (i.e. the frequency range over which the output voltage remains within specified limits, usually 3 dB) of such a critically-coupled arrangement is about 1·4 times that of a single tuned-circuit coupling. Further the overall bandwidth of a series of stages coupled by double-tuned circuits, as might be used in a drive unit, narrows much less rapidly as the number of stages is increased, compared with single tuned-circuit coupling. The same remarks apply to double-tuned circuits irrespective of whether they are coupled

by mutual inductance, common inductance or capacitance, or by link coupling as described in the following section.

The practical advantage gained therefore by the use of a properly adjusted bandpass system is that after the initial setting up of the circuits, the drive to the final stage can be made to remain virtually constant over the width of an amateur band without the necessity of any tuning adjustments.

The circuit shown in Fig. 29 is a simple practical bandpass coupling arrangement. To avoid capacitive coupling effects which would modify the bandpass characteristic in an undesirable and unpredictable way, the grid end of the secondary winding should be situated at the opposite end from the anode end of the primary. It is quite a simple matter to measure the frequency-response characteristics (as typified by Fig. 30) merely by using the v.f.o. as the source of variable-frequency input voltage and observing the variations in the grid current of the driven stage. The voltage produced by the v.f.o. (or by an untuned buffer stage following it) can be assumed to be reasonably constant over a limited frequency range. The correct degree of inductive coupling can then be found from a progressive series of measurements. If the bandwidth obtained with critical coupling is found to be too small, it is usually possible to broaden it by increasing the L/C ratio of the tuned circuits.

Sometimes it can happen that at first only one voltage peak is observed, although in fact the over-coupled case shown in curve D is being obtained. The other peak may be lying outside the range of measurement.

Link Coupling

The practical disadvantage of simple bandpass inductive coupling between a pair of tuned circuits is that it may be difficult to arrange for the necessary mechanical adjustment. This can be overcome by using a variable link coupling between the two coils.

A small coil having a very few turns of wire is coupled to the driver tank circuit, thus transforming the output from a high impedance to a low impedance. A flexible transmission line transfers the energy at this low impedance to another similar coil coupled to the tuned input circuit of the driven valve where it is again transformed to the high impedance value required by its grid: see **Fig. 31**. The degree of coupling is adjusted by altering the position of either of the link coils or by altering the number of turns in them.

The link coils should be situated at the "cold" or "earthy" ends (i.e. the ends having zero r.f. potential) of the tank coils since the capacitance coupling which exists between the link and the tuned circuits will otherwise result in spurious tuning effects and the transference of unwanted harmonics. It is also beneficial to earth one side of the link circuit because this eliminates the possibility of stray capacitive coupling between the tuned circuits through the link.

The link line may in theory be of any length, but in practice, unless it is limited to about 2 ft. the resulting reactance presented by the link may make adequate coupling difficult. However, if the line is initially adjusted to have a "flat" characteristic, this difficulty should not arise. The link reactance may also be tuned out by making the link circuit resonant; this is usually accomplished by the addition of capacitance in parallel or in series with one of the link coils. The method is not always satisfactory since the correct adjustment varies with the operating frequency and the losses in the line and the radiation from it are increased. A further advantage of link coupling is that it simplifies the problem of coupling a single-ended stage to a push-pull (or push-push) amplifier, as shown at (B) in Fig. 31. Balanced low-impedance line, such as flat-twin cable of 80-ohms impedance, is suitable for this purpose; coaxial cable (outer braid earthed) can also be used and this may be desirable in order to reduce radiation from the line. Good quality flex has also been used but is not recommended where alternatives are available.

Parallel Anode Feed

If desired, the d.c. anode voltage of the driver valve can be removed from the associated coupling components in any of the coupling arrangements so far described. The basic principles are shown in **Figs. 32** and **33**. The choke RFC_1 presents a high impedance over a reasonably wide range of frequencies including the operating frequencies, and the necessary r.f. voltage is developed across the tuned circuit to which it is coupled through the isolating capacitor C_1.

Apart from the increased factor of safety achieved by removing the anode voltage from the tuned circuits, the peak voltage across the tuning capacitor is reduced and one

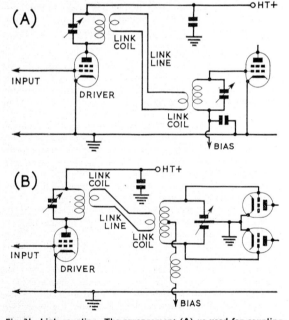

Fig. 31. Link coupling. The arrangement (A) us used for coupling two single-ended stages, while (B) shows how a single-ended driver can be coupled to a push-pull amplifier. The link coils must always be placed at the "cold" parts of the tuned-circuit inductances to avoid unwanted capacitive coupling. Suitable numbers of turns for the link coils are as follows:

Frequency (Mc/s)	1·8	3·5	7	14	21	28
No. of turns	4—5	4—5	3	2	1	1

In certain circumstances it may be desirable to earth one side of the link line.

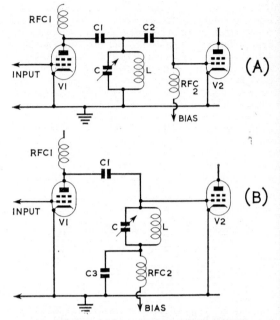

Fig. 32. Parallel anode feed in capacitance-coupled amplifiers. In these arrangements the resonant circuit LC is the anode load and is connected in parallel with the anode choke RFC_1. In (A) the bias for V_2 is applied direct through the grid choke RFC_2, whereas in (B) it is applied in series with the tuned circuit. C_1—isolating coupling capacitor (0·001—0·01 μF); C_2—inter-stage coupling capacitor (100 pF); C_3—by-pass capacitor (0·001—0·01 μF); LC—tank circuit of driver stage V_1.

of smaller voltage rating may therefore be used—a matter of some importance in high-power driver stages or power amplifiers. The capacitor C_1 should be rated to withstand the d.c. anode voltage plus the peak r.f. voltage and should preferably have a mica dielectric.

R.F. Chokes

As mentioned above, the r.f. choke must present a high impedance at the operating frequency. If the latter is variable over a very wide range as in an all-band transmitter covering 1·8–30 Mc/s appreciable losses may occur in the choke owing to the effects of self-capacitance and perhaps resonance. The difficulty may be partially overcome by the use of two or more different chokes connected in series.

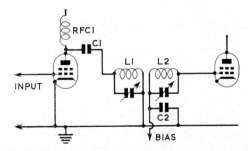

Fig. 33. Parallel anode feed in an inductively-coupled amplifier. C_1—isolating capacitor (0·001—0·01 μF); C_2—by-pass capacitor (0·001—0·01 μF); L_1L_2—inductively-coupled coils.

A good compromise for an all-band choke is one having an inductance in the region of 2·5 mH, but its self-capacitance should be low.

Where r.f. chokes are present in both the grid and the anode circuits of a valve amplifier, it is advisable to make them of different inductance values since otherwise there is a possibility of low-frequency parasitic oscillations being generated by feedback in the tuned-anode/tuned-grid circuit thus formed.

Interstage Pi-network Coupler

The pi-network coupler is often used for delivering power to an aerial or an aerial feeder but it is equally suitable for coupling together two intermediate stages as shown in **Fig. 34.** The impedances of the two stages can be matched by adjusting the tuning capacitors C_2 and C_3. The properties

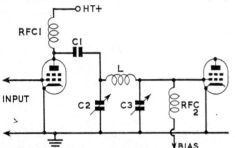

Fig. 34. Inter-stage pi-network coupler. By varying C_2 and C_3 the impedances of the two stages can be matched: see text for design data. The blocking capacitor may be 0·001—0·01 μF.

of a pi-network coupler are further discussed on page 187, and the method of finding the coil and capacitor values is given. When used as a matching device between two class-C stages the following values may be taken:

Output resistance of driver stage—

$$R_o = \frac{(0·57 \times V_{ht})^2}{P} \text{ ohms}$$

where V_{ht} = d.c. anode voltage (volts)

P = output power (watts)

Input resistance of driven stage—

$$R_i = \frac{6·22 \times P_D}{I_G^2} \times 10^5$$

where P_D = driving power required by the driven stage (watts)

I_G = d.c. grid current of driven stage (mA).

The pi-network coupler also acts as a low-pass filter, and therefore it helps to prevent the transfer of undesirable harmonics from the driver to the following stages. In fact, the harmonic output from a transmitter stage using such a coupler is less than that produced by a normal tank circuit of the same Q by a factor of $1/n^2$ where n is the order of the harmonic.

FREQUENCY-MULTIPLIERS

A power output at a multiple of the generated frequency is often required in amateur transmitters to obtain, for example, multi-band operation or merely to gain the advantage of the higher frequency stability which results from operating the oscillator on a relatively low frequency.

Frequency multiplication is made possible by the distortion of the anode-current r.f. waveform which occurs in a class-C amplifier stage. As described on page 176, the current in such an amplifier flows only for a short time during the cycle in the form of pulses, and it can be shown that such a series of pulses behaves as though it is composed of a number of sine waves of frequencies, f, $2f$, $3f$ and so on (where f is the fundamental or input frequency), the amplitude of these *harmonics* as they are called gradually diminishing with increasing order. Their relative amplitudes depend upon the shape of the pulse, which is determined by the operating conditions of the valve.

By inserting a parallel-tuned circuit in the anode circuit of the valve, resonant at the desired harmonic frequency and therefore offering its highest impedance at this frequency, the passage of the harmonic current produces a corresponding voltage-drop across the circuit. The tuned circuit in this way acts as a selector for the appropriate frequency.

In order to increase the energy of the harmonic current contained within the pulse, and therefore the efficiency of the valve as a frequency-multiplying device, it is desirable to reduce the angle of flow of current (defined on page 176) to values somewhat below the normal class C amplifier levels, e.g. 90 degrees or less. This is accomplished by increasing the grid bias to beyond normal class C operation and driving the valve with a high r.f. grid voltage.

The maximum power output obtainable at various harmonic frequencies in a frequency-multiplier stage, relative to the output at the fundamental frequency are—

Second harmonic	..	55 per cent
Third harmonic	..	35 per cent
Fourth harmonic	..	25 per cent

The fourth harmonic is the maximum degree of multiplication usually attempted in one stage, although for low output-power requirements a frequency multiplication of up to seven or eight is occasionally used.

The increase of harmonic output power obtained by this method may be found to aggravate the problem of avoiding interference, and in general a frequency-multiplying stage should be operated at the lowest possible power level and preferably it should be followed by a further buffer amplifying stage before being used to drive the final power amplifier.

Neutralization of a frequency-multiplier is not required even with triodes since the grid and anode circuits are tuned to different frequencies, and self-oscillation is not possible.

Push-push Doubler

To improve the efficiency of frequency multiplication at the *even* harmonic frequencies a push-push doubler is often

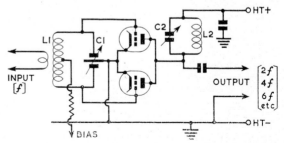

Fig. 35. The push-push frequency-multiplier circuit. The anode tank circuit L_2C_2 can be tuned to even multiples of the grid-circuit frequency.

used: see **Fig. 35**. The anodes of the two valves are connected in parallel to the normal tank circuit, whereas the grids are driven in push-pull. The tuned circuit thus receives pulses of current alternately from the two anodes and the harmonic energy supplied to the tuned circuit is thereby doubled. When operated as a doubler, such a stage is capable of giving efficiencies approaching that of a straight class C amplifier; at the higher even harmonics the output is correspondingly increased.

Push-pull Frequency-Multipliers

To increase the efficiency of a multiplier stage at *odd* harmonics a true push-pull circuit such as is shown in **Fig. 36** may be used, both the grids and the anodes being connected in push-pull. In this case, the even harmonics are self-cancelling in the anode circuit and the odd harmonics are reinforced.

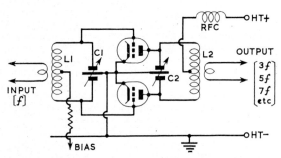

Fig. 36. The push-pull frequency-multiplier circuit. The output tank circuit L₂C₂ is tuned to ODD multiples of the grid-circuit frequency.

Design Features and Adjustments

Although triodes may be suitable for frequency multiplication, the drive-power requirement for tetrodes or pentodes is much lower. In many amateur transmitters a drive unit consisting of a number of successive pentode frequency-multiplying stages preceded by a v.f.o. or crystal oscillator are used. All these stages are operated at low power to reduce the possibility of TVI and other forms of interference. The output of any of these multiplier stages may be selected at will to provide drive for the power amplifier on the desired frequency band.

In modern designs, the coupling between stages is in the form of wide-band couplers as described in the previous section which give a notable reduction in the transference of undesired harmonics. Furthermore, once the circuits have been initially tuned no further adjustments are necessary.

The first step in setting up a frequency-multiplying stage is to reduce its h.t. supply voltage. The drive can then be applied and the grid circuit adjusted to resonance (as indicated by a maximum reading on the grid-current meter). On varying the tuning of the anode circuit one or more dips in the value of the anode current will be noticed, corresponding to resonance at the various harmonic frequencies. The dips become progressively less deep as the order of harmonic selected is increased.

The possibility of tuning to an incorrect harmonic should be borne in mind and it is advisable to check the frequency

with a suitable absorption wavemeter coupled to the tank circuit; alternatively the effect of the absorption wavemeter on the anode current of the multiplier at resonance can be observed. The current should vary as the wavemeter is tuned through the harmonic frequency.

POWER AMPLIFIERS

As already explained, the generation of r.f. power must be at a low level to ensure complete stability, and this level is raised to the desired value by means of r.f. power amplifiers. The amplification must take place without the introduction of any spurious or harmonic frequencies which if radiated might cause interference to other services. According to the terms of the Amateur (Sound) Licence the maximum d.c. power input to the anode circuit of the final amplifier must be limited to a certain specified value, depending on the frequency band in use and other factors, and therefore in order to radiate the greatest possible power for the limited input the anode-circuit efficiency of the amplifier (i.e. conversion of d.c. power to r.f. power) must be as high as possible. For this reason and also on the grounds of economy, the two classes of r.f. power amplifier in common use are the class B and class C types, described below.

Class C Operation

In a class C amplifier the standing grid-bias voltage is increased to approximately twice the value required to cut off the anode current in the absence of r.f. drive to the grid. The r.f. drive voltage must be of sufficient amplitude to swing the grid potential so far that it becomes positive with respect to the cathode during the positive half-cycle. The resultant anode current is thus in the form of a succession of pulses, flowing only during a part of the r.f. drive cycle; the " angle of flow " (which measures its duration) is usually about 120 electrical degrees in a class C amplifier, i.e. about one-third of a full cycle (360 degrees), whereas for comparison the angle of flow in a class B amplifier is 180 degrees.

Fig. 37 shows the conditions existing in a class C amplifier. The broken horizontal line AB at about one-third of the

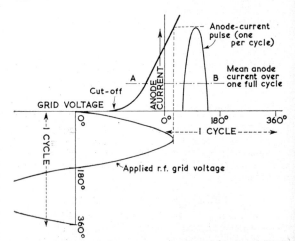

Fig. 37. Class C operation. The application of a large-amplitude sinusoidal grid voltage superimposed on a grid bias greater than the cut-off value causes the anode current to flow in pulses. The output is rich in harmonics.

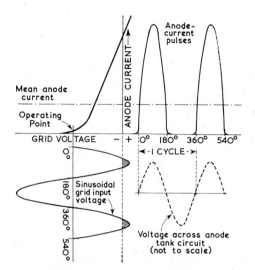

Fig. 38. Class B operation. The anode-current pulses are approximately of half-cycle duration and appreciable grid current flows owing to the positive incursions of the grid drive voltage.

peak pulse height represents the mean anode current during one cycle, as would be indicated by a moving-coil milli-ammeter.

Although the anode current flows in the form of pulses, the r.f. voltage developed across a resonant circuit connected to the anode is approximately sinusoidal, owing to the " flywheel " action of the resonant circuit, i.e. its tendency to allow the oscillations to continue after the removal of the current pulse.

As the angle of flow of anode current is reduced the efficiency increases. This is accomplished by increasing the negative grid bias and increasing the drive, which results in increased peak amplitude of the anode current pulses and increased peak anode current. Because the pulses are narrowed the power output will fall, but because of the increased efficiency it will fall proportionately less than the anode input power. The increase in efficiency achieved by narrowing the angle of flow to less than 120 degrees is small and is rarely worth while. Taking into consideration the increased drive and the higher peak current which the valve must provide, the efficiency to be expected at 120 degrees is about 75 per cent.

Class B Operation

In the class B amplifier, the anode-current pulses flow for approximately 180 degrees, i.e. half of the r.f. cycle as indicated in **Fig. 38**. The negative grid bias is sufficient to reduce the anode current in the absence of drive only to the cut-off point, and the applied grid voltage swing drives the grid slightly positive once in each cycle, as represented by the shaded areas.

Owing to the larger angle of flow the anode efficiency is less than in class C operation, but even so it may reach 60–65 per cent for c.w. operation. The r.f. voltage in the output circuit is proportional to the r.f. grid excitation voltage; i.e. the power output is proportional to the square of the grid excitation voltage. This class of amplifier may

therefore be used for the amplification of amplitude-modulated signals (including single-sideband modulated signals). Since the anode efficiency varies with the grid excitation level, the mean efficiency for the amplification of modulated signals is considerably less than the value of 60–65 per cent quoted above and is dependent on the nature of the amplified signal.

Triode R.F. Amplifiers

The fundamental circuit of an r.f. amplifier using a triode is shown in **Fig. 39**. The grid is connected to a tuned resonant circuit which is coupled to the oscillator or driver valve by any of the means previously suggested, while the output is derived from a resonant circuit connected to the anode and tuned to the same frequency as the grid circuit.

When adjusting a class C amplifier the load is first coupled loosely to the anode tank circuit and drive power is fed to the grid. On varying the tuning of the anode circuit it will be found that an appreciable dip in anode current occurs at resonance. The magnitude of the anode-current dip is proportional to the efficiency of the anode tank circuit if the load is disconnected. It is important to remember, however, that the p.a. valve should not be operated with the load disconnected unless the anode voltage is considerably reduced, because of the danger of developing high r.f. voltages which may cause " flash-over " in the valve or the associated components.

It will be found that the r.f. power output increases as the drive is increased, and this increase continues up to a certain point beyond which no further increase of power output is achieved: the amplifier is then said to be *saturated*. The drive power should be set slightly higher than the level at which saturation commences; at this point, the anode current can be adjusted to the value corresponding to the required power input by increasing the load coupling. Slight

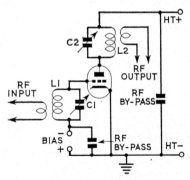

Fig. 39. Basic triode amplifier circuit.

readjustment of the tank tuning may then be required, and finally the excitation should again be varied to ensure saturation. It is inadvisable to allow the grid excitation to rise much higher than the value at which saturation occurs since not only is the grid dissipation thereby increased but the production of harmonics is enhanced and there is no significant increase in efficiency.

With class B amplifiers the method of adjustment is similar except that the drive power is considerably less than the saturation level.

Tetrode or Pentode R.F. Amplifiers

In a tetrode or pentode amplifier the screen grid is held at a constant potential and it therefore reduces the capacitance between the control grid and the anode to an extremely low value. If suitable auxiliary external screening is provided, the coupling between the input and output circuits can be almost completely eliminated. At the same time the electric field of the anode is prevented from influencing the ability of the grid to control the current flowing through the valve, and consequently much less power is required to drive a tetrode or pentode than a triode; i.e. a greater power gain is available.

Because the characteristics of a tetrode or pentode valve tend to make it operate like a constant-current device, very high voltages may occur in the anode tank circuit if this circuit is tuned to resonance in the absence of an output load or if it is very inadequately loaded, and therefore no attempt should be made to explore the anode-current dip with such valves except with greatly reduced power input.

It is more satisfactory to supply the screen through a series voltage-dropping resistance from the anode supply than directly from a fixed source, since in this way the screen is protected from the danger of excessive current if the control grid should be overdriven. The series dropping resistance also protects the screen from excessive dissipation in the event of the load being removed from the anode circuit. Moreover, by feeding the screen from the anode h.t. supply the possibility of damage owing to the application of screen voltage without the normal anode voltage is diminished.

If, however, it is considered that overdriving and underloading are not likely to occur, it will be found easier to obtain full output from the valve when the screen voltage is fixed at its correct value by the use of a potential divider across the h.t. supply or a separate constant-voltage source. The high power-sensitivity of pentodes and tetrodes and the fact that neutralization is not normally required are the main reasons for their popularity as r.f. amplifiers. The small drive requirements enable a complete multi-band transmitter to be built within a single screened container, and the possibility of television interference resulting from the leakage of r.f. power is thus greatly reduced.

Push-pull Operation

A pair of identical valves in a push-pull circuit will produce double the power output obtainable from a single valve, and although this is likewise true of a pair of valves connected in parallel there are several theoretical advantages to be gained from the inherent balance which exists in the push-pull arrangement.

If the valves are similar in characteristics the second harmonic and other even harmonics are balanced out in the common tank circuit. Similarly, the currents set up by one valve in the common by-pass circuits are cancelled by those of opposite phase set up by the other. Since these currents can become quite large, particularly at the higher frequencies, increased stability is attainable by the use of push-pull operation. In practice, however, it is unlikely that a perfect balance will be found to exist.

A further advantage is that the L/C ratio of the tank circuits may be made higher than with single-ended stages, since the capacitances of the valves are presented in series across the coils. This feature is likely to be of greater value at frequencies of 21 Mc/s and above where the desired L/C ratio is difficult to achieve.

Parallel Operation

The output power obtainable from a push-pull or parallel arrangement is the same, provided that the correct impedances are presented to the anode and the grid circuits by use of correct L/C ratios in the tank circuits. It may prove impossible to satisfy this condition when certain valves of high anode-to-earth capacitances are used in the parallel arrangement above about 21 Mc/s, but nevertheless this circuit is often considered preferable to the push-pull arrangement, owing to the simpler construction involved and in view of the fact that the theoretical advantages of the push-pull circuit mentioned earlier are not easily obtained in practice.

Neutralization

It will be noticed that the basic circuit of an r.f. amplifier, shown in Fig. 39, corresponds to that of a tuned-anode/tuned-grid oscillator. Unless something is done to prevent it, the amplifier will oscillate at a frequency determined by the tuned circuits, because of the feedback from the anode to the grid through the inter-electrode capacitance.

Only in pentode or tetrode valves designed specifically for r.f. work will the anode-to-grid capacitance be small enought to prevent the occurrence of self-oscillation. Amplifiers using valves such as the 807 which has an anode-to-grid capacitance of about 0·25 pF will not generally oscillate on any amateur h.f. band, and neutralization may not be required unless the layout is very poor (although it is quite likely to be beneficial). On the other hand, single-ended tetrodes such as the 6L6 or 6V6 which are intended for a.f. application will require neutralizing even on the lower frequency amateur bands. All triodes without exception require neutralizing on all amateur bands.

The r.f. voltage fed back through the anode-to-grid capacitance can be neutralized or cancelled by injecting an equal and opposite voltage on the grid through a separate path. There are two main methods by which this may be achieved: (a) anode neutralization, (b) grid neutralization.

Anode Neutralization

In this method a centre-tapped anode tank circuit is used in place of the simple coil-and-capacitor so that an

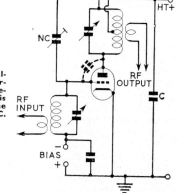

Fig. 40. Anode neutralization. In this arrangement the centre-tap of the tank coil is earthed through the r.f. bypass capacitor C.

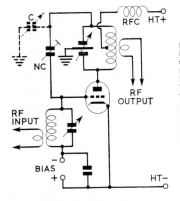

Fig. 41. Anode neutralization using a split-stator capacitor to provide the zero-potential centre-tap in the tank circuit. The diagram also shows a balancing capacitor C for cancelling the anode-to-earth capacitance of the valve: if desired it can likewise be added to the circuit in Fig. 40.

the anode-to-*earth* capacitance of the valve. It may be found especially beneficial whenever the neutralizing adjustment shows a tendency to vary from one band to another, although with the spit-stator circuit this does not normally occur.

Grid Neutralization

A less commonly used circuit is shown in **Fig. 42**. This system is analogous to anode neutralization, the only important difference being that the voltage-phase reversal is achieved in the grid circuit. The method of adjustment is otherwise similar to that required for anode neutralization. Its chief advantage is that it allows a normal anode tank circuit to be retained.

Link Neutralization

The required feedback voltage may be coupled from the anode tank circuit to the grid tank circuit by means of a link line connecting the two, as shown in **Fig. 43**. The phase

out-of-phase voltage is made available for neutralizing the feedback from the anode. **Fig. 40** shows such an arrangement in which the anode tuning inductance is centre-tapped and is fed at this point from the h.t. line thereby producing an r.f. voltage at the end of the coil opposite to the anode equal in value to the anode voltage but 180 degrees out-of-phase with it. To neutralize the internal feedback due to the anode-to-grid capacitance (shown dotted), the neutralizing capacitor *NC* should therefore be equal in value to this inter-electrode capacitance; in most valves this is quite small—less than 10 pF—but its effect is important and an accurate balance is required.

With this circuit a certain amount of undesirable feedback is usually present when the operating frequency is higher than about 7 Mc/s owing partly to the difficulty of tapping the coil at its exact radio-frequency centre and partly to the inevitable inductance of the leads connected to the neutralizing capacitor.

An improvement on this arrangement is shown in **Fig. 41**. Here a split-stator capacitor is used to provide the zero-potential centre-tap in the tank circuit. The voltages to earth of the opposite ends of the coil are determined by the relative capacitance values of the two sections of the capacitor and an accurate balancing of the two voltages is thus more easily obtained. The balancing of the circuit may be further improved by the addition of the small variable capacitor *C* shown dotted in Fig. 41. This serves to balance

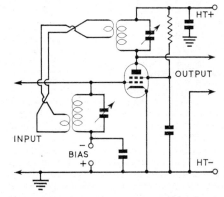

Fig. 43. Link neutralization. This arrangement is particularly suitable for pentode or tetrode circuits where the required amount of neutralization is relatively small.

is determined by the polarization of the two coils, and if incorrect the connections to one or other of the coils should be reversed. The method is useful when a suitable neutralizing condenser is not available or cannot easily be fitted into the layout. It is also suitable for neutralizing a tetrode or pentode amplifier which has been built without provision for neutralization and subsequently has been found slightly unstable.

Series-capacitance Neutralization

Another neutralizing circuit using a capacity potential divider is shown in **Fig. 44**. A small capacitor *NC* is connected between the valve anode and a large capacitor in series with the grid tank circuit or the anode tank circuit of the preceding valve. The relative values of *NC* and *C* may be selected from the following expression:

$$\frac{NC}{C} = \frac{C_{ga}}{C_{in}}$$

where C_{ga} = anode-to-grid capacitance
C_{in} = input capacitance of the valve plus stray capacitance across the input circuit.

It is advisable not to use a value greater than 5 pF for

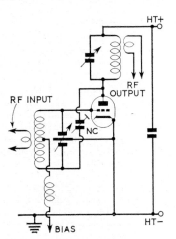

Fig. 42. Grid neutralization.

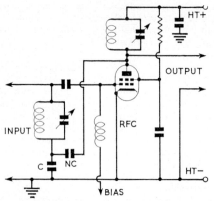

Fig. 44. Series-capacitance neutralization. The balancing voltage is derived from the potential divider comprised by the capacitors NC and C. Typical values for an 807 are NC = 5 pF and C = 1000 pF.

NC because this capacitance is effectively in parallel with the output of the valve and the L/C ratio of the tank circuit may be reduced undesirably.

Push-pull Neutralization

In a push-pull amplifier, neutralization can be easily applied, as shown in **Fig. 45** since a centre-tapped coil is already an essential feature of the circuit. Perfect balance can be obtained, and if the connecting leads are kept short the neutralization setting remains the same over a wide range of frequency including perhaps several of the amateur bands. It is common practice to use split-stator condensers in both the grid and the anode circuits and to earth the rotors, preferably by the shortest and thickest possible connections to ensure that harmonics are effectively by-passed.

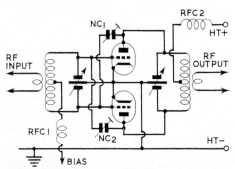

Fig. 45. Neutralization of a push-pull r.f. amplifier. Owing to the symmetry of the arrangement, excellent balance is usually easy to obtain: one setting of the neutralizing capacitor will hold over several amateur bands provided that the connecting leads are kept short.

Grid Bias

There are three possible methods by which bias may be obtained, any of which may be used either singly or in combination: see **Fig. 46**.

(a) *Fixed bias*, applied directly to the grid through an r.f. choke from a battery or suitable power supply (with the positive terminal earthed).

(b) *Cathode bias* (sometimes known as *automatic bias*), obtained by the voltage drop across a resistor inserted in the cathode lead of the valve.

(c) *Grid-resistance bias*, produced by the voltage-drop across a resistance in the grid-circuit return lead caused by the flow of rectified grid current when the drive is applied.

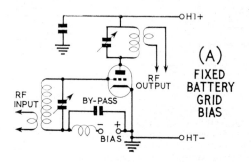

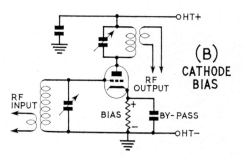

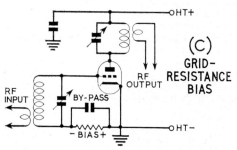

Fig. 46. Methods of providing grid bias in a class C amplifier

Fixed Bias

The simplest method for the production of fixed bias is a battery. For two reasons, however, its use may be found unsatisfactory: (i) As the battery ages its resistance increases and an additional bias gradually develops owing to the grid current flowing through the battery. (ii) Grid current, which flows in a direction opposite to the normal discharge from a battery, tends to charge up the battery and its voltage may be caused to rise well above the nominal value.

These drawbacks can be avoided by using a small mains-driven power unit incorporating the usual rectifier and ripple filter. The chief requirement in such a supply is that the output resistance must be low enough to prevent excessive auxiliary bias being developed across it by the flow of grid current. One method of ensuring this is to place a low-resistance bleeder across the output terminals, in which case the power supply must be designed to supply a considerably larger current than is necessary for the actual biasing purposes. The difficulty is best met by the use of a voltage-stabilizing valve which will maintain the output voltage constant irrespective of grid-current changes. The output from this voltage stabilizer must then be applied directly to the valve without the inclusion of an external resistance or a potential-divider network. In practice the minimum bias voltage obtainable by the use of voltage regulator valves will be 60–80 volts.

A most important advantage of fixed bias is that the valve will be fully protected in the event of a failure of the r.f. drive. This is quite likely to occur during tuning operations, and some form of fixed bias is therefore always advisable particularly in high-power stages.

Suitable fixed-bias circuits are described in Chapter 17 (*Power Supplies*).

Cathode Bias

Cathode bias is normally used in conjunction with fixed or grid-resistance bias for a class C stage because of the high value of bias which such a stage requires. The voltage-drop across the cathode resistor must be subtracted from the h.t. supply in calculating the effective anode-cathode voltage, and it may be uneconomical to derive the whole of the required bias from the voltage-drop across the cathode resistor. The most valuable feature of cathode bias is that it automatically protects the valve by preventing the flow of excessive anode current if the auxiliary sources of bias should fail. The cathode resistor is generally chosen so that, without auxiliary grid bias, sufficient voltage is developed across it to limit the anode dissipation to within the maximum ratings. The method of calculation follows from Ohm's law ($R = E/I$):

$$Cathode\ resistance\ (ohms) = \frac{Bias\ voltage\ (V) \times 1,000}{Cathode\ current\ (mA)}$$

In the case of a tetrode or a pentode, the cathode current is equal to the sum of the screen and anode currents. As an example, consider a tetrode which requires a bias of 10 volts to limit the anode current to 70 mA, the screen current being 10 mA. From the above formula—

$$Cathode\ resistance = \frac{10 \times 1,000}{10 + 70} = 125\ ohms$$

The power dissipated in this resistor is given by I^2R, where I is the total current; thus—

$$Power = (0·08)^2 \times 125 = 0·8\ watts$$

In practice a 1-watt resistor would be chosen.

When a drive voltage is applied, the cathode current is augmented by the current flowing in the grid circuit but since this is relatively small it can safely be ignored in these calculations.

Grid-resistance Bias

In class C operation the r.f. grid drive is large enough to cause the grid potential to become positive at peak values, with the result that a rectified current flows in the grid circuit. If a resistance is inserted into the grid return lead the voltage-drop across this resistance due to the grid current

causes the grid to be biased more negatively. This provides an automatic biasing action, the amount of bias varying with the drive power and thus to some extent adjusting the actual peak drive voltage to the operating requirements of the valve.

Since failure of the drive would result in the loss of the whole of the bias if this were derived solely from a grid resistor, it is recommended that grid leak bias should only be used in conjunction with sufficient fixed or cathode bias to limit the anode dissipation to a safe value should the drive fail.

To illustrate the method of choosing the relative proportion of fixed, cathode and grid-resistance bias, the following example is given.

EXAMPLE: *An 807 is to be operated under maximum power input conditions (I.C.A.S. rating) with a combination of grid-resistance bias and fixed bias. It is required to calculate the value of the grid resistance and the fixed bias voltage.*

The relevant operating conditions are obtained by reference to the published valve data:

Anode voltage ..	750	volts
Anode current ..	100	mA
Anode dissipation	30	watts
Grid bias ..	−45	volts
Grid current ..	4	mA
Driving power ..	0·3	watts

First it is necessary to calculate the minimum bias required to limit the anode current to a safe value in the absence of r.f. drive. At 750 volts the maximum current permissible for a dissipation of 30 watts would be 40 mA. By referring to the characteristic curve, the bias needed is found to be approximately −20 volts. With the r.f. drive applied an additional bias of 25 volts is therefore required to raise it to the specified −45 volts. However, if the fixed bias is supposed to be obtained from a mains-driven power unit having an internal resistance of, say, 1000 ohms, there will be an extra voltage developed due to the flow of grid current through this internal resistance: since the grid current is expected to be 4 mA, this extra voltage-drop will be $1000 \times 0·004 = 4$ volts. The fixed-bias supply unit (nominally supplying 20 volts) will therefore develop an effective bias, under drive conditions, of 24 volts. This means that the series grid resistance which is going to be relied upon to provide the additional bias to bring the total up to 45 volts need only contribute 21 volts. For a grid current of 4 mA, a resistance of 21/0·004 = 5250 ohms would thus be required.

If the fixed bias were to be obtained from a 20-volt battery (the internal resistance of which is negligibly small), the extra bias to be contributed by the series grid resistance would be 25 volts and its value would have to be increased to 25/0·004 = 6250 ohms.

In either case the total resistance in the grid circuit is 6250 ohms and the total resistive voltage-drop amounts to 25 volts.

Clamp Valve

If the grid bias is derived solely from the flow of r.f. current through the grid resistance, the valve will take excessive anode current when the drive is removed. To prevent this occurrence in a tetrode or pentode amplifier, a *clamp* valve connected as in **Fig. 47** may be used. During normal operation the p.a. grid-resistance bias also constitutes a bias for the clamp valve and thus renders it ineffective. On removal of the excitation, the bias on the grid of the clamp valve becomes zero and its anode/cathode resistance falls to a relatively low value. The resulting increased voltage-drop across the screen resistance R reduces the screen voltage of the p.a. stage sufficiently to limit the anode current to a safe value.

For effective clamp operation, a valve should be selected which is capable of passing almost the whole current available through the screen resistor. Thus, for a p.a. valve operating with a series screen dropper of 30,000 ohms from

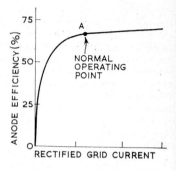

Fig. 48. The anode efficiency of a class C power amplifier initially rises rapidly with a small increase of grid current up to about 65 per cent, after which the increase of efficiency with drive becomes relatively slight.

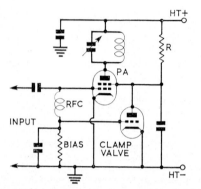

Fig. 47. Clamp valve circuit. On removal of the grid drive to the p.a. stage the clamp valve conducts and reduces the screen voltage applied to the p.a. valve, thus limiting its anode current.

an h.t. supply of 750 volts, the clamp valve should be capable of passing a current of—

$$\frac{30{,}000 \text{ ohms}}{750 \text{ volts}} = 0.025 \text{ amperes} = 25 \text{ mA}$$

The pentode chosen must, however, have a grid base sufficiently short to ensure cut-off under normal drive conditions, a requirement not difficult to meet with the 6V6 or a similar type if the bias derived across the grid resistor is greater than about 25 volts.

Grid-drive Requirements

Grid Current. In normal class C operation the rectified grid current is sufficiently small to cause only a moderate rise in the temperature of the grid, but if the valve is over-driven the temperature rise may become great enough to produce grid emission and possibly cause permanent physical damage to the grid itself. Where the valve is a pentode or tetrode over-driving may also result in excessive screen dissipation. Another danger is the production of undesirable harmonics. A curve drawn to show the relation between grid current and the anode efficiency of a class C p.a. stage will have the form shown in **Fig. 48.** The efficiency initially rises quickly for a small increase of grid current from zero after which it remains substantially constant over quite a wide range. The grid current should therefore be kept as low as possible consistent with a reasonable efficiency being obtained (65–70 per cent); for example, by operating at point A.

Drive Power. The drive power required is made up of (i) the power required to drive the grid current against the

bias voltage, (ii) the power dissipated in the grid of the valve and (iii) the loss in the coupling arrangement.

The power in the bias source is the product of the grid current times the total bias voltage from all sources and is the same no matter how the bias voltage is obtained. The power dissipated in the grid of the valve is approximately equal to the product of grid current times the peak positive grid excursion which is often about the same as the power in the bias source. The loss in the coupling components will depend on the quality of the components used and on the layout and this is usually at least as great as the total drive power specified for the valve. The drive power available should be at least five times the power lost in the bias sources. Valves in parallel or push-pull require twice as much drive as a single valve of the same type.

In an amplitude modulated output stage the drive power and bias must be large enough to accommodate modulation peaks during which the anode voltage may rise to twice its normal maximum value in the unmodulated condition and the drive power requirement correspondingly increased.

Grid Tank Circuits

A grid tank circuit should be designed to have a Q value of about 12, for reasons which are outlined later in the discussion on *Anode Tank Circuits*. The required Q value is obtained by adjusting the L/C ratio of the tank circuit, although the relative values of L and C are also dependent on the type of circuit in use. **Fig. 49** shows a selection of the more popular arrangements.

The optimum value of C for a grid tank circuit in any of these arrangements can be found directly from the abac in **Fig. 50.** To use this abac the data required are (a) the operating frequency, (b) the grid-drive power and (c) the grid current. In the case of parallel or push-pull circuits, the grid-drive power and the grid current will be double the values corresponding to a single-ended circuit.

EXAMPLE A. *Find the grid tank-circuit capacitance and inductance required in the 3·5 Mc/s band for an 807 valve in class-C telegraphy operation. The drive power required is 0·25 watts and the grid current 3·5 mA.*

Using Fig. 50 join the values 3·5 mA and 0·25 watts on the grid-current and power scales by a straight-edge. This intersects the X_L/X_C scale at $1 \cdot 17 \times 10^3$ ohms. Join this value to the 3·5 Mc/s band marker on the frequency scale. The tank-circuit capacitance is then read off as 36 pF: in practice this would be made up by a capacitor of 25 pF in parallel with the valve input capacitance of 11 pF.

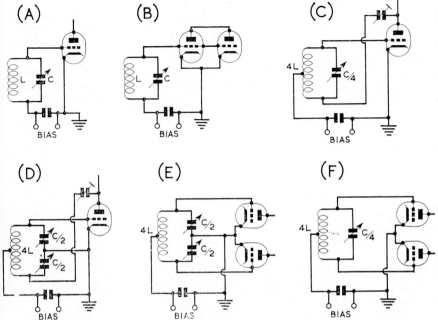

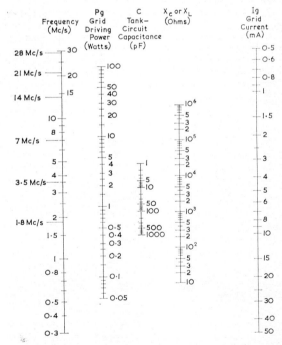

split-stator capacitor should have half the indicated value of C, i.e. 32·5 pF.

As the operating frequency is raised it will be found that the optimum value of C derived from the abac in Fig. 50 becomes smaller, and it may easily happen that it is less than the input capacitance of the valve. For instance, this would have occurred in Example A if the operating frequency had been raised to 14 Mc/s; here the optimum value of C would be 3 pF whereas the input capacitance of an 807 is 11 pF. In such circumstances, the circuit will have to be allowed to operate with more than the optimum capacitance (i.e. a lower L/C ratio): the only serious disadvantage will be a lowering of the efficiency of power transfer from the driver to the grid circuit of the p.a. stage. To offset this there will

Fig. 49. Grid tank-circuit arrangements. The values of C and L can be obtained from Fig. 50.

The corresponding tank-circuit inductance (for an operating frequency at the mid-point of the band, i.e. 3·65 Mc/s) is given by—

$$L = \frac{1 \cdot 17 \times 10^3}{2\pi \times 3 \cdot 65} = 51 \ \mu H$$

EXAMPLE B. *For a pair of 807 valves operating in push-pull (grid-circuit arrangement as shown at E in Fig. 49), each valve working under the same conditions as those prescribed in Example A, what is the grid tank-circuit capacitance and inductance required for the 3·5 Mc/s band?*

The total grid driving power is 0·5 watts and the total grid current is 7 mA. From the chart in Fig. 50—

$$X_c = 6 \times 10^2 \text{ ohms}$$

and $C = 65$ pF

For an operating frequency of 3·65 Mc/s as before—

$$L = \frac{6 \times 10^2}{2\pi \times 3 \cdot 65} = 26 \cdot 2 \ \mu H$$

The total value of the grid-circuit inductance is four times this value, i.e. 105 μH, and each of the two sections of the

Key to Fig. 50. Join the selected values of P_g and I_g by a line **PQR**. Note the point **Q** on the X_C/X_L scale. Join the point **Q** to the appropriate frequency **T** on the extreme left-hand scale. The required value of C is given at the point **S**. The corresponding value of L is given by the reactance value X_L at the point **Q** divided by 6·28 × frequency (in Mc/s). Alternatively, L can be obtained from the reactance chart in Chapter 22 (General Data).

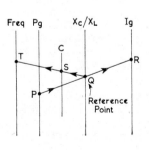

Fig. 50. Abac for determining grid tank circuit capacitance for a Q-value of 12 in the circuit arrangements shown in Fig. 49. For push-pull and parallel connections, the appropriate values of grid current and power are those for the two valves taken together.

183

be the advantage of a reduction in the harmonic content of the grid-voltage waveform and a reduced likelihood of interference due to harmonic radiation.

Anode Tank Circuits

The correct design of an anode tank circuit must fulfil the three following conditions:

(a) The anode circuit of the valve must be presented with the proper operating impedance in relation to the valve impedance to ensure efficient generation of power.

(b) The power delivered by the valve to the tuned circuit must be transferred to the load or aerial without appreciable loss.

(c) Owing to the nature of the anode-current pulses, the Q of the circuit when it is loaded by the aerial must be sufficiently high to maintain a good " flywheel " action and produce a close approximation to a sinusoidal r.f. voltage waveform.

A valve will deliver the maximum power when the output load is equal to the source impedance. For practical purposes a p.a. stage has an r.f. source impedance equal to that of an imaginary resistance proportional to a figure which is obtained by dividing the anode voltage by the anode current, and the load is represented by the tank circuit shunted by the aerial load. The efficiency of the tank circuit depends on the ratio of its dynamic resistance when unloaded to its value when loaded. Because the dynamic resistance is proportional to Q, the efficiency depends on the ratio of the " unloaded-Q " to the " loaded Q."

For a given Q value the dynamic resistance can be raised or lowered by changing the reactance of the coil or capacitor, i.e. by altering the L/C ratio. In a good tank circiut the unloaded Q is likely to be of the order of 100–300, while the loaded Q will be much lower. Reducing the loaded Q will reduce the circulating currents in the tank circuit, and because of the diminished heating effect it will be practicable to use smaller components. However, if the Q of the tank circuit under load is reduced too severely the

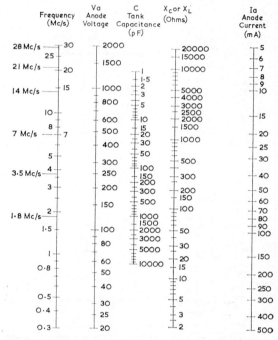

Fig. 52. Abac for determining anode tank-circuit capacitance for a loaded-Q of 12 in the circuit arrangements shown in Fig. 51. For push-pull and parallel connections, the appropriate value of anode current is that for the two valves taken together.

" flywheel " effect becomes too small, and the harmonic content of the output increases as a consequence of the non-sinusoidal waveform. A compromise between the two requirements which has been generally accepted for use in amateur transmitters is represented by a loaded Q value of 12.

A slight increase of Q above 12 will in fact slightly lower the efficiency, but at higher Q values two other factors become significant. Firstly, distortion can occur if the stage is modulated or if it is amplifying a modulated carrier, owing to the reduction in the impedance of the tank circuit at the sideband frequencies relative to the carrier frequency. The effect is to give an apparent lack of modulating power at the higher audio frequencies. Secondly, the frequency band over which substantially constant power output can be obtained without re-tuning the tank circuit will become narrower, and the serviceable bandwidth will then obtainable may be much less than is required for normal frequency

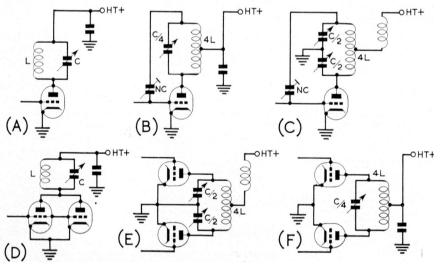

Fig. 51. Anode tank-circuit arrangements. The values of C and L corresponding to a loaded Q of 12 can be obtained from Fig. 52.

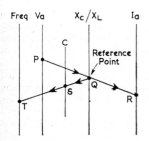

Key to Fig. 52. Join the selected values of V_a and I_a by a line **PQR**. Note the point **Q** on the X_C/X_L scale. Join the point **Q** to the appropriate frequency **T** on the extreme left-hand scale. The required value of **C** is given at the point **S**. The corresponding value of **L** is given by the reactance value X_L at the point **Q** divided by $6\cdot28 \times$ frequency (in Mc/s). Alternatively, **L** can be obtained from the reactance chart in Chapter 22 General Data).

changes within the permitted frequency band. The second effect will be much more significant than the first since the modulating frequencies are low in comparison with the carrier frequency.

The correct operating Q value can be obtained by adjusting the L/C ratio, but it must be remembered that the optimum proportions of L and C also depend on the particular form of anode tank circuit which is used. Several popular arrangements are shown in **Fig. 51**. An abac for the direct estimation of C for any given operating frequency will be found in **Fig. 52**: the only other data required are the operating anode voltage V_a and the anode current I_a.

EXAMPLE: *Find the anode tank capacitance and inductance required at 7 Mc/s for a pair of 5763 valves connected in parallel in a class-C telegraphy output stage: the anode current for a single valve is 50 mA and the h.t. supply is 300 volts.*

Using Fig. 52, join the values 100 mA and 300 volts on the anode-current and anode-voltage scales respectively by a straight-edge. This line intersects the X_L/X_C scale at the reference point of 150 ohms. Join this point to the 7 Mc/s-band marker on the frequency scale. The optimum tank-circuit capacitance is then read off as 150 pF. The anode-to-earth capacitance of the two valves (plus stray capacitances) is about 15 pF, leaving about 135 pF to be provided by the actual tank capacitor.

The inductance is given by—

$$L = \frac{X_c}{2\pi f(\text{Mc/s})} \text{ microhenrys}$$
$$= \frac{150}{6\cdot28 \times 7} = 3\cdot4 \ \mu\text{H}$$

As in the grid circuit, the desired L/C ratio cannot always be achieved in practice at the higher frequencies with some valve types, and a lower L/C ratio must then be accepted with some loss of efficiency.

PARASITIC OSCILLATIONS

Under certain conditions, the amplification of an r.f. drive voltage may be accompanied by the production of oscillations within the amplifying stage itself. The frequency of these *parasitic oscillations* is usually quite unrelated to the normal carrier frequency, and therefore interference may be caused to other services outside the amateur bands. They may be found to occur at a relatively low frequency or at a very high frequency.

Low-frequency Parasitics

Low-frequency parasitics are likely to be generated when the r.f. chokes in the grid and anode circuits happen to resonate at approximately the same frequency. The use of two similar chokes in these positions should be avoided, or it may be better to use a grid resistance in place of a choke. The frequency of oscillation is normally below about 1–2 Mc/s and the reactance of the tank coils to such low frequencies is therefore very small except on the lower-frequency bands.

V.H.F. Parasitics

The causes of v.h.f. parasitic oscillation are somewhat more subtle than those of the l.f. parasitics and it is not at first obvious how they can be produced. They are more common in tetrode and pentode amplifiers where the valve has a relatively high mutual conductance; often valves such as the 807 are viewed with suspicion for this reason but the prevention of parasitic oscillation is quite simple provided that the cause is understood and the proper precautions are taken.

A tuned circuit is formed by both the grid and anode circuits as shown by the heavy lines in **Fig. 53** and is likely

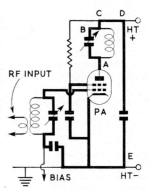

Fig. 53. Typical power-amplifier circuit showing how v.h.f. parasitic oscillations may be generated. The heavy lines indicate the respective v.h.f. grid and anode circuits, the inductance being constituted by the connecting leads. A neon lamp can be used to indicate the presence of such oscillations: if it is moved, for example round the path **ABCDE**, the intensity of the glow will be found to diminish progressively.

to have a resonant frequency in the range 100–200 Mc/s. At these frequencies the by-pass and other capacitors (and their connecting leads) act as inductive reactances and the capacitance which resonates with them is that of the grid and anode circuits and other stray capacitances. If the resonant frequencies of the grid and anode circuits are not greatly different from each other, oscillation may occur. By reducing the stage gain at the frequencies concerned, or alternatively by separating the v.h.f. resonance frequencies of the grid and anode circuits, oscillation can be prevented. Further, by connecting to the tank circuits with thick short leads, the inductance of the wiring may be reduced sufficiently to increase the resonant frequency to a value so high that the amplification afforded by the valve is insufficient to maintain oscillation.

Simple methods of suppressing v.h.f. parasitics are available and one or other of them should always be used as a safeguard. The most commonly adopted method is the inclusion of " stopper " resistances in the leads to the valve electrodes: see **Fig. 54(A)**. These are connected directly at the valve socket or at the cap on the valve. These resistances should be of carbon and should not have a higher value than is necessary to stop the parasitic oscillation; suitable values are 10–100 ohms for R_1 and 10–22 ohms for R_3. Unnecessarily high values would seriously reduce the efficiency at the operating frequency. The stopper resistance in the screen circuit is usually of about 50 ohms and is included because there is often quite a large mutual conductance between control grid and screen, with the consequent possibility of v.h.f. parasitics also being generated in the screen circuit. The presence of this resistance, while preventing the screen from being properly earthed at the carrier frequency, is unlikely to make neutralization necessary. If difficulty is in fact encountered, the use of two or

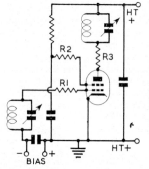

Fig. 54 (A). To suppress parasitic oscillations stopper resistances can be inserted in the grid, screen and anode leads. Typical values are:
Grid stopper R₁=10—100 ohms. Screen stopper R₂= 10—22 ohms. Anode stopper R₃=47—100 ohms.

more bypass capacitors of different values in parallel (e.g. 0·01 μF and 100 pF) to give a low impedance over both h.f. and v.h.f. ranges may be tried as an alternative to the use of the screen stopper.

Small r.f. chokes may be used in the parasitic-generating circuits to inhibit the tendency to oscillate: see **Fig. 54(B)**. Occasionally these chokes are tuned to the v.h.f. parasitic

Fig. 54 (B). To prevent parasitic oscillations an alternative to the use of simple stopper resistors is the insertion of small r.f. chokes consisting of about 24 in. of thin wire wound round a small resistor of high value. Occasionally it may be beneficial to tune one of the chokes by the addition of a parallel capacitor, as shown for RFC₃. A suitable maximum value would be 20 pF.

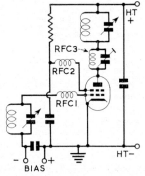

as shown in the anode circuit. Such chokes offer a high impedance at the parasitic frequency, but have a negligible effect at the operating frequency.

Another worthwhile component to try in dealing with parasitics is a *ferrite bead*. These, as their name suggests, are beads of ferrite material which can be slipped on to the wiring to the valve electrodes. The magnetic field surrounding the wire which is produced by the current flowing through it is concentrated by their high permeability and the inductance of the wire is thereby increased. Several beads may be used close together in series if required.

Identification of Parasitics

The presence of either type of parasitic oscillation will render the tuning characteristics of the amplifier erratic and will reduce the efficiency at the operating frequency. In some cases, the valve is overloaded owing to the parasitic oscillation and may be damaged as a result. Therefore, apart from the possibility of interference by unwanted radiation, these parasitics should be eliminated so as to

allow the full efficiency to be obtained. The tendency of the p.a. stage to oscillate can be investigated in the following way. The r.f. drive to the amplifier should be removed and the grid bias adjusted so that the anode current does not exceed the safe maximum value. If it happens that self-oscillation at a frequency corresponding to the actual tuning circuits is taking place owing to lack of screening or neutralization, an adjustment of either of the tuning capacitors will alter the frequency (which will be heard on a receiver possibly as a rough unstable note): the anode current will also vary with the tuning adjustment. Such self-oscillation must first be eliminated either by improving the screening arrangements or by ensuring that the amplifier is properly neutralized.

If the parasitic oscillation is of the l.f. type, the tuning capacitors will have very little effect on its frequency, and a neon lamp held near the anode circuit will glow with a darkish red colour at any part of it, including the apparently "earthy" end. In the case of v.h.f. parasitics, the neon lamp will glow with a reddish-purple colour when held near the anode, but the intensity of the glow will diminish as the neon is moved round the "parasitic" anode circuit (ABCDE in Fig. 53). It may happen that parasitics are more readily generated when the tank capacitors are at their maximum values, and the capacitors should therefore be varied throughout their full ranges to ensure all possible conditions are examined.

AERIAL COUPLING

A convenient way of transferring power from a power amplifier tank circuit to the aerial is by link coupling. The link (which consists of a few turns of wire, the number depending on the frequency band in use) is generally variable in position with respect to the tank coil, and a similar link coil at the other end of the link line is coupled to the coil of the aerial tuning unit or perhaps to a dipole itself.

The anode impedance of the p.a. valve is usually several thousands of ohms and the tank coil likewise has a high impedance, but by tapping the coil nearer to the h.t. end (i.e. the end which is at zero r.f. potential) a relatively low-impedance output connection can be obtained. Such a tapped-coil arrangement could be used to transfer energy

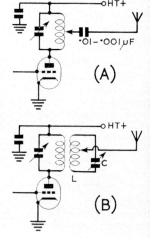

Fig. 55. Two methods of coupling an aerial to a power amplifier. The position of the aerial tap on the coil is adjusted to give correct loading and negligible change of reactance at the anode when the aerial is connected.

direct to an aerial (through a blocking capacitor) as shown at (A) in **Fig. 55**, any small reactance presented by the aerial being tuned out by adjusting the capacitance of the tank capacitor. However, the method suffers from several important disadvantages and its general use is not recommended except as a possible means of effecting the necessary coupling in an emergency where other components are not available.

Any harmonics, key clicks, and spurious radiation, which may be produced by the amplifier or other sections of the exciter are transferred direct to the aerial. An improvement on this simple method is to couple a separate tuned circuit LC to the tank circuit as shown at (B), the impedance match then being made in the separate tuned circuit. The inclusion of this extra tuned circuit gives a useful reduction in the amount of harmonic energy and of other spurious radiations transferred to the aerial.

Multi-band Tank Circuits

It is usually preferred to have a different tank coil for each frequency band, the selection being made either by the use of plug-in coils or by switching the required coil into the circuit, but if certain compromises are accepted the number of tuning components for multi-band operation can be appreciably reduced.

A multi-band arrangement which avoids both the changing

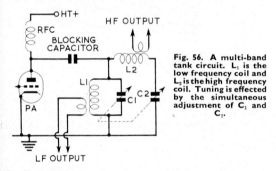

Fig. 56. A multi-band tank circuit. L_1 is the low frequency coil and L_2 is the high frequency coil. Tuning is effected by the simultaneous adjustment of C_1 and C_2.

of coils and the use of a selector switch is shown in **Fig. 56**. It comprises two fixed coils and two variable condensers: L_1 is the tank coil for the lower frequency bands (e.g. 3·5 and 7 Mc/s) and L_2 is the tank coil for the higher frequency bands (e.g. 14, 21 and 28 Mc/s). On the lower frequencies the arm of the circuit L_2C_2 presents a capacitive reactance across L_1C_1 and acts as extra tuning capacitance; by varying C_1 (in conjunction with C_2 if necessary) the total capacitance variation across the low-frequency coil L_1 can be made sufficient to cover two bands, say 3·5 and 7 Mc/s. The output at the lower frequencies is of course taken from L_1. On the higher frequencies, L_1 has a high inductive reactance and may be regarded as an r.f. choke in parallel with the circuit L_2C_2. Control of the resonant frequency is effected by varying C_1 and C_2, as before, and two or three higher-frequency bands may be covered by choosing suitable component values. The output on the higher-frequency bands is taken from L_2. If C_1 and C_2 are assembled so as to have a common shaft or are in the form of a split-stator capacitor, single-knob control may be obtained over several bands.

The simplicity of such a system is, of course, obtained at the expense of efficiency, owing to the large variation in

L/C ratio from one band to another, and whether or not this variation is acceptable will depend on several other factors, which must be decided for the individual case.

The Pi-network Coupler

A pi-network coupler can be made to function both as an aerial coupling unit and as an anode tank circuit, and when correctly designed it can perform these two functions more

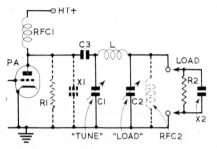

Fig. 57. Basic pi-network impedance matching circuit for feeding an unbalanced load. R_1 and X_1 represent the output resistance and reactance of the valve: R_2 and X_2 are the resistance and reactance of the load. The proper matching of R_1 and R_2 is effected by varying the relative values of C_1 and C_2, and the reactances X_1 and X_2 can be cancelled by the positive or negative variation of these capacitors. In practice, a choke RFC_2 is often added to prevent the appearance of the h.t. supply voltage across the load terminals in the event of an insulation-breakdown in C_3.

efficiently than the two units used separately, and a wide range of load impedances may be matched.

The basic pi-network coupler arrangement is shown in **Fig. 57**. The resistance R_1 (shown dotted) represents the output resistance of the valve which is to be matched through the network to the aerial or load impedance (equal to $R_2 + X_2$). In order to achieve a correct match, the reactive part of the aerial impedance must be eliminated when presented through the network to the valve. At the same time, the loaded Q of the network when regarded as a tank circuit should normally be in the region of 12 so as to provide the necessary " flywheel " effect.

To meet these requirements, the two capacitors C_1 and C_2 and the inductance L should have certain values of reactance as given by the following formulae:

$$X_{C1} = \frac{R_1}{Q} \left(1 + \sqrt{\frac{R_2}{R_1}} \right) \qquad \ldots.(1)$$

$$X_{C2} = X_{C1} \sqrt{\frac{R_2}{R_1}} \qquad \ldots.(2)$$

$$X_L = \frac{R_1}{Q} \left(1 + \sqrt{\frac{R_2}{R_1}} \right)^2 \qquad \ldots.(3)$$

where Q is the loaded Q of the circuit.

For any particular frequency, the corresponding values of C_1, C_2 and L can be calculated from the reactance charts shown on page 188 or from the basic formulae.

The maximum practicable ratio between the resistance R_1 and the resistive component of the load R_2 is about 100:1. Correct matching will be more easily obtained if the ratio is appreciably smaller than this.

The value of R_1 representing the effective p.a. anode

impedance can be calculated by assuming that the peak r.f. voltage swing at the anode is about 80 per cent of the d.c. supply voltage, V_{ht}. It will then be given by—

$$R_1 = \frac{(0.57 \times V_{ht})^2}{P} \text{ ohms} \qquad \ldots(4)$$

where P is the power *output* of the valve in watts. It is much simpler, however, to measure the power *input*, and if an

330 ohms. The chart for X_L shows a corresponding value of about 380 ohms.

From equation (2)—

$$X_{C2} = 330 \sqrt{\frac{70}{3450}} = 47 \text{ ohms}$$

From the reactance chart below, the value of the capacitance corresponding to a reactance C_1 of 330 ohms

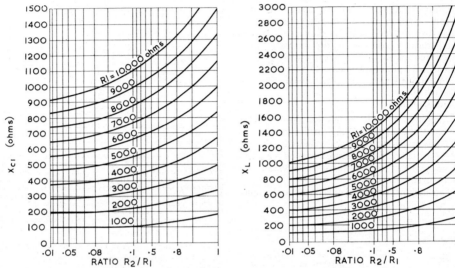

Fig. 58. Reactance charts for the design of pi-network couplers: see text for details.

assumption is made with regard to the anode efficiency the expression can be converted into a more useful form. Thus, if the stage is assumed to be 70 per cent efficient, the expression becomes—

$$R_1 = 464 \times \frac{V_{ht}}{I_a} \text{ ohms} \qquad \ldots(5)$$

where I_a is the anode current in milliamperes. Either of the expressions (4) or (5) may be calculated from the operating data given in the valve manufacturer's catalogue.

A chart derived from equations (1) and (3) is given in **Fig. 58** from which X_{C1} and X_L may be determined for a required ratio R_2/R_1, assuming that the Q of the loaded circuit is 12. The value of X_{C2} is then obtained from equation (2). The following example shows how this chart is to be used.

EXAMPLE. *A single-ended p.a. stage using an 807 valve is to operate at 750 volts anode voltage and 100 mA anode current, and is to be matched by a pi-network coupler to a load of 70 ohms, the Q of the circuit being* 12.

From equation (5)—

$$R_1 = 460 \times \frac{750}{100} = 3450 \text{ ohms}$$

The ratio R_2/R_1 is 70/3450, i.e. approximately 0·02, which is well within the practical limit ($R_1/R_2 \gg 100$) and a proper impedance match will therefore be obtainable with a Q value of 12.

Referring to Fig. 58, for a ratio R_2/R_1 of 0·02 and a value of 3450 ohms for R_1, the reactance of C_1 is approximately

on the appropriate frequency band may be estimated. Thus, on the 3·5 Mc/s band (3·65 Mc/s mid-frequency), this reactance corresponds to a capacitance of 132 pF. Likewise C_2 would be 925 pF, and the correct value of the inductance L is similarly seen from the chart to be 16·4 μH.

Twin Pi-network Coupler for Balanced Stages

For matching a push-pull p.a. stage to a balanced aerial feeder a pi-network coupling of the type shown in **Fig. 59**

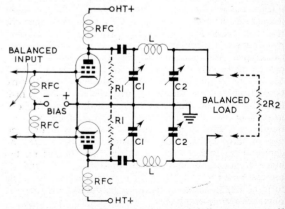

Fig. 59. Twin pi-network coupler for a push-pull output stage. If preferred the pairs of capacitors C_1C_1 and C_2C_2 can be replaced by single capacitors, the earthed centre connections then being ignored.

can be used. The values of the circuit components are calculated in the foregoing manner by taking the valve resistance as R_1 for each arm of the network and the total load value as $2R_2$ (i.e. a resistance of R_2 in each arm). The values of L will be about 10 per cent less than for an unbalanced circuit if mutual coupling happens to exist between the two halves of the coils.

In cases where the feeder impedance is not purely resistive matching can usually be effected satisfactorily, since an adjustment of C_2 will tune out this reactance and the resulting reactance presented to the valve anodes is then zero. Unwanted reactance is, of course, not eliminated at the aerial end of the feeder, nor are any standing waves on the feeder which may be caused by this reactance.

The pi-network coupler possesses a further important theoretical advantage over the normal tank circuit previously described; this arises from the possibility of reducing the amplitude of harmonic voltages fed to the output circuits. The circuit is similar to that of a low-pass filter which permits the transfer of power at the fundamental or carrier frequency, but cuts off at higher frequencies. Higher-order harmonics circulate within the filter, and for this reason if good harmonic reduction is to be achieved the components must be carefully placed. The capacitors C_1 and C_2 should be earthed direct to the chassis, if possible, or with a short thick strip of copper. The outer conductor of the coaxial feeder (in an unbalanced circuit) should be earthed at the same point as the rotor of C_2, and the screening of this lead should be continued to a point as near as possible to C_2. The capacitor C_1 should be mounted as closely as possible to the valve.

Practical Considerations

The actual amounts of capacitance to be used will have to take into account the stray circuit and valve capacitances, and generally it is permissible to rely on estimated values. In the case of C_1 the most important item will be the anode-to-cathode capacitance of the p.a. valve.

In the event of the aerial impedance not being accurately known, a rough estimate can usually be made which will be adequate for practical purposes. Even if the error in estimation is large there will probably be no difficulty in finding the correct adjustment of the pi-network coupler since it is capable of dealing with quite a wide range of impedance values.

One value of inductance is generally used to cover a single amateur band, and for other bands another coil of different inductance is provided. An alternative method is the use of a single coil in which sections are progressively short-circuited by a switch for operation on the higher-frequency bands.

The use of an r.f. choke (shown as RFC_2 in Fig. 57 across the capacitor C_2) is recommended for two reasons; firstly, if the blocking capacitor C_3 should fail, the d.c. connection from the aerial to earth through the choke acts as a safeguard against the full h.t. line voltage appearing on the aerial: secondly, an appreciable d.c. voltage may appear across the output owing to slight leakage through the blocking capacitor C_3 even when it is of high quality, and the presence of the r.f. choke will avoid this possibility and thus make it unnecessary to use a loading condenser C_2 of extravagantly high voltage rating.

Owing to the tendency of an r.f. choke to resonate at

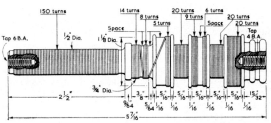

Fig. 60. Construction of an all-band r.f. choke suitable for a parallel-fed p.a. stage. The former may be made of Tufnol or p.t.f.e. The wire used is 30 s.w.g. d.s.c.

various frequencies, depending on its design, some caution is necessary when using a parallel-fed tank circuit. A choke suitable for an all-band high-power parallel-fed p.a. stage is illustrated in **Fig. 60**. This has been designed so that no resonances are present within the amateur bands; nevertheless the possibility of an unexpected resonance should be borne in mind since a metal chassis or a screening partition in the vicinity of the windings can alter the characteristics appreciably. Resonance will be noted by a loss in efficiency and by overheating of the choke windings. The choke former should be made from a material with good electrical properties and capable of withstanding without softening the temperature which it may acquire by being mounted close to the p.a. valve. A suitable material is *Tufnol*, or if available p.t.f.e. would be ideal.

Adjusting the Pi-network Coupler

To tune a pi-network coupling the following procedure will be found most satisfactory. First short-circuit the output of the network and tune the anode capacitor (C_1 in Fig. 57) for minimum p.a. anode current, with a low power input to avoid possible damage to the valve. Remove the short-circuit, connect the aerial load or its equivalent and decrease the capacitance of C_2 slightly from its maximum value; this capacitor C_2 can conveniently be regarded as a " loading " control. Next, C_1 should be readjusted for minimum anode current. The procedure is then repeated until a value of C_2 is found at which the output into the load is a maximum and at the same time a dip in anode current of 10–15 per cent can still be obtained by varying C_1, the dip being coincident with maximum output.

If the p.a. loading is found to increase as the value of C_2 is increased, the ratio between the impedances R_1 and R_2 is too great to allow correct matching to take place. In this event, it is preferable to modify the load impedance R_2, usually by connecting a capacitance in series; its optimum value will best be determined by experiment. This capacitor should be suitably designed to carry the relatively heavy output-load current and one having a good mica dielectric should prove satisfactory.

ADJUSTING THE P.A. STAGE

To avoid possible damage to the valve it is desirable to make the preliminary tuning adjustment of the grid circuit with the anode and screen supplies removed. The normal bias should be applied, and if link coupling is used both links should be adjusted to give rather less than maximum coupling, say, about half. A milliammeter in the grid circuit of the p.a. stage will indicate when optimum coupling has been obtained; the procedure is to tune the driver-anode tank circuit to give minimum anode current in the driver, and, with the links set as above, the grid circuit is tuned to give maximum drive as indicated by the grid milliammeter. The link coils may then be readjusted to give tighter coupling, followed by further slight retuning of the driver-anode and p.a. tank circuits, if necessary, to give maximum grid current. The latter should have a value 30-40 per cent greater than the normal specified operating value since it will fall by approximately this amount when the anode voltage is applied later.

Where the circuit needs to be neutralized the adjustment of the neutralizing control should be checked under the same conditions as described in the preceding paragraph and without any load coupled to the output circuit. If the anode tank circuit is effectively screened from the grid tank circuit, as it always should be, the variation of the anode tank capacitor through resonance will have no influence on the grid-current reading, provided that the neutralizing control is adjusted correctly; if the grid current is found to vary, the neutralizing control should be readjusted until a setting is obtained such that a variation of the anode-circuit tuning has no effect on the grid current. Sometimes the effect cannot be entirely elimated but this does not necessarily mean that the circuit will not function properly. However, the greatest care should always be taken to achieve the lowest possible degree of interaction. In a push-pull amplifier the two neutralizing capacitors should be varied together (i.e. with roughly similar values) so that an approximate balance is maintained during the process. The final correct balance may be found to occur with slightly different settings of the two capacitors but if the values are greatly different the balance may be upset when the operating frequency is changed to a different band. A well designed and constructed amplifier, when correctly neutralized, should remain so over the full range of frequencies 1·8–30 Mc/s. The neutralizing adjustments are preferably made first on the *highest* frequency band, where the effect of a small feedback capacitance is most noticeable.

A final check should be made by applying a low anode voltage, removing the grid drive, and adjusting the bias so that it produces a standing anode current corresponding to about half the maximum permissible anode dissipation. If the neutralizing setting is incorrect, self-oscillation is almost certain to occur. This can be detected in various ways, e.g. by the glow in a neon lamp held near the " hot " parts of the anode circuit, by the lighting of a pea-lamp connected to a loop of wire when coupled to the tank coil, or by an absorption wavemeter or a heterodyne frequency meter. Anode-current variations will also be observed when the grid or anode tank capacitor is tuned through resonance.

If it appears impossible to achieve proper neutralization the cause of the difficulty may lie in the presence of parasitic oscillation. Methods for suppressing such oscillations are described on page 185.

When the amplifier has been neutralized, a suitable load should be coupled to the anode tank coil and then the grid drive may be applied though still with reduced anode and screen voltages. This load may consist of an ordinary domestic lamp of suitable power rating or a number of carbon resistors in parallel sufficient to dissipate the expected output. It can be tapped across a portion of the tank coil, or alternatively connected to a link coil consisting of a few turns inductively coupled to the tank circuit. The optimum number of turns is best found by experiment. It can be assumed that the circuit is correctly loaded if the dip in anode current when the tank circuit is tuned through resonance is 10–15 per cent. If a lamp is used as the load it should be connected to the coil by the shortest practicable leads, the wires being soldered directly to the lamp-cap contacts.

After the amplifier has been thus tuned at reduced power, full power may be applied. A rough estimate of the power output may be made by observing the brilliance of the lamp. Finally the anode efficiency and dissipation should be calculated to ensure that the valve is being operated within its ratings.

If it is found that varying the anode tank capacitor about the resonance position causes the grid current to change sharply at any point, it is a sign that feedback is taking place and closer attention should be paid to the screening or to the neutralizing adjustments. Besides being troublesome in other ways such feedback can cause intermittent spurious emissions in telephony operation and produce effects similar to those of over-modulation.

Sometimes the tuning adjustment that produces the maximum output from the power amplifier does not coincide with the tuning adjustment for minimum anode current. This can often be traced to a variation in the screen voltage as the circuit is tuned through resonance, and in this event the remedy is to stabilize the screen voltage.

POWER RATINGS OF R.F. AMPLIFIERS

The maximum permissible ratings at which a valve may be operated are specified in the valve manufacturers' published data. In the case of some American valves, the manufacturers specify two different ratings: (i) the C.C.S. or *Continuous Commercial Service* rating, in which long life and consistent performance are the chief requirements, and (ii) the I.C.A.S. or *Intermittent Commercial and Amateur Service* rating in which high output from the valve is a more important consideration than long life. The term " intermittent " applied to ON periods (key down) not exceeding five minutes followed by OFF periods (key up) of the same or greater duration. This must be remembered if it becomes necessary, as for instance while testing, to keep the key closed so that the valve is then in *continuous* operation.

Tables showing the ratings of a selection of valve types commonly used by the amateur are given at the end of this chapter: where applicable the data quoted are the I.C.A.S. ratings.

The following are the main features to be borne in mind when considering the power-handling capabilities of a valve.

Power Input

The power input to the valve is the d.c. power P_i fed to the anode circuit from the h.t. supply. It is given by—

$$P_i = \frac{I_a \times V_{ht}}{1000} \text{ watts}$$

where I_a = anode current (mA)
V_{ht} = anode voltage (V)

Power Output and Anode Efficiency

Not all of the h.t. power supplied to the valve is converted into r.f. energy; part is expended in heating the anode. Thus, the power-handling capacity of the valve is limited by the maximum permissible dissipation of heat by the anode through radiation and conduction. The anode efficiency is given by—

$$\text{Efficiency} = \frac{P_o}{P_i} \times 100 \text{ per cent}$$

where P_o = r.f. power output
P_i = d.c. power input to the anode circuit

The maximum r.f. power output obtainable from a valve may be predicted from a knowledge of the anode dissipation. For example, consider a valve with a maximum permissible anode dissipation of 12 watts, operating in class C, the efficiency being about 70 per cent. Of the d.c. power input, 70 per cent will appear as r.f. energy and 30 per cent as heat which must be dissipated by the valve anode. This amount of heat is limited by the valve rating to 12 watts. Thus—

$$\text{Maximum dissipation} = 12 \text{ watts} = \frac{100}{30} \times \text{d.c. input power}$$

Therefore—

$$\text{Maximum power input} = 12 \times \frac{100}{30} = 40 \text{ watts}$$

For two such valves operating under the same conditions, either in parallel or in push-pull, the maximum power input would be 80 watts.

If the anode efficiency is less than 70 per cent, the maximum power output would be correspondingly lower.

Screen Dissipation

All the d.c. power supplied to the screen circuit is expended in heating the screen. Since the screen is constructed of relatively thin wire mesh, the valve may be permanently damaged if the permissible dissipation is exceeded even for a relatively short period.

Screen Voltage Supply

If the screen voltage is applied through a series dropping resistance, as shown at (A) in **Fig. 61**, the calculation of the correct resistance value is very simple. Consider, for example, the requirements for an 807 valve:

Screen voltage	= 250 volts
Screen current	= 6 mA
Supply line voltage	= 750 volts

The series resistance must drop $750 - 250$ volts (i.e. 500 volts) for a current of 6 mA. Therefore its resistance must be—

$$R_1 = \frac{750 - 250}{0 \cdot 006} = 83,000 \text{ ohms}$$

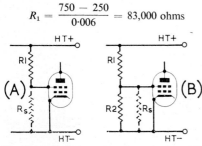

Fig. 61. Calculation of resistances in screen-voltage supply circuits: see text. R_s is the equivalent screen/cathode resistance under the operating conditions.

Under these conditions the power dissipated in the resistance will be $(750 - 250)\text{V} \times 6 \text{ mA} = 3$ watts.

If the supply to the screen is derived from a potential divider, as shown at (B) in Fig. 61, the procedure is slightly more complicated since it is necessary in effect to calculate the screen/cathode resistance which is now in parallel with the lower section R_s of the potential divider. Taking the example of the 807 again—

$$\text{Screen/cathode resistance } R_s = \frac{250}{0 \cdot 006} = 42,000 \text{ ohms approx.}$$

Assuming that the purpose of the potential-divider network is to prevent the screen potential from varying too widely under different current conditions in the valve, the lower section R_2 of the potential divider must be of relatively low resistance so that variations in the value of the parallel screen/cathode resistance will not greatly affect the voltage distribution across R_1 and R_2. Since R_s is about 42,000 ohms, R_2 could reasonably be 15,000 ohms. Then the resultant resistance of R_s and R_2 in parallel is—

$$\frac{R_s R_2}{R_s + R_2} = \frac{42,000 + 15,000}{42,000 \times 15,000} = 11,000 \text{ ohms approx.}$$

Across this combined resistance there must be a voltage drop of 250 volts. Therefore the current flowing through both resistances taken together must be—

$$\frac{250 \text{ volts}}{11,000 \text{ ohms}} = 23 \text{ mA approx.}$$

This is the current which when passing through R_1 produces a voltage drop of $750 - 250$ volts. Hence—

$$\frac{(750 - 250) \text{ volts}}{23 \text{ mA}} = 22,000 \text{ ohms}$$

Power dissipated in $R_1 = (750 - 250)$ volts $\times 23$ mA $= 11 \cdot 5$ watts

Power dissipated in $R_2 = 250$ volts $\times \dfrac{250 \text{ volts}}{15,000 \text{ ohms}} = 4 \cdot 2$ watts approx.

It is important to note that the total power dissipated in the screen and the screen supply circuit is much greater in the case of the potential-divider system than in the simple series-resistance method. In the example considered here, it is 17·25 watts as compared with 4·5 watts. The total power could be reduced by choosing a higher value for R_2 but this would, of course, mean reduced stability of the screen voltage.

Capacitor Ratings

A fixed capacitor which is used in r.f. circuits where any loss of power must be avoided should have a mica or ceramic dielectric. These types have the required low dielectric loss, low inductance values and high insulation resistance. Low inductance is a particularly important requirement of decoupling and other bypass capacitors since they should have negligible reactance over the entire working frequency range (and above) and it is recommended that feed-through or other disc types be used for low-power circuits where the h.t. supply does not exceed about 500 volts. For normal h.f. transmitter use, the values of decoupling, d.c. blocking and r.f. coupling capacitors lie within the range 0·001–0·01 μF.

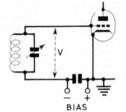
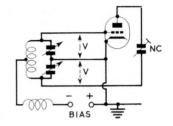
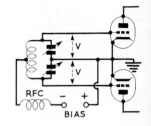

Fig. 62. Grid-tank capacitor voltage ratings. The peak voltage, V, across each section is equal to the bias voltage plus 25 per cent of the applied d.c. anode voltage.

BIAS   BIAS   BIAS

To allow a margin of safety, the voltage rating of a capacitor should be at least 50 per cent greater than the peak voltage which is likely to occur across it, and its size should be adequate to carry the r.f. current without overheating. The following notes should enable the reader to determine the necessary voltage rating of any capacitor used in an r.f. amplifier.

Grid Coupling Capacitors. The peak applied voltage is approximately the sum of the grid bias voltage of the driven stage and the d.c. anode voltage of the driver stage; the voltage rating of a grid coupling capacitor should therefore be about 50 per cent higher than this peak value.

Grid Tank Capacitors. The peak voltage across the grid tank capacitor depends on the circuit arrangement and is indicated in **Fig. 62.**

Screen By-pass Capacitors. The voltage rating should be 1·5 times the anode voltage, or 2·5–3 times this value when anode-and-screen modulation is used.

Anode Decoupling and Blocking Capacitors. In c.w. transmitters the peak voltage across the anode decoupling and blocking capacitors is equal to the d.c. anode voltage; in telephony operation it rises to at least twice this value on full-modulation peaks.

Neutralizing Capacitors. The neutralizing capacitor is subjected to peak voltages equal to the sum of the peak grid voltage and the peak anode voltage, amounting in the case of an unmodulated amplifier to about 2·3 times the d.c. anode voltage, and for a modulated amplifier about twice this value.

Anode Tank Capacitors (including pi-networks). The peak voltage across an anode tank capacitor depends on the arrangement of the circuit, e.g. single-ended, split-stator or push-pull. The values given in **Fig. 63** assume that the amplifier is correctly loaded. In circuits where the d.c. supply voltage also exists across the capacitor, as at (C) and (F), twice the rating is required, and it is therefore an

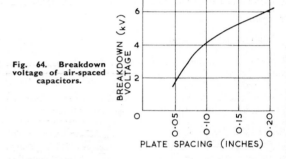

Fig. 64. Breakdown voltage of air-spaced capacitors.

advantage in high-power stages to remove this voltage from the capacitor by the use of parallel feed or other suitable arrangements. The application of 100 per cent modulation doubles the peak voltages occurring in any of the above circuits.

Although the necessary plate-spacing of an air-spaced capacitor for a given peak voltage rating depends to some extent upon the constructional features such as the shape of the plates and the rounding of their edges, a useful guide to the voltage at which breakdown occurs for different values of spacing will be found in **Fig. 64.**

Pi-network Output (Loading) Capacitor. The peak voltage E occurring across a pi-network output capacitor is given by—

$$E = \sqrt{2P_o R_2} \text{ volts}$$

where P_o = power output of the amplifier (watts)

R_2 = resistive component of the load or aerial impedance.

With a low-impedance load (e.g. a coaxial line not exceeding 100 ohms) the peak voltage is not likely to be higher than about 300 volts, even in

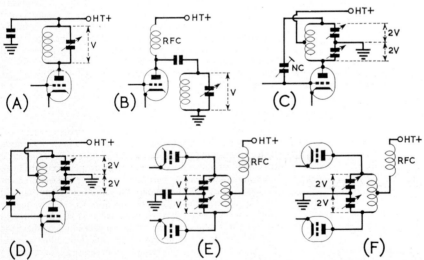

Fig. 63. Anode-tank capacitor voltage ratings. The peak V may be taken as 80-90 per cent of the h.t. supply voltage.

a 150-watt modulated transmitter, and a receiving-type variable capacitor should be quite satisfactory. In many cases it may be convenient to use a good-quality 3- or 4-gang receiving-type capacitor so as to obtain a maximum capacitance of 1500–2000 pF, which may be necessary on 1·8 Mc/s and 3·5 Mc/s. The sections may be switched out progressively on changing to operation on the higher-frequency bands.

EXAMPLE. *A 150-watt phone transmitter is operating into a 72-ohm line through a pi-network coupler. What is the peak voltage across the output capacitor?*

Since the peak power input occurring on modulation peaks is $4 \times 150 = 600$ watts, and if the anode efficiency of the p.a. stage is assumed to be 70 per cent, the peak power output will not exceed 420 watts. The peak voltage occurring across the pi-network output capacitor would therefore be—

$$E = \sqrt{2 \times 420 \times 72} = 264 \text{ volts}$$

TRANSMITTER DESIGNS

The necessity of taking strict precautions against television interference has had a marked effect on transmitter construction in recent years. Layouts devoid of screening to prevent radiation from intermediate amplifiers and frequency doublers have had to be abandoned

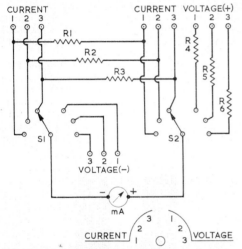

Fig. 65. A simple switching system for enabling one meter to be used for measuring three different currents and three different voltages. The switches S_1 and S_2 can be of the ganged-wafer type. The resistors R_1, R_2, R_3 (current range shunts) and R_4, R_5, R_6 (voltage-range series resistances) are selected according to the required ranges and the full-scale current of the meter.

in favour of all-metal construction with careful attention to the filtering of outgoing leads and connections. At the same time, the availability of smaller and more efficient valves has enabled a reduction in overall size to be accomplished. It is generally considered desirable to design the transmitter so that all leads can be kept short, and the rack-and-panel system so long popular in amateur designs is not normally necessary unless an input power greater than about 150 watts is required.

The transmitters described here are typical of modern amateur practice and have been designed to conform with the general principles outlined in this chapter. They can be

recommended as being relatively simple to construct and adjust whilst being capable of first class results. Some practical points concerning the construction of transmitters are also described as a preliminary to the specific designs.

Metering

Although it is necessary to meter the current and/or the voltage at several different parts of the transmitter to ensure that all the various stages are operating correctly, an economy in regard to the inclusion of instruments is made possible by the fact that one single reading (of the anode current in the p.a. stage, for example) is usually all that is required for noting quickly whether the transmitter is operating normally. A single instrument of about 1 mA f.s.d. in conjunction with a multi-way switch to allow connection to the appropriate points is therefore often found adequate. Such an arrangement is shown in **Fig. 65**.

The resistances R_1, R_2 and R_3 in this circuit are the shunt resistances necessary to give a convenient range-multiplication factor for the current to be measured, and they are left permanently in the circuit to be monitored; owing to their low resistance values, the operation of the circuit is not affected. The actual values are calculated as suggested in Chapter 19 (*Measurements*). On the voltage ranges, the series resistances R_4, R_5 and R_6 will likewise be selected to give a convenient full-scale deflection for the meter. Their values are also calculated as in Chapter 19.

The selector switch should be of the wafer type, with ceramic insulation for the higher voltage circuits, and the contacts should be of the break-before-make type to avoid a short-circuit when changing from one circuit to the next. For voltages above about 300 volts it may be necessary to use double spacing between adjacent contacts to prevent flash-over, and the circuit should be arranged, where possible, so that adjacent contacts are at approximately similar potentials.

As an alternative to switching, closed-circuit jacks are sometimes used. These are jacks which keep the circuit closed except when the plug is inserted. The advantage of the method is that an independent external meter may be used but this advantage is outweighed by the simplicity and convenience of the switched meter arrangement. Further, all possibility of spurious radiation is eliminated when the meter and the associated wiring are completely contained within the transmitter enclosure.

A PRACTICAL WIDE-BAND COUPLER

The coupler described in the following paragraphs is suitable for coupling between the stages of a transmitter and utilises the properties of tuned coupled circuits discussed

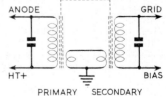

Fig. 66. Wide-band coupling. Small link windings are used in addition to inductive coupling between the main windings.

on page 26. When it is correctly adjusted, almost constant transfer of drive power will be maintained over the entire width of each amateur band to which the coupler is appropriate.

The two tuned coils L_1 and L_2 constituting the primary and secondary windings are coupled mutually by virtue of their proximity, but are simultaneously coupled through the use of small link windings, as shown in **Fig. 66.**

The capacitance across each winding is provided by small mica capacitors and final tuning adjustments can be carried out by means of the variable dust-iron cores.

The mechanical details of the arrangement are shown in **Fig. 67.** The coil formers are Ekco type F804, fitted with dust-iron cores, as used in some television receivers. The

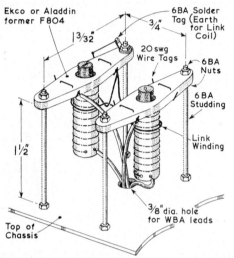

Fig. 67. Constructional details of a wide-band coupler. A suitable screen is a standard 1⅜-in. square aluminium i.f. transformer can, 2-in. high, having a ¼-in. flange for mounting on the chassis. Two ⅜-in. diameter holes should be drilled on the top of the can to allow the cores to be adjusted.

outside diameter is ⅜ in. and the winding length available is ⅞ in. They are mounted with a spacing of ¾ in. between centres by means of 6 B.A. studding to provide convenient adjustment of the cores from the top of the chassis. A suitable screen should be fitted over the whole assembly to prevent stray coupling either to or from the coils. The link coupling is provided from one winding to the other, additionally to the mutual coupling at the " cold " ends (i.e. the h.t. and bias ends of the coils; it consists of 22 s.w.g.

TABLE 5
Wide-band Coupler Design

Frequency Band (Mc/s)	No. of turns		Wire Size (s.w.g.)	Link Coil (turns)	Approx. Trimmer Capacitance*	
	Pri.	Sec.			Pri.	Sec.
3·5	88	88	38	4	10 pF	—
7	55	55	30	2	10 pF	—
14	28	28	24	2	10 pF	—
21	15	15	24	1	—	—
28	10	10	24	1	—	—

* The optimum values are determined by experiment.

enamelled copper wire, and one side of it is earthed. If other methods of mounting are preferred, care should be taken not to allow the screening material to approach the coils too closely since this would seriously reduce the Q value. If the coil-former flanges are to be used for mounting purposes, they should be spaced at least 1/16 in. from any metal surface.

An alternative link-coupling arrangement for the separate link coils described above, is as follows. The h.t. end of the primary is connected to a short length of 22 s.w.g. enamelled copper wire and taken round the end of the secondary winding for the appropriate number of turns. It is then soldered to a tag made by inserting a shaped piece of 22 s.w.g. tinned copper wire through the small holes located for this purpose on the coil-former base flanges. The h.t. by-pass capacitor is soldered to this point and becomes an integral part of the unit. With this construction the link is thus really a continuation of the primary winding and it may increase the inductance of the winding sufficiently to make unnecessary the use of the fixed parallel condensers.

Table 5 gives winding data of the coils and links for all the amateur bands from 3·5 Mc/s to 28 Mc/s.

A SIMPLE TWO-VALVE CLAPP V.F.O. UNIT

This v.f.o. unit covers a frequency range of 3·5–3·8 Mc/s and is suitable as an oscillator for the five-band transmitter described on page 199. Owing to its small dimensions it may be mounted within a suitable all-band exciter unit with the addition only of a tuning dial.

As shown in Fig. 68, it consists of a Clapp v.f.o. (V_1) followed by an untuned buffer amplifier stage (V_2) to ensure complete isolation between the v.f.o. and the output circuit; keying may be carried out in the cathode of V_2 as indicated, although it may be preferable to introduce it in a later stage. The whole unit is built into an Eddystone type 650 die-cast metal box 4 11/16 in. $\times$ 3 11/16 in. $\times$ 2¼ in. deep ready for direct mounting on the exciter chassis: see **Fig. 69.**

Fig. 69. Clapp v.f.o./driver unit for 3·5 Mc/s. The circuit diagram is shown in Fig. 68.

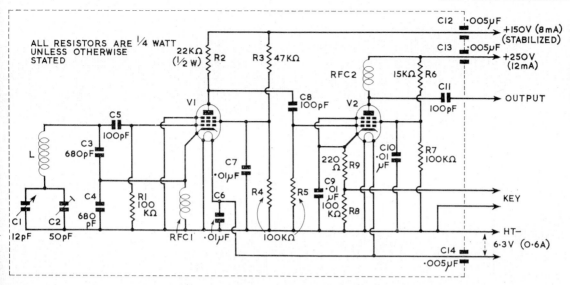

Fig. 68. A Clapp v.f.o./driver unit for 3·5 Mc/s. The inductance L consists of 45 turns of No. 24 s.w.g. enamelled copper wire close-wound on a 1 in. diameter ceramic former. Suitable valves for V_1 and V_2 are 6AM6, EF91, Z77, etc. Silvered mica capacitors should be used for C_3, C_4 and C_5.

The output voltage from the unit at the centre of the 3·5 Mc/s band with a capacitance of about 20 pF between the anode of V_2 and earth should be about 20 volts. It is important to reduce the output capacitance as far as possible by the use of a direct connection from the anode of V_2 to the following stage. Low-capacitance coaxial cable should be used if screening is required, and its length must be kept as short as possible.

The power requirements are—

Heaters ..	..	..	6·3 volts,	0·6 amps
Buffer (unstabilized)	..	250	volts, 12	mA
Oscillator (stabilized)	..	150	volts, 8	mA

A suitable stabilizer for the 150 volt supply would be a VR150/30 tube.

A THREE-BAND 25 WATT OUTPUT TRANSMITTER FOR 3·5/7/14 Mc/s

The general arrangement of this transmitter can be seen clearly in the block diagram shown in Fig. 70. A Hartley-type

e.c.o. (V_1) generates r.f. power in the 3·5–3·8 Mc/s band and this is amplified by a tuned buffer amplifier (V_2). The output of this amplifier can be switched either to V_3 or to V_4. If the transmitter output is required in the 3·5 Mc/s band the output of V_2 is fed direct to V_4, the latter acting as a further buffer amplifier preceding the power-amplifier stage V_5.

For 7 Mc/s operation, the output from V_2 is fed into V_3, which then acts as a frequency doubler from 3·5 to 7 Mc/s and V_4 operates as a buffer amplifier as before.

For 14 Mc/s operation, both V_3 and V_4 are used as frequency doublers.

A circuit diagram of the transmitter is shown in Fig. 71. The oscillator valve V_1 is supplied with h.t. at 150 volts, stabilized by the valve V_6 from the 250 volt line. The oscillator anode circuit is flatly tuned to cover the 3·5 Mc/s band by the adjustable inductance L_2 resonating with the stray capacitances: its output is capacitively coupled to V_2. Keying is effected in the cathode circuit of V_4. A resistor of 68 kilohms is connected between the cathode and earth

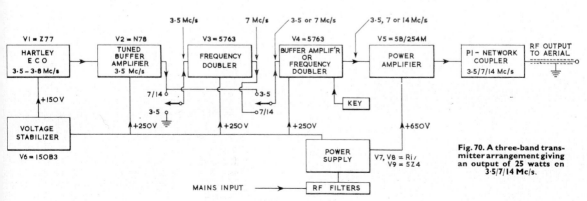

Fig. 70. A three-band transmitter arrangement giving an output of 25 watts on 3·5/7/14 Mc/s.

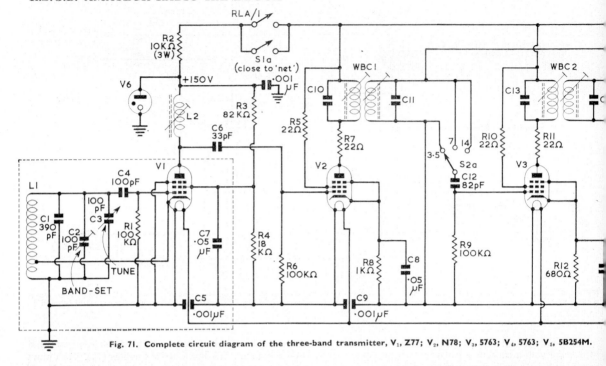

Fig. 71. Complete circuit diagram of the three-band transmitter, V₁, Z77; V₂, N78; V₃, 5763; V₄, 5763; V₅, 5B254M.

to ensure that the heater/cathode voltage does not exceed the manufacturer's rating when the key is open.

The amplified output from V_2, also at 3·5 Mc/s, is fed through the wide-band coupler WBC_1. The winding details for this and the other wide-band couplers are given in Table 5. A suitable alternative design is given on page 194.

The valve V_3 is not required on the 3·5 Mc/s band and its grid is therefore earthed in the "3·5" position of S_2. The output of WBC_1 is then switched directly to the grid of V_4. This valve (type 5763) requires neutralization when acting as a buffer amplifier on the 3·5 Mc/s and 7 Mc/s bands. In this design the series-capacity method of neutralizing (page 179) is used.

Likewise, the p.a. stage V_5 benefits by being neutralized and the same method is also adopted here. The wide-band couplers WBC_3, WBC_4 and WBC_5 between V_4 and V_5 for the 14, 7 and 3·5 Mc/s bands respectively are switched into

circuit by means of the third and fourth wafers on the switch S_2, the first and second of which simultaneously select the required conditions for the earlier stages. A separate band-change switch S_3 is needed to select the pi-network inductances L_3 and L_4 in the p.a. stage owing to the physical separation between these inductances and the earlier stages. For the 3·5 Mc/s band, extra capacitance to augment the existing tank capacitors is automatically connected by S_{3B} and S_{3C}.

The p.a. valve is a Brimar 5B/254M (a miniature version of the 807) but there is no reason why the normal version of this valve may not be used. Adequate space exists within the p.a. compartment for the larger bulb of the 807, which may then be run at the I.C.A.S. rating of up to about 75 watts input; the circuit would of course require certain modifications, including greater h.t. voltages and the substitution of fixed bias for cathode bias.

To economize in the number of stages in this transmitter, a frequency multiplier has been relied upon to feed the p.a. stage directly, a method which is normally deprecated owing to the possible transfer of harmonics to the p.a. stage. However, in this design, owing to careful screening, the attenuation of harmonics by the pi-network output circuit and the use of a quarter-wave open-circuited stub across the output terminals, no television interference is likely to occur in an area of normal field strength. The quarter-wave stub should be tuned to the frequency of the local television channel and it then acts as a virtual short-circuit to harmonics around this frequency: see Chapter 18 (*Interference*).

To avoid the use of separate bias supplies the grid bias for each stage is obtained by the use of cathode and grid resistances. The cathode resistance of V_5 has been selected

COIL DATA FOR FIG. 71

L_1—4·5 μH: 13 turns of No. 18 s.w.g. enamelled on 1¼-in. diameter former, length 2 in. Tapped 3½ turns from earthed end.
L_2—90/190 μH: 110 turns of No. 36 s.w.g. enamelled, pile-wound ¼ in. wide on ½-in. diameter *Aladdin* former, with dust-iron core.
L_3—3·5 μH: 12 turns of No. 16 s.w.g. on 1½-in. diameter former, spaced at 8 turns per inch.
L_4—20 μH: 28 turns of No. 22 s.w.g. on 1½-in. diameter former, spaced at 20 turns per inch. Tapped at 16 turns.
WBC_1 & WBC_5 (3·5 Mc/s)—Each winding 44 turns of No. 36 s.w.g. s.c.c., pile-wound ¼-in. wide on ¼-in. diameter former, ¼-in. spacing between windings.
C_{10}, C_{11}, C_{23}—68 pF C_{26}—56 pF
WBC_2 & WBC_4 (7 Mc/s)—Each winding 30 turns of No. 36 s.w.g. s.c.c., pile-wound ¼-in. wide on ¼-in. diameter former, ¼-in. spacing between windings.
WBC_3 (14 Mc/s)—Each winding 24 turns of No. 30 s.w.g. enamelled, C_{13}, C_{14}, C_{22}—33 pF C_{25}—15 pF
close-wound on ¼-in. diameter former, ¼-in. spacing between windings.
C_{21}—18 pF C_{24}—nil

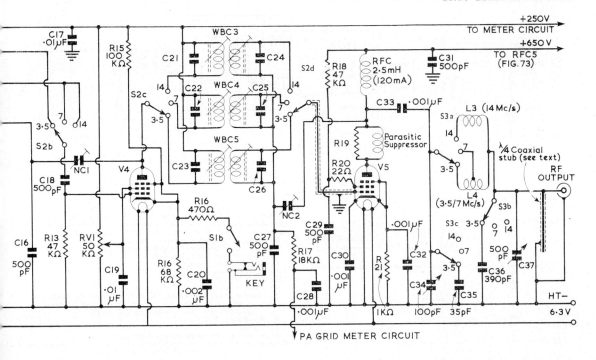

PA GRID METER CIRCUIT

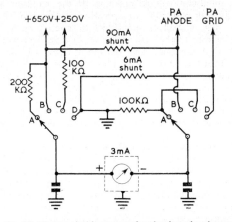

Fig. 72. Meter switching system for the three-band transmitter. This allows measurement of the two h.t. supply voltages and the grid current and anode current to the p.a. stage. A 2-pole 4-way switch is used: the connections are arranged to give minimum voltage between adjacent contacts. The switch must be of the break-before-make type.

Range	F.S.D.	Circuit
A	900 V	650 V h.t. supply
B	90 mA	Anode current to p.a.
C	300 V	250 V h.t. supply
D	6 mA	Grid current to p.a.

so that under no-drive conditions and with the h.t. voltage shown the standing p.a. anode current is limited to a safe value. This results in a fairly high value of resistance, and the d.c. power input to the valve is limited to about

45 watts under normal drive conditions as a result of the voltage-drop in the resistance.

All external connections to the transmitter are brought through small filter units each consisting of an r.f. choke and a by-pass capacitor to prevent radiation from the leads. These filters are screened by a small metal enclosure adjacent to the terminals.

Anode-and-screen modulation may be applied to the power amplifier from a separate modulator of about 25 watts output power.

The meter circuit, shown in **Fig. 72**, is designed to monitor only four items—p.a. grid current, p.a. anode current and the two h.t. line voltages—and it is thereby kept comparatively simple. The instrument itself is screened at the rear and feed-through capacitors are used to avoid any spurious radiation through the meter aperture which may arise if the meter itself is " alive " with r.f. currents.

Power Supply

The power supply provides two separate outputs of 250 volts and 650 volts respectively from a single h.t. transformer. In this arrangement a pair of diodes V_1 and V_2 (see **Fig. 73**) operate as a conventional full-wave rectifier for the 250 volt supply except that the two cathodes are returned to the ends of the 350-volt winding instead of the anodes. The centre-tap of the h.t. winding is then the positive side of the output instead of the negative, as is more usual. The output voltage is somewhat below the transformer voltage because the filter is of the choke-input type. This filter comprises the swinging choke CH_1 on the negative side in combination with the capacity-input filter C_{13}, CH_2, C_{14} on the positive side. For the 600 volt supply the diodes V_1 and V_2 operate simultaneously with the

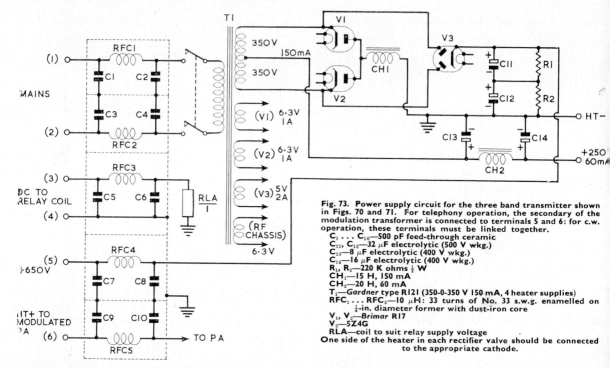

Fig. 73. Power supply circuit for the three band transmitter shown in Figs. 70 and 71. For telephony operation, the secondary of the modulation transformer is connected to terminals 5 and 6: for c.w. operation, these terminals must be linked together.
$C_1 \ldots C_{10}$—500 pF feed-through ceramic
C_{11}, C_{12}—32 μF electrolytic (500 V wkg.)
C_{13}—8 μF electrolytic (400 V wkg.)
C_{14}—16 μF electrolytic (400 V wkg.)
R_1, R_2—220 K ohms ½ W
CH_1—15 H, 150 mA
CH_2—20 H, 60 mA
T_1—*Gardner* type RI21 (350-0-350 V 150 mA, 4 heater supplies)
$RFC_1 \ldots RFC_5$—10 μH: 33 turns of No. 33 s.w.g. enamelled on ¼-in. diameter former with dust-iron core
V_1, V_2—*Brimar* RI7
V_3—5Z4G
RLA—coil to suit relay supply voltage
One side of the heater in each rectifier valve should be connected to the appropriate cathode.

double-diode V_3 as a bridge rectifier, and in this case the filter circuit comprises merely the swinging choke CH_1 and the two electrolytic capacitors C_{11} and C_{12} in series.

The rectifiers V_1 and V_2 carry the total current required by both h.t. supplies, as does CH_1, and they are therefore selected to carry the sum of the currents required by the two h.t. lines (about 120 mA).

Tuning and Adjustment Procedure

For initial tuning purposes the h.t. supply should be

Fig. 74. Top view of the 3-band transmitter with the cover removed. The p.a. compartment appears at the bottom right, and the v.f.o. (cover in position) at the bottom centre.

disconnected from the p.a. stage by removing the link joining the terminals 5 and 6 (Fig. 73). The drive potentiometer VR_1 controlling the screen of V_4 should also be set at the minimum voltage position. If the stabilizer valve V_6 is lighting correctly, the operation of the v.f.o. can be tested. This is best accomplished by connecting a short length of wire to the aerial terminal of a receiver working in the 3·5 Mc/s band and placing it close to L_2. The signal from the v.f.o. can be thus monitored and checked for quality. The bandset capacitor C_2 is then adjusted so as to allow full coverage of the 3·5 Mc/s band on the v.f.o. dial (C_3). Next, the frequency should be set to 3·65 Mc/s and the core of L_2 adjusted so that maximum grid current is obtained in the next stage, V_2, which is measured by an external meter.

Place the band-change switches in the " 3·5 " position and note the grid current of V_4 with S_1 in the " net " position. The coupler WBC_1 may then be tuned by disconnecting the capacitor C_{11} from the secondary and adjusting the core of the primary winding for maximum grid current in V_4; this capacitor is then replaced and the primary capacitor C_{10} temporarily removed. The secondary winding is likewise tuned. On replacing the capacitor across the primary, very slight readjustment of both primary and secondary tuning may be necessary to give substantially constant drive to V_4 over the frequency range 3·5–3·8 Mc/s.

Set the drive control RV_1 to about its mid-position and repeat the above operations for WBC_5, this time monitoring the p.a. grid current by the normal metering circuit. After this coupler has been roughly tuned, V_5 should be neutralized by adjusting NC_2, using the method described on page 179. The coupler WBC_5 can then be finally adjusted for maximum output at 3·65 Mc/s. The grid current obtainable

198

Fig. 75. Underside view of the three-band transmitter.

in the p.a. stage is about 3–4 mA, falling at the edges of the band to approximately 2 mA.

Reduced h.t. can now be applied to the p.a. stage by inserting a 5000-ohm resistor (20-watt rating) between terminals 5 and 6 (Fig. 73). The r.f. output socket should be connected to a 25-watt lamp. The pi-network coupler can be tuned and loaded (as described on page 189), after which full h.t. may be applied to the power amplifier. Finally, the drive should be adjusted to give maximum r.f. power output.

The transmitter should next be tuned for the 7 Mc/s band with, of course, the band-change switches S_2 and S_3 in their appropriate positions. Since the coupler WBC_1 has already been adjusted, WBC_2 can be tuned to the centre of the 7 Mc/s band by the normal procedure indicated previously. The 7 Mc/s wide-band coupler, WBC_4, which drives the p.a. grid circuit can likewise be tuned, and finally the p.a. anode circuit, as before.

Finally, the transmitter is tuned on 14 Mc/s, on which band only the coupler WBC_3 will require adjustment.

There is no need to neutralize V_4 on the 3·5 Mc/s band but on the 7 Mc/s band it may be found beneficial: the adjustment is made during the tuning of WBC_2, in the same manner as for the p.a. stage. The neutralizing adjustment of the latter should be checked on each band.

If the circuit is functioning correctly, an output of at least 25 watts should be obtained on all three bands with an input of 40 watts to the power amplifier (66 mA at 600 volts).

Keying is accomplished by breaking the cathode connec-

tion of V_4. The cathode potential is limited under key-up conditions by the potential divider formed by R_{15} and R_{16} across the 250 volts h.t. line. A check should be made to verify that keying characteristics are satisfactory and that there is no spacer wave with the key up; poor characteristics could be caused by the incorrect neutralization of V_4 or V_5 and this should be investigated if trouble is experienced.

Owing to the physical layout used the connection from the p.a. grid to the switch S_2 is rather long and it is therefore made in the form of a length of screened cable. This cable is of a low-capacitance type (12 pF/ft.), in order not to add too much capacitance to the tuned circuits, and the fixed secondary tuning capacitors of WBC_3, WBC_4 and WBC_5 are selected on this basis. If the type of cable or its length is changed, the capacitors must be modified accordingly. The type of construction and layout adopted in this transmitter are illustrated in **Figs. 74** and **75**.

A FIVE-BAND 150 WATT TRANSMITTER

This transmitter, based on a design originally developed by G. Gibbs (G3AAZ), operates on five frequency bands (3·5–28 Mc/s) with a maximum power input on c.w. of 150 watts. It is also capable of accepting the full power input of 150 watts in a.m. telephony operation.

The required amateur band is selected by a band-switching arrangement. As a result of the basic design and constructional technique the transmitter is capable of operating at full power in normal television service areas without any TVI troubles.

The transmitter is designed to accept on input from a separate v.f.o. unit operating in the 3·5 Mc/s band. A design for a suitable v.f.o. is suggested earlier in this chapter.

Four low-level stages are used, the first being a simple amplifier working at 3·5 Mc/s. The second stage doubles the frequency to 7 Mc/s and the third multiplies this output either to 14 or to 21 Mc/s. The fourth low-level stage doubles from 14 Mc/s to 28 Mc/s. These low-level stages are followed by an 807 " straight-through " driver stage which is capacitance-coupled to the 813 power amplifier. The latter is connected into a pi-network output circuit.

Circuit Details

A diagram of the complete circuit is given in **Fig. 76**. For the low-level stages, four 6F12 (EF91) r.f. pentodes are used, all of which are triode-connected except the first stage. The triode-connection has been adopted partly to simplify the wiring by dispensing with screen-circuit components and partly to increase the bandwidth over which the r.f. output remains constant. The stages are coupled by a Labgear wide-band frequency-multiplier unit, a device

TABLE 6
Pi-network Component Values for 813 Output Tank Circuit in Fig. 76

Component	Reactance (ohms)	Frequency (Mc/s)				
		3·65	7·2	14·15	21·5	28·5
C_{27}	330	132 pF	68 pF	34 pF	23 pF	17 pF
C_{29}	45	1000 pF	500 pF	250 pF	167 pF	125 pF
L_4	375	16·4 μH	8·4 μH	4·2 μH	2·8 μH	2·1 μH

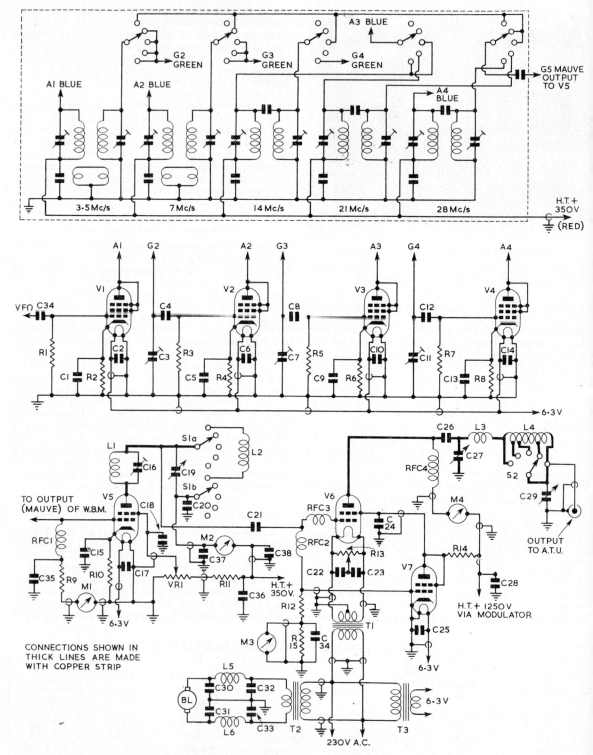

Fig. 76. Circuit diagram of the five band 150-watt transmitter. The components within the dotted line are part of the Labgear wideband multiplier unit. In the interests of safety, 2·5mH r.f. choke should be wired in parallel with C_{29}.

which contains all the necessary wide-band couplers together with the band-switch within a compact unit.

The 807 driver stage (V_5) is of normal design and its output is controllable by the potentiometer VR_1. It is capacitance-coupled to the power amplifier.

The 813 p.a. stage (V_6) is provided with a pi-network output circuit designed in accordance with the suggestions given earlier in this chapter. The output impedance of the 813 was taken as 3500 ohms, and the load value was assumed to be 72 ohms. **Table 6** gives the calculated ideal component values for the pi-network. The input capacitor has a maximum value of 200 pF and a very low minimum, while the output capacitor C_{29} has a maximum value of 1500 pF. A good-quality three-gang 500 pF tuning capacitor is satisfactory as C_{29}.

The anode-to-earth capacitance of the 813 is 14 pF, and it is therefore impossible to reduce the stray pi-network input capacitance at 28 Mc/s to less than 17 pF, as is desired. The coil size is instead slightly reduced and a lower L/C ratio accepted; the 28 Mc/s tuning point occurs with C_{27} almost at its minimum value. In order to preserve the effici-

Fig. 77. Underside view of the 5-band 150-watt transmitter.

ency of the circuit at 28 Mc/s, a separate coil L_3, of heavy-gauge copper tubing is used. Unwanted series inductance in the tank circuit is reduced by using heavy copper strap or braiding to connect the anode to the blocking condenser, and the tapping points of the coil to the switch.

A clamp valve, V_7, is connected to the screen of the p.a. valve. With an h.t. supply of 1250 volts and a grid-return resistance of 15,000 ohms, the standing anode current of the amplifier valve is maintained at 30 mA, which corresponds to an anode dissipation of 37·5 watts. In both the driver and p.a. stages, careful attention has been paid to layout and decoupling to avoid any form of instability. The heater and screen by-pass capacitors must be mounted on the valveholder tags and earthed by direct soldering to the chassis at a common point. To ensure effective decoupling even on the lowest frequency band a 0·001 μF capacitor is used as an anode by-pass in the p.a. stage. With these precautions, no traces of feedback should be found on any of the bands.

Constructional Details

The transmitter is entirely enclosed in a box constructed from $\frac{1}{16}$ in. flat brass sheet, the sides of the box being built up around a chassis measuring 17 in. × 13 in. × 3 in. Joints and corners are made " r.f.-tight " by the use of $\frac{3}{8}$ in. brass angle soldered to the sides, the total length required being about 24 ft. Ventilation in the top is provided by holes covered with copper gauze, the cooling air being supplied from a blower mounted below the chassis. The top and bottom cover plates are screwed to the angle strips with $\frac{1}{4}$ in. countersunk 4 B.A. bolts. These bolts

COMPONENTS DATA FOR FIG. 76

BL—motor blower
C_1, C_2, C_5, C_6, C_9, C_{10}, C_{13}, C_{14}, C_{17}, C_{18}, C_{25}, C_{35}—0·01 μF disc ceramic
C_3, C_7, C_{11}, C_{16}—30 pF air trimmer (*Polar*)
C_4, C_8, C_{12}, C_{34}—100 pF tubular ceramic
C_{15}, C_{22}, C_{23}, C_{36}, C_{37}, C_{38}—0·001 μF disc ceramic
C_{19}—120 pF max. (*Raymart*)
C_{20}, C_{32}, C_{33}—0·01 μF mica
C_{24}—0·001 μF mica, 2 kW wkg.
C_{26}, C_{28}—0·001 μF tubular ceramic, 5 kV wkg.
C_{27}—200 pF *Eddystone* type 833, sections in parallel
C_{29}—1500 (receiver-type 3-gang, 500 pF sections in parallel
C_{30}, C_{31}—470 pF disc ceramic
L_1—6 turns, 18 s.w.g. $\frac{1}{2}$ in. o.d. spaced one wire diam. (TVI trap)
L_2—*Labgear* turret type E.5023 B
L_3—4 turns, $\frac{1}{4}$-in. diam. copper tube spaced $\frac{3}{16}$-in. on $1\frac{1}{8}$-in. diam. former (28 Mc/s)
L_4—20 turns, 14 s.w.g. enamelled on $2\frac{1}{2}$-in. diam. former (*Eddystone* type 1090) tapped at 10, 17, 19 turns from junction with L_3
L_5, L_6—TV chokes, 1 amp. type (*Radiospares*)
M_1—5 mA m.c. meter
M_2—50 mA m.c. meter
M_3—15 mA m.c. meter
M_4—200 mA m.c. meter
R_1, R_3, R_5, R_7—27 kΩ, $\frac{1}{2}$ W
R_2, R_4—470 Ω, $\frac{1}{2}$ W
R_6, R_8—1000 Ω, $\frac{1}{2}$ W
R_9—15 kΩ, $\frac{1}{2}$ W
R_{10}—350 Ω, 1 W
R_{11}—15 kΩ, 5 W
R_{12}—18 kΩ, 10 W
R_{13}—40 Ω wire-wound, centre-tapped
R_{14}—75 kΩ, 50 W, wire-wound
R_{15}—200 Ω, 1 W
RFC_1, RFC_2—1·25 mH (*Eddystone* type 1010)
RFC_3—8 turns 18 s.w.g. $\frac{3}{8}$-in. diam.
RFC_4—see text and Fig. 60
S_1—part of *Labgear* turret type E.5023 B
S_2—single-pole 5-way heavy-duty switch
T_1—10 V 5A (*Woden* type DTF22)
T_2—12 V 1A (to suit blower)
T_3—6·3 V 4A (*Partridge*)
V_1, V_2, V_3, V_4—6F12
V_5—807
V_6—813
V_7—6L6
VR_1—25 kΩ, 5 W potentiometer
Wideband Multiplier—*Labgear* type E.5026

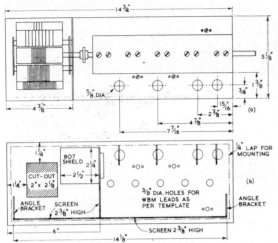

Fig. 78. Layout of components in the exciter section of the five-band 150-watt transmitter: (a) view from above, (b) underside view.

should be spaced not more than 4 in. apart to ensure effective sealing. The exciter chassis is designed for easy removal, and as can be seen in **Fig. 77** it is connected through a multi-way plug-and-socket to the main assembly and held down by four 6 B.A. bolts inserted into tapped holes. The only other connections to be removed when detaching the sub-unit are the coaxial input plug and the flexible coupler to the condenser C_{19}.

The layout of the exciter unit is illustrated in **Fig. 78.** This should prove useful as a basis for construction, even if the exact details are not followed. Although the coil turret and wide-band coupler are joined by a flexible coupler, care should be taken to align the spindles correctly, since any misalignment may strain the switch wafers besides

Fig. 79. Top view of the five-band 150-watt transmitter with the cover removed. The pairs of trimmers on the wideband multiplier unit can be seen to the left of the rear compartment. Reading from right to left, the frequency bands are 3·5, 7, 14, 21 and 28 Mc/s. The right-hand trimmer in each case is for grid tuning, and the left-hand trimmer is for anode tuning.

increasing the torque required to turn the switch. If exact alignment is not possible two flexible couplers should be used. The mounting for the right-angle drive for the exciter selector switch is formed from $\frac{5}{8}$ in. × $\frac{1}{8}$ in. brass strip bent while hot into U-form. The shaft bearings are $\frac{1}{4}$ in. bushes soldered into place, the bevel gears being 1:1 ratio, $\frac{5}{8}$ in. in diameter, to accept $\frac{1}{4}$ in. shafting. With a little ingenuity, it would be possible to gear the exciter switch with the p.a. band-change switch, thus simplifying band-changing operations still further and removing the asymmetrical appearance of the panel due to the extra control.

It was found that forced air cooling was desirable for the transmitter when operating at full power, and this is supplied from a small blower motor mounted at the rear of the chassis, visible in the view of Fig. 77 at the bottom right-hand corner. Air is blown through a 1-in. diameter gauze-covered hole in the side of the chassis directly on to the penultimate valve V_6 and from there through to the p.a. compartment above chassis. The warm air finally escapes through the holes provided in the top of the cabinet. The blower unit shown was designed to operate on 27 volts d.c. but performs satisfactorily with 12 volts a.c. supplied by the heater transformer. By mounting the blower on sponge rubber, the mechanical noise is reduced to a negligible level.

The 813 valve socket is arranged on a sub-assembly, the ceramic socket forming the main component. It is spaced below the chassis on distance pieces so that the top of the metal valve-base is level with the deck of the chassis; on the chassis itself is a flange plate to which is soldered a length of copper tube 3 in. in diameter and 1 in. high. This tube directs air from beneath the chassis uniformly over the glass bulb and also provides additional screening between the grid and anode circuits.

The various components associated with the 813 are supported on a copper framework mounted on the socket itself, and two strips of springy brass are provided for earthing the valve-base shell.

The r.f. choke RFC_4 used for the p.a. anode feed was constructed according to the details given in Fig. 60. The mounting position of this choke can be seen in the top view of the transmitter, **Fig. 79.** Also visible in this illustration is the clamp valve (top right-hand corner of the p.a. compartment) and the 813 heater transformer (bottom right). All leads feeding into the screened meter compartment are carried from beneath the chassis through a copper conduit, although screened cable would be equally satisfactory. Braided screened cable is used for all the wiring except that carrying r.f. current, and the braiding is earthed at both ends whenever possible.

A front view of the transmitter is shown in **Fig. 80.**

Adjustment and Tuning

First the exciter unit should be correctly tuned, and for this purpose it may conveniently be removed from the main chassis. The grid and anode meters and the drive control can be temporarily connected to the terminal block at the rear, from where permanent connections are made subsequently.

The tuning of the unit is carried out as follows, with the aid of an insulated trimming tool, after first removing the h.t. voltage from the 807 driver stage. Turn the band-change switch to the 3·5 Mc/s position and apply drive to the input

Fig. 80. Front view of the five-band 150-watt transmitter.

from the v.f.o. Adjust the tuning to give maximum drive to the 807 at the low-frequency end of the band with the grid trimmer and at the high-frequency end with the anode trimmer; repeat as necessary to secure reasonably constant drive over the whole band. Having correctly tuned the 3·5 Mc/s band, repeat the process for the next pair of trimmers, with the switch in the 7 Mc/s position, and so on throughout all bands. When one pair of trimmers has been set correctly, it is not necessary to adjust it again when aligning the trimmers on the other bands. The trimmers C_3, C_7 and C_{11} are adjusted to compensate for the extra capacity which is present when the stage in use is switched to the grid of the

807. In tuning the couplers, no attempt need be made to cover a greater band than is necessary since this would merely result in a general reduction in drive and possibly a reduction in harmonic attenuation of the wide-band circuits.

A dummy load consisting of a loop of wire and a 10-watt lamp can now be coupled in turn to each of the coils in the anode circuit of the 807 driver. On applying h.t. to this stage it should be possible to light the lamp to full brilliance. The grid current should not be less than 2·5 mA at any point in any band.

The exciter should now be replaced in the main chassis so that the amount of grid drive current for the 813 p.a. stage can be examined. This should be done before the h.t. supply is connected to it. The drive available should be 12–15 mA on all bands.

Initial adjustments to the p.a. stage should be carried out with reduced h.t. supply (about 600 volts) and a dummy load consisting of a 100-watt 75-ohm resistor or a suitable lamp connected across the output terminals. Tests for stability should be made on all bands without any grid drive as suggested on page 186; the standing anode current will be about 15 mA. The drive can be applied if the circuit appears to be stable and the pi-network circuit adjusted to give full output. The settings for the tank and loading capacitors can be noted and tabulated for quick reference when changing from one band to another.

A LOW POWER C.W./PHONE TRANSMITTER
FOR 1·8/3·5 Mc/s

The transmitter described here represents one of the simplest practicable arrangements under present-day conditions

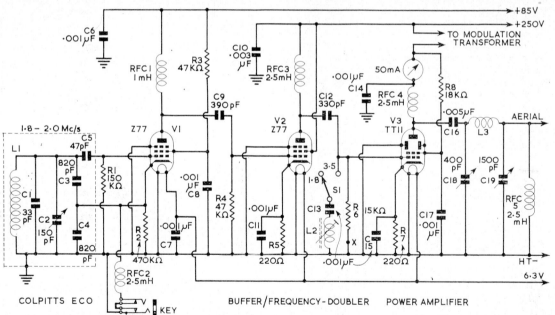

Fig. 81. Low-power transmitter for 1·8/3·5 Mc/s (designed by D. White, G3JKA). C_1 is a temperature-compensating capacitor, type N750K. C_3, C_4 and C_5 should be silvered-mica capacitors. C_{19} can be a triple-gang receiving-type capacitor (500 pF per section)

L_1—32 turns of No. 22 s.w.g. enamelled on 1-in. diameter former.

L_2—60 turns of No. 36 s.w.g. enamelled pile-wound on ⅜-in. diameter former with dust-iron core.

L_3—50 turns of No. 22 s.w.g. enamelled on 1-in. diameter former.

Alternative valve types for V_1 and V_2 are 6AM6, EF91, etc. The anode current in the TT11 output stage is 30-40 mA and the grid current through R_6 is 1 mA on both frequency bands. An efficiency of 60 per cent on the 1·8 Mc/s band should be obtained.

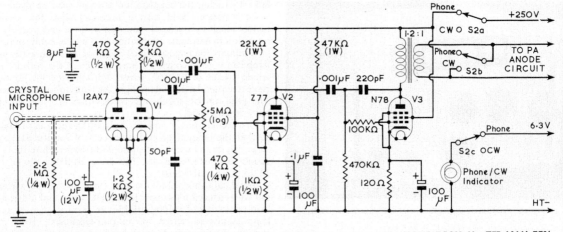

Fig. 82. Modulator for the low-power 1·8/3·5 Mc/s transmitter. Alternative valve types: V₁—12AX7, ECC83; V₂—Z77, 6AM6, EF91. The c.w./phone change-over switches S2A, S2B, S2C can be combined as a 3-pole 2-way wafer-type.

for low power operation on the 1·8 Mc/s and 3·5 Mc/s bands. It is designed for an input power of 10 watts, phone or c.w., and is free from television-interference troubles. Owing to its simplicity it can be recommended as an ideal beginner's transmitter.

Circuit Arrangement

The circuit of the r.f. section is given in **Fig. 81**. It consists of a Z77 Colpitts type of v.f.o. operating in the 1·8–2 Mc/s band. This drives a second Z77 stage which is designed to operate either as an untuned buffer amplifier on 1·8 Mc/s or as a frequency doubler. The change-over is effected by switching in the inductance L_2: in combination with the effective grid-to-earth capacitance of the p.a. valve this introduces a wide-band tuned circuit between the driver valve V_2 and the p.a. stage. The capacitor C_{13} serves merely as a blocking capacitor to prevent the short-circuiting of the grid bias.

For the p.a. stage a type TT11 valve is used and a pi-network coupler transfers power direct from the anode to the aerial. The pi-network is tuned to either of the two

bands by adjusting the tuning and loading capacitors C_{18} and C_{19}. This means that a compromise has to be made in choosing the values of L_3, C_{18} and C_{19}, but in practice the loss of efficiency is negligible.

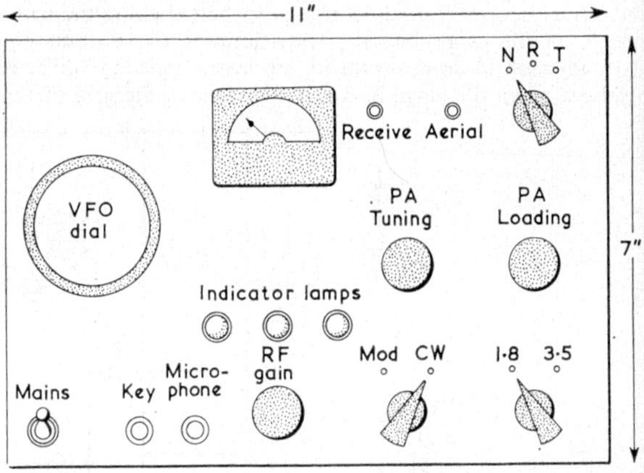

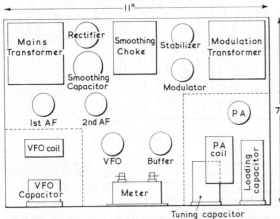

Fig. 84. Panel layout of the low-power 1·8/3·5 Mc/s transmitter.

For telegraphy operation the key is inserted in the cathode lead of the oscillator valve V_1, a high resistance R_2 being added between cathode and earth to ensure that the heater/cathode voltage does not rise to a dangerous value.

The p.a. stage is anode-and-screen modulated by the modulator shown in **Fig. 82**. It consists of a simple four stage amplifier and is suitable for use with a crystal microphone; the high frequency response is purposely restricted to about 3000 c/s in order to reduce the bandwidth of the radiated signal. When operating on c.w., the modulator is switched off and the secondary of the modulation transformer is short-circuited to prevent the generation of voltage surges across the windings which may be caused by sudden changes of anode current in the p.a. valve during keying.

A suitable layout for the chassis is shown in **Fig. 83** and the corresponding panel layout is shown in **Fig. 84**.

Fig. 83. Chassis layout of the low-power 1·8/3·5 Mc/s transmitter

In the power supply unit an orthodox full-wave rectifier circuit is used, as shown in **Fig. 85.** The v.f.o. valve is supplied separately from a stabilized h.t. line of 85 volts.

Tuning the Transmitter

A 10-watt lamp should first be connected between the r.f. output terminals to simulate aerial loading. With the switch S_1 (Fig. 81) in the c.w. position, the frequency range of the v.f.o. unit should be checked to verify that it covers the 1·8–2 Mc/s band, and its frequency stability and the quality of the keying should be observed. With the band-change switch S_1 in the 1·8 Mc/s position, the p.a. grid current (measured at the point X) should be found to remain constant at about 1–1·5 mA over the entire band. The tuning and loading capacitors C_{18} and C_{19} respectively should then be adjusted as suggested on page 189 and their settings noted for future convenience. On full load, the anode current to the output stage will be about 40 mA at 250 volts (i.e. 10 watts power input) and the 10-watt lamp should glow quite brightly.

Next the transmitter may be tuned on the 3·5 Mc/s band by tuning S_1 to the appropriate position and setting the v.f.o. to 1·83 Mc/s (i.e. approximately the mid-point of the 3·5 Mc/s band). The core of L_2 can then be adjusted to bring the p.a. grid current to about 1 mA at this frequency: there should be only a slight variation over the full range 3·5–3·8 Mc/s. The pi-network output circuit can finally be tuned, as explained earlier in this chapter.

Modulation is tested by switching S_2 to the "phone" position. On modulation peaks, the increase of r.f. output power should be apparent by the brightening of the lamp. The amplitude and the quality of the modulation should then be monitored by any suitable method as described in Chapter 9 (*Modulation*).

TRANSMITTER WITH BREAK-IN FACILITIES FOR 14, 21 AND 28 Mc/s.

Circuit Details

The transmitter shown in **Fig. 86** was designed by G. F. GEARING (G3JJG) to provide a high stability c.w. signal with provision for full break-in. A crystal oscillator-mixer type v.f.o. is employed. By using this technique, the problem of v.f.o. stability is simplified and, as both oscillators have to be run at low level (with consequently low harmonic content), the possibility of interference to other services is reduced.

The v.f.o. output frequency range is from 7·0 Mc/s to 7·15 Mc/s. The variable low frequency oscillator covers 1·5 Mc/s to 1·65 Mc/s and is mixed with the output of a crystal oscillator on 5·5 Mc/s. When operating on 28 Mc/s the frequency multiplication is only four times so the effects of drift are kept to a minimum. If the v.f.o. were on 1·75 Mc/s, as in conventional designs, the multiplication factor would be 16 times, i.e. a drift of 100 c/s at the fundamental would be 1600 c/s at 28 Mc/s.

The mixer stage may be keyed for break-in operation, effectively keying the v.f.o. output but without the transient responses which may occur when an oscillator is keyed. A netting facility is provided which brings the mixer into operation but not the buffer amplifier.

The multiplier chain uses 5763s in conventional circuitry,

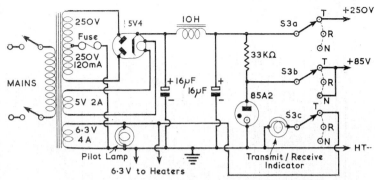

Fig. 85. Power supply for the low-power 1·8/3·5 Mc/s transmitter. The switches S3A, S3B S3C may be combined as a 3-pole 3-way wafer-type giving TRANSMIT—RECEIVE—NET One side of the heater should be connected to the cathode.

followed by the power amplifier, a v.h.f. double tetrode (Mullard QQV06-40) with the two sections in parallel. A pi-network tank is utilized, output being taken through an electronic aerial relay to the 70 ohm load.

The circuit chosen for the low frequency oscillator (V_1) is the low-capacity Colpitts.

As may be seen from **Fig. 87,** the grid blocking capacitor C_1 has been placed in series with C_4 and C_5, so that the shunt capacitance is effectively reduced to approximately 60 pF, permitting L_1 to be large and C_2 small. Random variations in the input capacity of V_1 are accordingly swamped by C_4.

Coupling to the oscillator tank circuit is controlled by the value of C_1, which is dependent on the Q of L_1. As the stability of an oscillator is improved if the power dissipated by the tuned circuit is reduced, C_1 should be as small as possible consistent with steady oscillation. Drift which occurs whilst warming-up is counteracted by the negative temperature co-efficient capacitor C_3. A stability exceeding 0·005 per cent is possible with the circuit values given.

The tuning range is from 1500 kc/s to 1650 kc/s with a small overlap either side. This may be reduced by removing one rotor plate from the specified tuning capacitor, C_2.

The output of the two oscillators appear at the mixer (V_3) anode together with their sum and difference frequencies. When the l.f.o. is tuned to 1500 kc/s, these frequencies are

Fig. 86. The above-chassis layout showing the p.a. box at the top left and the l.f.o. and crystal oscillator components to the right. The large transformer at the lower left is the heater transformer.

205

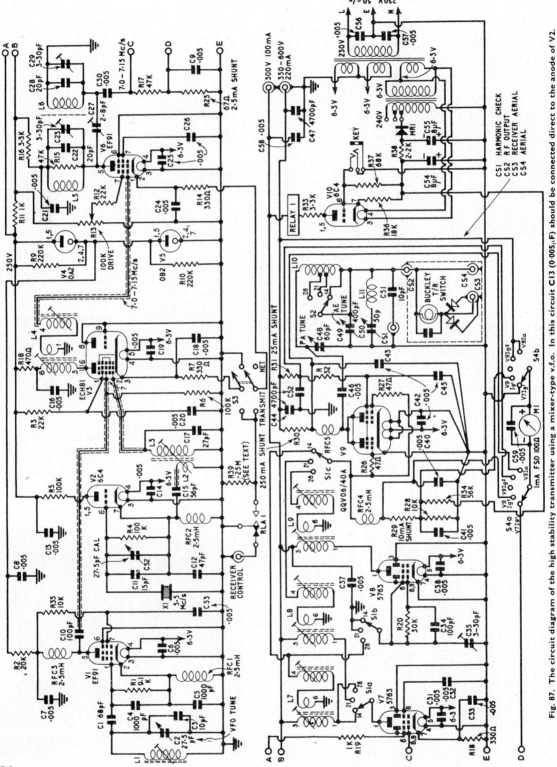

Fig. 87. The circuit diagram of the high stability transmitter using a mixer-type v.f.o. In this circuit C13 (0·005 μF) should be connected direct to the anode of V2.

(h) Tune the primary and secondary of L_4, C_{23} and C_{29} for maximum drive. Tune to 7·0 Mc/s and adjust the top slug of L_4. Adjust the bottom slug at 7·15 Mc/s. Drive will be at a maximum at 7·075 Mc/s. C_{27} is increased till the drive is at maximum at the band edges with a small drop towards band centre. C_{27} must be as low capacity as is possible. L_2, L_3 may now be adjusted for a final peak in drive. The grid current in V_7 should be greater than 1·5 mA at all frequencies.

(i) Monitor V_9 grid and select 14 Mc/s on S_1, S_2.

(j) Adjust the top slug of L_7 at 14 Mc/s and the bottom slug at 14·3 Mc/s. Continue these adjustments alternately until a level response is obtained.

(k) On 21 Mc/s, tune L_8 at 21 Mc/s and at 21·45 Mc/s.

(l) On 28 Mc/s tune L_9 at 28 Mc/s and adjust C_{35} at 28·6 Mc/s.

(m) With the 5·5 Mc/s crystal removed, the residual drive should be less than 100 microamps at all settings of the l.f.o.

(n) H.t. may now be applied to the p.a., and the transmitter loaded into a 70 ohm resistive load. The spacing of the turns of L_{10} may be varied if the p.a. will not tune to all frequencies in the three bands.

TRANSMITTER RATINGS

Methods of calculating power input for A1 and A3 transmitters (p.a. anode voltage multiplied by the anode current in amps. gives the input power in watts) are well known but other systems, particularly single sideband and grounded grid amplifiers present a somewhat different problem.

Single Sideband Transmitters

The Post Office states that: " The peak r.f. power input from an A3a transmitter shall not exceed that obtained from the A3 transmitter working at an overall efficiency of 66 per cent. The power shall be measured by the following process:

(i) Apply a pure sinusoidal tone to the transmitter and adjust the input to 150 watts d.c.; the deflection on a cathode-ray tube by the r.f. envelope shall be measured. (D.c. input power is the total d.c. input to the anode circuit of the valve(s) energizing the aerial.)

(ii) Replace the tone by speech; the maximum deflection on the cathode-ray tube showing the r.f. output caused by the peaks of speech shall not be greater than twice the previously measured deflection for the tone input."

Earthed or Grounded Grid Power Amplifiers

In the opinion of the Society's Technical Committee, the power input, effectively, to a grounded grid power amplifier stage should be reckoned as 10 per cent greater than the product of the anode voltage and anode current to that stage. One proviso is, however, that to prevent unreasonable driving power being used the power input to the driver stage should not exceed 50 per cent of the d.c. power input to the driven stage.

Pulse Modulation

The use of pulse modulation is permitted in the bands 2350–2400, 5700–5800, 10050–10450 and 21,150–21,850 Mc/s, the systems specified being P1, P2d, P2e, P3d and P3e. These may be defined as follows:

P1 —Telegraphy without the use of a modulating audio frequency signal.

P2d—Amplitude modulation of the pulse by audio frequencies for telegraphy.

P2e—Width modulation of the pulse by audio frequencies for telegraphy.

P3d—Amplitude modulation of the pulse by audio frequencies for telephony.

P3e—Width modulation of the pulse by audio frequencies for telephony.

The maximum mean d.c. power input is 25 watts and 2·5 kW peak input power at the crest of the pulse. The limit of 2·5 kW peak d.c. input implies a maximum peak-to-mean ratio of 100 : 1, or a 1 per cent duty ratio.

The duty ratio is defined as the ratio between pulse duration and pulse repetition period. For example, if the pulse duration is t and the interval between the beginning of one pulse and the beginning of the next is T, then t/T is the duty ratio.

It is essential for a station employing pulse modulation to have a suitable cathode-ray oscilloscope in order to set up the transmitter. To display the envelope of the r.f. pulse, some of the r.f. output should be applied to the Y plates of the tube, the X plates being operated from the time base which should be locked at a sub-multiple of the repetition frequency.

Frequency Modulation

The Post Office states that: " The carrier frequency (of an f.m. signal) must be at least 10 kc/s within the limits of the frequency band in use and that the maximum deviation of carrier frequency shall not exceed 2·5 kc/s. The maximum effective modulating frequency shall be limited to 4 kc/s ,and the audio frequency input to the frequency modulator at any frequency above 4 kc/s shall be not less than 26db below the maximum input at lower frequencies."

Although the Post Office does not state the maximum effective modulating frequency for other types of phone operation, it is good practice to restrict the bandwidth to 4 kc/s or less (a frequency response of 500 to 2500 c/s is generally considered adequate for communication purposes).

CHAPTER 7

V.H.F./U.H.F. TRANSMITTERS

TRANSMITTERS for the 4m, 2m and 70cm bands employ the same general principles as those used on the h.f. bands: a stable oscillator followed by frequency-multiplying and power-amplifying stages. On the 23cm band, however, both stabilized transmitters and self-excited oscillators feeding directly into the aerial are in use. The reasons for this are (a) that circuit development on the 23cm band is not so far advanced as on the lower frequencies, (b) narrow-band techniques are as yet unnecessary owing to lower activity, (c) the higher initial cost involved in the construction of frequency-multiplying and amplifying stages for 23cm.

A major difference between h.f. and v.h.f. transmitters is that the v.h.f. equipment is invariably designed to operate on one band only. This is mainly due to the r.f. losses that would result from a band-switching device, and also to the difference in the form of tuned circuit, the transition from lumped circuits to parallel-line circuits and ultimately from parallel-line to coaxial-line circuits as the frequency is increased.

As the 2m band and part of the 70cm band are in harmonic relationship it is common practice to use an existing 2m transmitter as a driver, the output of the 2m transmitter being applied to a push-pull tripler stage which in turn is used to drive a power amplifier on 70cm. With this arrangement a transmitter operating between 144 and 146 Mc/s will produce an output having a frequency between 432 and 438 Mc/s. Similarly, a 70cm p.a. can be used to drive a tripler to 23cm, resulting in frequencies between 1296 and 1314 Mc/s. The usual operating range for frequency stabilized equipment on this band is 1296–1300 Mc/s.

CRYSTAL CONTROLLED OSCILLATORS

The majority of v.h.f. transmitters are crystal controlled, although in a few 2m transmitters the drive is derived from a stable variable frequency oscillator. The need to tune the local transmitter to the same frequency as that of the station being called, which is one of the customary requirements for operation on the h.f. bands, does not exist in v.h.f. practice. Normally the only justification for a shift in frequency within one of the v.h.f. bands is to avoid interference from another transmitter operating on an adjacent channel.

The crystal-oscillator circuits used in v.h.f. transmitters are similar to those employed for the lower frequencies. Crystal frequencies are usually in the range 6–12 Mc/s, and owing to the high multiplication factor in the transmitter to reach the final radiated frequency, the oscillator arrangement adopted is generally one that produces a large harmonic output. A common example is the modified Pierce oscillator (Chapter 6, Fig. 5(c)), in which the anode circuit is tuned to the third harmonic of the crystal frequency. Suitable

valves in the miniature range to employ in this circuit are the EF91 (CV138, 6AM6), EL91 (CV136, 6AM5) and QV03–12 (CV2129, 5763).

Overtone Oscillators

In addition to operation on their fundamental frequency it is possible for crystals to oscillate on odd multiples, or overtones, of the fundamental. The term overtone is used in preference to harmonic operation, as the resultant frequency of oscillation is not an exact multiple of the crystal frequency.

The most suitable crystals for overtone operation are AT-cut or BT-cut, operating in the thickness shear mode, in which the frequency is determined by the thickness of the crystal. **Figs. 1 (a)** and **(b)** show the deformation in the thick-

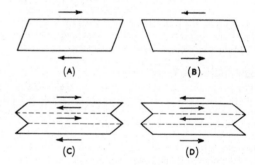

Fig. I. Operation of a crystal on its fundamental and third overtone.

ness of a crystal operating on its fundamental frequency at successive peaks of each half-cycle. **Figs. 1 (c)** and **(d)** show the deformation of a crystal operating on its third overtone; in each instance the arrows indicate the direction of mechanical movement. It will be seen that the crystal now operates as if it consists of three distinct layers; for fifth overtone operation it would appear to consist of five layers and so on. When the crystal is functioning as an overtone oscillator, there is no fundamental frequency component, the lowest frequency generated being that of the particular overtone.

For successful overtone operation crystals must be very accurately ground. At the frequencies used for oscillators in v.h.f. transmitters each layer of the crystal is only a few thousands of an inch thick, and any irregularity in the grinding will result in failure to oscillate. Excessive pressure on the surfaces of the crystal by the mounting will also prevent oscillation.

Crystals specially processed for overtone are available giving output frequencies up to approximately 100 Mc/s.

Certain crystals ground for fundamental frequency operation are suitable for use on the third and fifth overtones, notably the type FT243 in the frequency range 5·5 to 8·5 Mc/s. In transmitter circuits it is recommended that operation is restricted to the third or fifth overtone, due to the low output voltage obtainable at the higher orders.

To cause a crystal to oscillate on its overtone additional feedback at the overtone frequency must be provided. Sufficient feedback to sustain oscillation only is required: too much feedback will result in the crystal losing control and self-oscillation taking place. Adjustment of feedback is usually quite critical, fundamental frequency crystals requiring more feedback than those specially processed.

The evacuated B7G type of crystal having sputtered electrodes is also very suitable for overtone operation, provided that a moderate h.t. voltage only is applied to the oscillator and feedback is not excessive. Too high an h.t. voltage will result in fracture of the crystal.

The advantages of employing overtone oscillators in v.h.f. transmitters are that an economy in valves is effected, and also due to the fact that the lowest frequency generated is that of the overtone, there is less chance of causing spurious emissions than from a fundamental frequency oscillator. Disadvantages are that initial adjustment to obtain good frequency stability may be critical, and that the overtone frequency generated is not an exact multiple of the crystal frequency; this second fact must be borne in mind when working close to the edges of a frequency band.

Typical overtone oscillator circuits are shown in **Fig. 2.** The simple circuit of **Fig. 2 (a)** is suitable for use with crystals intended for overtone operation but cannot be employed with fundamental crystals as insufficient feedback is provided to cause oscillation. L_1 is tuned to the overtone frequency.

Fig. 2 (b) shows the Squier circuit which is in common use with fundamental type crystals in transmitters and as the local oscillator in v.h.f. converters. Feedback between anode and grid circuits is by direct inductive coupling, the degree of feedback being determined by the position of the h.t. tap on the inductor L_1; the tap is at earth potential to r.f. and feedback increases with the number of turns between the tap and the grid end of the inductor.

When overtone crystals are used in this circuit the amount of feedback required is small, but it must be increased with fundamental type crystals. L_1 is slug tuned to the frequency of the particular overtone selected. The position of the tap should be adjusted to provide sufficient feedback to initiate and maintain oscillation only and should be approximately one-quarter of the total number of turns from the grid end of the winding. This may require adjustment when initially setting up the oscillator. As with all overtone circuits too much feedback will result in the crystal losing control and self-oscillation taking place.

The circuit shown in **Fig. 2 (c)** is similar in operation to the Squier circuit, feedback in this case being provided by a separate winding L_2 coupled to L_1 which is tuned to the overtone frequency. The amount of feedback is determined by the number of turns in L_2 and its proximity to L_1. L_2 must be wound in the same sense with respect to L_1 to cause oscillation.

Fig. 2 (d) illustrates the Robert Dollar circuit. In this circuit feedback is controlled by the two capacitors C_2 and C_3. Decreasing the capacitance of C_2 increases the feedback. Typical values for C_2 and C_3 are shown in the diagram, but if desired, C_2 may be a pre-set capacitor to give some

flexibility of adjustment. L_1 is tuned to the overtone frequency.

A variant of the Butler circuit, due to Cathodeon Crystals Ltd., is shown in **Fig. 2 (e).** This circuit, which is suitable for use with overtone crystals, consists of a grounded grid amplifier (V_{1a}) and a cathode follower (V_{1b}). The anode circuit of the amplifier is tuned to the overtone frequency; the anode circuit of the cathode follower is tuned to a harmonic of this frequency, usually the second or third, as output at harmonics higher than these is generally too low to provide adequate drive in transmitter circuits. If r.f, output at the overtone frequency only is required this may

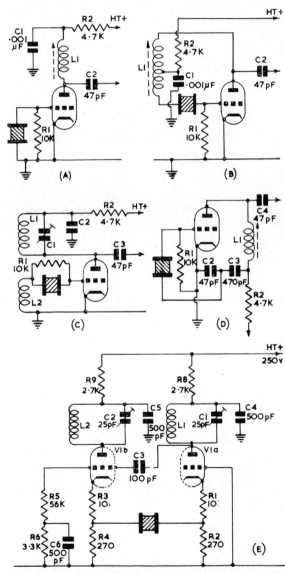

Fig. 2. Typical overtone oscillator circuits. (a) Suitable for use with crystals ground for overtone use. (b) The Squier circuit. (c) A somewhat similar arrangement to the Squier in which feedback is provided by a separate winding. (d) The Robert Dollar circuit. (e) Modified Butler circuit.

be obtained from an inductive coupling to L_1; in this instance the anode of the cathode follower should be earthed to r.f. and the tuned circuit L_2, C_2 omitted.

It is recommended that low Q inductors are used in this circuit. The type wound on polystyrene formers and tuned by adjustable dust-iron cores are suitable. The resistors in the cathode circuits of the valves form a transmission line and should be matched in value to achieve lowest loss. It may be necessary to experiment to obtain the optimum value for these components because the r.f. output rises but the frequency stability of the circuit falls as the value of resistance is increased. Lowering the value of the resistors increases the stability but the output will be reduced to a point at which oscillation ceases. A compromise should be aimed at between good frequency stability consistent with r.f. output adequate to drive the succeeding stage of the transmitter.

Triode valves are shown in all the circuits previously described but tetrodes and pentodes may also be used satisfactorily. Valves in the miniature range are to be preferred; the normal practice is to use double triodes, one section functioning as the oscillator, the output of which is fed into the grid of the second section, which acts as a frequency multiplier. Suitable valves to employ in the circuits of Fig. 2 are the ECC81 (CV455, 12AT7, B.309), ECC91 (CV858, 6J6) and ECC82 (CV491, 12AU7). The triode pentode ECL80 is suitable for use as a triode overtone oscillator and pentode frequency multiplier. A recommended valve in the double triode range for the Butler circuit of Fig. 2 (e) is the ECC81; suitable pentodes for this circuit are two type EF95 (CV850, 6AK5).

As with the more normal type of crystal oscillator, resonance in an overtone circuit is indicated by minimum anode current. It will be found when tuning the circuit that the anode current will fall very sharply on the low frequency side and will rise rather more gradually on the high frequency side of resonance. The final adjustment should be such that the circuit is tuned slightly to the high frequency side of the resonant point, which will result in maximum stability being obtained.

The resonance condition of the oscillator circuits described in this Chapter may be conveniently determined by tuning for maximum grid current in the following stage. The overtone circuit L_1, C_1 of Fig. 2 (e) may be adjusted for maximum grid current in V_{1b}, as indicated by a milliammeter connected across R_6.

FREQUENCY MULTIPLIERS

Frequency multiplying stages usually incorporate tetrode or pentode valves for greatest sensitivity and efficiency; high sensitivity is desirable because a large amount of grid drive may not be available from the preceding stage, particularly as the frequency of operation is increased. As the frequency increases the efficiency of multiplying stages falls off and for this reason it is advisable that any quadrupling or tripling is confined to the early stages of the transmitter and that doubling only takes place in the later stages where the efficiency is lowest.

To minimize the generation of unwanted frequencies, which would increase the possibility of interference to other services, multiplying stages should be designed to give maximum output at the desired harmonic and minimum output at all other frequencies. This is achieved by the use of high Q tuned circuits, inductive or link coupling between stages, and operation at the lowest power level consistent with obtaining adequate drive to the succeeding stage.

At frequencies up to 145 Mc/s single ended stages are usually employed. Most of the valves listed in Table 1 are satisfactory for use as multipliers; suitable types for low power operation are the EF91 (CV138), QV03–12 (CV2129, 5763) and QV04–7 (CV309). R.f. double tetrode valves are commonly used as push-pull frequency triplers and can also be used as push-pull doublers with the two anodes connected in parallel.

Triode frequency multipliers are sometimes employed in low power fixed and mobile transmitters, and their use in crystal-oscillator/multiplier circuits has already been mentioned in the section dealing with overtone oscillators.

POWER AMPLIFIERS

Power amplifying stages may employ triode or tetrode valves, used either singly or in push-pull. Tetrodes have the advantage that the power gain is greater and a lower grid drive is required, an important factor at the higher frequencies where in many instances only a low output is available from the preceding driver stage.

For low and medium power 2m and 70cm transmitters undoubtedly the most popular is the r.f. power double tetrode, some versions of which are suitable for operation up to 600 Mc/s. In the low power class, up to 10 watts anode dissipation, these valves are of miniature single-ended construction; examples are the Mullard QQV02–6 and QQV03–10. For higher power ratings up to a maximum of 40 watts anode dissipation a double-ended construction has been adopted, as exemplified by the Mullard QQV03–20A and QQV06–40A. These valves incorporate internal neutralizing capacitances and no external neutralization is necessary provided that input and output circuits are shielded from each other.

Single tetrodes are commonly employed in high power 2m transmitters, or a pair may be used in push-pull; suitable valves are the Mullard QY3–65 and QY3–125. For 70cm a typical high power amplifier consists of an S.T.C. 4X150A forced air cooled tetrode in a coaxial circuit; such an amplifier can be operated at the maximum input of 150 watts at 435 Mc/s. Amplifiers for 23cm make use of planar electrode triodes in a coaxial circuit.

A list of valves suitable for operation as power amplifiers and in the later frequency multiplying stages of v.h.f. and u.h.f. transmitters appears in **Table 1.** Detailed information on these types and in many instances application notes may be obtained from the valve manufacturer.

TUNED CIRCUITS

At frequencies up to approximately 150 Mc/s lumped circuits are efficient and are generally used throughout the transmitter in both multiplying and amplifying stages. Above this frequency the efficiency of an inductor-capacitor tuned circuit falls off and use is made of parallel resonant lines up to frequencies of approximately 500 Mc/s. At higher frequencies the spacing between parallel lines becomes appreciable compared to the wavelength and loss occurs due to radiation from the lines; for this reason coaxial resonant lines in which the outer conductor is at earth potential

TABLE

Make	Type No.	Class	Base	Cathode			Limiting Values			Max. freq. full ratings (Mc/s)	Output at full ratings (W)	Max. freq. reduced ratings (Mc/s)	Output at reduced ratings (W)
				Type	V	A	P_A	V_A	V_{G2}				
M-O Valve Mullard S.T.C. U.S.A. CV	L77 EC90 6C4 6C4 133	Triode	B7G	IH	6·3	0·15	5	350	—	54	5·5	150	2·5
Mullard U.S.A. CV	ECC91 6J6 858	Double-triode	B7G	IH	6·3	0·45	2 × 1·5	300	—	80	3·5	—	1·0 at 250 Mc/s
M-O Valve Mullard CV	DET23 TD03-5 354	Disc-seal triode	—	IH	6·3	0·4	5	350	—	2000	—	—	—
S.T.C. CV	33A/158M 1884	Double-triode	B8G	IH	6·3	0·8	6	300	—	100	15·5	—	—
Mullard	EC56	Disc-seal triode	Octal	IH	6·3	0·65	10	300	—	—	—	4000	0·5
Mullard	EC57	Disc-seal triode	Octal	IH	6·3	0·65	10	300	—	—	—	4000	1·8
M-O Valve Mullard CV	DET22 TD03-10 273	Disc-seal triode	—	IH	6·3	0·4	10	350	—	1000	2·8	3000	0·5
S.T.C. CV	33B/152M 1540	Double-triode	B9G	IH	6·3	0·92	15	375	—	300	28	—	—
M-O Valve Mullard CV	DET24 TD04-20 397	Disc-seal triode	—	IH	6·3	1·0	20	400	—	600	23	2000	3·5
S.T.C. CV	3B/240M 2214	Triode	B8G	IH	6·3	1·1	24	375	—	200	24	—	—
M-O Valve CV	ACT22 257	Disc-seal triode	—	IH	6·3	4·0	75	600	—	1000	90	—	—
Mullard CV	TY2-125 1924	Triode	B5F	DH	6·3	5·4	135	2500	—	150	390	200	245
Mullard CV	QQV02-6 2466	Double-tetrode	B9A	IH	6·3 12·6	0·8 0·4 }	2 × 3	275	200	200	6	500	5
Mullard CV	QV04-7 309	Tetrode	B9G	IH	6·3	0·6	7·5	400	250	20	7·9	150	6·3
Mullard U.S.A. CV	QQV03-10 6360 2798	Double-tetrode	B9A	IH	6·3 12·6	0·8 0·4 }	2 × 5	300	200	100	16	225	12·5
M-O Valve CV	TT15 415	Double-tetrode	B9G	IH	6·3	1·6	2 × 7·5	400	—	200	12	250	—
Mullard U.S.A. CV	QQV04-15 832A 788	Double-tetrode	B7A	IH	6·3 12·6	1·6 0·9 }	2 × 7·5	750	250	100	26	250	18
M-O Valve Mullard U.S.A. CV	TT20 QQV03-20A 6252 2799	Double-tetrode	B7A	IH	6·3 12·6	1·3 0·65 }	2 × 10	600	250	200	48	600	20
Mullard U.S.A. CV	QV06-20 6146 3523	Tetrode	Octal	IH	6·3	1·25	20	600	250	60	52	175	25
Mullard U.S.A. CV	QQV06-40A 5894 2797	Double-tetrode	B7A	IH	6·3 12·6	1·8 0·9 }	2 × 20	750	250	200	90	475	60
Mullard U.S.A. CV	QQV07-40 829B 2666	Double-tetrode	B7A	IH	6·3 12·6	2·5 1·25 }	2 × 20	750	225	100	87	250	60
Mullard U.S.A. CV	QY3-65 4-65A 1905	Tetrode	B7A	DH	6·0	3·5	65	3000	400	50	280	220	110
Mullard U.S.A. CV	QY3-125 4-125A 2130	Tetrode	B5F	DH	5·0	6·5	125	3000	400	120	375	200	225
Mullard S.T.C. U.S.A. CV	QV1150A 4X150A 4X150A 2519	Tetrode— forced-air cooled	B8F	IH	6·0	2·6	150	1250	300	165	195	500	140

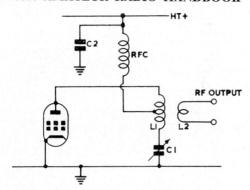

Fig. 3. Series tuned anode circuit.

to r.f. are employed at ultra high frequencies. The transition from one type of tuned circuit to the other takes place gradually and some overlap exists in the choice of a particular tuned circuit for a given frequency; for instance although the majority of 2m transmitters make use of lumped circuits throughout, a quarter wavelength line is sometimes employed as the tank circuit in a medium or high power amplifying stage. At 70cm the tendency is to use parallel-line circuits at low and medium powers and coaxial circuits in high power transmitters.

Examples of all the types of tuned circuit previously discussed appear in the transmitters described subsequently in this chapter.

The inductors used in lumped circuits should be of self-supporting air spaced construction, and can conveniently be wound with soft drawn enamelled copper wire, having a gauge between 12 and 22 s.w.g., the wire gauge increasing as the power rating of the stage and the frequency of operation increases. For power ratings in excess of 100 watts, it is advisable to use $\frac{3}{16}$ or $\frac{1}{4}$ in. o.d. copper tube, preferably silver plated to minimize loss due to skin effect which can be appreciable at the frequencies under consideration. As a v.h.f. transmitter is essentially a one band device, an inductor can be soldered directly across the associated tuning capacitor; this eliminates any plug and socket connection which cause losses if used in an r.f. circuit.

In tuned circuits associated with driver stages it is common practice to dispense with the tuning capacitor and to resonate the inductor with the stray and circuit capacitances. Tuning is effected by opening out or compressing the turns of the inductor.

Certain single-ended tetrodes have a high output capacitance which precludes their use at v.h.f. with a normal parallel-tuned circuit because it is not possible to employ sufficient inductance to form an efficient circuit. This type of valve can be used, however, if a " series-tuned " anode circuit is adopted (Fig. 3). In this arrangement the tuning capacitor C_1 and the output capacitance of the valve are in series across the inductor. The effective parallel capacitance is less than that due to the valve alone and the external inductance can be increased to a value that results in an efficient circuit.

Linear tuned circuits are most conveniently employed in push-pull stages and may be any multiple of a quarter wavelength ($\lambda/4$) long. This refers to the electrical length of the line, the actual length in practice being somewhat

shorter due to the valve acting as an extension of the line, so that the added inductance of the leads and the inter-electrode capacitance result in a physical shortening of the line. A quarter wavelength linear anode circuit for a push-pull stage is shown in Fig. 4 (a). Tuning may be effected either by varying the physical length of the line by adjustment of a shorting bar or by a variable capacitor C_1 connected across the open circuited end of the line adjacent to the valve. To maintain circuit balance a split-stator capacitor should be used for tuning with the rotor left floating and not connected to earth. For the same reason the h.t. feed connection at the voltage antinode of the line should be left unbypassed. An electrical centre-tap on the circuit is provided by the valve inter-electrode capacitances.

A push-pull anode circuit employing a half wavelength line is shown in Fig. 4 (b). The valve and tuning capacitance are connected at opposite ends of the line and h.t. is applied at the electrical centre of the line, i.e. the voltage node. Half wavelength lines are sometimes employed in grid circuits at the higher frequencies where the valve leads and inter-electrode capacitances are such that the natural frequency of

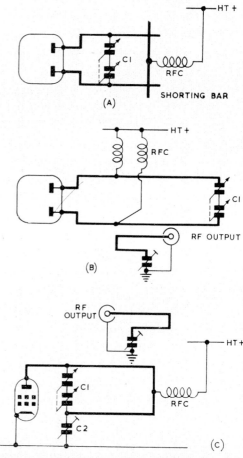

Fig. 4. Linear tuned circuits. (a) Quarter wavelength tuned circuit. (b) Half wavelength line for push-pull use. (c) Linear tuned circuit for use with a single ended stage.

the valve grid assembly is lower than the frequency of operation. All parallel-line circuits should be shielded to minimize loss due to r.f. radiation from the lines which becomes greater as the frequency of operation increases.

Linear tuned anode circuits can be used in single ended stages as shown in **Fig. 4 (c)**. The capacitor C_2 is necessary to balance the output capacitance of the valve connected across the other half of the line.

Aerial Coupling to Parallel-line Tank Circuits

The usual method of coupling the output of a v.h.f. transmitter to a low impedance coaxial feeder is by a one or two turn coupling winding located adjacent to the earthy end of the p.a. tank inductor. One side of the coupling circuit is invariably earthed, either directly or through a small preset capacitor which is adjusted to cancel out the inductive reactance of the coupling coil. With a parallel-line tank circuit a hairpin loop is employed, as shown in Fig. 4 (b) and

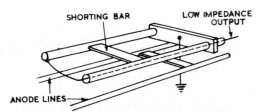

Fig. 5. Aerial coupling to a linear (parallel line) tank circuit.

(c). This arrangement is satisfactory with the unbalanced circuit of Fig. 4 (c) but when used with the push-pull anode circuit of Fig. 4 (b) it results in some unbalance being reflected back into the tank circuit.

One method of overcoming this is to use a linear balance-to-unbalance and impedance transformer—balun **(Fig. 5)**. The amount of coupling is determined by the distance between the balun and the anode lines, and also by the length of the balun lines which is dependent on the position of the shorting bar.

Coaxial Circuits

Coaxial circuits are usually employed at 435 Mc/s and above. At 1260 Mc/s planar-electrode valves are incorporated in grounded grid circuits with quarter wavelength cathode and anode cavities, though three-quarter wavelength cavities are sometimes found. Use of a grounded grid amplifier obviates the necessity for neutralization but as the amplifier and its driver stage are effectively connected in series, both stages must be modulated for telephony transmission. The audio power is not wasted, however, as the modulated r.f. output of the driver stages is added to the output of the amplifier.

Design of Transmission Line Resonators

When designing a resonator to be used as a tank circuit it is necessary to know first how long to make the lines. The resonant frequency of a capacitatively loaded shorted line, open-wire or coaxial, is given by the following well-known expression:

$$\frac{1}{2\pi fC} = Z_0 \; tan \; \frac{2\pi l}{\lambda}$$

where f is the frequency
C is the loading capacity
λ is the wavelength
l is the line length
Z_0 is the characteristic impedance of the line.

The characteristic impedance is given by

$$Z_0 = 138 \; log_{10} \; \frac{R_1}{R_2}$$

for a coaxial line with inside radius of the outer R_1 and outside radius of the inner conductor R_2

or

$$Z_0 = 276 \; log_{10} \; \frac{2D}{d}$$

for an open-wire line with conductor diameter d and centre-to-centre spacing D.

The results obtained from these expressions have been put into the form of the simple set of curves shown in **Fig. 6.**

In the graphs, fl has been plotted against fC for different values of Z_0, with f in Mc/s, C in pF and l in centimetres.

In the case of coaxial lines (the righthand set of curves) r is the ratio of conductor diameters or radii and for open-wire lines (the lefthand set of curves) r is the ratio of centre-to-centre spacing to conductor diameter.

The following examples should make the use of the graphs quite clear:

Example 1

How long must a shorted parallel-wire line of conductor diameter 0·3 in. and centre-to-centre spacing 1·5 in. be made to resonate at 435 Mc/s, with an end-loading capacitance of 2 pF (the approximate output capacitance, in practice, of a QQV03-20 push-pull arrangement)?

First, work out f x C, in Mc/s and pF.

$$fC = 435 \times 2$$
$$= 870$$
$$= 8·7 \times 10^2.$$

The ratio, r, of line spacing to diameter is:

$$r = \frac{1·5}{0·3} = 5·0$$

Then, using the curved marked " parallel-wire lines," $r = 5·0$ in. project upwards from 8·7 x 10² on the horizontal "f x C" scale to the graph and project across from the point on the graph so found to the vertical "f x l" scale, obtaining:

$$fl = 2800$$

therefore, $l = \frac{2800}{435} = 6·45$ cm approximately.

The anode pins would obviously absorb quite a good deal of this line length but, if the lines were made 6cm long, with an adjustable shorting-bar they would be certain to be long enough.

Example 2

A transmission line consisting of a pair of 10 s.w.g. copper wires spaced 1 in. apart and 10cm long is to be used as part of the anode tank circuit of a TT15 or QQV06-40 p.a. at 145 Mc/s. How much extra capacitance must be added at the valve end of the line to accomplish this?

For a pair of wires approximately $\frac{1}{8}$ in. in diameter spaced 1 in. r is about 8. Also f x l is equal to 145 x 10, i.e. 1450. Estimating the position of the " $r = 8$ " curve for a parallel-wire line between " $r = 10$ " and " $r = 7$," f x C is found

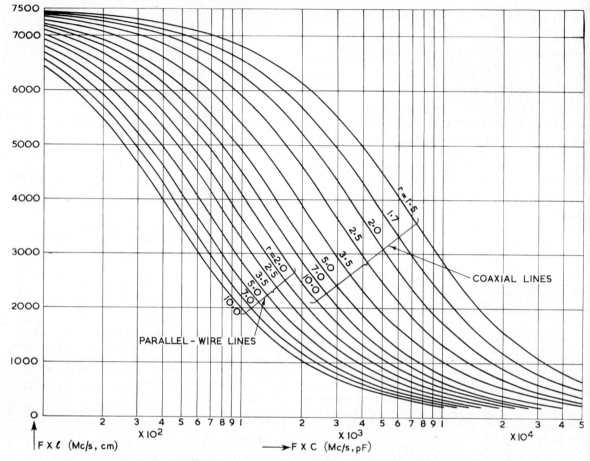

Fig. 6. Resonance curves for capacitively loaded transmission line resonators.

to be about 1·55 x 10³, i.e. 1550. Hence the total capacity C required is given by

$$145 \times C = 1550$$
$$C = 1550 \div 145$$
$$= 10.7 \text{ pF.}$$

Now the output capacitance of a TT15 or QQV06-40 push-pull stage is around 4 pF in practice, so about 7 pF are required in addition. A 25 + 25 pF split stator capacitor should therefore be quite satisfactory giving 12 to 15 pF extra at maximum capacity.

Example 3

A coaxial line with outer and inner radii of 5·0 and 2·0cm, respectively, is to be used as the resonant tank circuit (short-circuited at one end of course) for a 4X150A power amplifier on the 70cm amateur band. What length of line is required?

In this case:

$$f \times C = 435 \times 4.6$$
$$= 2001.$$

Using the " $r = 2.5$ " curve for coaxial lines,

$$f \times l = 4620$$

Hence

$$l = 4620 \div 435$$
$$= 10.6\text{cm approximately.}$$

This length would include the length of the anode and cooler of the 4X150A of course but, as in Example 1, a line 10cm long would be certain to be long enough, especially as the output capacity used in the calculations is that quoted by the manufacturers for the valve, the effective capacity being somewhat greater in practical circuits. A shorting bridge would be the best method of tuning the line to resonance.

Designing for Maximum Unloaded Q

The tank circuit efficiency is given by

$$Efficiency \text{ (per cent)} = \frac{unloaded\ Q - loaded\ Q}{unloaded\ Q} \times 100$$

It is obvious that the highest possible unloaded Q is needed to get the greatest tank circuit efficiency. The Q is greater for radial and coaxial resonators than for comparable parallel-wire circuits and the former types should always be used where possible. It should perhaps be explained that unloaded Q is the Q of the tank circuit with the valve in position and all voltages and drive power applied, but with no load coupled up to it. The loaded Q is, of course, that measured when the load is correctly coupled to the tank circuit.

For parallel-wire lines, unshielded, the unloaded Q is usually quite low because of power loss by radiation from the line and the best value is obtained by using a small conductor spacing.

To obtain the best Q, the material of the line should be copper or brass fairly smoothly finished, although a highly polished surface is not necessary. To improve its conductivity, the surface of a coaxial or radial line can be silver plated. However, if one lives in an industrial or city atmosphere, the silver plating is rapidly attacked by atmospheric gases and the surface conductivity suffers far more than does that of a copper or brass line. The best solution is to apply a " flash " of rhodium to the silver plating but this is rarely possible for the amateur.

The Q of a coaxial line depends also upon the ratio of conductor diameters and, for fairly heavily capacitatively loaded resonators, which is true in most practical cases, this ratio should be between about 3 and 4·5 to 1.

Care should be taken that the moving contacts on the bridge (if one is used) are irreproachable and they should preferably make contact with the line a little way away from the shorting disc, where the line impedance is somewhat higher than at the current antinode. It is better to use a large number of springy contact fingers rather than to use a few relatively rigid ones.

Attention to these points will often make all the difference between a reliable, satisfactory resonant circuit of high Q and one which possesses none of these qualities.

Disc-Type Capacities

Parallel lines or concentric tuned circuits are conveniently tuned by means of a variable air capacitor comprising two parallel discs, but the calculation of the capacitance range of different size discs with differing spacing can be tiresome.

The chart in **Fig. 7** plots the capacitance between two parallel discs of various convenient diameters with spacings between $\frac{1}{4}$ in. and 1/128 in. calculated according to the formula

$$C_{pF} = \frac{0 \cdot 244 \text{ x area } (inches)}{spacing \ (inches)}$$

The diameter of the disc employed may be fixed by space considerations but it determines the minimum and maximum capacitance and the range available. Very close spacings should be avoided unless extremely accurate parallelism can be maintained, and must be avoided where high voltages exist, as in transmitters.

For example, a cathode concentric tuned circuit tuned by a disc capacitor is required for a 2C39A valve to be used as a tripler from 432 to 1300 Mc/s. This valve has an input capacitance of $6 \cdot 5 \pm 1$ pF. If the cavity has an outer diameter of $2\frac{3}{8}$ in. and an inner conductor of $\frac{3}{8}$ in. the ratio is 7 : 1 and at 430 Mc/s the curves in **Fig. 7** show that if C is taken as 7·5 pF plus a minimum disc capacitance of, say 0·5 pF, i.e. 8 pF, the inner conductor length is 4·2cm or 1·65 in. If a $\frac{1}{2}$ in. disc capacitor is chosen then the range of tuning is from 0·2 pF at $\frac{1}{4}$ in. spacing to 1·5 pF at $\frac{1}{32}$ in. spacing. As the drive voltage is of the order of 100 volts closer spacing must not be used. It is clear that a $\frac{1}{2}$ in. disc will not do as the spread between top and bottom limit values is 2 pF so that $\frac{3}{4}$ in. discs will have to be used giving a range of 0·4 to 3·0 pF which is sufficient for fixed frequency working, but if it is necessary to cover a frequency band then a greater range is required. If at times the drive frequency were 420 Mc/s then this would require a maximum capacitance across the tuned circuit of the original 8 pF multiplied by the square of the frequency ratio, i.e. $\frac{(430)^2}{(420)^2}$ or 1·05. This means a maximum disc capacitance of 2·4 pF and the $\frac{3}{4}$ in. diameter will still just do but $\frac{5}{8}$ in. would not.

If it is found that the range of the capacitance is larger

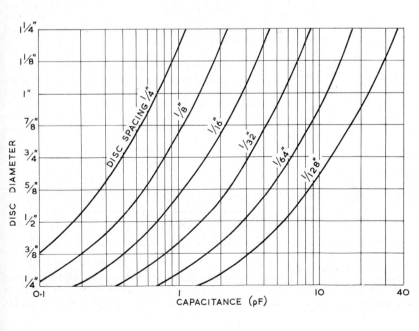

Fig. 7. Capacitance between two parallel discs of various diameters.

than the maximum size disc that can be accommodated, then the solution is to use two sets of discs located, for example, each side of a cavity and use one as tuning and one as a kind of band-set. Valve capacitance limits must be taken into account otherwise the replacement of a valve can result in the circuit no longer tuning. Where the tolerances in input and output capacitance are not known they can be taken as ± 30 per cent which would adequately cover most cases.

Neutralization

With triode valves and tetrodes operating below their self-resonant frequency the normal methods of neutralization apply: the application of an antiphase feedback voltage from anode to grid of the valve. The residual anode-to-grid capacitance of modern v.h.f. tetrodes is quite low, in some instances being less than 0·1 pF. Provided that adequate screening exists between grid and anode circuits, operation of certain types of valve in the lower part of the v.h.f. spectrum (up to 70 Mc/s) is permissible without neutralization being required. At higher frequencies although the reactance of this capacitance is still not sufficiently low to cause oscillation, it will result in the stage being regenerative and neutralization will be necessary.

A convenient method of providing the small capacitance required for neutralizing push-pull double tetrode stages consists in using each valve anode as one plate of the capacitor, and a wire connected to the grid of the opposite valve as the other plate (Fig. 8 (a)). The capacitance (C_n) is adjusted by bending each wire nearer or farther away from the respective anode. In single ended circuits the capacitance is formed by a wire connected at one end to the grid and positioned so that the other end is adjacent to the appropriate side of the anode tank circuit (Fig. 8 (b)). Heavy gauge enamelled copper wire (12 to 16 s.w.g.) should be used, and a metal tab may be attached at the end of the wire to increase the capacitance should that provided by the wire alone be insufficient.

When the valve is operated above the self-neutralizing frequency the neutralizing capacitor must be connected directly between anode and grid of the valve (Fig. 8 (c)). Alternatively a variable capacitor may be connected between screen grid and earth and tuned with the screen lead inductance to form a series resonant circuit at the frequency of operation, thus providing a low screen-to-earth impedance and effectively placing the screen grid at earth potential with respect to r.f. (Fig. 8 (d)). It must be remembered that this method of neutralization is frequency-sensitive, and any considerable change in the operating frequency will necessitate re-adjustment of the variable capacitor.

MODULATION

For telephony service a v.h.f. transmitter may be modulated by any one of the normal methods, though high level modulation of the final amplifier is the system usually adopted. For satisfactory modulation it is essential that there is adequate grid drive to the modulated amplifier and that the stage is correctly neutralized.

Experience has shown that it is desirable to maintain a high average level of modulation in a v.h.f. transmitter and the use of speech clipping or compression is therefore recommended (see Chapter 9—*Modulation*).

Instability in the modulator may be experienced due to r.f. feeding back into early stages of the speech amplifier. To

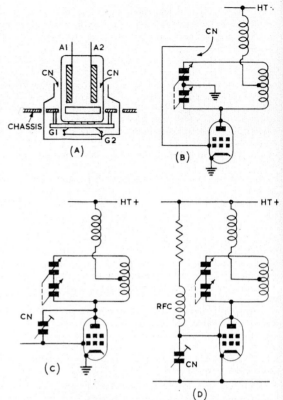

Fig. 8. Neutralizing circuits. (a) Neutralization of push-pull double tetrode stage. (b) Similar method for single ended stage. (c) Neutralization of a valve operating above the self neutralizing frequency. (d) Screen neutralization of single ended stage.

eliminate this the microphone input circuit should be completely shielded and the effect of inserting grid stopper resistors, particularly in low level speech amplifying stages, and the inclusion of an r.f. filter in the grid circuit of the first valve should be investigated.

FOUR METRE TRANSMITTERS

For the newcomer to the v.h.f. bands 4m offers many interesting possibilities. It is the lowest v.h.f. band allocated to British amateurs and the frequency (70·3 Mc/s) is sufficiently close to that of the high frequency 28 Mc/s band to warrant no great change in transmitter design and

TABLE 2
Crystal frequencies and multiplication factor for 4m transmitters

Crystal frequency range (kc/s)	Multiplication factor
5,850·0 to 5,866·6	12
7,800·0 to 7,822·2	9
8,775·0 to 8,800·0	8
11,700·0 to 11,733·3	6

construction techniques; in some respects they are simpler because crystal controlled oscillators are usually employed on 4m, whereas h.f. transmitters invariably require a v.f.o.

It is thus possible for a high efficiency 4m transmitter to be built without having to use the more expensive valves and components necessary to achieve optimum results on the other v.h.f. bands. Provided that short, low impedance connections are made in r.f. circuits, and this is probably the most important factor in v.h.f. transmitter construction, a successful 4m transmitter is assured.

From an operating point of view the band has distinct attractions. For local communication the results are similar to those obtained on the 2m band and excellent results can be obtained with transmitters having a power input of 10 to 15 watts. For ranges in excess of say, 100 miles, under poor or average conditions it appears that the transmission path on 4m is better than that obtained on 2m. In addition, the 4m band has the distinct advantage that DX working, up to distances exceeding 1000 miles, is possible under certain conditions by virtue of tropospheric refraction.

A range of suitable crystal frequencies and the multiplying factors necessary to give a final frequency between 70·2 and 70·4 Mc/s is listed in **Table 2**.

A 50 WATT PHONE AND C.W. TRANSMITTER

The three stage transmitter shown in **Figs. 9 to 12** consists of a crystal oscillator multiplier followed by a second frequency multiplier and power amplifier. The final stage, which may be run at the maximum permissible input of 50 watts on both phone and c.w., employs a Mullard QV06–20 v.h.f. power tetrode which is suitable for operation at frequencies up to 175 Mc/s and makes an economical and efficient power amplifier for a 4m transmitter. At the frequency under consideration an efficiency of approximately 75 per cent may be obtained.

Provision is made for keying the transmitter in the h.t. lead to the screen of the multiplier valve. Protection of the p.a. stage during " key up " periods is achieved by a clamp valve which reduces the screen voltage and thus limits the anode current of this stage. Anode and screen modulation of the final amplifier may be effected by an external modulator with an audio output power of 25 to 30 watts, which can be obtained, for example, from two 6L6 valves operating in class AB1. H.t. and heater supplies of 400 volts at 175 mA. and 6·3 volts at 2·65 amps respectively are required to operate the transmitter.

Fig. 9. A 50 watt phone and c.w. transmitter for 70 Mc/s.

Circuit

The circuit diagram is shown in **Fig. 10**. An EL91 a.f. pentode (V_1) functions as a crystal controlled oscillator-multiplier in a modified Pierce circuit; the crystal frequency is in the 7·8 Mc/s range, and the multiplier anode circuit is tuned to the third harmonic, i.e. approximately 23·4 Mc/s. R.f. output from V_1 is capacitively coupled to the grid of V_2, which is a QV03–12 tetrode also operating as a frequency tripler, the anode circuit L_2, C_9 being tuned to the final radiated frequency between 70·2 and 70·4 Mc/s, dependent on the actual frequency of the crystal used. Grid bias for V_2 is obtained by flow of grid current through R_4; a low value resistor R_5 is connected in series with the grid resistor, and enables the oscillator-multiplier anode circuit to be tuned by monitoring the grid current on a meter connected between test point 1 and earth. A closed circuit jack J_1 is connected in series with the screen supply to V_2 and enables this stage to be keyed for c.w. working.

The anode circuit of V_2 is link coupled via L_3 and L_4 to the grid circuit L_5, C_{12} of the tetrode valve V_3. This stage functions as a straight amplifier; r.f. output from the anode circuit L_6, parallel-tuned by a split-stator capacitor C_{18}, is inductively coupled through a low impedance loop L_7 to the coaxial output socket CS_1; C_{20} is connected in series with the output circuit, and in operation its capacitance is so adjusted that the reactance cancels out the inductive reactance of L_7.

The split-stator tuning capacitor is desirable in the anode circuit of V_3 so that an r.f. voltage in antiphase to that at the anode is available to be applied to the grid through C_{14} to effect neutralization of the p.a. stage. The grid anode capacitance of V_3 is so low that the stage is stable and may be operated without neutralization at 70 Mc/s but the inclusion of a neutralizing capacitance is recommended so that optimum working conditions may be obtained. The capacitance required in practice is very small and C_{14} is formed by a wire connected at one end to the grid of V_3, the other end being adjacent to the stator plates of C_{18} remote from the anode of V_3.

Grid leak bias only is also applied to the p.a. valve and is obtained by the grid current through R_8 and the monitor resistor R_9 in series; a milliammeter may be connected between test point 2 and chassis to give an indication of resonance of the anode circuit of V_2. An EL90 a.f. pentode (V_4) is connected between the screen grid of V_3 and earth; the grid of V_4 is decoupled by C_{15} and is connected to the grid return circuit of V_3, so that when V_3 is being driven the negative bias voltage developed across R_8 and R_9 in series is applied to the grid of V_4. This voltage, which is approximately 90, biases V_4 well beyond cut-off and the valve has no effect on the operation of the circuit.

When the drive to V_3 is removed, the negative bias applied to the grids of both V_3 and V_4 is removed also; the clamp valve conducts heavily, resulting in an increased voltage drop across R_{10} and a consequent reduction in the screen voltage to a very low value. This reduces the anode current of V_3 sufficiently to prevent the maximum permissible dissipation (20 watts) of the valve being exceeded. With 400 volts h.t. applied this is represented by an anode current of 50 mA; in practice the anode current falls to less than 25 mA when the drive is removed.

Anode and screen modulation of the 400 volts h.t. supply to the p.a. is effected by connecting the output of the modulator to SK_1. The anode current taken by V_3 is continuously monitored by M_1.

An h.t. supply line of 300 volts is required for the crystal oscillator and frequency multiplier stages. This may be obtained from a separate power unit capable of delivering approximately 50 mA at 300 volts, or alternatively from the main 400 volts line through a 2K ohm 5 watt series resistor. The heaters of V_1, V_2 and V_3 are decoupled by C_{21}, C_{22} and C_{23} respectively, connected directly between the heater tag on each valveholder and chassis.

Constructional Details

The 4m transmitter is assembled on a chassis measuring $10\frac{3}{4}$ in. long $\times$ 6 in. wide $\times$ $2\frac{1}{2}$ in. deep fabricated from 18 s.w.g. aluminium. The layout may be seen in **Figs. 9** and **11.**

The crystal and the oscillator-multiplier valve V_1 are located at the lefthand side towards the rear, with the anode tuning capacitor C_4 immediately in front of the valve. Nylon-loaded p.f. (phenolformaldehyde) valveholders are used for this stage and for the frequency multiplier V_2. It is essential that a screening can is not fitted to V_2 because this would restrict the dissipation of heat from the valve. As the multiplier is unscreened it is necessary to fit a shield on top of the chassis between this stage and the power amplifier; the shield which is located at the middle and runs from front to rear of the chassis, measures $5\frac{3}{4}$ in. long $\times$ $3\frac{1}{2}$ in. high and is made from 20 s.w.g. aluminium.

The feedthrough bypass capacitors C_7 and C_{13} enable the grid currents of V_2 and V_3 to be monitored conveniently from the top side of the chassis. All inductors are self-supporting and are soldered directly across the associated tuning capacitor. If desired the multiplier anode inductor L_2 can be made more rigid by cementing two or three thin strips of polystyrene or Perspex along the axis of the inductor on the inside.

The two coupling loops L_3 and L_4 are supported by a small insulator measuring $1\frac{1}{2}$ in. $\times$ $\frac{1}{2}$ in. made from $\frac{1}{8}$ in. polystyrene, which carries two $\frac{1}{2}$ in. lengths of 18 s.w.g. tinned copper wire pushed through two holes spaced $\frac{3}{16}$ in. apart near to one end of the block. Each single turn loop is insulated with polythene sleeving and soldered to opposite ends of the pair of wires; the loops are pushed between the turns of L_2 and L_4 adjacent to the earthy end of each inductor.

A ceramic valveholder is employed for the final stage and is secured to the *underside* of the chassis by its mounting plate. The base of the QV06–20 valve carries three cathode pins, and each of the relevant tags on the valveholder, together with the base shield and heater return connections are wired directly to the chassis with the shortest possible leads; a separate connection is made between each of the tags and chassis **(Fig. 12 (a))**. A heavy gauge conductor should be used for these connections; in the transmitter illustrated 18 s.w.g. tinned copper wire is employed. A woodflour-loaded p.f. valveholder is used for V_4 as no r.f.

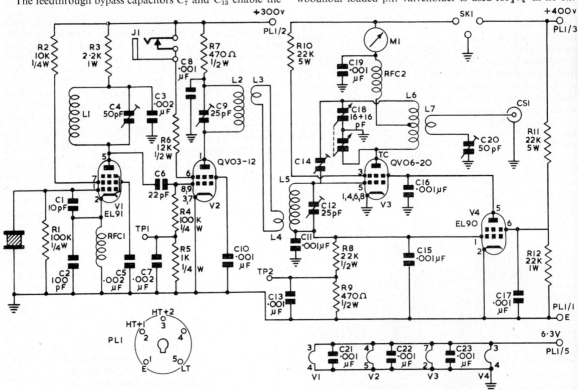

Fig. 10. Circuit diagram of the 70 Mc/s transmitter shown in Fig. 9. $C_{7, 8, 10, 11, 13}$, ceramic feedthroughs; C_{14}, see text; $C_{15, 16, 17, 21, 22, 23}$, 0·001 μF ceramic; C_{19}, 0·001 μF 1250V d.c. wkg.; L_1, 9 turns 20 s.w.g. enam. $\frac{3}{4}$ in. o.d. $\frac{7}{8}$ in. long; L_2, L_5, 3 turns 16 s.w.g. enam. $\frac{3}{4}$ in. o.d. $\frac{1}{2}$ in. long; L_3, L_4, 1 turn 18 s.w.g. tinned copper $\frac{3}{4}$ in. o.d. insulated with polythene sleeving; L_6, 6 turns 16 s.w.g. enam. 1 in. o.d. 1 in. long $\frac{3}{8}$ in. gap at centre for L_7; L_7, 2 turns 18 s.w.g. tinned copper 1 in. o.d. insulated with polythene sleeving; M_1, 0–150 mA d.c. meter; RFC_1, 2·5 mH (Eddystone No. 737); RFC_2, 50 turns 28 s.w.g. enam. $\frac{1}{4}$ in. diam. $1\frac{1}{4}$ in. long wound on Eddystone former type 685; V_1, EL91 or 6AM5; V_2, QV03-12 or 5763; V_3, QV06-20 or 6146; V_4, EL90 or 6AQ5.

ig. II. A view under the chassis of the 70 Mc/s transmitter.

losses can be incurred in the circuit associated with this valve.

The anode tuning capacitor C_{18} for the final amplifier is mounted vertically above the chassis with the rotor spindle projecting through to the underside. This enables a relatively short connection, made of thin copper strip $\frac{1}{8}$ in. wide, to be obtained between the valve anode and the p.a. tank circuit. An additional nut is screwed on to the threaded rotor bush before the capacitor is mounted so that the ceramic end plate is raised $\frac{3}{16}$ in. above the chassis; this is necessary to avoid the possibility of a short circuit between the stator screws of the capacitor and chassis.

The neutralizing capacitor C_{14} is formed by two 18 s.w.g. wires, one connected to the grid tag of the p.a. valveholder, and projecting through a hole in the chassis immediately in front of the valveholder; this hole is lined with a polystyrene bush to prevent a short circuit and minimize r.f. loss. The oppposite plate of the capacitor is a similar wire connected to a 6 B.A. soldering tag inserted under the stator column of the tuning capacitor in place of one of the existing two washers.

The tuning control for the p.a. tank capacitor is mounted on the front of the chassis and a right-angle drive is obtained through two 1 in. brass bevel gears. The shaft is of $\frac{1}{4}$ in. diameter mild steel and measures $3\frac{1}{4}$ in. long; the rear bush is carried by an 18 s.w.g. aluminium bracket located approximately $2\frac{1}{2}$ in. from the front of the chassis. The two bevel gears should be tightly meshed to avoid any backlash between the control knob and rotor of the capacitor.

The output coupling loop L_7 is supported by a block of $\frac{1}{4}$ in. polystyrene mounted on an aluminium bracket. The turns of the loop are insulated with polythene sleeving, the ends being inserted through holes in the block and cemented in position. A short length of 75 ohm coaxial cable is used to connect the loop to the r.f. output socket and the capacitor C_{20}.

Alignment

During initial alignment h.t. voltage should be applied to each stage successively as the preceding one is tuned. V_2 and V_3 may conveniently be made inoperative by inserting a plug in J_1 and leaving SK_1 open circuited. The lining-up procedure is then as follows:

(i) Connect a low range (0–5) milliammeter between TP_1 and chassis. Adjust C_4 for maximum meter reading.

(ii) Connect the milliammeter between TP_2 and chassis. Apply h.t. to the screen of V_2 and adjust C_9 for maximum meter reading. Adjust the position of L_3 and L_4 to obtain optimum grid current in V_3.

(iii) Connect a dummy load, e.g. a 230 volts 40 watt lamp, to CS_1, apply h.t. to V_3 and tune C_{18} to resonance, observed as a sharp dip in the anode current reading of M_1. Adjust the neutralizing capacitance C_{14} by bending the two wires towards or away from each other until maximum r.f. output corresponds to minimum anode current. Care should be taken when moving the wire connected to h.t. Adjust the coupling between L_6 and L_7 and the value of C_{20} until an anode current of 125 mA, corresponding to an input of 50 watts, is obtained.

(A very convenient method of " hot " neutralization of an r.f. amplifier, i.e. neutralization with h.t applied to the stage, consists in observing the change in grid current as the anode tuning capacitor is detuned each side of resonance. When the stage is correctly neutralized the condition of minimum anode current at resonance corresponds to maximum grid current. If the grid current falls as the anode circuit is detuned the stage is perfectly balanced; if the grid current rises at either side of the resonant point, the neutralizing capacitor should be adjusted until the correct condition is achieved. It will be found that very accurate neutralization of the p.a. stage in this transmitter can be obtained.)

(iv) Check the operation of the clamp valve by removing h.t.

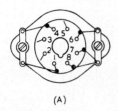

(A)

V 3 valveholder - earth connections
viewed from underside of chassis.

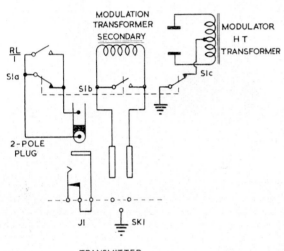

(B)

Phone/CW changeover switching.

Fig. 12. (a) P.a. valveholder earthing. (b) Phone/c.w. switching.

from V_1 and V_2 or inserting a plug into J_1. The anode
current of V_3 should fall to approximately 25 mA.

Operation

When operating on c.w. the transmitter can be run at the
maximum permitted input of 50 watts to the final stage
(125 mA at 400 volts). The screen circuit of V_2 should be
keyed through a relay operated from a low voltage supply to
prevent h.t. voltage appearing directly on the key contacts.
For telephony operation the output of a 25 watt modulator
matched into 3,225 ohms is connected to SK_1, and the
keying plug either removed from J_1 or short circuited by a
switch. The anode current of V_3 should be reduced to a
value not greater than 112 mA at 400 volts (48 watts) by

TABLE 3
Typical current readings for the 4m transmitter

Valve	Grid current	Screen current	Anode current
V1	—	2·5 mA	15 mA
V2	1 mA	6 mA	26 mA
V3	4 mA	12 mA	112 mA

222

adjusting the position of L_7. If this is not done the rating of
the QV06–20 at this frequency will be exceeded.
A simple switching system for changing over from c.w.
to telephony operation is shown in Fig. 12 (b). Contacts of
the switch S_1 are shown in the telephony position.

TWO METRE TRANSMITTERS

A range of crystal frequencies suitable for use in 2m
transmitters, and the required multiplication factors are
given in Table 4.

TABLE 4
Crystal frequencies and multiplication factors to give
frequencies between 144 and 146 Mc/s

Crystal frequency (Mc/s)	Multiplication factor
6·0 to 6·083	$\begin{cases} \times 3 \ \times 2 \ \times 2 \ \times 2 \\ \times 4 \ \times 3 \ \times 2 \end{cases}$
8·0 to 8·111	$\times 3 \ \times 3 \ \times 2$
9·0 to 9·222	$\begin{cases} \times 2 \ \times 2 \ \times 2 \ \times 2 \\ \times 4 \ \times 2 \ \times 2 \end{cases}$
12·0 to 12·166	$\times 3 \ \times 2 \ \times 2$

A SIMPLE PHONE AND C.W. TRANSMITTER

The three valve, four stage transmitter shown in Figs. 13
and 14 employs a QV06–20 tetrode valve as a single ended
amplifier, which can be run at an input of up to 35 watts in
telephony, and up to 45 watts in c.w. service. In these conditions the power requirements are an h.t. supply of 320 volts
at 200 mA, and a heater supply of 6·3 volts at 2·3 amps.
Approximately 20 watts of audio power are required for full
anode and screen modulation, the impedance presented by
the p.a. stage to the modulator being 2,700 ohms.

Circuit Description

In the circuit diagram shown in Fig. 15, V_{1a}, one half of an
ECC81 double triode valve functions as a crystal oscillator
and uses an 8 Mc/s type FT243 crystal in a Squier overtone
circuit. The slug tuned inductor L_1 is resonated at the third
overtone of the crystal frequency. Capacitive coupling is

Fig. 13. A simple phone and c.w. transmitter for 144 Mc/s employing
a QV06–20/6146 valve in the p.a.

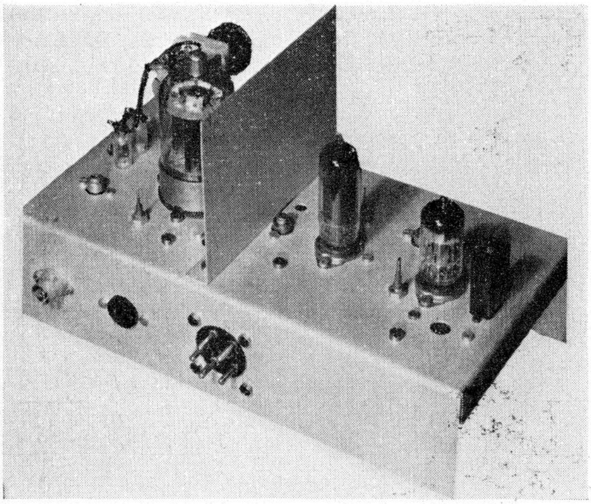

Fig. 14. A rear view of the simple 144 Mc/s transmitter.

employed between the anode of V_{1a} and the grid of the second section of the double triode, V_{1b}, which operates as a frequency tripler. The anode circuit L_2, C_6 is tuned to approximately 72·5 Mc/s, the exact frequency being dependent on the frequency of the crystal being used.

The output of V_{1b} is also capacitively coupled to the input of V_2, a QV03–12 tetrode operating as a frequency doubler. The anode circuit of this valve, which comprises L_3 and C_{11}, is tuned to approximately 145 Mc/s, and is inductively coupled to the series-tuned grid circuit of the QV06–20 tetrode power amplifier V_3. Grid resistors R_{11} and R_{12} of V_3 are connected between the centre-tap of L_4 and earth.

The anode circuit of V_3 is also series-tuned and is formed by L_5 and C_{16}. H.t. is fed to the anode via the meter M_1, choke RFC_2 and the centre-tap of L_5. R.f. output is fed to the coaxial socket CS_1 by the single turn link L_6, which is coupled to the centre of L_5, and the tuning capacitor C_{18}.

Screen neutralizing of the amplifier stage is effected by the pre-set capacitor C_{14} connected between the screen of V_3 and earth. C_{14} is adjusted so that its capacitance, in conjunction with the screen lead inductance and stray capacitance, form a series-tuned resonant circuit from screen to earth. This places the screen of the valve at earth potential with respect to r.f. and effectively eliminates any feed-back between anode and grid circuits through the valve.

Modulation is applied to the anode and screen of the p.a. via SK_1. Use of a three pole socket for this purpose allows a screened connecting cable to be earthed to the chassis of the transmitter if desired.

Power supplies are connected to the transmitter through the five pole plug PL_1, only three pins of which are normally used. The resistor R_{10} reduces the voltage on the h.t. line feeding V_1 and V_2 from 320 to 300 volts.

Resonance of the oscillator and multiplier anode circuits and the grid circuit of the amplifier stage is indicated by maximum grid current in the following stage; the grid

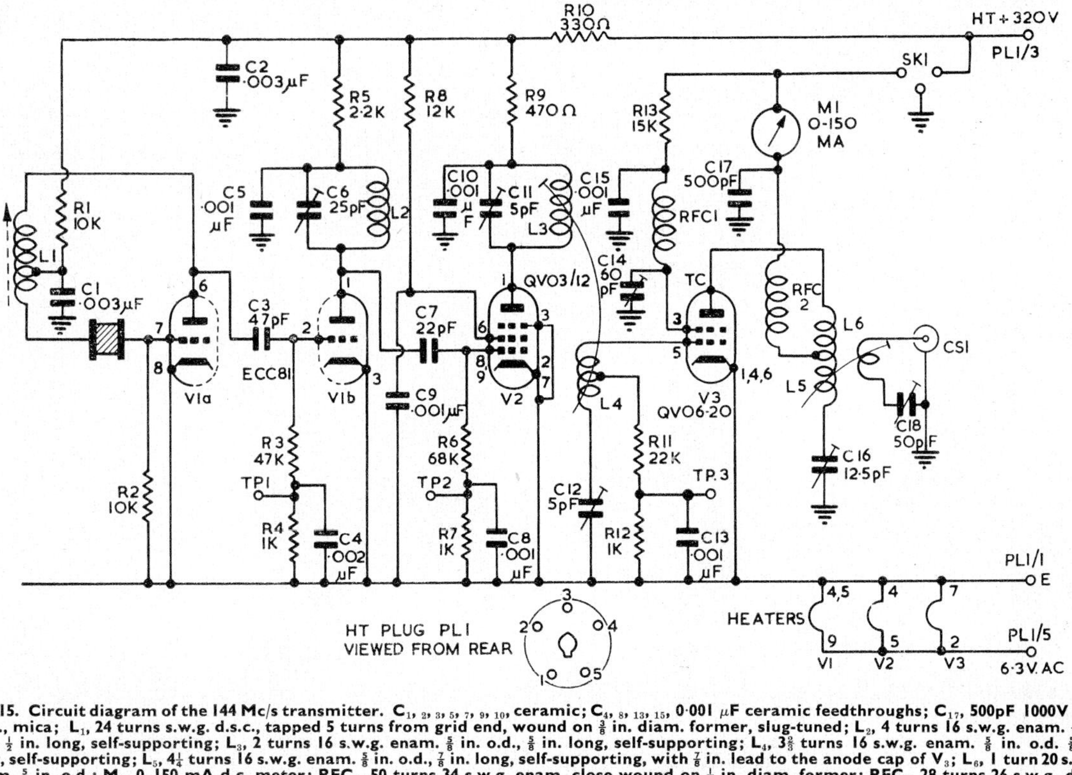

Fig. 15. Circuit diagram of the 144 Mc/s transmitter. $C_{1, 2, 3, 5, 7, 9, 10}$, ceramic; $C_{4, 8, 13, 15}$, 0·001 µF ceramic feedthroughs; C_{17}, 500pF 1000V d.c. wkg., mica; L_1, 24 turns s.w.g. d.s.c., tapped 5 turns from grid end, wound on $\frac{3}{8}$ in. diam. former, slug-tuned; L_2, 4 turns 16 s.w.g. enam. $\frac{5}{8}$ in. o.d., $\frac{1}{2}$ in. long, self-supporting; L_3, 2 turns 16 s.w.g. enam. $\frac{5}{8}$ in. o.d., $\frac{5}{8}$ in. long, self-supporting; L_4, $3\frac{2}{3}$ turns 16 s.w.g. enam. $\frac{5}{8}$ in. o.d. $\frac{5}{8}$ in. long, self-supporting; L_5, $4\frac{1}{4}$ turns 16 s.w.g. enam. $\frac{5}{8}$ in. o.d., $\frac{7}{8}$ in. long, self-supporting, with $\frac{7}{8}$ in. lead to the anode cap of V_3; L_6, 1 turn 20 s.w.g. enam. $\frac{5}{8}$ in. o.d.; M_1, 0–150 mA d.c. meter; RFC_1, 50 turns 34 s.w.g. enam. close wound on $\frac{1}{2}$ in. diam. former; RFC_2, 28 turns 26 s.w.g. d.s.c. $\frac{1}{4}$ in. diam. $1\frac{1}{4}$ in. long wound on Eddystone former type 863; V_1, ECC81 or 12AT7; V_2, QV03-12 or 5763; V_3, QV06-20 or 6146.

Fig. 16. Under-chassis view of the transmitter of Fig. 15.

current is read by connecting a milliammeter between the relevant test point (TP$_1$, TP$_2$ or TP$_3$) and chassis. Resonance of the p.a. anode circuit is indicated by minimum anode current shown on the meter M$_1$.

Constructional Details

The transmitter is built on an 18 s.w.g. aluminium chassis measuring 10 in. long $\times$ 5 in. wide $\times$ 2$\frac{1}{2}$ in. deep with a $\frac{5}{8}$ in. lip turned down at each end to increase its rigidity. The position of components can be located from the under-chassis view **(Fig. 16)** and the drilling plan **(Fig. 17)**.

Shielding between the p.a. valve anode circuit and the doubler valve V$_2$ is effected by a vertical screen across the chassis at a distance of 4$\frac{3}{4}$ in. from the righthand end. The screen is of 20 s.w.g. aluminium and measures 5 in. wide $\times$ 3$\frac{1}{2}$ in. high with the addition of a $\frac{5}{8}$ in. wide lip by which it is secured to the chassis by three 4 B.A. screws and nuts. The p.a. anode tuning capacitor C$_{16}$ is mounted on an 18 s.w.g. aluminium bracket at a height of 1$\frac{1}{4}$ in. above the chassis.

All bypass capacitors, with the exception of C$_{17}$ are of the hi-K ceramic type; C$_{17}$ is a 1,000 volt working, silvered mica type. These capacitors are connected into the circuit with the shortest possible leads. The grid circuit capacitors are of the feedthrough type; one lead of each capacitor projects through the chassis to form the test points TP$_1$, TP$_2$ and TP$_3$.

The aerial coupling loop L$_6$ consists of a single turn of 18 s.w.g. enamelled copper wire, insulated with polystyrene sleeving and inserted at the centre of L$_5$. This loop is supported by two $\frac{3}{4}$ in. polystyrene stand-off insulators and is connected to the coaxial output socket via a short length of 75 ohm twin feeder, which is lead through a grommeted hole in the chassis. The output coupling capacitor is connected between one leg of the twin feeder and chassis.

Nylon-loaded valveholders are employed for V$_1$ and V$_2$. The holder for V$_3$ is a ceramic type, and is mounted on the underside of the chassis; the tags on the valveholder that connect to the three cathode pins and brass sleeve of V$_3$ and the heater return (pins 1, 4, 6, 7 and 8) are bent over and earthed by individual connections to soldering tags located

under the two fixing nuts of the valveholder. These connections should be as short as possible and made with a heavy gauge conductor, not less than 18 s.w.g. tinned copper wire.

Setting up

Before power is applied to the transmitter it is recommended that the resonant frequencies of the tuned circuits are checked with a grid dip oscillator. L$_1$ should be tuned to approximately 24 Mc/s; L$_2$, C$_6$ should be tuned to 72·5 Mc/s; L$_3$, C$_{11}$, L$_4$, C$_{12}$ and L$_5$, C$_{16}$ should be tuned to 145 Mc/s. As no protective grid bias is applied to any stage of the transmitter, it is recommended that initial adjustments are carried out with a low h.t. voltage, not greater than 200 volts, applied to V$_1$ and V$_2$. For the same reason h.t. should not be connected to the anode and screen of V$_3$ until the oscillator and multiplier stages have been adjusted and bias is being developed across the p.a. grid resistor. The most convenient method of removing h.t. from the p.a. stage is to leave the modulator socket SK$_1$ open-circuited.

The procedure to be adopted in tuning the transmitter is as follows:

(i) Connect a 0–5 mA meter between TP$_1$ and chassis (positive to chassis). Adjust the dust-iron core of L$_1$ to obtain maximum current reading, then de-tune the circuit

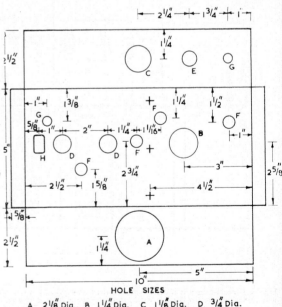

HOLE SIZES

A 2$\frac{1}{8}$" Dia.   B 1$\frac{1}{4}$" Dia.   C 1$\frac{1}{8}$" Dia.   D $\frac{3}{4}$" Dia.

E $\frac{5}{8}$" Dia.   F $\frac{1}{2}$" Dia.   G $\frac{3}{8}$" Dia.   H $\frac{3}{4}$" $\times$ $\frac{7}{16}$"

Fig. 17. Drilling plan (above-chassis view).

TABLE 5
Typical current readings for the 35 watt transmitter of Fig. 14

Valve	Anode current	Screen current	Grid current
V_{1a}	8·5 mA	—	—
V_{1b}	11 mA	—	1·2 mA
V_2	32 mA	4 mA	0·6 mA
V_3	30 mA (unloaded)		
	110 mA (loaded) (telephony)		
	140 mA (loaded) (c.w.)	8 mA	2·25 mA

slightly to the high-frequency side of this position; this will result in a small drop in grid current.

(ii) Connect the meter to TP_2 and chassis and tune C_6 for maximum grid current in V_2. (A better indication is obtained if a 0–1 milliammeter is used in this position.)

(iii) Connect the meter between TP_3 and chassis; tune C_{11} and C_{12} in that order for maximum grid current in V_3. Re-adjust C_{11}.

(iv) Check the neutralization of V_3 by tuning C_{16} through resonance. Adjust C_{14} until the minimum change in grid current results as the p.a. anode circuit is swung through resonance.

(v) Short-circuit the modulator socket. Connect a dummy load to the aerial socket. (A 15 watt lamp may be used as a load or alternatively a Morganite Type 7101 80 ohm resistor.) With the low voltage still applied to the transmitter, tune C_{16} to resonance.

(vi) Apply 320 volts to the transmitter and load the p.a. by increasing the coupling between L_5 and L_6 and adjusting C_{18} until an anode current at resonance of 110 mA is obtained. Check that the neutralizing is correct, i.e., that maximum r.f. output corresponds to minimum anode current; re-adjust C_{14} if necessary.

The loosest coupling between L_5 and L_6 consistent with obtaining the required power input should be the aim. It may be necessary to adjust the inductance of L_3, L_4 and L_5 to enable these circuits to be peaked at the actual frequency being used. The coupling between L_3 and L_4 should be adjusted to give maximum grid current in V_3 and it will be found that these circuits must be tightly coupled to obtain sufficient drive to the amplifier.

Typical values of anode and grid current readings are given in **Table 5**.

For c.w. operation of the transmitter it is recommended that the screen of the doubler valve V_2 is keyed, and a clamp valve incorporated in the p.a. circuit to reduce the screen voltage of V_3 in the spacing condition. The clamp circuit may be identical to that employed in the 4m transmitter shown in Fig. 10.

Unless the h.t. supply to the transmitter has good regulation, anode voltage for the oscillator and first multiplier should be derived from a separate source in order to avoid excessive variation in the anode voltage applied to these stages when the transmitter is keyed.

A 15 WATT PHONE TRANSMITTER

The three valve transmitter of **Fig. 18** employs a double tetrode valve in the output stage which can be operated at a maximum input of 15 watts; in this condition it delivers

approximately 6 watts r.f. into an aerial. The power supply requirements are an h.t. voltage of 200 to 250 volts at 120 mA and a heater supply of 6·3 volts at 1·33 amps.

The circuit of the transmitter is shown in **Fig. 19.** V_1 is an ECL80 triode pentode valve, the triode section (V_{1a}) of which functions as an overtone crystal oscillator, employing an 8 Mc/s fundamental frequency type FT243 crystal. The dust cored inductor L_1 is tuned to the third overtone of the crystal frequency, approximately 24 Mc/s. Capacitive coupling is employed between the anode of V_{1a} and the grid of the pentode section V_{1b}, which operates as a frequency doubler, the anode circuit L_2, C_3 being tuned to 48 Mc/s.

V_2 is an EL91 pentode operating as a frequency tripler. The anode circuit of this stage consists of L_3, parallel-tuned to approximately 145 Mc/s by C_9, which is connected between the anode of the valve and earth. Link-coupling is used to couple the tripler anode circuit to the grid circuit of the QQV03–10 push-pull power amplifier V_3; both link windings L_4 and L_5 are coupled to L_3 and L_6 respectively at points of low r.f. potential, that is, at the h.t. end of L_3 and the centre of L_6. The grid inductor L_6 is self-resonant at 145 Mc/s with the input capacitance of V_3 and stray circuit capacitances.

The p.a. tank circuit consists of L_7 parallel-tuned by the split-stator capacitor C_{14}. R.f. is fed to the coaxial output socket CS_1 via a low impedance winding L_8 coupled to the centre of L_7. Modulated h.t. is applied to the screen and anode of V_3 through R_9 and R_{10} respectively.

Grid bias for all stages is derived from the flow of grid current through the respective grid resistor when excitation is applied, that is, when V_1 is oscillating. Test points TP_1, TP_2 and TP_3 permit the grid current of V_{1b}, V_2 and V_3 to be monitored when the transmitter is being initially tuned.

The transmitter is built on an 18 s.w.g. aluminium chassis measuring $7\frac{1}{2}$ in. long $\times$ $4\frac{1}{2}$ in. wide $\times$ $2\frac{1}{2}$ in. deep. All components, with the exception of the three valves and the crystal are mounted below the chassis **(Fig. 20).** The dust-iron core of L_1 and the two tuning capacitors C_3 and C_9 are accessible for adjustment from the underside of the chassis. C_9 is spaced 1 in. from the chassis, being mounted

Fig. 18. A 15 watt 144 Mc/s transmitter for phone operation.

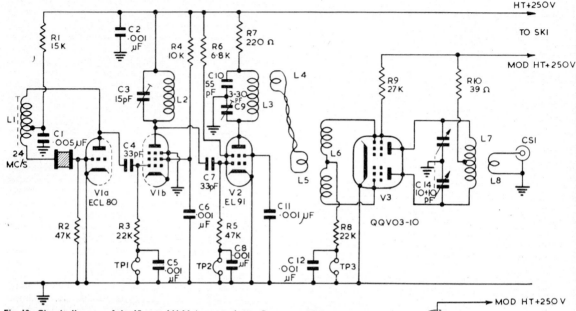

Fig. 19. Circuit diagram of the 15 watt 144 Mc/s transmitter. $C_{2, 6, 10, 11}$, hi-K ceramic; $C_{1, 7}$, ceramic; L_1, 22 turns 22 s.w.g. enam. tapped $7\frac{1}{2}$ turns from grid end wound on $\frac{3}{8}$ in. diam. former slug tuned; L_2, 6 turns 18 s.w.g. enam. $\frac{1}{2}$ in. diam. $\frac{1}{2}$ in. long; L_3, 4 turns 18 s.w.g. enam. $\frac{1}{2}$ in. diam. $\frac{1}{2}$ in. long; L_4, 2 turns 18 s.w.g. enam. $\frac{1}{2}$ in. diam. interwound with earthy end of L_3; L_5, 2 turns 18 s.w.g. enam. $\frac{1}{2}$ in. diam; L_6, 4 turns 18 s.w.g. enam. $\frac{1}{2}$ in. diam. $\frac{3}{8}$ in. long split at centre for L_5; L_7, 4 turns 18 s.w.g. enam. $\frac{3}{4}$ in. diam. $\frac{3}{8}$ in. long split at centre for L_8; L_8, 2 turns 20 s.w.g. enam. $\frac{3}{8}$ in. diam.; V_1, ECL80; V_2, EL91 or 6AM5; V_3, QQV03-10 or 6360. In this diagram, C_9 should be connected to the junction of C_{10}, L_3 and R_7. There is no C_{13}.

SKI VIEWED FROM REAR

on a 2 B.A. threaded stud to which the rotor connection of the capacitor is soldered.

The link inductors L_4 and L_5 are connected directly to the tags of a small ceramic standoff insulator. L_4 is interwound with the low-potential (h.t.) end of L_3; L_4 should be insulated with thin sleeving to prevent a short-circuit between the windings should this be considered necessary.

The grid resistors R_3, R_5 and R_8 are returned to chassis via single-point tag strips, which form the three test points. The bypass capacitors C_5, C_8 and C_{12} are connected between the relevant tag strip and earth; each capacitor is bridged by a low value resistor, one end of which is disconnected when it is desired to monitor the grid current during initial tune-up. A switch can then be arranged to switch a low reading milliammeter across each test point.

Underneath the chassis the p.a. grid and anode circuits are isolated by a screen mounted across the chassis. The screen is 2 in. deep, to provide clearance between the upper edge and the p.a. valveholder contacts. Fig. 21 shows how the screen is located across the diameter of the valveholder which is positioned so that pins 4 and 9 are in line with it.

In the transmitter illustrated the p.a. anode tuning capacitor C_{14} is mounted by two 6 B.A. screws which engage in threaded holes in one of the bars forming the capacitor frame. Each screw carries a $\frac{1}{4}$ in. diameter spacer located between the frame of the capacitor and the chassis. Alternatively C_{14} may be mounted on a small aluminium bracket for which three hole fixing is provided on the capacitor. A small epicyclic slow-motion drive is fitted to C_{14}.

Screening cans are fitted to V_1 and V_2; the can fitted to V_2 is essential as the capacitance between the earthed can

and the anode of V_2 forms part of the anode circuit tuning capacitance. Owing to the amount of heat generated by V_3 it is not permissible to use a screening can for this valve.

Alignment

Initial adjustments should preferably be carried out with a low h.t. voltage, not exceeding 200 volts, applied to V_1 and V_2 only. H.t. is most conveniently removed from the anode and screen of V_3 by leaving $SK_{1/3}$ disconnected.

The procedure to be adopted in tuning the transmitter is as follows:

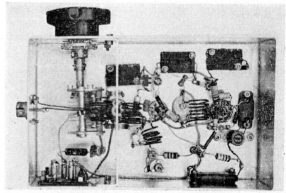

Fig. 20. Under-chassis view showing the layout of the components. Note the screen across the p.a. valveholder.

(i) Disconnect the jumper from TP_1 and connect a low-range milliammeter across the test point. Adjust the dust-iron core of L_1 for maximum grid current in V_{1b}, then detune slightly to the h.f. side of resonance. Remove the meter and reconnect the jumper.

(ii) Tune the anode circuits of V_{1b} and V_2 by adjusting C_3 and C_9 for maximum grid current in the meter when connected to TP_2 and TP_3 respectively. Adjust the coupling of the link windings L_4 and L_5, and the inductance of L_6 so that maximum grid current in V_3 is obtained.

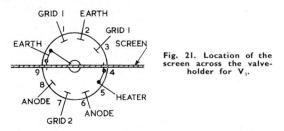

Fig. 21. Location of the screen across the valve-holder for V_3.

(iii) Connect a dummy load across CS_1, apply h.t. to the anode and screen of V_3 by connecting a 0–100 milliammeter between $SK_{1/3}$ and $SK_{1/4}$. Tune C_{14} to resonance as indicated by the dip in anode current. (A suitable dummy load consists of two 12 volt 0·3 amp. M.E.S. bulbs connected in parallel. These lamps should light to full brilliance when an h.t. voltage of 250 is applied to the transmitter.)

Typical current readings are shown in **Table 6.**

The transmitter is modulated by connecting the secondary winding of the modulation transformer between $SK_{1/3}$ and $SK_{1/4}$. With the aerial connected the coupling between L_7 and L_8 should be adjusted to give the required anode current to the p.a. stage, up to the maximum permissible limit of approximately 60 mA. In this condition, with 250 volts h.t. applied to V_3, the impedance presented by the p.a. to the modulator is 4,200 ohms; approximately 7 watts of audio are required for 100 per cent modulation.

TABLE 6

Typical current readings for the 15 watt 2m transmitter of Fig. 18

Valve	Anode current	Screen current	Grid current
V_{1a}	5 mA	—	—
V_{1b}	26 mA	5 mA	0·6 mA
V_2	22 mA	3 mA	1·25 mA
V_3 (unloaded)	30 mA		
V_3 (loaded)	60 mA	3 mA	2 mA

LOW POWER TRANSMITTER FOR PORTABLE OR MOBILE STATIONS

The small telephony transmitter shown in **Fig. 22** is primarily intended for portable or mobile operation but can also be used in a fixed station. A Mullard QQV02–6 miniature v.h.f. double tetrode is employed in the power amplifier stage, which may be run at a maximum input of 7·5 watts;

with this input an r.f. power output of approximately 5 watts can be obtained. A two-valve modulator is incorporated, which effects anode and screen modulation of the p.a. stage The circuit is shown in **Fig. 23.**

Power requirements are an h.t. voltage of 220 volts at approximately 115 mA, and a 12 volts d.c. supply which is used to heat the valves and operate a receive-to-transmit changeover relay. When used as a fixed station transmitter an a.c. heater supply of either 6 or 12 volts may be used by connecting the heaters in parallel or series-parallel respectively but a suitable d.c. voltage must be available to operate the aerial change-over relay.

In the transmitter illustrated a $4\frac{1}{2}$ volt battery is used to energise the carbon microphone, but an alternative method whereby the microphone current is derived from the h.t. supply may be substituted if desired.

Circuit Description

The circuitry of the crystal oscillator and first multiplier stages is similar to the corresponding stages in the 35 watt transmitter of Fig. 15. In this design a 6J6 double triode valve (V_1) is employed, using an FT243 type crystal having a frequency in the 8 Mc/s range; the anode circuit of the

Fig. 22. Low power 144 Mc/s transmitter for portable or mobile service.

Squier oscillator (V_{1a}) and the multiplier (V_{1b}) are tuned to frequencies of approximately 24 and 72 Mc/s respectively. The oscillator anode inductor L_1 is slug-tuned and the doubler anode inductor L_2 is parallel-tuned by the air trimmer C_4. Capacitance coupling is used between the anode circuit of V_{1a} and the grid circuit of V_{1b} and in all interstage coupling circuits throughout the transmitter. A second 6J6 (V_2) with the electrodes of each section connected in parallel to form a single triode, functions as a doubler from 72 to 144 Mc/s. H.t. supply to the anodes of V_2 is applied via a centre-tap on L_3, parallel-tuned by C_6.

The p.a. valve V_3 is a QQV02–6 double-tetrode; as in the earlier stages of the transmitter, the cathodes of this valve are earthed directly and grid leak bias only is applied. Grid circuit decoupling is effected by a feed-through capacitor

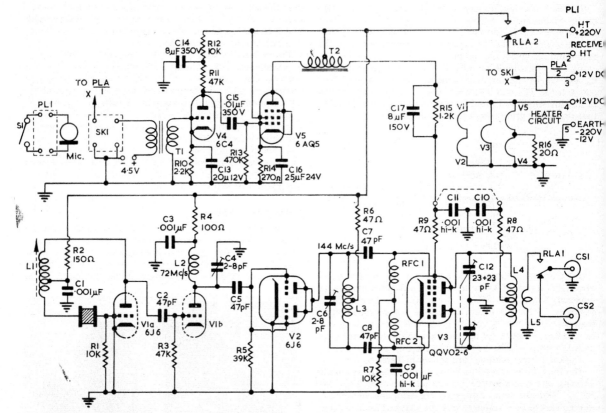

Fig. 23. Circuit diagram of the low power transmitter. $C_{1, 3}$, 0·001μF ceramic; $C_{9, 10, 11}$, 0·001μF hi-K ceramic feedthroughs; L_1, 20 turns 24 s.w.g. enam. tapped 5 turns from grid end, wound on ⅜ in. diam. former, slug-tuned; L_2, 6 turns 20 s.w.g. tinned copper ½ in. o.d. ½ in. long; L_3, 3 turns 18 s.w.g. tinned copper ½ in. o.d. ½ in. long; L_4, 3+3 turns 20 s.w.g. tinned copper ¾ in. long, ¼ in. gap at centre for L_5; L_5, 2 turns 22 s.w.g. tinned copper ¾ in. o.d., p.v.c. insulated; $RFC_{1, 2}$, 35 turns 30 s.w.g. enam. close wound on ⅛ in. diam. 470K ohm ½ watt resistor; T_1, microphone transformer ratio 1 : 60 (Wearite type 207 suitable); T_2, push-pull speaker output transformer, primary only used; $V_{1, 2}$, 6J6 or ECC91; V_3, QV02-6; V_4, 6C4, or EC90; V_5, 6AQ5 or EL90. The relay RL_1 is a miniature 12 volt type with double pole changeover contacts.

C_9; R_7 is located so that the earthy end is readily detached from the chassis to permit insertion of a meter in series with the resistor when initially tuning the transmitter. Anode and screen circuits are decoupled by R_8, C_{10} and R_9, C_{11} respectively; the screen resistor is not bypassed directly to earth. R.f. output from the anode circuit of the p.a. is taken from a link winding L_5 inductively coupled to the centre of L_4.

A simple two stage resistance coupled amplifier consisting of a 6C4 triode (V_4) and 6AQ5 pentode (V_5) is employed which provides 100 per cent modulation when used in conjunction with a single-button carbon microphone. Operation of the send-receive switch on the microphone S_1 energizes the coil of the changeover relay $RLA/_2$ from the 12 volt d.c. supply; RLA_1 disconnects the aerial socket (CS_1) from the receiver socket (CS_2) and connects CS_1 to the output of the transmitter; RLA_2 disconnects the h.t.+ supply line from the transmitter and modulator, and extends the supply to $PL_{1/2}$, where it is available to operate a receiver.

If desired the microphone current may be obtained from the h.t. supply, thus eliminating the need for a separate battery. A suitable arrangement which may be substituted for the microphone circuit in Fig. 23 is shown in **Fig. 26**.

Coupling between the modulator and p.a. valves is effected

Fig. 24. Under-chassis view of the low power phone transmitter. The microphone transformer is at the lower right and the p.a. tuning capacitor at the top left.

mounted; each plate of this capacitor consists of a brass disc $1\frac{3}{4}$ in. diameter attached to a threaded stud which engages in a tapped hole in a brass block soldered to the lines. A fine thread (e.g. 40 t.p.i.) should be cut on the studs to ensure smooth movement of the capacitor plates. A slot should be cut at the end of one stud to engage with a small metal blade fixed to the end of a $\frac{1}{4}$ in. diameter polystyrene rod which forms the tuning control; this rod may be spring-loaded to avoid any tendency of the blade to jump out of the slot as the control is rotated.

It will be found that resonance occurs when the two plates are approximately $\frac{1}{8}$ in. apart and they should be adjusted so that this distance is obtained when the front plate is at the mean position of its travel. The threaded studs should be a reasonably tight fit in the tapped holes to ensure that there is no electrical discontinuity between the capacitor and the lines. It is advisable for the rear plate to be locked in position after resonance has been determined.

Anode connectors must be used and can conveniently be made of $\frac{5}{16}$ in. brass rod $\frac{3}{4}$ in. long, similar to those employed for the 70cm transmitter (Fig. 43). Copper strip $\frac{1}{4}$ in. wide and $2\frac{1}{4}$ in. long is used to join the end of the lines to each anode connector. The anode circuit lines are supported at the end by a $\frac{1}{4}$ in. thick Paxolin plate to which the short-circuiting strip is screwed, and by two polystyrene blocks mounted on an aluminium bracket located $4\frac{1}{2}$ in. from the end of the lines.

Operation

To set up the unit apply heater voltage only and connect a load to CS_2. Excitation may then be applied to CS_1 and C_1 tuned to resonance. The output of the exciter and coupling between L_1 and L_2 should be adjusted to give a grid current of 4 mA. H.t. may then be applied to the amplifier and C_3 tuned; the dip in anode current at resonance should correspond to maximum r.f. output. Coupling

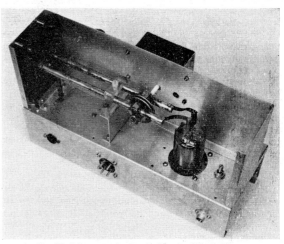

Fig. 28. Linear tank circuit for the 144 Mc/s p.a.

between L_3 and L_4, and the capacitance of C_5 should then be adjusted to load the stage to the required rating. Finally, the value of R_2 and R_4 should be adjusted to obtain maximum r.f. output for a given d.c. input to the stage, without exceeding the rated anode and screen dissipation of the valve. After the anode circuit has been tuned, h.t. voltage may be applied without grid drive, as the clamp valve effectively reduces the input to anode and screen of the valve to a very low value.

SEVENTY CENTIMETRE TRANSMITTERS

The portion of the 70cm band generally occupied by crystal controlled transmissions ranges from 432 to 436 Mc/s.

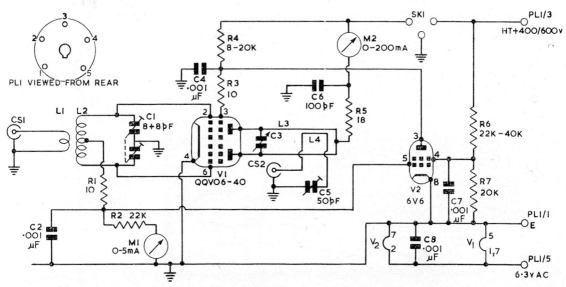

Fig. 29. Circuit diagram of the 144 Mc/s p.a. C_2, $_4$, $_7$, $_8$, 0.001μF mica; C_3, see text; C_6, 100 pF 2500V d.c. wkg., mica; L_1, 1 turn 20 s.w.g. enam. $\frac{3}{8}$ in. diam. insulated with polythene sleeving, at centre of L_2; L_2, 4 turns 16 s.w.g. enam. $\frac{3}{8}$ in. i.d. $1\frac{1}{4}$ in. long; L_3, parallel-line anode circuit consisting of two $\frac{3}{8}$ in. diam. copper tubes, 8 in. long, silver plated; L_4, output coupling loop, 16 s.w.g. enam. $2\frac{1}{4}$ in. long, 1 in. wide; $R_{1,3}$, 10 ohms wire wound; R_4, 8–20K ohms (see text); R_6, 22–40K ohms (see text); V_1, QQV06–40 or QQV06–40A; V_2, 6V6.

231

This has been chosen because it is in harmonic relationship with the 2m band, and thus an existing 2m transmitter may be used to drive a tripler stage to give output in the 70cm band without any duplication of existing equipment. In practice the majority of crystal controlled transmissions take place in the range 432 to 434 Mc/s.

Although some transmitters make use of a tripler stage only following the 2m transmitter or exciter, the majority consist of a tripler followed by a straight amplifier on 70cm. In addition to the increased efficiency obtained from an amplifier as compared to a frequency multiplying stage, its use is desirable to minimize radiation at 145 Mc/s which results if a tripler stage feeds the aerial directly.

A LOW-POWER TRIPLER-AMPLIFIER

The introduction of a range of r.f. double-tetrode valves suitable for operation at maximum frequencies of between 500 and 600 Mc/s makes possible the construction of efficient amplifiers in 70cm transmitters. A simple tripler amplifier unit intended for use in conjunction with an existing low power 2m transmitter or exciter having an r.f. output of between 1 and 2 watts is shown in **Figs. 30** and **31**. Mullard QQV02–6 miniature r.f. double tetrodes are employed in both stages. This type of valve, which is of single ended construction, incorporates built-in neutralizing capacitors, thus eliminating the need for any external neutralization of the p.a. stage, provided that input and output circuits are adequately shielded. When used as an amplifier at 435 Mc/s the valve is capable of delivering an r.f. output power of nearly 6 watts in c.w. telegraphy and 4 watts in telephony service, with an anode efficiency in excess of 50 per cent.

Circuit Description

In the circuit diagram (**Fig. 32**) V_1 functions as a push-pull frequency tripler from 145 to 435 Mc/s. The output of the 2m driver is inductively coupled to L_2, which is resonant with the input capacitance of the valve and circuit capacitances at 145 Mc/s. The centre-tap of L_2 is earthed to r.f. by C_1; this is necessary to maintain equal grid drive to each section of the valve, regardless of any mismatch in the valve input capacitances, which would otherwise cause unbalance in the drive to each grid.

The anode circuit of the tripler stage consists of a quarter wave line L_3 tuned to 435 Mc/s by C_2, which is connected across the line at a short distance from the end. This results

Fig. 30. Low power tripler-amplifier for 430 Mc/s.

in a longer line than would be obtained if the capacitor were connected directly across the open circuited end, with a consequent slight increase in the Q of the line. The tripler anode circuit is inductively coupled to the quarter wave input line (L_4) of the amplifier V_2, as in the preceding stage; this circuit has no added capacitance. The centre-tap of L_4 is capacitively earthed through C_3.

Another quarter wave line L_5 tuned by C_4 forms the anode circuit of the power amplifying stage; in this instance the capacitor is connected approximately half-way along the line. Both V_1 and V_2 anode circuits are unbypassed to avoid loss that would result due to any asymmetry in these circuits causing r.f. current to flow through the bypass capacitor to earth. In accordance with normal practice for v.h.f. double tetrodes, the screen grid leads to both valves are also unbypassed. An unbalanced r.f. output coupling circuit is employed, consisting of a loop L_6 and series capacitor C_5, which is provided to cancel out the inductive reactance of the loop.

Grid bias for both stages is provided by current flow through R_1 and R_6 when excitation is applied to the unit. Resistors R_2 and R_7 in series with the grid resistors enable the grid currents of the tripler and amplifier valves to be monitored on a meter connected to test points TP_1 and TP_2 respectively and earth. Anode current to each stage may be measured by a milliammeter connected across the 100 ohm resistors R_4 and R_9. Heater circuits should be decoupled by r.f. chokes (RFC_{2-5}) in each lead located as close to the

Fig. 31. Under-chassis view of the low power tripler-amplifier. The p.a. valveholder is on the right of the picture.

valveholder as possible, and bypass capacitors C_6 and C_7 connected directly across the relevant tags of the valve-holders; only the bypass capacitors are incorporated in the unit illustrated, but it may be found that omission of the chokes may result in greatly increased grid drive being necessary to obtain a given r.f. output from the valves. H.t. and l.t. supplies are bypassed by feedthrough capacitors C_8 and C_9, respectively, which also provide a convenient method of termination between the unit and external supply leads.

Construction

The unit is built on a 20 s.w.g. aluminium chassis measuring 9 in. long × 3 in. wide × 2 in. deep, a drilling plan for which is shown in **Fig. 33**.

All tuned circuits are connected directly to the appropriate tags on the valveholders. The bypass capacitor C_1 and grid resistor R_1 for the tripler stage should be fitted before the grid inductor L_2 is connected in circuit. Details of the 435 Mc/s tuned circuits are shown in **Fig. 34**. The ends of each line are bent inwards slightly to correlate with the grid and anode tags on the valveholders, and bent down slightly so that the tripler anode line L_3 is spaced $\frac{1}{2}$ in. The amplifier lines L_4 and L_5 are spaced $\frac{3}{4}$ in. from the underside of the chassis. This allows a spacing of $\frac{1}{4}$ in. between L_3 and L_4 (Fig. 34 (b)); the distance separating these two circuits is not critical and may be adjusted during initial alignment to obtain the correct amplifier grid current. Each of the anode lines is supported at the h.t. feed point by a small ceramic stand-off insulator $\frac{1}{2}$ in. high; the grid line L_4 is supported by

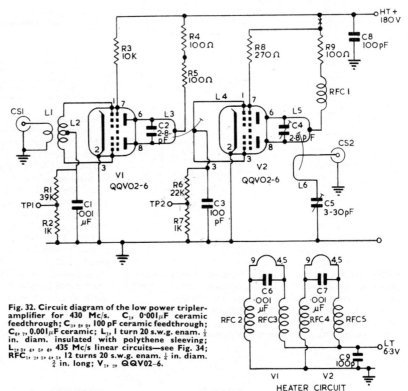

Fig. 32. **Circuit diagram of the low power tripler-amplifier for 430 Mc/s.** C_1, $0.001\,\mu F$ ceramic feedthrough; $C_{3, 8, 9}$, 100 pF ceramic feedthrough; $C_{6, 7}$, $0.001\,\mu F$ ceramic; $L_{2, 3, 4, 5, 6}$, 435 Mc/s linear circuits—see Fig. 34; $RFC_{1, 2, 3, 4, 5}$, 12 turns 20 s.w.g. enam. $\frac{1}{4}$ in. diam. $\frac{3}{4}$ in. long; $V_{1, 2}$, **QQV02-6.**

C_3. This capacitor and the grid resistor R_6 should be fitted before the line is soldered in position. Anode circuit tuning capacitors C_2 and C_4 are soldered directly across the lines in the positions indicated in Fig. 34, and project through the $\frac{5}{8}$ in. holes in the chassis. The rotor connection of C_5 is connected to a 6 B.A. soldering tag mounted under one of the securing screws for CS_2. A nominal spacing of $\frac{3}{8}$ in. should be provided between L_5 and L_6.

The test points TP_1 and TP_2 each consist of a length of 18 s.w.g. tinned copper wire projecting through a hole in the chassis from which they are insulated by a small grommet. The wire is connected to a tag strip which forms a junction between the grid bias and monitoring resistor. Anode current monitoring resistors R_4 and R_9 are connected to tag strips which facilitate the insertion of a meter into the circuits.

For reasons of cooling and performance at u.h.f. screening cans must not be fitted to either of the valves. Screening between amplifier grid and anode circuits is provided by a 20 s.w.g. aluminium shield measuring 3 in. long × $1\frac{1}{2}$ in. wide, with a $\frac{1}{2}$ in. lip at each end for attachment to the chassis. There is thus a gap of $\frac{1}{2}$ in. between the underside of the chassis and the upper edge of the shield, which gives clearance for the valveholder tags while providing sufficient isolation between the circuits.

Alignment

The unit requires power supplies of 180 volts h.t. at approximately 80 mA, and 6·3 volts at 1·2 amps. To avoid over-running the valves it is essential that the h.t. voltage

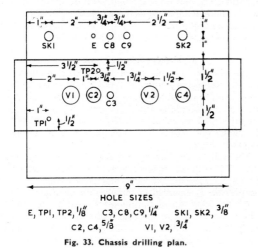

HOLE SIZES

E, TP1, TP2, $\frac{1}{8}''$ C3, C8, C9, $\frac{1}{4}''$ SK1, SK2, $\frac{3}{8}''$

C2, C4, $\frac{5}{8}''$ V1, V2, $\frac{3}{4}''$

Fig. 33. Chassis drilling plan.

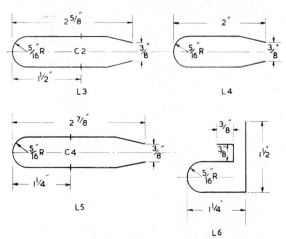

Fig. 34 (a). Construction of the 435 Mc/s linear circuits made from 16 s.w.g. enamelled wire.

TABLE 7

Typical current readings for the low power 70cm tripler-amplifier

Valve	Grid current	Screen current	Anode current
V_1	2·0 mA	5 mA	26 mA
V_2	1·25 mA	9 mA	40 mA

When the QQV02–6 is operated as a frequency tripler the r.f. output greatly exceeds the drive required by the same type of valve operating as an amplifier at 435 Mc/s. It is therefore recommended that the h.t. voltage applied to anode and screen of V_1 is reduced to as low a value as possible (by the inclusion of a series resistor in the h.t. supply line to this valve) that will result in the required grid drive to the amplifier stage being obtained.

Typical current readings for the 70cm low power tripler-amplifier when operated as a telephony transmitter are shown in **Table 7**. Anode and screen modulation may be effected by disconnecting R_8 and R_9 from the common h.t. line at the point marked x on the circuit diagram and inserting the secondary of the modulation transformer at this point. The modulator, which should have a power output of 5 to 6 watts, should be adjusted to match into an impedance of 3600 ohms.

When operated as a c.w. transmitter the amplifier stage may be run at an increased input up to a maximum of 10

specified is not exceeded, and if a power unit delivering a higher voltage is used, the voltage applied to the h.t. line of the tripler-amplifier must be reduced accordingly.

The output of the 2m exciter should be connected to CS_1 through a short length of coaxial cable; heater voltage only should be applied, and a dummy load, which may consist of

Fig. 34 (b). Layout of the linear circuits below the chassis.

a 12 volt 0·3 amp. M.E.S. bulb, connected to CS_2. The procedure for alignment is as follows:

(i) Connect a low range (0–5) milliameter between TP_1 and chassis (positive to chassis) and adjust the turns spacing of L_2 for maximum meter reading. Adjust the coupling between L_1 and L_2 or the output of the 2m exciter until a grid current in V_1 of approximately 2 mA is obtained.

(ii) Connect the meter between TP_2 and chassis and apply h.t. to V_1 only. The most convenient way of doing this is to disconnect one end of the 270 ohm resistor in the screen lead of V_2. Adjust C_2 for maximum meter reading. The total grid current for the QQV02–6 when used as an amplifier in this unit is approximately 1 mA; the coupling between L_3 and L_4, and the screen voltage of V_1 should be adjusted until this current is obtained. It will be found that the rated current will be obtained with loose coupling between the anode and grid circuits.

(iii) Apply h.t. to the amplifier valve and adjust C_4 and C_5 for maximum brilliance of the lamp load. If the 3·6 watt bulb specified is used, it should light up to full brilliancy.

Anode current to V_1 and V_2 may be monitored by connecting a meter (0–50 mA) across R_4 or R_9, respectively. It will be noticed that as C_2 and C_4 are tuned to resonance, a pronounced dip in anode current will occur, but this may not correspond exactly with maximum r.f. output from the stage.

watts by increasing the coupling between L_5 and L_6 until the p.a. valve draws a total anode current not exceeding 55 mA. For telegraphy service fixed grid bias must be applied to both valves in the tripler-amplifier. On no account must h.t. voltage be applied to the unit when the drive is removed, as the anode dissipation of the amplifier valve will increase to such a value that the valve will be damaged; the tripler valve is protected to a certain extent by the high value screen resistor.

A 24 WATT TRIPLER-AMPLIFIER

Fig. 35 shows a higher power 70cm tripler-amplifier that is intended for use in conjunction with a 2m transmitter having an r.f. output of not less than 5 watts. With an input of 24 watts to the amplifier stage this unit will deliver a power output of 12 watts at 435 Mc/s. Mullard QQV03–20A double-tetrode valves are employed in both tripler and amplifier stages.

The unit requires an h.t. supply of 300 volts at 200 mA and a 230 volts a.c. mains supply; the latter is necessary to obtain 6·3 volts for the valve heaters, for which purpose a transformer is mounted underneath the chassis.

All the 70cm tuned circuits are formed by parallel lines which are shielded to minimise radiation and thus increase their efficiency. Forced-air cooling of the valves is unnecessary unless the amplifier stage is run at an input greater than

24 watts. Anode and screen modulation of the p.a. stage may be effected by a modulator having an audio output of 15 to 20 watts; with an input of 24 watts to the power amplifier the impedance of the modulated stage is 3750 ohms.

Circuit Description

The circuit of the tripler-amplifier is shown in **Fig. 36.** R.f. drive from the 2m exciter is applied to CS_1 and via L_1, L_2 to the push-pull grids of the tripler valve V_1. L_2 is tuned by the valve input capacitance and stray circuit capacitances to a frequency of approximately 145 Mc/s; coupling between L_1 and L_2 is variable and can be adjusted to obtain the rated grid current for V_1. Grid-leak bias for the tripler valve is derived from flow of grid current through R_1, which is returned to chassis through the monitoring resistor R_2, bypassed by C_1.

The anode circuit of V_1 is tuned to 435 Mc/s and consists of a quarter wave parallel strip line L_3 tuned by C_2, which consists of the capacitance between opposite legs of the strip line. This capacitance is made variable by gradually introducing a block of insulating material, in this instance Keramot, between the line, so that the permittivity of the dielectric and

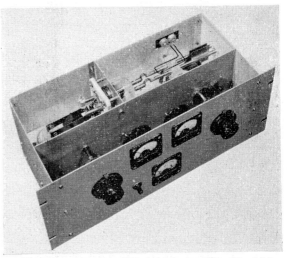

Fig. 35. Front view of the 24 watt tripler-amplifier. The tripler tuning is on the left and the p.a. tuning on the right. The anode meters M_2 and M_3 are at the top of the panel.

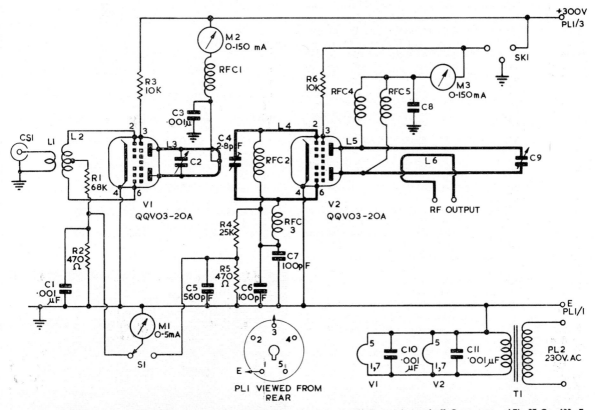

Fig. 36. Circuit diagram of the 24 watt tripler-amplifier for 435 Mc/s. $C_{1, 2, 3, 11, 12}$, 0.001 μF ceramic stand-off; C_3, see text and Fig. 37. $C_{6, 7}$, 100 pF ceramic feedthrough; C_8, approximately 220 pF (see text and Fig. 42 (d)); C_9, see text and Fig. 38; L_1, 1 turn 20 s.w.g. enam. $\frac{3}{8}$ in. o.d. (see Fig. 41); L_2, 4 turns 16 s.w.g. enam. $\frac{3}{4}$ in. o.d. approximately $\frac{1}{2}$ in. long, centre tapped; L_3, copper strip 18 s.w.g. $\frac{1}{2}$ in. wide, total length $6\frac{3}{8}$ in. bent into U form (see Fig. 43 (a)); L_4, two $\frac{1}{4}$ in. diam. brass rods $1\frac{3}{4}$ in. long drilled and tapped as shown in Fig. 43 (b); L_5 two $\frac{1}{4}$ in. diam. brass rods $5\frac{1}{2}$ in. long plus anode connectors, see text and Fig. 43 (c); L_6, loop 2 in. long $\frac{1}{2}$ in. wide of 16 s.w.g. enam.; M_1, 0–5 mA m.c. meter; $M_{2, 3}$, 0–150 mA m.c. meter; RFC$_{1, 2, 3, 4, 5}$, 12 turns 20 s.w.g. enam. $\frac{1}{4}$ in. o.d. approximately 1 in. long; T_1 230V 50 c/s primary, 6.3V 3A secondary; $V_{1, 2}$, QQV03–20A (6252). The valveholders for V_1 and V_2 are modified as described in the text.

235

Fig. 37. Close-up view of the tripler anode circuit and p.a. grid circuit Note the variable dielectric between the lines forming L_3.

hence the effective capacitance of the circuit is changed. This method of tuning, which is also employed in the p.a. anode circuit has been adopted to maintain balance between each section of the valve. It has commonly been found that the more normal method of tuning push-pull circuits by using a split-stator capacitor having the rotor either earthed or left floating, results in unbalance of the circuits when employed at frequencies of the order of 435 Mc/s. A material such as polystyrene having a lower power factor than Keramot, may be used but even with the less efficient dielectric employed the r.f. drive to the amplifier grids is more than adequate.

H.t. supply to the anode of V_1 is decoupled by RFC_1 and the feed-through capacitor C_3. The screen supply is reduced from 300 volts to a maximum of 250 volts by R_3, the value of which should be adjusted during initial setting-up of the unit so that maximum r.f. output is obtained from the valve when operated within the permissible rating. The screen of V_1 is unbypassed.

Inductive coupling is employed between V_1 anode circuit and the grid circuit of V_2. The tuned grid circuit L_4 of the power amplifier is a half-wave long when loaded by the input capacitance of the valve, and RFC_2 and RFC_3 are connected at the approximate electrical centre of the line. The two grid circuit chokes are returned to earth through the bias resistor R_4 and monitoring resistor R_5 in series; these resistors are by passed by C_5, C_6 and C_7.

Another half-wave line L_5, tuned by C_9, forms the anode circuit of V_2. In this instance the anode tuning capacitor is formed by the capacitance between two copper plates soldered to the line; the dielectric of this capacitor in the transmitter illustrated is also of Keramot but it is recommended that polystyrene be used so that the highest possible efficiency is obtained in this circuit. H.t. is fed to the p.a. anodes through RFC_4 and RFC_5, connected to the line at the voltage node. The anode circuit is decoupled by C_8, which is specially constructed to provide a low impedance bypass at the operating frequency. As with the tripler circuit, the screen of V_2 is unbypassed.

Anode and screen modulation of the power amplifier is obtained by connecting the output of the modulator to

SK_1. A screened lead between modulator and p.a. may be employed, with the screen connected to the chassis of the r.f. unit at SK_1 if necessary.

A balanced output loop L_6 is coupled to L_5 adjacent to the point corresponding to the voltage node on the line, and is connected to two polystyrene feedthrough insulators mounted on a strip of paxolin fixed to the rear screen. The paxolin strip ensures a low capacitance between the insulators and the earthed screen. If a coaxial cable is used to feed the aerial array, it is recommended that a balance-to-unbalance transformer be interposed between L_6 and the cable; the coupling circuit shown in Fig 5 is suitable for this purpose.

The cathodes of both V_1 and V_2 are connected directly to earth and no protective grid bias is employed. Current in the grid circuits of V_1 and V_2 is monitored by switching M_1 across R_2 and R_5 respectively. The heater transformer T_1 is included in the unit to avoid voltage drop that would occur in the connecting lead if the heater voltage was obtained from a separate power unit. For the same reason connections between the secondary of T_1 and heater tags on the valveholders should be made with a heavy gauge conductor, preferably not less than 16 s.w.g. For efficient operation of the valves it is essential that the voltage across the actual valve heaters should be maintained at 6·3 volts. The heaters of V_1 and V_2 are bypassed at the valveholders by C_{10} and C_{11} respectively.

Construction Details

Views of the tripler and amplifier stages, and the underside of the chassis appear in **Figs. 37, 38** and **39**; details of the chassis drilling are shown in **Fig. 40**. Panel, chassis, front and rear screens are made from 16 s.w.g. aluminium; the side screens and vertical shield on which the tripler valveholder is mounted are of 18 s.w.g. aluminium. The panel fitted to the transmitter illustrated measures 17 in. long × 7 in. high, but the length may be increased to 19 in. if it is desired to mount the unit in a standard rack. The U-shaped chassis on which the two stages are mounted measures 15 in. long × 4 in. wide × 2½ in. deep, and the side screens are secured to it by 2½ in. × ½ in. aluminium angle brackets at each corner on the underside. When making the two side screens, the rear flange on each should be formed so that it is flush with the edge of the screen and hence with the rear drop of the chassis when fitted in position. Cheesehead 6 B.A. screws and nuts are used in the assembly of the

Fig. 38. The anode circuit of the power amplifier.

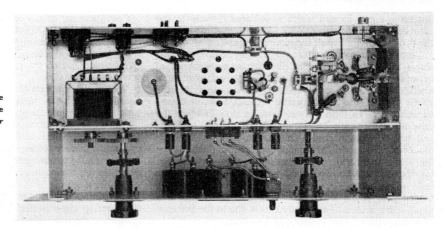

Fig. 39. Under-chassis view. The tripler stage is on the right. The transformer at the left is for the heaters.

unit, with the exception of the front panel, which uses six 4 B.A. round-head screws and nuts.

At the extreme left of the unit the tripler stage valveholder is mounted underneath the chassis on four spacers $\frac{1}{2}$ in. long, made from $\frac{1}{4}$ in. diameter brass rod drilled and tapped 4 B.A. A small fibre washer is inserted between the valveholder and each spacer and under the head of each fixing screw to prevent fracture of the ceramic holder as the screws are tightened.

The input coupling loop L_1 is mounted on a thin strip of polystyrene attached to a paxolin support by a small angle bracket (Fig. 41), on which it is pivoted by a single 8 B.A. screw; this permits adjustment in the position of L_1 relative to L_2. The paxolin support is secured to the underside of the tripler valveholder by two of the 4 B.A. securing screws. L_1 is insulated with polystyrene sleeving; the ends of the wire are bent at right-angles and passed through two small holes in the polystyrene to which it is secured with cement.

Decoupling capacitors C_1 and C_{10} are mounted on an aluminium bracket (Fig. 42) fixed to the underside of the chassis adjacent to the tripler stage valveholder; the cathode is connected to this bracket through a short length of $\frac{1}{2}$ in. wide copper strip.

The amplifier valveholder is mounted on the interstage screen in a similar manner to that employed for the tripler valveholder. Before the holder is fitted in position it is

necessary to remove the two control grid contacts so that the p.a. grid lines may be fitted directly on to the valve pins. This is done by drilling out the rivets which secure the spring contacts to the base; the holes in the base are then enlarged to a diameter of not less than $\frac{5}{16}$ in., using a tungsten-carbide tipped drill (Mason Master or Rawlplug) with turpentine as a lubricant. Extreme care must be exercised when enlarging the holes to avoid fracture of the ceramic base.

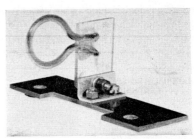

Fig. 41. Coupling loop from the 144 Mc/s exciter to the tripler grid circuit.

The valveholder is positioned on the screen so that the cathode contact is nearest to the chassis; this permits a short, low inductance cathode connection formed by a 20 s.w.g. aluminium bracket (Fig. 42 (b)) to be obtained. At the top of the

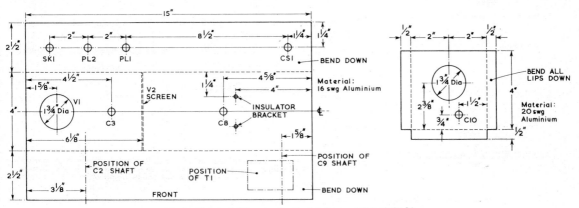

Fig. 40. Chassis drilling plan for the tripler-amplifier of Fig. 36.

bracket a tag is located which is soldered directly to the cathode tage on the valveholder. This bracket also carries the two grid circuit bypass capacitors C_6 and C_7.

Details of the mounting for the p.a. anode lines are also shown in Fig. 42 (c). The $\frac{1}{4}$ in. diameter lines are supported between two polystyrene blocks fixed to an aluminium bracket by two 2 B.A. screws and nuts; the cut-out at the base of the bracket is to accommodate the anode circuit bypass capacitor C_8. To form the semi-circular slots in which the lines are seated in the blocks, clamp both blocks together, and with centres marked 14mm apart, drill through the blocks with a $\frac{1}{4}$ in. drill at the junction between them. When the blocks are fitted in the transmitter they are clamped together by a 2 B.A. nylon screw passing through a clearance hole in the upper block and engaging in a corresponding tapped hole in the lower one. Nylon in preference to a metal screw is used to avoid any effects due to the presence of metal in the r.f. field between the two lines.

Constructional details of the anode circuit bypass capacitor C_8 are shown in Fig. 42 (d). The capacitor consists of two circular brass plates, $1\frac{1}{8}$ in. in diameter, made from 16 s.w.g. brass sheet; a heavier gauge metal may be used with advantage. One of the plates is mounted above and the other below the chassis, from which each plate is insulated by a $1\frac{1}{4}$ in. square sheet of 0·004 in. mica. A $\frac{5}{16}$ in. diameter hole is drilled in the chassis to clear the 2 B.A. screw by which the plates are clamped together and a paxolin washer having a thickness corresponding to the gauge of metal used for the chassis, which in the present instance is $\frac{1}{16}$ in. The two active surfaces of the brass plates should preferably be faced in a lathe to ensure their flatness. A capacitor made as described has a capacitance of approximately 300 pF.

Details of the 435 Mc/s tuned circuits are shown in **Fig. 43.** The tripler anode line is attached to the valve anode pins by two small spring clips made from 24 s.w.g. beryllium copper secured to the line with 4 B.A. nuts and screws. The block

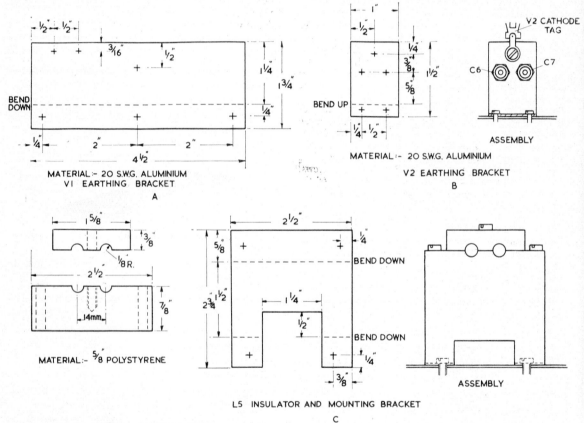

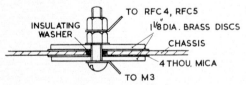

Fig. 42. Details of the various brackets used in the 24 watt tripler-amplifier. At the left is shown the construction of the bypass capacitor C_8 for the anode circuit of V_2

of dielectric used for tuning the circuit measures 1 in. square × $\frac{9}{16}$ in. thick, and has a $\frac{1}{4}$ in. diameter hole drilled at a distance of $\frac{1}{4}$ in. from the bottom edge; the $\frac{1}{4}$ in. diameter Keramot spindle is filed down slightly to be a push fit in this hole.

Across one end of the amplifier grid lines the tuning capacitor C_4 is mounted on soldering tags secured to the line by 6 B.A. screws; the other end of the line is pushed over the grid pins of the valve and secured by 6 B.A. grub screws. In the unit illustrated the grid circuit chokes RFC_2 and RFC_3 are connected to soldering tags which are attached to the lines by 8 B.A. screws; a better method is to use small anode top cap connectors similar to those used to connect the anode circuit chokes in this transmitter.

Each of the amplifier anode lines (L_5) is joined to the valve anode connector through a $1\frac{1}{4}$ in. length of thin copper strip $\frac{1}{4}$ in. wide. This provides a flexible connection between the rigidly mounted lines and the valve anodes to prevent fracture of the valve envelope due to unequal expansion of the glass and metal. Considerable dissipation of heat from the anodes is effected due to the use of heavy connectors fitted to the anode pins. The plates of the tuning capacitor C_9 measure $1\frac{1}{2}$ in. square and are made from 16 s.w.g. copper soldered at a centre distance of $1\frac{1}{4}$ in. from the end of the line. The variable dielectric is $\frac{1}{8}$ in. thick and $1\frac{1}{4}$ in. square and is fitted to the insulated control spindle in a manner similar to that employed for the tripler stage. Anode chokes RFC_4 and RFC_5 are attached to the line through two small valve anode top cap connectors; this enables the point of connection of the chokes to the line to be adjusted.

Both tuning controls are fitted with slow motion dials; the tripler stage capacitor is driven directly, but the amplifier capacitor is driven from the slow motion head through two $1\frac{1}{2}$ in. gear wheels, which enables a symmetrical front panel layout to be obtained.

In the unit illustrated the two anode current meters are connected into circuit through plugs and sockets mounted on the front drop of the chassis. This is not essential but prevents leakage of air if the transmitter has to be blown. The heater transformer T_1 is mounted underneath the chassis at the extreme righthand end.

Adjustment and Operation

The output of a 2m transmitter or exciter should be coupled to CS_1 through a short length of coaxial cable, and a 230 volts a.c. mains supply connected to PL_2. The tripler and power amplifier tuned circuits should then be adjusted in that order by adopting the following procedure:

(i) Set the meter switch S_1 to read tripler grid current and with no h.t. applied to the unit, adjust the turns spacing of L_2 for maximum grid current in V_1. Adjust the coupling between L_1 and L_2, or the output of the 2m exciter to obtain optimum current (see Table 8);

(ii) Switch S_1 to read p.a. grid current, and apply approximately 200 volts h.t. to the tripler stage only. (The most convenient method of doing this is to leave SK_1 open circuited.) Then tune C_2 and C_4 to resonance as indicated by maximum grid current in V_2. At resonance about half the effective capacitance of C_2 should be in circuit;

(iii) Connect a dummy load, which may consist of a 230 volts 15 watts lamp, to the output terminals of the transmitter. Apply h.t. to both stages, then tune C_9 and adjust the coupling between L_5 and L_6 for maximum

brilliance of the lamp load. It will generally be found that quite a loose coupling is required.

An aerial may now be connected to the output terminals and 300 volts h.t. applied. It will be found that the anode currents of V_1 and V_2 do not dip as the associated circuits are tuned and therefore some form of r.f. output indicator will be required to show resonance of the p.a. anode circuit. The ideal arrangement is to make use of a reflectometer (see Chapter 19, *Measurements*) connected in the aerial feeder but failing this, a simple r.f. output monitor located adjacent to the feeder will be suitable.

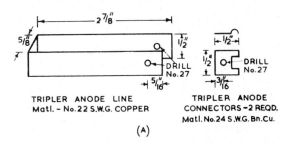

TRIPLER ANODE LINE
Matl. – No. 22 S.W.G. COPPER

TRIPLER ANODE
CONNECTORS – 2 REQD.
Matl. No. 24 S.W.G. Bn. Cu.

(A)

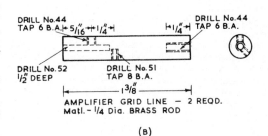

AMPLIFIER GRID LINE — 2 REQD.
Matl. – $\frac{1}{4}$ Dia. BRASS ROD

(B)

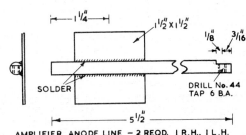

AMPLIFIER ANODE LINE — 2 REQD. 1 R.H., 1 L.H.
Matl. – LINE – $\frac{1}{4}$ Dia. BRASS ROD
CAPACITOR PLATE – No. 16 S.W.G. COPPER

(C)

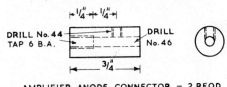

AMPLIFIER ANODE CONNECTOR — 2 REQD.
Matl. $\frac{5}{16}$ Dia. BRASS ROD

(D)

Fig. 43. Construction of the tuned circuits for the 24 watt tripler-amplifier.

The value of the two screen resistors R_3 and R_6, and the value of the p.a. grid resistor R_4 should be adjusted for optimum results within the rating of the valves. The position of RFC_4 and RFC_5 on the p.a. anode line should be adjusted to correspond to the voltage node on the line. A convenient way of doing this is to line up the transmitter into a lamp load, and then repeatedly tap a pencil along each line until a point is found such that when the pencil is touched on the line no diminution in r.f. output results; the clip attached to the choke is then slid along the line to this point.

Table 8 shows typical current readings obtained with an h.t. supply of 300 volts; it is important that the anode current of the two valves does not exceed the figures shown unless

Fig. 45. The cruciform Perspex insulator and the tuning capacitor.

TABLE 8

Typical current readings for the 70cm transmitter of Fig. 35

Valve	Anode current	Screen current	Grid current
V_1	80 mA	5·0 mA	2·5 mA
V_2	80 mA	6·0 mA	2·0 mA

forced air cooling is employed. If the d.c. power input to either valve exceeds 24 watts it will be necessary for such cooling to be used. In this event the two stages must be completely enclosed by fitting a base and top cover to the section in which the valves are located. A motor blower can conveniently be mounted at the rear of the chassis. Holes must be drilled in the chassis beneath the anodes of the p.a. as shown in Fig. 38 to allow the passage of air past this valve, and in the top cover immediately above both valves; enough clearance for cooling purposes already exists between the envelope of the tripler valve and the chassis. If cooling is resorted to, the r.f. section must be sufficiently airtight to minimize leakage through joints between the chassis and screens; sealing may be effected by applying polystyrene cement to all joints with a small brush. The blower should have sufficient capacity to maintain the pin temperature of the valves at not more than 180° C.

A HIGH POWER AMPLIFIER FOR 70CM

A 70cm power amplifier incorporating a 4X150A tetrode in an grounded cathode coaxial circuit is shown in **Fig. 44.** This unit will handle comfortably an input of 150 watts and

will also operate at high efficiency with a considerably lower power input; forced air cooling of the valve is employed under all conditions.

Constructional details are shown in the assembly drawing of **Fig. 46.** The coaxial input circuit, L_2, is three-quarter wave long and has a characteristic impedance of 80 ohms; the circuit is tuned to resonance by a parallel-plate capacitor C_2 connected between the inner and outer conductors near to the open circuited end of the line. A Perspex insulator of cruciform shape supports this end of the line; this insulator and the tuning capacitor may be seen in **Fig. 45.**

The series input capacitor C_1 is mounted in a small housing which can be seen on the left in Fig. 46. Self-capacitance between the housing and the capacitor is minimized by mounting C_1 on two Perspex spacing pillars and securing with two 10 B.A. screws and nuts.

At the closed circuited end of L_2 the flange on the inner line is insulated from the end plate of the outer line by a mica disc 0·005 in. thick; this arrangement forms the grid circuit bypass capacitor C_3. Four 6 B.A. screws hold the inner line in position; these screws pass through Tufnol bushes in the end plate of the outer and engage in tapped holes in the flange of the inner line. The negative pole of the grid bias supply is connected to one of the 6 B.A. screws.

A view of the bracket on which the valveholder is mounted, as seen from the anode end of the amplifier appears in **Fig. 47.** Connection between the control grid pin of the valve and the inner line of the coaxial input circuit is achieved by a combined plug and socket, which is held centrally in the flange of the valveholder by a Perspex insulator similar in form to that shown in Fig. 46. The socket, which can be seen in Fig. 47, makes contact with the grid pin of the valve and the banana plug fits into the open end of the inner conductor. Earthing of the four cathode pins of the valve is effected at the valveholder which also incorporates an integral screen bypass capacitor. The outer conductor of the grid line is secured to the valve socket flange by four 6 B.A. screws, which also hold the Perspex insulator in position at the end of the line.

A shallow circular groove, concentric with the valveholder, having an internal

Fig. 44. High power amplifier for 70cm employing a 4X150A.

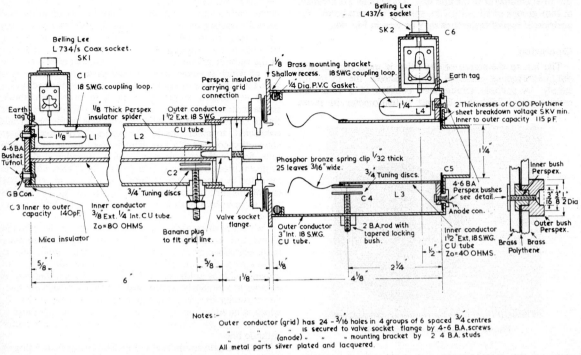

Notes :-
Outer conductor (grid) has 24 - 3/16" holes in 4 groups of 6 spaced 3/4" centres
  "   "   " is secured to valve socket flange by 4-6 B.A.screws
  "   "   (anode) "   "   "   " mounting bracket by 2 4 B.A.studs
All metal parts silver plated and lacquered.

Fig. 46. Construction of the 4X150A amplifier for 70 cm. C_1, 10 pF trimmer (Polar type C32–01); C_2, see text and Fig. 45; C_3, 140 pF, see text; C_4, see text; C_5, 115 pF, see text; C_6, 10 pF trimmer. The valveholder is a type B8F (Ediswan Clix VH 88/802).

diameter of 3 in., is turned in the brass mounting bracket to provide a register for the coaxial anode line assembly (**Fig. 48**).

The anode line L_3 is a quarter-wave long and is adjusted to resonance by C_4, which is similar in construction to C_2. Contact between the inner conductor of L_3 and the valve anode is effected by a phosphor bronze finger strip soldered to the end of the inner line. The h.t. bypass capacitor C_5 is formed in a similar manner to C_3; in this instance two thicknesses of 0·010 in. polythene sheet provide insulation between the inner and outer lines, as it is essential that the capacitor has a breakdown voltage of not less than 5 kV. A detail drawing of the Perspex bush by which each of the 6 B.A. securing screws is insulated from the outer conductor is shown at the lower right in Fig. 46. The positive pole of the h.t. supply is connected to one of these screws.

The complete anode line assembly is fixed to the mounting bracket by two 4 B.A. threaded studs positioned diametrically opposite at the end of the outer conductor. These studs engage in the two holes at the sides of the bracket which can be seen in Fig. 47, and are secured by two 4 B.A. nuts. A flange is soldered to the inside of the 3 in. diameter tube to carry a gasket which ensures an airtight seal between the anode line assembly and the valve mounting bracket.

The capacitor C_6 in series with the output loop L_4 is mounted in a similar manner to that employed for C_1; C_6 is mounted on two $\frac{1}{4}$ in. long Perspex pillars and secured with 8 B.A. screws and nuts.

For highest efficiency all fabricated metal parts should be silver plated and subsequently lacquered to prevent corrosion of the plating. The amplifier must be forced air cooled under

all conditions of service to limit the temperature of the base and seals of the valve to 150° C; the air must be applied simultaneously with the heater voltage. The blower output is coupled to the $1\frac{1}{4}$ in. diameter tube at the end of the anode line; flow of air is then down the inner conductor of the anode line, through the anode radiator and past the valve base seals.

Outlet for the air is provided by 24 $\frac{3}{16}$ in. diameter holes in

Fig. 47. The valveholder for the 4X150A and its mounting bracket.

the outer conductor of the grid line. These holes are arranged in four groups of six, with $\frac{1}{4}$ in. spacing between holes. The position of two of the groups may be seen in Fig. 44.

Operation

The h.t. to the screen of the valve is most conveniently obtained from a potential divider across the main h.t. supply. A suitable arrangement consists of a 15K ohm resistor and a 25K ohm 25 watt potentiometer in series,

Fig. 48. Coaxial anode line assembly

with one end of the potentiometer connected to h.t. positive and the slider connected to the valve screen grid. A series resistor from the h.t. supply must not be used for supplying the screen, as should primary screen emission occur, the voltage can increase to a value that may result in destruction of the valve.

A grid resistor of 10 K ohms in series with a 0–10 milliammeter should be connected between the grid bias negative termination and the outer of the grid line. With the drive and load connected to SK_1 and SK_2 respectively, C_1 and C_2 should be tuned for maximum grid current, which is approximately 8 mA for correct operation.

With 800 volts h.t. applied, the slider of the screen potentiometer should be adjusted so that the screen voltage does not exceed 250. C_4 and C_6 should be adjusted for maximum r.f. output (the best indication is obtained on a reflectometer connected between SK_2 and the load or aerial feeder). A dip in anode current of between 10 and 15 mA as C_4 is tuned to resonance should be obtained. The screen voltage should be adjusted so that an anode current of 100 mA is obtained; in this condition the r.f. output will be approximately 45 watts. For 150 watts input the anode voltage may be increased to 1,200 volts, when an r.f. output in excess of 100 watts should be obtained.

A 23CM TRIPLER

A 23cm tripler stage employing a 2C39A triode valve in a grounded grid coaxial circuit is shown in **Fig. 49.** Constructional details, including all necessary dimensions, are given in **Fig. 50.**

The outer line of the 70cm cathode cavity (**Fig. 51**) is fabricated from 18 s.w.g. brass tube, $2\frac{1}{2}$ in. outside diameter and $2\frac{3}{16}$ in. in length. One end of the tube is closed by a brass end plate of similar gauge on which are mounted con-

centrically the inner conductor of the cathode cavity and the heater connection. A number of holes are drilled in the end plate for cooling purposes. A flange, formed by a brass ring $3\frac{3}{4}$ in. o.d., $2\frac{1}{2}$ in. i.d. and made from $\frac{3}{16}$ in. brass sheet is soldered to the other end of the tube. The inner conductor of the cathode circuit is formed by a $\frac{3}{8}$ in. diameter tube, one end of which is soldered to the end plate; the other end is split for a distance of approximately $\frac{3}{4}$ in. and formed into a slight bell-mouth to provide a push fit over the cathode sleeve termination of the valve. This also forms the heater return circuit, as the cathode and one side of the heater are connected together inside the valve. The live heater connection consists of a $\frac{1}{4}$ in. diameter tube inside the cathode tube, fixed to the end plate by a 6 B.A. threaded stud which projects through a central hole in the plate, from which it is insulated by a bush made of Tufnol or a similar material. The end of this tube is shaped in a similar manner to the cathode tube so as to be a push fit over the heater termination of the valve.

Two brass discs each $\frac{7}{8}$ in. in diameter form the cathode circuit tuning capacitor C_2. The disc forming the fixed plate is soldered to a small bracket attached to the inner line at approximately $\frac{5}{8}$ in. from the closed circuit end; the moving plate is soldered to a 2 B.A. threaded stud which engages in a similarly tapped bush soldered to the outer line. Series tuning of the input coupling loop is effected by C_1 which is mounted on two insulating pillars $\frac{3}{8}$ in. long and is contained in an external housing attached to the outer cathode line.

The 23cm grid anode cavity (**Fig. 52**) is made from a ring of $3\frac{3}{4}$ in. diameter 18 s.w.g. brass tube, $\frac{7}{8}$ in. long, each end of which is closed by an 18 s.w.g. circular plate, having a central hole $1\frac{1}{2}$ in. in diameter, which carry the grid and anode contact rings. If brass tube is not available the cavity may

Fig. 49. A 23 cm tripler stage employing a 2C39A valve.

ing is capable of giving results which are almost as good
h.t. supply keying. However, unless special precautions
taken, the cathode potential tends to float when the
is open and may rise to such a high value that there
a serious danger of breakdown of the heater/cathode

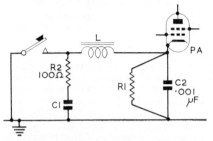

. 3. Cathode keying. The rise-time is determined by L, a low-
istance choke of 1–5 henrys. The decay time is determined by
which can have a value of 0·5–2 μF. Rl is a safety resistance and
should not be more than 0·25 Megohms.

ulation. To avoid this excessive potential difference a
istor not exceeding 0·25 Megohm should be connected
tween the cathode and the heater.

When a drive voltage is applied to the valve and the key
open, the cathode-to-heater voltage will rise to the sum
the cut-off bias plus the peak positive drive voltage, and
is therefore desirable to avoid any unnecessary rise by
suring that the driver stage has good output voltage
gulation.

If directly-heated valves are used a separate heater winding
ll be needed for the keyed valve, and unless a limiting
sistance equivalent to R_1 in Fig 3 is included there may
quite high voltages developed across the key.

The optimum component values of the click filter circuit
pend partly on the magnitude of the cathode current
d are best found by experiment. When the key is
pressed, the condenser C_1 is short-circuited through the
y (the resistance R_2 being included to limit the discharge
rrent to a reasonable value) and the condenser therefore
ays no part in determining the rise-time of the carrier.
us the first step is to choose a suitable inductance value
give an acceptable " make," the rise-time being determined
this inductance value. When a suitable choke has been
und, the value of C_1 may be altered to give the desired
cay-time, or " break " characteristic.

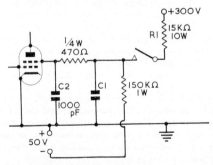

g. 4. Screen-grid keying. The values shown are suitable for a
lve of the 807 class but may be varied widely. Rl will be somewhat
wer than would be required if it were a simple series dropper
sistance. The condenser Cl is chosen to give suitable hardness
the keying: a typical value is 0·25 μF. C2 is the r.f. by-pass
condenser.

The d.c. resistance of L produces a certain amount of
cathode bias, and the operating conditions of the stage
should be adjusted to allow for this. The condenser C_2
is an r.f. by-pass and is small enough to have no perceptible
effect on the keying characteristic.

Screen-grid Keying

Screen-grid keying permits a high-power amplifier stage
to be keyed with contacts and filter components of lower
power rating than would be necessary in the case of h.t.
supply keying. In its simplest form, the method consists
in breaking the positive supply line to the screen, but unfortunately most pentodes and tetrodes do not completely
cease to conduct when the screen is isolated (owing to
current leakages and screen primary emission) and it is
usually necessary to apply a negative bias of the order of
20–50 volts in the key-up condition to eliminate the spacer
wave. The bias may be derived from a battery or a separate
bias unit.

A typical screen-grid keying circuit suitable for valves
of the 807 class is shown in **Fig. 4.** It may be worth noting
that this arrangement has the slight disadvantage of causing
the " make " to be harder than the " break."

Grid-block Keying

If a sufficiently large negative bias is applied to the control
grid of a p.a. stage, no cathode current will flow even in

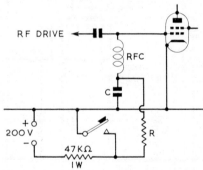

Fig. 5. Grid-block keying. The resistance R has the normal bias
value, and the keying envelope is determined mainly by the time
constant of R and C. The product of R (in kilohms) and C (in
microfarads) should be about 5. The bias supply should be capable
of supplying 4 mA in the key-down condition and should have an
open-circuit output of about 200 V.

the presence of drive voltage. For most tetrode or pentode
power amplifiers a bias of about 200 volts will be found
adequate. A suitable circuit is shown in **Fig. 5.** In this
circuit the voltage across the key contacts will rise to 200
volts with the key up, but the impedance is high enough
to prevent dangerous currents from flowing, and a hand
key may safely be used. The voltage must not be allowed
to exceed the specified maximum d.c. negative control-grid
potential: otherwise there is a danger of flash-over, particularly in high-slope valves.

This method is also sometimes known as *blocked-grid
keying.*

Suppressor-grid Keying

The output from a pentode amplifier may be reduced

249

to zero by the application of a sufficiently high negative voltage to the suppressor grid, but this is seldom used as a method of keying. When the suppressor is biased to cut-off, heavy screen-grid current will flow and the screen-grid dissipation limit may be exceeded. Moreover, the suppressor potential is a very insensitive form of control in most pentodes, and the keying voltage required is therefore large.

Keyer Valves

In any class C amplifier every electrode (except the suppressor grid in a pentode) normally passes a current. This means that the keying circuit must be able to deal with power and not merely voltage, and local interference may be caused by arcing at the contacts or by radiation from the key leads.

Also in most circuits it is difficult to obtain the desired degree of softness at both make and break with the same component values, and a compromise is necessary.

Both of these drawbacks may be overcome by the introduction of an auxiliary valve used as a variable resistance in series with the h.t. supply to some convenient valve in the transmitter, the key being used to control the grid bias on the auxiliary valve. **Fig. 6** shows a circuit in which a 12AU7 (with the two sections connected in parallel) is

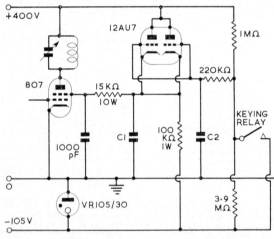

Fig. 6. **Valve keying of screen-grid supply. This circuit is suitable for inputs of 25-35 watts using a p.a. valve of the 807 class. The condensers C1 and C2 determine the hardness at "break" and "make" respectively: suitable values for normal keying are C1 = 0·1 μF and C2 = 0·005 μF. Note that the arrangement utilizes the back contacts of the key: i.e. the carrier is radiated only when the contacts are open. A separate heater supply is required for the 12AU7 keyer valve and the heaters should be strapped to the cathodes through a 220K ohm resistor.**

used to key the screen supply to an 807. An important point to note is that this method utilizes the back contact of the key. The steady current flowing through the key contacts is only 0·5 milliamperes in the key-up condition, though the open-circuit voltage (i.e. with the key depressed) is about 400 volts. If desired, the current could be reduced by using higher resistance values in the keyed circuit, but generally there would be little advantage in doing so.

If the transmitter is controlled by a semi-automatic morse keyer, it is often possible to dispense with relays

in this arrangement since suitable voltages may be deriv directly from the keyer circuit. With a 12AU7 keyer va as in Fig. 6 the two grids should be at +300 volts to ea with the key down and −100 volts with the key up.

BREAK-IN OPERATION

The essential feature of a break-in system is that t operator is able to receive incoming signals in the spac between his own transmitted morse characters so th duplex operation becomes possible. Much time is there saved, particularly in multiple contacts or when interferen is present, and the advantages in contests or when hunti DX are obvious. Transmissions are prefaced with t sign " BK " and the call-signs are given at frequent interv to conform with the conditions of the licence.

When using break-in, the functions of the normal sen receive switch must be performed quickly and in the prop sequence, and all the necessary operations must be controll automatically by the key. Ideally the station will return the receiving condition at the sensitivity level requir by the operator between each dot and dash of the tra mitted message, but this is not essential; many operat are content to listen only between complete letters or ev complete words.

No attempt is made here to give a foolproof method achieving ideal break-in, but an outline is given of t problems involved and of the methods by which they m be solved.

Transmitter Keying Requirements

In order to prevent break-through on the receiver duri listening periods, additional requirements are imposed the transmitter keying system. It will normally not be poss ble to leave the v.f.o. running, unless this is exceptional well screened or unless its fundamental frequency is ve low compared with the final frequency and the multipli stages are keyed. An exception to this is the mixer type master oscillator in which case the two oscillators may left running and the mixer stage keyed.

Perfect keying characteristics cannot be achieved keying the v.f.o. alone; however carefully designed a constructed the v.f.o. may be the resultant output w brobably show a marked chirp or troublesome key-click and more usually both. The best approach is to key bo the v.f.o. and the p.a. stage and to ensure that the p. keying is the controlling factor in shaping the keyi envelope. To do this the v.f.o. must be keyed with a sho time constant and be so arranged that it is active at a times when the p.a. conducts and quiescent at other time

A reliable method is to use a keying relay with at lea two pairs of contacts, one pair switching the v.f.o. an another the p.a. stage. The contact springs should be be so that the v.f.o. contacts close as soon as the armatu starts to move, the p.a. contacts closing later in its trave On release, the sequence is reversed so that the v.f.o. sta on for a short time after the p.a. contacts have opened. difficulty here is that the time interval between the operatio of the two pairs of contacts is limited to a few millisecon and therefore the keying cannot be made very soft.

Muting the Receiver

When the key is depressed the receiver must lose sensitivi quickly enough to prevent a click being produced from th

ding edge of the transmitted signal; when the key is
eased the gain should remain low until radiation has
ased and then rise rapidly. It is usually convenient to
te the receiver by breaking the cathode return of the
, and i.f. stages and replacing the normal r.f./i.f. gain
ntrol with a " monitor level " control of higher resistance
ue: the normal control can be restored in parallel with
s through the back contacts of the key or a pair of similar
ntacts on the keying relay, adjusted to open at the same
e or a little earlier than the instant when the v.f.o.
ntacts close. **Fig. 7** shows a circuit of this kind.

In order to obtain a sufficiently rapid fall in sensitivity
en the key is depressed it may be necessary to reduce the
ues of the r.f. and i.f. cathode decoupling condensers
in the receiver to the minimum required for proper
rking, or in mild cases to reduce the value of the bleed
istor R_1 which usually exists between the h.t. line and the
thode line, thus reducing the charging time of the cathode
ndensers.

When the key is released, the gain will rise rapidly owing
the relatively low value of the normal gain control
tentiometer R_2, which forms the main discharge path
the cathode condensers. The process may be delayed
the addition of a choke L of several henrys inductance
th a rectifier MR acting as a spark suppressor. Note
at the d.c. resistance of this choke may result in a consider-
le reduction in the maximum gain of the receiver unless
bias resistors are suitably adjusted.

Further troubles may arise from the beat-frequency oscilla-
r in the receiver. If the b.f.o. injection point is followed by
gain-controlled stage, the high b.f.o. voltage at the second
tector will be modulated by the muting voltage, and for
st rates of muting this will produce a click or thump at
output. The remedy is either to inject the b.f.o. voltage
a later stage or to remove the gain control from the
age in question.

Another problem may arise from the use of a crystal
ter especially if it is placed at the beginning of the i.f.
plifier chain, e.g. in the anode circuit of the mixer. In
ch a receiver, the crystal filter is followed by at least
e gain-controlled stage, and in the key-down condition
e signal voltage at the crystal may be many times that
ich corresponds to a reasonable output when the receiver
being operated at maximum sensitivity. Due to the very
all bandwidth (very high Q value) of the filter this voltage
nnot die away quickly even after the transmitter output
s fallen to zero, and if the gain of the following stages of
e receiver is allowed to increase rapidly to normal after the

key is released this signal will be heard as a loud click in
the receiver immediately after the instant of break. A
possible remedy is to avoid controlling the i.f. gain and to
rely on controlling the r.f. gain, although with this arrangement it will often be found impossible to reduce the overall
gain sufficiently. In a case such as this it may be satisfactory
to extend the gain control to include the mixer stage. As a
last resort, the cathode choke L (Fig. 7) may be made large
(e.g. 20 henrys) and some loss of sensitivity during brief
key-up periods may have to be tolerated.

The a.g.c. line is sometimes used for muting, but it is then
necessary to reduce the time constants drastically, and a
separate bias supply will be needed.

Aerial Switching

A simple expedient often used in a break-in system is to
erect a separate aerial for the receiver. This usually has the
disadvantage that the polar diagram of the receiving aerial
differs from that of the transmitting aerial, invalidating
the adage that " *if you can hear them, you can work them.*"
Also there is often trouble from absorption effects owing
to the close proximity of two aerials tuned to the same
frequency.

If only one aerial is available it may of course be switched
by means of a relay. The operation of its contacts must however be timed accurately in relation to the transmitter
keying and receiver muting; this is easy only if all these
functions are performed by contacts on the same relay.

Alternatively a transmit/receive switch of the contactless
type may be installed. Transmit/receive switches may be
divided into two classes: (a) those which require the application of some control voltage or current synchronized with
the key, and (b) those which act as limiters and are entirely
automatic. With either type the transmitter is connected
permanently to the aerial, the receiver being connected
to it through the t.r. switch. In the key-down condition
the t.r. switch must not absorb any appreciable fraction
of the transmitter output power, nor must it permit any
excessive amount of power to reach the receiver. The switch
is usually arranged so that it presents a high impedance
in the key-down condition and is connected to the aerial
at a point of low impedance and thus of low voltage.

The t.r. switch may consist of an additional stage of
amplification preceding the main receiver, so arranged
that it will withstand the full transmitter output voltage
without being damaged. This requirement precludes the
provision of any useful amount of impedance step-up in

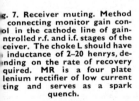

g. 7. Receiver muting. Method
connecting monitor gain con-
ol in the cathode line of gain-
ntrolled r.f. and i.f. stages of the
ceiver. The choke L should have
inductance of 2–20 henrys, de-
nding on the rate of recovery
quired. MR is a four plate
lenium rectifier of low current
ting and serves as a spark
quench.

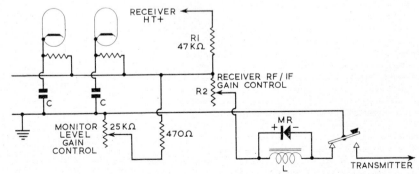

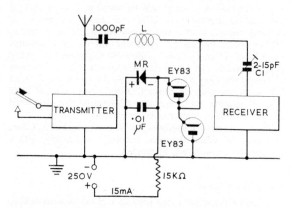

Fig. 8. Receiver input limiter. The aerial feeder and the receiver input should both be of low impedance. The trimmer is adjusted for best reception at the centre of the band in use. MR is a six-plate 150 mA selenium rectifier (S.T.C. type H35–6–1W) and serves to maintain a more constant bias voltage than would be possible if a resistor were used in this position. The maximum permissible r.f. power exceeds 100 watts in 75-ohm feeder on all bands from 1·8 Mc/s to 21 Mc/s. For use at moderate power on the 1·8 Mc/s and 3·5 Mc/s bands a 6AL5 valve may replace the EY83's if the inductance values are approximately doubled and if the r.m.s. aerial voltage is restricted to 100 V. on 1·8 Mc/s and 50 V. on 3·5 Mc/s.

Frequency Band	Value of L
1·8 Mc/s	275 μH
3·5 Mc/s	77 μH
7 Mc/s	20·5 μH
14 Mc/s	5·1 μH
21 Mc/s	2·3 μH

its grid circuit, and the noise factor of the receiver may be worsened. The best form of circuit is probably the grounded-grid arrangement using a small high-slope triode: this may be muted either by applying a large negative bias to its grid or by breaking its d.c. cathode return lead, whichever is the more easily adaptable to the muting system used for the main receiver. A carrier power of 100 watts in a 75-ohm circuit gives a peak voltage of about 125 volts (provided that there are no standing waves); at least this amount of bias must be applied to prevent conduction in the t.r. switch valve, and the peak grid/cathode voltage with the carrier applied will therefore be 250–300 volts. This is beyond the rating of most high-slope valves, but the majority of samples will withstand it without premature failure.

The heater/cathode insulation is subjected to voltages of the same order and it may be necessary to insert r.f. chokes in the heater supply leads, each heater pin being by-passed to the cathode with a 1,000 pF condenser.

If too high a voltage appears between grid and cathode, it will be necessary to insert a tuned circuit or a wide-band transformer between the aerial and the t.r. switch, tapping the switch down to a point where the voltages involved fall below the manufacturer's ratings for the valve used.

Other forms of amplifier may be preferred but it should be remembered that pentodes generate more valve noise than triodes, while triodes in circuits other than the grounded-grid circuit give excessive break-through owing to the anode-grid or grid-cathode capacitance.

A receiver-input limiter which is very effective for moderate carrier power at frequencies up to about 21 Mc/s is shown in **Fig. 8.** The inductance L is made to resonate with the trimmer condenser C_1 and the stray circuit capacitances approximately at the centre of the band.

In the absence of any r.f. output from the transmitter t two diode sections (which are effectively in series for d.c are prevented from conducting by a small positive bi and in this condition there is only a small reduction receiver sensitivity due to losses in the coil L. When t key is depressed sufficient r.f. voltage appears across t diodes to overcome the bias and the diodes conduct, there providing an effective short-circuit for the receiver inpu The limitation on power is that the rectified current in t diodes should not exceed the maximum safe value. Th may readily be checked by inserting a d.c. milliammet in series with the selenium rectifier MR and observi the change in reading when the key is depressed. T rating for an EY83 is 250 mA which is unlikely to exceeded; if a 6AL5 is used the current should not exce 9 mA.

As the frequency is increased the problem becom rapidly more difficult. It is then necessary to use larg rectifiers and this means greater stray capacities and smal coils, which lead to yet higher currents in the diodes and larger voltage appearing at the receiver input termina

Any limiter using diodes or other rectifiers is liable produce harmonic radiation, owing to the very distort waveform of the currents flowing in the diodes wh transmitting. The limiter should therefore be connect to the aerial system at a point between the transmitter a the harmonic filter or aerial coupling unit. Also stro harmonics of the local broadcasting station may be hea in the receiver as a result of rectification in the diode a wave-trap tuned to its frequency should overcome th defect.

ELECTRONIC KEYERS

A semi-automatic keyer can greatly increase the pleasu of morse operating by lessening the fatigue of long spe of sending, particularly at high speeds. The type of key most widely used produces a series of dots or of dash when the moving arm or paddle is held against one other of two fixed contacts. In these keyers, once a dot dash has been started it will be completed irrespecti of what happens to the paddle, and a space of the corre

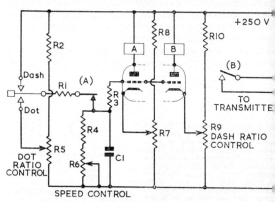

Fig. 9. Electronic keyer. The relays A and B may be Post Offi type 600 (small type) with 3000–6000 ohm coils. Relay A has o break contact and relay B has one or more make contacts.
C1 — 0·2 μF; R1 — 470 ohms, $\frac{1}{4}$ W; R2 — 15 k ohms, 5 W; R3 — 2 Megohms, $\frac{1}{2}$ W; R4 — 220 K ohms, $\frac{1}{2}$ W; R5, R7, R9 — 10 K ohms, wir wound variable; R6 — 1 Megohms carbon variable; R8, R10 — 33 ohms, 5 W. The valve may be a 6SN7 or 12AU7.

length will be left before the start of the next dot or dash. The timing of the hand movements is thus very much less critical than when using a " straight " key; the result will be either correct Morse or complete gibberish.

A simple form of keyer, developed by OZ7BO, is shown in **Fig. 9.** Each half of the double triode valve is biased beyond cut-off by the potential dividers R_7R_8 and R_9R_{10}. When the paddle is moved on to either contact a positive voltage is applied to the two grids. Both triodes then conduct and both relays operate. Relay A has a " break " contact (A) which isolates the grids from the paddle, while relay B has a " make " contact (B) which keys the transmitter. The grids are held positive by the charge on C_1, but this charge leaks away through R_4 and the speed control R_6. The potentiometers R_7 and R_9 are adjusted so that the cathode of V_2 is held more positive than that of V_1; therefore as the grid voltage falls relay B releases before relay A. The transmitter is switched off when relay B releases, but the cycle of operations cannot repeat until relay A has released, thus giving the required space between the letter elements.

When the paddle closes on the dash contact, a higher positive voltage is applied than when it closes on the dot contact. The time of discharge of the condenser C_1 through R_4 and R_6 is therefore longer and a longer time elapses before the relay B releases, but the space period after this is the same for both dot and dashes.

Some care may be required in selecting suitable relays. The design of relay B is not critical, except that it must operate quickly and solidly on about 5 mA; the relay A must also operate solidly on about 5 mA but it should not open too quickly, because C_1 may then not be fully charged before the circuit is broken by the A-relay contact. Post Office type-600 relays with 3000–6000 ohm coils are recommended though they tend to be noisy. High-speed relays could be used, but it may be necessary to shunt the coil of relay A with a condenser to retard its operation.

To adjust the keyer, first set R_7 and R_9 so that V_1 and V_2 are both just beyond cut-off. Hold the paddle in the *dash* position, adjust the speed control R_6 for a convenient rate of sending and then set R_9 for the correct on/off ratio for dashes (i.e. 3 units *on*, 1 unit *off*). Now hold the paddle in the *dot* position and adjust R_5 for the correct dot ratio (i.e. equal times *on* and *off*). This may be done aurally,

or more accurately by observing the anode current of a keyed stage in the transmitter (provided that the current is zero in the key-up condition). A series of dots should result in an average anode current equal to half the steady carrier value, while a series of dashes should give three-quarters. The ratios should remain correct for quite a wide range of speeds.

KEYING MONITORS

There are few operators who can send perfectly correct Morse, particularly when using a semi-automatic key, without being able to hear what they are sending. It is

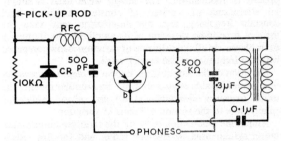

Fig. 10. **Simple transistorized c.w. monitor. The crystal diode CR may be a OA81 and the transistor a medium gain audio type. A suitable transformer is the Repanco type TT9. If co-ax feeder is in use, a capacitive tap should be made to the centre conductor instead of using a pick-up rod.**

of course practicable to use the main receiver as a monitor simply by reducing its gain sufficiently but some operators prefer a monitor whose note does not depend on the receiver tuning.

An audio-frequency tone generator may be keyed from the transmitter key (using auxiliary contacts or a relay) and fed into the a.f. section of the receiver. Alternatively a low-consumption valve or an equivalent transistor-type of a.f. oscillator may be supplied with power derived from the transmitter output by a simple rectifier and filter circuit. A method which enables a direct check to be kept on the transmission but without involving the main receiver is to use a heterodyne wavemeter or a simple uncalibrated oscillating detector as a monitor, screened if necessary to avoid overloading.

CHAPTER 9

MODULATION

A RADIO-FREQUENCY carrier wave can be used for the transmission of speech by subjecting it to a process of modulation. The carrier wave itself is simply an alternating r.f. current of constant amplitude and constant frequency, and the modulation may take the form of a periodic variation of its amplitude, its frequency or its phase. In all cases the rate of variation is low compared with the frequency of the carrier wave.

Variation of the amplitude is known as *amplitude modulation*, generally abbreviated to a.m. In a similar manner the terms *frequency modulation* (f.m.) and *phase modulation* (p.m.) refer to the two other forms of variation.

Amplitude modulation is by far the most common modulation system used in amateur radio, and for this reason the present chapter is confined entirely to a consideration of the various aspects of amplitude modulation.

Production of Sidebands

No matter what system is employed, the process of modulation produces additional frequencies above and below that of the carrier wave. Thus the modulated carrier wave consists of a band of frequencies as distinct from the single frequency of the carrier. The bandwidth depends upon the modulation system and the frequency of the modulating signals.

The bands of frequencies produced above and below the carrier-wave frequency by complex modulating signals (i.e. those composed of many different frequencies as in speech or music) are known as the upper and lower *sidebands* respectively. In the case of amplitude modulation the highest sideband frequency is equal to the *sum* of the carrier frequency and the highest modulation frequency; similarly the lowest sideband frequency is the *difference* between the carrier frequency and the highest modulation frequency. Thus the total bandwidth occupied is equal to *twice* the highest frequency in the modulating signal. For example, if the highest frequency in the modulating signal is 15 kc/s and the carrier frequency is 1000 kc/s, the sidebands will extend from 1015 kc/s to 985 kc/s. The total bandwidth occupied is therefore 30 kc/s.

Modulation Depth

The amplitude-modulated wave is shown graphically in **Fig. 1.** Here (A) represents the unmodulated carrier wave of constant amplitude and frequency which when modulated by the audio-frequency wave (B) acquires a varying amplitude as shown at (C). This is the modulated carrier wave, and the two curved lines touching the crests of the modulated carrier wave constitute the *modulation envelope*. The modulation amplitude is represented by either x or y (which in most cases can be assumed to be equal) and the ratio of this to the amplitude of the unmodulated carrier wave z is known as the *modulation depth* or *modulation factor*. This ratio may also be expressed as a percentage. When the amplitude of the modulating signal is increased as at (D) the condition (E) is reached where the negative peak of the modulating signal has reduced the amplitude of the carrier to zero, while the positive peak increases the carrier amplitude to twice the unmodulated value. This represents 100 per cent modulation, or a modulation factor of 1.

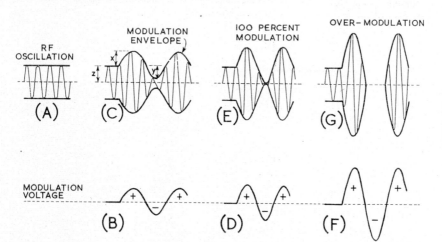

Fig. I. Graphical representation of amplitude modulation: (A) unmodulated carrier wave; (B) modulating signal; (C) modulated carrier wave; (D) (E) 100 per cent modulation; (F) (G) over-modulation.

Further increase of the modulating signal amplitude as indicated by (F) produces the condition (G) where the carrier wave is reduced to zero for an appreciable period by the negative peaks of the modulating signal. This condition is known as *over-modulation*. The breaking up of the carrier in this way causes distortion and the introduction of harmonics of the modulating frequencies which will be radiated as spurious sidebands; this causes the transmission to occupy a much greater bandwidth than necessary, and considerable interference is likely to be experienced in nearby receivers. The radiation of such spurious sidebands by over-modulation (sometimes known as *splatter* or *spitch*) must be avoided at all costs.

Modulation Power

In the special case of a sinusoidal modulating signal, corresponding to a single pure tone, it can be proved mathematically that the effective power in such a wave at 100 per cent modulation is 1·5 times the unmodulated carrier power. Thus, in order to modulate the carrier fully with a sinusoidal wave, the average power in it must be increased by 50 per cent. This extra power must be supplied from the modulator. For example, to modulate fully a radio-frequency stage operating with a d.c. power input of 150 watts, the amount of audio-frequency power required would be 75 watts.

It must not be assumed, however, that the aerial current of a fully modulated transmission will increase by 50 per cent. The relationship between the modulated and unmodulated aerial current for sine-wave modulation is given by—

$$I_m = I_0 \sqrt{1 + \frac{m^2}{2}}$$

where I_m = r.m.s. value of modulated aerial current,
I_0 = r.m.s. value of unmodulated aerial current,
m = modulation factor.

Thus, for 100 per cent modulation by a sinusoidal signal—

$$I_m = I_0 \sqrt{1 + \tfrac{1}{2}}$$
$$= 1 \cdot 226 \, I_0$$

In other words, the aerial current will increase by 22·6 per cent.

The position is somewhat different when the modulating signal consists of the "peaky" waveform of speech. Assuming that the peaks drive the transmitter into full modulation, the 22·6 per cent increase will occur at these peaks, but for most of the remainder of the time the modulation depth is much lower; the increase in aerial current will also be much lower. The average modulation depth when the peaks are fully modulated will be of the order of 30 per cent, and the average increase in aerial current as seen on a typical ammeter will then be only a few per cent.

Modulation depth may also be expressed in terms of the a.f. power actually supplied and the unmodulated d.c. power supply to the modulated stage; thus—

$$m = \sqrt{2A/W}$$

where A = a.f. power supplied,
W = d.c. input power.

Table 1 gives the values, calculated from this expression, for the amount of a.f. power required for various depths of modulation. It will be seen that to produce 70 per cent modulation requires only one half of the a.f. power required for 100 per cent modulation. The corresponding increases in aerial current are shown in the same table.

Linearity of Modulation

Ideally, for all modulation depths up to 100 per cent the difference in the amplitudes of the r.f. output between the crests and the troughs of the modulation involved should be proportional to the amplitude of the modulating signal; i.e. the modulation characteristic should be linear.

Non-linearity is most often manifest as a flattening of the crests of the modulation waveform, and this causes considerable distortion. It may be minimized by careful design and correct adjustment of the modulated stage, particularly with respect to the amount of r.f. grid drive and the aerial loading. Linear and non-linear modulation characteristics are shown in **Fig. 2**.

Bandwidth of a Modulated Wave

For the faithful reproduction of speech and music it is necessary to transmit frequencies in the whole range of the audio spectrum (i.e. approximately 40–15,000 cycles per second). The total bandwidth for this purpose would therefore be 30 kc/s. For a communication system, however, it is the intelligibility and not the fidelity which is of prime importance, and experience has shown that for the intelligible transmission of speech it is sufficient to transmit frequencies up to about 2·5 or 3 kc/s. Thus the transmitted bandwidth

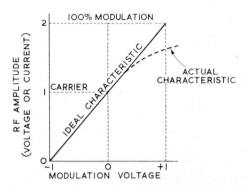

Fig. 2. The ideal modulation characteristic is a straight line. Often the actual characteristic is found to be non-linear, and the form of non-linearity shown here is due to the failure of the r.f. voltage (or current) amplitude to rise to twice its normal value at the positive peaks of the modulating signal.

TABLE I

Effect of Modulation on Aerial Current

Depth of modulation (per cent)	Ratio: $\dfrac{\text{a.f. power}}{\text{d.c. power}}$	Increase in aerial current (per cent)
100	0·5	22·6
90	0·405	18·5
80	0·32	15·1
70	0·245	11·5
60	0·18	8·6
50	0·125	6·0

need not exceed approximately 5 kc/s. In the overcrowded conditions of the present-day amateur bands it is obviously important to ensure that no transmission occupies a greater bandwidth than is necessary for intelligible communication.

Modulating Impedance

The impedance that an r.f. stage which is being modulated presents to the source of the modulating signal, i.e. the modulator, is called " modulating impedance." It is the ratio of the anode voltage and anode current of the r.f. stage or

$$Zm = \frac{Ea}{Ia} \times 1000$$

where Zm = modulating impedance
   Ea = anode voltage of r.f. stage
   Ia = anode current of r.f. stage (in mA).

Mathematical Representation of Sidebands

The mathematical equation for a carrier wave of constant frequency which is amplitude-modulated by a signal of constant frequency is—

$$e = E_0 (1 + m.\sin 2\pi f_m.t) \sin 2\pi f_c.t$$

where m = modulation factor,
   f_m = frequency of modulating signal,
   f_c = frequency of carrier wave,
   E_0 = amplitude of unmodulated carrier

This equation may be expanded, giving—

$$e = E_0 \sin 2\pi f_c.t + m\frac{E_0}{2}\cos 2\pi(f_c-f_m)t - m\frac{E_0}{2}\cos 2\pi(f_c+f_m)t$$

Inspection of this expanded form shows that it is made up of three separate terms. The first, $E_0 \sin 2\pi f_c.t$, represents the original carrier, while $m\frac{E_0}{2} \cos 2\pi(f_c-f_m)t$ and $m\frac{E_0}{2}$ $\cos 2\pi(f_c+f_m)t$ correspond to the lower and upper side-frequencies respectively which are the result of applying a modulating signal of frequency f_m. The total bandwidth of this amplitude modulated wave is $(f_c + f_m) - (f_c - f_m)$ or $2f_m$; i.e. the bandwidth is equal to twice the modulating frequency.

It should be noted from the last equation that the carrier wave is not fundamentally essential to communication since all the intelligence is contained in the sidebands. The carrier wave can therefore be suppressed and need not be transmitted; indeed, it is sufficient to transmit only one of the sidebands. This method is often used and is known as *single-sideband* operation (s.s.b.). Although it requires more complicated equipment than ordinary amplitude modulation, it has the obvious advantage of transmitting the same intelligence within a smaller bandwidth and without a carrier.

Basic Modulation Equipment

In the foregoing paragraphs the fundamentals of the process of amplitude modulation have been reviewed. It thus now becomes possible to specify the modulation equipment required for a communications transmitter. This consists of—

(a) An a.f. power amplifier capable of developing the required power over the minimum frequency range for intelligible speech, and its associated d.c. power unit.

(b) A means of coupling, with correct matching of impedances, the a.f. power to the r.f. stage.

(c) A microphone.

(d) A speech amplifier to amplify the output of the microphone to a suitable level to drive the a.f. power amplifier.

The manner in which these elements are associated in a typical communications transmitter is illustrated in the block diagram shown in **Fig. 3**. The term *modulator* is often applied to the whole of the a.f. amplifying section, but strictly speaking it should be applied only to the final stage of the a.f. amplifier.

AMPLITUDE MODULATION SYSTEMS

As already defined, amplitude modulation consists of variation of the envelope of the r.f. carrier in accordance with the waveform of the intelligence which it is desired to transmit. There are several possible ways of applying amplitude modulation to a carrier wave. They can be classified according to the manner in which the modulating voltage is applied to the stage to be modulated, giving the following broad classifications:

(a) Anode modulation
(b) Control-grid modulation
(c) Suppressor-grid modulation
(d) Screen-grid modulation
(e) Cathode modulation.

Modulation should be applied only to an r.f. stage which is driven from a source of constant frequency, e.g. a crystal oscillator or a stable variable-frequency oscillator followed by at least one isolating stage. This is to prevent the production of spurious frequency modulation such as would result from the direct modulation of a self-excited oscillator. In the case of a triode p.a. stage, neutralization must be perfect, and where neutralization is not employed, as in some tetrode or pentode power amplifiers, great care must be taken to avoid parasitic oscillation which may occur only on the peaks of modulation.

Anode Modulation

Anode modulation of a class C r.f. stage is accomplished by superimposing the modulating voltage on the d.c. anode voltage. For full modulation the anode voltage of the p.a. is swung from zero to twice its normal value, thus

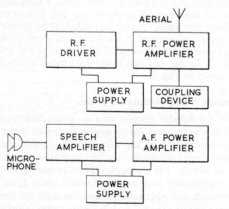

causing a corresponding variation in the amplitude of the r.f. output. If the r.f. stage is operated under the correct conditions, the r.f. output current will be proportional to the anode voltage applied to the p.a., and the modulation will be distortionless.

Anode modulation may be achieved in a variety of ways:

(a) Transformer modulation.

(b) Choke modulation.

(c) Series modulation.

(d) Anode modulation of tetrodes and pentodes.

(a) **Transformer Modulation.** The most straightforward means of anode modulation is the use of a transformer

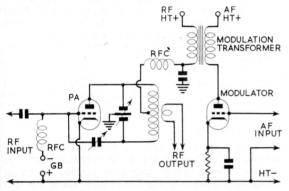

Fig. 4. Anode modulation using transformer coupling. The system is sometimes referred to as " transformer modulation."

known as a *modulation transformer* to couple the modulator to the p.a. stage: the basic circuit arrangement is shown in **Fig. 4.** The ratio of the transformer should be such that it will match the impedance of the modulated r.f. stage to the load required by the modulator valve(s). Although in Fig. 4 a single triode modulator is shown, it should be realized that triodes, tetrodes or pentodes, either in push-pull or single-ended operation, may be used.

In order to obtain linear modulation the r.f. amplifier should be carefully adjusted in accordance with the operating conditions recommended by the manufacturer for the particular valves concerned. In general, it can be said that the r.f. stage must be operated under class C conditions for peak output, and the aerial coupling must be adjusted to provide the correct modulating impedance.

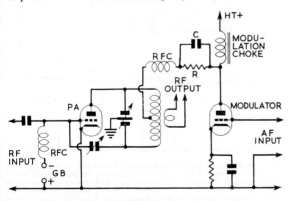

Fig. 5. Choke modulation of a class C r.f. amplifier.

Although the *effective* power input is modulated, the *average* power input remains constant because each positive excursion of the anode voltage is immediately followed by a corresponding negative one. This means that the anode current, as measured by a moving-coil d.c. meter, does not vary during modulation because such a meter measures average current. However, the aerial current is usually measured on a thermal meter which indicates the r.m.s. value and, as was shown earlier, the effective or r.m.s. value of the aerial current does depend upon the amount of modulation. Although the thermal ammeter in the aerial circuit should show a rise of current on modulation, the moving-coil " average-current " meter in the anode circuit should remain constant, and any movement of this meter during modulation indicates incorrect operation.

Anode modulation is the commonest form used, and it is probably the simplest system to adjust and operate. Moreover it is a system which enables the r.f. amplifier to operate at a constant high efficiency, and is capable of full modulation with the least amount of distortion. For most valves the output rating, under anode-modulation conditions, is of the order of two-thirds of the maximum output under c.w. conditions.

(b) **Choke Modulation.** An alternative method of anode modulation employs a choke as the coupling impedance between the modulator and the r.f. stage, as shown in **Fig. 5.**

The modulation choke must have an impedance at audio frequencies which is high compared with the impedance of the modulated r.f. stage when carrying the combined anode currents of that stage and the modulator. Obviously in this system both valves operate at the same h.t. voltage. The undistorted output voltage from the modulator which is developed across the choke must be less than the h.t. voltage and therefore it cannot modulate the r.f. stage to 100 per cent. For this reason the p.a. stage is run at a lower h.t. voltage than that of the modulator, the excess voltage being dropped across the resistor R which is by-passed at audio frequency by the condenser C. The h.t. voltage on the p.a. stage should be reduced by this means to about 60–70 per cent of the modulator h.t. voltage. Since a push-pull arrangement in the modulator is obviously precluded, class-B operation cannot be employed without excessive distortion, and such modulators must operate under class A conditions. This may necessitate the use of very large modulator valves, or several in parallel, and for this reason choke modulation is only economic for low-power operation, e.g. up to about 15 watts input to the r.f. amplifier.

(c) **Series Modulation.** In this case the modulator and the p.a. valves are connected in series across one h.t. supply, as shown in **Fig. 6.** Thus both will pass the same current, the method of adjustment being to vary the operating conditions (i.e. the amount of grid drive, the aerial loading and the grid bias of the p.a. stage) so that it is operating at a lower anode-to-cathode voltage than the modulator. This system has the advantage that one power unit feeds both the p.a. and the modulator, and that no modulation transformer or choke is required. Valves such as the 807 can be used in both positions in a series-modulation system from a 1000 volts supply. The operating conditions of the p.a. stage should be such that there is 500–600 volts across the modulator, and between 400–500 volts across the p.a. For higher power two such valves may be used in parallel

257

as the modulator, and two more either in push-pull or in parallel as the p.a. Although Fig. 6 shows the modulator connected to the positive end of the supply, the modulator and p.a. may be interchanged so that the modulator is earthed and the p.a. is connected to the positive supply terminal. It is immaterial which arrangement is used as long as appropriate precautions are taken, e.g. the valve connected to the positive end of the power supply must have a separate heater transformer capable of withstanding

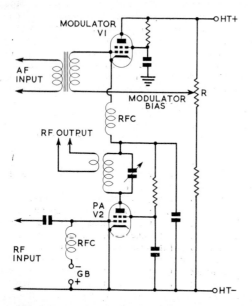

Fig. 6. Series modulation. The relative positions of the a.f. modulator V1 and the r.f. output valve V2 between the h.t. line and earth can be interchanged if desired. The appropriate negative bias on the control grid of V1 with respect to its cathode is obtained by adjusting the potentiometer R1.

approximately one half of the total h.t. voltage, and its grid circuit (a.f. or r.f. as the case may be) must have transformers or condensers with insulation rated for this voltage.

(d) **Anode Modulation of Tetrodes and Pentodes.** True anode modulation can be applied only to triodes. The characteristics of tetrodes and pentodes demand that both the screen and anode voltages are modulated to obtain a linear modulation characteristic. This may be done as in **Fig. 7** where it will be seen that the screen-grid voltage is obtained from the modulated anode voltage through a series resistance *R*. A potentiometer cannot be used for this purpose. The screen by-pass condenser *C* must have a reasonably high reactance at audio frequencies in order not to short-circuit the modulation voltages. The modulator load impedance in this case is the ratio of the anode voltage to the sum of the anode and screen currents, and the audio power required is one half of the product of the anode voltage and the sum of the anode and screen currents.

Efficiency Modulation Systems

The remaining methods of amplitude modulation are usually grouped together under the general heading of *Efficiency-Modulation Systems.* In these systems the efficiency

(i.e. the ratio between the r.f. power output and the d.c. power input) is varied by altering the voltage on either the control-grid or the screen-grid, whereas in anode modulation the efficiency is constant and the required variation in r.f. output is obtained by altering the power input. The term *efficiency modulation* should not be taken to imply that this system results in a high efficiency: on the contrary, the overall average efficiency is low. The maximum efficiency for a class C stage is of the order of 70 per cent in anode-modulation systems and this remains constant throughout the modulation cycle. This figure is only achieved, however, on the peaks of modulation in efficiency-modulation systems; the average efficiency is only one half of this figure, and frequently a little lower, say about 30 per cent. The average r.f. output power for a given d.c. input power to the p.a. is appreciably less than for anode modulation. However, the extra r.f. power output which is delivered at modulation peaks is a consequence of the higher operating efficiency at these peaks rather than the effect of additional audio power from the modulator. In efficiency modulation systems the audio power required is generally insignificant compared with the d.c. input to the r.f. stage.

Grid Modulation

This is probably the most common form of efficiency modulation. It may be applied to practically any type of valve, whether triode, tetrode or pentode. A circuit arrangement is shown in **Fig. 8** in which It will be seen that the audio-frequency voltage is applied in series with the r.f. voltage to the grid of the r.f. amplifier. With this system of modulation it is more difficult to make adjustments which will give full modulation with low distortion than in the case of anode modulation. The requirements are as follows:

(a) The r.f. drive must have good regulation, i.e. the r.f. grid voltage must remain substantially constant in spite of the varying grid-current load of the r.f. amplifier. This is generally arranged by providing much more drive than is really necessary and dissipating the excess in a lamp or other resistance load.

(b) The modulator must have a low-impedance output

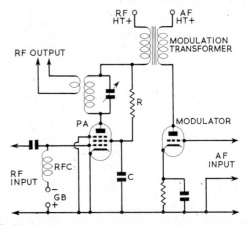

Fig. 7. Anode-and-screen modulation. When the modulated stage consists of a pentode or a tetrode, the screen voltage as well as the anode voltage should be modulated by a proportionate amount in order to ensure linear modulation. A r.f. decoupling capacitor should be connected between the junction of R and the tuned circuit and earth.

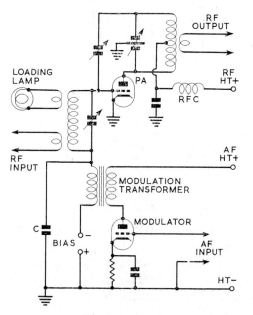

Fig. 8. Grid modulation. The lamp is used to absorb an appreciable proportion of the grid-driving power and thus improve the grid-drive regulation. The condenser C serves as an r.f. by-pass: it must be small enough to present a high reactance at the highest modulation frequency.

(e.g. 100–130 volts in the case of the 807). Unless this is done, the upward excursions of the screen voltage during modulation would be limited by the sharp rise in screen current. The positive peaks of the modulated r.f. output waveform would thus be flattened and the modulation would become asymmetrical.

The low average screen voltage results in a rather low r.f. carrier output power, as in the case of control-grid modulation, and it may therefore be worthwhile to incorporate two r.f. valves in push-pull when using this system. Screen-grid modulation does not call for critical adjustment of the grid drive to the modulated stage but the unmodulated screen voltage must be very carefully adjusted to allow the greatest possible depth of modulation without distortion. This maximum is generally of the order of 75–80 per cent. The audio power required, as in other efficiency modulation systems is quite low, 4–6 watts being sufficient to modulate an input of 150 watts.

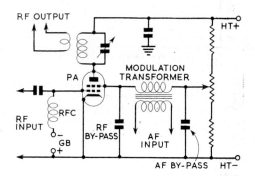

Fig. 9. Screen modulation. The screen supply voltage must be obtained from a potentiometer R to enable the necessary critical adjustment to be made for maximum depth of modulation.

to avoid waveform distortion due to the varying grid load of the r.f. amplifier. A triode operating in class A is preferable, but if a tetrode or pentode is used it is advisable to connect a swamping resistance across the secondary of the modulation transformer.

(c) The grid-bias supply must have good voltage regulation; either battery bias or a voltage-stabilized supply is required.

The chief advantage of grid modulation is the relatively low audio power required, a few watts generally sufficing to modulate a 150-watt stage.

The power input to the p.a. valve must be limited to such a value that the maximum permissible anode dissipation is not exceeded, assuming the low average efficiency of 35 per cent. The adjustment generally consists of setting the grid drive (which is about 20–25 per cent of that necessary when maximum efficiency as a c.w. output stage is required), and adjusting the grid bias and the aerial loading until the appropriate amount of aerial-current increase is obtained without causing any variation of the p.a. anode current. The audio-frequency gain is then adjusted so that the desired peak modulation is obtained: in this system the peak modulation will usually have to be limited to about 90 per cent to prevent the occurrence of distortion.

Screen-grid Modulation

The general circuit arrangement used for screen-grid modulation is shown in Fig. 9. Popular types of beam tetrodes, such as the 807 and the 813 are well suited to this system.

The main drawback of screen modulation is that the screen-grid voltage must be reduced to a fairly low value

Clamp Modulation

The so-called clamp-modulation system is an interesting variation of screen-grid modulation. The purpose of a "clamp" valve is to reduce the screen voltage of a tetrode r.f. amplifier to a low value in the absence of grid excitation, so that it acts as a protective device and allows the exciter to be keyed for c.w. operation without the necessity for using fixed bias on the p.a. stage. A typical circuit is shown in Fig. 10. The clamp valve V_2, which may be of the KT66 or 6L6 class, is cut off by the operating bias of the r.f. stage V_1 which is developed across R_1. When the excitation is removed, there is no bias on V_2 and hence it passes a large anode current which develops a high voltage-drop across R_2, the screen resistor of V_1. This reduction in the screen voltage of V_1 reduces the anode current to a very low and safe value.

For the purposes of modulation the grid of the clamp valve may be switched from the r.f. bias resistor R_1 to the output of a speech amplifier V_3 so that the screen of V_1 receives the audio output voltage through V_2.

When V_2 is switched for telephony operation its bias should be arranged to be such that its anode voltage, i.e. the screen voltage of V_1, is about one half of the value which it has in the c.w. position. Tuning-up can take place

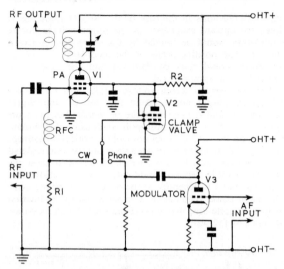

Fig. 10. Clamp modulation. This is an elaborated form of screen modulation which enables the transmitter to be easily switched to c.w. operation.

in the c.w. position, but when V_2 is switched to the telephony position the carrier output of V_1 will of course fall. When modulating, the audio gain should be such that the anode current of V_1 on modulation peaks does not exceed about three-quarters of the normal c.w. value.

Suppressor-grid Modulation

The gain of a pentode may be controlled independently of the other voltages by varying the voltage applied to the suppressor-grid. This forms the basis of the suppressor-grid modulation system in which the a.f. modulating voltage is added to the suppressor-grid bias, as shown in **Fig. 11(a)**. This form of modulation is one of the simplest to adjust, and is capable of producing up to about 95 per cent modulation with very little distortion, and requires only a small amount of a.f. power. Adjustment is carried out by changing the grid bias in a negative direction by an amount which reduces

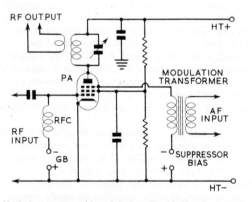

Fig. 11(a). Suppressor-grid modulation. The bias on the suppressor grid needs to be carefully adjusted. The suppressor grid should be decoupled to earth by an r.f. by-pass capacitor.

the anode current to one half of that obtained for c.w. working. The peak value of the a.f. voltage applied to the suppressor will need to be equal to this change of suppressor-grid bias, and under these conditions practically full modulation will be obtained.

Grid-leak Modulation

A form of grid modulation which is occasionally used for low-power operation is called *grid-leak modulation*. If, in an r.f. amplifier which obtains its operating bias solely by the grid-leak method, the value of the grid leak is varied, the grid bias and hence the output will also be varied. In practice this may be accomplished by using a valve as the grid leak (**Fig. 11(b)**). The usual adjustments should be made of grid drive and aerial loading for approximately one half of the normal c.w. output. Under these conditions the aerial current should rise during modulation by the normal amount.

The power efficiency of this system is very low, being about 25–30 per cent, but on the other hand it is probably the most

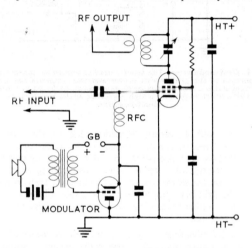

Fig. 11(b). Grid-leak modulation. This system requires the minimum amount of audio equipment but the r.f. efficiency is low.

economical system since it can be made to function successfully with only a carbon microphone and its transformer and one small triode.

Cathode Modulation

Modulation may alternatively be applied to the cathode circuit of the p.a. as illustrated in **Fig. 12**. This is known as *cathode modulation*. In effect both anode and grid voltages are varied simultaneously with respect to the cathode. Cathode modulation is therefore a compromise between anode modulation at high output efficiency and grid modulation at low output efficiency. By suitable adjustment, any desired proportion of each form may be achieved.

The ratio of the respective amounts of anode modulation and grid modulation is controlled by the value of the grid bias on the p.a., which in turn will determine the amount of audio-frequency power required. The latter determines the amount of anode modulation, while the former determines the amount of control that a given value of

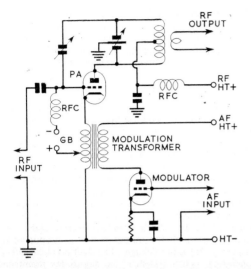

Fig. 12. Cathode modulation. This method is a combination of (a) anode modulation with its high output efficiency and high-modulation-power requirement and (b) grid modulation with its low output efficiency and low modulation-power requirement.

modulating voltage will have. The grid bias, of course, will depend upon the value of the r.f. and a.f. voltages. A greater range of adjustment in the grid circuit may be obtained if the grid return can be taken to a variable tap on the secondary winding of the modulation transformer; for this reason a multi-ratio type of transformer is preferable.

The setting-up of such a circuit can be fairly complicated because in addition to the normal adjustments, the proportion of grid and anode modulations should be adjusted to obtain full modulation. However, once set up the system is capable of very good results.

Series Gate Modulation

Series gate modulation is a form of screen modulation of fairly recent origin. It is simple and effective and appears to justify the claims made for it. The name " series gate " modulation was given to it by the originator, but it does not indicate clearly the mode of operation.

The basic series gate modulator circuit is shown in **Fig. 13(a).** This employs only one valve, a twin triode, but there is, of course, no reason why two separate triodes should not

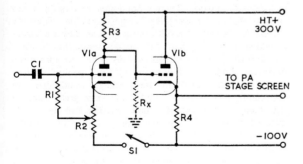

Fig. 13(a). Basic " series gate " modulation circuit.

be used. The circuit is essentially a voltage amplifier V_{1a} direct-coupled to a cathode-follower V_{1b}.

When the slider of R_2 is at the cathode end of its travel, V_{1a} is operating without bias; there is, therefore, a large voltage drop across R_3 and the anode voltage of V_{1a} is reduced to a low value, of the order of 15V. This voltage is direct-coupled to the cathode-follower V_{1b}, and so about 95 per cent of this voltage or 14V appears across the cathode load R_4. Thus the screen voltage of the r.f. amplifier is also 14V and the r.f. output is low. If the slider of R_2 is moved away from the cathode end, the bias on V_{1a} increases and the voltage drop across R_3 is reduced. The anode voltage of V_{1a}, and hence the grid voltage of V_{1b}, then rises to the order of 250V. The screen voltage of the p.a. stage will therefore be increased to somewhat less than this as a result of the cathode-follower action of V_{1b}. Thus the output of the p.a. stage will be increased towards its maximum.

The setting of R_2 therefore makes it possible to vary the output of the r.f. stage from a low level to almost full c.w. ratings. If S_1 is opened, V_{1a} is inoperative and the anode of V_{1a} and the grid of V_{1b} rise towards the anode supply voltage and the screen voltage of the p.a. stage is limited by the flow of grid current of V_{1b} through R_3. The screen

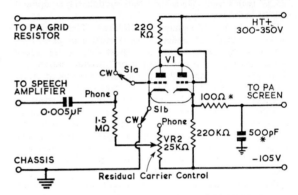

Fig. 13(b). Practical series gate modulator. For p.a. inputs up to 75 watts, suitable valves are the 6SN7 and 12AU7. For higher inputs, a 12BH7 may be used. Alternatively, two 6J5s or triode connected 6V6s are suggested. The 100 ohm resistor and 500 pF capacitor marked with asterisks are the normal screen decoupling components mounted close to the p.a. valveholder.

potential is then the highest obtainable with this particular circuit arrangement. The maximum screen voltage may be set by the introduction of R_x. R_3 and R_x then form a potentiometer across the h.t. supply which holds the grid voltage of V_{1b} constant.

Modulation may be achieved by applying an a.f. voltage to C_1. Assuming that the bias on the grid of V_{1a} is set (by R_2) to $-1V$, the d.c. voltage applied to the screen of the p.a. is low and so the r.f. output is low. If an a.f. voltage of 1V peak is now applied to the grid of V_{1a}, it will be amplified by V_{1a} and appear at the p.a. screen and so modulate the low r.f. output to a depth of approximately 95 per cent, the mean d.c. potential of the p.a. screen remaining constant. If the a.f. voltage applied to V_{1a} is increased, grid current will flow in V_{1a} and a negative charge will build up on C_1 proportional to the peak value of the a.f. voltage. This additional d.c. bias applied to the grid of V_{1a} will cause the potential on its anode and the grid of V_{1b} (and of course the mean screen voltage of the p.a. stage) to rise, resulting in

261

increased r.f. output from the p.a. stage. Since the period of time for which this potential is raised depends upon the time it takes for C_1 to discharge through R_1, the time constant of R_1 and C_1 is important and must be considerably longer than the time corresponding to the lowest audio frequency used.

The increased a.f. voltage at the grid of V_{1a} will appear as an amplified voltage at the p.a. screen relative to its previous value, but as the mean screen potential has also been raised the carrier is again modulated to a level of about 95 per cent.

A practical series gate modulator is shown in **Fig. 13(b).** It will be seen that this is virtually the same as the basic circuit shown in Fig. 13(a) the only addition being the phone/c.w. switch S_1, the 500 pF capacitor and 100 ohm resistor. The latter are the normal p.a. screen decoupling components which of course should be mounted as close a possible to the p.a. valveholder. For inputs to the p.a. of up to 75 watts, recommended valves are the 6SN7 or 12AU7. For higher inputs, a 12BH7 is to be preferred. Alternatively separate valves such as the 6J5, L63 or triode-corrected 6V6's (or similar) may be used.

This series gate modulator may be conveniently preceded by a simple two-stage speech amplifier using, for example, a 12AX7 twin triode. Thus the whole modulating equipment may be made very small.

The method of adjustment is as follows. The transmitter should be tuned and loaded in the normal manner with S_1 set to c.w. Switch to PHONE and adjust VR_2, i.e. the screen voltage of the p.a., to give an input or " residual carrier " of about one-fifth to one-eighth of the full carrier input under c.w. conditions. The audio gain control in the speech amplifier should then be slowly advanced while speaking into the microphone until the anode current rises on peaks to the value obtained under c.w. conditions. If too small a value of residual carrier is used, the signal tends to become difficult to tune in initially. When receiving a series gate modulated signal it is preferable to switch off the receiver a.g.c.

The advantages of series gate modulation may be summarized as follows:

    (i)   Overmodulation on positive peaks cannot occur because as the a.f. voltage applied to C_1 (Fig. 13(a)) is increased, limiting will occur in V_{1a} and hence the a.f. voltage applied to the p.a. screen cannot increase.

    (ii)   Splatter caused by the breaking up of the carrier by overmodulation on the negative peaks cannot occur because the screen voltage cannot fall below the value selected by the residual carrier control VR_2. Thus a simple but effective means of speech clipping is available merely by slightly advancing the audio gain control beyond the point specified above. Too much clipping in this manner will, however, tend to decrease intelligibility rather than increase it as is usual.

    (iii)   In the cw position of S_1 the modulator functions as a normal clamp circuit and so protects the p.a. under key-up conditions.

The disadvantage is that a negative bias supply is required. This is not necessarily available with the widespread use of a clamp valve on the p.a. stage. A battery or a well-smoothed supply is necessary.

Thus even a 150W input r.f. power amplifier may be modulated by a small unit using two twin triodes. The small size and power requirements of such a modulator make it ideal for mobile or portable equipment. It is also a convenient way of modifying a c.w. transmitter for telephony operation with the minimum of expense and addition.

Low-level Modulation

The modulation systems so far considered are known as " high-level " systems because the modulation is applied to the r.f. stage working at the highest power level. There is no reason why the modulation should not be applied to a low-power stage, the modulated output of which is then amplified. This " low-level " modulation system is occasionally used in amateur practice. The modulated r.f. voltage can be amplified to increase the output power, but in order to avoid distortion of the modulated wave the r.f. amplifiers following the modulated stage must be of the so-called linear type. Such amplifiers operate under class B conditions in which the output power is proportional to the square of the input voltage. The chief practical difficulty in operating such a system is the day-to-day maintenance of the operating conditions which are more critical than those in a high-level class C modulated amplifier. The impedance of the grid circuit of such amplifiers varies appreciably over the modulation cycle, and a low-impedance source of grid power is required for the reasons already explained in the case of grid modulation. The regulation of the driving stage may be improved by dissipating some of the output from the previous stage in a resistance load. The linear amplifier stage must not be operated as a frequency multiplier since the depth of modulation would thereby be increased and distortion introduced.

Choice of Modulation System

There is little doubt that anode modulation is the most effective system of amplitude modulation from all points of view. It has, however, the disadvantage that the audio-frequency power requirements are the highest, and thus the modulator and associated power supply are expensive and often complicated pieces of equipment.

It may be argued that the overall power efficiency of a transmitter employing one of the so-called efficiency-modulation systems is much higher on account of the smaller amount of audio power required. This may well be a powerful argument in the case of portable, mobile or battery-operated equipment, but such systems are not often adopted for fixed-station work. There is not a great deal of difference between any of the variable-efficiency methods. They are all capable of excellent results, but in general they are harder to adjust correctly than the anode-modulation system. The published valve ratings usually refer to maximum sinusoidal conditions, but owing to the " peaky " nature of the speech waveform the average conditions are appreciably less arduous, and with very great care in adjustment and operation these circuits can be safely operated at somewhat higher ratings than those usually published for a given valve. Perhaps the greatest advantage of variable-efficiency systems is that they present a convenient method of telephony operation to the amateur whose main interest lies in c.w. operation.

MICROPHONES

The microphone is the starting point of any electrical system of communication by speech, as it is the device which converts the energy of the sound wave of the human voice into electrical energy. The output voltage or current can then be amplified and used to modulate a radio transmitter.

Basic Acoustical Principles

A sound wave is a wave of alternating pressure and rarefaction spreading out from the source, in which the instantaneous air pressure at any fixed point varies above and below the mean atmospheric pressure by an amount which determines the intensity of the sound. The waveform of this pressure variation is a curve whose shape determines the characteristics by which one sound differs from another. For example, a pure sine wave of pressure results in a single tone described as " pure," the frequency determining the pitch. Different musical instruments all playing a note of the same pitch produce waves of varying harmonic content, the proportions of which determine the tonal quality or *timbre* of the sound. Harmonics (or overtones) similarly determine the characteristic differences between the male and female singing voices. The important parts of the waveshape of speech sound are the harmonics of the fundamental pitch and the transient wave-shapes.

The pressure of a sound wave represents the variation about the mean pressure, and is usually measured in dynes per square centimetre. When referring to sinusoidal waves either the peak value or the r.m.s. value may be used as in other alternating quantities, the r.m.s. figure being more generally quoted.

In an electrical circuit an e.m.f. or electrical pressure produces an electrical current, the magnitude of which depends upon the electrical resistance. In an analogous manner an acoustical pressure-wave is accompanied by a movement of the air particles, which may conveniently be measured by the velocity of these particles. This velocity depends upon the *acoustic impedance* of the air space upon which the pressure is acting. This impedance depends in turn on the distributed mass and elasticity of the air, and can be regarded as a " characteristic impedance " similar to the characteristic impedance of a cable or transmission line which is determined by the distributed inductance and capacitance.

The wavelength of an acoustic wave is derived in the same way as that for a radio wave, except that the wave velocity in air is approximately 344 metres/second compared with 300,000,000 metres/second for electromagnetic waves. This wave velocity is a constant figure for any given gas or liquid at a specified temperature and must not be confused with the particle velocity referred to above, which depends upon the acoustic pressure.

Thus, the wavelength corresponding to a frequency of 100 c/s is given by—

$$\lambda = \frac{34,000}{100} = 344 \text{ cm.}$$

and that corresponding to a frequency of 10,000 c/s by—

$$\lambda = \frac{34,000}{10,000} = 3 \cdot 44 \text{ cm.}$$

Microphones can be designed so that their electrical output voltage is proportional either to the acoustic pressure or to the particle velocity, thus giving rise to the terms *pressure microphone* and *velocity microphone*.

The pressure microphone, provided it is small enough to avoid complications due to reflection of the wave, will give a constant output no matter in what direction it is facing relative to the direction of travel of the wave. In practice, however, when the frequency is high enough for a half-wave to approximate to the size of the microphone, or higher, the microphone will be more responsive to sounds from a direction facing the microphone than to those from the sides or the rear. Thus, at 10,000 c/s where the half-wavelength is 1·72 cm. the " front-to-back " ratio would be quite high for a microphone 3 in. in diameter, whereas at 100 c/s, corresponding to a half-wavelength of 172 cm., the same microphone would give the same output regardless of the direction of the sound.

The term *velocity* has no meaning unless it is associated with a direction as well as a magnitude, since sound waves consist of longitudinal movements of the air particles in

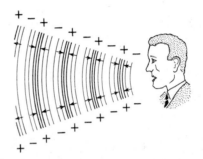

Fig. 14. Sound waves consist of successive variations of pressure above and below the normal undisturbed pressure and can be represented by alternate regions marked + and —. When sound is radiated from a point source, the wavefront is spherical in shape, the centre of the sphere being at the source of the sound.

the direction in which the wave is travelling. The velocity at any point is at a maximum in a direction facing the source, and zero in a direction at right angles to this. Thus a velocity microphone, i.e. one in which the output is designed to be proportional to the particle velocity, will have maximum output when facing towards or away from the source and zero output when at right angles to the source; moreover, the output is independent of any refraction effects referred to earlier, i.e. it is zero in the perpendicular direction, even at the lowest frequencies. **Fig. 14** represents the radiation of sound waves from a point source. Regions in which the maximum instantaneous pressure is above or below atmospheric pressures are indicated by + and — signs respectively. The air particles will, of course, move from the regions of high pressure to the regions of low pressure, so that the groups of arrows shown in the diagram represent the displacement of the air particles. The positions of maximum velocity will be the same as those of maximum pressure in free space, although there they will be in quadrature with respect to time.

An ideal pressure microphone has a polar diagram consisting of a circle, while a velocity microphone has a diagram like a figure-of-eight, similar to that of a dipole aerial. These diagrams apply in any plane, which means that for a pressure microphone the solid polar diagram is a sphere, while that for a velocity microphone is two spheres touching at the point represented by the microphone.

Basic Electro-mechanical Principles

All practical microphones consist of a mechanical system in which some part moves in sympathy with either the acoustic pressure or the particle velocity, or a combination of both. The pressure microphone comprises a closed chamber containing air at normal atmospheric pressure, part of this chamber being made in the form of a diaphragm which, if it is small and light, will move in sympathy with the variations in air pressure produced by the sound wave outside the chamber above and below the mean pressure of the air inside the chamber.

In a velocity microphone, however, a very light membrane with both sides open to the air is used. When the plane of the membrane is at right angles to the direction of the air movements, it will move with the air, and its velocity will be almost the same as that of the air particles if it is light enough.

To convert a movement of the diaphragm of the pressure microphone or of the membrane of the velocity microphone into an electrical output either the resistance of a circuit may be varied, as for instance by the use of carbon granules, or electromotive forces may be produced by electro-magnetic induction or the piezoelectric effect.

Microphone Characteristics

Brief details are given below of the construction and characteristics of the more common types of microphone. Reference should be made to the manufacturers' literature for more detailed information.

The Carbon Microphone. In this microphone a small capsule filled with carbon granules is attached to a diaphragm, and the effect of the varying pressure of the sound waves is to cause a similar variation in the resistance of the capsule. When connected to a source of constant voltage the microphone thus produces a varying current. The normal resistance of the capsule is generally between 200 and 1000 ohms and the polarising current should be in the range 5–40 mA according to the particular design of capsule.

The source of current may be a small dry battery or a potential divider connected across the h.t. supply to the speech amplifier, as shown at (A) and (B) in **Fig. 15**. To match the low impedance of the microphone circuit to the high impedance of the input grid circuit of the amplifier, a trans-former with a large turns-ratio is required; any ratio between 1 : 30 and 1 : 100 should prove satisfactory.

Although these microphones are very sensitive, the frequency response is poor compared with that of most other types. An output of between 5 and 15 volts can be expected across the secondary of the transformer when speaking close to the microphone, depending on the transformer ratio and the polarizing current. To avoid distortion, the latter should be kept as low as possible consistent with the output required. It will be appreciated that a microphone which utilizes the change in pressure between a multitude of contact points cannot be as free from distortion as some of the more elaborate types described below.

The carbon microphone is particularly convenient for portable use as its high output is capable of fully driving valves such as the KT66 and 6L6 directly from the micro-phone transformer. An alternative method of using a carbon microphone is shown at (C) in Fig. 15. Here the microphone acts as the cathode bias resistance of the first valve, the grid being earthed. This form of connection avoids the use of a transformer and a separate polarizing supply, and is capable of somewhat better quality, although the output may be lower.

The Transverse-current Microphone. This is another form of resistance microphone employing carbon granules. It has a mica diaphragm, usually rectangular in shape, behind which is a shallow chamber containing very fine carbon granules. The polarizing current passes between carbon electrodes which are placed at opposite edges of the chamber so that the granules form a thin layer of carbon through which the current passes from one edge to the other. As with the simple carbon microphone a polarizing current and step-up transformer are required. Because the diaphragm is heavily damped all over its surface by the carbon granules, the frequency response is much better than that of the capsule type, although the sensitivity is lower. An output in the order of 0·1–0·5 volt across the transformer secondary can generally be obtained.

The Moving-coil Microphone. This microphone is an electrodynamic type. Its construction is very similar to that of a moving-coil loudspeaker, except that the whole con-struction is very much smaller. The impedance of the coil is generally 20–50 ohms. When the diaphragm is caused to vibrate by the sound pressure an e.m.f. is developed in the coil and no polarizing supply is necessary. A step-up transformer, however, is required to feed the grid of the first amplifier valve. A very good frequency response can be obtained, and this type of microphone is commonly

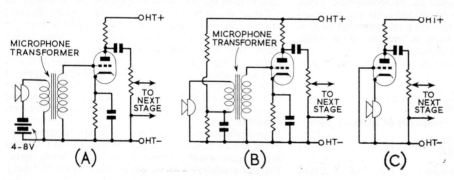

Fig. 15. Typical carbon microphone input circuits. In (A) the polarizing current is obtained from a small battery: in (B) a potential divider across the h.t. supply is used as a substitute for the battery: in (C) the microphone is used to modulate the cathode current directly by acting as a variable cathode-bias resistance.

used in broadcasting studios. The output from the secondary of a suitable transformer is usually not more than about 0·05 volt. A miniature moving-coil loudspeaker can sometimes be made to serve as a fairly satisfactory microphone, but its frequency response will not be as good as that of a specially designed instrument

The Ribbon Microphone. This type of microphone has an output proportional to the velocity of the air particles. The main difference between its operation and that of a pressure microphone is that it has a figure-of-eight polar diagram; it is thus necessary to align its axis with that of the direction of the sound source.

The most common form consists of a very thin strip of aluminium foil (about 1 in. long, 0·1 in. wide and 0·00003 in. thick) supported between the poles of a permanent magnet. As the ribbon vibrates it cuts the magnetic field between the poles, and so an e.m.f. is induced in the strip. A step-up transformer is normally placed within the microphone case to transform the very low ribbon impedance to 50–250 ohms to make the microphone impedance suitable for working into a cable, and a further step-up transformer is used at the amplifier input. No polarizing current is required, and the frequency response can be very good, although the sensitivity tends to be rather low.

The Condenser Microphone. The condenser microphone consists of a thin conducting diaphragm which forms one plate of a condenser whose capacitance varies when actuated

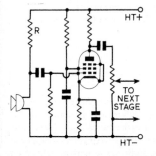

Fig. 16. Condenser microphone input circuit. The resistance R must be very high and is usually of the order of several megohms.

by sound waves. A polarizing voltage of 100–200 volts is required in series with a very high resistance across which the output voltage is developed. The usual circuit arrangement is shown in Fig. 16 where R is the resistance across which the output voltage appears. Because the capacitance of any connecting cable will reduce the output, it is necessary for the first stage of the amplifier to be close to the microphone. Consequently the first stage of the amplifier is often built into the microphone housing. Owing to this complication and to the fact that the normal output is generally very low, condenser microphones are not commonly used in amateur stations.

The Crystal Microphone. This type of microphone utilizes the piezoelectric effect whereby any mechanical strain applied to a suitably cut piece of certain materials such as quartz or Rochelle salt generates an e.m.f. between opposite faces. Such microphones are very popular amongst amateurs since their frequency response is usually very good, and neither a polarizing voltage nor a transformer is required. They can be connected directly to the grid of the first amplifier stage through a moderate length of screened cable (up to about 8 ft.). A high resistance must, however, be connected across the output at the grid of the valve, as shown

in **Fig. 17.** This should be 2–5 megohms; any lower value than 2 megohms will impair the output at low frequencies. In normal conditions an output of 0·05 volt can be obtained.

There are two types of crystal microphone in general use. The most common consists of a diaphragm which acts

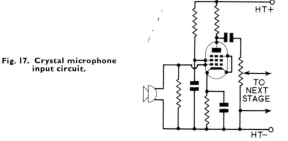

Fig. 17. Crystal microphone input circuit.

directly on the crystal (normally Rochelle salt). In the second type, known as the " cell " type, the diaphragm is dispensed with, and the sound waves act directly on a pair of crystals which form the surface of a flat cell. Both types are capable of excellent quality, the latter type having a better frequency response but being less sensitive.

Relative Sensitivities

In commercial practice the output of a microphone is generally specified in decibels relative to a reference level of one volt per dyne per square centimetre of acoustic pressure. For amateur purposes, however, it is more convenient to be able to estimate the actual voltage output which is likely to be obtained from the various types of microphone described above when the microphone is held in the hand of the speaker and is actuated by normal speech. An approximate indication of typical output voltages is given in Table 2.

SPEECH AMPLIFIERS

The term *speech amplifier* is generally applied to the stage or stages of an a.f. amplifier whose function is to amplify the low output voltage of a microphone to a level suitable for driving the modulator valves which form the last stage in the audio frequency chain. The speech amplifier may consist entirely of *voltage amplifiers*, i.e. amplifiers which increase the signal voltage without having to supply power

TABLE 2

Voltage Output of Various Microphones

Type	Transformer Ratio	Voltage at Grid
Carbon (capsule) ..	30–100	5 –15 volts
Transverse-current ..	20– 40	0·1– 0·3 volts
Condenser	—	0·05 volts
Ribbon	10	0·03 volts
Moving-coil	30– 50	0·1– 0·5 volts
Crystal (diaphragm)	—	0·05 volts
Crystal (cell) ..	—	0·01 volts

into the load, or in some cases the final stage of the speech amplifier may be a *power amplifier*. This is only necessary when the modulator valves are driven so hard that grid current begins to flow.

Voltage Amplifiers

Audio-frequency voltage amplifiers may be divided into two categories, viz. resistance-capacity (*RC*) coupled amplifiers, and transformer-coupled amplifiers. The basic circuit of an *RC*-coupled amplifier is shown in **Fig. 18**. The voltage amplification of such a stage is given by the expression—

$$\frac{V_{out}}{V_{in}} = \mu \left(\frac{R_L}{R_L + r_a} \right)$$

where μ = amplification factor of V_1
r_a = anode resistance of V_1
R_L = external anode load impedance

It is assumed that the value of R_g, the following grid resistor, is greater than $R_L r_a/(R_L + r_a)$, a condition which is generally fulfilled.

It will be seen from this relationship that in order to achieve high gain, R_L must be large compared with r_a. If, however, R_L is made too large, the d.c. voltage-drop across it will be excessive and a high d.c. voltage will be necessary in order to maintain adequate voltage at the anode of V_1. In practice, R_L is generally made 3–5 times as large as r_a. Grid bias for V_1 is provided by the voltage-drop across the cathode resistor R_1, which is by-passed by C_1, to prevent negative current feedback with resulting loss of gain.

When V_1 is a pentode R_L cannot satisfactorily be made greater than r_a because the latter is normally of the order of several megohms, and values of R_L between 100,000 and 330,000 ohms are normally used with pentode amplifiers.

The frequency response of such a stage (i.e. the variation of gain over the frequency range) is determined principally by the values of three capacitances:

(i) The cathode by-pass condenser C_1.
(ii) The coupling condenser C_c.
(iii) The total input capacitance C_s of the following stage V_2.

The first two affect the response at low frequencies and have negligible effect at high frequencies, while the third affects the high-frequency response.

The capacitance of the cathode by-pass condenser C_1 should be such that its reactance at the lowest frequency at which amplification is desired should be small compared with the value of the cathode bias resistance. This condenser also serves a useful purpose in that it by-passes

a.c. hum voltages between the cathode and the heater; hence it is advantageous to use a somewhat larger condenser than that dictated by low-frequency response considerations. For most practical purposes a 25 μF condenser is adequate.

At low frequencies, the reactance of the coupling condenser C_c increases, and since C_c and R_g form a potential divider the voltage appearing across R_g, which is the input to the following stage, tends to fall. The relative gain at a low audio frequency, with respect to that at frequencies in the middle of the audio range, may be found from the expression—

$$\frac{R_g}{\sqrt{R_g{}^2 + \dfrac{1}{\omega^2 C_c{}^2}}} \times 100\%$$

where R_g and C_c are the values of the grid leak and the coupling condenser respectively of the following stage and $\omega = 2\pi f$. In practice this means that the value of coupling condenser must be about 0·5 μF for good low-frequency response. However, for speech, where good response below 300 c/s is not essential, a value of 0·01 μF is adequate for use with a grid leak R_g of 0·1 MΩ or more.

At high frequencies the reactance of C_s falls, and as this capacitance is, in effect, in parallel with the output of the previous stage, appreciable high-frequency loss can occur if its value is too great. This capacitance C_s is composed of the input capacitance of the valve V_2 and the various stray capacitances of the circuit components.

The input capacitance of an amplifier valve with a resistance load is—

$$C_{input} = C_{gc} + (M + 1) C_{ga}$$

where C_{gc} = grid/cathode capacitance of the valve
C_{ga} = grid/anode capacitance of the valve
M = stage gain

This reflection of the grid-to-anode capacitance into the grid circuit is known as the *Miller Effect*, and in some circumstances it may make the input capacitance quite high. The relative amplification at high audio frequencies compared with that in the middle of the audio range may be calculated from the expression—

$$\sqrt{\frac{1}{1 + (\omega R C_s)^2}} \times 100\%$$

where R = equivalent resistance of R_L, r_a and R_g in parallel
C_s = total shunt capacitance

This high-frequency loss can be very important in the design of high-fidelity amplifiers, but for speech communication where an upper frequency limit of about 3000 c/s is acceptable it is not usually of great significance.

Resistance-capacity coupling is a cheap and convenient form of inter-stage coupling and is in almost universal use. It has the added advantage that it is not prone to pick up hum from stray magnetic fields, which can sometimes be troublesome with transformer-coupled circuits. It may be used with either triodes or pentodes, and in fact it is the only suitable form of coupling with high-μ valves because of the difficulty of making a transformer suitable for operating with the high load impedances associated with such valves.

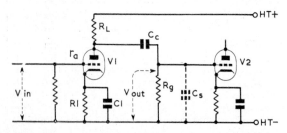

Fig. 18. Basic circuit of a resistance-capacity voltage amplifier.

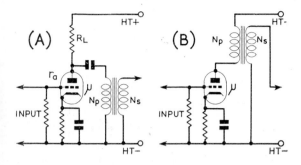

Fig. 19. **Alternative arrangements of transformer-coupled amplifiers.**

Transformer-coupled Amplifiers

Transformer-coupled amplifiers are ordinarily used only when it is desired to amplify power rather than voltage, or when a push-pull output is required from a single-ended input. For most effective operation low-μ triodes operating in class A are generally used because the low anode loads required make the design of the transformer easier.

Two alternative arrangements are shown in **Fig. 19**. In (A) a parallel feed to the transformer is shown, in which there is no d.c. flowing through the primary and thus there is no reduction in the impedance of the primary winding. The over-all voltage gain of this arrangement is—

$$\text{Gain} = \mu \left(\frac{R_L}{R_L + r_a} \right) \left(\frac{N_s}{N_p} \right)$$

In the arrangement shown at (B) in Fig. 19 the transformer carries the d.c. anode current of the valve, and to prevent undue reduction of the primary inductance due to this effect the transformer may need a core with a suitable air gap. The voltage amplification, assuming no grid-current load on the secondary, is given by—

$$\text{Gain} = \mu \quad \left(\frac{N_s}{N_p} \right)$$

The frequency response of such stages is governed mainly by the characteristics of the transformer. At very low frequencies, the inductive reactance of the primary winding falls, and as this forms either part of or the whole of the anode load of the valve, the amplification will be correspondingly reduced. Thus, a high primary inductance is necessary for good response at low frequencies. At the upper end of the audio-frequency range the self-capacitance and leakage inductance of the transformer become important, and may cause a resonant rise in the amplification. To maintain a uniform high-frequency response such transformers are generally constructed with sectionalized windings to reduce the leakage inductance and the self-capacitance.

Multi-stage Amplifiers

Several amplifiers may be operated in cascade, in which case the overall voltage amplification is then the product of the individual voltage amplifications of each stage. It is necessary to proportion the amplification of individual stages to avoid overloading. In high-gain amplifiers it is

essential to prevent stray coupling between the stages, both by correct layout of components to avoid unwanted capacity couplings, and also by adequately decoupling the h.t. supply to each stage. A resistance of 10,000–33,000 ohms, and a condenser of 4–8 μF is normally sufficient.

Gain controls should be introduced as near to the input as possible in the amplifier chain to prevent overloading of the early stages by strong signals. This may often mean inserting the control in the grid circuit of the first stage of the amplifier, in which case the circuit should be adequately screened to prevent the pick-up of hum voltages. In such circumstances it may be advisable to include a gain control in the next stage.

Push-pull Amplifiers

A push-pull stage requires the two grids of its two valves to be driven by identical voltages of opposite polarity. In class-A stages no grid current will be produced by this voltage, but in class-B stages grid current will be caused to flow, and the driver stage must be able to supply power for this purpose. It should have a low impedance so that no waveform-distortion of the voltage is caused by the

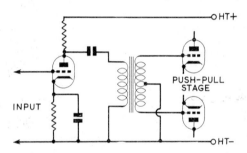

Fig. 20. **By using a transformer which has a centre-tapped secondary winding, a balanced output suitable for driving a push-pull stage is obtained.**

variation of the grid current over the audio cycle. The various methods of obtaining the push-pull driving voltages are discussed below.

Centre-tapped Transformers. The transformer-coupled amplifier using a transformer with a centre-tapped secondary, as shown in **Fig. 20**, is the easiest way of obtaining a push-pull output. It can be used for supplying a push-pull

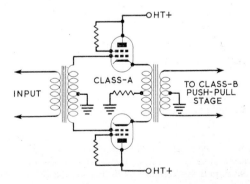

Fig. 21. **Push-pull cathode-follower driver stage. The cathode output circuit has a low impedance and is suitable for working into a step-up transformer for driving a class-B push-pull output stage.**

grid circuit from a single-ended stage, a step-down ratio often being employed to obtain the required low impedance in the drive circuit when the push-pull stage is of the class-B type. **Fig. 21** shows another arrangement in which the input transformer is a step-up transformer driving the push-pull stage in class A, while the following push-pull stage (not shown) is driven from the cathodes of the first stage through a transformer having centre-tapped primary and secondary windings. This utilizes the property of the low-impedance output of the cathode follower circuit, and hence it is not necessary for this transformer to have a step-down ratio for driving a class-B push-pull output stage.

A transformer with a centre-tapped primary is the almost universal method of coupling a push-pull power amplifier to its load.

Cathode-coupled driver stages can be connected to the grid circuit of the output stage directly, without the use of push-pull transformers, in the manner shown in **Fig. 22**. If the push-pull input to the driver stage is obtained from one of the circuits which follow, no transformers other than the modulation transformer are required.

Phase-splitting Circuits. There are a number of circuits capable of producing balanced voltages of opposite polarity (where grid current is not involved) for driving grid circuits in push-pull without the use of transformers. They all utilize modified forms of RC coupling with single or double valves, and are of course essentially voltage amplifiers.

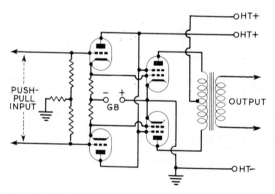

Fig. 22. Push-pull cathode-follower driver stage using direct coupling from the cathode load resistances to a class B output stage.

Such circuits are generally referred to as *phase-splitting* circuits.

(i) *Paraphase Circuit.* This arrangement employs two similar valves, generally in the form of a double-triode, as shown in **Fig. 23**. V_1 acts as a normal voltage amplifier, its output appearing across the series combination $R_1 + R_2$. The part of this output which appears across R_2 is applied to the grid of V_2 and this, due to the phase reversal which occurs in a voltage amplifier, produces an output in R_3 of opposite polarity to that of the voltage across R_1 and R_2. If the output voltages are to be balanced, two conditions are necessary—first that $R_1 + R_2$ should be equal to R_3, and secondly that $(R_1 + R_2)/R_2$ should be equal to the voltage gain of V_2. The use of close-tolerance high-stability resistors

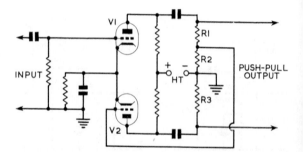

Fig. 23. Paraphase phase-splitting circuit. The two triodes may conveniently be in the form of a double-triode.

is recommended for R_1, R_2 and R_3. The value of the cathode bias resistor should be half the normal value for a single valve of the type used.

(ii) *Split-load Phase Inverter.* This circuit uses a single valve, the output voltage appearing across two resistances,

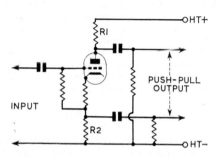

Fig. 24. Split-load phase-inverter circuit.

one in the anode circuit (R_1) and the other in the cathode circuit (R_2) as shown in **Fig. 24**. Since the same current flows in R_1 and R_2, equal voltages are developed across both resistors. The impedances to earth at the two output terminals are, however, different because the anode impedance and the cathode impedance of the valve are not the same.

(iii) *Cathode-coupled Phase-splitter.* This circuit (**Fig. 25**) uses two similar valves coupled together by a common cathode bias resistance R. The signal is applied to one grid only, the other grid being connected to earth through a grid leak. A push-pull output is obtained from the two anodes, but the overall gain is rather less than half that of a single valve under normal RC conditions.

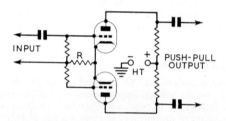

Fig. 25. Cathode-coupled phase-inverter circuit.

Balancing Adjustments. The amount of unbalance which may be permitted between the two halves of the output of a push-pull speech amplifier is really dependent on the amount of distortion which can be tolerated. In high-fidelity work, accurate balancing is essential, but in amateur transmitting practice this is not so important, and the use of high-stability resistors with a tolerance of $\pm$ 2 per cent or even $\pm$ 5 per cent in the appropriate positions generally ensures an adequate degree of balance.

Nevertheless, it must not be deduced from this that it is unnecessary to check the balance of the input voltages to a push-pull modulator. This may be done by direct measurement of the two halves of the output by a high-resistance a.c. voltmeter (rectifier type), or preferably a valve voltmeter. An alternative method which requires a pair of headphones is shown in **Fig. 26**. When the system is balanced, the voltages across R_1 and R_2 will be equal, and therefore the potential of their junction to earth will be zero. This can be tested by connecting a pair of headphones between the junction of R_1 and R_2 and earth. With a test signal applied to the input, the slider of VR_1 may be adjusted until a position is found where minimum sound can be heard in the headphones. It is desirable (but not essential) to short-circuit the phone jack when the phones are removed, by the use of break-contacts as shown.

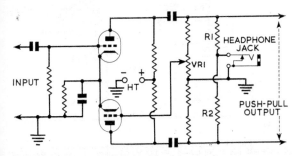

Fig. 26. Balancing adjustment for push-pull driver stage. In a typical amplifier, R1 and R2 may be about 220 K ohms. The potentiometer VR₁ is adjusted for minimum sound in the headphones.

The Cathode Follower

Several of the preceding circuits have employed fairly high resistances in the cathode circuits of valves. The cathode-follower circuit incorporates a form of negative feedback which arises from the inclusion in the input circuit of the potential developed across the cathode resistor. If this resistance is high enough the signal voltage appearing on the cathode will nearly equal the voltage applied to the grid. Such a circuit is therefore called a *cathode follower*, and although the output voltage is no higher than the input voltage, it appears across an effective resistance which is very low and is therefore capable of delivering substantial current without waveform distortion.

The Anode Follower

Another circuit of this type which can be used as a phase-splitter is known as an *anode follower*. In this case feedback is arranged so that the output voltage from the anode is similar to that of the input grid voltage, the effective

output impedance again being very low. Whereas in the case of the cathode follower the output voltage is of the same polarity as the input voltage, in the anode follower the output voltage from the anode is of opposite polarity to the input voltage.

Fig. 27 shows how this circuit can be used to produce a balanced push-pull output. The resistance R_1 is made

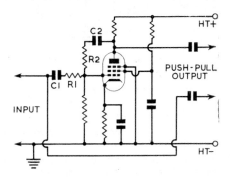

Fig. 27. The anode follower used as a phase inverter.

equal to R_2, and the capacitance C_1 equal to C_2. The voltage appearing on the anode will be almost equal to the input voltage if the stage gain, in the absence of feedback, is made very high. This is achieved by the use of a pentode with a high anode resistance load. The push-pull output is taken from the anode and the input terminals respectively through suitable blocking condensers. The output impedance of the half taken from the anode will, however, probably be much lower than that taken from the input, its impedance being equal to $2/g_m$, where g_m is the mutual conductance of the valve which is used.

Negative Feedback

Negative feedback is commonly used in audio-frequency amplifiers, but it is not often applied to the modulators of amateur transmitters. Negative feedback consists of feeding back to an earlier stage a proportion of the output of the amplifier in such a phase relationship that the feedback voltage has an opposite polarity to the input voltage which produces it. Since the effect of the feedback voltage is thus to reduce the effective grid voltage of the earlier stage, the overall result is to reduce the gain, but in return the distortion, the hum and the noise are reduced; in addition there are a number of other advantages of which the following are the most important:

  (i) Less change in amplification due to changes in supply voltages and valve characteristics.

 (ii) Improvement of frequency response.

(iii) Reduced harmonic and inter-modulation distortion.

(iv) The ability to increase or decrease the output and input impedances of the amplifier, if desired.

It is this last property which can be of great value in modulator design, as it presents a convenient means of providing a low-impedance driver stage for a push-pull modulator working under class-B conditions.

The feedback voltage may be obtained in various ways,

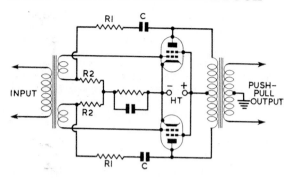

Fig. 28. Application of negative feedback to push-pull driver stage.

the two most commonly used being—

(a) The provision of a separate secondary winding on the output transformer.

(b) A fairly high-resistance potentiometer across the output of one stage, the tapping point of which is returned either to the input of the same stage or a suitable earlier one.

A typical circuit showing the use of negative feedback in the push-pull driver stage is illustrated in **Fig. 28**. The magnitude of the feedback voltage is governed by the proportions of the potential dividers R_1R_2, suitable values for which are 150,000 and 33,000 ohms respectively. The two blocking condensers C may have a capacitance of 0·1 μF and should be rated at about twice the h.t. voltage used. It will be seen that when a voltage at one of the grids is increased the corresponding anode voltage will be decreased, and hence a feedback voltage opposite to that of the input voltage will be added to the grid, thus providing a negative feedback.

Overall Negative Feedback

The use of negative feedback need not be confined to the a.f. equipment only, but may be applied over the whole chain from the radio-frequency output of the transmitter right back to the first stage of the speech amplifier. The basic arrangement of such an application is shown in **Fig. 29**. Here L is a small coil loosely coupled to the output

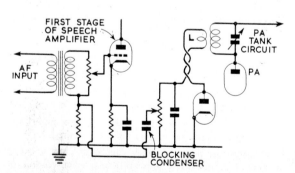

Fig. 29. Overall negative feedback. Part of the modulated r.f. output voltage is rectified and fed back to the first stage of the speech amplifier.

of the transmitter. The voltage developed across this coil is then rectified, and the resulting voltage may be fed back to the speech amplifier.

Such a scheme has the advantage that it takes account of distortion appearing anywhere in the transmitter, a particularly valuable feature since most of the distortion occurs in the modulation transformer and the modulation system. It can also reduce hum introduced from the h.t. supply and from the a.c. used for filament heating. It should be pointed out, however, that negative feedback cannot reduce the distortion resulting from over-modulation once the r.f. output has been reduced to zero any more than it can reduce the distortion in an ordinary a.f. amplifier due to overloading which is severe enough to cut off the anode current.

Simple Speech-amplifier Circuit

A simple general-purpose speech amplifier is shown in **Fig. 30**. This consists of an EF37A a.f. pentode (Mullard) which is connected as a triode, followed by a small triode (type 6J5) having a transformer with a centre-tapped

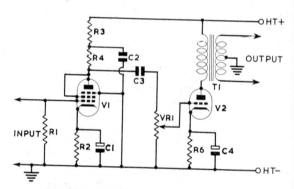

Fig. 30. Simple general purpose speech amplifier.
C1, C4—25 μF, 25 V; C2—4 μF, 250 V; C3—0·01 μF, 250 V; R1—1 M ohms, $\frac{1}{2}$ watt; R2—4·7 K ohms, $\frac{1}{2}$ watt; R3—47 K ohms, $\frac{1}{2}$ watt; R4—33 K ohms, $\frac{1}{2}$ watt; R5 (VR1) 500 K ohms potentiometer; R6—1·5 K ohms; T1—push-pull driver transformer, ratio 1 : 4; V1—EF37A; V2—6J5.

secondary in its anode circuit. For an input of 0·25 volt to the grid of the EF37A, and with the gain control at the halfway position, an output of 77 volts + 77 volts is available at the transformer secondary. The total h.t. consumption is 7·5 mA at 275 volts. If more gain is required, the first valve may be connected as a pentode by taking its screen grid to the h.t. line through a 1 Megohm resistor and by-passing it to earth by means of a 0·1 μF condenser. The other components would be unaltered. Under these conditions an output of 72 volts + 72 volts is provided by an input of 0·05 volt to the grid of the first valve.

The particular characteristics of some valves commonly used in speech amplifiers are given in Table 3.

THE MODULATOR STAGE

In a voltage-control type of modulation system, such as grid modulation, it is sufficient to use a voltage amplifier as the modulator stage since only a negligible amount of power is required. Other systems, such as the very popular anode modulation, require considerable power output from the modulator stage which must therefore be designed specifically as a *power amplifier*.

One of the dominant factors in the design of a power amplifier is the anode-circuit efficiency. It is uneconomical, for example, to operate such an amplifier in class A owing to the inherently low efficiency of this method, and the majority of modulators are arranged to operate in class AB or class B. This naturally leads to the use of a push-pull circuit incorporating a pair of valves in order to keep the distortion to a minimum.

As already explained the grids and anodes of the valves in a push-pull circuit are connected to opposite ends of balanced circuits, generally in the form of centre-tapped transformers. Because of the close magnetic coupling between the two halves of the windings the grid and anode voltage excursions of one valve are equal and opposite to those of the other; thus the momentary increase in the anode current of one valve during modulation is associated with a decrease in anode current of the other. These changes in anode current are combined in the output transformer so that the current in the secondary load represents an effective addition of the two anode current changes. Any even harmonics which are produced will be automatically balanced out and there will be no such harmonic current in the output. For this reason a greater distortionless output power can be obtained from two valves working in push-pull than from the same two valves connected in parallel.

The various modes of operation of valves as power amplifiers have been described in Chapter 2 (*Valves*), but the salient differences in the operating conditions are summarized here in order to emphasize the widely differing characteristics of amplifiers operating in each class.

Class A Amplifiers

Class A operation may be defined as that in which the values of grid bias and alternating input voltage are such that the anode current flows during the *whole* of the cycle of input voltage. In order that there should be no distortion in the output waveform it is necessary for the grid bias to be chosen so that equal positive and negative excursions of input voltage cause equal positive and negative changes in the anode current. This implies that the operative portion of the valve characteristic should be as nearly linear as possible. The anode current in the presence of a signal remains at the same steady value as in the absence of a signal, since the equal positive and negative changes in anode current do not effect the average value. Thus there is a continuous dissipation of power in the valve, and hence the efficiency of a class A amplifier will always be low.

Class B Amplifiers

A class B amplifier is one in which the grid is biased approximately to the cut-off voltage, i.e. in the absence of any input signal the anode current is almost zero. Anode current therefore only flows for approximately half of the

TABLE 3
A Selection of Valves Commonly Used as Speech Amplifiers

Type	Class	Heater		E_a	E_{g2}	g_m (mA/V)	r_a	μ	Base
		V	A						
6C5	Triode	6·3	0·3	250	—	2·0	10,000 ohms	20	Octal
6F5★	Triode	6·3	0·3	250	—	1·5	66,000 ohms	100	Octal
6J5	Triode	6·3	0·3	250	—	2·6	7,700 ohms	20	Octal
6C4	Triode	6·3	0·15	300	—	1·7	7,700 ohms	17	B7G
6SC7GT.. ..	Double-triode	6·3	0·3	250	—	1·3	53,000 ohms	70	Octal
6SL7GT.. ..	Double-triode	6·3	0·3	250	—	1·6	44,000 ohms	70	Octal
6SN7GT.. ..	Double-triode	6·3	0·6	250	—	2·6	7,700 ohms	20	Octal
12AT7	Double-triode	6·3 / 12·6	0·3 / 0·15	250	—	5·5	10,000 ohms	55	B9A
12AU7	Double-triode	6·3 / 12·6	0·3 / 0·15	250	—	2·2	7,700 ohms	17	B9A
12AX7	Double-triode	6·3 / 12·6	0·3 / 0·15	250	—	1·6	62,500 ohms	100	B9A
6AC7	Pentode	6·3	0·45	300	150	9	1 M ohms	—	Octal
6J7★	Pentode	6·3	0·3	250	100	1·25	1·5M ohms	—	Octal
EF50	Pentode	6·3	0·3	250	250	6·5	1 M ohms	—	B9G
SP41★	Pentode	4	0·95	200	200	8·5	0·7M ohms	—	M.O.
SP61★	Pentode	6·3	0·6	200	200	8·5	0·7M ohms	—	M.O.
6AM6	Pentode	6·3	0·3	250	250	7·5	1 M ohms	—	B7G
6BR7	Pentode	6·3	0·15	250	100	1·25	2·3M ohms	—	B9A
6BS7★	Pentode	6·3	0·15	250	100	1·25	2·3M ohms	—	B9A
EF80/Z719 ..	Pentode	6·3	0·3	170	170	7·4	0·4M ohms	—	B9A
EF86/Z729 ..	Pentode	6·3	0·2	250	140	1·8	2·5M ohms	—	B9A
EF37A★	Pentode	6·3	0·2	250	100	1·8	2·5M ohms	—	Octal

★ Grid top cap.

full cycle. In order to obtain high power-efficiency, class B amplifiers are commonly operated with a large input voltage, the peak value of which may be greater than that of the grid bias, causing grid current to flow over the part of the cycle where the grid potential becomes positive. Because this grid current flows for only part of the cycle, the driver stage must have good regulation to avoid distortion of the input wave by the loading effect of the grid current.

Because the anode current flows for only half of each cycle, class B operation at audio frequencies demands the use of two valves in push-pull in order that both halves of the input waveform may be reproduced without distortion. Such a push-pull class B amplifier can have a high anode efficiency since, in the absence of an input signal, the anode current is very low. However, owing to the variation in anode current with the input voltage, an anode power supply of good regulation is essential. Provided that the requirement of low grid-circuit impedance is met, class B operation enables full advantage to be taken of the portion of the anode-current/grid-voltage curve which lies in the positive grid region. This part of the curve is usually fairly linear. The lower portion of the characteristic is badly curved, but the curved portions of the two valve characteristics compensate each other when they are combined in the output circuit. Thus waveform distortion can be kept reasonably low, while still retaining high anode efficiency, so that class B amplification is well suited for use in high-power audio amplifiers.

Special valves with a high amplification factor, which are suitable for operating at zero grid bias, have been developed for this class of operation, typical examples being the DA41 and the DA42 which when used in pairs will give an output of up to 200 watts.

Class AB Amplifiers

In class AB operation, which is an intermediate stage between class A and class B, the grid bias is insufficient to reduce the anode current to zero, and hence anode current flows for more than half of the input cycle but for less than the whole cycle. In class AB_1, the input signal is not permitted to be large enough to drive the grids positive, whereas in class AB_2 grid current is allowed to flow, and consequently the driver stage must be capable of delivering appreciable power. Since the fixed grid bias is higher than in class A, larger signals can be handled without grid current, and the standing anode current is less. The efficiency and maximum power output are therefore greater than for class A. Operation in push-pull is, of course, still

necessary to avoid distortion arising from the use of the curved part of the valve characteristic.

To summarize the foregoing, as the mode of operation is changed from class A through class AB to class B, the reduction in standing anode current and anode dissipation under no-signal conditions results in a considerable increase in the power-handling capacity and the anode efficiency. Against this, however, must be set the fact that both the h.t. and grid-drive requirements become more critical. A greater input voltage is required and, in the case of class AB_2 and class B operation, the driver stage must be designed to supply the grid power and to have good regulation. Since the anode current varies over a wide range the anode power supply must also have good regulation.

As a general rule class B operation is liable to produce more distortion than class A, but it must be remembered that the overall distortion depends on many factors, and provided that the regulation of the power supplies and the driver stage is good, and particularly if negative feedback is employed, the overall distortion can be reduced to a very low level.

MODULATOR DESIGN AND CONSTRUCTION

To design any particular modulating equipment it is necessary first of all to know (a) the voltage output of the microphone to be used and (b) the maximum audio output power required to modulate the transmitter fully. The intermediate stages can then be designed to provide the necessary voltage gain. The initial step in the design is the choice of a suitable output stage which will deliver the calculated amount of power.

Power Required for Full Modulation

As stated at the beginning of this chapter, the audio power required for 100 per cent modulation of a triode amplifier when using the anode-modulation system is one half of the d.c. power input to the r.f. amplifier, but in practice it must be remembered that the modulation transformer will not be free from losses: a typical efficiency is about 90 per cent. For this reason, about 10 per cent more audio power than the theoretical value should be provided. Thus, in order to anode-modulate fully a p.a. stage having an input of 150 watts an audio power of 75 watts + 10 per cent, say 83 watts, is required from the modulator valves. In a tetrode or pentode p.a. stage in which both the anode and the screen grid are modulated, a further 10–20 per cent of audio power is required for the screen grid. Hence it is necessary to use modulator valves

Table 4

Modulation Power obtainable under various circuit conditions

Type of Valve	Class A	Class AB1	Class AB2	Class B
Noval-based	5 watts	12–15 watts	25– 30 watts	—
25 watt tetrode/pentode (single-ended)	15 watts	30 watts	50– 70 watts	—
25 watt tetrode/pentode (double-ended)	23 watts	30–50 watts	80–120 watts	120 watts
35 watt tetrode/pentode (single-ended)	25 watts	60 watts	100 watts	150 watts
40/50 watt triode	20 watts	40 watts	100 watts	150–200 watts

capable of delivering about 100 watts of audio power in order to modulate fully such stages when the input is 150 watts. Since a small factor of safety is always desirable, a suitable figure on which to base such a design could be reckoned as 120 watts.

Typical Modulator Valves

The approximate economic ranges of audio power which may be obtained from different types of valves operating in various circuit conditions are given in **Table 4.** It will be seen that the maximum requirements of the British amateur station may be most conveniently met by using tetrodes or pentodes of 25 or 35 watts anode dissipation operating in class AB₁, AB₂ or B.

Basic operating conditions of valves commonly used as modulators in this country are given in **Table 5.** Reference to this table shows that under class AB₂ or class B conditions

there is considerable variation in both anode and screen-grid currents between zero and maximum signal conditions. There will consequently be a similar variation in the bias if this is obtained from the voltage drop across the cathode resistor, and also in the screen grid voltage if this is obtained through the usual dropping resistor.

The effect of such voltage variation is to cause the operating conditions of the valves to be continuously changing between zero and maximum signal levels, thereby preventing the full output of the valves from being obtained.

It must be emphasized therefore that in order to obtain the maximum output from tetrodes or pentodes operating in class AB₂ or class B it is essential that all supply voltages, anode and screen grid and grid bias, are maintained as nearly constant as possible. As a general rule, all supply voltages should not vary by more than 5 per cent between zero and maximum signal conditions.

It will be appreciated, therefore, that fairly stringent

TABLE 5
Characteristics of Typical Modulator Valves

Type	Class	Heater		E_a (V)	E_{g2} (V)	I_a (No signal) (mA)	I_{g2} (No signal) (mA)	I_a (Max. signal) (mA)	I_{g2} (Max. signal) (mA)	Peak Input Voltage (grid-to-grid) (V)	Load Resistance (anode-to-anode) (ohms)	Power Output (watts)
		(V)	(A)									
6AM5 ..	A	6·3	0·2	250	250	2× 11	2×1·6	2× 13	2× 4·1	32	24,000	4
12A6 ..	A	12·6	0·15	250	250	2× 30	2×3·5	2× 33	2× 8	20	7500	6·8
EL32 ..	A	6·3	0·3	250	250	2× 27·5	2×4·4	2× 32	2× 8	20	7000	7
6AQ5 ..	AB₁	6·3	0·45	250	250	2× 35	2×2·5	2× 39·5	2× 6·5	30	10,000	10
6N7 ..	B	6·3	0·8	300	—	—	—	2× 35		58	8000	10
6V6 ..	AB₁	6·3	0·45	285	285	2× 35	2×2	2× 46	2× 7	35	8000	14
EL84 ..	AB₁	6·3	0·76	300	300	2× 40	2×3	2× 72	2× 8	70	8000	17
6L6 ..	A	6·3	0·9	270	270	—	—	2× 72·5	2× 8·5	35	5000	18·5
6F6 ..	AB₂	6·3	0·7	375	250	2× 54	2×8	2× 74	2×18	55	10,000	19
6L6 ..	AB₁*	6·3	0·9	360	270	2× 44	2×2·5	2× 65	2× 8·5	45	9000	24·5
KT55 ..	AB₁	52	0·3	200	200	2×110	2×7·5	2×113	2×22·5	29	4500	25
5763 ..	AB₂	6	0·75	300	225	2× 13·5	2×1·1	2× 70	2× 9	71	4500	25
6BW6 ..	AB₂	6·3	0·45	315	285	2× 35	2×2	2× 77·5	2× 8	70	8000	30
KT66 ..	AB₁	6·3	1·27	390	275	2× 52	2×2·5	2× 62·5	2× 9	80	3400	40
KT88 ..	AB₁	6·3	1·8	330	330	2× 85	2×7·5	2× 95	2×20	80	3400	40
6L6 ..	AB₁*	6·3	0·9	360	270	2× 44	2×2·5	2×102·5	2× 8	72	6000	47
807 ..	AB₁	6·3	0·9	600	300	2× 40	2×3	2× 75	2× 9	60	10,000	47·5
KT66 ..	AB₁*	6·3	1·27	480	375	2× 40	2×1·5	2× 87·5	2× 9·5	80	5000	50
KT88 ..	AB₁*	6·3	1·8	450	345	2× 50	2×4	2×120	2×17·5	75	4000	65
EL37 ..	AB₁*	6·3	1·4	400	400	2× 50	2×6	2×138	2×36	60	3250	69
KT88 ..	AB₁*	6·3	1·8	600	330	2× 50	2×3	2×125	2×16	70	5000	100
EL34 ..	AB₂*	6·3	1·5	800	400	2× 25	2×3	2× 91	2×19	67	11,000	100
807 ..	AB₂*	6·3	0·9	750	300	2× 26	2×2·5	2×120	2×10	92	7000	120
807 ..	B	6·3	0·9	750	—	2× 6	—	2×120	—	554	6650	120
6146 ..	AB₁	6·3	1·25	750	195	2× 12	2×1	2×110	2×13	100	8000	120
KT88 ..	B	6·3	1·8	750	—	2× 10	—	2×140	—	360	6000	150
DA41 ..	B	7·5	2·5	1000	—	2× 22	—	2×140	—	220	7000	175
TT21 ..	AB₁*	6·3	1·6	1250	300	2× 28	2×1	2×130	2×13	90	15,000	200

*Fixed bias. The figures shown here relate to pairs of valves operating in push-pull (except type 6N7 which is itself a double-triode).

requirements are placed upon the design of the power unit for such amplifiers. In particular, the grid bias voltage should be obtained from a small separate supply.

These conditions are not encountered to the same extent when triodes, and particularly those designed for zero bias operation, are used. However, such valves require a higher anode voltage and more grid driving power for the same power output.

A compromise which is fairly commonly used is a pair of triode-connected 807s operating in class B with zero bias. In this arrangement, shown in **Fig. 31**, the input taken to the screen grids to which the control grids are connected through 22,000-ohm resistors. This circuit is

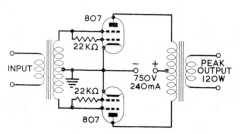

Fig. 31. A pair of beam tetrodes, each with its two grids connected together, may be used as zero-bias triodes in a class B amplifier.

capable of an output of 120 watts and requires an anode supply of 750 volts at 240 mA. These figures are similar to those for a pair of 807s operating in class AB$_2$. However, in the latter condition stable sources of anode and grid bias voltages are essential (although a grid-drive power of only 0·2 watt is required), whereas the zero-bias class B circuit does not require any grid bias or screen-grid supplies, but it does require a speech amplifier having a low-impedance output and capable of supplying 5·5 watts. Other valves may, of course, be used in this arrangement, e.g. the G.E.C. type KT88 is capable of an output of 150 watts at an anode voltage of 750 volts and a grid driving power of 7 watts.

The Modulation Transformer

The modulation transformer is a most important component, for its object is to superimpose the output of the modulator upon the d.c. supply to the r.f. stage in order to produce the required modulation: it must also convert the modulating impedance of the r.f. amplifier to the load impedance required by the modulator valves. To avoid distortion the iron core should be of generous proportions, and modulation transformers should always be used well within their ratings.

The choice of a suitable modulation transformer should receive careful attention. Two conditions must be fulfilled: (a) the ratio must be correct in order to transform the impedance of the modulated r.f. amplifier to the optimum load required for the modulator, and (b) the transformer must be capable of handling the maximum power output over the whole of the audio-frequency range without undue distortion. Multi-ratio modulation transformers, of which the Woden types UM1 and UM3 are excellent examples, are frequently used, since they enable adjustments of the matching conditions to be made. The use of miscellaneous transformers, such as mains transformers, which are

not designed for audio work is not recommended as they rarely have the correct impedance ratio, and magnetic saturation of their cores is likely to occur even with relatively low values of direct current.

The Driver Stage

When the basic design of the output stage has been determined, the next step is the choice of a suitable driver stage appropriate to the manner in which the output valves are to be run. As discussed in the previous section, operation in class B or class AB$_2$ is usual, in which case medium-power triode valves or triode-connected tetrodes such as the 6V6 are commonly chosen. It is advisable to employ a driver stage which is capable of providing about 50 per cent more power than the estimated power required to drive the output stage. If the output valves are to operate in class A or class AB$_1$ the driver stage need only be a voltage amplifier using either transformer coupling or *RC* coupling to the output stage with one of the centre-tapped transformer or phase-splitting circuits already described. The voltage-amplifying stages preceding the driver stage must have sufficient gain to produce the necessary amount of drive to the output stage when supplied with the normal output voltage from the microphone. It is good practice to make the first stage a high-gain amplifier (e.g. a pentode), but if further amplification is required one or two stages of medium gain are preferable to a second high-gain stage in order to avoid instability.

Frequency Range

The frequency range of the modulator should be restricted to the minimum necessary for intelligible communication, i.e. to about 300–3000 c/s. The low frequency response may be controlled by a suitable choice of grid coupling capacitor and grid leak (see section on voltage amplifiers). However, this is not of overriding importance as the l.f. response inevitably tends to be reduced by any transformers used in the speech amplifier and particularly by the modulation transformer.

It is the reduction of the upper frequency limit which is far more important as this defines the overall bandwidth of the transmission. The upper frequency limit may be restricted by the inclusion of shunt capacitors (value 0·005–0·01 μF) across the anode loads of any R-C coupled valves in the speech amplifier or by connecting a capacitor of similar value and of suitable

A typical modulator valve for amateur use—the G.E.C. KT88. (Photo by courtesy of M-O Valve Company).

working voltage across the secondary winding of the modulation transformer. A more satisfactory method of reducing the bandwidth is by the use of a low pass filter. Such filters form part of a speech clipping circuit and are described later in this chapter.

Modulator Power Supplies

The power supplies required by class A or class AB1 modulators are relatively simple in view of the small variation of current drawn. A capacitor input smoothing circuit is generally adequate. Class AB or class B operation requires supplies having very good regulation. This implies that the transformer and choke should be of generous design with windings having low d.c. resistance. A single section choke-input filter with the largest possible value of smoothing capacity should be used. The regulation may be further improved by the use of mercury vapour rectifier valves. A separate well regulated supply should be used for the screen voltage; alternatively it may be obtained from the anode supply by utilizing the voltage drop across gas stabilizer valves such as the VR150 or S130. The negative bias voltage may be conveniently obtained from a small separate supply which uses a reversed 240 volts/6·3 volts heater transformer fed from the heater circuit.

Reference should be made to Chapter 17 for details of the design of power units.

Construction Practice

No matter how good the theoretical design of a modulator may be its virtues will be wasted unless the construction is given careful thought. In addition to the usual practical points contributing to good workmanship, it is necessary to ensure the correct choice of components suitable for the appropriate working conditions in regard to their structural features as well as their circuit values. It is particularly important that full consideration be given to the layout of the components and the supply leads in order to avoid unwanted feedback between points of the circuit having high signal-potential differences and between low-level input circuits and power-supply circuits. This matter of unwanted couplings between different parts of the circuit forms one of the most difficult problems in the construction of audio-frequency apparatus.

The general layout of the modulator is usually determined to a large extent by its power rating. As an example, consider a modulator suitable for a 25-watt transmitter. This would need to have a maximum output of about 15

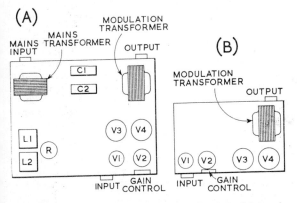

Fig. 32. Suggested alternative layouts for a 15-watt modulator. In (A) the power supply is incorporated with the amplifier-modulator on a 17 in. × 12 in. chassis. In (B) the power supply is excluded and the size of the modulator chassis can be considerably smaller. VI, V2 speech-amplifier valves; V3, V4 modulator valves; CI, C2 smoothing condensers; LI, L2 smoothing chokes; R power-supply rectifier.

watts, and would most likely use a pair of small tetrodes operating in class AB₁. All the components, including the modulation transformer and power supply would be of quite small dimensions, and such a modulator could easily be accommodated on a chassis measuring 17 in. × 12 in. A suggested layout is shown at (A) in **Fig. 32**. The main requirement in such a scheme is that both the modulation transformer and the low-level input stages should be situated as far as possible from the mains transformer.

The stray magnetic field from a power-supply transformer or from a filter choke can induce mains-hum pick-up in an

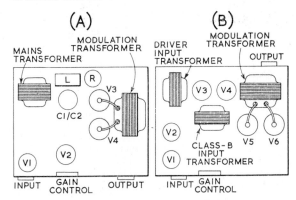

Fig. 33. Suggested alternative layouts for a high-power modulator. In (A) the small power supply required for the speech amplifier is included. In (B) the power supplies are excluded as the space is needed for the driver-input and class B input transformers. A suitable chassis size is 17 in. × 12 in.

a.f. transformer if their cores happen to be oriented in such a way that there is mutual coupling between them. Such coupling is best minimized by a trial-and-error method, moving one or other of the transformers to various positions and placing it at various angles while the equipment is in operation and thus finding the setting where the hum pick-up is eliminated. Likewise there may be stray coupling between the input and output transformers of the a.f. amplifier itself, and the result may then be an appreciable amount of feedback (either positive or negative) which could seriously affect the performance. This is rather more difficult to detect and to cure, but if the transformers are widely separated and if their cores are arranged to be mutually at right angles, the centre of one transformer being located on the magnetic axis of the other, the stray coupling will quite probably be negligible.

The layout shown at (B) in Fig. 32 suggests an alternative arrangement in which the power supply is not included, thus permitting a smaller chassis to be used.

Turning now to the other extreme and considering a modulator with an output power of up to 120 watts, the modulation and h.t. transformers, the smoothing chokes and the condensers become large and heavy, and so it becomes necessary to separate the modulator and the power supply to avoid an unduly heavy unit. Generally the most convenient way to do this is to use one chassis to accommodate the modulator and speech amplifier and the power supply for the speech-amplifier stages, and a second chassis to accommodate the power supply for the output stages. A typical layout for such a scheme is shown at (A) in **Fig. 33**. The power supply for the speech-amplifier stages need only use a small transformer (e.g. a standard 250 volt 60 mA type), a small choke and a two-section electrolytic condenser. If a separate heater transformer for the output stage is required, it is advisable to mount this on the modulator chassis as it reduces to a minimum the number of inter-connecting wires required. Another suitable layout for a high-power modulator using a driver stage coupled with a driver transformer is shown at (B) in Fig. 33.

In order to keep the microphone leads short when the transformer is remote from the operating position, it is sometimes convenient to make the first one or two stages of the speech amplifier as a *head-amplifier* unit separate from the remainder of the modulator. Such a head amplifier, which can have its own gain control, may be combined with any other transmitter controls at some suitable position on the operating desk.

The actual mechanical form of construction is not very important, the most convenient being the familiar inverted-tray type of chassis. Quite successful amplifiers may be built on a simple chassis consisting of a flat sheet of metal supported on a wooden frame. Where rack mounting is desired an alternative form of construction which can be especially recommended for high-power equipment is to mount the heavy components such as transformers and chokes directly on the panel, the smaller components such as the valves being supported on brackets mounted on the transformers. In this way the use of a chassis is avoided.

GENERAL DESIGN FEATURES

Without doubt the most critical stage in any a.f. amplifier is the first voltage-amplifying stage. Its grid circuit is very prone to pickup hum and the signal voltage in it is quite low, resulting in a poor signal-to-hum ratio. Consequently it is advisable to screen the microphone input jack and all the wiring, together with the microphone transformer (if any) and the grid resistor, right up to the grid of the valve. The valve itself should at least have a screened top cap and preferably a complete screening can. A double-ended type of valve, i.e. one in which the grid connection is at the top cap, is preferable in this position since many single-ended valves are susceptible to hum pick-up between the grid and heater pins in the base. For similar reasons the gain control should be inserted *after* the first valve rather than in its grid circuit.

Another troublesome fault frequently encountered in the input stage is *microphony* which is apparent as a ringing sound when the valve is tapped and is due to the vibration of the valve electrodes. It can usually be cured by sub-stituting one of the special valves such as the G.E.C. type Z729, Mullard EF86 (B9A base), and Mullard EF37A (octal base) which are provided with a very high degree of internal bracing for reducing the relative movement between the electrodes.

By comparison with the input stage, the remainder of the amplifier is relatively straightforward. If the layout is logically arranged and if adequate decoupling is included, the biggest bugbear of amplifier construction—undesired feedback—can be avoided. Any layout which brings the input circuit of the amplifier near to the output circuit, or which brings the wiring of an anode circuit near to a grid circuit, should be avoided at all costs.

The Output Stage

If single-ended valves are used in the output stage, it is advisable to mount them in ceramic or other good-quality valve-holders, as the high voltage appearing at the anode pin has been known to break down the insulation of ordinary moulded bakelite valve-holders. Stopper resistances for the grid circuits and/or anode and screen circuits, where used, should be placed as near as possible to the appropriate valve pins. Such resistances should have the lowest value that will ensure the prevention of parasitic oscillations. Typical values are 10 ohms for anode stoppers, 100 ohms for screen stoppers and 1000 ohms for grid stoppers. The grid stoppers of valves with top-cap grids should be attached directly to the grid connector.

Heater Wiring

If the heater winding of the power supply transformer has a centre tap it should be earthed and the valve heaters wired with twisted flex or screened cable to reduce the electric and magnetic fields. In any case the grid and anode leads should be kept as far away from the heater wiring as possible. The heater wiring is preferably laid along the corners formed by the ends and sides of the chassis, and if this is done screened cable will probably be unnecessary. If in spite of these precautions the hum from the heater wiring still persists it is sometimes beneficial to disconnect the centre tap from earth and connect a small potentiometer or " humdinger " across the heater circuit, the slider being connected to earth. A careful adjustment of this potentio-meter will generally balance out the last traces of hum.

A major difficulty in tracing hum in new designs is that it may be arising from several different causes, so that changes which reduce hum from one source may have little effect on others. It is also very easy to produce misleading symptoms: for example, clipping on extra smoothing capacitors may actually cause the hum level to rise because incorrect earth-ing of the capacitor may inject some of the ripple current into a signal circuit—but this would not indicate that the unit had excessive smoothing. Smoothing capacitor con-nections to the earth "bus" line are, in fact, important and should be the mirror image of the h.t. positive distribution system (for this reason common earth connections in multiple section capacitors are sometimes to be avoided).

The importance of using twisted leads for a.c. heater wiring is well known and correct and incorrect methods are shown in Fig. 49 in Chapter 4. It is also necessary to see that twisted leads, sensibly routed, are used for pilot lamps and a.c. primary wiring. While a.c. leakage from the heater circuit usually produces 50 c/s hum as opposed to the 100 c/s hum from full-wave h.t. ripple, it is worth noting that electronic conduction between cathode and heater, due to the heater acting as an "anode" with low applied a.c. potentials (the heater voltage), can cause either 50 or 100 c/s hum. The remedy for this type of hum is to put a positive bias of about 50 volts on the heater line, provided that the cathode/heater insulation will stand this. The bias potential saturates the electronic conduction.

Where equipment develops hum after being in use for some time, it can usually be traced to defective valve inter-electrode insulation, dried-out electrolytics or transformer field leakage.

Earthing

The actual earthing of the various points of the circuit should be carefully planned. Indiscriminate earthing of components to various points on the chassis is liable to set up circulating currents in it. It is better to take all the earth connections belonging to each stage to one point, as in r.f. technique. An alternative method particularly applicable to a.f. amplifiers is to run a busbar of thick tinned copper wire (10 or 12 s.w.g.) along the whole length of the chassis to which all earth connections may be made. One end of this busbar should be reliably connected to the chassis. It is important that all connections to the windings of input transformers should be made by means of twisted wires going through the same hole. On no account should leads to low-impedance transformer windings be taken through separate holes in a steel chassis.

Choice of Components

As in any other electronic device, the use of components of adequate rating is essential for reliable operation and long life. A power rating of $\frac{1}{4}-\frac{1}{2}$ watt is adequate for many resistors in audio equipment, but anode resistors will often need to be of a higher rating. The actual dissipation should be checked in each case from a knowledge of the current which the resistor carries, and a reasonable factor of safety allowed. This is also important for the cathode bias and screen-voltage potential dividers in which the power to be dissipated is sometimes quite high. All condensers should have a reasonable safety factor in regard to the working voltage. Grid-coupling condensers should be of the mica type because even a very slight leak may have disastrous effects on the following valve.

Metering

It is helpful to be able to measure the anode or cathode current of each valve in the modulator since this provides an immediate check on the operating conditions of each stage. A low resistance can be wired in series with each valve, a single low-reading milliammeter being switched across each resistance. The resistance should be considerably higher than that of the meter in order not to affect its accuracy appreciably. As an alternative a meter may be plugged into each stage by means of a closed-circuit jack which completes the circuit when the plug is removed.

The two valves in the output stage should preferably have independent anode-current meters of their own, although commonly a single meter for the combined anode currents is employed. If separate meters are not incorporated, some means whereby a voltmeter can conveniently be connected across the two cathode resistors should be provided in order to check the balance of the two output valves when setting-up the modulator and during operation: the two currents should not differ normally by more than 10 per cent.

Interconnections

All interconnections should be as short and direct as possible, with emphasis on the adequate bonding together of the chassis of the modulator and its power unit and the transformer with thick copper wire. Circuits of either 200 or 600 ohms impedance are commonly used for distribution of audio-frequency energy, but for the short cable lengths commonly encountered in amateur equipment this is not important, and audio input and output circuits of any convenient impedance up to several thousand ohms can be connected with good quality screened flexible cables.

Microphone-to-modulator. Microphones of the moving-coil or carbon type are preferably connected to the modulator or head amplifier by screened twin flex but coaxial cable is often used for crystal microphones. In order to reduce hum pick-up a preferred scheme for crystal microphones is to use screened twin flex with the screening connected to the microphone case at one end and, together with the " earthy " microphone lead, to the earthed chassis at the other end. The other lead connects the live side of the microphone to the grid of the valve. As far as possible the screening should be continuous from the microphone to the grid of the first valve. If coaxial cable is used the appropriate coaxial plugs and sockets will be required. When screened twin cable is used a screened two-pin connector should be used. The use of coaxial cable for low-impedance moving-coil microphones is bad practice since it may result in serious hum pick-up: a screened twisted-pair cable is much to be preferred.

Modulator-to-transmitter. Owing to the high voltages which exist across the secondary of the modulation transformer, it is necessary to use a good quality heavily insulated wire for making the connections from it to the transmitter. The leads should be as short as possible, and preferably placed clear of metalwork and other leads. A point often overlooked is that in a transmitter which is also used for telegraphy, the secondary winding of the modulation transformer should be either short-circuited or disconnected from the power-amplifier h.t. supply altogether during telegraphy operation. If this is not done the high voltage induced in the windings when the current through the secondary is keyed is liable to cause quite severe key clicks and may result in the breakdown of the transformer insulation.

Radio-frequency Pick-up

Instability in a telephony transmitter can often be caused, particularly when working on the higher frequency bands, by the existence of r.f. fields or currents in the vicinity of the high-gain a.f. amplifiers, the first voltage-amplifying stage being usually the most susceptible. Rectification of the modulated r.f. voltage takes place, and the resulting a.f. voltage is fed back into the transmitter through the modulator. At some frequency the phase will probably be such as to produce positive feedback, and the whole system will oscillate at an audio frequency. This form of instability can only be cured by excluding the r.f. fields from the a.f. equipment. The problem is similar to that of the suppression of TVI. Short, direct and screened wiring between the modulator, transmitter and power circuits, in conjunction with the liberal use of r.f. chokes and by-pass condensers of 0·001–0·01 μF at each end of the power line is generally sufficient to effect a cure.

SPEECH CLIPPING AND VOLUME COMPRESSION

Before considering speech clipping in detail it is necessary to examine further some aspects of radio telephony which were discussed earlier in this chapter.

Over-modulation, or the breaking up of the carrier wave by excessive audio output power from the modulator, gives rise to severe harmonic distortion and of the production of spurious sidebands. This may cause the total bandwidth occupied by an over-modulated transmission to extend to 50 kc/s or more. While this excessive bandwidth may not be apparent to a distant listener to whom it may only appear as a badly distorted signal of little more than normal bandwidth, it can cause extreme inconvenience to stations in the immediate vicinity. These spurious sidebands, which only occur on the peaks of modulation, may be received at considerable strength at stations within a radius of a few miles. This form of interference, or " splatter " as it is usually known, obviously prevents the reception of weak signals on frequencies adjacent to the over-modulated transmission.

For intelligible communication by speech, it is not necessary to transmit audio frequencies higher than about 3 kc/s. Hence the total bandwidth of an a.m. communications transmitter need not exceed 6 kc/s. This important point is perhaps not appreciated as much as it should be. With the possible exception of those frequency bands which are used exclusively for local working, there is unquestionably no justification in the over-crowded amateur bands of today for telephony transmissions which occupy a bandwidth greater than that really necessary for intelligible communication.

Although a pure sine wave and a speech waveform may have the same peak value, due to the peaky nature of the speech waveform, the average value of the latter is lower that that of a sine wave. This is shown in **Fig. 34,** where (A) represent a pure sine wave having just sufficient amplitude to modulate a given transmitter to a depth of 100 per cent. (B) is a typical speech waveform also with just sufficient amplitude to give 100 per cent modulation on peaks. In the latter case, if the audio level is conscientiously adjusted to give 100 per cent modulation on peaks which may not occur very often, the average modulation depth will be much less than 100 per cent, probably of the order of 30 per cent. If

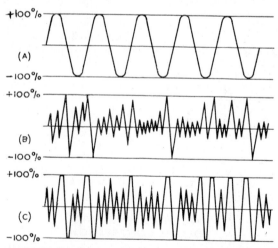

Fig. 34. Speech clipping. (A) represents a sinusoidal modulating signal the peak amplitude of which is sufficient to modulate a given carrier wave to a depth of 100%. (B) shows a typical speech waveform of equivalent peak amplitude to (A). Full 100% modulation is reached relatively infrequently and the average modulation level is low. In (C) the same speech waveform has had its peaks removed by clipping, and the mean amplitude of the modulating voltage has been increased so that 100 per cent modulation is again reached. As compared with (B), there is greater average speech power in the clipped waveform (C).

278

the audio level is increased in order to increase the average modulation depth, then overmodulation will obviously occur on the peaks.

Principle of Speech Clipping

The process of speech clipping consists simply of clipping or limiting the audio level at the value corresponding to 100 per cent modulation and at the same time increasing the audio level as shown in Fig. 34 (C). Thus overmodulation is prevented and the average level is increased.

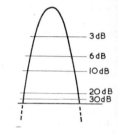

Fig. 35. The degree of speech clipping is expressed in decibels. The diagram shows the corresponding amounts by which the maximum amplitude of the waveform must be reduced.

The degree to which this process can be carried is limited by the amount of distortion of the speech waveform that can be tolerated, and if taken to excess the quality of the speech will deteriorate and intelligibility will be diminished. Furthermore the squaring of the individual peaks as shown at (C) in Fig. 34 would introduce very high audio-frequency components which would defeat the object of the operation by again increasing the bandwidth occupied. Any speech-clipping system must therefore be followed by a low-pass filter to restrict the audio bandwidth to the required 3 kc/s. The degree of speech clipping is defined as the ratio of the peak level to the clipped level, as shown in **Fig. 35.** Small amounts of clipping, of the order of 4–6 dB, will give an appreciable increase in signal strength with only a slight loss of naturalness. When the clipping is increased to about 10 dB distortion becomes noticeable, while at 20–25 dB some intelligibility is lost.

In Fig. 34 both positive and negative peaks are shown clipped (*symmetrical clipping*). This is by no means essential but is sometimes preferable. Either peak may be clipped (*asymmetrical clipping*) provided that the phasing of the audio chain is adjusted so that it is the *unclipped* peak that *increases* the carrier amplitude. Asymmetrical clipping results in the displacement of the effective zero line of the speech waveform. Normal intervalve couplings adjust themselves to give equal areas above and below the zero line, and asymmetrical clipping will upset this equality, giving a momentary shift in the zero axis. It is advisable to make all succeeding coupling capacitances small enough so that the time constant of the coupling circuits is short enough to allow rapid restoration of the normal zero position. It is quite possible for this momentary displacement of the zero axis, owing to the presence of a.c. intervalve couplings, to cause the clipping level to be exceeded and therefore permit over-modulation in spite of the speech-clipping action. A similar effect can occur even in symmetrical clipping circuits owing to the asymmetrical characteristic sometimes experienced in speech waveforms. It may be obviated by ensuring that there are the fewest possible couplings after the clipper stage, i.e. the clipper should be as late as possible in the audio chain.

In principle speech clipping may be effected equally well at either high or low level. High-level clipping, as its name suggests, is introduced between the modulator and the modulated r.f. stage, while low-level clipping is introduced at some point preceding the modulator. The necessary filter for attenuating the higher audio-frequency components may also be inserted at either high or low level, but the filtering action must, of course, always take place *after* the clipping.

High-level clipping has the disadvantage that the associated circuit components must have a correspondingly high voltage rating, but on the other hand the filter would then also serve to remove any high audio frequencies that might be produced anywhere in the whole a.f. chain from the microphone input to the modulation transformer. Another disadvantage of high-level clipping is that the severe voltage transients which it causes may break down the insulation of the modulation transformer and possibly also damage the modulator valves, but to some extent these troubles could be encountered even without clipping in the event of extreme over-modulation. A reasonable factor of safety should therefore be allowed in the design of such equipment.

Low-level Clippers

The limiting of the peaks that occur in speech waveforms resembles the limiting of impulsive interference by a conventional noise limiter. The circuits employed are very

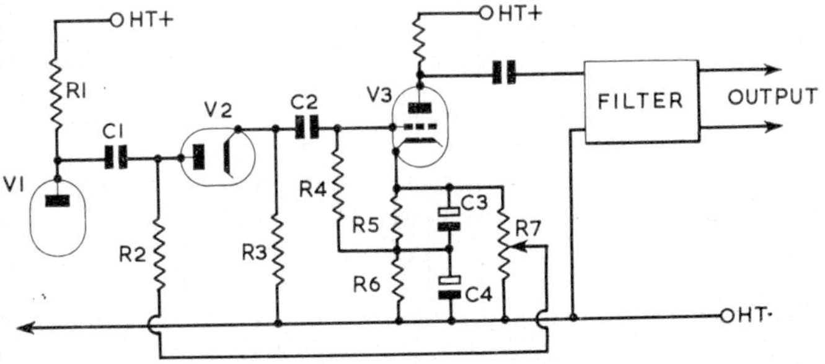

Fig. 36. Low-level asymmetrical series clipper. CI, C2—0·05 μF; C3, C4—25 μF; RI—47 K ohms; R2, R3—2·2 M ohms; R4—I Megohm; R5 + R6—bias resistor for V3; R7—100 K ohms potentiometer; VI, V3—normal a.f. stages; V2—one section of 6H6, 6AL5, etc.

similar and consist of a series or shunt arrangement of diodes suitably biased to give the desired clipping level. A typical low-level asymmetric series clipper is shown in

Fig. 36. If the anode of V_2 is held at, say, + 5 volts by means of potentiometer R_7, signals at all amplitudes up to 5 volts peak will be passed on unchanged, but any *negative* peak which exceeds — 5 volts will cause the diode to become nonconductive, and hence to become clipped.

The corresponding shunt diode clipper is shown in **Fig. 37**. In this case the diode V_2 is normally non-conducting, but it conducts when the *positive* peak voltage at its anode exceeds the positive bias applied to the cathode from VR_1

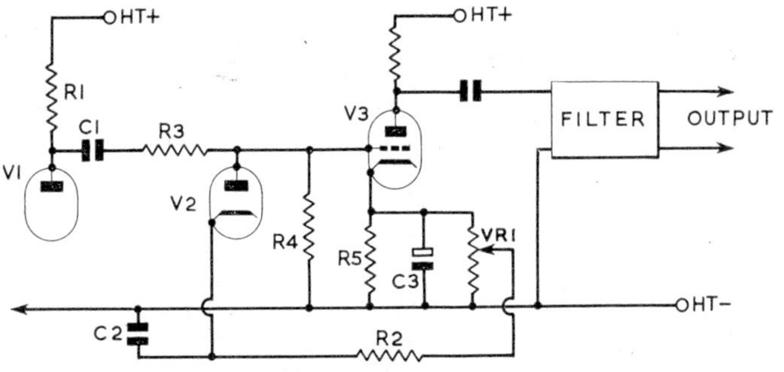

Fig. 37. Low-level asymmetrical shunt clipper CI, C2—0·05 μF; C3—25 μF; RI—47 K ohms; R2, R3—2·2 M ohms; R4—I M ohms; R5—bias resistor for V3; VRI—100 K ohms potentiometer; VI,V3—normal a.f. stages; V2—one section of 6H6, 6AL5, etc.

and thus all positive peaks which exceed this value are by-passed by the diode.

The corresponding symmetrical series and shunt clipping circuits are shown in **Figs. 38** and **39** respectively. The series circuit includes an extra pair of diodes to equalize the load on the previous stage. Whenever either of the series diodes stops conducting and in effect disconnects the following stage, its partner conducts and presents an equivalent dummy load. The diodes in these low-level clipping circuits may be double-diodes of the 6H6 or 6AL5 class (or their equivalent); alternatively miniature metal rectifiers such as the Westinghouse type WX2 or S.T.C. "Sentercel" type H5 may be used. The latter has three advantages: (*a*) no heater power is required, (*b*) a more compact layout is possible, and (*c*) there is no risk of hum being introduced into the clipper stage from the heater circuit.

The sharpness of the clipping action depends upon the characteristics of the diodes used. Thermionic diodes, provided that the input is large enough, give almost perfect

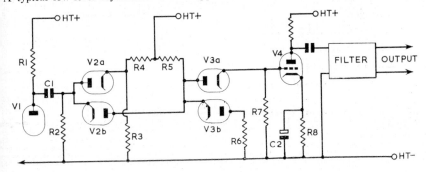

Fig. 38. Low-level symmetrical series clipper. This circuit provides a constant load for the preceding stage. CI—0·05 μF; C2—25 μF; RI—47 K ohms; R2—100 K ohms; R3, R4, R5, R6, R7—220 K ohms; R8—bias resistor for V4; VI, V4—normal a.f. stages; V2, V3—6H6, 6AL5, etc

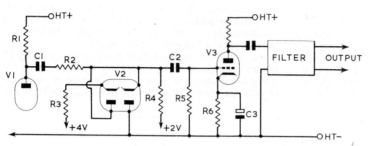

Fig. 39. Low-level symmetrical shunt clipper. C1, C2—0·01 µF; C3—25 µF; R1—47 K ohms; R2, R3, R4—100 K ohms; R5—1 M ohms; R6—bias resistor for V3; V1, V3—normal a.f. stages; V2—6H6, 6AL5, etc.
The small positive bias voltages applied through R3 and R4 to the cathodes of the double-diode V2 can be conveniently obtained from taps on the cathode bias resistor R6 of the following amplifier stage V3.

limiting, i.e. the clipped peaks are flat-topped. In the case of the smaller metal rectifiers, such as the copper-oxide instrument type, the limiting action is not so sharp and the output waveform resembles a "compressed" signal rather than a limited one. Assuming that the circuit is suitably adjusted to prevent over-modulation, this is not necessarily a condition to be avoided since it makes the succeeding filter somewhat simpler, the filter not then being required to remove such a wide range of undesired harmonics. A low-level clipper is sometimes combined with the first stage of the speech amplifier, the combination being a separate unit from the rest of the audio equipment in the form of a pre-amplifier. A typical example of such an arrangement is shown in **Fig. 40**. In this circuit V_1 and $V_{2(a)}$ are voltage amplifiers, and V_3 acts as a symmetrical shunt clipper which is followed by a further amplifier $V_{2(b)}$ and the low-pass filter.

High-level Clippers

The high-level series-diode negative-peak clipper is the commonest arrangement. The circuit is shown in **Fig. 41**. The diode V conducts only when its anode is positive with respect to its cathode. Therefore the modulated anode volt-

age cannot swing the anode of the r.f. amplifier negative. For use in a 150-watt transmitter, the diode V may be a rectifier of the 500 volt 250 mA class with the two anodes connected together. It should be noted that the filament transformer T must have a primary-to-secondary insulation suitable for at least twice the anode voltage of the r.f. stage. Such a clipper used in conjunction with a good filter makes a very effective "splatter" suppressor. It has the advantage that relatively few extra components are required, although the filter components are likely to be rather bulky if entirely satisfactory performance is to be achieved.

Volume Compression

A *volume compressor* is an automatic gain control which causes the gain of an audio amplifier to vary inversely with the output level. In other words it reduces the gain when the level is high and increases it when the level is low. The volume range of the signal is automatically reduced or "compressed," and the intelligibility of a transmitted signal will therefore be increased by the consequent rise in the average level of the speech power.

Volume compression is often used for increasing the

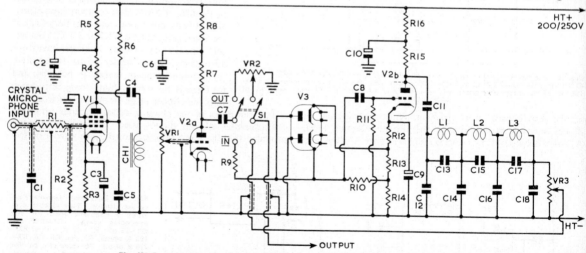

Fig. 40. Combined low-level symmetrical series clipper, speech amplifier and filter.
C1—47 pF Ceramicon ; C2, C6, C10—3 × 8 µF, 350 V electrolytic; C3, C9—10 µF, 50 V-T.C.C. " Picopack "; C4, C7, C8, C11—0·01 µF tubular paper; C5—0·1 µF tubular paper; C12, C13, C15—0·015 µF tubular paper; C14—0·003 µF tubular paper; C16—0·05 µF tubular paper; C11—0·003 µF tubular paper; C18—0·06 µF tubular paper; CH1—10 H midget choke (primary of Wearite type 202 midget a.f. transformer suitable); L1, L2, L3—12 mH filter coils (Denco Ltd.); VR1—500 K ohms potentiometer; VR2—10 K ohms potentiometer (pre-set); VR3—2,500 ohms potentiometer R1—4,700 ohms, ¼ watt; R2—1 M ohms, ¼ watt; R3, R12—1,000 ohms, ¼ watt; R4, R7, R9, R10—100 K ohms, ¼ watt; R5, R8, R16—10 K ohms, watt; R6 R11—470 K ohms, ½ watt; R13, R14—1,200 ohms, ½ watt; R15—47 ohms, ¼ watt; S1—toggle switch d.p.d.t.; V1—EF91, 6AM6, Z77, V2—ECC91, 6J6; V3—EB91, 6AL5, D77.

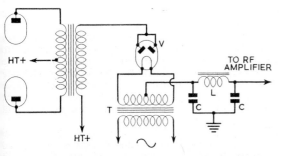

Fig. 41. High-level series-diode negative-peak clipper. The transformer T must be insulated for at least twice the anode voltage of the r.f. stage. V may be a 500 V, 250 mA rectifier. Suitable values of L and C can be calculated from the basic filter design equations (see text).

average depth of modulation in commercial radio telephony and also in sound recording, but its application in Amateur Radio is not as common as speech clipping.

Such a circuit may be used to increase the average modulation depth of a telephony transmitter, without causing over-modulation. There is a practical limit to the amount of compression of the volume range because if it is carried too far any hum or background noise in the speech input will be increased to an unacceptable level. The increased

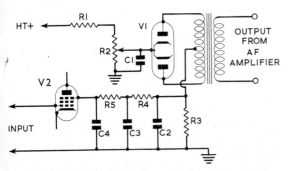

Fig. 42. Simple volume compressor. As the average speech amplitude rises above a certain level, set by the potentiometer R2, the gain of the amplifier V2 is reduced by the rise in the suppressor-grid bias. C1, C2, C3, C4—0·1 μF; R1—220 K ohms; R2—50 K ohms potentiometer; R3, R4, R5—220 K ohms; V1—6H6, 6AL5, etc.; V2—first stage of speech amplifier.

gain at low input levels will also increase the risk of trouble due to overall feedback. The maximum amount of volume compression which can normally be used is that which will reduce gain by about 20 dB at peak level. As in the case of speech clipping, the received signal sounds louder because the average modulation power has been raised.

Volume compression is achieved by rectifying a portion of the output from the a.f. amplifier, passing the resultant rectified voltage through a smoothing circuit which eliminates the audio-frequency components, and then applying the smoothed output to the control grid or suppressor grid of one of the early voltage-amplifying stages in the chain. A simple circuit is shown in **Fig. 42**. A fraction of the output from the audio amplifier is applied through the transformer to the double-diode V_1. The resulting rectified voltage which is developed across R_3 is smoothed by the RC network composed of $C_2 R_4 C_3 R_5 C_4$. The

smoothed voltage is then applied to the suppressor grid of V_2 which is the first stage of the speech amplifier. The voltage at which the circuit begins to operate is controlled by applying a positive bias to the cathodes of V_1 by the potentiometer R_2 which may be conveniently supplied through R_1 from the h.t. line of the speech amplifier.

The audio input to the compressor circuit may be obtained (a) directly from the modulator output, (b) from the input transformer of a class B output stage, or (c) from a separate amplifier valve fed from the last stage of the speech amplifier. Owing to the load presented by the rectifiers it is not usually satisfactory to feed such a circuit directly from a voltage-amplifier.

The distortion which results from volume compression is not so troublesome as that caused by the clipping of a signal, and therefore a low-pass filter is not essential after the variable-gain stage. Distortion of a less severe type can, however, be produced in the variable-gain stage, but this can be kept to a minimum by the use of two valves connected in push-pull for this stage, which will cause even harmonics to be cancelled.

Clipping-v-Compression

A volume compressor circuit may not necessarily be as effective as a properly designed and adjusted speech clipper and filter system, however it is somewhat simpler in application because a low-pass filter is not required.

Since the object of clipping and compression circuits is to raise the average modulation level, it is important

Speech amplifier clipper-filter unit, the circuit of which is shown in Fig. 40.

that the transmitter and its power supplies should be capable of operating at the higher average modulation level which will result. As already pointed out, while simple speech circuits without clippers operate at low average-signal conditions owing to the presence of the peaks, a speech transmitter with volume compression or speech-clipping circuits should preferably be designed as if it were required to operate with a sine-wave modulation signal. These are the conditions which are usually quoted in valve data.

It cannot be too strongly emphasized that the use of a speech clipper or a volume compressor is no cure for modulation troubles which may exist due to overloading of the modulator stage, bad impedance matching, etc.

Negative Cycle Loading

It has been stated that the maximum depth of modulation which may be obtained is 100 per cent. This fact arises, of course, because the carrier wave is broken up and splatter occurs if the modulation depth on the negative peaks exceeds 100 per cent. The modulation on the positive peaks is therefore automatically limited to 100 per cent because of the symmetry of the modulating waveform.

It would obviously be advantageous to be able to increase the depth of modulation on positive peaks without at the same time breaking up the carrier by over-modulation on the negative peaks. This would enable the amount of power in the sidebands to be increased and a stronger signal would result. This process would inevitably cause the modulation envelope to be unsymmetrical and if carried too far would result in excessive distortion.

Various methods of achieving this state of affairs (e.g. "Ultra Modulation") have been suggested from time to time but do not appear to have had much application.

One such system is based on the unsymmetrical loading upon the modulator which occurs during the modulation cycle. Analysis shows that at the negative peak of the modulation cycle the loading on the modulator output stage is reduced to zero. The immediate result of this is that there is no voltage drop in the secondary winding of the modulation transformer. Inevitably it follows that on the positive half cycle, the modulating voltage applied to the p.a. stage is reduced by the amount of this voltage drop. The waveform of the modulating voltage is therefore unsymmetrical and so splatter may occur before the 100 per cent modulation level on positive peaks is reached. This effect is accentuated considerably if the modulator is being overrun or has bad regulation. The absence of load upon the modulator at the peaks of the negative half of the modulation cycle may be compensated for by the addition of a load which functions only during the negative half cycle. This takes the form of a diode and a resistor in series across the secondary winding of the modulation transformer. The diode (e.g. a rectifier of adequate voltage rating) is connected with its anode to the h.t. end of the winding. The resistor should be equal in value to half of the modulating impedance of the p.a. stage. The power rating of the resistor should, of course, be one half of the output power of the modulator. This system enables almost symmetrical loading on the modulator to be obtained and so the modulation depth on positive peaks is increased. It does not, however, appear to have had much application except in conjunction with high power class B modulators.

The "Ultra Modulation" system is similar to the above but uses two additional diodes. The cathodes of these are commoned and taken to the anode of the p.a. stage. The anode of one diode is taken to one end of the secondary winding of the modulation transformer, while the other anode is taken to a tap on the resistor which is in series with the first diode across the secondary winding. In this case the resistor should be equal in value to this modulating impedance. It is claimed that by suitable adjustment of the resistor tap it is possible to achieve modulation depths of much greater than 100 per cent on positive peaks without creating splatter on the negative peaks.

It should be noted that as with speech clipping, such systems as described above cannot make a badly designed or incorrectly adjusted telephony transmitter into a good one. These systems should only be used with discretion after careful setting up on an artificial aerial. The complete transmitter should be designed for continuous operation under sinewave conditions as in the case of speech clipping.

FILTERS

Every speech-clipping stage must be followed by a filter to remove the harmonics generated by the action of speech clipping on the waveform. Such filters must obviously be put into the circuit after the clipping has taken place. Transmitters which only include volume compression do not introduce waveform distortion of the same type as clippers, but such transmitters, and even those without either clipping or compression can, with advantage, incorporate a low-pass filter to remove any modulation frequencies above about 3 kc/s, thus restricting the total transmitted bandwidth to about 6 kc/s.

The filter by itself will not prevent splatter resulting from over-modulation, but assuming over-modulation is avoided by adequate gain control of the amplifier stages, a filter to restrict the bandwidth is a worthwhile addition.

Filter Design

The complete design of filters is outside the scope of this Handbook, but the following notes should enable the amateur to design and make satisfactory filters without very much trouble.

Before the design can be commenced, three factors must be known:

1. The "cut-off" frequency, i.e. the frequency separating the regions of high attenuation and low attenuation.
2. The amount of attenuation required in the attenuating band.
3. The impedances between which the filter is to operate.

It is upon the first two of these factors that the degree of splatter-suppression achieved will depend. A recommendation of the I.A.R.U. Congress (Paris), May 1950, is that the response of the modulator in an amateur telephony transmitter at 4 kc/s should be 26 dB below the response at 1 kc/s. A suggested method of achieving this is by the use of two

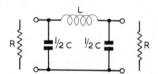

Fig. 43. Low-pass "prototype" or "constant-k" filter. It is also referred to as a "pi-network" filter. Its function is to attenuate all voltages having frequencies above a certain value determined by the filter components. See text for design equations.

filters, one in the speech amplifier with an attenuation of 20 dB at 4 kc/s and a second between the modulation transformer and the r.f. amplifier having an attenuation of 6 dB, the second filter having a higher cut-off frequency than the first. It would be reasonable to consider these attenuation figures as being the minimum acceptable, particularly in the case of a high-power transmitter.

The operating impedance of the filter is not critical, and normally considerable variation is possible. In the case of a high-level filter, it should be designed to work from the modulating impedance of the r.f. amplifier.

The simplest form of low-pass filter is the pi-network illustrated in **Fig. 43**. This is known as a " prototype" or " constant-k " filter. If the impedance of the two circuits which are coupled by the filter are assumed equal, the design equations are as follows:

$$R = \sqrt{\frac{1000\,L}{C}} \qquad L = \frac{R}{\pi f} \qquad C = \frac{1000}{\pi f R}$$

where R = terminal impedance (ohms)
$\quad L$ = inductance in filter (mH)
$\quad C$ = total capacitance in filter (μF)
$\quad f$ = cut-off frequency (kc/s)

Thus L and C may be calculated for any chosen values of R and f. In a low-pass filter for the purpose described f could have a value of 3·3 kc/s.

Such a filter by itself has an attenuation curve which does not rise very steeply beyond the cut-off frequency, and would only give an attenuation of about 6 dB at 4 k/cs and about 30 dB at 10 kc/s. It would, however, be suitable for a high-level filter if a filter of higher attenuation is included in the speech amplifier.

The simplest method of increasing the attenuation of a

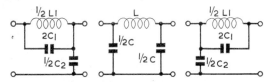

Fig. 44. An improved low-pass filter having a more sharply-defined cut-off frequency than the simple filter shown in Fig. 43. The diagram illustrates the three separate sections comprising a single-section "prototype" filter preceded and followed by an "m-derived" section. See text for design equations.

filter is to connect several identical sections in cascade. Three sections of the type just referred to give an attenuation of about 20 dB at 4 kc/s and about 60 dB at 10 kc/s. Thus a three-section constant-k filter in the low-level amplifier plus a single section of similar type for the high-level filter would just about meet the specified requirement. If a steeper attenuation/frequency curve is desired, use may be made of what are called " m-derived " half-sections. The arrangment of a filter having a single constant-k section and an m-derived section at each end is shown in **Fig. 44**. The design equations for the m-derived sections at the ends are—

$$L_1 = mL \qquad C_1 = \frac{1 - m^2}{4m}\,C \qquad C_2 = mC$$

The general attenuation characteristic of such section has a very sharp peak of attenuation followed by a reduced attenuation remote from the cut-off frequency, as compared

with the constant-k sections which have a slow but steadily increasing attenuation. The quantity m in the above equations is determined by the separation between the frequency of peak attenuation and the cut-off frequency. A convenient value of m for design purposes can be taken as 0·6, and these equations then become—

$$L_1 = 0.6L \qquad C_1 = 0.27C \qquad C_2 = 0.6C$$

A filter consisting of a single constant-k section and two m-derived half-sections would give an attenuation of about 30 dB at 4 kc/s.

It will be seen from the above equations that the value

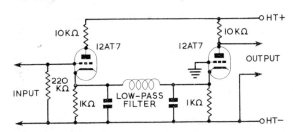

Fig. 45. A suggested circuit arrangement for a low-impedance type of low-pass filter. The use of a cathode follower and a grounded-grid stage provides relatively low terminal impedances. The values of the filter components can be calculated from the basic filter design equations (see text).

of inductance required is proportional to the terminal impedance of the filter. High values of inductance introduce difficulties owing to the presence of self-capacitance, and for this reason it is often preferable to avoid filters of higher impedance than, say, 10,000–15,000 ohms. Such filters, however, may not provide adequate load impedance for voltage amplifiers, and a means of using a low-pass filter with a terminal impedance as low as 500–1000 ohms is shown in **Fig. 45**. The filter is connected between a cathode follower and a grounded-grid stage.

Filter Construction

As the values of L and C required in a filter depend upon the choice of impedance and the cut-off frequency, these values may be selected in order to utilize existing components. Obviously the use of close-tolerance components enables the filter to fit the exact requirements, but this is sometimes rather a luxury in amateur practice.

The layout of filters is not usually very critical. However, care should be taken to avoid undesired couplings between filter coils by suitable spacing. The mounting of such coils with their axes at right-angles will reduce the coupling between them, provided that the axis of one coil intersects the axis of another at its centre.

Condensers. The capacitance values required rarely coincide with those easily obtainable, and series or parallel arrangements are usually necessary. Good-quality paper condensers are satisfactory, although mica ones are better, but if these are not readily available the extra expense involved is rarely justified, provided that the working voltage of the condensers is adequate. In a high-level filter the voltage rating of the condensers should be at least twice the anode voltage of the r.f. amplifier.

Inductances. In the case of a high-level filter, the inductances must be capable of carrying the h.t. current of the modulated stage, and they therefore tend to be of larger

283

dimensions than those intended for low-level filters where the current may be only a few milliamperes.

Either air-cored or iron-cored inductances may be used, but air-cored ones are simpler to design and make. This applies particularly to inductances for high-level filters.

Inductances with an accuracy of 5–10 per cent may be

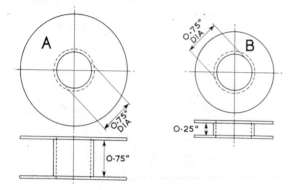

Fig. 46. Dimensions of bobbins for inductances wound according to Table 6. The inductances are all air-cored.

made by reference to Table 6 which shows the number of turns of wire required to give the stated values of inductance when wound on one or other of the two bobbins illustrated in **Fig. 46.** For the larger bobbin (A) the wire size is 32 s.w.g. (enamelled), and inductances wound with this wire

TABLE 6

Winding Data for Air-cored Inductances

Approximate Inductance (mH)	Number of Turns	Outside Diameter	
		Bobbin A	Bobbin B
80	2030		
100	2240		
120	2400	2½ in.	1¼ in.
150	2620		
180	2800		
200	2930		
250	3200	3 in.	1½ in.
300	3450		
350	3660		
400	3850		
450	4030		
500	4200	3½ in.	1¾ in.
600	4570		
700	4840		
800	5160		
900	5480	4 in.	2 in.
1000	5800	4 in.	2⅛ in.

For bobbin A the wire size is 32 s.w.g. enamelled.
For bobbin B the wire size is 40 s.w.g. enamelled.

will carry 200 mA without overheating, thus being suitable for high-level filters. The largest coil listed (1 henry) will take about 1 lb. of wire and will have a resistance of about 260 ohms.

For the smaller bobbin (B) the wire size required is 40 s.w.g. (enamelled), and the largest size shown will need about 2¼ oz. of wire and will have a resistance of about 850 ohms. These inductances are suitable for low-level filters.

In either case inductances of intermediate values may be found by simple interpolation.

Typical A.F. Filters

The filter shown in **Fig. 47** is a single-section constant-*k* filter suitable for use at high level, feeding an r.f. amplifier having an input of 150 watts. Assuming an anode supply

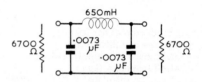

Fig. 47. Single-section "prototype" filter suitable for feeding a 150 watt modulated r.f. stage.

of 1000 volts and a current of 150 mA, the terminal impedance required is 1000 volts/0·15 amp. which equals 6700 ohms. The values of the components shown will give a cut-off frequency of 3·3 kc/s.

Fig. 48 shows a filter having a single constant-*k* section with *m*-derived end sections which would be suitable for use at low levels in a voltage amplifier. It is designed for

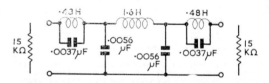

Fig. 48. Low-pass filter suitable for use at low levels in a voltage amplifier having an output impedance of 15,000 ohms. The cut-off frequency is 3 kc/s. The filter comprises a "constant-k" section with an "m-derived" section at each end.

a terminal impedance of 15,000 ohms and has a cut-off frequency of 3 kc/s.

Resistance-capacitance Filters

By careful design, a filter of the type just described may be made to have a characteristic which is flat to 2·5 kc/s or so and then falls rapidly to the order of −50db at 4 kc/s.

It is considered by some that such a filter gives a too unnatural sound to the voice and that a filter with a much slower fall-off in its characteristic is preferable.

Such a characteristic may be obtained from a resistance-capacitance filter. A single section RC filter may be considered as a potentiometer composed of the resistance and the reactance of the capacitor. The ratio of the potentiometer, therefore, is dependent on the frequency of

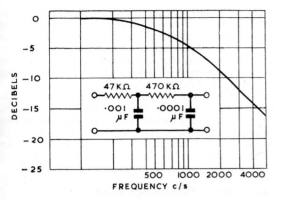

Fig. 49. Typical two stage R-C filter and approximate Loss/
Frequency characteristic.

the input voltage. A two-section RC filter is shown in
Fig. 49 which also shows its approximate loss/frequency
characteristic.

This type of filter is obviously not as effective as the
conventional LC type, particularly when used after heavy
speech clipping, but it has the merit of simplicity.

ADJUSTMENT AND MONITORING

The importance of thoroughly checking the overall performance of a telephony transmitter cannot be over-
emphasized. Unfortunately it is a task which can present
considerable difficulties, especially in the case of a transmitter with a power input as high as 150 watts. Nevertheless, it should be the aim of every amateur to test his
modulator as far as the facilities available will permit by
applying its output to the transmitter, and also to test the
complete system with some form of dummy load before
using it to radiate a signal.

The principal tests which should be applied to any telephony system are as follows:

(1) *On the modulator:*

    (*a*) maximum undistorted power output,

    (*b*) frequency distortion (i.e. variation of gain over
    the required frequency range),

    (*c*) amplitude distortion (i.e. introduction of har-
    monics and other unwanted frequencies),

    (*d*) hum level.

(2) *On the complete system:*

    (*a*) depth of modulation,

    (*b*) overall fidelity.

Testing the Modulator

After the wiring of the modulator has been thoroughly
checked the heaters should be switched on, and after a
few minutes the h.t. may be applied. The voltage on the
various electrodes of each valve should be measured with
a high-resistance voltmeter having a sensitivity of at least
1000 ohms-per-volt, and the results can then be compared
with the design figures.

In order to avoid possible damage to some of the components the h.t. voltage should on no account be applied

to the output stage unless it has a suitable load. This should
consist of a non-inductive resistor having a dissipation
rating at least equal to the expected power output of the
modulator. It should have a resistance approximately
equal to the modulation impedance of the r.f. stage, or
alternatively of such a value that it can be matched to this
impedance by suitable adjustment of the taps of a multi-
ratio modulation transformer.

The ideal set-up for the overall performance checking
of any audio amplifier is shown in **Fig. 50**. A signal of
known frequency and known voltage is fed into the amplifier
from an a.f. oscillator. The amplifier output is dissipated
in the resistive load *R*, the voltage across the load being
measured by the voltmeter *V*. This must be an a.c. voltmeter
suitable for use over the audio frequency range. Many
multi-range test meters are suitable for this purpose. A
preliminary calculation to find the approximate value of
the output voltage is advisable in order to set the range
correctly and avoid burning out the voltmeter. It will be
found convenient to plot a graph of the calculated power
output against the voltmeter reading for the load resistance
selected, so that the actual output power from the amplifier
can be determined under the various conditions of test.

The output voltage is observed on the cathode-ray oscilloscope the input to which may be tapped down the resistance
load if necessary, to avoid overloading the oscilloscope.
The maximum undistorted power output at any frequency
is readily found by increasing the gain control in the amplifier, or by increasing the output of the oscillator until distortion becomes apparent on the output waveform. It is
advisable to check the output of the oscillator with the
oscilloscope to be certain that there is no inherent distortion
of the input waveform. Such distortion tests should be made

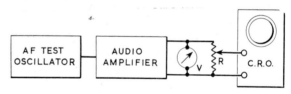

Fig. 50. Ideal arrangement using a test oscillator and an oscilloscope
for checking the overall performance of an audio amplifier.

at low and high frequencies as well as at medium frequencies.
With the gain control of the modulating system left at the
same setting, the input signal should be removed and the
residual hum measured on the voltmeter and observed
on the oscilloscope. The hum voltage should preferably
be less than 1 per cent of the maximum undistorted signal
output voltage. If it is more than this the origin of the hum
may be traced by applying the oscilloscope to the output
of each stage in turn.

By varying the frequency of the oscillator and measuring
the modulator output voltage, keeping the input voltage
constant, the frequency response of the modulator can be
determined. Any low-pass filters which it is intended to
use should be included in the equipment when such tests
are made.

Another method of estimating distortion is to apply the
input and output voltages of the modulator to the hori-
zontal- and vertical-deflector plates respectively of the oscilloscope, with the internal time base inoperative. The gain

in the horizontal- and vertical-deflection amplifiers should be adjusted so that vertical and horizontal lines of equal length are obtained when each is tested separately. When both inputs are applied simultaneously, the resulting pattern will be a straight line inclined at 45 degrees to the horizontal and vertical axes. Any phase shift originating in the amplifier, which will be most noticeable at the lower and upper frequency limits, will cause this straight line to open out into

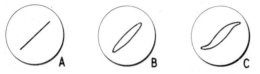

Fig. 51. Oscilloscope patterns produced by applying the input and output voltages of the modulator to the X- and Y-plates respectively. The straight-line trace A shows the complete absence of phase-shift or distortion. The simple loop shown at B indicates slight phase-shift but no distortion. The twisted loop C indicates both phase-shift and distortion.

an ellipse. Distortion produced in the modulator will show up as a curving at the ends of the straight line or at the tips of the ellipse. Examples of the patterns which may be observed in this way are shown in **Fig. 51**.

Before beginning such tests it is advisable to apply the oscillator voltage to both of the oscilloscope amplifiers to verify that there is no appreciable distortion in these amplifiers.

Simpler methods are available when an oscilloscope and audio oscillator are not available. The output of the modulator can be monitored by means of a pair of headphones connected across the low resistance in series with the load resistance, as shown in **Fig. 52**. The value of *r* should be adjusted to give a comfortable signal strength in the headphones; generally 2–3 ohms is sufficient. As a safety precaution it is very important that one side of the headphones should be earthed, and that the resistance *r* should be of a very reliable type and very securely connected across the headphones. Such a simple testing method will

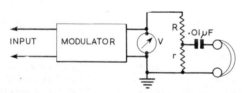

Fig. 52. A simple method of checking the audio performance of the modulator by a direct listening test. Special care must be taken to ensure that no dangerously high voltage ever reaches the headphones.

enable any serious distortion to be heard when the modulator is driven either from the microphone to be used or from a musical signal derived from a broadcast receiver or a gramophone.

Testing the Complete System

Before the output of the modulator is applied to the transmitter, it is essential to make certain that the r.f. amplifier which is to be modulated is itself operating satisfactorily. Neutralization, if used, should be as complete as possible. The correct values of grid bias and grid drive

should be applied, and the aerial coupling should be adjusted so that the stage is drawing the required anode current. This ensures that the modulating impedance of this stage is of the correct value. As suggested earlier, the first trials of any telephony transmitter should be carried out with some form of dummy aerial to avoid causing unnecessary interference to other stations.

When it is certain that the r.f. stage is operating satisfactorily, the modulation may be applied and steadily increased up to the maximum amplitude which the system in use is capable of accepting. Almost 100 per cent should be possible in the case of anode modulation, but 75 per cent is as much as can be expected without distortion for the various forms of grid modulation.

Measurement of Modulation Depth

The cathode-ray oscilloscope is the best instrument for measuring the depth of modulation since it enables a quick visual check to be made. There are two distinct methods

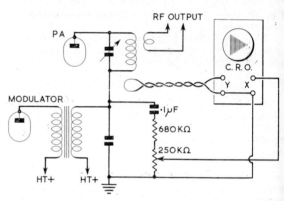

Fig. 53. Trapezium test for checking the modulated output from the r.f. power amplifier. Here r.f. voltage is applied to the Y-plates and a.f. voltage is applied to the X-plates. No time-base is required in the oscilloscope.

of measuring modulation depth with an oscilloscope; one is dependent on the use of a time base and the other is not.

The method which does not require a time base is illustrated in **Fig. 53**. A small fraction of the modulated output voltage is fed to the *Y*-plates of the oscilloscope by a pick-up loop loosely coupled to the output tank circuit while the a.f. modulating voltage is fed to the *X*-plates. With a steady modulating signal a trapezoidal or wedge-shaped pattern will be produced on the screen. **Fig. 54** shows the variations in this pattern for various degrees of modulation. The modulation depth is calculated as follows:

$$m = \frac{P - Q}{P + Q} \times 100 \text{ per cent}$$

where *P* and *Q* are the lengths of the vertical sides of the pattern. *P* and *Q* can be measured with reasonable accuracy by means of a pair of dividers. For 100 per cent modulation a triangular pattern is produced.

The oscilloscope pattern can also be used to examine the overall performance in other respects besides the actual modulation depth. If the operating conditions are correct so that there is no distortion in the modulation process, the sloping sides of the trapezoidal pattern will be perfectly

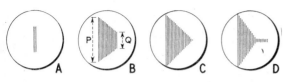

Fig. 54. Typical oscilloscope patterns obtained by the method shown in **Fig. 53.** The vertical line **A** shows the unmodulated-carrier amplitude. In **B** the carrier is modulated 50 per cent, while in **C** it is modulated 100 per cent. Where the sloping edges of the pattern are flattened, as in **D**, the carrier is over-modulated.

straight: any curvature of these sides indicates non-linear modulation. Typical patterns for various fault conditions in both anode- and grid-modulation systems are shown in **Figs. 55** and **56** respectively. The audio voltage applied to the X-plates may be derived directly from the audio input to the amplifying system of the transmitter instead of from the output of the modulator, in which case any distortion in the audio part of the system will become apparent. The apparatus required for this test is very simple

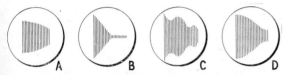

Fig. 55. Fault conditions in anode modulation: **A**—insufficient drive: **B**—over-modulation: **C**—instability in power amplifier: **D**—incorrect matching of modulator to p.a.

and consists only of a small cathode-ray tube and its associated power supply. The whole apparatus can be conveniently built up on a 3-in. panel for rack mounting.

The alternative method, which requires the use of a time base, produces the envelope of the modulated wave on the screen. In the arrangement shown in **Fig. 57** the modulated r.f. voltage is applied to the Y-plates as in the previous method, and the normal time base which is of course applied to the X-plates is adjusted so that the audio-frequency

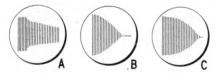

Fig. 56. Fault conditions in grid modulation. **A**—excessive drive: **B**—over-modulation: **C**—power amplifier insufficiently loaded.

components of the envelope are suitably displayed. A rectangular patch of constant height will be observed when there is no modulation, and this will show the appropriate change of shape during modulation. The type of patterns displayed on the cathode-ray tube are shown in **Fig. 58.** By measuring the height R corresponding to a modulation peak and the height S of the unmodulated carrier the depth of modulation can be calculated directly:

$$m = \frac{R - S}{R} \times 100 \text{ per cent}$$

The patterns resulting from incorrect operation of the transmitter are more difficult to interpret in this method,

and for this reason the trapezium test is usually found more satisfactory.

Whichever method is used the results are easier to interpret when a constant sinusoidal input is applied to the modulator, but for many purposes the signal obtained from a sustained whistling into the microphone is sufficient.

In the absence of a cathode-ray oscilloscope the most convenient way to determine the depth of modulation is to measure the aerial current with and without modulation. A rearrangement of the formula shown on page 255 gives the expression for modulation percentage with a sinusoidal signal as—

$$m = \sqrt{2 \left[\left(\frac{I_m}{I_0}\right)^2 - 1 \right]} \times 100 \text{ per cent}$$

This method of measurement assumes that there is no distortion in the modulating system. If such distortion is present it may even cause the aerial current to decrease on modulation, and unreliable results are frequently obtained when using this method. Moreover the formula does not apply to modulation by speech. For these reasons the first method of using the cathode-ray oscilloscope described above is much to be preferred.

In an anode-modulation system the modulation percentage may be obtained approximately by measuring the a.c. voltage across the modulation choke or the secondary

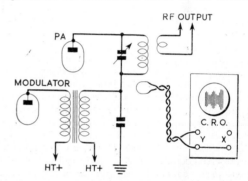

Fig. 57. Alternative methods for checking the modulated output from the r.f. power amplifier. The test signal is applied to the Y-plates, while the X-plates are supplied with a linear time-base voltage of any suitable frequency.

of the modulation transformer. If the test signal has a sinusoidal waveform, the modulation percentage is given by—

$$m = \frac{\text{a.c. modulation voltage (r.m.s.)}}{\text{d.c. voltage applied to p.a.}} \times 141 \text{ per cent}$$

If, however, the test signal is not sinusoidal or if for any reason it is more convenient to measure the *peak* value of

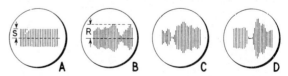

Fig. 58. Typical oscilloscope patterns obtained by the method shown in **Fig. 57.** **A**—unmodulated carrier: **B**—50 per cent modulation: **C**—100 per cent modulation: **D**—over-modulation. Since the time-base frequency is independently fixed the patterns obtained with a normal speech input are constantly varying in position on the horizontal axis.

the modulation voltage instead of the *r.m.s.* value, the factor 141 in this formula must be reduced to 100.

The formulae given here are only applicable to the use of a sine-wave modulation voltage. In the case of speech the rise in average aerial current from the measured modulation voltage for 100 per cent modulation will be considerably less.

Modulation Monitors and Over-modulation Indicators

Even if no means of measuring the exact depth of modulation is available, some indication of the presence of over-modulation is essential. There are several ways of doing this.

In a class B or class AB$_2$ modulator the anode current of the modulator varies appreciably with the amplitude of the signal input. If a device to measure the actual modulation percentage can be borrowed a mark can be made on the scale of the modulator anode-current meter corresponding to 100 per cent modulation, so that the gain control can always be adjusted to ensure that this value is not exceeded. Similarly a high-resistance a.c. voltmeter connected to the output of the modulator can be calibrated to show percentage modulation from the formula shown above. It should be noticed, however, that sluggishness in the operation of such a meter may give rise to a false impression, and it should be of a type which will give as rapid an indication as possible.

Since the average anode current of an anode-modulated amplifier is constant, any variation in the reading of the anode milliammeter may be taken to indicate over-modulation provided that the modulating system is free from distortion such as that due to insufficient grid drive or grid bias on the modulated stage, which will also cause the meter needle to flicker. Any instability of the r.f. stage can likewise cause variations in the anode current, and consequently the results of such a test are not always easy to interpret.

The sudden interruptions of the carrier which occur in over-modulation as a result of the frequent reduction of the p.a. anode current to zero are the principal cause of interference to local receivers, and it is therefore particularly important this should be avoided. A simple means of showing the presence of this effect is shown in **Fig. 59**. The milliammeter in series with the rectifier will show a

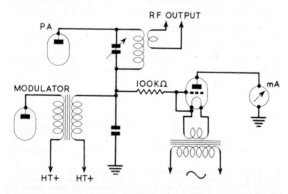

Fig. 59. Over-modulation indicator. The meter needle will flicker when the depth of modulation exceeds 100 per cent.

288

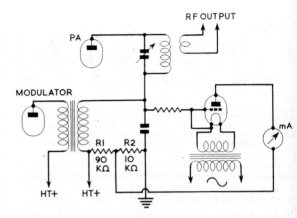

Fig. 60. Over-modulation indicator biased to show when the depth of modulation exceeds 90 per cent. The critical percentage can be altered by suitably proportioning the potential divider R1R2.

reading whenever there is a peak of modulation which carries the instantaneous voltage on the anode of the modulated r.f. stage below zero into the negative region. The diode cannot conduct as long as the negative peak of the audio output voltage is less than the d.c. voltage applied to the r.f. stage. Both the rectifier and its heater transformer must be capable of withstanding a voltage equal to the sum of the peak r.f. and a.f. voltages. Any high-voltage low-current rectifier or an old transmitting triode with the grid and cathode strapped together will serve as the diode. A low-reading milliammeter (e.g. one with a full-scale deflection of about 5 mA) is a suitable indicator.

If an indication of any modulation depth less than 100 per cent is required, the meter may be returned to a point on a potentiometer connected across the h.t. supply instead of to earth. For example, if a maximum of 90 per cent is to be indicated, the voltage across the earthed section of the potentiometer should be 10 per cent of the d.c. voltage. Such an arrangement is illustrated in **Fig. 60**.

Taking everything into account, the use of a speech-clipping system which will automatically avoid over-modulation is to be recommended in preference to a non-limited system which has to be continuously monitored to avoid over-modulation. Nevertheless the monitoring of the speech quality by means of headphones, using the station receiver (generally referred to as *side-tone*), provides a valuable overall check. It is necessary, however, that the receiver should have a gain control in the first r.f. stage and that it should be well screened in order to prevent overloading and the resultant distortion of the signal. Such a monitoring receiver cannot be considered satisfactory unless it is possible to reduce the r.f. gain so that the transmission can be rendered completely inaudible.

Downward Modulation

Downward modulation is the name given to a condition, sometimes occurring in amateur telephony transmitters, in which the power level of the modulated carrier is found to *diminish* as the modulation amplitude increases. It is easily detectable by connecting a small lamp in the aerial lead or coupling it to the p.a. tank coil; if downward modulation is occurring the lamp will be seen to decrease in brilliance as the modulation level is raised.

This spurious condition is somewhat similar to the " under-modulation " phenomenon in v.h.f. transmitters, and is caused only by incorrect adjustment or bad design. The main features to be suspected are as follows:

(a) Incorrect grid drive and/or bias on the p.a. stage,

(b) Power-amplifier stage not being run under the valve maker's recommended conditions, or alternatively lack of cathode emission,

(c) Presence of parasitic oscillations in the p.a. stage,

(d) Incomplete neutralization in the case of a triode p.a.,

(e) In the case of a tetrode or pentode p.a., incorrect time-constant of the screen circuit; the value of the screen decoupling capacitor should be such as to give a suitably high reactance (e.g. higher than the screen dropping resistor) at the highest modulation frequency in use. If too great a time-constant is used, the screen potential will not be able to " follow " the modulating voltage; generally this implies that the screen decoupling condenser should not be greater than 0.002μF,

(f) Inadequate regulation of the h.t. supply to the p.a. stage,

(g) Modulation transformer or modulator being grossly overrun,

(h) Aerial coupling too tight.

The remedy for all these defects is fairly obvious. In this respect, the value of checking the linearity of any modulated amplifier by means of an oscilloscope cannot be over-emphasized.

TYPICAL MODULATORS

Beginners' Low-power Modulator (25 watts)

This is a low-power modulator suitable for the newcomer to telephony work. As shown in **Fig. 61** the circuit consists of three stages, a voltage amplifier driving a paraphase phase-inverter, which drives a pair of beam tetrodes (type KT66) operating in class AB_1. Resistance-capacity coupling is used throughout and since the output stage operates in class AB_1 the h.t. current requirement is not heavy.

Beginners' low-power modulator

The input valve V_1 is an r.f. pentode (EF36). This is coupled by a condenser C_3 of 0.001 μF capacity and the gain control potentiometer R_6 to a twin-triode $V_{2a}V_{2b}$ (type B65), which acts as the paraphase phase-inverter. The input to one of the output valves, V_3, is obtained through C_6 in the normal way from V_{2a}, while the other output valve V_4 is fed through C_7 from V_{2b}. The grid voltage for V_{2b} is obtained from the output of V_{2a} by means of a tap on the following grid leak, which is made up of R_{10} and R_{11} in series.

Grid stoppers (R_{13} and R_{15}) and screen stoppers (R_{16} and R_{17}) are connected in the appropriate leads to the KT66s. The screen voltage for the output valves is obtained from a voltage divider, R_{18} and R_{19}, across the h.t. supply. The h.t. supply for V_1 and V_2 is also taken from the same point. The modulation transformer is a Woden multi-ratio type UM1.

A condenser of 0.01 μF (working voltage 1000 volts) is connected across the secondary of the modulation transformer in order to reduce the high-frequency response. The low-frequency response is restricted by the use of comparatively low values for the grid coupling condensers C_3, C_6 and C_7.

The modulator is built on an aluminium chassis 14 in. $\times$ 9 in. $\times$ $2\frac{1}{2}$ in. which will allow room for future additions.

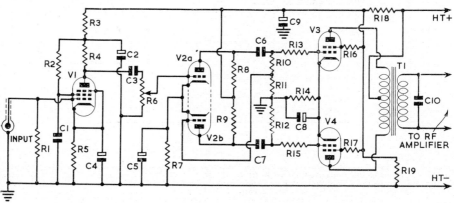

Fig. 61. Low power class ABI modulator. CI—0·1 μF, 250 V; C2, C9—8 μF, 500 V; C3—0·001 μF, 350 V; C4, C5—25 μF, 25 V; C6, C7—0·01 μF, 500 V; C8—25 μF, 50 V; C10—0·01 μF, 1,000 V; RI, R2,470 K ohms, $\frac{1}{2}$ watt; R3—33 K ohms $\frac{1}{2}$ watt; R4—330 K ohms, $\frac{1}{2}$ watt; R5 —3,300 ohms, $\frac{1}{2}$ watt; R6— 250 K ohms potentiometer; R7—4,700 ohms, $\frac{1}{2}$ watt; R8, R9—100 K ohms, $\frac{1}{2}$ watt; R 10, R12—220 K ohms, watt; R11—22 K ohms, $\frac{1}{2}$ watt; R13, R15—4,700 ohms, $\frac{1}{2}$ watt; R14—250 W, 5 watts; R16, R17—100 ohms, $\frac{1}{2}$ watt; R18—4,700 ohms, 10 watts; R19—15 K ohms, 10 watts; TI—Woden UMI; VI— EF36 (see text); V2, B65 (see text); V3, V4—KT66 (see text).

The layout of the valves and modulation transformer, and the position of the input jack (which should be screened) and the gain control can be seen from the photograph.

As the h.t. current varies by only about 25 mA between zero input and full input, the regulation of the power supply is not important, and the circuit may consist of a conventional full-wave rectifier with a condenser-input smoothing filter. Adequate smoothing will be given by a 20H choke and an 8 + 16 μF condenser.

On test, the maximum undistorted output of this modulator into a 6600-ohm load resistance was found to be 26·5

A 30 watt modulator for a Table Top transmitter

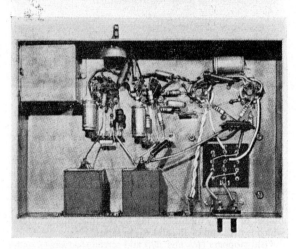

Under-chassis view of beginners' low-power modulator

watts for an input to V_1 of 0·05 volt r.m.s. The maximum d.c. input to the modulator under these conditions was 147 mA at 420 volts.

Similar results could be obtained by using valves other than those specified, but it is not practicable to give details of all the changes in resistor and condenser values which

this may require. The valve manufacturers' data should be consulted as the guide on this point. Possible alternative output valves are the 807, 6L6 and EL37, while V_2 may be replaced by a 6SN7 or two single triodes of type 6C5, 6J5 or L63. Almost any octal-based r.f. pentode may be used for V_1.

If the modulator is required for use with a microphone of unusually high output, the microphone output voltage must be stepped down by a potentiometer, or alternatively the gain of V_1 should be reduced by decreasing the anode load R_4 and using the valve as a triode by connecting the screen grid to the anode.

A Modulator (30 watts) for a 50-watt "Table Top" Transmitter

This modulator was designed for a transmitter using a single 807 as the r.f. power amplifier. The input to the p.a.

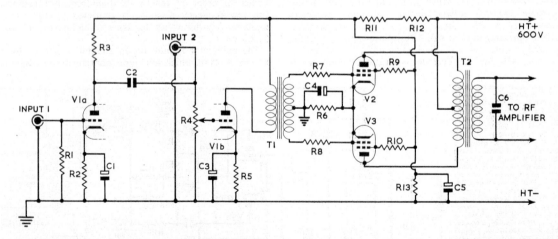

Fig. 62 A simple 30-watt modulator suitable for modulating a single 807 r.f. power amplifier. The two 807s used in the push-pull modulator shown here are operated in class A. C1, C3—25 μF, 25 V; C2—0·01 μF 350 V; C4—25 μF, 50 V; C6—0·01 μF, 1,000 V; R1—470-K ohms, $\frac{1}{4}$ watt; R3—33 K ohms, $\frac{1}{2}$ watt; R4—250 K ohms potentiometer; R2, R5, 1·5 K ohms $\frac{1}{2}$ watt; R6, 250 ohms 5W; R7, R8—4,700 ohms, $\frac{1}{4}$ watt; R9, R10—100 ohms, $\frac{1}{2}$ watt; R11—2,200 ohms, 3 watts; R12—10 K ohms, 10 watts; R13—15 K ohms, 10 watts; T1—push-pull driver transformer, ratio 1 : 4; T2—Woden UM1; V1—6SN7GT; V2, V3—807.

stage, when using telephony, is approximately 85 mA at 600 volts, i.e. about 50 watts. The audio output power required is about 30 watts, and this is obtained from two 807s running at the same anode voltage as the r.f. stage. In order to reduce the variation of current drawn from the power unit to the minimum the 807s are operated as closely as possible to class A conditions.

As will be seen from the circuit diagram shown in **Fig. 62**, the voltage amplifier consists only of a 6SN7GT double-triode, or its equivalent. The first section is resistance-capacity coupled to the second section which is transformer-coupled to the push-pull 807s. The transformer used has an overall step-up ratio of 1 : 4 and has a centre-tapped secondary winding. Sufficient gain is available to give full output when using a crystal microphone driving the first stage or a moving coil microphone driving the second stage, two input jacks being provided.

Grid stoppers (R_7 and R_8) and screen stoppers (R_9 and R_{10}) are fitted to the output valves V_2 and V_3. The screen voltage for V_2 and V_3 (300 volts) and also the anode supply for the speech amplifier are obtained from the potential divider consisting of R_{11}, R_{12} and R_{13}. The response at the high-frequency end is limited by the condenser C_6 (0·01 μF) connected across the secondary of the modulation transformer. The total h.t. current is 90–110 mA.

The complete modulator is built on an aluminium chassis which measures 10 in. × 5 in. × $2\frac{1}{2}$ in., and is bolted to one side of the transmitter chassis. The output terminals and the grommet to insulate the h.t. and heater supplies are therefore

Under-chassis view of 30 watt modulator

conveniently located towards the rear of one side of the chassis, as shown in the photograph.

Simple High-power Modulator (100 watts)

The output stage of this modulator uses a pair of KT88 beam tetrodes. These valves have several advantages for amateur work; in particular they will provide an output of 100 watts in push-pull class AB_1 with an anode voltage of only 600 volts. As can be seen from the circuit arrangement shown in **Fig. 63**, a split-load phase-inverter V_1 (type 6J5)

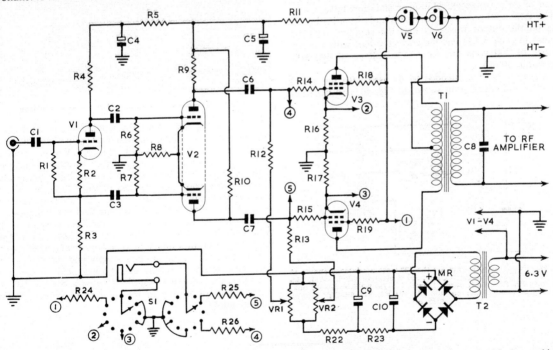

Fig. 63. High-power modulator capable of providing a peak audio output of 100 watts. This circuit may be used with the combined speech amplifier and clipper unit shown in Fig. 40. C1—0·01 μF, 350 V; C2, C3, C6, C7, 0·05 μF 350V wkg. C4, C5—8 μF, 500 V; C8—0·01 μF, 2,000 V; C9, C10—4 μF, 350 V; R1—1 M ohms, $\frac{1}{2}$ watt; R2—1,500 ohms, $\frac{1}{2}$ watt; R3, R4—33 K ohms, $\frac{1}{2}$ watt; R5—33 K ohms, 1 watt; R6, R7— 470 K ohms, $\frac{1}{2}$ watt; R8—1,000 ohms, $\frac{1}{2}$ watt; R9, R10—33 K ohms, $\frac{1}{2}$ watt; R11—4,700 ohms, 1 watt; R12, R13—100 K ohms, $\frac{1}{2}$ watt; R14, R15 —10 K ohms, $\frac{1}{2}$ watt; R16, R17—1·66 ohms (23″ of 26 s.w.g. Eureka wire); R18, R19—270 ohms, $\frac{1}{2}$ watt; R20, R21 (VR1, VR2)—20 K ohms, potentiometer; R22—10 K ohms, 5 watts; R23, 4·7 K 5 watts; R24—1·2 M ohms; R25, R26—300 K ohms; S1—2 bank, 11 way switch; T1— Woden UM3; T2—230 V/6·3 V (small heater transformer suitable); V1—6J5; V2—6SN7GT; V3, V4— KT88; V5, V6—S130; MR—RM.O (or similar)

Simple high-power modulator

supplies the push-pull input to the double-triode V_2 (type 6SN7GT) which drives the KT88 output valves in class AB_1, resistance-capacity coupling being used throughout. A fixed bias of about -50 volts is required for the KT88s, and this is provided by a small power unit employing bridge-connected metal rectifiers (type RM–0) and a reversed 6·3 volts heater transformer, the 6·3 volts winding being fed from the heater supply to the valves. An important safety feature to note is that the bias is thereby applied to the valves as soon as the heaters are switched on.

The screen voltage of about 300 volts required by the KT88s is derived from the main h.t. line (600 volts) through a pair of series-connected S130 neon stabilizer tubes.

The setting-up procedure consists simply in adjusting the bias on the output valves so that the standing no-signal current in each KT88 has the correct value: with a screen voltage of 300 volts and an anode voltage of 600 volts this will be 50 mA.

This modulator is intended to be used with the speech amplifier and clipper unit shown in Fig. 40, and if desired

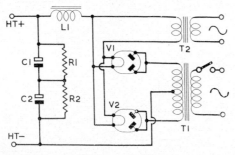

Fig. 64. Power supply unit for the 100 watt modulator shown in Fig. 62. C1, C2—64 μF (or higher), 500 V electrolytic; L1—5H, 250-300 mA; R1, R2—100 K ohms, 1 watt; T1—750-0-750 V, 250-300 mA; T2—heater transformer to suit V1, V2; V1, V2—5R4GY U18/20, U19, etc.

space can be provided for it on the chassis. This close proximity is not essential and the two units may be separated by a reasonable distance if this would be more convenient.

Full metering facilities are provided. A meter plugged into the jack nearest to the output valves is switched by S_1 to read the following:

Position 1. Screen voltage of V3 and V4

Position 2. Cathode current of V3

Position 3. Cathode current V4

Position 4. Negative bias on V3

Position 5. Negative bias on V4.

The current shunts and multiplier resistance shown on the circuit diagram are designed to give full scale deflections of 600 volts, 150 mA, 150 mA, 150 volts, 150 volts respectively when a 0·5 mA, 500 ohm meter is used.

The construction should present no difficulty if the guidance given earlier in this chapter is followed. The size of the chassis shown in the photograph is 17 in. × 8 in. × 3 in. and the bias supply is built as a sub-unit on a piece of bakelite or similar material 5 in. × 2½ in.

The recommended circuit for the h.t. power supply unit

Under-chassis view of simple high-power modulator

is shown in **Fig. 64**. Since the maximum current drain is 250–300 mA the regulation should be as good as possible, and for this reason a choke-input type of filter is essential. The lowest practicable capacity of the smoothing condenser is about 32 μF, and 50 μF will give noticeably better results. A pair of electrolytic condensers of suitably large capacity may be connected in series as shown, the shunt resistors R_1 and R_2 being included to equalize the voltage-drop across the two condensers. The rectifier valves may be type 5R4GY, U18/20 or U19. On full load, the output voltage of this power unit should be approximately 600 volts.

The components for the bias supply and the neon stabilizers for the screen supply may be mounted on the same chassis as the h.t. power supply if desired, but this has the disadvantage of adding to the number of interconnecting leads required.

CHAPTER 10

SINGLE SIDEBAND

SINGLE sideband suppressed carrier telephony (commonly called s.s.b.) is a specialized refinement of amplitude modulated telephony and a brief examination of basic amplitude modulation theory is therefore an essential preliminary to any description of the more advanced system.

A numerical example is probably easier to grasp than an abstract one. Consider what happens when a 3700 kc/s carrier of 100 watts output is modulated 100 per cent by a pure audio tone of 1000 c/s. If the output were to be monitored on an oscilloscope, the pattern would resemble that shown in **Fig. 1,** which at a cursory glance might suggest that the modulated waveform consists of a single frequency oscillation which varies in amplitude in sympathy with the modulation. In fact, the pattern is the resultant of the following three superimposed r.f. oscillations:

(i) the original carrier of 3700 kc/s, which remains unchanged in amplitude;

(ii) a new sine wave of 3,701 kc/s formed by the addition of the modulating frequency and the carrier frequency. This is known as the *upper sideband* and at full modulation has an amplitude equal to one-half of that of the carrier;

(iii) a similar sine wave at 3699 kc/s, formed by the subtraction of the modulating frequency from the carrier frequency. This is the *lower sideband*.

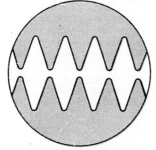

Fig. 1. Oscilloscope pattern of a carrier wave modulated to almost 100 per cent by sinusoidal audio tone.

The frequency and amplitude relationships of the carrier and its sidebands are shown graphically in **Fig. 2.** This form of representation is no mere mathematician's trick; each of the component waveforms has an individual existence, as may be readily proved by tuning a highly selective receiver through the signal. In the general case of a carrier fc modulated by an audio tone fm, the upper and lower sidebands are $(fc + fm)$ and $(fc - fm)$ respectively. Both sidebands are identical in amplitude, and are precise mirror images of one another as regards phase and frequency displacement from the carrier.

When the single tone modulating signal is replaced by the output of a speech amplifier, the picture grows more complex. It may, however, still be analysed into the original carrier, unchanged in amplitude and frequency, about which are displaced symmetrically the upper and lower sidebands. The sidebands will of course undergo continuous change in amplitude and frequency as the voice changes in inflexion and intensity, but they may never exceed half the amplitude of the carrier if overmodulation is to be avoided. Their

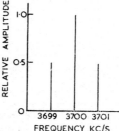

Fig. 2. Amplitude/frequency relationships of carrier and sidebands when a 3700 kc/s carrier is modulated to 100 per cent by a sinusoidal tone at 1000 c/s.

maximum excursion in frequency is limited by the highest frequency component of the voice; for practical communications purposes this may be taken as 3 kc/s. **Fig. 3** illustrates in diagrammatic form the relationship of the carrier and its sidebands under speech modulation; it is this representation, rather than that of Fig. 1, which forms the foundation stone on which to build a solid understanding of s.s.b. There is, however, one noteworthy point which is more immediately evident from Fig. 1 than from the alternative representation. On upward modulation peaks, the instantaneous amplitude of the waveform becomes double that of the unmodulated carrier. If the modulated stage in the numerical example

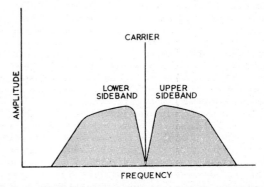

Fig. 3. Amplitude/frequency relationships of carrier and sidebands with 100 per cent speech modulation.

approximates a pure resistance, the peak output power therefore rises to 400 watts. In addition, the voltages at the anode and screen rise on modulation peaks to twice the applied d.c. potentials so the components in these circuits must be appropriately rated to avoid breakdown.

COMMUNICATIONS EFFICIENCY

The amplitude of each sideband is limited to half that of the carrier, so its maximum power will be one quarter of the unmodulated output power. In the numerical example already quoted the maximum power in one sideband would be 25 watts; both sidebands together would produce 50 watts. It is not, however, possible to specify the effectiveness of the transmission until something is known about the equipment on which it is being received. The sidebands necessarily occupy a band of frequencies stretching 3 kc/s to either side of the carrier, so that if the receiver has a bandwidth of 6 kc/s they both add in phase and contribute to the total *talk power*. If a more selective receiver of 3 kc/s bandwidth is used, only one sideband contributes to its output. Under the crowded conditions which obtain in the amateur bands, high selectivity is almost invariably a necessity, so that only 25 watts of the signal actually conveys intelligence to the listener. This is not a particularly profitable return for the generation of 100 watts of carrier power, not to mention the cost, weight and bulk of a high level modulator and associated power supply.

As the carrier remains constant in frequency and amplitude it conveys no intelligence from transmitter to receiver, and serves merely as a datum line against which the sidebands are demodulated. All the intelligence is conveyed in the sidebands, so that the carrier may be omitted and the signal demodulated perfectly clearly if the reference function is transferred to a local oscillator at the receiving end. The attractiveness of substituting for the 100 watt carrier a few volts of r.f. from a small oscillator valve at the receiver is obvious. The reduction of heterodyne interference within the amateur bands, which results from carrier suppression, may alone appear to be adequate justification for making the change, but there are other advantages.

The power amplifier which produces a 100 watt carrier must be capable of a peak output of 400 watts. With modifications, the full capacity of this amplifier may be utilized to radiate intelligence-conveying sideband energy. This does not necessarily mean that the peak envelope power output of the hypothetical amplifier will be 400 watts, because there are important differences between the operating conditions of anode-modulated class C amplifiers and the class AB or B linear amplifiers customarily employed in s.s.b. output stages. The question of linear amplification will be dealt with in detail later in this chapter, but as a rough guide it may be said that a 100 watt a.m. stage ought to be able to produce about 250 watts peak output in s.s.b. service. The whole of these 250 watts will contribute to the talk power at the receiving end, which compares very favourably with the 50 watts which produce speech output from a conventional a.m. transmission at a receiver of 6 kc/s bandwidth, and even more favourably still if the receiver has a narrower bandwidth.

There is no difficulty at all in suppressing the carrier: a miniature double triode, or a pair of crystal diodes, together with a few resistors and capacitors are all that is necessary, leaving only the problem of how to get rid of one of the sidebands. It has already been said, however, that a receiver of 6 kc/s bandwidth is capable of combining the two sidebands so that both may contribute to the audio output. Furthermore, it matters little at the transmitting end whether the linear amplifier is producing single sideband or double sideband output, so long as the peak power remains substantially the same in both cases. It is however desirable to eliminate one sideband in order to simplify the demodulator process in the receiver. Even if the local oscillator at the receiver can be made stable enough to simulate the precise frequency of the suppressed carrier, that alone is not sufficient. It must also be identical *in phase*, otherwise the two sidebands will not combine to produce anything approaching the original modulating waveform. The best way to utilize fully a double sideband suppressed carrier (d.s.b.) signal is to tune it in on a wideband receiver to which is coupled an adapter capable of synchronising the local oscillator to the required frequency and phase by means of information derived from the sidebands themselves. The main disadvantage of this system of detection lies in its susceptibility to lose synchronization because of interference from random noise or from strong adjacent-channel signals.

If, however, one of the sidebands is eliminated as well as the carrier, reception becomes fairly easy. The local oscillator may wander quite a few cycles away from the correct frequency before intelligibility suffers appreciably and does not have to be locked in phase. The best place to eliminate the unwanted sideband is clearly at the transmitter, because the full capacity of the p.a. stage may then be used to amplify the wanted sideband. In addition, the transmission will occupy only 3 kc/s. Alternatively the conversion from d.s.b. to s.s.b. may be effected at the receiving end. This is relatively simple because increasing interference has already led many amateurs to increase the selectivity of their receivers to a point at which it is possible to reject one half of a d.s.b. transmission and deal with the remainder as if it were a true s.s.b. signal. When received in this way d.s.b. is considerably more difficult to tune than s.s.b., and is only half as efficient. Half of the power radiated by the transmitter is not used for reception and merely serves to increase the general level of interference. In this respect it is no worse than conventional a.m., although it has the advantage of having no resting carrier to cause a constant heterodyne whistle. When the fact that a d.s.b. transmitter is simpler and cheaper than an a.m. rig of comparable power output is considered, the reasons for its increasing popularity become evident, though it is to be hoped that users of the system will come to regard it as a stage on the road towards s.s.b., and not as an end in itself.

SUPPRESSING THE CARRIER

The usual way to eliminate the carrier is to phase it out in a balanced modulator. The possibilities for varying the circuit design are virtually limitless, so there is some excuse for assuming the balanced modulator is complicated. In fact, it is a straightforward application of the bridge circuit and there is no reason why the simplest designs should not perform as well as the more elaborate ones. Balanced modulators fall into the following two sub-divisions:
   (i) The high impedance type which employs amplifier valves, and
   (ii) the pure bridge or ring circuit which uses diodes and operates at a much lower impedance.
Stripped of non-essentials, the r.f. circuitry of the high

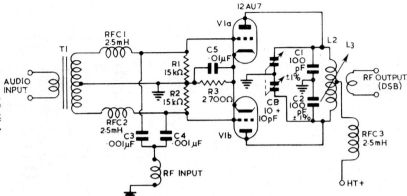

Fig. 4. Twin triode balanced modulator. Almost any centre-tapped interstage audio transformer may be used at T_1. Balance is adjusted by the 10 + 10pF capacitor C_B which should be the differential type

impedance type is as shown in **Fig. 4.** An r.f. voltage applied to the grids of V_1 and V_2 will appear in amplified form at the anodes. This will cause r.f. currents to flow in opposing directions through the two halves of L_2. If the circuit is so adjusted that the signal induced in one half of L_2 is balanced exactly by that induced in the other half, no energy whatsoever will be passed on to L_3. Balance is governed primarily by the amplification factors of V_1 and V_2; ideally these valves should be identical, but this is difficult to achieve in practice and the best that can be done is to choose a pair whose characteristics match as closely as possible. The two units in a double triode envelope often match fairly well, and if half a dozen valves are available at least one should be good enough for balanced modulator service. Almost any valve type can be made to give good results, but for ease of adjustment and long-term stability of balance a low-mu triode such as the 12AU7 or 12BH7 is recommended. Better still is the G.E.C. A.2900. The characteristics of high mu types such as the 12AT7 are more prone to change as the valve ages. A valve which has seen enough service to permit its characteristics to stabilize is more likely to prove satisfactoy than a brand new one; if a new valve must be used it should be aged artificially by operating it at normal heater voltage and a few milliamperes of anode current for 50–100 hours before it is tested for use in a balanced modulator. The importance of selecting the right valve cannot be overstressed. While it is possible to balance out large inequalities by external means, the circuit will drift out of balance quite rapidly, and will require continual readjustment.

Although a well matched pair of valves will give about

25db carrier suppression on their own, this is rarely enough, and additional balancing is required. If the remainder of the circuit permits, the simplest way is to vary the operating point of one or other of the valves by altering the standing bias. An example of this method will be seen later in the cathode circuit of V_1 and V_2 in Fig. 8. The balancing method of widest application is obtained by varying the point of virtual earth on L_2. As this point is governed by the ratio of C_1 to C_2 an adjustment of this ratio is all that is called for. In practice it is more convenient to use identical components for C_1 and C_2 and to parallel them with a small differential capacitor of about 10 pF capacity than to attempt to vary C_1

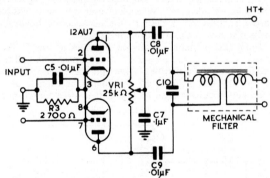

Fig. 6. Resistive method of balancing suitable for input to a mechanical filter.

and C_2 directly. The preferred scheme, shown in Fig. 4, enables resonance and carrier balance to be adjusted independently of one another.

The basic arrangement may of course be varied widely to suit particular conditions, but there are certain pitfalls for the unwary. As the effective earth must be determined by the capacitors the tapping point on the coil at which the h.t. supply is fed to the valves must *never* be brought to r.f. earth potential by means of a bypass capacitor. An r.f. choke as shown in Fig. 4 will ensure that the tapping point will " float " in the required manner, and if the consequent voltage drop can be tolerated this component may be replaced by a resistor of 10K ohms or more. When the circuit is used at signal frequency the coil is usually tapped, but at intermediate frequencies the necessity frequently arises to feed h.t. in parallel by means of two resistors in the manner

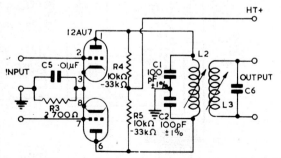

Fig. 5. Resistive method of supplying anode voltage to a twin-triode balanced modulator where it is inconvenient to tap the anode inductor

295

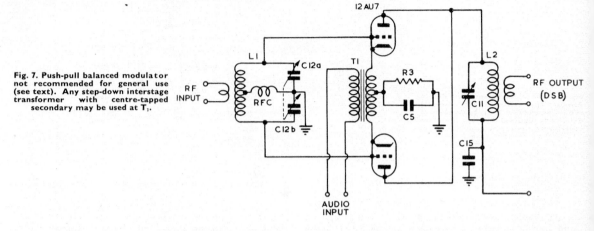

Fig. 7. Push-pull balanced modulator not recommended for general use (see text). Any step-down interstage transformer with centre-tapped secondary may be used at T_1.

shown in **Fig. 5.** From this arrangement arose a classic misconception about balanced modulators. Because the Collins Radio Company of America modified it to provide input to their mechanical filters (see Chapter 4, *H.f. Receivers*) and used a variable resistor to allow for adjustment of balance (see **Fig. 6),** many amateurs jumped to the conclusion that resistive balancing is effective under all conditions. If the balanced modulator is followed by a mechanical or crystal filter giving 20db attenuation or more at the carrier frequency it is unnecessary to strive for maximum carrier suppression by the balanced modulator itself, and the circuit of Fig. 6 may indeed prove adequate. When, however, the best possible carrier suppression is desired, the capacitative balancing method shown in Fig. 4 is to be preferred.

From time to time, circuits on the lines of **Fig. 7** have appeared in which the grids are excited in push-pull and the anodes strapped in parallel. Although there is no obvious reason why this arrangement should not be capable of as good performance as that of Fig. 4, it is often found more

difficult to adjust and less stable in operation. It has the further disadvantage that (because of its similarity to the well known push-push doubler) even-order harmonics are accentuated in its output and may give rise to spurious signals. Unless considerations external to the balanced modulator dictate the use of the push-push configuration, it is best ignored.

Multi-grid valves may be substituted for triodes in the circuits already described. Their performance is not inherently better than that of triodes, but the isolation offered by the separate grids makes them attractive for some applications. **Fig. 8(a)** and **8(b)** show configurations which are suitable for pentodes and pentagrids respectively. The r.f. carrier is applied in parallel to the control grids of the pentodes and to the oscillator injection grids of the converter valves. Modulating voltage is applied in push-pull to the screen grids of the pentodes, and to the signal injection grids of the pentagrids. Adjustment of r.f. balance is simple: the balancing potentiometer merely varies the operating

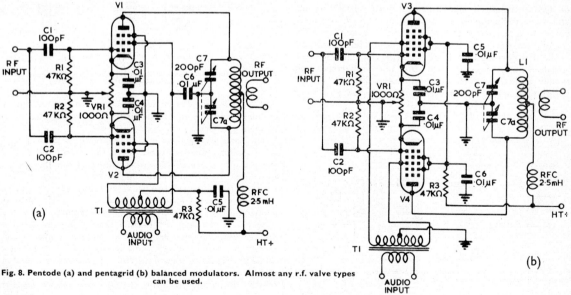

Fig. 8. Pentode (a) and pentagrid (b) balanced modulators. Almost any r.f. valve types can be used.

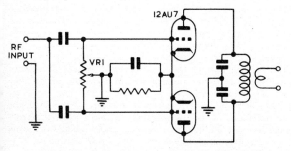

Fig. 9. Unreliable method of balancing (see text).

points of the valves by altering the applied cathode bias. Circuits have been described in which balance is adjusted by the differential variation of the r.f. excitation applied to the grids. This may be done by replacing R_1 and R_2 by a potentiometer, the slider of which is returned to earth, and by substituting fixed resistors for the adjustable cathode network of Fig. 8. The general arrangement may be gathered from the skeleton diagram in **Fig. 9.** The disadvantage of this scheme is that both ends of the balancing potentiometer are at r.f. potential, so that the stray capacitance of this component is likely to introduce phase shifts which are as unpredictable as they are undesirable. The method has nothing to commend it and should be avoided.

If a high degree of balance is to be maintained over a considerable time, it is essential to stabilize the anode supply to triode balanced modulators, and the screen supplies to multigrid valves. Gas filled regulator tubes are convenient for this purpose. No matter what precautions may be taken, however, the circuits described will ultimately drift because the characteristics of the valves will change as they age. Although this is likely to be a long-term trouble which may be remedied by monitoring and readjustment, it can cause considerable inconvenience if the balancing controls are so positioned that the whole transmitter has go be taken out of its case to allow them to be reset.

The Radio Corporation of America has recently introduced a new valve to overcome the limitations of conventional types in balanced modulator and balanced mixer service. This valve, the 7360, is available in Great Britain

from importers of U.S. radio equipment. The resemblance between the 7360 and the conventional electrostatically deflected cathode ray tube will be apparent from the diagram of the electrode layout shown in **Fig. 10(a).** Cathode, control grid and screen grid form an electron gun, the screen being so constructed that the number of electrons which it attracts to itself is only a fraction of the stream which it accelerates on its way towards the twin anodes. As the screen is earthed for r.f. by means of a bypass capacitor, it effectively isolates the triode section from the deflection assembly. The triode section may therefore be operated with complete stability as a hot-cathode Hartley or Colpitts oscillator, so that a separate oscillator valve is unnecessary. The beam of electrons emitted by the gun passes between a pair of deflecting plates on its way to the two anodes; if the valve were perfectly symmetrical, the r.f. would be divided equally between each anode in the absence of any difference of potential between

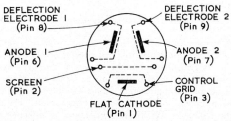

Fig. 10(a). Electrode layout of the beam-deflection valve type RCA 7360. The heater (6·3 volts, 0·35 amp) is connected to pins 4 and 5

the deflecting plates. Absolute symmetry is rarely met in practice, but the deflecting electrodes operate satisfactorily over the range $\pm$ 100 volts d.c., so balance is easily achieved by applying a fixed positive bias of approximately 20 volts to one of the plates and arranging for the bias on the other plate to be adjustable to a limited extent. With the beam centred, no r.f. voltage appears in a push-pull tank circuit connected between the anodes.

A practical balanced modulator employing the 7360 is shown in **Fig. 10(b).** In addition to the potentiometer VR_1 which provides for amplitude balance, adjustment for phase balance is permitted by the inclusion of VR_2 in the anode

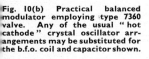

Fig. 10(b) Practical balanced modulator employing type 7360 valve. Any of the usual "hot cathode" crystal oscillator arrangements may be substituted for the b.f.o. coil and capacitor shown.

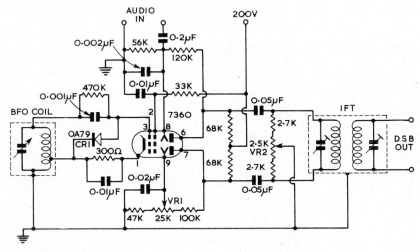

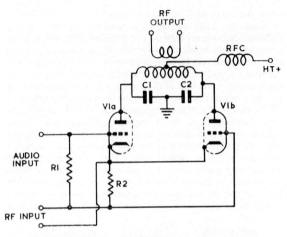

Fig. II. Single-ended excitation of balanced modulator (see text).

circuit. By setting these two controls appropriately, at least 60db of carrier suppression may be effected. The application of an a.f. signal, which should not exceed 1 volt R.M.S. or 2·8 volts peak-to-peak to one of the deflecting plates will cause a double sideband signal of approximately 4 volts peak-to-peak to appear across the output tank circuit. The other deflecting plate is, of course, maintained at effective earth potential for a.f. by the 0·02μF bypass capacitor.

The only critical feature of the 7360 is that it will not operate properly unless the control grid is maintained negative with respect to cathode at all times. In the circuit of Fig. 10(b), where the triode portion is used as a self-oscillating carrier generator, the crystal diode CR₁ ensures that this condition is met. If separate excitation is preferred, the control grid may be connected to earth through a resistor not exceeding 0·47 Megohm in value and excitation applied via a 0·001μF capacitor. The value of the cathode resistor should be increased to 1,200 ohms. The applied r.f. voltage measured at pin number 3 should not exceed 3 volts R.M.S.

The long term stability of a balanced modulator employing the 7360 is inherently high, because the electron flow to both anodes is derived from a single source, and the division of

current between the anodes depends upon the potential difference between the deflecting electrodes, rather than the d.c. potential applied to them. On the other hand, the circuit of Fig. 10(b) employs more components than a twin triode balanced modulator and is considerably more costly. It therefore falls to the constructor to weigh the relative merits of the two arrangements in the light of his own particular requirements.

It will be noted that, except in the case of the 7360, the introduction of a.f. modulation in push-pull is recommended with all high-impedance balanced modulators using conventional amplifier valves. Simplified circuits such as that of **Fig. 11** have been designed in which modulation is applied to one of the valves only. The drawback of such a simplification is that the amount by which the carrier may be suppressed is only about half that obtainable with push-pull modulation: 20–25db represents creditable performance for the circuit of Fig. 11. For best results, it is essential to provide push-pull audio excitation.

Although there are many possible variations of the low impedance diode modulator, they all stem from the four-diode ring modulator which has given the telephone companies such excellent service in landline s.s.b. work. The basic modulator, shown in **Fig. 12,** is rarely used by amateurs, but a number of derivatives have become popular. The diode balanced modulator requires impedance transformation in both the audio and the r.f. circuits, and is often less convenient to incorporate in a transmitter than the high impedance type. It may also prove more difficult in initial adjustment, but its long-term stability is claimed to outweigh all other considerations.

The shunt-connected circuit shown in **Fig. 13,** is capable of excellent results, and is suitable for providing input to filters operating at intermediate frequencies. The key to successful operation lies in the selection of a pair of diodes whose characteristics match closely, and in the correct transformation of impedances at both audio and radio frequencies. It is not sufficient to select a pair of diodes whose forward resistances are indicated by a multirange test meter to be approximately equal. Both forward and back resistances should be measured at a number of applied voltages between 0 and 10, and a set of curves plotted. If a number of diodes are available to choose from, it will rarely prove difficult to find a suitable pair. When soldering them into position, an efficient heat shunt should be used to prevent the heat of the iron causing the characteristics to change. In addition, the diodes should be located well clear of components which might generate enough heat to affect their performance. Many a mediocre balanced modulator owes its indifferent operation to the fact that it has been placed too close to a valve or a high wattage voltage-dropping resistor.

The selection of operating impedances is something of a compromise. The resistor R₂ is included to prevent the carrier being shorted to earth through the audio transformer T₁, and the input of the i.f. transformer must be modified as shown in the diagram so that it will not act as a short circuit at audio frequencies. Carrier input must be at low impedance: a standard i.f. transformer modified as suggested in the caption to Fig. 13 will be found satisfactory.

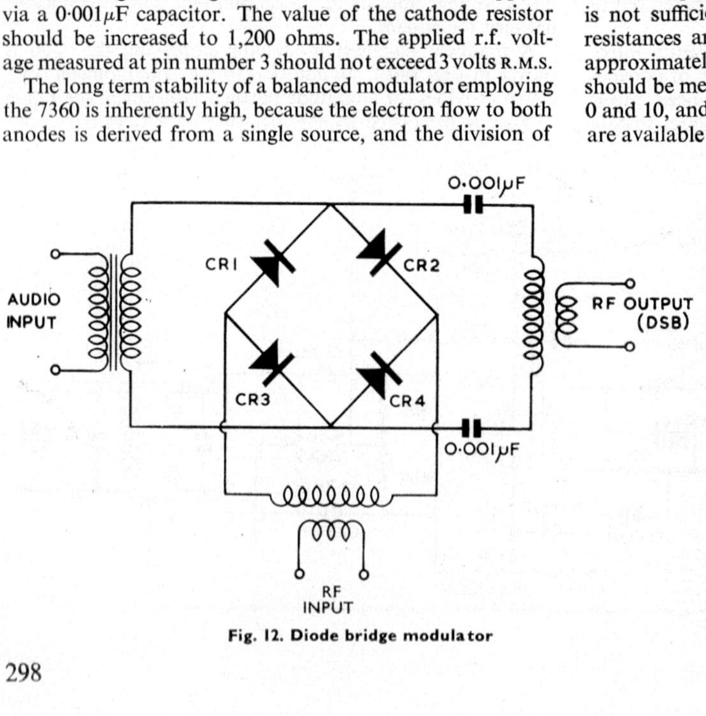

Fig. 12. Diode bridge modulator

If the potentiometer VR_1 does not alone give sufficient carrier suppression, it may be supplemented by a small variable capacitor of 3–30 pF connected between earth and one or other of the points marked P_1 and P_2 in Fig. 13. If the balancing capacitor is needed, its correct placement and adjustment may quickly be determined by trial and error. The application of modulation causes the bridge to become unbalanced at audio rate, and double sideband energy to appear at the output. For minimum distortion, the carrier voltage should be about ten times as great as the peak audio voltage. Several volts of r.f. and a fraction of a volt of audio are the usual operating levels.

The series-connected balanced modulator shown in **Fig. 14** often presents less of a constructional problem than the shunt circuit. Almost any audio transformer may be used, as long as it is bypassed at carrier frequency by C_1, while a standard i.f. transformer will serve at the output end. The same considerations as in the shunt-connected modulator apply to the carrier input transformer and to capacitative balancing. An attractive feature of the series modulator is that audio input may be provided by a cathode follower instead of a transformer. **Fig. 15** shows an arrangement used by the Collins Radio Company in a commercial transmitter employing a mechanical filter. The 100K resistor was included to match the input impedance of the mechanical filter, and should be omitted if the balanced modulator is followed by a device of higher impedance such as a crystal filter.

Although the series and shunt balanced modulators are suitable for use at intermediate frequencies to feed filter units, a pair of them may not be connected conveniently in parallel in the manner required for the generation of s.s.b. output by the phasing method. The modified ring-circuit designed by

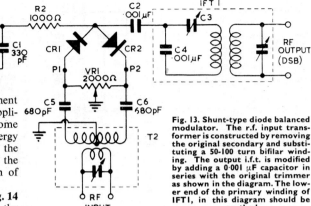

Fig. 13. Shunt-type diode balanced modulator. The r.f. input transformer is constructed by removing the original secondary and substituting a 50-100 turn bifilar winding. The output i.f.t. is modified by adding a 0·001 μF capacitor in series with the original trimmer as shown in the diagram. The lower end of the primary winding of IFT1, in this diagram should be earthed

D. E. Norgaard (W2KUJ) and reproduced in **Fig. 16**, overcomes this difficulty. Almost all the commercial phasing-type transmitters made in the U.S.A. which employ diode balanced modulators make use of this arrangement. An ordinary loudspeaker transformer with a 15 ohm secondary will be suitable for T_1, while L_1 is a three or four turn link wound over the cold end of the carrier oscillator coil and

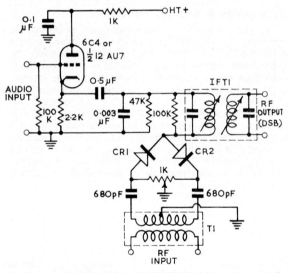

Fig. 15. Method of substituting an a.f. cathode follower for an audio transformer with series-type diode balanced modulator.

adjusted to give about 4 volts of r.f. across VR_1. The push-pull tank circuit resonates at the desired output frequency. The choke RFC is essential for the correct operation of the circuit and must not on any account be omitted.

In describing balanced modulators the convention of rating a circuit in terms of " so many decibels of carrier suppression " has been followed. This may be misleading to the uninitiated, because in fact the circuits work the other way round. To be strictly correct, the rating of a balanced modulator ought to be expressed as the number of decibels by which the output at maximum audio drive exceeds the minimum resting output in the absence of modulation. The point of making this distinction is to show that for the highest

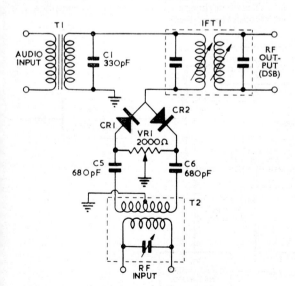

Fig. 14. Series-type diode balanced modulator. The r.f. input transformer is modified as for Fig. 13.

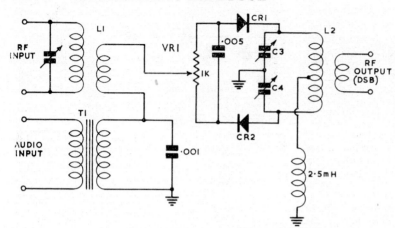

Fig. 16. Modified ring type balanced modulator. T_1 is an audio transformer with low impedance secondary winding; a ratio between 1 : 8 and 1 : 12 is recommended. L_1 is a three or four turn link wound over the cold end of the input tank inductor and adjusted to give 3 or 4 volts r.m.s. across its output. Any matched pair of diodes may be used for CR_1 and CR_2. The input and output r.f. circuits should resonate at the operating frequency.

degree of carrier suppression any balanced modulator should be driven to its maximum undistorted output. The drive to the final stages of a transmitter should be controlled *after* the s.s.b. signal has been generated, and not by reducing the audio input to the balanced modulator; if it is not, the carrier suppression of the system as a whole will suffer.

Construction of Balanced Modulators

No matter what circuit configuration may be chosen, the operation of the balanced modulator will ultimately depend upon the care with which the constructor assembles the components. Leads carrying r.f. should be short and direct, the output and input should be screened from one another, and components should be arranged symmetrically to minimize unbalance arising from stray capacitance. All components should be anchored firmly, nothing being permitted to move or vibrate in the wiring. With high impedance modulators, the resistors and capacitors should be soldered directly to the valveholder tag. As the balance of both high and low impedance types is affected to a considerable extent by the amplitude of the applied r.f. carrier,

excitation should be obtained from an oscillator of highest stability. The voltage to the oscillator anode should of course be stabilized, as should the anode supply to the valves in the high impedance balanced modulator.

SIDEBAND ATTENUATION

The double sideband signal generated by any of the balanced modulators described is of little value for communications purposes, so it has to be turned into s.s.b. by attenuating one of the sidebands. No matter what system may be used, the unwanted sideband is not eliminated completely; it is merely attenuated to the extent at which its nuisance effect at the receiving end becomes negligible. An attenuation of 30–35db has come to be regarded as the minimum acceptable standard. With care, suppression of 50db or more is attainable, but it is debatable whether there is any practical advantage in striving after greater perfection.

The unwanted sideband may either be phased or filtered out. The two methods are totally different in conception, and will be discussed in detail.

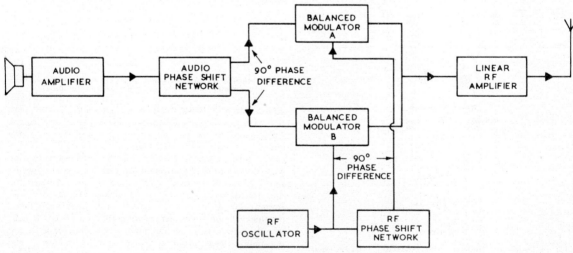

Fig. 17 Block diagram of a phasing exciter.

The Phasing System

Although the filter method provides the classic way to generate a single sideband signal, the phasing system will be described first, because it was invented, pioneered and developed by amateurs. The system is based upon a mathematical theory which is not capable of explanation in simple language, but fortunately an understanding of a few basic principles is all that is required to enable the theory to be translated into practice.

A block diagram of a phasing type transmitter is shown in **Fig. 17,** from which will be seen that the output of an r.f. oscillator is fed into a network in which it is split into two separate components, equal in amplitude but differing in phase by 90°. Similarly, the output of an audio amplifier is split into two components of equal amplitude and 90° phase difference. One r.f. and one a.f. component are combined in each of two balanced modulators. The double sideband suppressed carrier energy issuing from the two balanced modulators is fed into a common tank circuit. The relative phases of the sidebands produced by the two balanced modulators are such that one sideband is balanced out, while the other is reinforced. The resultant in the common tank circuit is a s.s.b. signal. The main advantages of a phasing exciter are that sideband suppression may be accomplished at the operating frequency and that selection of the upper or lower sideband may be made by merely reversing the phase of the audio input to one of the balanced modulators. These facilities are denied to the user of the filter system.

If it were possible to arrange for absolute precision of phase shift in the r.f. and a.f. networks, and absolute equality in the amplitude of the outputs, the attenuation of the unwanted sideband would be infinite. In practice, perfection is impossible to achieve, and some degradation of performance is inevitable. Assuming that there is no error in audio amplitude adjustment, a phase error of 1° in either the a.f. or the r.f. network will reduce the suppression to 40db, while an error of 2° will produce 35db, and 3·5° will result in 30db suppression. If, on the other hand, phase adjustment is exact, a difference of amplitude between the two audio channels will similarly reduce the suppression. A difference between the two voltages of 1 per cent would give 45db attenuation, an error of 2 per cent would result in 40db, and 4 per cent 35db approximately. These figures are not given to discourage the intending constructor, but to stress the need for high precision workmanship and adjustment if a satisfactory phasing-type s.s.b. transmitter is to be produced.

There are many ways of obtaining r.f. phase shifts, but the two most satisfactory are those which use a pair of loosely-coupled tuned circuits, and the so-called *low-Q* network which uses a combination of resistance, inductance and capacitance. The former is shown diagrammatically in **Fig. 18,** and is based on the property of coupled circuits which provides that if both are tuned to resonance the voltage induced in the secondary will lag behind that appearing

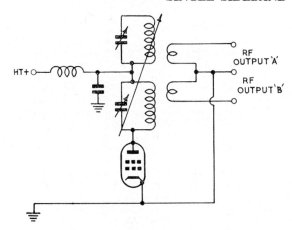

Fig. 18. Method of obtaining 90° r.f. phase shift by coupled tuned circuits.

across the driven primary by 90°. In practice it may prove difficult to tune both circuits to the precise point of resonance because of mutual interaction, but if this effect is encountered it may be easily overcome. The recommended method is to start by detuning the secondary completely, or to shunt it by a resistive load of about 200 ohms so that it cannot react upon the primary. The primary is tuned to resonance, using a valve voltmeter or other r.f. indicator, and is then detuned to the high frequency side until the voltage drops to 70 per cent of that indicated at resonance. The secondary is next brought to resonance (with its shunt removed) and finally detuned to the low frequency side until the indicated voltage drops to 70 per cent. The voltages across the two circuits will then differ in phase by precisely 90°. Because of losses, it is unlikely that the voltage appearing across the secondary will be of exactly the same amplitude as that across the primary. It is therefore inadvisable to use capacitive coupling from the hot ends of the windings. Link coupling, as shown in Fig. 18, is preferable because it allows compensation to be made for inequalities in amplitude.

The low Q network shown in **Fig. 19** is often considered to be the most flexible and least critical way of phase-shifting at r.f. It is a differential device, which operates on the basic theory that if an alternating voltage is applied to a resistance and a reactance in series, the voltage at the junction of the components will lead or lag behind the applied voltage, dependent on whether the reactance is inductive or capacitive.

TABLE I

Component values for Low Q R.F. Phase Shift Network of Fig. 19.

f	R_1R_2	C	L
3·75 Mc/s	50 ohms	851 pF	2·13 μH
3·75 Mc/s	300 ohms	142 pF	12·8 μH
9·0 Mc/s	50 ohms	355 pF	0·85 μH
9·0 Mc/s	300 ohms	59 pF	5·1 μH

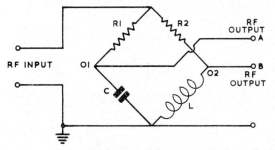

Fig. 19. Low Q phase shift network. At the operating frequency X_C and X_L should be equal to R_1 and R_2. For component values, see Table I.

The resistors R_1 and R_2 may be chosen to have any convenient value between 50 and 300 ohms, and L and C are adjusted so that they offer a reactance at the carrier frequency exactly equal in value to the resistors. The voltage at point O_1 will then lead the applied voltage by 45°, and that at O_2 will lag behind the applied voltage by the same amount. The total phase difference between the points will therefore be 90°, and the signals will be of equal amplitude. When the network is correctly adjusted its input impedance is purely resistive and is equal to the ohmic value of either of the resistors. The circuit should be operated directly into the associated valve grids, and should not be loaded by low value grid resistors, neither should it be employed with valves which draw grid current, otherwise its performance will be degraded. One attractive feature of the low Q circuit is its ability to maintain the required 90° phase shift over a considerable frequency range. There will be some variation in amplitude between the two output channels as the frequency is altered from the exact design-centre value, but this is unimportant. It may be proved mathematically and confirmed by practical experiment that small inequalities in the amplitude of r.f. excitation to the two balanced modulators have no degrading influence upon the degree of sideband suppression, provided that equality in the amplitude of the audio modulation is maintained. The extent to which this theory may be exploited in a practical exciter depends largely upon conditions imposed by associated circuitry, and is best determined by

experiment in each case. As a minimum it should be possible to arrange perfect coverage of at least 100 kc/s of the 3·5 Mc/s band. This makes the network particularly suitable for use at the operating frequency in single band exciters designed to cover only a portion of the chosen band. If, however, optimum results are desired, it is best to design the network to operate at a fixed frequency outside the amateur bands, and to heterodyne the output of the exciter to the required band or bands by means of an external v.f.o. This method will be discussed in greater detail later in this chapter.

Stray capacitances start to have an appreciable effect on the low Q circuit at frequencies greater than 14 Mc/s, and may also give trouble if an attempt is made to incorporate it into any form of band-switching arrangement. **Table 1** gives values of L and C appropriate for operation at 3·75 Mc/s and 9 Mc/s with resistors of 50 and 300 ohms. The values for 9 Mc/s have been included because this frequency has been found convenient for the construction of a fixed-frequency exciter the output of which may be heterodyned into all the amateur bands from 3·5 to 28 Mc/s inclusive.

Audio Phase Shift Networks

Unfortunately, it is not quite so easy to obtain the required phase shift over the total audio frequency range to be covered. Although it is quite practicable to construct a network capable of covering from 50 to 5000 c/s, the results scarcely justify the high cost involved. Experiments have shown conclusively that frequencies below 200 and above 3000 c/s contribute little to the intelligence conveyed by the human voice, and that under conditions of high ambient noise there is a decided advantage in accentuating the higher-frequency speech components and in progressively attenuating those components which lie below 500 or 600 c/s. The naturalness of the voice under this kind of treatment must necessarily suffer, but to a lesser degree than might be expected. The Post Office telephone lines have a frequency response no better than that mentioned, and their quality is adequate for normal aural communication.

A straightforward circuit giving an exact 90° shift over the total audio spectrum is impossible to realize, but by restricting the range to the minimum required for satisfactory communication, a tolerably good network may be constructed from simple fixed capacitors and resistors. Like the low-Q r.f. circuit, this device operates differentially; that is, the voltage at one of the output terminals leads applied a.f. voltage by an amount which varies according to the frequency, while the output at the other terminal lags behind the applied voltage. The values of the components may be chosen so that the total phase shift between both output terminals approximates 90°.

Figs. 20(a) and 20(b) show two types of network which are suitable for amateur use. **Fig. 20(a)** is similar in configuration to that used by W2KUJ in his famous "S.S.B. JR" which popularized single sideband in the U.S.A., but the circuit values have been modified to enable more easily obtainable components to be used. The network operates over the range 300-3000 c/s, and if it is constructed of components of 1 per cent tolerance the maximum deviation from the ideal phase shift of 90° will be within 1·5°. Sideband suppression is therefore better than 35db at the worst frequency within the audio range. The network should be fed from a relatively high impedance source, such as the secondary of an interstage audio transformer, and the output terminals must be connected to a load of infinite impedance,

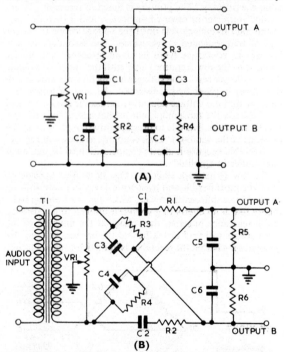

(A)

(B)

Fig. 20(a). "S.S.B. JR" passive a.f. phase shift network. $C_{1,2}$, 680pF ± 1% silvered mica; $C_{2,4}$, 430pF (330pF + 100pF) ± 1% silvered mica; R_1, 487,500 ohms (470K + 15K + 2·2K in series); R_2, 777,000 ohms (500 + 270K in series); R_3, 125,000 ohms (100K + 15K + 10K in series); R_4, 198,000 ohms (150K + 47K in series); VR_1, 500 ohms. All fixed resistors are high-stability ± 1% ½ watt made by TSL. (b) The Dome passive phase shift network. C_1, 0·0242 μF; C_2, 0·00535μF; C_3, 892 pF; C_4, 0·00403 μF; C_5, 0·00806 μF; C_6, 0·00178 μF. All capacitors ± 1% silvered mica. $R_{1,2}$, 20K ohms (two 10K in series); $R_{3,4}$, 120K ohms (100K + two 10K in series); $R_{5,6}$, 60K ohms (50K + 10K in series). All resistors ± 1% high stability type. VR_1, 250-500 ohms.

such as the grids of a pair of class A amplifier valves. The potentiometer VR_1 is adjusted to give amplitude balance, and as the insertion loss of that half of the network which feeds one of the following amplifiers is much greater than that of the other half, this control will be some distance away from midpoint when properly set.

The circuit in **Fig. 20(b)** is that of the original passive network devised by R. B. Dome (W2WAM) and is sometimes considered to be more convenient to construct than Fig. 20(a). Provided it is built of components of 1 per cent tolerance, it is capable of maintaining a phase shift of $90 \pm 1 \cdot 5°$ over the audio range from 200 to 2000 c/s. As with the simpler network, VR_1 adjusts amplitude balance, and the same conditions of input and output impedances apply.

As the audio phase shift network is the heart of a phasing exciter, no effort should be spared in constructing it as closely as possible to specification. Close tolerance silvered mica capacitors and high stability resistors should be used exclusively. They cost more than ordinary components, but are much more reliable. It may sound attractive to select

the required values from stock 20 per cent stacked mica capacitors and carbon resistors, but such components are not designed for long term stability and will invariably drift with use. Some of the values required for the networks are not in the standard range, and will have to be made up by the series or parallel connection of two or more components. Radiospares 1 per cent tolerance resistors and capacitors are freely available at reasonable cost and in a wide range of values, and any co-operative supplier ought to be able to make up the required combinations from his normal stocks. Alternatively, plug-in phase shift units may be purchased ready-made from dealers specializing in components for the radio amateur.

If the speech amplifier used to drive either of the networks described does not have its response restricted to the range over which they are effective, objectionable distortion will result. An adequate degree of roll-off at low frequencies may be obtained by using low value coupling capacitors in the speech stages preceding the network. Insufficient high frequency attenuation will not necessarily make the signal as difficult to tune and read as poor low frequency cut-off, but

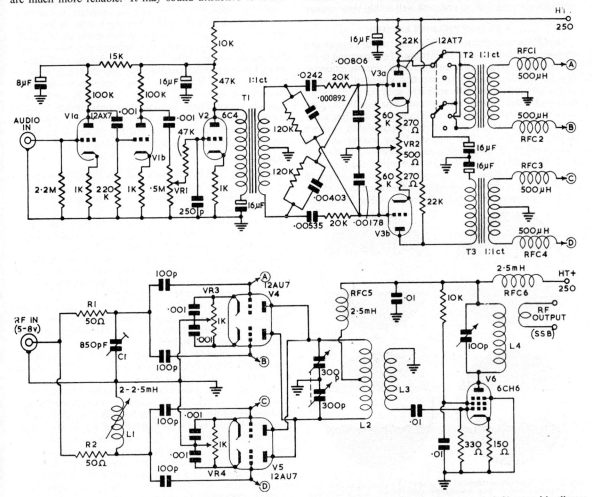

Fig. 21. 3·5 Mc/s phasing exciter. L_2 is 32 turns, I in. diam., $1\frac{1}{2}$ in. long, with an 8 turn link, L_3, wound at the centre; L_4 is 20 turns, I in. diam I in. long, with a 3-6 turn link wound over the cold end.

it will cause splatter and interference to users of adjacent channels. This may be minimized by restricting the high frequency response of the audio amplifier in the manner shown in Chapter 9 (*Modulation*).

A stage of class A amplification must be interposed between each of the output channels of the phase shift network and its associated balanced modulator for three reasons: to provide amplification, to offer the correct terminating impedance, and to isolate the network from the somewhat variable load presented by the balanced modulator. The necessity of building these two amplifiers as really high fidelity devices is frequently overlooked, but it is vitally important. Unless the frequency response is excellent, the amplifiers may introduce phase-shifts on their own account and nullify the good work done by the phase shift network. If *RC* coupling is employed, large-value capacitors are essential, while audio transformers should be of proven high quality and wide frequency response. Shunt feed is recommended with transformer coupling to obviate the ill-effects of direct current flowing through the primary. Finally, the valves themselves should be operated on the most linear part of their characteristic curves and kept well within their ratings.

A 3·5 MC/S PHASING EXCITER

Fig. 21 shows an exciter which works straight through and provides s.s.b. output with an existing v.f.o. operating in the 3·5 Mc/s band. The speech amplifier stages are conventional. The 12AX7 dual triode provides two stages of resistance coupled amplification with sufficient gain for a crystal or high impedance dynamic microphone. The coupling capacitors and resistors are chosen to favour the audio frequency range of 250–3000 c/s over which the phase-shift network performs efficiently. The output of the second stage is capacitively coupled through a gain control to a 6C4 which drives the audio phase shift network through the push-pull interstage transformer T_1. The centre-tapped secondary of this transformer delivers voltages of equal amplitudes to the network, which is the Dome configuration of Fig. 20(b). The

output of the network is fed to the two halves of a 12AT7 dual triode V_3, from which it passes via the audio transformers T_2 and T_3 to the two 12AU7 balanced modulators V_4 and V_5. These stages are cathode balanced by the potentiometers VR_3 and VR_4. Audio balance is provided by the potentiometer VR_2 in the cathode circuit of the two halves of the a.f. modulator valve V_3.

Excitation from an external v.f.o. operating in the 3·5 Mc/s band is applied through a length of coaxial cable to the low Q r.f. phase shift network R_1, R_2, L_1 and C_1, and from thence it is coupled capacitively to the grids of the balanced modulators. The r.f. chokes in the leads from the audio driver transformers to the balanced modulators are essential to prevent interaction between the r.f. and a.f. sections of the exciter. The switch S_1 between V_{3a} and T_2 has three positions. By changing the phase of the audio excitation to the balanced modulator it enables upper or lower sideband transmission to be selected at will, and in the third position it disables V_4, with the result that a double sideband signal will be produced when audio modulation is applied. (A double sideband signal is extremely useful for aligning linear amplifiers.) Only a few volts of r.f. excitation are required, and in most cases this may be obtained by winding a three or four turn link over the earthy end of the output tuned circuit in the v.f.o. Alternatively, a cathode follower driver may be used. The common tuned circuit fed by the two balanced modulators follows normal practice, but care should be taken to mount the coil L_2 so that stray capacitances from one end or the other do not unduly affect the balance to earth. The 6CH6 in the r.f. driver position V_6 is conventional in every respect. Operating conservatively in class A, it is capable of providing more than enough excitation for any of the linear amplifiers to be described later in this chapter.

Alignment

Alignment is straightforward, but it does call for a certain amount of reliable test equipment. An oscilloscope is essential, but it need not be expensive or complicated. A simple instrument will be found adequate. A valve voltmeter capable of making r.f. and a.f. measurements is also highly desirable, and like the oscilloscope, an inexpensive home constructed instrument will be just as effective as a highly-priced commercial one. Finally, a simple audio oscillator capable of generating a good sine wave at about 1500 c/s will be found extremely useful. Suitable instruments are described in Chapter 19 (*Measurements*).

The first step is to apply r.f. input, and to adjust all the tuned circuits to resonance at the desired output frequency. The fashionable part of the band for s.s.b. operation in the U.K. is between 3·75 and 3·8 Mc/s.

The valve voltmeter is the most useful output indicator at this stage of alignment, but if one is not available a simple r.f. indicator may be employed.

The carrier should be balanced out, using VR_3 and VR_4. If it cannot be reduced almost completely one of the balanced modulators requires attention. A fraction of a volt of audio may next be applied to the microphone input, care being taken not to overload any of the amplifier stages, otherwise misleading results will be obtained. Adjustment of VR_2 will enable the modulating voltage applied to the balanced modulator grids to be brought to equality, as indicated by a valve voltmeter. An oscilloscope is required from this point onwards, and should be coupled to the output of the exciter in such a manner as to display a conveniently large pattern

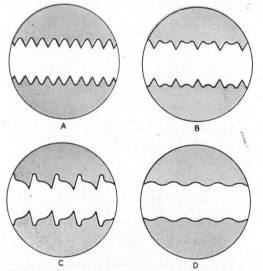

Fig. 22. Oscilloscope patterns of the output of a phasing exciter: (a) r.f. phasing correct but amplitude unbalanced; (b) amplitude correct, but r.f. phasing not properly adjusted; (c) amplitude unbalanced, and incorrect r.f. phasing; (d) optimum adjustment.

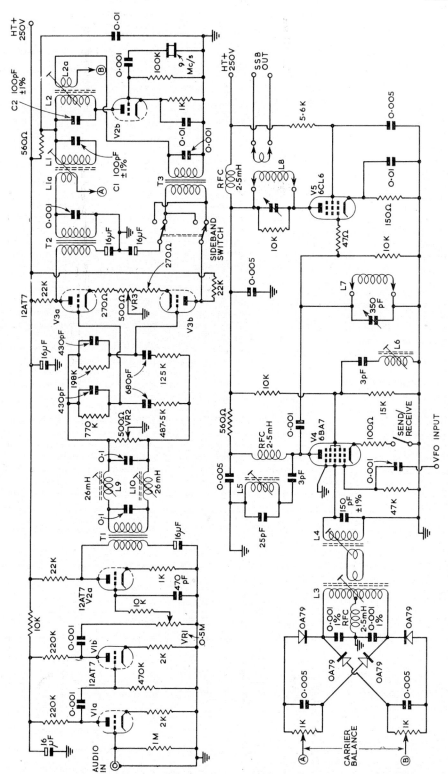

Fig. 23. Circuit diagram of a 9 Mc/s phasing exciter. L_1, L_2, 25 turns 20 s.w.g. enam. Closewound on $\frac{3}{8}$ in. diam. slug tuned former. L_{1a} and L_{1b} are 4 turn links wound over the "cold" ends. The spacing between L_1 and L_2, which should be approximately $1\frac{1}{2}$ in., may be adjusted to give optimum phase shift. L_3, 8 turns, centre tapped, $\frac{3}{8}$ in. diam. and $\frac{3}{4}$ in. long, with two turn link at centre. L_4, 25 turns 20 s.w.g. enamel, close wound on $\frac{3}{8}$ in. diam. slug tuned former. L_5, L_6, Trap coils, 18 turns 20 s.w.g. enamel, closewound on $\frac{3}{8}$ in. diam. slug tuned former. L_7, L_8, See winding data in Table 2. T_1 may be any step-down audio transformer with a ratio not less than 1:5. Standard loudspeaker transformers are suitable for T_2 and T_3. For details of the low pass audio filter, see text. The commercial B & W type 2Q4 audio phase-shift network may be substituted for the components shown in the diagram.

when modulation is applied. To simulate working conditions, a non-inductive dummy load of appropriate wattage dissipation should be coupled to the output tank circuit. With a steady a.f. tone applied to the input, and the switch set to either of the s.s.b. positions, the pattern on the cathode ray tube should be examined. With perfect sideband suppression, a smooth band will be obtained, similar to that produced by an unmodulated carrier wave. In the initial stages of alignment, however, it is likely that the r.f. phasing and amplitude will be out of adjustment, and an appreciable amount of modulation ripple may be seen. Phasing and amplitude adjustments interlock in the low Q network, so it is advisable to obtain the correct phase difference first and deal with the amplitude later. Preliminary phase adjustment may be effected by varying the position of the tuning slug in L_1. The correct position will be indicated by the regular pattern of **Fig. 22(a)**. The patterns resulting from incorrect conditions of alignment are shown for reference in **Figs. 22(b) and (c)**. When correct phasing has been obtained, amplitude may be equalized by the differential adjustment of L_1 and C_1 until the smoothest obtainable pattern is shown on the display. A final adjustment may then be made to the audio balance control VR_2 to ensure that it is in the optimum position; it should not, however, require more than a trace of movement if the preliminary setting with the valve voltmeter has been done correctly. The amount of residual ripple will indicate the degree to which the unwanted sideband has been suppressed. A peak-to-peak ripple of 3 per cent indicates suppression approaching 30db, 2 per cent represents about 35db, and 1 per cent 40db.

A 9 MC/S PHASING EXCITER

A somewhat more elaborate phasing exciter is shown in **Fig. 23**. This circuit is a development of the S.S.B. Jr, designed by D. E. Norgaard (W2KUJ). Optimum performance is ensured in the modified circuit here presented by carrying out the r.f. phasing at a crystal controlled frequency of 9 Mc/s. An external v.f.o. at about 5·25 Mc/s enables output to be obtained in either the 3·5 or the 14 Mc/s band. There is no particular disadvantage in generating the initial s.s.b. signal at a fixed frequency, because band changing must

TABLE 2

Coil winding data for Class A amplifier stage of phasing exciter shown in Fig. 23 and filter exciter in Fig. 34.

Band	Grid			Anode		
	Turns	Diam.	Length	Turns	Diam.	Length
3·5 Mc/s	60	$\frac{3}{8}$ in.	1 in.	30	1 in.	$1\frac{1}{2}$ in.
7 Mc/s	30	$\frac{3}{8}$ in.	1 in.	20	1 in.	$1\frac{1}{2}$ in.
14 Mc/s	16	$\frac{3}{8}$ in.	1 in.	12	1 in.	$1\frac{1}{2}$ in.
21 Mc/s	9	$\frac{3}{8}$ in.	1 in.	8	1 in.	1 in.
28 Mc/s	7	$\frac{3}{8}$ in.	1 in.	6	1 in.	1 in.

* The 3·5 Mc/s grid inductor should be shunted by a fixed silvered-mica capacitor of 50–75 pF.

be effected by a heterodyning operation in any event. In common with all other forms of amplitude modulated telephony, band changing by frequency multiplication *after* modulation has been applied is out of the question. In the exciter shown in Fig. 23, the application of a heterodyning signal from a v.f.o. at 2, 12 or 20 Mc/s will result in output in the 7, 21 or 28 Mc/s bands respectively. The tuned circuits in the mixer and amplifier stages will, of course, have to be appropriately modified.

The audio amplifier is almost identical to that of the exciter in Fig. 21. Because diode balanced modulators are used, less audio voltage is required, so the overall gain is reduced by using a 12AT7 in the first two stages instead of a 12AX7. Low frequency response is curtailed by appropriately chosen coupling capacitors, and the low pass audio filter which is interposed between T_1 and the phase-shift network gives a high frequency cut-off which will be appreciated by other operators because of the resulting reduction in splatter. The inductors L_9 and L_{10} may be adapted from standard television width-control coils, which should be adjusted to resonate at about 3200 c/s with a 0·1 μF capacitor in parallel. The minimum inductance varies from one manufacturer to another, and with some types of coil it may be necessary to remove turns before resonance at a high enough frequency becomes attainable. The audio phase shift network is identical to that already described in Fig. 20(a). The input potentiometer VR_2 should be a carbon-track component (not wirewound) and should be set initially with the aid

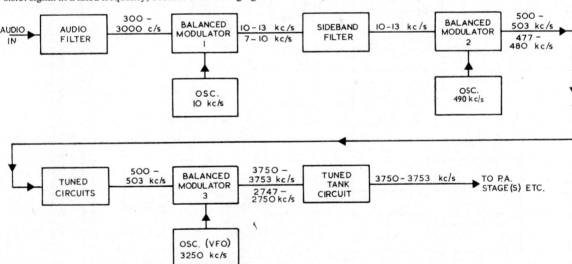

Fig. 24. Simplified block diagram of low frequency system of generating an s.s.b. signal.

of an ohmmeter so that the ratio of resistance between points *A-B* and *B-C* is close to 2 : 7. If the component measures up accurately at 500 ohms, appropriate meter readings will be 110 and 390 ohms. When this potentiometer has been set it should be sealed and forgotten, all subsequent audio balance adjustments being made by VR_3. Standard transformers designed to feed a 15 ohm loudspeaker are ideal for use at T_2 and T_3.

Phase shifting at r.f. is accomplished by the coupled circuits L_1, C_1 and L_2, C_2 in the anode circuit of the crystal oscillator valve V_{2b}.

Most of the instructions given for the alignment of the exciter previously described are equally applicable to this one. The r.f. adjustments are perhaps a little simpler because phase and amplitude may be regulated independently of one another. Phasing adjustment was dealt with fully in the section relating to the phasing network. R.f. amplitude may be equalized by tightening or loosening the coupling between one of the link windings L_{1a} or L_{2a} and its associated tuned circuit.

The s.s.b. output at 9 Mc/s is link coupled from the tank circuit of the double balanced modulator to the oscillator injection grid of the 6BA7 pentagrid mixer, V_4. The mixer is conventional, except for the trap circuits in the screen and anode circuits which attenuate the third harmonic of the

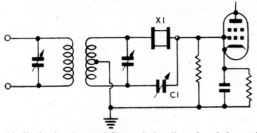

Fig. 25. Single signal crystal filter. C_1 is adjusted to balance the self-capacity of the crystal.

5 Mc/s v.f.o. so that it will not cause a spurious radiation when operation in the 14 Mc/s band is required. If a grid dip oscillator is available, it will be found useful in setting the traps to frequency.

Coil winding details for all bands from 3·5 to 29·7 Mc/s are given in **Table 2**. If desired, a band switching coil pack may be substituted for the individual coils indicated in the circuit diagram. The table also includes winding data for the tuned circuit in the output stage. This stage, which uses a 6CL6 miniature high gain pentode, also follows normal practice, and is capable of providing enough excitation for any of the linear amplifiers described later.

CRYSTAL FILTERS

Although crystal filters have been used for many years to increase the selectivity of receivers, it is paradoxical that their application to transmission did not come until amateur interest in s.s.b. had been awakened by the development of the phasing method. The filter system is the classic way to generate s.s.b., and the earliest designs used *LC* filters which, to be effective, had to work in the region of 10–20 kc/s. Low frequency filters have not gained widespread popularity amongst amateurs because they are comparatively difficult and costly to build. They also require at least one intermediate stage of heterodyne conversion before reaching

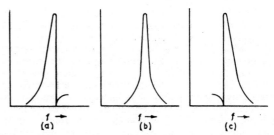

Fig. 26. Response curves of single signal crystal filter shown in Fig. 25. (a) C_1 smaller than capacitance of X_1; (b) C_1 equal to capacitance of X_1; (c) C_1 greater than capacitance of X_1.

operating frequency if objectionable image-response is to be avoided. The block diagram of **Fig. 24** shows what is required.

A quartz crystal filter, operating in the 400–500 kc/s region, can give results at least as good as the low frequency *LC* variety, and may be heterodyned directly to the signal frequency in a single operation. Although the theory of crystal

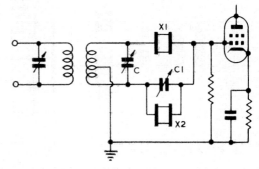

Fig. 27. Bandpass crystal filter. X_2 is approximately 2 kc/s higher in frequency than X_1.

filters is quite complicated, intelligent application of broad principles is sufficient to enable an excellent filter to be built from standard i.f. transformers and inexpensive crystals from war surplus sources.

The best filter for home construction with limited test equipment is undoubtedly the half-lattice configuration. Its operation may most easily be understood by examining the way in which it is derived from the common single-crystal

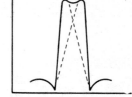

Fig. 28. Response of bandpass crystal filter. The dotted line shows how the response of the two crystals adds to form the bandpass curve.

receiver filter of **Fig. 25**. As the quartz plate is a very high Q device, the passband will be extremely narrow in comparison to that of the best *LC* circuit at the same frequency. When the shunt capacitance of the crystal and its holder is just balanced by C_1, the response curve is perfectly symmetrical, as shown in **Fig. 26(b)**. If C_1 is made smaller, a rejection notch appears to the high frequency side as in Fig. 26(a); if larger, the notch appears on the low frequency side as in

Fig. 26(c). By shunting C_1 with a second crystal approximately 2 kc/s higher in frequency than X_1 as shown in **Fig. 27,** the response waves of Fig. 26(a) and 26(c) will combine to form the bandpass curve shown in **Fig. 28.** The value of C_1 will of course have to be adjusted to give the optimum response. In most cases, a value in the region of 2 pF is required, and this may conveniently be obtained by twisting together two short pieces of insulated wire. Should the balancing capacitor be inadvertently placed across the lower frequency crystal, the skirts will spread and a pronounced dip appear in the centre of the passband. With the input circuit tuned to the centre of the passband, it is possible to obtain a virtually flat-topped curve about 3 kc/s wide. The skirts will be steep and regular, and the response at least 35db down at 6 kc/s bandwidth.

The constants in the input and output circuits have a considerable effect on the performance of the filter, and must therefore be carefully chosen. A high C/L ratio in the input transformer will make it impossible to obtain a flat-topped

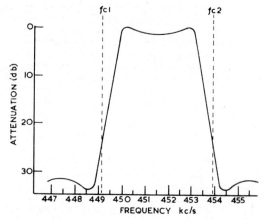

Fig. 31. Carrier placement with symmetrical bandpass crystal filter Upper sideband output is obtained when the carrier is at fc_1 and lower sideband when it is at fc_2.

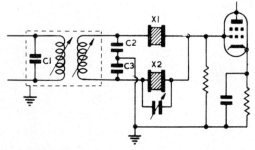

Fig. 29. Recommended method of adding a capacitive centre-tap to a standard i.f. transformer ($C_2 = C_3 = 2C_1$).

curve. Two distinct peaks will appear at the resonant frequencies of the crystals, separated by a deep trough, which renders the filter quite useless. For practical purposes in the 400–500 kc/s range, the tuning capacitor C should not exceed 100 pF. Centre-tapped transformers are rare, but equally good results will result from capacitance-tapping as shown in **Fig. 29.** Circuits have been published in which the tap is obtained by adding two small capacitors to the existing tuning capacitor as shown in **Fig. 30;** this is bad practice, because it invariably leads to poor balance and indifferent filter performance. The existing capacitor should be cut out, and replaced by two close-tolerance silver-mica components of double its value in series. Experiment has proved that there is no advantage in squeezing these capacitors into

the transformer screening-can. Provided they are mounted close to its base, they work just as well outside.

The correct terminating impedance for the filter depends amongst other things on the crystal parameters, and with surplus crystals in type FT241 holders the value should be in the region of 70K ohms. A resistor will serve as shown in the various figures, or an r.f. choke of appropriate value may be substituted. Best of all is a tuned circuit or i.f. transformer resonated at the centre of the passband and loaded by a 68K ohm resistor. It enables a flatter-topped curve to be obtained than the resistor alone, and increases the attenuation outside the passband. An unloaded tuned circuit must not, however, be used, because it presents too high a terminating impedance and will nullify the effect of the crystals.

The two-crystal circuit of Fig. 27 has formed the heart of many simple s.s.b. exciters. By arranging the carrier frequency at about 20db down either of the passband skirts, a tolerable signal may be obtained. The general idea may be

TABLE 3

Combinations of two-digit (54th harmonic) and three-digit (72nd harmonic) type FT241 surplus crystals suitable for sideband filters in the 400–500 kc/s intermediate frequency range.

Upper Sideband			Lower Sideband		
Shunt Crystal	Series Crystals		Shunt Crystal	Series Crystals	
	Lower	Upper		Upper	Lower
289	17	291 (18)	291	18	289 (17)
293	20	295 (21)	295	21	293 (20)
297	23	299 (24)	299	24	297 (23)
301	26	303 (27)	303	27	301 (26)
305	29	307 (30)	307	30	305 (29)
309	32	311 (33)	311	33	309 (32)
313	35	315 (36)	315	36	313 (35)
317	38	319 (39)	319	39	317 (38)
321	41	323 (42)	323	42	321 (41)
325	44	327 (45)	327	45	325 (44)
329	47	331 (48)	331	48	329 (47)
333	50	335 (51)	335	51	333 (50)
337	53	339 (54)	339	54	337 (53)
341	56	343 (57)	343	57	341 (56)
345	59	347 (60)	347	60	345 (59)
349	62	351 (63)	351	63	349 (62)
353	65	355 (66)	355	66	353 (65)
357	68	359 (69)	359	69	357 (68)

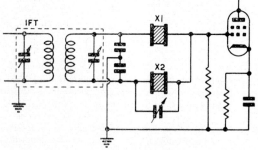

Fig. 30. Common, but unreliable, method of adding a capacitive centre-tap to a standard i.f. transformer.

The three-digit series of crystals shown in the third column of each of the above tables are recommended as giving optimum frequency response over a modulating range of 300–3,000 c/s with an appropriate oscillator crystal. The two-digit series (shown in brackets) may be substituted in the event of the three-digit series being unobtainable, but the a.f. response will be adversely affected.

seen from **Fig. 31.** The disadvantage of this elementary arrangement is that modulating frequencies below 1000 c/s are sharply attenuated by the filter, which makes the transmission sound unnatural. Despite this, the sideband suppression close to the carrier is not quite good enough, and the signal sounds harsh or gritty. An improvement may be made by sharp low frequency cut-off in the speech amplifier, but this step is scarcely justified because it is easier and better to improve the filter itself.

The steepness of either of the skirts may be sharpened by shunting the input or output circuit by a third crystal

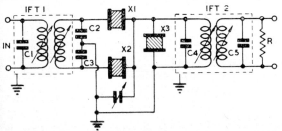

Fig. 32. Bandpass crystal filter with additional shunt element. X_2, approximately $X_1 + 2$ kc/s; X_3, approximately $X_1 - 500$ c/s; R, 68 K ohms Standard i.f. transformers are suitable, provided the trimmer capacitance does not exceed 100 pF. Wearite type M800 are recommended ($C_2 = C_3 = 2C_1$).

approximately 500 c/s above the frequency of the higher filter crystal, or below that of the lower frequency unit as shown in **Fig. 32.** It matters little whether this crystal is placed across the input or the output, but experiment

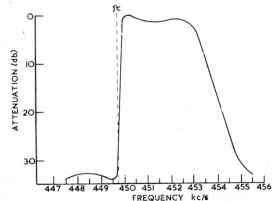

Fig. 33. Response of the crystal filter shown in Fig. 32.

suggests that it is marginally better in the position shown in Fig. 32. The shunt crystal acts as a highly selective series-resonant trap which shorts the output circuit at its resonant frequency. Either skirt may be steepened, but with surplus FT241 crystals it is easier to obtain a flat-topped curve if the shunt crystal is to the lower side of the passband. Advantage may be taken of the frequency relationships between the 54th harmonic and 72nd harmonic surplus crystal series to construct a filter having a response-curve resembling that shown in **Fig. 33.** A number of suitable crystal combinations between 400 and 500 kc/s are given in **Table 3.** With the carrier frequency placed about 30db down the steep-sided skirt, all modulating frequencies between 200 and 3000 c/s will be faithfully reproduced, and the attenuation of the unwanted sideband will be about 35db. For better results, two

half-lattice sections in cascade sharpen the pass band still further, and in theory can give sideband suppression approaching 70db. Because of unavoidable leakage around the filter, the performance of a practical unit will fall short of the ideal. Approximately 50db represents creditable attenuation for a two-stage filter of amateur construction.

A FILTER TYPE EXCITER

The high quality exciter of **Fig. 34** has been designed around a filter of this type. The speech amplifier consists of and EF86 low-microphony pentode (V_1), resistance coupled through a gain control to one half of the 12AU7 double triode V_{2a}. The other portion of the double triode, V_{2b}, acts as a phase-splitter to drive the 12AU7 balanced modulator V_4. The double triode V_3 acts as carrier oscillator and impedance-matching cathode follower to supply r.f. excitation to the cathodes of the balanced modulator. Carrier reinsertion for test and netting purposes is available by means of the potentiometer in the cathode circuit of V_{3b}. A single 7360 could of course be eliminated for V_3 and V_4; if this is preferred, V_2 could be eliminated as well, provided that a high-gain twin triode such as the 12AX7 were substituted for the EF86

Two switched crystals are shown in the oscillator circuit; one at the correct carrier frequency, and one centred in the filter passband to provide a double sideband test signal for linear amplifier alignment and to verify the performance of the balanced modulator. The frequency of either or both these crystals may have to be changed slightly as described elsewhere in this chapter.

To prevent leakage of the carrier around the filter, the amplitude of oscillation is deliberately held as low as possible, and generous decoupling is provided in the h.t. supply to V_3. The filter itself follows the circuit already described. Because they tune with a low value of capacitance, Wearite M800 i.f. transformers have been found ideal for T_1, T_2 and T_3. The output of the filter is fed to the EF89 amplifier V_5. This particular valve type has proved most satisfactory in this position, but it may, if desired, be replaced by other types such as the 6AU6. Television pentodes such as the EF80 should, however, be avoided, because they are prone to self oscillation unless the tuned circuits are damped to an unacceptable degree. The i.f. amplifier is included to raise the output of the filter to a level at which it can effectively operate the balancer mixer V_6. If it were omitted, the output of the crystal oscillator and the first balanced modulator would have to be raised so much that carrier leakage would be almost inevitable. It would also be possible for the balanced modulator and the first filter section to be overloaded.

The balanced mixer V_6 is quite conventional and about 5 volts excitation from an external v.f.o. at about 4·2 Mc/s will provide lower sideband output at the high frequency end of the 3·5 Mc/s band. The potentiometer VR_4 enables the v.f.o. signal to be balanced out of the mixer output. The switching system in the output from V_6 permits the 3·5 Mc/s signal either to be passed directly to the 6CL6 class A amplifier V_8, or via the 12AT7 heterodyne converter V_7 to provide upper sideband output at 14, 21 or 28 Mc/s. The self-balancing action of V_7 greatly reduces spurious radiations from the oscillator V_{12}. Spurious emission is further minimized by operating X_{12} as a third-overtone oscillator. To set up the oscillator, switch to the 28 Mc/s crystal, and adjust L_{osc} until a kick in the voltage across the

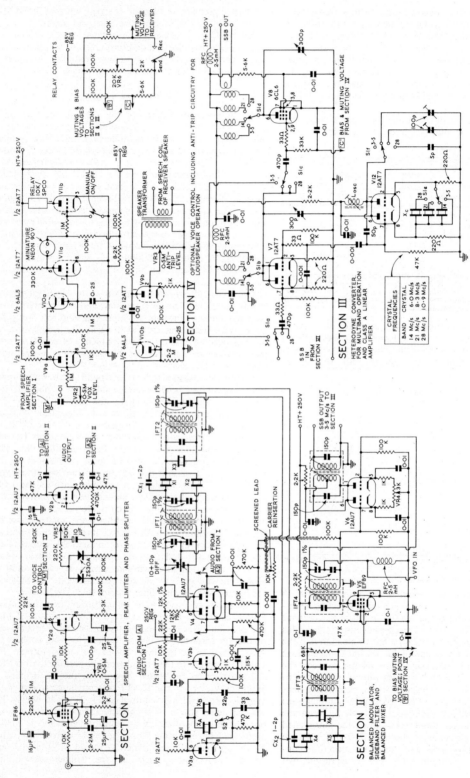

Fig. 34. Filter type exciter for 3·5 14, 21 and 28 Mc/s. In Section I, VR₃ should be adjusted to limit the peaks of highest amplitude only. If severe speech clipping is attempted, considerable distortion will result. For crystal frequencies in Section II, see Table 2. The carrier crystal X_A should be adjusted as described in the text so that the carrier falls at the appropriate point on the steeper-sided skirt of the filter passband. X_B, which gives a d.s.b. signal for test purposes, is optional; if included it should be adjusted to the mid-point of the filter passband. The excitation of the final amplifier should be controlled by VR₅, shown in the insert to Section IV. This potentiometer adjusts the gain of the variable-mu pentode V₅. Details of the anode inductors for V₇ and V₈ in Section III are given in Table 3. L_{OSC} consists of 6-8 turns close-wound on $\frac{3}{8}$ in. diam. slug tuned former. For method of setting up the oscillator, see text. In the interests of clarity, a link winding has been shown on one of the output coils only. In practice, each must be provided with an appropriate link winding. In this diagram, the lower ends of the primaries of IFT₂ and IFT₃ should be earthed.

47K ohm indicates that the crystal is oscillating in the over-tone mode. Then switch in turn to the 21 and 14 Mc/s crystals, and adjust the appropriate trimmer capacitors until third-overtone operation is established.

Voice Control

Voice controlled operation may, if desired, be obtained by including V_9, V_{10} and V_{11}. Audio from the second speech amplifier stage is coupled through a gain control to the grid of V_{9a}. The voltage at the anode of V_{9a} is rectified by V_{10a}, and appears as a negative bias which switches V_{11a} from its normally conductive state to complete cut off. This in turn switches V_{11b} from cut off to saturation, operating the high-resistance relay and turning on the transmitter. The neon-tube d.c. coupling ensures a very clean switching action. The time constant of the RC combination in the grid return of V_{11a} controls the length of hold-on, and may require variation to suit individual taste. Loudspeaker operation is permitted by the inclusion of the anti-trip amplifier V_{9b} and its associated rectifier V_{10b}. These valves together produce a negative bias which reduces the sensitivity of V_{9a}. When VR_2 and VR_3 are correctly adjusted, the receiver may be operated at full gain without tripping the relay, yet a single syllable into the microphone will mute the receiver and activate the transmitter.

Although extremely convenient, voice control is by no means essential. Rapid break-in operation may be achieved by substituting a hand or foot operated push-to-talk switch in place of the relay contacts.

Layout

Any convenient layout may be adopted, provided that the filter components are arranged in a straight line and the oscillator valve V_3 and the balanced modulator V_4 are located as remotely as possible from V_5 and all following r.f. amplifiers. Power supply leads should be routed and de-coupled so that they do not offer a path by which the carrier or the suppressed sideband may leak around the filter. Good shielding between the input and output circuits, coupled with the generous use of stopper resistors, is usually enough to stabilize the output valve V_8, but in stubborn cases of self-oscillation capacitance-bridge neutralization may have to be added.

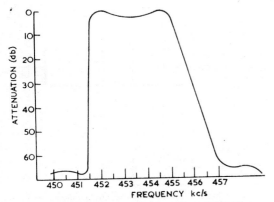

Fig. 35 Response curve of exciter shown in Fig. 34.

Alignment

The filter may be aligned by means of a simple test oscillator (capable of covering about 5 kc/s each side of the nominal carrier frequency) and a valve voltmeter with a diode probe. The calibration of these instruments need not be particularly precise, so long as the tuning rate of the oscillator is slow and positive, and the relative readings on the voltmeter are reliable.

The initial adjustment is made by connecting the voltmeter probe to either grid of V_6, and aligning T_3 and T_4 to mid-frequency of the filter passband. All crystals should be removed before making this adjustment, and the oscillator connected to the secondary of T_2. The balancing capacitor C_{x2} will allow enough signal to be fed to T_3, but will prevent its tuning being upset by the loading of the oscillator. The test signal should then be injected into one of the grids of the balanced modulator V_4 so that T_1 and T_2 may be adjusted to resonance. The crystals X_1, X_2, X_4 and X_5 should be re-placed, and the response of the filter examined by tuning the test oscillator through the passband and plotting the voltmeter readings. It is likely that one of the peaks will be considerably higher than the other, in which case the secondaries of T_1 and T_2 should be adjusted *a little at a time* until equality is obtained. Any dip in the centre of the passband may be minimized by slight adjustment of the primaries of T_1, T_2 and T_3, together with the phasing capacitors C_{x1} and C_{x2}. All these adjustments interlock, so the constructor should be prepared to repeat the sequence many times until a satisfactorily symmetrical curve is obtained with steep skirts and a mid-frequency dip not exceeding 3db. Care must be taken not to make C_{x1} and C_{x2} too large, otherwise the lobes outside the passband proper may become obtrusive. The shunt crystals X_3 and X_6 may finally be inserted, and the tuning touched up until the curve of **Fig. 35** is obtained. With patience and care, it is possible to achieve sideband attenuation better than 60db, but measurement becomes difficult when this point is reached. No difficulty should, however, be encountered in adjusting the filter to give at least 50db suppression, which is adequate for normal purposes.

When the filter has been aligned, the tuning cores of the i.f. transformers should preferably be sealed with wax so that they may not be disturbed by vibration. The carrier crystal should be adjusted to a frequency about 30db below peak response on the steep side of the passband. With a v.f.o. signal applied to the input of V_6, the operating frequency tuned circuits should be resonated, and the exciter is ready for use.

ADJUSTING CRYSTAL FREQUENCIES

In constructing filters it will probably be found necessary to change the frequencies of some of the crystals if government surplus types are used. The frequency may be raised a few hundred cycles by removing the crystal from its holder and grinding the top edge of the quartz plate on grade 200 wet-and-dry abrasive paper placed on a flat surface such as a sheet of glass. This is a rather delicate operation, and if possible some practice should be obtained by grinding an unwanted crystal before starting on a valuable one.

Copper plating may be used to lower the frequency. A standard plating solution may be made by adding 15 gm of copper sulphate, 5 cc of concentrated sulphuric acid and 5 cc of alcohol to 100 cc of distilled water. The solution should be poured into a glass vessel in which is placed a piece of clean copper wire bent so that it clamps the edge of the vessel and extends about 1 in. into the liquid. The wire should be connected in series with a 330 ohm resistor to the positive terminal of a 1·5 volt dry cell. Both pins of the crystal are then connected together and wired to the negative side of the battery. When the crystal is dipped into the solution, a copper deposit will be formed which will lower its frequency. The exact variation may be determined by trial and measurement; if the process is accidentally carried too far, it may be reversed by changing the polarity of the dry cell and removing some of the copper. The process is not necessarily reversible with *all* crystals so caution is recommended. When the frequency of a crystal has been increased by grinding or lowered by plating, the unit should be washed in carbon tetrachloride before being returned to service.

THE THIRD METHOD

In addition to the methods already described, details have been published of a third method of generating a s.s.b. signal. Because it is rather more complicated, insofar as it combines the principles of both phasing and filter-type equipment, the third method has not attracted much interest amongst amateurs. A brief description is however included, because the system is said to preserve a higher degree of fidelity than a sharp-cutting filter, and to give better sideband suppression than a straightforward phasing exciter.

In a filter-type transmitter with a bandpass characteristic similar to Fig. 33, it becomes imperative to locate the carrier in exactly the right frequency relationship to the pass band. Should the carrier drift into the passband, sideband suppression at low audio frequencies will be degraded. The signal will become hard to tune at the receiving end, and will sound harsh or gritty. Drift in the opposite direction will remove the lower audio frequencies from the wanted sideband, and although suppression will not suffer, the signal will sound decidely odd to the listener. It therefore follows that the carrier oscillator must be capable of critical adjustment, and must have exceptional stability. Even if the carrier oscillator is perfect, some loss of naturalness is likely because of the filter itself. This arises from the fact that the

response curve of Fig. 33 is only strictly applicable to single-frequency excitation of constant amplitude and an extremely low rate of frequency change. The response of most filters under dynamic conditions is likely to be very different, as may be proved experimentally by displaying the curve on an oscilloscope with the help of a frequency-modulated oscillator. The trace will be seen to undergo considerable change as the repetition rate is increased. With speech input, the effect manifests itself as a kind of grittiness and loss of true fidelity. Paradoxically, the better the sideband rejection, the more pronounced may be the distortion.

The phasing system does not detract from speech quality, but the difficulty of designing wideband networks to provide 90° phase shift over the required audio spectrum imposes a limit upon the degree of sideband suppression. In practice, 30db attenuation with a phasing exciter is creditable and anything exceeding 35db is excellent.

The third method combines the principles of both systems in such a way that a wideband audio phase-shift network is unnecessary, and although filters are used, their cut-off characteristics are not abrupt enough to detract from speech quality. The method is shown diagramatically in **Fig. 36.** The output of a pilot audio frequency oscillator P is applied to a differential phase-shift network, preferably of low Q. The two components emerging from the network are adjusted to be approximately equal in amplitude, and to differ in phase by exactly 90°. The frequency of the oscillator is not particularly critical; the system can be made to work at any point from 1600 c/s to 4-5 kc/s, but as will be seen later there is an incidental dividend in remaining within the range 1600-1800 c/s. The quadrature signals from the first phase-shift network PS_1 are applied to two identical balanced modulators BM_{1a} and BM_{1b}. Audio excitation from a conventional speech amplifier is fed in parallel to the other inputs of BM_{1a} and BM_{1b}. Because of the low frequencies involved, it is possible to achieve an exceptionally high order of pilot carrier attenuation in the balanced modulators, and the output of each will consist solely of two sidebands at audio frequency, $(f_p + f_m)$ and $(f_p - f_m)$. Amplitudes and waveforms will be identical, but the sidebands from one balanced modulator will be 90° out of phase

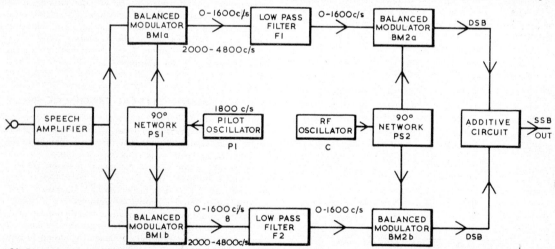

Fig. 36. Block diagram of the third method of generating a s.s.b. signal. For lower sideband transmission, the nominal output frequency will be fp+fc and for upper sideband transmission, the nominal output will be fc−fp. The nominal output frequency itself is not generated.

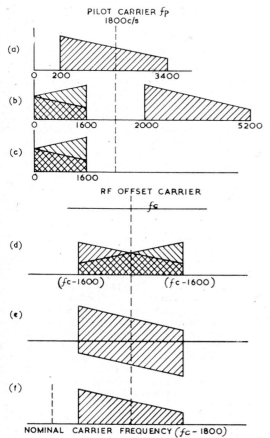

PILOT CARRIER f_p
1800c/s

(a)

0   200   3400

(b)

0   1600   2000   5200

(c)

0   1600

RF OFFSET CARRIER

f_c

(d)

(f_c-1600) (f_c-1600)

(e)

(f)

NOMINAL CARRIER FREQUENCY $(f_c - 1800)$

Fig. 37. Frequency relationships in a third method transmitter:
(a) a.f. input spectrum to BM_{1a} and BM_{1b}; (b) a.f. output from
BM_{1a} and BM_{1b} for a pilot carrier frequency of 1800 c/s. Note how
the lower sideband is folded; (c) a.f. output from lowpass filters F_1
and F_2; (d) r.f. output from upper modulator chain in Fig. 36; (e)
r.f. output from lower modulator chain in Fig. 36; (f) single sideband
output from additive tank circuit in which (d) and (e) are combined.
By reversing the phase of the output from either BM_{2a} or BM_{2b},
upper or lower sideband transmission may be selected at will.

with those from the second. The higher-frequency sidebands
are eliminated from both channels by a pair of identical
low-pass audio filters. If a pilot frequency of 1800 c/s is
assumed and a minimum modulating frequency of 200 c/s,
each filter will be required to pass all frequencies up to
1600 c/s, and to attenuate rapidly above 1600, reaching
maximum rejection at 2000 c/s. It is comparatively easy to
attain this performance with standard tolerance components, and high stability is not essential in either the pilot
oscillator or the filter itself. The phase shift network PS_1
is the only part of the circuit calling for precision adjustment,
but a simple differential arrangement will take care of more
drift than is likely to be met in any practical pilot carrier
oscillator.

The quadrature audio signals issuing from F_1 and F_2 are
applied to a further pair of balanced modulators, where they
modulate quadrature r.f. carriers from PS_1 exactly as in a
conventional phasing transmitter. The r.f. excitation may be
at the desired output frequency, or if multiband operation is
contemplated, at a neutral frequency convenient for heterodyning into the required bands. When the double sideband

signals from the two balanced modulators are combined in
an additive tank circuit, the wanted components reinforce
one another, and the unwanted sideband balances itself out
to an extent which depends upon the accuracy of the two
90° networks PS_1 and PS_2. It is claimed that attenuation
exceeding 40db is achievable.

The main advantage of using as low an audio frequency
as possible for the pilot carrier lies in the resulting simplification of the low-pass filter design. In the numerical
example quoted, the response of the filter is required to
change from zero to full attenuation in the 400 cycles
between 1600 and 2000 c/s; that is, in 25 per cent of the
highest frequency to be passed. Had 3600 c/s been chosen
as the pilot frequency, the slope off the filter response curve
would have to be twice as steep in proportion if the same
performance were to be maintained. This would naturally
call for more sophisticated filter design. An incidental
advantage of a low pilot frequency stems from the fact that
the modulating spectrum becomes "folded" upon itself for
all audio frequencies exceeding that of the pilot oscillator.
In the earlier numerical example, a tone of 1000 c/s would
beat with the pilot carrier to give a difference frequency of
800 c/s. If, however, the audio tone were 2600 c/s, the difference frequency would also be 800 c/s, but the phase would
be altered by 180°. Taking the system as a whole, it follows
that imperfect sideband suppression manifests itself as
inverted speech superimposed upon the wanted sideband
and not as adjacent channel interference. The protagonists
of the third method claim that the listener's ear can discriminate more readily against this type of imperfection than
against the type of interference caused by poor suppression
in a conventional s.s.b. transmitter. The validity of this
argument is open to question, because many amateurs now
use highly selective receivers capable of rejecting image-
type interference. Selectivity at the receiving end affords no
improvement to a poor third method transmission.

There is however some rough justice in the fact that a badly
adjusted third method transmitter causes more irritation to
its owner than to the occupants of adjacent channels, while
the reverse is usually true of a poor transmitter of more
conventional design.

A fuller explanation of audio spectrum folding would
require mathematical treatment beyond the scope of this
Handbook. The description in the preceeding paragraph in
conjunction with the diagrams of **Fig. 37** should, however,
show in broad outline how the system operates. Readers
who desire a deeper understanding of the third method are
referred to the excellent article by D. K. Weaver in the
Proceedings of the I.R.E. for December 1956.

A third method transmission is received in exactly the
same way as s.s.b. generated by either of the more common
systems. As will be seen from Fig. 37, the carrier insertion
oscillator will have to be offset from the nominal frequency
of transmission by an amount equal to the frequency of the
pilot audio oscillator. The receiving operator will not, however, be conscious of this fact. Imperfect carrier suppression
will show up, not as a steady heterodyne against which the
carrier insertion oscillator may be zeroed, but as an audio
tone at the frequency of the pilot oscillator in the transmitter.

FREQUENCY CONVERSION

In a c.w. or conventional a.m. telephony transmitter,
multiband operation is normally effected by generating a
carrier at the frequency of the lowest band to be used.

313

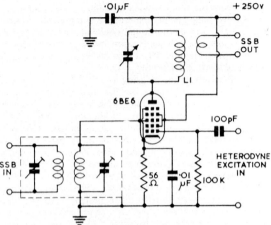

Fig. 38. Simplest form of frequency converter using a pentagrid valve. The tuned circuits should resonate at the appropriate input and output frequencies.

Because of the fortunate harmonic relationship between the amateur h.f. allocations, the higher bands are reached by interposing a chain of frequency multipliers between the oscillator and the modulated p.a. stage. Multiplication may not be carried out *after* modulation, mainly because the frequency relationship between carrier and sidebands would be falsified to such an extent as to make reception impossible by any normal method. This axiom applies to all forms of a.m. telephony, including such specialized branches as s.s.b. Multiband operation of an s.s.b. transmitter normally involves the generation of the signal at a fixed frequency, and the provision of one or more heterodyne converters to enable output to be obtained in the required amateur bands.

The circuitry is straightforward, so the secret of distortion-free frequency conversion lies in the care with which the conditions of operation are chosen. Excitation is critically important, and must be adjusted so that inter-modulation distortion is reduced to negligible proportions. The cause and effect of intermodulation are discussed in detail in the section on linear amplifiers, but it must be emphasized that a mixer which operates under non-linear conditions can have just as bad an effect as an improperly adjusted amplifier stage.

The pentagrid valve, of which the 6BE6 is representative, is probably the best known type of frequency converter. The circuit of **Fig. 38** is typical, and may be used either to raise the output from a filter in the i.f. range to the 80 metre band, or to change the transmitter frequency from one band to another. For linearity, the oscillator excitation to grid 1 should be close to 2·5 volts R.M.S. and the s.s.b. signal at grid 3 should not be allowed to exceed 0·1 volt R.M.S. at peak input. Should the s.s.b. output of the preceding stage exceed this value, a voltage divider should be interposed to reduce the excitation to the recommended level. The excitation could of course be reduced by turning down the audio gain but this would impair the ratio of sideband signal to resting carrier and nullify the good work done by the balanced modulator or modulators. It is a sound principle of s.s.b. transmission that the audio gain control should be used solely to secure optimum operating conditions for the balanced modulator, and that the excitation of the converter or amplifier stages should be adjusted *after* the single sideband has been generated.

Apart from its low level of output, the only serious shortcoming of the simple pentagrid converter lies in its inability to discriminate against the unwanted energy from the heterodyning oscillator if the s.s.b. signal is to be raised in frequency by a ratio of more than five or six to one. The following numerical example will make the reason clear. Assuming that the output of a 460 kc/s crystal filter is to be converted to 3760 kc/s, the heterodyning oscillator will operate at 3300 kc/s or 4220 kc/s. A single tuned anode circuit of good quality (high Q), adjusted precisely to 3760 kc/s, will present roughly 25 times the impedance to the wanted s.s.b. signal as it will to the steady off-tune oscillator signal. The oscillator input voltage will, however, have been adjusted to at least 25 times the amplitude of the peak s.s.b. input, so despite the selective effect of the output tank circuit, the steady oscillator voltage across it will be just about the same as the peak s.s.b. voltage. Subsequent amplifier stages will, of course, afford further discrimination against the oscillator signal, but if the tuned circuits are wide-banded or swamped in the interest of linearity, enough energy may leak through to produce an appreciable spurious signal outside the amateur bands. For conversion ratios exceeding three to one, it is desirable to employ a critically coupled pair of really high Q tuned windings in the anode circuit.

With appropriate changes to circuit values, any receiving-type frequency converter may be substituted for the pentagrid in Fig. 38. If the oscillator is crystal controlled, a valve envelope may be saved by using the triode section of a triode-hexode as oscillator, but it may prove difficult to adjust the excitation to the precise value for maximum linearity. A self-excited oscillator should preferably be isolated from the frequency converter by a buffer stage, otherwise pulling and frequency modulation may be experienced.

Although multielement valves are convenient and efficient, comparable results may be obtained with double triodes such as the 12AU7 and 12AT7. A representative circuit is shown in **Fig. 39.** It may be operated at the same voltage levels as those recommended for the 6BE6 and has the same shortcomings.

When the conversion ratio exceeds three to one, many designers prefer to attenuate the oscillator voltage in the

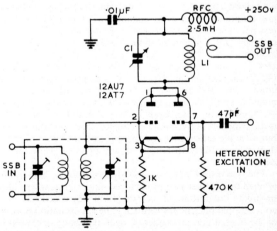

Fig. 39. Double triode frequency converter in its simplest form. The tuned circuits should resonate at the appropriate frequencies.

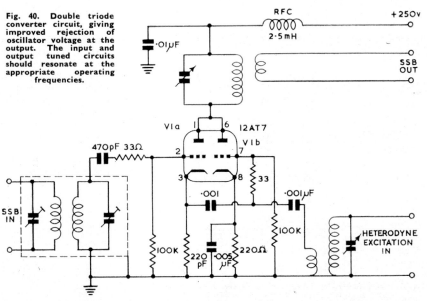

output circuit by a system of phasing or balancing. The principle is identical to that of carrier elimination by balanced modulator. An unusually straightforward circuit, capable of attenuating the oscillator output by about 25db, is shown in **Fig. 40.** Excitation of between 2·5 and 3 volts R.M.S., which must be obtained from a low impedance source such as a cathode follower or a link winding on the oscillator tank inductor, is applied in parallel to the cathode of V_{1b} and the grid of V_{1b}. As V_{1a} operates in the grounded grid mode as far as the oscillator signal is concerned, its output is in phase with the input. The other triode operates as a grounded-cathode amplifier, so its output is 180° out of phase with the input. As the two anodes are strapped, and the voltages thereat are approximately equal in amplitude but opposite in phase, the voltage developed across the tuned anode load is negligible. The application of s.s.b excitation, which for optimum linearity should not exceed 0·1V R.M.S. will produce output at the selected frequency. As with all converters, an unwanted image signal will also be generated, but a single tuned circuit will give adequate discrimination at ratios as high as ten to one.

By employing centre-tapped input and output tuned circuits, even greater attenuation of the oscillator frequency may be attained. The circuit of V_6 in the exciter shown in Fig. 34 is representative. With care in construction, symmetrical disposition of the components about the valve base, and good isolation between input and output, there should be no difficulty in reducing the oscillator voltage by at least 40db. The balance control should be adjusted for minimum voltage across the tuned circuit in the absence of s.s.b. excitation.

An outstanding balanced mixer, designed around the 7360 beam deflection valve, is shown in **Fig. 41.** Because of the unique geometry of this valve, the electron-gun portion may be used as a self-excited oscillator without fear of frequency modulation by the deflection assembly. The oscillator excitation voltage, which is less critical up to the grid-current point than with the more conventional valves, is automatically regulated by the OA79 crystal diode. The maximum s.s.b. input should not exceed 3 volts R.M.S. and oscillator attenuation, which is adjusted by the 5000 ohm potentiometer, will be at least 40db. Should separate excitation be preferred, the crystal diode should be removed and the cathode returned to earth via a 1200 ohm resistor bypassed by a 0·1 μF capacitor. With the oscillator input adjusted to give 4 volts R.M.S. at grid 1, approximately 15 volts of s.s.b. energy will be developed across the output tank circuit. The 7360 is intolerant of over-excitation. Even the minutest amount of grid current will have a disastrous effect on oscillator attenuation.

Where multiband operation is contemplated from the outset, it is sound practice to design the transmitter so that frequency conversion may be effected at low level by one or other of the arrangements described above. It sometimes happens, however, that the output of an existing exciter, capable of delivering several watts of power in one band only, has to have its output heterodyned to a different band. In this case, receiving-type valves are out of the question, and conversion has to be effected by a small transmitting tetrode or pentode. The neatest of the many possible circuit configurations is that shown in **Fig. 42.** With no heterodyning voltage applied to grid 1, the valve operates as a

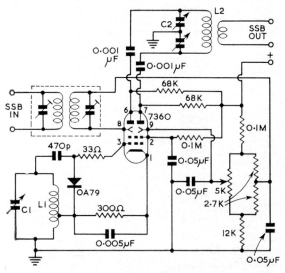

Fig. 4I. Balanced mixer utilizing a beam deflection valve type 7360. L_1C_1 should oscillate at the desired mixing frequency. L_2C_2 should resonate at the output frequency.

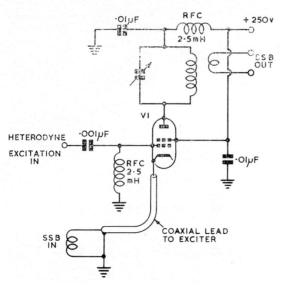

Fig. 42. Suggested high level frequency converter. Any small transmitting tetrode or pentode may be used (see text).

conventional grounded-grid amplifier, drawing an anode current of about 15 mA. There is no variation of anode current with signal. When heterodyning voltage is applied, the valve operates as a converter, and the anode current rises slightly on voice peaks. It is important to note that both the s.s.b. and the heterodyne signal sources must have excellent regulation, as they have to be capable of delivering power to the mixer valve. The output tank circuit should be designed for high Q in exactly the same way as if the stage were to operate as a conventional power amplifier. Almost any valve may be used; the 807, 6146 and even the 813 are known to work satisfactorily in this application.

If incorrectly driven or loaded, the high-level mixer is prone to intermodulation distortion. The most practical way of combatting this tendency is to monitor the output of the transmitter under normal operating conditions, and to adjust drive and loading until distortion is eliminated.

THEORY OF LINEAR AMPLIFICATION

As the exciters already described in this chapter are incapable of producing an output of more than a few watts of r.f. power, it is usually desirable to amplify their signals considerably before they reach the transmitting aerial. Much effort will have gone into the construction and adjustment of an exciter capable of an acceptable degree of carrier and sideband attenuation, so care must be taken to ensure that subsequent amplifier stages do not degrade the overall performance of the transmitter by introducing avoidable distortion. This makes it essential to operate all s.s.b. amplifiers under linear conditions.

The r.f. linear is less well understood than most other types of amplifier. Constructionally, it bears a close resemblance to the more familiar class C stage, from which it differs only in its conditions of drive, bias and loading. It has been suggested that it has more in common with class A and AB audio amplifiers than with other classes of r.f. amplifier, but this approach is liable to obscure several important issues and to lead to misconceptions.

By definition, a linear amplifier is one which produces at its output a faithful but magnified facsimile of any signal applied to its grid. The valve must not add anything to the applied signal. Unfortunately, the perfect valve has not yet been made, and the waveform at the anode of any practical amplifier will differ slightly from that at the grid. This difference is the distortion which is so unpopular in high fidelity audio circles. The manifestation of distortion in r.f. linears is, however, totally different to that in audio amplifiers and it is vitally important for those concerned with the design and operation of s.s.b. amplifiers to understand where this difference lies. In the description which follows use will be made of diagrams and numerical examples but it should be remembered that these are deliberately over-simplified with the intention of conveying a broad but clear picture to the newcomer in this sphere.

The diagrams in **Fig. 43(a)** and **(b)** show an audio amplifier and an r.f. linear respectively. It will be assumed that a 1000 c/s sine wave is applied to the grid of V_1 in Fig. 43(a) and that the amplifier is so poor that the waveform comes out as badly " bent " as is shown in the drawing. Basic principles show that *any* waveform may be resolved into a fundamental sine wave, to which has been added a number of its harmonics. A more complete treatment of this subject will be

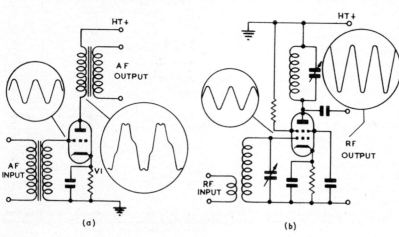

Fig. 43. (a) Class A audio frequency amplifier, showing effect of harmonic distortion on output waveform; (b) class A radio frequency amplifier.

found in standard text books under *Fourier's Theorem.* In Fig. 43(a) the distorted waveform at the anode of V_1 contains the fundamental component of 1000 c/s, plus harmonics at 2000 c/s and 3000 c/s, 4000 c/s and 5000 c/s. If the audio transformer T_2 is a reasonably good one, it will respond to the harmonics just as effectively as to the fundamental, and the waveform passed to the following audio stage will be the replica of that appearing at the anode of V_1. For obvious reasons this is known as harmonic distortion and is the type which valve manufacturers and audio designers have in mind when they say that a certain circuit has " less than 1 per cent distortion at 10 watts output." The effect of harmonic distortion is that the sound which issues from the loudspeaker is not a true reproduction of that which went into the microphone; it cannot cause inconvenience or offence to anyone except the owner of the amplifier and his immediate friends and relations. There are of course other forms of distortion to be encountered in audio amplifiers, but except in really high fidelity equipment they are insignificant in comparison to harmonic distortion.

With the r.f. linear of Fig. 43(b), a different set of conditions exist. Assuming that a pure r.f. wave at a frequency of

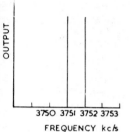

Fig 44 (a) Output of a perfect s.s.b. transmitter of nominal carrier frequency 3750 kc/s, modulated by two audio tones of 1000 and 2000 c/s

3750 kc/s is applied to the grid and that V_2 introduces as much distortion as V_1 in Fig. 43(a), the waveform *at the anode* will be the same as that in the audio amplifier. When analysed, it will be found to consist of the fundamental at 3750 kc/s, and harmonics at 7500 kc/s, 10,250 kc/s, 15,000 kc/s and 18,750 kc/s. The anode load, which is provided by the tuned circuit L_2C_2, behaves very differently to the audio transformer in Fig. 43(a). It presents a very high impedance to the fundamental of 3750 kc/s and little or none to the harmonics. The waveform passed on to subsequent amplifier stages is therefore a more-or-less pure sine wave at the fundamental frequency, no matter how much distortion is inherent in V_2. If the output of sideband exciters consisted of nothing but single-frequency waveforms, subsequent amplification would present no problem, but this is quite impracticable if the transmission is to convey intelligence. As was mentioned earlier in this chapter, speech modulation covers a band stretching from about 200 c/s to 3000 c/s to one side or other of the nominal carrier frequency. This complexity of the modulating waveform is the root cause of distortion in r.f. linear amplifiers.

An analysis of any particular speech waveform would be extremely complicated to follow, but a representative picture may be obtained by examining what happens when a modulating signal consisting of only two audio tones is applied to a s.s.b. exciter. Assuming that the nominal carrier frequency is 3750 kc/s, and that the modulating waveform

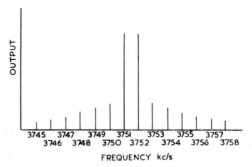

Fig. 44 (b) Output of a s.s.b. transmitter of nominal carrier frequency of 3750 kc/s, modulated by two tones of 1000 c/s and 2000 c/s, and followed by an amplifier exhibiting extreme non-linearity.

may be analysed into two pure audio tones of 1000 c/s and 2000 c/s, and upper sideband exciter will produce two r.f. sine waves at 3751 kc/s and 3752 kc/s. As it is always easier to achieve perfection in a hypothetical circuit than in a real one, it will be taken that the carrier and the lower sideband have disappeared completely. The diagram in **Fig. 44(a)** shows the frequency relationships of the component signals in graphical form. If these signals are applied to a valve which suffers from non-linearity, the output at the anode will contain r.f. components at the two original frequencies of 3751 and 3752 kc/s, plus harmonics at 7502, 7504, 10,253, 10,256 kc/s and so on. If, as in Fig. 43(b), the anode load is a tuned circuit of adequate Q, the harmonics will not be passed on to the following stage, so it might seem that they are incapable of causing trouble. Unfortunately, this is not so.

The valve itself is the villain of the piece. When it operates in a non-linear fashion, it not only generates harmonics, but acts as a mixer as well. The sum and difference frequencies arising from the applied signals are at 7503 kc/s and 1 kc/s respectively, which is well outside the response of the tuned anode load and causes no trouble. When, however, the second harmonic of the 3751 kc/s signal beats with the fundamental of the 3752 kc/s signal, a spurious signal is formed at 3750 kc/s (7502–3752), which is right on the frequency of the carrier which so much care was taken to suppress. Taking the second harmonic of the 3752 kc/s signal with the fundamental of that at 3751 kc/s gives a further spurious response at 3753 kc/s (7504–3751). The anode load will not discriminate against these distortion products, because they fall so close to the wanted signal to which it is tuned. Nor is this the full picture, because the third harmonic at 10,253 kc/s will react with the second at 7054 kc/s to produce a spurious signal at 3749 kc/s, right in the place where the lower sideband was suppressed. This analysis could be carried on indefinitely, but it has gone far enough to demonstrate that a non-linear amplifier can produce intermodulation distortion products stretching many kilocycles to either side of the signals which were required to be amplified. These spurious products are illustrated graphically in **Fig. 44(b)**, which represents the type of response which might be expected if a highly non-linear amplifier such as a class C stage were used with the two-tone signal in the example cited. It will be appreciated that a waveform covering the full range of speech frequencies will produce an even worse result, and that a perfectly good exciter capable of an output like that shown in Fig. 44(a) can have its work undone by a non-linear amplifier which will turn out something like Fig. 44(b).

317

Unlike the audio case, in which distortion is readily apparent and strictly local in effect, non-linearity in an s.s.b. amplifier does not manifest itself at the transmitting end, but shows up as splatter spreading across the band on both sides of the intended signal. This makes the signal difficult or impossible to read, causes annoyance to other amateurs, and is of course a breach of the licence conditions. The picture may seem depressing, but it has not by any means been overdrawn. If they are allowed to occur, the effects of non-linearity can be most objectionable, but they may be reduced to negligibly low levels. As has already been said, the perfect valve does not exist, but by selecting the most suitable types for the purpose, and arranging for them to operate under optimum conditions, it is quite practicable to build an amplifier in which the distortion products at maximum output will be between 40 and 50db below the wanted signal. In other words, a well-built transmitter capable of 400 watts peak output will radiate spurious signals no more powerful than 40 milliwatts, which is not likely to cause noticeable interference.

The linear amplifiers which are likely to interest the s.s.b. enthusiast fall into three broad groups: class A, class AB1 and class AB2. As each group has certain characteristics peculiar to it alone, the three classes will be dealt with separately.

The Class A Linear Amplifier

The class A linear, of which a representative diagram is given in **Fig. 45,** will be seen to bear a strong family resemblance to the r.f. and i.f. amplifiers in receivers. Care must, however, be taken not to presume too far upon this relationship, otherwise trouble in the form of unexpected distortion may result. A true class A stage must be so biased and driven that the valve operates at all times on the linear part of its characteristic curve. The r.f./i.f. amplifier is essentially a small-signal amplifier; that is, the signal applied to its grid is only a fraction of a volt, so the valve will operate linearly no matter how it is biased. Furthermore, the stage is not required to produce any power and works into the constant load provided by the grid of the following stage. In s.s.b. service few class A stages work under such favourable conditions. They are usually called upon to produce a reasonably large voltage swing, and perhaps several watts of output power as well. If they are to drive a class AB2 stage, the loading will require some kind of stabilization to minimize fluctuations. There is, therefore, limited scope for small receiving valves in s.s.b. linears. It pays to follow the lead of the designer of high fidelity audio equipment who customarily builds an amplifier of far higher power handling capability than is really needed. By underrunning valves, the problem of distortion is avoided.

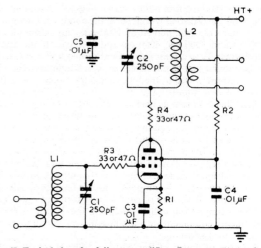

Fig. 45. Typical class A r.f. linear amplifier. For component values not shown on the diagram, see Table 4.

No valves have yet been specifically designed as class A linear power amplifiers in s.s.b. service, but as a general principle any small power pentode or beam valve which gives a good account of itself in low or medium power audio stages will work satisfactorily in class A linear service. Valves which have proved their suitability include the 6AG7, 6CL6, EL84/6BQ5 and the 5763. At somewhat higher power levels, the QV06–20 (6146), 807 and 1625 perform well. One excellent type is the 5B/254M. This value is a miniaturized version of the 807 on a loctal base with cathode and screen leads so short that decoupling is really effective and stability is far above average.

At very low power levels receiving types may be used, but it is advisable to avoid television valves such as the 6AM6 and EF80. These valves have a very high amplification factor, and are intended to operate with low Q input and output circuits. Uncontrollable regeneration may be encountered if they are used with circuits of the Q value desirable in s.s.b. work. Much more predictable results will be obtained by heeding the advice of the valve manufacturers who recommend that valves designed for r.f. and i.f. amplifier service in *radio* receivers should be used for applications of this kind. Typical examples are the 6AU6, 6BA6, 6AH6 and EF89.

Cathode bias will necessarily result in negative voltage feedback which will in turn increase distortion and reduce the power and amplification obtainable from the stage. If it is essential to obtain maximum performance, fixed negative bias should be applied to the grid.

The efficiency of a practical class A stage varies from zero

TABLE 4

Typical operating conditions of a representative selection of r.f. tetrodes and pentodes in class A linear amplifier service.

	6AU6	EF89	6CH6	6CL6	EL84	5763	6146	807
V_a	250V	250V	250V	300V	250V	300V	500V	500V
I_a	10mA	9mA	40mA	30mA	48mA	40mA	40mA	50mA
V_{g2}	150V	100V	250V	150V	250V	225V	150V	200V
I_{g2}	4·5mA	3mA	6mA	7mA	5·5mA	2·4mA	2mA	1·6mA
V_{g1}	−1V	−2V	−4·5V	−3V	−7·5V	−7·5V	−22V	−15V
R_k	68 ohms	180 ohms	100 ohms	82 ohms	135 ohms	175 ohms	470 ohms	280 ohms

The fixed bias voltage and the cathode resistor in the table above are alternatives.

under no-drive conditions to about 30 per cent at full input which means that the maximum output is limited to something less than one-third of the rated anode dissipation of the valve used. Provided that the internal insulation is built to stand it, operation at high voltage and low current will give greater efficiency and better linearity than low voltage and high current. It is impossible to list recommended operating conditions for all suitable valves under all circumstances, but **Table 4** gives a representative set of typical working conditions for the valves already mentioned. Suitable conditions for valves not included in the table may be deduced from the audio frequency power amplifier ratings given in manufacturers' characteristic sheets.

The construction of a class A stage follows common practice; input and output circuits should be well shielded from one another to prevent self-oscillation, and high frequency parasitics should be eliminated by the generous use of stopper resistors. If oscillation at operating frequency should prove troublesome, the capacitance bridge neutralizing arrangement will provide a sure remedy.

Class AB Amplifiers—Triodes

Although it would be technically possible to achieve sufficient output for amateur purposes by using class A amplifiers exclusively, the result would certainly be uneconomical. Greater efficiency is essential in any practical transmitter, and this may be obtained by operating the high level stages in class AB or class B. For the purposes of this chapter, the precise shade of difference between a class AB amplifier and a true class B stage is unimportant and will be ignored.

When examining the ratings of power valves, it is important to note that the efficiency and typical operating conditions sometimes quoted for r.f. amplifier service in valve data sheets refer to the amplification of carrier type a.m. waveforms and are not directly applicable to s.s.b. use. The linear amplifier is a variable efficiency device: its efficiency in the absence of drive is zero, rising in a regular manner to between 50 and 75 per cent at maximum drive. The greatest efficiency obtainable depends on a number of interdependent variables, as well as upon the valve itself, but 66 per cent may be taken as a rough generalisation. The figures given in manufacturers' literature relate to d.c. measurements under conditions of no modulation; on modulation peaks, input and efficiency double, and in troughs both drop to zero. In s.s.b. service there is no carrier to provide a reference point against which to strike an average, so peak input and peak power handling capacity are the standards of measurement normally used. Conveniently enough, these standards are used by manufacturers themselves when rating valves for audio frequency linear amplifier service. When available, these audio ratings provide a more convenient guide as to what may be expected in an r.f. linear than any other published data.

In theory, any r.f. valve may be used as a class AB or class B linear, but there are a number of external factors which narrow the field considerably. Except in the special case of the zero-bias triode, fixed negative bias is essential, and if the stage is driven into grid current the voltage must have excellent regulation so that it does not vary over any part of the input cycle. Dry cells are inexpensive and may be used if the amount of grid current flowing through them is strictly limited. At high values of reverse current any battery will quickly develop enough internal resistance to cause the instantaneous bias voltage to fluctuate with input. The life of the cells under such conditions would be uneconomically short. Battery bias is therefore restricted to tetrode and pentode stages.

Most important of all is the effect of the amplifier on the preceding driver stage. With any valve which draws grid current over only a part of the input cycle, the onset of grid current will cause the load presented to the driving stage to fall from something approaching infinity to a fairly low value. Wide fluctuations in loading would have a disastrous effect on the linearity of the driver so some way has to be found to minimize the variation. The most practical method is to load the driver with a resistor chosen to dissipate at least ten times the peak load presented by the driven stage. In this way the load on the driver increases only 10 per cent at the onset of grid current, and distortion is kept within bounds. Resistive loading gives rise to no difficulty with tetrodes or pentodes, which require a watt or less of driving power, but rules out low-mu triodes, which would need far too large a driver stage to make them either practical or economical.

One possible way to use low-mu triodes is to bias them to cut-off and to adjust the drive so that they will not operate beyond the negative grid-voltage region; that is, in class AB1. The peak efficiency in this mode of operation is only 40–50 per cent, because the peak current which the valve can draw at zero grid voltage is relatively low. A high voltage bias supply has also to be provided. Zero bias triodes such as the 805, 811 and TZ40 are a much more favourable proposition. As grid current flows throughout the whole of the driving cycle, the load presented to the driver *during the time at which it is delivering power* is virtually constant. To understand the full implication of this statement, it is necessary to remember the discussion of the nature and cause of distortion in linear amplifiers.

Fig. 46 shows a zero bias triode driven by a pure sine wave. Only that portion of the driving waveform which is depicted by the solid line can, however, result in r.f. output; when the driving signal enters the region represented by the dotted line the valve is cut off, and the positive excursion of the output waveform is provided by the flywheel effect inherent in the anode tank circuit. As the valve itself is cut off, it cannot produce intermodulation distortion, and it isolates its output circuit from any distortion which may occur in the driver stage because of the change in loading. Some distortion close to the cross-over point is, of course, inevitable, but practice has

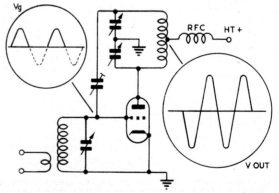

Fig. 46. Waveforms at grid and anode of a class B zero bias linear amplifier.

proved that this has negligible effect on the signal. It is the distortion at maximum input which causes trouble.

In a practical zero bias amplifier it matters little whether the conventional push-pull configuration is followed or whether the stage works in single-ended fashion. If the popular pi-section output coupler is used, single ended construction is simpler, but on the other hand neutralization is easier with the push-pull arrangement. In Great Britain the choice of types is rather restricted, and valves such as the 805 and 811 are likely to find favour.

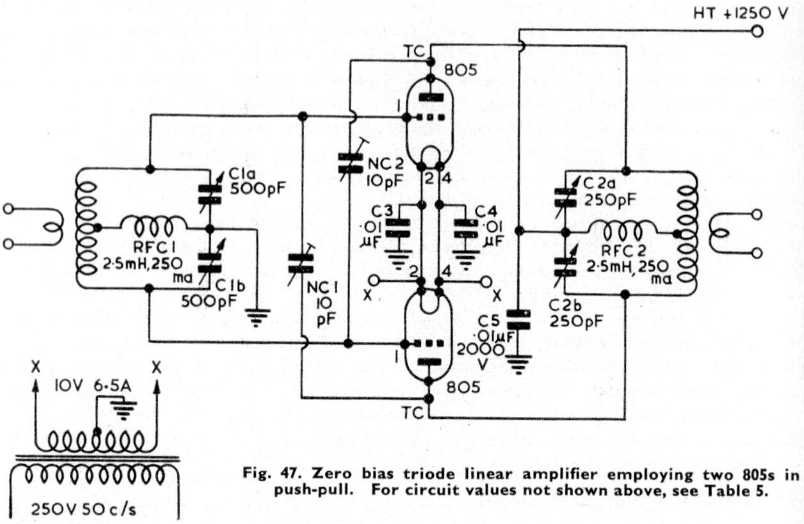

The 805 was originally designed as a high quality class B audio amplifier, and is difficult to find a better valve for linear service at peak outputs up to 150 watts. A pair in push-pull (or parallel) will deliver 300 watts and require only 7 watts of driving power, which can be supplied fairly comfortably by a single 807 in class A. The circuit of a typical amplifier is given in **Fig. 47.** The diagram is self-explanatory, but the factors governing the design of the various tank circuits will be examined in detail so that those wishing to adapt the design for use with different valve types may be able to do so without difficulty. The makers' recommended operating conditions for the two in push-pull are given in **Table 5,** from which will be seen that the optimum load for highest undistorted output is 6,700 ohms. An output circuit Q of about 15 is desirable which, from the theory of Chapter 6 (*H.F. Transmitters*), necessitates that the reactance of both the tank capacitor and the inductor at resonance shall be $\frac{6700}{15}$ or 430 ohms approximately. The required tank capacitance may easily be calculated from the formula

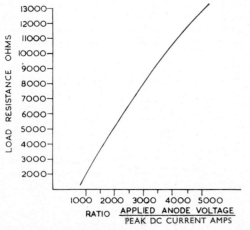

Fig. 47. Zero bias triode linear amplifier employing two 805s in push-pull. For circuit values not shown above, see Table 5.

$X_c = \dfrac{1}{2\pi f C}.$ This is, however, the total value of C_3 and C_4 in series, so the value of each half of the split stator capacitor requires to be double that obtained by calculation. Suitable values for all amateur bands from 3·5 to 28 Mc/s are given in **Table 6,** together with coil winding instructions based on the Eddystone 2½ in. diameter ceramic formers.

If a different valve type is used, it is advisable to obtain the manufacturer's recommendation about anode loading, and to calculate capacitor and inductor values in the manner demonstrated. Loading information is readily available for most of the valves likely to be encountered, but if it should prove difficult to locate for any particular valve, an approximate value may be obtained from the graph in **Fig. 48.**

TABLE 5

Recommended operating conditions for two type 805 triodes in class B push-pull zero bias.

D.c. anode volts	1,250 volts
Grid excitation—peak-to-peak	235 volts
Anode current—zero signal	148 mA
Anode current—maximum signal	400 mA
Grid driving power—maximum signal	6 watts
Anode input—maximum signal	500 watts
Power output—maximum signal	400 watts
Anode-to-anode load	6,700 ohms

The calculation of circuit values for the grid tank may be performed in exactly the same manner as for the anode circuit, and the results will be as shown in Table 6. Some manufacturers do not quote the grid load impedance in direct form, but for zero-bias valves this may be calculated from the stated grid driving-power and peak grid-to-grid input voltage by means of the simple formula

$$R_{grid} \simeq \frac{(Peak\ Input\ Voltage)^2}{2 \times Driving\ Power}$$

The relatively large values of capacitance for the grid circuit are neither the result of miscalculation nor misprint; they arise from the characteristics of the valve under consideration. A two-gang receiving type variable capacitor will

Fig. 48. Graph showing anode load resistance for various conditions of operation. As the values obtainable from the graph are approximations, they should only be used when manufacturers' recommendations on working conditions are unobtainable.

TABLE 6

Anode and grid circuit values for push-pull zero-bias class B amplifier using type 805 triodes.

Band	Anode			Grid		
	C		L	C		L
3·5 Mc/s	200 + 200pF		20 turns CT	300 + 300pF		32 turns CT
7 Mc/s	100 + 100pF		14 turns CT	150 + 150pF		20 turns CT
14 Mc/s	55 + 55pF		8 turns CT	75 + 75pF		12 turns CT
21 Mc/s	35 + 35pF		8 turns CT double spaced	50 + 50pF		12 turns CT double spaced
28 Mc/s	25 + 25pF		6 turns CT double spaced	40 + 40pF		10 turns CT double spaced

Anode inductors are wound on Eddystone or similar 2½ in. diam. ceramic formers. The 21 and 28 Mc/s coils should be double spaced, and because stray inductance has an appreciable effect at these frequencies, pruning may be necessary in individual cases.
Grid inductors are wound on ⅞ in. or 1 in. diameter formers, threaded 20 or 21 turns per inch.
Capacitor settings are "in use" values and include valve capacitances and circuit strays.

probably be found more convenient than a standard transmitting component, for under no circumstances should the tabulated values of capacitance be reduced, because the proper operation of linear amplifiers in general is vitally linked with the choice of correct component values in the tuned circuits.

As the driver stage operates in class A the calculation of tank circuit values is less critical, and an approximation obtained from the graph in Fig. 48 will be close enough to ensure satisfactory operation. Any zero bias triode may be substituted for the 805. In addition, beam power valves such as the 807, 1625 and 813 may be connected as high-mu triodes in the manner shown in **Fig. 49.** The triode-connected tetrode usually requires a much higher excitation voltage than

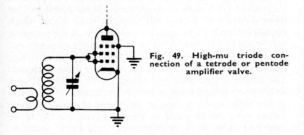

Fig. 49. High-mu triode connection of a tetrode or pentode amplifier valve.

a conventional triode, but is otherwise capable of similar performance. For greatest efficiency, the highest anode voltage which will allow anode dissipation to be kept within ratings should be applied. Valves such as the 807 may be operated from supplies as high as 1,200 volts, but this entails a certain amount of overrunning, which will be dealt with in greater detail later in this chapter.

Class AB Amplifiers—Tetrodes and Pentodes

Because of their ready availability and comparatively low cost, the multi-electrode valves which are most likely to interest amateurs are the 807 (or its equivalents), the QV06–20 (6146), the 813 and the TT21. The following information is therefore directed towards the use of these valves in particular, but the general principles may be applied to any other type which may be available. To simplify treatment, it will be assumed that tetrodes, pentodes and beam power valves

behave identically, unless special reference is made to the contrary.

The introduction of the screen grid opens wider possibilities to the constructor in quest of linear amplification than in other fields of amateur endeavour. The presence of the screen enables peak outputs to be obtained which would be quite impossible with triodes of the same anode-dissipation rating. As full input can be obtained from all the valves mentioned with a fraction of a watt of drive, excitation obviously presents no problem and will be ignored for the present. With zero-bias triodes the maximum anode voltage which may be applied is limited by the anode-dissipation in the absence of drive, and operating conditions preclude the application of fixed bias to reduce this dissipation. With tetrodes, fixed bias is necessary in any event, and the anode voltage is limited only by the maximum which the valve will bear without flashover. The 807 and the other small types will stand 1,200 volts quite comfortably, and the 813 will take at least 4,000 volts. These figures, which have been proved in practice, are indirectly confirmed by the valve manufacturers, who rate the 807 at 600 volts in a.m. service and the 813 at 2,000 volts. At 100 per cent amplitude modulation peaks the applied potentials are momentarily doubled, without damage to the valve. Similarly, the screen voltages may be increased above the values customarily used in class C r.f. service, but here more caution is called for, because a temporary screen overload can cause permanent damage or even the total destruction of a valve. The screen voltages quoted for class B audio service form a good guide for general use.

In the absence of drive, the anode current of the valve must be adjusted by varying the applied grid bias until the dissipation is within that permitted for class C telegraphy service. There may be some doubt as to what is to be gained from using higher-than-normal supply voltages, and why are they inadvisable for c.w. work. The reason stems from the intermittent nature of the sideband signal produced by voice modulation. In c.w. transmission, the signal has a duty-cycle of about 45 per cent—in other words, the power amplifier delivers full output for 45 per cent of the time taken to radiate intelligence, and rests for the remaining 55 per cent. During certain words and passages, the duty-cycle rises to over 60 per cent. In any event, the manufacturer rates valves conservatively so that they will withstand the efforts of the unskilled operator who will make all his adjustments with the key held firmly down.

With s.s.b. voice transmission, the average power is somewhat less than 20 per cent of the peak, and unless the operator gives a sustained whistle into his microphone, the drive is truly intermittent. Under such conditions it is reasonable to expect a valve to stand input peaks far in excess of those which it could handle in c.w. service. As long as the average dissipation is maintained below the c.w. rating, the valve will come to no harm. This mode of operation is sometimes described as "intelligent ill-treatment" of a valve, but this is a misnomer, because an intelligent operator will apply the theory in such a way is to cause no illtreatment whatever to his amplifier. Most manufacturers refuse to commit themselves on this issue, because they like to have a fairly large safety margin in hand and recognize that incorrect operation will almost certainly result in the demise of a perfectly good valve. Two companies in the U.S.A., Penta Laboratories and Eitel McCullough, have, however, set the seal of approval on this theory by releasing special s.s.b. operating conditions for some of their valves.

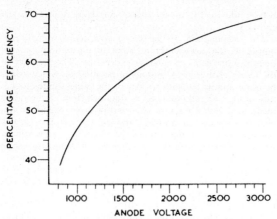

Fig. 50. Graph showing relationship between anode efficiency and applied d.c. potential in a class B linear amplifier.

Efficiency

Even if it is not desired to run a valve at large peak input, there is nevertheless a considerable latent advantage in employing the highest possible anode voltage. It will be recalled from the theory of valve amplification in Chapter 2 (*Valves*) that the valve is required to pass maximum current at the instant at which the anode voltage reaches its lowest point. The ideal valve would of course be able to pass an infinite current at zero voltage, but in practice the minimum instantaneous voltage which can be achieved is in the region of 200–400 for the types under consideration. A close approximation of anode efficiency may be obtained from the equation:

$$\text{Percentage efficiency} \simeq 78 \left(1 - \frac{E_{\text{min.}}}{E_{\text{app}}}\right)$$

from which will be seen that high applied voltages can result in an increase in efficiency. Just how marked this may be is illustrated graphically in **Fig. 50**.

Choice of Class of Operation

Before proceeding to a practical design, the question of whether the amplifier is to be operated in class AB1 or AB2 must be resolved. An advantage usually claimed for class AB1 is that, as grid current does not flow at any time, it is possible to drive the stage with a voltage amplifier incapable of delivering power, and that a regulated bias supply is unnecessary. There is little or nothing in the first point; any driver, no matter how heavily swamped by a resistive load, ought to be able to supply the fraction of a watt required to drive the amplifier to full input in class AB2. The second point is valid, but potentially dangerous. In most cases it is virtually impossible to guarantee that the grid will not be driven positive from time to time, and when this does happen the distortion will be excessive. Even if the intention is to operate an amplifier exclusively in class AB1 it is desirable to design the driver, input and bias circuitry as if operation in the grid-current region were intended. The extra complication in construction will be a small price to pay for effective insurance against high distortion if the stage is slightly over-driven.

MEDIUM POWER CLASS AB2 AMPLIFIER

A medium power design, employing a pair of 5B/254M in

TABLE 7

Typical operating conditions for a single 807 or 5B/254M in class AB2 r.f. linear amplifier service.

Va	750 V	1000V	1250V
Ia —zero signal	30mA	25mA	20mA
Ia —max. signal	120mA	90mA	75mA
V_{g_2}	300 volts	300 volts	300 volts
I_{g_2} —zero signal	< 1mA	< 1mA	< 1 mA
I_{g_2} —max. signal	8 mA	7mA	6mA
*V_{g_1}	−32V	−42 V	−55 V

*The grid bias figures quoted above are design centre values based on an average valve. For optimum linearity and efficiency, bias should be adjusted until the tabulated value of zero-signal anode current is drawn.

parallel, is shown in **Fig. 51**. This valve is particularly recommended because of its efficiency, ruggedness and high stability at frequencies up to and beyond 30 Mc/s. The 807 may be substituted with no change in circuit constants, but will prove a little less efficient and more difficult to stabilize if operation on the higher frequency bands is contemplated. Modifications necessary to permit the substitution of the 6146 will be given later in this section. The circuit is largely self-explanatory, and no attempt should be made to simplify it by omitting the stabilizing arrangements for the screen supply or increasing the value of the bleeder potentiometer VR_1 in the grid circuit. The electrolytic capacitor C_8 in the screen circuit is not absolutely essential, but improves the linearity on peaks. It is, however, capable of forming a relaxation oscillator in conjunction with the gas stabilizer tubes V_3 and V_4, if R_1 is incorrectly adjusted. If this resistor is set so that the standing current through the stabilizers in the absence of drive is approximately 25 mA, no trouble will be experienced.

Any of the normal methods of construction will prove satisfactory, but the input and output circuits must be well shielded from one another and bypassing and parasitic suppression have to be really effective. These points call for more attention in a class AB amplifier than in one which operates in class C, because the power gain of the former is very much higher than in the latter. Neutralization may not be absolutely essential to avoid self-oscillation at operating frequency, but it does help the linearity and is best included. The Bruene capacity-bridge system shown in Fig. 51 is a well proven arrangement in tetrode amplifiers. If the meter in the screen lead is omitted in the interest of economy, some means must be provided to enable screen current to be measured under working conditions. In a linear amplifier, screen current gives a far more reliable indication of correct operation than does anode current. This will be elaborated further in the section dealing with amplifier adjustment.

TABLE 8

Values of capacitance and inductance for the output tank circuit of the amplifier shown in Fig. 51.

f	$V_a = 750V$		$V_a = 1000$ V		$V_a = 1250V$	
	C2	L2	C2	L2	C2	L2
3·5 Mc/s	300pF	10 turns*	200pF	13 turns*	140pF	17 turns*
7 Mc/s	150pF	7 turns*	100pF	8 turns*	70pF	11 turns*
14 Mc/s	75pF	7 turns†	50pF	9 turns†	35pF	7 turns*
21 Mc/s	50pF	5 turns†	33pF	7 turns†	25pF	8 turns†
28 Mc/s	37·5pF	4 turns†	25pF	5 turns†	20pF	6 turns†

Notes — * = Coils wound on standard 2½ in. diameter ceramic formers.
　　　　† = Air wound coils 2 in. diameter, wound 4 turns per inch.
Capacitances shown are "in use" values, including valve output and circuit strays. In certain layouts it may be difficult to obtain the low values recommended for the 21 and 28 Mc/s bands, and the inductors will have to be adjusted to compensate.

Bias Supply

The mains operated bias supply may be replaced by dry cells of appropriate voltage, but the mains supply offers the convenience of precise adjustment of operating bias. This is often valuable when setting up an amplifier. If dry cells are used, they must be examined periodically and replaced when their internal resistance shows signs of increasing, otherwise the regulation of the supply will suffer when grid-current starts to flow.

Power Supply

Any available supply between 750 and 1,250 volts will serve for the anodes; typical operating conditions at 750, 1,000 and 1,250 volts are listed in **Table 7.** The anode voltage

will, of course, effect the output-circuit constants, and **Table 8** has been prepared to cover the three supply voltages mentioned. If other voltages are to be employed, suitable circuit values may be deduced from this table by interpolation. The average current drawn from the anode power supply will be quite low, so a much smaller transformer may be used than for a conventional constant-carrier transmitter. A component rated for continuous operation at about half the peak output of the linear stage will work comfortably without overheating. Screen voltage may either be taken from the anode power pack via a dropping resistor, or from a separate low voltage supply such as that provided for the exciter. The only real objection to using the anode supply is that an appreciable amount of power may be wasted in the dropping resistor if

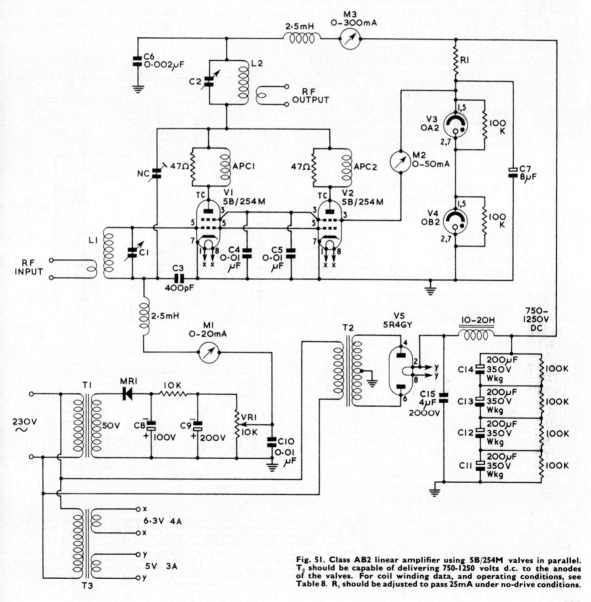

Fig. 5I. Class AB2 linear amplifier using 5B/254M valves in parallel. T₂ should be capable of delivering 750-1250 volts d.c. to the anodes of the valves. For coil winding data, and operating conditions, see Table 8. R₁ should be adjusted to pass 25mA under no-drive conditions.

the stage is operated at high voltage. This loss may be minimized by using the screen potentiometer network as the bleeder which is necessary to prevent the anode voltage from soaring under no-drive conditions. If, however, a separate screen supply is preferred, precautions must be taken to make sure that the anode supply is switched on *and delivering power* before screen potential is applied, and that the screen current will be interrupted instantly if the anode supply should fail. Unless some form of safety interlock is provided, the early demise of a pair of valves is likely. Should the linear amplifier screens be fed from the same pack as the exciter, adequate decoupling must be included to prevent feedback and self-oscillation. The value of the output capacitor in the anode supply power pack is the only other point which calls for comment. The larger the value of this component, the better will be the linearity and the higher the peak output obtainable. Not less than $40\mu F$ is recommended for the output position, and $100\mu F$ or greater is even more desirable. Oil-impregnated paper smoothing capacitors can be ruled out on grounds of price, but good results may be obtained at reasonable cost by connecting a number of high-capacitance electrolitic television smoothing capacitors in series in the manner depicted in Fig. 51. The bleeder resistors are essential to equalize the voltage across each of the electrolytics and must not be omitted. To prevent short-circuits and shocks, it is necessary to mount the components on an insulated board and to cover the cans with insulating material.

Alternative Valves

The circuit of Fig. 51 may be adapted to QV06–20s (6146s) by replacing the VR150s in positions V_3 and V_4 by a VR90 and a VR105 in series to reduce the screen potential to 195 volts. The applied grid bias must also be increased to the value given in **Table 9** appropriate to the voltage of the anode supply. The QV06–20 is far more critical than the 807 or its equivalents as regards screen supply, and a few *moments* operation at normal screen voltage in the absence of anode potential will ruin it irrevocably. Furthermore, the valve should never be controlled by interrupting the screen current and leaving the electrode floating, because the control grid is liable to suffer damage if drive is applied under such conditions. If it is to be used as a switching electrode in any safety interlock arrangement, the screen should be returned to earth in the OFF position. Unlike the 807, the QV06–20 has been designed expressly for class AB1 operation, and the minimal extra output obtained by driving it into the grid-current region is not worth the effort involved. It is therefore recommended that the meter 0-20 mA be replaced by a more sensitive instrument registering 500 microamps or one milliamp at total deflection, and that it be used to indicate when the stage is being overdriven.

Although the operating data in Tables 7 and 9 have been calculated for two valves in parallel, they may easily be converted for a single valve by halving

TABLE 9

Typical operating conditions for a type 6146 valve when substituted for the 5B/254M in the circuit of Fig. 51.

V_a	750V	1000V	1250V
I_a zero signal	28mA	20mA	not
V_{g1}	— 50V	— 62V	recommended

The grid bias figures are design centre values based upon an average valve. For optimum performance, the bias should be adjusted so that each valve draws the amount of anode current shown in the table. Care should be taken not to exceed the dissipation ratings recommended by the manufacturer. The 6146 is unusually susceptible to damage through overrunning.

the grid, screen and anode currents and the output power. The values of C_1 and C_2 will also require to be halved, and those of L_1 and L_2 to be doubled. Push-pull operation of a pair of valves is also a possibility, but experiment has confirmed that it is in no way superior to the parallel configuration.

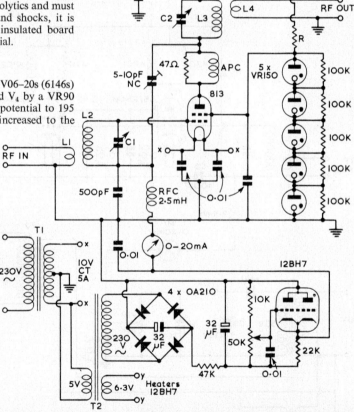

Fig. 52. High-power class AB2 linear amplifier using a single 813. C_1, 200pF; C_2, 120pF; L_2 wound on 1 in. diam formers threaded 20-21 t.p.i. 3·5 Mc/s—40 turns, 7 Mc/s—25 t., 14 Mc/s—12 t., 21 Mc/s—12 t. double spaced, 28 Mc/s—10 t. double spaced; L_3 wound on $2\frac{1}{2}$ in. diam. Eddystone or similar formers, 3·5 Mc/s—21 t. 7 Mc/s—16 t., 14 Mc/s—10 t., 21 Mc/s—6 t. L_3, 28 Mc/s—6 t. 2 in. long air wound. Stray capacitance and inductance may have an appreciable effect at 28 Mc/s and the anode inductors may require pruning in certain layouts. R should be adjusted to pass 35 mA under no-drive conditions. In this diagram, the 0-300mA meter should be to the left of the lead from the h.t. line to resistor R.

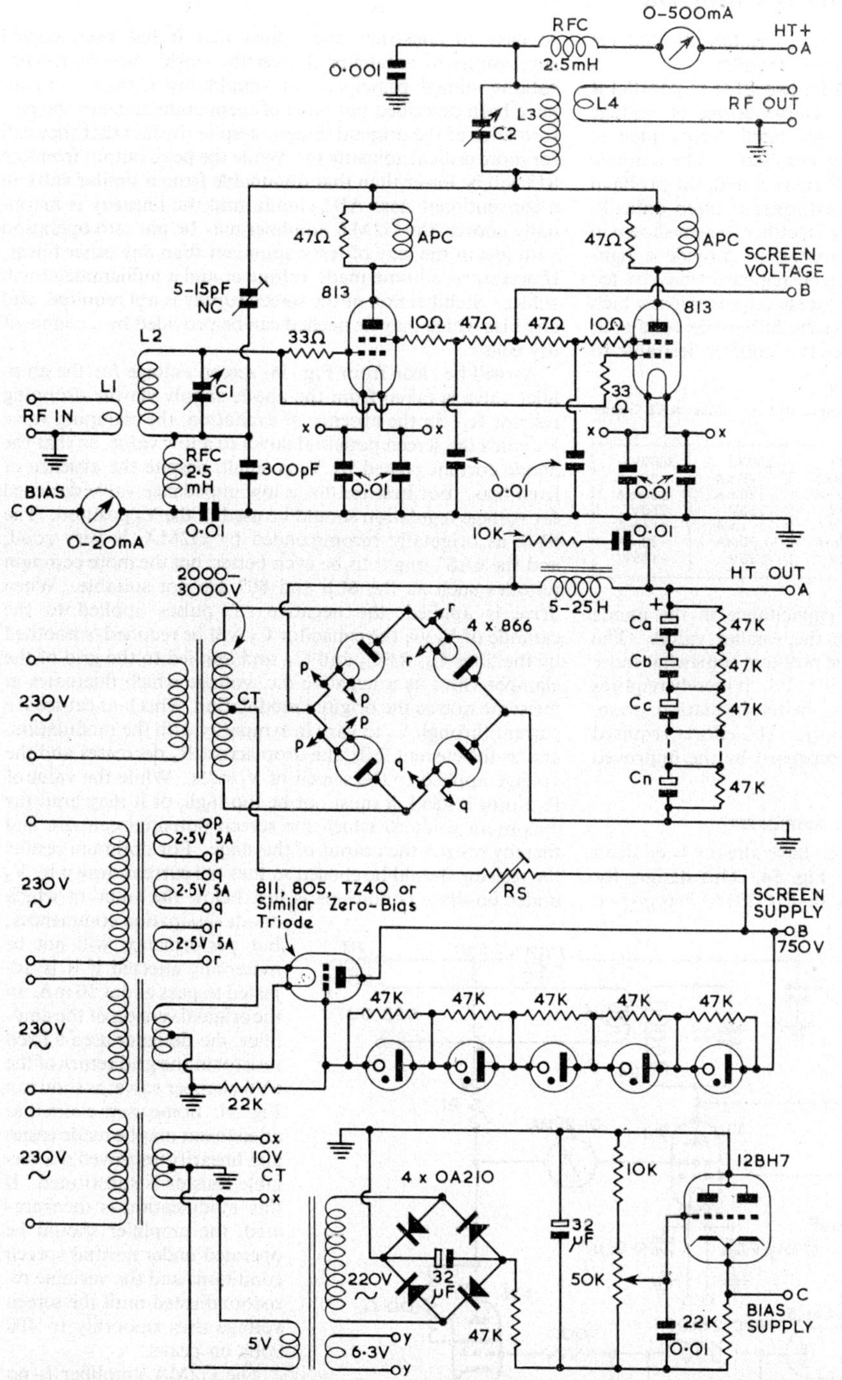

Fig. 53. High power linear amplifier using two 813s in parallel. C_1, 250pF; C_2, 180pF; L_2, wound on 1 in. dia. formers threaded 20-21 t.p.i., 3·5 Mc/s—30 turns, 7 Mc/s—20 t., 14 Mc/s—10 t., 21 Mc/s—10 t double spaced 28 Mc/s—8 t. doubled spaced; L_3, 3·5 Mc/s—16 turns, 7 Mc/s—10 t., 14 Mc/s—6 t.; wound on 2½ in. dia. Eddystone formers, 21 Mc/s—5 t. airwound 2 in. dia. 4 t.p.i., 28 Mc/s—4 t. airwound 2 in. dia. 4 t.p.i. Due to stray inductance and capacitance, L_3 for the higher frequency bands may require pruning in individual layouts. R_6 should be adjusted so that the shunt regulator valve draws 65mA under no-drive conditions. The number of capacitors C_a–C_n to be connected in series across the anode voltage supply depends upon the working voltage of the electrolytics available. The working capacitance should be 40µF or more. A choke input filter should be included between the centre-tap of the high-voltage transformer and R_6. The rectifier valves should be described as 866A.

SINGLE SIDEBAND

HIGH POWER 813 CLASS AB LINEARS

While the amplifiers already described are capable of a considerable output, they are unlikely to satisfy the high-power enthusiast who wishes to take advantage of the maximum permitted by the Amateur (Sound) Licence. The circuit of **Fig. 52** uses a single 813 in class AB2 to generate an output of between 200 and 250 watts dependent upon the voltage applied to the anode and will be powerful enough to satisfy all but the most discriminating. For the latter few the amplifier shown in **Fig 53** has been designed. Using a pair of parallelled 813s in class AB1, it certainly provides a de luxe method of producing the maximum allowed by the regulations. Anode voltage need not be greater than 2,000 or 2,500, distortion is extremely low, and the valves just loaf along even at prolonged peak outputs.

All the advice which has been given regarding the smaller amplifiers applies to their larger counterparts. Component ratings will naturally have to be increased to deal with higher potentials, but this is the only real difference. Operating conditions for the single valve stage at voltages between 2,000 and 3,000 are given in **Table 10**. The screen voltage should be stabilized at the recommended value of 750, which for a single 813 may be achieved by employing a string of VR150s in series as shown in Fig. 52. The adjustable regulated bias system shown in the diagram enables the operator to make the fine setting which is often necessary if the highest quality results are to be obtained. As will be seen from Table 10, however, the bias required at all recommended anode voltages falls very close to the standard values which may be obtained from the useful range of gas regulator tubes. Some simplification may therefore be made with little deterioration

325

in performance by substituting an appropriately selected VR tube for the 12BH7 and its associated circuitry.

The peak screen current drawn by two 813s in parallel is too great to be stabilized by a simple string of voltage regulator tubes, so a shunt-valve regulated supply such as that shown in **Fig. 53** becomes essential. When anode voltages in excess of 1,500 or 2,000 are required, the problem of obtaining a suitable power transformer is often difficult. This may be met by using the bridge-rectifier system shown in this circuit. The use of the centre-tap to provide a half-voltage supply from which the screen regulator may be fed forms a neat way to overcome the excessive power loss which would otherwise occur in dropping the full anode voltage to the value required for the screens. It is equally desirable to

TABLE 10

Typical operating conditions for a single 813 in class AB2 linear amplifier service.

V_a	2000V	2250V	2500V	3000V
I_a zero signal	35mA	30mA	28mA	25mA
I_a max. signal	150mA	160mA	180mA	150mA
V_{g_2}	750V	750V	750V	750V
I_{g_2} zero signal	0mA	< 1mA	< 1mA	< 1mA
I_{g_2} max. signal	25mA	27mA	30mA	30mA
V_{g_1}	−85V	−90V	−95V	−105V

provide a high value of output capacitance in the anode supply for the 813s as it is with the smaller valves. The higher voltages employed make the problem somewhat more difficult, but the same solution is still valid. It merely requires more electrolytics, more resistors, better insulation, more room, and more constructional work. The efforts required will, however, be more than recompensed by the improved linearity of the amplifier.

THE G2MA LINEAR AMPLIFIER

A contrast to the amplifiers which have already been dealt with is provided by the circuit of **Fig. 54**. This design, for which credit is due to David D. Marshall (G2MA), has proved so easy to construct and adjust that it has been copied successfully by amateurs all over the world. Several modifications, aimed principally at simplifying G2MA's circuit, have been described but none of them quite matches the performance of the original design, despite the fact that they call for more critical adjustment. While the peak output from the 813 will be lower than that obtainable from a similar valve in a conventional class AB2 circuit, and the linearity is marginally poorer, the G2MA amplifier may be put into operation with less in the way of test equipment than any other linear. If necessary, a home-made voltmeter and a milliammeter will suffice. Stabilization of the screen supply is not required, and any bias which may be needed can be provided by a couple of dry cells.

As will be clear from Fig. 54, screen voltage for the amplifier valve is taken from the anode supply via the dropping resistor R_1. In the absence of excitation, the clamping valve V_3 holds the screen potential down to a low value, so that the anode current passed by V_1 is small, despite the absence of fixed bias. For best results, a low impedance valve designed for voltage regulation should be used in the V_3 position. The 6Y6, as originally recommended by G2MA, is very good, and the 6AS7 ought to be even better, but the more common tetrodes such as the 6L6 and 807 are not suitable. When drive is applied, the negative r.f. pulses applied to the cathode of V_2 via the capacitor C_3 will be rectified, smoothed by the filter C_6, RFC$_3$ and C_7, and applied to the grid of the clamper valve as a negative d.c. voltage which fluctuates at the same rate as the original modulation. This bias causes the current through V_3 to vary in sympathy with the modulation, and as the current falls, the drop across R_1 decreases and the voltage applied to the screen of V_1 rises. While the value of R_1 is not critical, it must not be too high, or it may limit the maximum value to which the screen potential can rise and thereby restrict the output of the stage. For optimum results the resistor should be chosen so that the current drawn by V_3 under no-drive conditions is just below the value at which anode dissipation commences; but performance will not be materially affected if it is adjusted to pass about 50 mA. In the original version of the amplifier, the designer used a fixed resistor in the grid return of the 6Y6 clamper valve, as shown in Fig. 54. Some users claim that adjustment may be made easier and linearity improved if a variable resistor is substituted. If this modification is incorporated, the amplifier should be operated under normal speech conditions and the variable resistor adjusted until the screen voltage rises smoothly to 400 volts on peaks.

The G2MA amplifier is no exception to the general rule that the highest obtainable anode voltage should be used if maximum output is desired but when a supply much in excess of 1,500 volts is used, the power loss in R_1 becomes

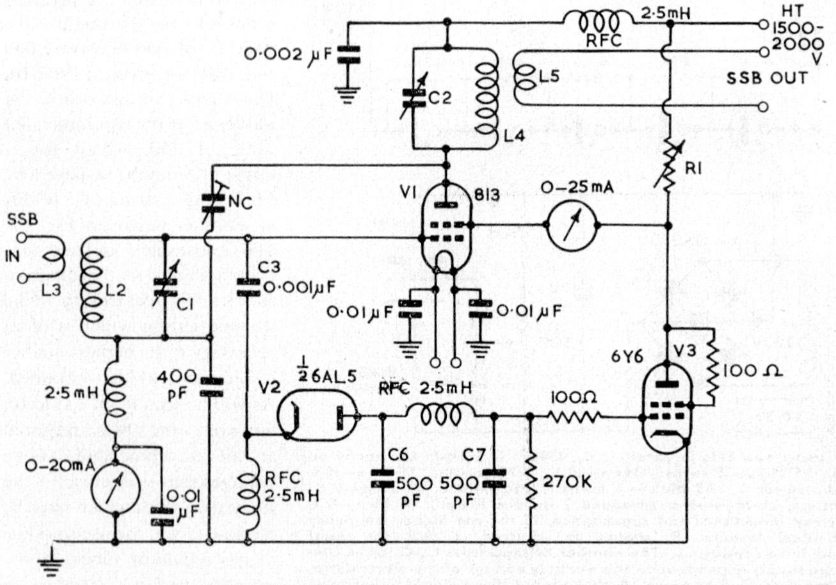

Fig. 54. G2MA linear amplifier. The coil-winding data given for the conventional amplifier of Fig. 52 may be used with this circuit. For adjustment of R_1 refer to text.

excessive. A separate low current supply of about 1,000 volts may be provided to reduce this loss, or if full wave bridge rectification is used in the power pack to the final amplifier, a half-voltage tapping may be taken off as in Fig. 53.

If maximum output is required, the G2MA amplifier should be aligned in the same manner as a conventional linear, using a two-tone test signal and oscilloscope. Tolerably good results may, however, be obtained at lower output by setting the drive so that the grid current meter reads 5 mA with steady modulation. In the absence of an audio oscillator, a sustained whistle into the microphone will serve. Loading should be increased smoothly, while observing the anode current meter closely. Beyond a certain point the current will cease to rise regularly with further increase in loading; the correct coupling occurs just before this point of inflexion is reached. The anode current should be noted, and when the amplifier is used with normal speech modulation, the meter should not be allowed to kick higher than one third to one half of the value under sustained single-tone modulation. The screen current will peak to about 10 mA. As a final test, a local amateur should be asked to monitor the signal for splatter. If any is found, the coupling should be reduced until it disappears. Some reduction in drive may also be needed. Although this procedure will enable a signal to be put on the air with a minimum of equipment, it leaves much to be desired, and adjustment with a cathode ray tube monitor is to be preferred.

THE TT21 LINEAR

The circuit of a linear amplifier designed by R. F. Stevens (G2BVN) and using a pair of G.E.C. TT21 valves is shown in **Fig. 55.** By virtue of its compact construction, this type of valve (an r.f. version of the KT88 audio valve) has shorter cathode leads than the 807 and the advantage of a screened base. It is capable of very much higher power input yet is easy to drive and inexpensive. In s.s.b. service it has been found to perform well at inputs up to the maximum permitted to U.K. amateurs.

In the TT21 linear, a parallel tuned high C input arrangement is used with link windings on the coils. One switch

position covers 28 and 21 Mc/s with separate inductances for the remaining bands. The grid circuit is damped by a 10K ohm non-inductive resistor while bias is supplied by batteries which will last practically their shelf life. A sensitive relay with a coil resistance of 8,000 ohms is wired in series with the lead from the battery and is used to light a 6·3 volt pilot bulb to indicate the flow of grid current. A regulated screen supply of 300 volts is derived from two VR150/30 valves mounted on the chassis of the amplifier.

Anode Circuit

The anode circuit is unconventional in that a multi-band tuning unit is employed instead of the more common pi-network. It will be seen from **Fig. 56** that if L_1 is replaced by an r.f. choke, C_1, C_2 and L_2 form a standard split-stator tank

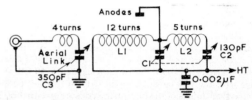

Fig. 56. Circuit of the multi-band tuner used in the output.

circuit. The inductance is adjusted so that the range 14 to 30 Mc/s is covered with some overlap at either end. If the r.f. choke is now removed and the coil L_1 substituted (at the same time shorting out L_2) the circuit is that of the usual single ended type with C_1 and C_2 in parallel and is adjusted to cover 3500 to 7100 kc/s. In practice, L_1 and L_2 are in circuit at all times. Both sections of the capacitor C_1 and C_2 are in series on the high frequency bands and in parallel on the low frequency bands, thus providing adequate L/C ratio for linear operation.

To cover both ranges without switching, L_2 acts as a long lead in the range 3500 to 7100 kc/s, whilst L_1 has the same effect as an r.f. choke on the range 14 to 30 Mc/s. The sequence in which the bands are tuned is shown in **Fig. 57.**

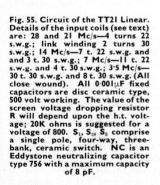

Fig. 55. Circuit of the TT21 Linear. Details of the input coils (see text) are: 28 and 21 Mc/s—4 turns 22 s.w.g.; link winding 2 turns 30 s.w.g.; 14 Mc/s—7 t. 22 s.w.g. and 3 t. 30 s.w.g.; 7 Mc/s—11 t. 22 s.w.g. and 4 t. 30 s.w.g.; 3·5 Mc/s—30 t. 30 s.w.g. and 8 t. 30 s.w.g. (All close wound). All 0·001µF fixed capacitors are disc ceramic type, 500 volt working. The value of the screen voltage dropping resistor R will depend upon the h.t. voltage; 20K ohms is suggested for a voltage of 800. S_1, S_2, S_3 comprise a single pole, four-way, three-bank, ceramic switch. NC is an Eddystone neutralizing capacitor type 756 with a maximum capacity of 8 pF.

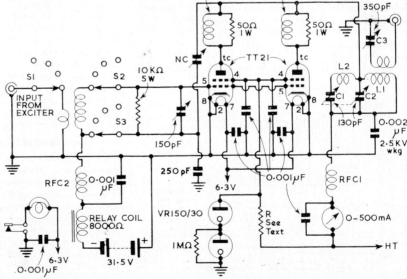

Coils L_1 and L_2 are wound on the same 2 in. diameter former at eight turns to the inch. L_1 should be wound first followed by L_2 and adjusted with a grid dip oscillator for coverage on the higher frequency range. A fixed capacitor of about 30 pF capacity should be connected in the circuit to replace the valve and stray capacities.

When the adjustment of L_2 is completed alterations may be made to L_1: such changes will not be reflected in L_2, but the reverse does not hold. The coils should be adjusted so that 28 Mc/s and 7 Mc/s or 14 Mc/s and 3·5 Mc/s do not appear

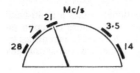

Fig. 57. Sequence in which the bands are tuned. Coverage of 14 Mc/s will occur at maximum capacity.

at the same dial setting. Very slight alterations to L_1 and L_2 will achieve the desired results. The link winding, which should be effectively insulated, is designed for working into a 72 ohm feeder and will need to be increased if a line of higher impedance is used. A variable capacitor of 350 pF in series with the link gives adequate control of the loading. The physical details of the multi-band coils are given in **Fig. 58.**

The split-stator capacitor should have a maximum capacity of about 130 pF per section and a reasonably low minimum capacity, with plate spacing suitable for the voltage to be used. It should be noted that the frame of the capacitor is connected to h.t. positive, making it necessary to use insulated feet and a good insulated coupling on the shaft.

The Eddystone neutralizing capacitor (NC) forms one arm of a bridge neutralizing circuit, the remaining arms being made up as follows: (i) the anode-to-control grid capacitor; (ii) the control grid-to-cathode capacitor, and (iii) the 250 pF fixed capacitor from the bottom of the grid circuit to earth.

Power Supply

The anode voltage may be in the range 800 to 1,000 from an external unit via a multi-way screened cable. The maximum indicated current drawn at 900 volts is 300 mA.

The h.t. supply is controlled by a toggle switch mounted on the front panel of the amplifier and connected in the earth return of a relay located in the power supply case. With this switch in the OFF position there should be no lethal voltage on the supply cable or in the amplifier unit itself. In addition to switching the h.t. supply an additional pair of contacts on the relay is used to operate a warning light on the power

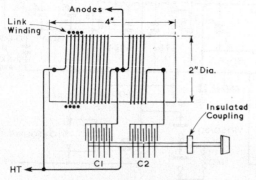

Fig. 58. Details of the multi-band coil.

A front view of the TT21 Linear. From left to right, input co-ax socket, grid circuit tuning, grid bandswitch, h.t. fuse and relay switch. Below the meter, the anode circuit tuning control with the link capacitor C_2 to the right. The grid current indicator is to the left of the meter with the heater circuit pilot lamp on the other side. Output is taken from the co-ax socket at the upper right.

supply panel. It is not necessary, and indeed inadvisable, to use more than a single section filter in the h.t. supply line, but the output capacitance should be at least 32μF to assist in maintaining good dynamic regulation. The rectifiers may be a pair of the 866A mercury vapour type or, if these are not available, the 5R4GY is suitable.

The heater current drawn by a pair of TT21 valves is 3·2 amps, and it is essential that the voltage measured at the heater pins should be 6·3 volts.

The TT21 valves should operate in class AB1 and any attempt to drive them too hard will result in unacceptable distortion. With miniature batteries of 22·5 volts and 9 volts in series the standing anode current is 75 mA.

Construction

In common with all equipment used for r.f. generation or amplification the unit should be completely enclosed with adequate provision for ventilation. The chassis used for the original amplifier measured 12 in. × 8 in. × 2 in. Input and output is by coaxial cable, and all power leads are filtered and bypassed with a large proportion of the wiring run in screened cable. All bypass capacitors are earthed at the nearest point on the chassis and the cathode leads are short and made from braid stripped from coaxial cable.

The grid coils and tuning capacitor are located beneath the chassis thus providing screening and short leads, with the larger multi-band tank components above the chassis adjacent to the anode top connections of the TT21 valves.

ALIGNMENT OF LINEAR AMPLIFIERS

By the application of the principles already set out and the exercise of care and skill, any amateur may construct an amplifier capable of functioning in a linear manner. Whether it will give undistorted output in practice will depend less upon the circuitry employed than on the attention which is devoted to its alignment. The old saying that any successful radio device is 10 per cent circuit and 90 per cent operator is as apt when applied to linear amplifiers as to anything else.

The fact that alignment is an unfamiliar word in connection with r.f. amplifiers need not deter anyone. It merely implies that the loading and drive have to be adjusted so that the stage is able to give the maximum output, efficiency and linearity of which it is capable.

One of the unfortunate features of a class AB or B amplifier is that the anode and grid current meters give no indication of whether the stage is working in a linear manner or not. It is therefore imperative to check the linearity on a monitoring oscilloscope. An audio oscillator capable of generating a pure sine wave at about 1,000 c/s is also essential and a valve voltmeter, although dispensable, is very useful. An operator who is prepared to sacrifice half the potential power handling capacity of his p.a. and to run it inefficiently, *may* produce a linear signal without an oscilloscope and oscillator, but test equipment is essential if the best results are desired. Suitable items are described in Chapter 19 (*Measurements*).

Two-Tone Test

The output of a s.s.b. transmitter modulated by a single tone is a pure single-frequency r.f. waveform at a frequency $fc \pm fm$. Nothing worthwhile may be deduced by displaying a pattern of this kind on an oscilloscope, so it has become accepted practice to use the signal shown in **Fig. 59** when adjusting a linear amplifiers. Because the pattern is produced by adding two pure sine waves, it is known as the *two tone test* signal. As it is merely a double sideband suppressed carrier signal in another guise, it may be generated in a phasing exciter by disabling one of the two balanced modulators and applying a single audio tone to the input of the

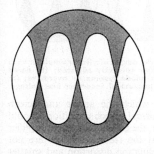

Fig. 59. Oscilloscope pattern of a two-tone test signal used for aligning linear amplifiers.

speech amplifier. In the filter exciter, the same result may be produced by applying single tone modulation and reinserting carrier of exactly the same amplitude as the s.s.b. signal passed through the filter. It is not necessary to go to the trouble of building an audio oscillator to give output at two separate frequencies.

Need for Alignment

The reason for aligning the amplifier will be apparent from an inspection of the characteristic curves in **Fig. 60**. The diagram relates to a popular class B zero-bias triode, but the curves for class AB beam power valves and pentodes are virtually identical in shape. They only differ as far as grid voltage values are concerned. Assuming a permissible peak current of 400 mA, it will be seen that the minimum instantaneous anode voltage may not fall below 250 volts. The peak grid voltage for this value of anode current is 100. When plotted graphically, the peak current point is represented by X on the diagram. With an applied anode voltage of 1,250, the resting voltage and current in the absence of drive is represented by the point O. By joining X to O, a line is obtained which represents in graphical form the load into

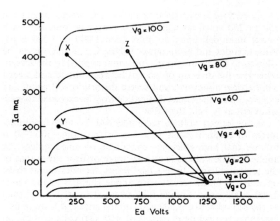

Fig. 60. Characteristic curves for a popular zero-bias triode showing (a) optimum load OX, (b) load too loosely coupled OY, and (c) load too tightly coupled OZ.

which the valve will perform under the conditions specified. The d.c. input, as indicated by a meter in the anode lead will be approximately

$$\frac{(I_{a\ peak} + I_{a\ min})}{2}$$

and the power output will be proportional to

$$(E_{a\ max} - E_{a\ min})\ I_{a\ peak}.$$

When monitored on an oscilloscope, the undistorted pattern shown in **Fig. 61(a)** will be displayed. Should the coupling be looser than optimum, the load line will move to a position such as OY in Fig. 60. The anode swing will remain virtually unchanged—but in the example shown the peak current will be reduced to half if distortion were to be avoided. Efficiency will not suffer, but input and output will be halved. Any attempt to raise the input by increasing the drive will result in distorted output waveform as shown in Fig. 61(b). Over-coupling, on the other hand, will result in the load line being shifted to a position such as OZ in Fig. 60. Although the amplifier may be made to draw the permitted peak anode current, the anode voltage swing will be less than maximum, so output and efficiency will both fall. Intermodulation distortion will not occur as long as the stage is not overdriven in an attempt to increase the output. The primary indication of overdrive will be excessive anode dissipation, a condition which may be avoided by visual inspection of the anode for signs of overheating. The secondary effect is much more serious. The cathodes of most amplifier valves are capable of considerably more than rated peak emission for short and intermittent periods. Prolonged operation at excessive currents will, however, impair the emissive properties of the cathode, and distortion from current limiting will occur. Damage from this cause is permanent and irreparable, so current-overloading should be avoided.

In tetrodes and pentodes, the screen confers the desirable property of allowing high signal power to be generated in the anode circuit for a relatively small amount of applied drive at the grid. The fact that there is a debit side to the balance sheet is, however, all too frequently ignored. In the simple triode, the instantaneous minimum voltage ($E_{a\ min}$) may be allowed to approach the instantaneous maximum positive voltage applied to the grid ($I_{g\ max}$). Values of

329

$E_{a\ min}$ realizable with the commonly used triodes range from 150 to 250 volts, so high efficiency may be obtained with power units delivering no more than 1,000 to 1,500 volts. With tetrodes and beam power valves, $E_{a\ min}$ may never be allowed to fall below the d.c. potential applied to the screen, otherwise the division of current between anode and screen will become abnormal, and severe distortion will result. In extreme cases, the screen dissipation may be exceeded to such an extent as to ruin the valve.

As the screen voltage recommended by most manufacturers of medium sized valves is in the range 500–750 it follows that high efficiency cannot be obtained unless the applied anode voltage is at least three or four times that of the screen voltage. In practical terms, tetrodes ought to be operated in linear service with anode supplies in the range 2,000–4,000 volts. Should it be essential to use a valve such as the 813 with, say, 1,500 volts on the anode, it is quite useless to try to operate in class AB1 with 600 volts or more on the screen. Much higher efficiency will result from dropping the screen potential to around 350 volts, and increasing the drive so that the stage operates in class AB2.

The belief appears to be fairly widespread that aligned radial-grid tetrodes such as the 4-125A and 4-250A have characteristics which make them especially suitable for s.s.b. linear amplifier service. Apart from the fact that they may be operated at higher frequencies than the cheaper 813, they have no outstanding advantages. In fact, they are rather more susceptible both to non linearity and to screen damage if overdriven.

Pentodes are more suitable as linear amplifiers than tetrodes, because with proper suppressor grid design an instantaneous anode voltage excursion well below the d.c. potential applied to the screen need have no ill effect. Unfortunately, few suitable pentodes are manufactured in the United Kingdom but valves specially designed for s.s.b. amplifier service are made by Penta Laboratories in the U.S.A., and are recommended to perfectionist constructors who do not mind paying anything from £12 to £20 for a single valve.

Practical Alignment Procedure

When a linear amplifier has been built and given a preliminary check for accuracy of wiring, the following alignment procedure is recommended:

(i) Apply reduced potentials to anode (and screen if applicable) and adjust the bias so that the valve is running that there is no trace of self-oscillation at the operating frequency or of parasitic oscillation at v.h.f. Correct neutralization is infinitely more important in a class B amplifier than in a class C stage used for telegraphy or A3 telephony.

(ii) Increase applied potentials to the values recommended by the valve manufacturer, making sure that neutralization remains effective no matter how the grid and anode tuning controls may be set.

(iii) Couple an oscilloscope to the output tank inductor by means of a link and coaxial cable. Adjust the coupling so that a display of convenient height is obtained when the drive is applied. If the amplifier is capable of delivering more than 420 watts power output to the load, the face of the oscilloscope should be calibrated by temporarily increasing the bias and operating the stage as a class C amplifier with the d.c. input adjusted to 150 watts. The amplitude of the pattern on the oscilloscope screen should be noted, and thereafter the

amplifier should be controlled so that the pattern will not exceed twice that amplitude under any circumstances.

(iv) Couple a load to the output tank and apply drive from an exciter generating a two-tone test signal.

(v) Adjust the drive and loading simultaneously until an undistorted pattern of maximum amplitude is obtained at the maximum d.c. input permitted under two-tone test conditions by the valve manufacturers' instructions. Should two-tone test data be unavailable, a value of 0·7 times the permitted d.c. peak input may be employed. A valve voltmeter with an r.f. probe will help to facilitate the adjustment of excitation to the value recommended by the manufacturer.

(vi) Examine the "cross-overs" on the oscilloscope critically. They should be sharp as in **Fig. 61(a).** If, however, they appear compressed as in Fig. 61(c) the bias should be adjusted until they are correct. With suitable valves, this type of distortion should not give trouble, but if it is persistent the bias supply should be suspected. The variable grid leak effect introduced by ageing dry cells is one of the more likely causes of cross-over distortion.

If the oscilloscope is to be left permanently in circuit as a monitor, a course which cannot be too strongly recommended, the transmitter may be put on the air without further preparation. If, however, permanent monitoring is not

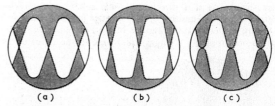

Fig 61. Oscilloscope patterns of the output of a linear amplifier with two-tone test input; (a) amplifier correctly adjusted; (b) peaks flattened because of insufficient anode loading or overdrive; (c) distortion at cross-over points because of incorrect bias voltage.

practicable, the reading to which the anode and screen current meters kick under normal speech conditions should be carefully noted. Thereafter, the gain of the speech amplifier should be controlled so that the recorded values are not exceeded, otherwise intermodulation distortion and splatter will result. If the transmitter tuning has to be adjusted in the absence of an oscilloscope, the screen current meter will be found more useful than the anode meter. As the tuning of a correctly loaded amplifier is rather flat, the anode current dip is not so pronounced as with a class C stage. Furthermore, maximum output does not always coincide exactly with minimum current. The screen current, on the other hand, will rise to an unmistakable peak as the anode tank circuit is tuned to resonance.

RECEPTION OF S.S.B.

The reception of s.s.b. is not difficult but it does necessitate the mastery of a technique which may be unfamiliar to many. As in so many other fields, an ounce of practice is worth a ton of theory. The most likely place to find a sideband station is between 3·75 and 3·8 Mc/s or around 14·3 Mc/s. As the receiver is tuned through the signal the noise issuing from the speaker will reach a peak and will then start to fall off, but it will at no time become intelligible. Until a datum frequency is introduced in place of the missing carrier, intelligibility is impossible. For a first essay into s.s.b. reception, the receiver b.f.o. may be used. With the noise peaked at maximum and

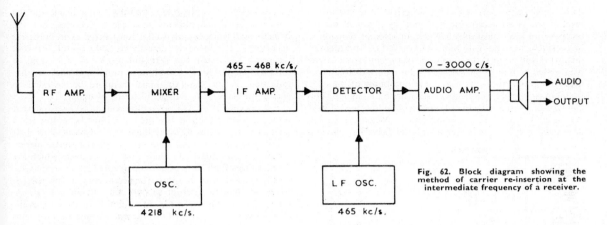

Fig. 62. Block diagram showing the method of carrier re-insertion at the intermediate frequency of a receiver.

the a.g.c. off, the b.f.o. should be switched on and the pitch control rotated slowly until the speech begins to sound recognizable. More likely than not, the output will sound heavily overmodulated, in which case an improvement may be made by backing off the r.f. and i.f. gain controls. A final touch to the pitch control, and the signal should become perfectly readable. If it sounds unnatural and overmodulated or like a gramophone record on a turntable which is not running evenly, the trouble is almost certain to stem from deficiencies in the receiver. The following aspects of receiver design, which supplement those discussed in Chapter 4, will assist anyone who is interested in obtaining top quality reception of sideband signals.

As has already been said, the insertion of a signal to take the place of the carrier is essential to the demodulation of a sideband signal. With a t.r.f. receiver, the only way of doing this is to couple into the front end the output of a local oscillator adjusted as closely as possible to the nominal frequency of the transmitting station. A similar system may of course be employed with a superhet receiver. The outstanding advantage of signal-frequency carrier insertion is that the intelligibility and quality of the audio output depends solely upon the stability of the carrier oscillator. As injection is done at the aerial terminals, nothing more than a small r.f.

signal is required, so the oscillator may be designed for quality of output rather than for quantity. A BC221 or one of the LM series frequency meters will be found ideal. Drift in the heterodyne oscillator of a superhet will have no more effect on s.s.b. signals received by front-end carrier injection than it will on conventional a.m. It may be irritating, but nothing more. With a poor and unstable receiver, this is the only worthwhile method to use. The drawback is that the receiver tuning must be adjusted in synchronism with the carrier oscillator when changing frequency. A minor point to watch is that the carrier oscillator must not overload the front-end of the receiver. If its amplitude is great enough to drive the r.f. stage into non-linearity, the receiver would become susceptible to cross modulation by any strong signal.

When using a superhet, it is more convenient to reintroduce the carrier at an appropriate frequency after the sideband has been converted to the intermediate frequency. A block diagram of this system is shown in **Fig. 62.** The b.f.o. is often pressed into service as carrier oscillator and produces regrettable results because it is asked to fill a role for which it was not designed. The average b.f.o. is a well built unit which has a slow tuning rate and is quite stable enough to take the place of the carrier. In 99 receivers out of 100, however, its output is via a small capacitor to the anode of a

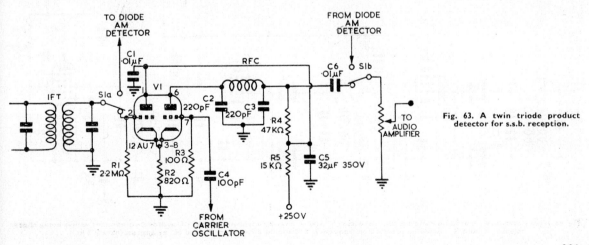

Fig. 63. A twin triode product detector for s.s.b. reception.

diode detector, and its amplitude is restricted to the lowest level at which an acceptable beat note is obtained for the reception of c.w. telegraphy. When an attempt is made to mix a sideband signal with that from the b.f.o., considerable distortion will occur if the amplitude of the simulated carrier is exceeded by that of the sideband. To reduce distortion to negligible proportions, the maximum amplitude of the s.s.b. signal must be held well below that of the b.f.o. signal. This can be done by reducing the r.f. and i.f. gain but this solution can never be more than a compromise. When the gain is advanced to read a weak signal, splatter becomes unavoid-

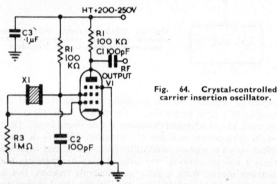

Fig. 64. Crystal-controlled carrier insertion oscillator.

able from any stronger signal which may happen to be adjacent. Increasing the output of the b.f.o. is rarely profitable, because stability is likely to suffer. In some receivers a considerable improvement may be effected by disconnecting the lead from the b.f.o. to the diode detector and connecting it to the grid of the first or second i.f. amplifier valves via a capacitor of 1 or 2 pF. This modification will not, however, work well if the i.f. stage is followed by a highly selective device such as a crystal or mechanical filter.

One answer to the problem is to replace the diode detector by a mixer-type demodulator. A representative circuit of this type is shown in **Fig. 63**. With this circuit, which is commonly called the *product detector*, the applied b.f.o. voltage is less critical than with a diode detector, yet the audio output is

much cleaner. It is possible to add the double triode and the few associated components into most receivers, but the detector will work equally well if constructed as an outboard accessory. The product detector is also useful for c.w. reception but it will not demodulate conventional a.m. or n.b.f.m. telephony. A switching arrangement such as that indicated on the diagram must therefore be included to enable the receiver to handle all forms of signal.

For successful i.f. carrier reinsertion, it is essential that both the local oscillator and the b.f.o. must be as free from drift as it is possible to make them. A consistent slow drift is not much of a handicap but erratic, short-term frequency jumps are particularly disconcerting. In receivers which are prone to this fault, it is usually more satisfactory to instal a crystal oscillator at an appropriate frequency within the i.f. passband than to attempt to cure the offending b.f.o. A typical circuit is given in **Fig. 64**. Suitable crystals are available at low prices from Government surplus sources, and instructions for altering their frequencies will be found earlier in this chapter. If the i.f. passband is wide enough to accept two sidebands, it will suffice to obtain one crystal of which the frequency should be centred in the middle of the passband. If, however, the passband approaches the more desirable selectivity characteristic of 3 kc/s, two crystals will have to be installed in a switchable circuit so that the carrier may be inserted to one side or the other of the passband, thereby permitting either upper or lower sideband reception at will. **Fig. 65** will give the idea much more quickly than a large number of words.

There are a few possible modifications which despite their simplicity may make a considerable improvement to many local oscillators. As drift is primarily caused by changes in the potentials applied to the various electrodes of the oscillator and mixer valves, stabilization of the h.t. supply by a gas regulator such as the VR105 is invariably beneficial. If the mixer valve is included in either the manual or the automatic gain control loops, it should be disconnected therefrom and the cathode and grid returns solidly earthed. An alteration to the send/receive switching is highly recommended in most receivers. The usual function of this switch is to disconnect the h.t. from all valves completely when it is

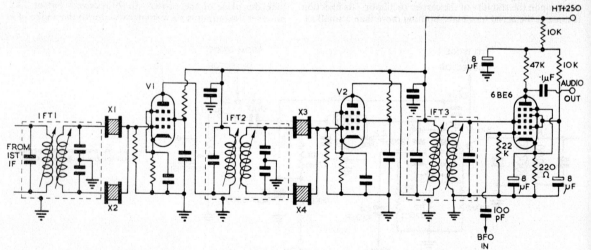

Fig. 66 Highly selective i.f. amplifier and product detector. V_1 and V_2 may be any usual type of r.f. pentode, component values being chosen to suit. X_1 and X_3 should be identical in frequency, and should differ from X_2 and X_4 by approximately 2 kc/s.

thrown to send, and a minor rearrangement of the wiring to permit the local oscillator and the b.f.o. to continue running will minimize erratic drift caused by alternate heating and cooling. The resulting improvement in stability will vary widely from one receiver to another, but will almost always be out of proportion to the simplicity of the modification.

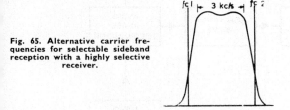

Fig. 65. Alternative carrier frequencies for selectable sideband reception with a highly selective receiver.

Finally, if the receiver is not particularly selective, the advisability of reducing its bandwidth to 3 kc/s may be worth considering. The advantage to be gained from this modification is not confined solely to s.s.b. work, but a single sideband transmission 3 kc/s wide tuned on a receiver with a 3 kc/s passband represents the highest efficiency and best signal-to-interference ratio at present attainable in telephony communication. The finest way to increase selectivity at reasonable

cost is to install two sections of half-lattice crystal filter in the i.f. amplifier. The remarks in the section dealing with crystal filters for transmission apply generally to receiver filters, but the symmetrical configuration is more suitable than the "lop-sided" variety used in the exciter of Fig. 34. The circuit of an i.f. strip and product detector that will give first-class results is given in **Fig. 66.**

DOUBLE SIDEBAND

This chapter would be incomplete without a brief reference to the double sideband system of communication which is simpler, cheaper and more efficient than conventional a.m. A low-power modulator of the type customarily used for grid-modulation is big enough to drive any of the popular tetrodes to a peak d.s.b. output greater than the same valves are capable of producing in anode modulated service. As d.s.b. is usually generated in the stage immediately preceding the aerial, the problem of linear amplification is avoided, and band changing is as simple as in a c.w. transmitter. There is no resting carrier, so voice control may be used as with s.s.b. Its disadvantages are that it occupies twice the bandwidth of s.s.b., and cannot be received without special equipment.

The simplicity of the transmitter may be gauged from the circuit in **Fig. 67.** The EF86 speech amplifier V_1 is resistance-coupled through the gain control VR_1 to the triode amplifier

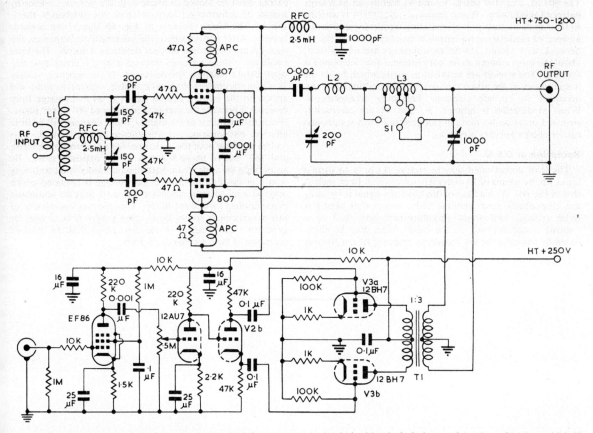

Fig. 67. Practical d.s.b. transmitter. L_1 should be selected to resonate in the desired band. L_2 is 4 turns, 1 in. diam., 1 in. long. L_3 is 17 turns 2½ in. diam., 2½ in. long, tapped at 1, 3 and 9 turns from the "hot" end. The 0·5 Megohm potentiometer in the grid circuit of V_{2a} is VR_1.

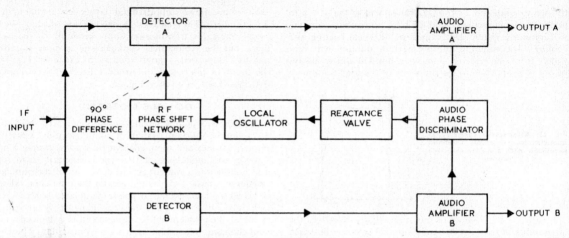

Fig. 68. Simplified block diagram of the synchronous detection system for d.s.b. reception. Audio output may be taken from either amplifier A or amplifier B, but not from both in parallel.

V_{2a}. This valve feeds the concertina phase-splitter V_{2b} which in turn drives the grids of the 12BH7 push-pull modulator V_3. Any step-up driver transformer will serve for T_1 but the Woden DT3, connected in reverse, is particularly suitable. The 807 r.f. amplifier valves V_4 and V_5 merely act as a large balanced modulator. Radio frequency excitation is applied to their grids in push-pull at operating frequency, and in the absence of modulation no output is developed across the pi-network tank circuit. Drive requirements are not critical; about the same amount as for conventional a.m. telephony is suitable. The screens are returned to earth, which holds the output down in the absence of modulation and makes it unnecessary to provide elaborate balancing arrangements. When modulation is applied, V_4 and V_5 are alternately switched on at audio rate, and double sideband suppressed carrier energy appears across L_2.

Reception of D.S.B.

The least complicated way to receive d.s.b. is to turn it into s.s.b. by means of an extremely selective i.f. filter such as that in Fig. 66. With a filter of this kind, the signal is virtually indistinguishable from genuine s.s.b., except that tuning is more critical, and slight misadjustment will lead to a " growl " superimposed on the audio. This may be eliminated by reducing the low frequency response of the receiver audio stages in the manner often recommended for transmitter speech amplifiers.

To make the most of d.s.b., both sidebands have to be accepted on a receiver with a passband of 6 kc/s, and the local carrier must be locked in phase with the nominal carrier by means of information derived from the sidebands themselves. The block diagram of **Fig. 68** shows one possible system. After conversion to the intermediate frequency, the signal is applied to two product detectors A and B. The local oscillator voltage is passed through a 90° r.f. phase shift network before reaching the detectors. If the injection voltage at A is in the correct phase relationship, maximum audio will appear in the output, but no signal at all will emerge from detector B because the carrier is introduced 90° out of phase. When the oscillator drifts slightly, the A channel will be little affected, but some output will start to appear from B. This will be in phase with the A channel for one direction of drift, and 180° out of phase for drift in the opposite sense. By amplifying the audio from both demodulators and combining it in a phase discriminator, a d.c. voltage is obtained which may be applied to a reactance valve to provide automatic phase control for the oscillator. The obvious complexity of this arrangement shows fairly clearly why it is simpler to generate a s.s.b. signal in the first place than to attempt reception of both sidebands of d.s.b.

CHAPTER II

FREQUENCY MODULATION

AMPLITUDE modulation is defined as modulation of the r.f. carrier wave by variation of its amplitude; this means that if the carrier wave is represented by the equation—

$$e = E_0 \sin(2\pi f + \phi)$$

the variation of E_0 gives rise to *amplitude modulation*. In a similar manner, the variation of f is known as *frequency modulation* and the variation of ϕ as *phase modulation*. The latter has no direct application in amateur radio communication but frequency modulation is widely used for high-fidelity broadcasting and under certain conditions may be used by the amateur radio operator.

Principles of Frequency Modulation

Frequency modulation may be represented graphically as shown in **Fig. 1.** Here A represents the unmodulated carrier wave, B the modulating signal, and C the frequency-modulated carrier wave. It will be seen that the frequency of the carrier wave is increased and decreased in sympathy with the amplitude and polarity of the modulating signal, but the amplitude of the carrier is not affected. The change in the frequency of the carrier wave is known as the *frequency deviation* or simply as the *deviation*. The total excursion of this frequency is called the *swing*; i.e. the swing is twice the deviation. The carrier frequency, for obvious reasons, is known in f.m. practice as the *centre frequency*. The deviation is proportional to the amplitude of the modulating signal, so that the limits of the swing are determined by the peaks of the modulating voltage. The rate at which the carrier frequency is deviated is equal to the frequency of the modulation signal. To quote a numerical example, if a carrier wave of frequency 7075 kc/s (i.e. the centre frequency is 7075 kc/s) is modulated by a 3 kc/s tone of specified amplitude to produce a deviation of 2·5 kc/s, the carrier frequency will swing between 7072·5

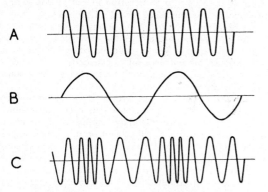

Fig. I. Graphical representation of frequency modulation. A—Unmodulated carrier wave. B—Modulating signal. C—Frequency-modulated carrier wave (i.e. its frequency is varied in sympathy with B).

kc/s and 7077·5 kc/s and back (i.e. the swing is 5 kc/s) 3000 times in one second. If the amplitude of the 3 kc/s tone were doubled, the carrier frequency would swing between 7070·0 and 7080·0 kc/s but the rate of variation would still be 3 kc/s.

The ratio of the deviation to the frequency of the modulating signal is known as the *modulation index*. This ratio is obviously not constant since the deviation depends on the amplitude of the modulating signal, and its limiting value, or the ratio of the maximum deviation to the highest modulating frequencies, is called the *deviation ratio*. In the example quoted earlier, the deviation ratio is 2·5 kc/s divided by 3 kc/s or 0·833 for the first given amplitude and 5·0 kc/s divided by 3 kc/s or 1·67 when the amplitude is doubled.

As in the case of amplitude modulation, sidebands are produced during the process of frequency modulation but with the important fundamental difference that a theoretically infinite number of side frequencies may exist. The side frequencies occur in pairs, one on each side of the carrier, and in the case of modulation by a single tone the spacing between the side frequencies on either side of the centre frequency will be equal to the frequency of the modulating tone. In the example just quoted of the frequency modulation of a 7075 kc/s carrier by a 3 kc/s tone, the first pair of side frequencies will occur at frequencies of 7078 kc/s and 7072 kc/s, the second pair at 7081 kc/s and 7069 kc/s, the third pair at 7084 kc/s and 7066 kc/s, and so on.

It should be appreciated that this concept of a number of sidebands and a fixed central carrier is an analytical representation of the effect of varying the frequency of the carrier, and the mental image of the process should not be confused by the supposition that the carrier passes through the frequencies occupied by these sidebands in the course of its frequency deviation.

The amplitudes of the sidebands produced are proportional to the modulation index; i.e. the amplitudes of the higher-order side frequencies (4th and above) increase from a value which is negligible when the modulation index is 1·0 to appreciable values when the modulation index is greater than 5. The manner in which the sidebands vary is shown in **Fig. 2** where their variation is plotted for values of the modulation index up to 5. It will also be seen that when the modulation index is 2·4, the carrier itself *disappears*, i.e. its phase reverses compared with the phase when modulation is absent. Further disappearances occur at higher values of modulation index.

It follows therefore that the question of the bandwidth required in the transmitter and receiver of an f.m. system has not such a straightforward answer as in the case of amplitude modulation.

In frequency modulation there is no condition equivalent to over-modulation. An increase in the amplitude of the modulating signal will merely cause an increase in the deviation produced. In the case of large deviations this effect will

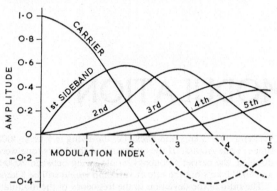

Fig. 2. Variation in relative amplitude of the carrier and the low-order sidebands in a frequency modulation system.

of course, introduce difficult problems into the design of the r.f. circuits of the transmitter and in the receiver, but these conditions do not occur in amateur communication equipment where the deviation is required by the terms of the Amateur (Sound) Licence to be kept relatively small.

At present the restrictions imposed by the G.P.O. on the use of frequency modulation by amateurs are as follows:

(a) The maximum deviation shall not exceed 2·5 kc/s.
(b) The maximum effective modulating frequency shall be limited to 4 kc/s and the a.f. input to the frequency modulator at frequencies higher than 4 kc/s shall be not less than 26 dB below the maximum input at lower frequencies.
(c) The carrier frequency shall be at least 10 kc/s within the limits of the frequency band in use.

The deviation ratio permitted is therefore 2·5 kc/s divided by 4 kc/s or 0·625. At this value, the carrier and the first-order sidebands are appreciable, and the second-order sidebands are almost small enough to be neglected while the third and higher orders may be ignored. Therefore, to a first approximation the bandwidth occupied may be considered as equal to twice the deviation or 5 kc/s. In other words, it is roughly equivalent to the bandwidth required for a " communication-quality " amplitude-modulated transmission. In contrast to the large deviations used in high-fidelity broadcasting, for which an international standard of 75 kc/s has been adopted, this restricted mode of operation has come to be known as *Narrow-Band Frequency Modulation*, generally abbreviated to n.b.f.m.

F.M. TRANSMITTERS

Frequency-modulated transmitters may be divided into two broad classes:

(i) Those which use a quartz crystal to determine the centre frequency.
(ii) Those which operate by the direct frequency variation of the master oscillator.

Transmitters in the first category are, in general, complicated in design and may involve the production of a phase-modulated signal which is then converted to a frequency-modulated one, the use of specially cut crystals or complicated chains of phase shifters, balanced modulators, frequency multipliers and mixers. However, they are capable of providing large deviations at extremely high degrees of stability of the centre frequency. For details, the reader is referred to the standard works on frequency modulation.

In the second category, the frequency of the master oscillator or v.f.o. is varied directly by placing a variable reactance across the tuned circuit of the oscillator. This of course implies that the frequency stability of the oscillator itself must be as high as possible. The stability of the present-day variable-frequency oscillator as used in amateur transmitters is usually adequate and this method of producing frequency modulation is therefore the one best suited to amateur use.

The Variable-Reactance Valve Modulator

The basic circuit of the variable-reactance or reactor type of modulator is shown in **Fig. 3**. Essentially it consists of a valve connected across the tuned circuit of an oscillator in such a way that it behaves like a variable capacitance or inductance. In the circuit shown, a potentiometer consisting of a condenser C_2 and a resistor R in series is connected from anode to earth and also, of course, across the tuned circuit. The centre point is taken to the grid of the valve. Provided that the resistance R is large compared with the reactance of C_2 at the resonant frequency of the tuned circuit, the grid will be fed with a voltage which is very nearly 90° out of

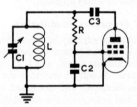

Fig. 3. Basic circuit of a variable-reactance frequency modulator. LC1 is the tuned circuit of the master oscillator.

phase with the voltage at the anode. A similar phase-shift but of the opposite sign may also be obtained by interchanging C_2 and R, in which case the reactance of C_2 would need to be large compared with the resistance R.

Since the anode current of a valve is in phase with its grid voltage, the current flowing through the reactance valve is 90° out of phase with the voltage across the tuned circuit due to the 90° phase-shift introduced by the combination of C_2 and R. Since the valve current also flows through the tuned circuit, the current through the tuned circuit is 90° out of phase with the voltage across it, which is equivalent to the result produced by connecting a reactance across the tuned circuit. This reactance may be either capacitive or inductive according to the configuration of the RC_2 potentiometer. In the arrangement shown in Fig. 3, the reactance will be inductive, while if R and C_2 are interchanged, the reactance will be capacitive. In either case, the effect of this reactance will be to change the resonant frequency of the tuned circuit.

The value of the reactance thrown across the tuned circuit and hence the change in resonant frequency will obviously depend on the value of the anode current of the reactance valve; in other words it will depend on the voltage applied to the grid of the valve. Thus the variable reactance valve presents a simple means of varying the frequency of an oscillator in sympathy with an a.f. voltage applied to the grid of the reactance valve. The amplitude of the grid voltage will govern the magnitude of the change in frequency; i.e. the deviation produced will be determined by the amplitude of the modulating signal and the rate at which the oscillator

found practicable to use an ordinary a.m. type of receiver provided that it has a suitable selectivity characteristic.

The basis of this method can be explained by reference to **Fig. 8**, which shows the selectivity curve of a typical i.f. amplifier. Normally, of course, for amplitude modulation the receiver is tuned so that the wanted signal is in the middle of the pass band or at the peak to give maximum amplitude, i.e. at point *A*. If, however, the receiver is detuned to one side or the other, to point *B*, it will respond to a signal of varying frequency, and if this variation itself occurs at a frequency within the audio range, the receiver will give an audio output the amplitude of which is proportional to the magnitude of the change in frequency. It is of course necessary to switch off the a.g.c. of the receiver.

The frequency/amplitude conversion is generally far from linear due to the fact that the i.f. response curve itself is not usually straight. It will also be seen from Fig. 8 that the effectiveness of this method will depend on the shape of the i.f. selectivity curve and also, for a given curve, upon the point on the curve at which the f.m. signal is received.

An a.m. communications receiver used in this manner is therefore a fairly effective means of receiving n.b.f.m. signals, but for serious work an f.m. discriminator is to be preferred.

F.M. Detectors and Discriminators

Many special circuits for the conversion of a frequency-modulated signal into a signal of varying amplitude have been evolved. Some of these require the input signal to be *limited*; i.e. all variations in amplitude must be removed, while others require the use of special multi-grid valves such as the nonode (EQ80) and gated-beam type (6BN6). Brief details and circuit diagrams of three of the more common discriminators are given in the following sections.

Limiters. The basic principle of a limiter requires first the amplification of all incoming signals, wanted or unwanted, to a high level, and secondly the application of these boosted voltages to a valve which is very easily overloaded. Above the threshold or limiting voltage, the valve will be *saturated* and any amplitude variations in the input signals will fail to appear in the output. Any noise components which are mainly amplitude-modulated that may be present will also fail to be reproduced, provided that they are of sufficient magnitude.

A common form of limiter consists of a pentode valve operating as an i.f. amplifier stage with low screen and anode voltages and with grid-leak bias. The screen and anode

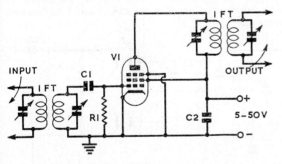

Fig. 9. Typical limiter circuit. CI — 100 pF; C2 — 0·01μF; RI — 100 K ohms, ¼ W; VI — r.f. pentode (short grid base).

voltages used are in the range 5–50 volts depending on the level at which the limiting action is required to commence. The time constant of the grid-leak and condenser should be short (of the order of 10 microseconds) so that the circuit can handle very short pulses of interference, e.g. ignition interference. A typical circuit is shown in **Fig. 9** and its limiting characteristic is given in **Fig. 10**. A single limiter stage does not give a perfect limiting action, as shown by the full line in

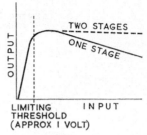

Fig. 10. Typical characteristics of single and double-stage limiters.

Fig. 10, but an improvement can be achieved by the use of two limiters in cascade which would give the almost ideal characteristic shown by the dotted line. However, a single limiter is generally adequate for amateur purposes.

The Double Tuned Circuit Discriminator. Although the double tuned circuit type of discriminator has been generally

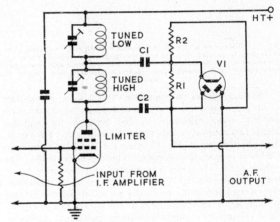

Fig. 11. Double tuned circuit (Travis) discriminator. There should be no coupling between the tuned circuits which should resonate above and below the i.f. of the receiver. CI, C2 — 100 pF; RI, R2 — 100 K ohms, ¼ W; VI — 6H6, or equivalent.

superseded by more modern types, it is capable of adequate performance where great bandwidth and good linearity of characteristic are not required; it also has the merit of simplicity and so is very suitable for amateur use. It is frequently referred to as the *Travis* discriminator.

A typical arrangement of this form of discriminator is shown in **Fig. 11**. The two tuned circuits resonate respectively at frequencies which are slightly above the upper deviation limit and slightly below the lower deviation limit. For example, if the intermediate frequency of the receiver is 465 kc/s, and the maximum deviation is 2·5 kc/s, the two tuned circuits would be tuned to about 460 kc/s and 470 kc/s respectively. The response curves of the two tuned circuits are shown at *A* in **Fig. 12.** Combination of these in the diode circuit gives the typical discriminator curve or characteristic shown at *B*. Ideally, the discriminator characteristic would be linear over a frequency range of at least twice the deviation in use.

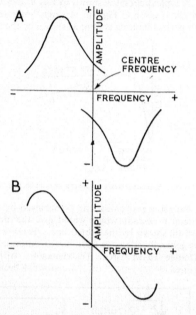

Fig. 12. Operation of the double tuned circuit discriminator. The individual responses of the tuned circuits are shown at A: these are combined in the diode circuit to form the discriminator characteristic shown at B. Ideally the resultant characteristic should be straight.

The Foster-Seeley Discriminator. This is sometimes known as the *phase-difference* type since it depends for its operation on the phase difference of 90° between the voltages across two coupled tuned circuits at resonance. The circuit diagram is shown in **Fig. 13** where L_1C_1 and L_2C_2 represent the tuned primary and secondary windings respectively. The voltage across the primary is injected into the centre-tap of the secondary through C_3. At the frequency of alignment, the voltages applied to the diodes are equal and the rectified voltages across the diode loads R_1 and R_2 are also equal. As these voltages are of opposite polarity, they cancel each other and so the circuit gives zero output across C_4. However, when the frequency changes, i.e. when the carrier is frequency-modulated, the voltage across one diode load increases and the other decreases, and an output proportional

to the frequency deviation is thereby produced. The Foster-Seeley discriminator is capable of giving better linearity than any other type and when preceded by a good limiter (which is essential) it proves the most effective f.m. discriminator, although it is the least sensitive.

The Ratio Detector. This is probably the most commonly used discriminator today in high-fidelity f.m. broadcast receivers. It belongs to the class of self-limiting detectors, but in spite of this the ratio detector is quite often preceded by a limiter. It is somewhat inferior to the Foster-Seeley type with regard to linearity of characteristic but has the advantage that it is appreciably more sensitive. A receiver having a ratio detector generally requires one less i.f. stage than a receiver using the Foster-Seeley circuit.

The circuit of the ratio detector is shown in **Fig. 14.** The resemblance to the Foster-Seeley circuit will be noticed, the main points of difference being the presence of the large condenser C_5 and the reversal of one of the diodes, but the mode of operation is quite different. If the voltages across the condensers C_3 and C_4 are represented by E_1 and E_2, the value of $E_1 + E_2$ will be constant because of the stabilizing effect of the large capacitance C_5 (which should be at least $8\mu F$). At the centre frequency, the voltages E_1 and E_2 are equal, but as the frequency varies so will the ratio E_1/E_2; hence the name *ratio detector*. The audio output resulting from the frequency modulation will be given by the difference $E_1 - E_2$. Since the value of $E_1 + E_2$ is kept constant by the capacitance C_5, the circuit is relatively insensitive to variations in amplitude of the input signal. Therefore a limiter is not essential, although it is often used. It should also be noticed that a controlling bias for a.g.c. purposes is available.

Discriminator Diodes

The diodes used in all forms of discriminator may be of the conventional double-diode type such as the 6H6 or 6AL5. Alternatively semiconductor diodes of the silicon or germanium type (e.g. the *G.E.C.* type GEX 34) may be used; these have the advantage that no heater supply is required and consequently there is no chance of hum pick-up in this part of the circuit. They may also be conveniently wired into the screening can containing the tuned circuits to give a very compact layout.

Alignment of F.M. Receivers

The alignment and adjustment of f.m. receivers is only slightly more complex than that of their a.m. counterpart. The tuning of the r.f. and i.f. circuits is of course similar, the only difference occurring in the adjustment of the discriminator itself.

Fig. 13. The Foster-Seeley discriminator. C1, C2 — tuning capacitors; C3, C4 — 50 pF; C5 — 0·05μF; R1, R2 — 100 K ohms, ¼ W; RFC — 2·5 mH r.f. choke; V1 — 6H6, or equivalent; L1C1 and L2C2 to resonate at i.f. of receiver.

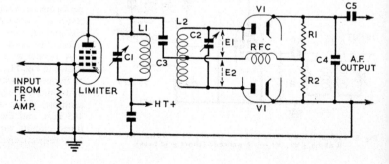

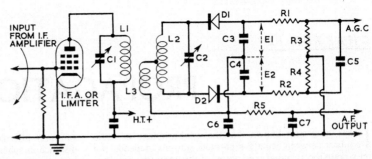

Fig. 14. The ratio detector. C1, C2 — tuning capacitors; C3, C4, C6 — 470pF; C5 — 8μF (min.); C7 — 0·002μF; R1, R2 — 1 K ohms, ¼ W; R3, R4 — 6·8 K ohms, ¼ W; R5 — 22 K ohms, ¼ W; D1, D2 — GEX34, or equivalent. L1C1 and L2C2 must both resonate at the i.f. of the receiver. L2 should be a close-wound bifilar winding. The tertiary winding L3 should have about a quarter of the number of turns used in L1 and should be wound over the end of the primary remote from the secondary.

The use of test equipment such as a frequency-calibrated a.m. or f.m. signal generator and some form of output meter obviously simplifies the lining-up procedure, but in the absence of either of these a discriminator can be lined-up by ear provided that the tuned circuits are known to cover the required frequency.

Assuming that all circuits preceding the discriminator have been lined up according to normal practice, the following notes should enable the discriminator itself to be aligned.

(*a*) **Two Tuned Circuit Type.** This is probably the easiest to deal with. The two tuned circuits must be adjusted to frequencies above and below the deviation limit; i.e. the resonant frequencies should be equal to the intermediate frequency of the receiver plus and minus about 5 kc/s. The modulated output of a signal generator should be set to each frequency in turn and the appropriate circuit tuned for maximum output.

(*b*) **Foster-Seeley Circuit.** This discriminator may be aligned by applying an amplitude-modulated signal of intermediate frequency and then tuning the primary of the discriminator transformer for maximum output and tuning the secondary for minimum output of the modulating signal. The output may be noted either aurally by a loudspeaker or by means of a high-impedance voltmeter connected across the output of the discriminator. Another method of alignment is to monitor the voltage across the primary of the discriminator transformer, tune the primary for a maximum with the secondary short-circuited, unshort the secondary and then tune the secondary until the primary voltage falls to a minimum.

(*c*) **Ratio Detector.** This circuit is most conveniently lined up by applying an f.m. signal at intermediate frequency The primary is then adjusted for maximum output and the secondary for minimum output as measured by a high-impedance voltmeter connected across R_3 in Fig. 14. The meter is then connected between the audio output and earth,

and the secondary is tuned for zero output. Next, with the meter reconnected across R_3, the primary is retuned for maximum reading on the meter. Optimum performance may then be obtained by applying an a.m. signal and adjusting R_1 and R_2 to give minimum a.m. output.

Advantages and Disadvantages of N.B.F.M.

As used in amateur radio communication, n.b.f.m. tends to be a compromise on account of the general absence of an f.m. discriminator and the small deviation used. It is therefore unlikely that the chief advantages of f.m. such as an improved signal-to-noise ratio and freedom from impulsive interference will be fully realized.

Although a conventional type of communications receiver can be used with reasonable success merely by detuning slightly so that the centre frequency of the f.m. signal is at the steepest part of the i.f. response curve, it is impossible to predict the effectiveness of this method with any certainty unless the shape of this curve is known. In the absence of a properly designed f.m. detector, an n.b.f.m. signal can sometimes be mistaken for a distorted a.m. signal.

Perhaps the most important advantage of n.b.f.m. is the fact that in troublesome cases of TVI it may often permit telephony operation when amplitude modulation is unworkable. Another considerable advantage is that, since the frequency-modulation process is originated in the frequency-determining stage of the transmitter, the size and complexity of the modulator are not governed by the output power level, and a large or expensive modulator is therefore not required for full-power operation. This may be particularly beneficial in portable or specially compact equipment.

Against these advantages it must be recognized that n.b.f.m. is more complex in its setting-up procedure than high-level a.m. and that for multi-band operation the deviation may have to be readjusted when changing bands.

CHAPTER 12

PROPAGATION

IT has long been known that the establishment of radio contact between widely separated stations depends not only upon the purposeful activities of the operators but also, in very many instances, upon the vagaries of the propagation characteristics in the intervening space. One of the most intriguing and exciting aspects of amateur communication is the variability of this medium, for although much research has been conducted in the study of radio-wave propagation much is still unknown there is still a wide field that remains open to further discovery.

Strictly speaking, the study of propagation must cover everything that happens to a radio wave from the moment when it leaves the transmitting aerial to the moment when it arrives at the receiving aerial, and this would include such phenomena as the reflection from buildings and hillsides and the absorption in forests, but the subject is so vast that only the major effects can be discussed in detail here. These are related mainly to the electrical characteristics of the atmosphere which in common with other meteorological conditions are constantly changing, and because they have such a dominant influence on radio communication the interested amateur will be amply repaid by his efforts to understand them.

Radiation

The radiation from an aerial may be regarded as a succession of concentric spheres of electric force or strain of ever-increasing radius, moving outward from the aerial at a constant speed. This distribution of electric force surrounding the aerial and extending over what are sometimes astonishingly great distances is known as the *electric field*. For many purposes it is convenient to suppose that an electric field is made up of " lines " of force, and the direction of these lines will indicate the direction of the electric force in any particular part of the field. The intensity of the field can be represented by the concentration of the supposed lines of force.

In the spherical field produced by a transmitting aerial the lines of force will have a form similar to the lines of longitude on a globe, the aerial being collinear with the polar axis. At considerable distances from the aerial it will be obvious that the lines are virtually parallel over relatively small areas in space.

At right angles to the electric field and inseparable from it, is the *magnetic field*, which is likewise conveniently supposed to be made up of lines of magnetic force. These two forces form a *wave* which travels outward at approximately the speed of light, i.e. 186,000 miles per second (300×10^6 metres per second). The exact velocity depends on the dielectric constant of the medium through which the wave passes.

Since the current in the aerial is alternating in direction at a high frequency the electric and magnetic fields are similarly alternating at the same high frequency, and the distance in space between successive peaks of field intensity will vary according to the rate of alternation of current in the aerial. The distance along the direction of propagation between two points where the field intensity is similar in magnitude and in sign is called the *wavelength* λ. This is related to the frequency of alternation f by the simple equation—

$$\lambda \text{ (metres)} = \frac{velocity\ of\ propagation \text{ (m/sec.)}}{f \text{ (cycles/sec.)}}$$

Taking the velocity as 300×10^6 metres per second, this relationship becomes—

$$\lambda \text{ (metres)} = \frac{300}{f \text{(megacycles/sec.)}}$$

A sinusoidal voltage in the transmitting aerial is continuously varying through a peak value in one direction, falling to zero, rising to a peak in the reverse direction and falling to zero again in each cycle, and in an exactly analogous manner the field strength at any given point remote from the aerial will undergo a cyclic change. How this induces a corresponding sinusoidal current or voltage in a receiving aerial is illustrated in **Fig. 1(A).** Spherical waves represented by the curved lines are radiated from the transmitter T and reach the point occupied by the receiver R. The sketch gives an instantaneous view of the field of electric force at the moment when the wave-front corresponding to a voltage peak at the transmitter has just reached the receiving aerial, and at this instant the electric and magnetic fields in the small section of the spherical wave-front in which the receiving aerial can be represented by **Fig. 1(B).** A quarter of a cycle later the front corresponding to zero intensity will reach the receiver, and after another quarter-cycle the wave-front corresponding to the opposite peak will arrive: at this moment the electric and magnetic fields will be reversed as shown in **Fig. 1(C).** As the succession of wave-fronts passes the receiving aerial so will a sinusoidal current be induced in it.

In each of these imaginary spheres the phase of the electric (or magnetic) force is uniform even though the wave-front may extend several miles up into the sky, but of course this does not mean that the intensity is uniform. The intensity, or *field strength*, at any part of the wave-front can be diminished by absorption, or *attenuation*.

Ideally, where the wave is propagated in " free space," i.e. where it is unaffected by the proximity of the earth and the various influences of its atmosphere, it would be a simple matter to calculate the field strength at a remote point since in these circumstances the intensity of the electric field is inversely proportional to the distance from the transmitter (and the power or energy density is inversely proportional to the square of the distance).

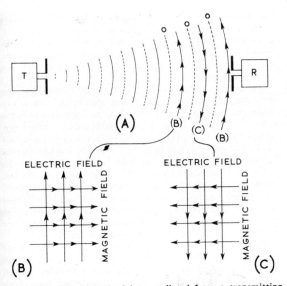

Fig. I. The electric field of force radiated from a transmitting aerial. In (A) the spherical waves emanating from the transmitter T are shown arriving at a receiver R. The patterns shown in (B) and (C) represent the electric and magnetic fields (which are mutually at right angles) in a small area of the spherical wave-front arriving at R. The reversal of sign corresponds to the reversal of the direction of current in the transmitting aerial. If the patterns are taken to represent peak values of electric (and magnetic) force there is a time-lapse of one half-cycle between (B) and (C). It should be noted that (B) and (C) are in a plane at right angles to the plane of diagram (A).

Near the earth's surface, however, the situation is very complex, and it may be necessary to take into account a large number of factors such as the frequency, the time of day, the season, the location of the station and the nature of the terrain. In fact there are so many variables, some of them unknown or incapable of measurement, that the prediction of the received field strength often becomes a matter of estimation based on statistics.

Polarization

The waves are said to be *polarized* in the direction of (or parallel to) the electric lines of force. With wire or rod dipoles the polarization is parallel to the length of the aerial and, since for convenience all dipole aerials are either vertical or horizontal, the radiation is in all practical cases either vertically or horizontally polarized. According to propagation conditions the polarization may change, especially over long distances where ionospheric reflection occurs. Waves may then be elliptically or circularly polarized, even though they started out with linear polarization. Ability to rotate the receiving aerial in all planes for optimum pick-up would be useful in these circumstances.

Field Strength

The intensity of a wave is generally stated in terms of *volts per metre* of space. This will be the strength of the electric lines of force at the receiving aerial (i.e. at right angles to the direction of propagation). Field strengths normally range from low values of one microvolt per metre to high values of 10–100 millivolts per metre.

At first sight it would appear that the greater the length of

the receiving aerial the greater the current induced by the field. This is true only up to the point when the wire is approaching a half-wavelength in electrical length. The reason is that the induced current-flow in the aerial moves at a speed rather less than that of the wave in space. Therefore the "distance" covered *in* the wire cannot be more than a half-wavelength before the electric field in the surrounding space has reversed and caused the current-flow to reverse. Thus in a wire several wavelengths long the current will, in effect, be divided into several short paths of a half-wavelength. Since the field strength is stated in terms of volts per metre it follows that the current induced in an aerial for a given field strength will be proportional to the wavelength.

Modes of Propagation

Considering a wave that is being radiated from an aerial relatively close to the ground, the effects outlined in the following paragraphs will be present to a greater or lesser degree depending on the frequency of the wave and on the height of the aerial above the ground.

As the wave travels outward it will be attenuated by an amount which depends on the nature of the soil or water and the vegetation and the buildings over which it passes. The attenuation will be less over water. At very high frequencies there will also be some absorption due to water-vapour droplets in the atmosphere.

On high frequencies particularly, in addition to the waves received by the direct path between transmitter and receiver, there will also be incoming waves which have been reflected from the ground or other relatively large objects. Since these reflected waves travel over rather longer distances, their time of arrival is slightly later than that of the direct ray. Thus they produce interference effects with the direct waves and cause the received signal to increase or decrease according to local phase relationships: see **Fig. 2**.

As the wave reaches the "optical" horizon, which will be decided of course by the respective heights of the receiver and transmitter aerials, the earth's curvature will cause a shadow effect. Under some conditions the wave will be

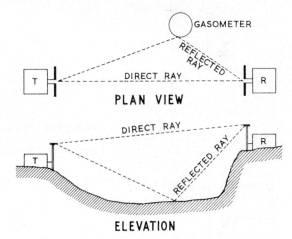

Fig. 2. Interference between direct and and indirect (reflected) rays. The strength of the received signal depends on the phase difference between the two rays when they arrive at the receiver and on their respective intensities.

rapidly attenuated beyond this point. At this stage, however, further and rather variable factors become important. The first of these is *diffraction* which, as with light rays, is a bending of the ray path around an opaque obstacle. According to prevailing weather conditions the wave will also be *refracted* around the earth's curvature to a greater or lesser degree. *Refraction* can be defined as a gradual change in the direction of propagation caused by progressive changes in the dielectric constant (k) of the medium, which in this case is the earth's atmosphere. This effect is important at relatively low heights (from zero to 1000 ft. or so). In order that the wave will follow the earth's curvature a diminution in k with height is required. This is normal and hence there is always some refraction taking place and fortunately the bending is in the desired direction. Changes in k will depend mainly on air temperature and humidity and are therefore directly related to the weather. The lower part of the atmosphere where these effects are important is known as the *troposphere*: see **Fig. 3.**

If, as occurs under certain weather conditions, there is a sudden diminution in k with height, *reflection* of the wave will take place at the boundary between the two air masses concerned.

Partial reflections and/or refraction of a wave at several isolated points over a relatively long path can take place, and this form of propagation is termed *tropospheric scatter*. The actual path covered will then not necessarily be the shortest distance between transmitter and receiver.

These tropospheric effects are detected on all frequencies but are important chiefly in v.h.f. communication because only by this form of propagation is the range extended beyond the optical horizon on frequencies above 70 Mc/s except in very abnormal and infrequent conditions.

The modes of propagation considered up to this point are important in the zone relatively near to the transmitter, possibly extending as far as the first 200 miles.

The propagation of radio waves to great distances over the earth's surface is mainly the result of single or multiple reflections from ionized regions in the upper atmosphere. These ionized regions are generally found at heights of 100–400 km. (60–240 miles) and are known collectively as the *ionosphere* (**Fig. 3**). At these heights the rarified air is partially ionized by the sun's radiations, i.e. some of the molecules are converted into ions and free electrons, and after sunset there is a gradual recombination of the ions with the electrons.

The degree of ionization is not constant with height and there are "layers" of more intense ionization. The actual heights of these layers vary from day to night and with the seasons, and to a lesser degree continuously. There are, however, three regions of chief importance. These are the E-layer at about 120 km., the F_1-layer at 200 km. and the F_2-layer at 300–400 km. At night and in mid-winter the F_1 and F_2 layers combine to form a single layer at 250 km. Below the E-layer there is a D-layer or region (at 50–90 km.) which generally is more important as an absorber than as a reflector of radio waves since the attenuation at this altitude is somewhat greater. The approximate heights of the various layers are shown in Fig. 3.

The theory of ionospheric reflection is a complex subject and will not be dealt with here. In brief, a wave can be said to undergo reflection when on reaching a suitably ionized region it sets in motion the free electrons which then move in a similar manner to the electrons in the transmitting aerial and "re-radiate" (i.e. reflect) the wave in a changed direction.

As the frequency is increased, a greater degree of ionization is necessary to cause reflection. The F_2-layer normally has the greatest degree of ionization and therefore reflects the highest frequencies. Patches of intense ionization in the form of clouds can, however, occur at E-layer height, especially in summer, and on certain occasions they will reflect radiation at frequencies up to about 100 Mc/s, i.e. higher than is normally the case with the F_2-layer. By reason of their nature these local layers of intense ionization are termed *sporadic-E*.

Sunspots

The solar radiation responsible for ionizing the atmosphere is continuously varying. A relationship has been found to

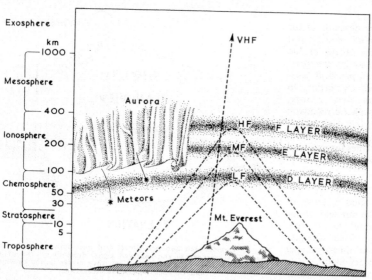

Fig. 3. The earth is surrounded at various heights by so-called layers of ionized gas, and the region in which these exist is known as the ionosphere. Other regions of the atmosphere are given various names according to their dominant properties and characteristics. The vertical scale is shown graded in such a way as to illustrate more clearly the detail at the lower altitudes.

exist between the number of sunspots appearing at any one time and the degree of ionization and, since the sunspot activity recurs cyclically, reaching a peak every ten years or so, there is a similar cyclic variation in the atmospheric ionization. Moreover, the sun rotates in approximately 27 days and this often causes a repetition of effects on a 27-day basis but to a lesser degree.

The seasonal effect due to the earth's movement round the sun and the tilt of its axis is also a major factor in that it causes considerable variations in the layers to occur in different parts of the world at a given time.

In addition to the ionizing radiations, the sun occasionally emits particles which arise from vast eruptions on its surface. On arrival at the earth, particularly in the polar regions, these particles tend to obliterate the ionized layers, the effect being most marked in the *F*-region. Thus communication may be interrupted for periods of a day or two over certain paths. This condition is known as an *ionosphere (or magnetic) storm*. Auroral displays are prominent at these times and radio waves will be reflected from the auroral zone.

Ionosphere storms are often preceded (by approximately two days) by what are called *sudden ionosphere disturbances (s.i.d.)*. Under these conditions "squirts" of abnormally strong solar ultra-violet radiation cause intense ionization in the low *D*-layer and waves are absorbed before reaching the *F*-region or are reflected at short distances. Thus long-distance communication is subject to fade-outs of an hour or two.

In addition to the modes of propagation described in the foregoing paragraphs, there are certain second-order effects. These are *ionospheric scatter* and *meteor-trail scatter*, and a brief account of them is given later in this chapter.

Ground-wave Propagation
Below 2 Mc/s

The lowest frequency band used by amateurs is at the upper limit where useful and consistent distances may be covered by the ground wave, both by day and by night, and perhaps it should be added that this refers to the ground wave proper and does not include tropospheric refraction. On frequencies over 2 Mc/s the ground-wave attenuation becomes greater and ionospheric reflection becomes more important. The effectiveness of ground-wave propagation depends largely on the conductivity and dielectric constant of the soil over which the transmission path extends. Paths of good conductivity such as sea-water give the longest ranges.

It has also been found that, in this frequency range, vertically polarized waves suffer far less attenuation than horizontally polarized waves.

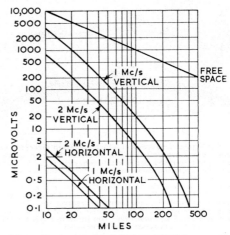

Fig. 4. Attenuation curves for 1 Mc/s and 2 Mc/s ground waves. The curves show the strength of the received signals under typical conditions from a medium-power transmitter.

Field strengths for ground-wave propagation have been measured over a wide range of conditions, and within certain limits it is possible to predict performance reasonably accurately. Thus Fig. 4 shows the effect of the attenuation over average soil of 1 Mc/s and 2 Mc/s waves, vertically and horizontally polarized, compared with propagation in free space. At night particularly, extended range will be obtained on these frequencies by ionospheric reflection and considerably higher field strengths obtained.

Ionospheric Propagation
1–70 Mc/s

The frequency range of 1–70 Mc/s covers the lower and upper limits where ionospheric reflection is the controlling factor in the propagation of waves over distances which may encircle the globe.

The maximum frequency which is reflected by the ionosphere over any particular path is known as the *maximum usable frequency (m.u.f.)*. It has been found to depend on (a) time of day, (b) season, (c) latitude, (d) period of sunspot cycle. It also depends to some degree on the height of the aerial above the ground. The *highest* m.u.f. with normal aerial heights corresponds to a distance determined by the layer height and a ray path directed horizontally, i.e. leaving the earth at a tangent, so that the ray approaches the layer at as oblique an angle as possible: see **Fig. 5**. This distance is generally found to be about 4000 km. (2500 miles) for the F_2-layer. At the m.u.f. a wave leaving at a greater angle to the earth's surface will penetrate the ionosphere, and in order to ensure reflection the frequency will have to be reduced.

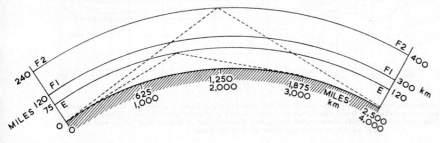

Fig. 5. Paths of waves leaving tangentially to the earth's surface producing oblique or grazing incidence at the reflecting layers. Such waves reach the most distant points possible and their frequency is the maximum usable frequency (m.u.f.) for this distance. For radiation at steeper angles to the earth's surface, the m.u.f. is somewhat lower.

345

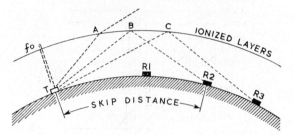

Fig. 6. The highest frequency at which radiation directed vertically upwards from a transmitter T is reflected back to earth by an ionized layer is termed the critical frequency (f_o). At higher frequencies the radiation penetrates the layer, and for such higher frequencies reflection can occur only if the angle of radiation is lowered to a sufficiently small angle: see A and B. The nearest point at which the radiation can be reflected back to earth (R2) is therefore at some distance from the transmitter. This is known as the skip distance. Inside this distance (e.g. at RI) no signals will be received from T by reflection. The limiting angle for reflection depends on the frequency.

When a wave is sent vertically upwards (i.e. angle of radiation 90° or "normal incidence") the highest frequency for which reflection by any particular layer will occur is termed the *critical frequency*, f_o. This frequency is much lower than the m.u.f. for oblique incidence. At frequencies higher than f_o the radiation will penetrate the layer and be lost in outer space and will continue to do so as the angle of radiation is progressively lowered until an angle is reached at which reflection begins to occur. This limiting angle is called the *critical wave angle*: see **Fig. 6**. Signals will then be received at a distant point R_2. Radiation at

lower angles will obviously be reflected to greater distance such as R_3. At points nearer to the transmitter such as R_1 no signals will be received by ionospheric reflection, but when R_1 is sufficiently close to come within the range of the ground wave the signals will again be heard. In between there is an area of no reception and this is known as the *skip zone*. The distance from the transmitter to the nearest point at which the radiation is reflected back to earth is known as the *skip distance*.

The critical wave angle for any particular ionospheric layer depends upon the frequency of the radiation and becomes smaller as the frequency increases. Therefore the skip distance increases as the frequency increases and the m.u.f. is the limit which must not be exceeded if the receiver is to remain in the area of reception just outside the skip zone. In other words, the more closely the operating frequency approaches the m.u.f. the more nearly does the skip distance extend towards the receiver.

By reflection from the ground a wave may be returned to the layer two or more times and thus arrive at a more distant receiver by "multi-hop" propagation. World-wide distances may be covered in this way under suitable ionospheric conditions.

The critical frequencies for the E, F_1 and F_2 layers are measured continuously at many scientific stations in various parts of the world, notably the D.S.I.R. at Slough in England and the C.R.P.L. (*Central Radio Propagation Laboratory*) in Washington, D.C., U.S.A. Over a period of years it has been possible from these measurements to build up world maps of the distribution of critical frequency at various

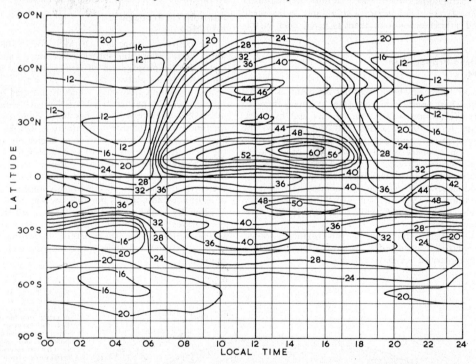

Fig. 7. A typical distribution map showing how the m.u.f. for transmission from a given site over distances of 4,000 km. (2,500 miles) using reflection from the F2-layer varies during a 24-hour period (local time). The map changes throughout the year (the example shown here being the distribution in November 1947), but it can be applied to transmitter sites on any latitude.

easons and stages of the sunspot cycle. This is of value
because there is generally a simple but approximate relationship between the critical frequency f_o and the m.u.f. for a
particular layer. Thus for the F_2-layer the m.u.f. for a distance of 4000 km. (2500 miles) is approximately three
times the F_2 critical frequency, and for the E-layer the m.u.f.
for a distance of 2000 km. (1250 miles) is approximately
five times the E-layer critical frequency.

From these factors the f_o-distribution maps can be converted to show the m.u.f. distribution. One such typical
map is shown in **Fig. 7**. These maps form a very useful
basis for forecasting, under normal conditions, the optimum
operating frequency for any particular path.

As the frequency is reduced the reflection tends to occur
in the lower ionospheric layers, and, particularly in the *D*-
layer, the density of the atmosphere begins to have an
appreciable effect in the absorption of the energy in the
wave. The increased absorption is due to the higher rate of
collision between the electrons which are set in motion by
the wave and the air molecules. The effect is greater as the
frequency is lowered, and the limit for any particular path
is reached at what is termed the *lowest usable high frequency*
(l.u.h.f.).

A further reason for the loss of signal strength on the lower
frequencies is that to arrive at a distant point a relatively
low-frequency wave may have been reflected several times
between the ionosphere and the ground, as illustrated in
Fig. 8. This is likely to occur because the lower-frequency
wave does not penetrate so high but rather is reflected at
short distances by the E-layer. On the other hand, a higher-
frequency wave may cover the distance in one hop by pene-
trating the E-layer and being reflected in the higher F-region.
Each reflection by the ground or by the ionosphere results
in some loss of energy in the wave and the lower-frequency
wave is attenuated to a greater extent.

It should be clear from the foregoing that there will be
the least attenuation of the radiated energy (i.e. maximum
signal strength for any given power) when the frequency
is chosen to be as high as practicable without exceeding
the m.u.f. for the particular path to be covered.

Ionospheric absorption is much less at night than during
the day and therefore the attenuation of the lower-frequency
signals (of the order of 1–5 Mc/s) at night is very little
different from that of higher frequencies in the 20 Mc/s
region. Since the m.u.f. at night over a particular path will
generally be less than half that of the daytime figure, this
means that for night-time long-distance communication

it is possible to use considerably lower frequencies and still
maintain good signal strength. Broadly speaking, the m.u.f.
for a particular path is higher during the winter months
than it is during the summer months, but during periods
of ionospheric storms the m.u.f. may become much lower

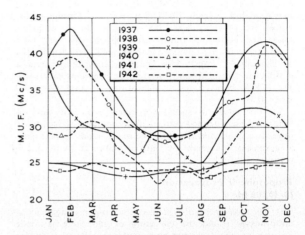

Fig. 9. The curves show how the average daytime m.u.f. for all
directions (recorded at G6DH) varied over a period of six years
(1937–42). Note the high winter peaks in the sunspot-maximum
year 1937 and the small variation as between winter and summer in
the sunspot-minimum period 1941–42.

for transmission in certain directions but higher in other
directions.

The variation of the average daytime m.u.f. over six
successive years is shown in **Fig. 9**. The first year represented
by these records (1937) coincided with a sunspot maximum,
and it will be noticed that the m.u.f. is exceptionally high
throughout this period, whereas during the sunspot minimum
(1941–42) the m.u.f. was consistently low.

In planning optimum working frequencies for any particular time, distance and direction, it is therefore necessary to
take all these variations into account. Readers who may
wish to go deeper into the subject can obtain the C.R.P.L.
monthly *Basic Radio Propagation Predictions* on subscription
from the National Bureau of Standards, Washington 25, D.C.,
U.S.A. Maps of the type shown in Fig. 7 are included in
this publication.

Over very long distances the distribution of sunlight may
be such that part of the transmission path is in darkness.
This will of course apply particularly to east-west routes and
be of less importance on north-south routes. Over a mixed
light-and-dark path the m.u.f. may be much lower than that
of the daylight zone and will usually be determined by the
m.u.f. for the dark region of the required path. The normal
procedure in estimating the m.u.f. in such circumstances
is to note the m.u.f. for the F_2-layer for each end of the long-
distance circuit and take the lower of these two frequencies
as the m.u.f. for the whole path.

In the summer months the determining factor in propagation will frequently be reflection by the *sporadic-E* layers.
The cause of this intense ionization is not yet fully known
but appears to be due to a combination of the usual sun's

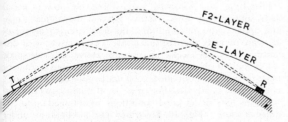

Fig. 8. A relatively low-frequency wave, which is reflected from a
low-altitude layer (such as the E-layer) may reach a distant receiver
by successive reflection between the earth and the layer. Attenuation of the wave is relatively greater since reflection occurs at a
low altitude. A higher-frequency wave is reflected at a higher
altitude and covers the distance in one hop.

347

ionizing radiation and another factor local to the earth's atmosphere. The area of the reflecting "clouds" may be quite small and is seldom more than a few square miles. Directional checks have shown that these reflecting zones move at variable and at times quite high speeds of the order of 200–400 km. per hour. The m.u.f. for this E_s reflection may at times go up to 80 Mc/s or even 100 Mc/s but as a rule it seldom exceeds 70 Mc/s in Europe. Optimum distances are generally 600–1,000 miles in the 25–60 Mc/s range and multi-hop transmission has hardly ever been known to occur, presumably due to the localized nature of the E_s "clouds." Nevertheless, the frequency of occurrence is sufficient to cause many interference problems in Europe and U.S.A. between television stations situated 800–1,000 miles apart.

The formation of sporadic-E layers does not seem to follow a closely defined pattern, although there is a tendency towards a 27-day recurrence. The m.u.f. tends to be higher at a sunspot maximum but not so markedly as in the F-region.

Tropospheric Propagation
20–30,000 Mc/s

It has already been explained that the propagation of radio waves round the curvature of the earth is made possible by the fact that they undergo reflection and/or refraction as the result of the small increase in the dielectric constant (k) and hence in the refractive index with height. The actual dielectric constant of un-ionized air is very little more than unity and the changes of k with height are extremely small. The presence of water vapour increases the value of k and is indeed the main factor in determining the degree of refraction and/or reflection which takes place. Water in droplet form, such as fog or rain, has little effect on metric wavelengths (1–10 m.), though it causes absorption and scattering of centimetric waves (below 1 m.). It is the invisible water-vapour content that is important in affecting the value of k. The maximum amount of water vapour that can be held by air increases with the temperature and tropospheric propagation effects are therefore more marked in warm moist air than in cold dry air. Because the temperature of the atmosphere lapses with height at some 6·5°C. per kilometre (i.e. 2°C. per 1,000 ft.), the moisture content, or humidity, becomes very low as the altitude increases, and therefore tropospheric propagation is mainly confined to

the lower atmosphere at heights of up to 2 km. (about 6,000 ft.).

A knowledge of meteorology will be found useful in the forecasting of tropospheric propagation conditions and the interested reader is advised to study the various publications which are available. As a general guide, the main effects of weather may be stated as follows:

(A) For maximum extended range there should be either a condition of high humidity at ground or low level followed by a rapid decrease in humidity with height or an *increase* in temperature with height (temperature inversion). Generally the two conditions occur simultaneously but not necessarily.

(B) For normal coverage, i.e. no extension of range by tropospheric effects, a well-mixed atmosphere, with a high lapse rate of temperature and low lapse rate of humidity, is the required condition.

Condition (A) is satisfied by fine, warm anticyclonic, settled weather, and condition (B) by rough, cold cyclonic and "frontal" weather. Between these two extremes there will, of course, be intermediate weather conditions where from simple observation it may be difficult to forecast radio conditions.

Anticyclonic conditions, when established, often remain much longer than the faster-moving depressions, and patches of favourable tropospheric conditions may therefore last for a week or two. In summer and warmer weather generally, tropospheric propagation will be more reliable than in cold winter months. In stable weather, conditions are most suitable over *land* for the formation of temperature inversions after sunset. As the ground cools off, the air in contact with it is likewise cooled while the air above remains almost at daytime temperature. Also, during the day, there will be less turbulence caused by uneven heating of different ground surfaces.

Over the sea there is a much smaller diurnal variation and conditions are influenced more by the weather system prevailing and by the sea temperature.

In the frequency range under consideration, i.e. 20–3000 Mc/s, the effect of frequency on observed tropospheric conditions is not very marked. If, for instance, good conditions are observed on 70 Mc/s, likewise on 144 Mc/s and 420 Mc/s conditions will also be good. This is quite different from the case of ionospheric propagation on lower frequencies.

Distances covered by tropospheric propagation will, of course, depend to some extent on the heights of the transmitting and receiving aerials and on power, aerial gains and receiver noise factor. Beyond the optical range and under optimum conditions, the field strength decreases at approximately the free-space rate (i.e. inversely with distance). At times peaks up to 6dB above the free-space values may be obtained. Typical range extensions of four or more times may be obtained, i.e. if under poor or "standard" atmospheric conditions the range is 50 miles similar signal strengths may under good conditions be obtained up to 200 miles or more. **Fig. 10** illustrates the attenuation under "standard" and free-space conditions beyond a horizon of 20 miles.

As a general rule, on very high frequencies results are not materially different according to whether the aerial polarization is horizontal or vertical.

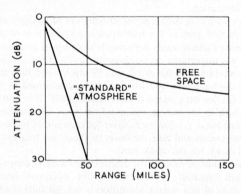

Fig. 10. Attenuation of the received signal by a so-called standard atmosphere beyond a horizon of 20 miles.

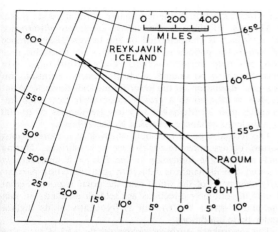

Fig. 11. Back-scatter propagation. A skeleton map showing the probable path by which signals radiated from PA0UM were received at G6DH. The time was 14.00 G.M.T. on a winter day. Both aerial beams were directed approximately north-west.

Propagation by Scatter

There are times when the more orthodox modes of propagation fail to provide a satisfactory means of communication and one or other of the various forms of propagation by scatter may then offer a useful alternative: these include *tropospheric scatter*, *ionospheric scatter* (which may be either *forward* or *backward*), *auroral reflection* and *meteor-trail scatter*.

Tropospheric Scatter. This is similar in character to ordinary tropospheric propagation except that advantage is taken of small local variations in the atmosphere, such as clouds, which afford partial reflection and refraction at a number of isolated points along the transmission path. However, the attenuation is much greater than by the normal tropospheric mode and it becomes necessary to use relatively high power and aerials with high gains. The distances which can be covered in this way may be as much as 500 miles.

Ionospheric Scatter. In this form of propagation ionospheric "clouds" are used to provide a reflecting surface for low-angle radiation of relatively high frequency. The reflection may take place also from the ground so that by a series of hops the wave is propagated over a more or

less straight line to a distant point: this is known as *forward scatter*. It is a comparatively regular phenomenon and is being increasingly used for communication purposes but like tropospheric scatter it requires high power because of the considerable attenuation: often the power required exceeds that normally permitted to amateurs. The frequencies employed are of the order of the m.u.f. for the F_2-layer or somewhat higher, and will usually lie in the range 35–60 Mc/s. The exact frequency will of course depend on the period in the sunspot cycle.

Partial reflection may occur at acute angles from a remote ionospheric cloud and from the ground, and the reflected radiation may be picked up by a receiver located relatively near to the transmitter: this is known as *back scatter*. It is of particular interest to amateurs since it can be used for communication over distances *within* the skip zone, especially in the 21 Mc/s and 28 Mc/s bands. For example, the skip distance may be 1,200 miles and stations within this distance may not be able to establish communication when the receiving and transmitting aerials are directed towards each other over the shortest path of, say, 100 miles. However, if the aerials are *both* directed to a distant point—of the order of 1500 miles from either station—it will be found that weak but consistent reflection occurs: see **Fig. 11**. According to relatively local ionospheric conditions the best direction for this form of partial reflection (or back scatter) will change with the time of day and also from day to day. Therefore, both the transmitting beam aerial and the receiving beam aerial should be rotated simultaneously around the compass in order to establish the best distant reflecting area in the ionosphere. Generally in the temperate latitudes of the northern hemisphere the best directions will be found between north-east through south to north-west and seldom to the north: see **Fig. 12**. This is because the regions of higher ionization generally lie to the south in these latitudes. Low-angle radiation is required for this purpose and the normal Yagi beams are quite suitable.

Auroral Reflection. Similar to ionospheric back scatter but less frequent is *auroral reflection* (or *auroral scatter*) from the auroral zones around the polar regions. This occurs during ionosphere or magnetic storms when there is marked auroral activity, and the frequencies at which this kind of reflection has been known to take place extend up to 150 Mc/s. Usually the reflection is not noticeable above about 70 Mc/s. The reflected waves are generally characterized by a very rapid fluctuation (10–50 cycles per

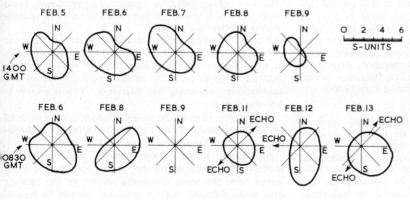

Fig. 12. Typical day-to-day variation in back-scatter directional characteristics. The absence of a pattern on Feb. 9 at 08.30 G.M.T. means that no signals could be heard. This was due to ionosphere disturbance.

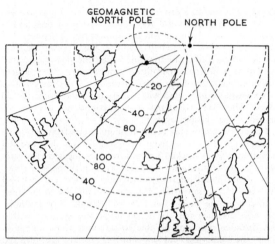

Fig. 13. Distribution of visible aurora in northern hemisphere. The contours represent the percentage of days on which aurora were seen. The propagation path for communication by auroral reflection between England and Holland is indicated.
(Courtesy U.S. National Bureau of Standards)

second) which makes telephony difficult but has no harmful effect on telegraphy. To make use of auroral reflection, directive aerials are essential and they should be pointed in a northerly direction in the northern hemisphere (southerly in the southern hemisphere). In this way communication can sometimes be established between stations located some 500 miles or more apart: see **Fig. 13.** Since auroral activity disrupts the ordinary forms of ionopheric propagation, a transmission path which crosses a polar region suffers a complete fade-out during such periods, and auroral reflection may then offer a means of maintaining contact.

Meteor-trail Scatter. This phenomenon is of very short duration, possibly less than a minute. When a meteor passes through the upper atmosphere it produces a trail of ionization which will, for a short period lasting from less than a second to two minutes, cause partial reflection of v.h.f. waves. Most trails are in the region of the E-layer (i.e. about 100 km.) and consequently the distances covered are similar to those of sporadic-E reflection, i.e. up to 1,200 miles for forward scatter. The aerials should of course be directive and should be oriented in a similar manner to that described for ionospheric or auroral back scatter but generally to a point rather less distant—say 500 miles. The best directions vary with the time of day and the rate of meteor occurrence. Any frequency band between 21 Mc/s and 144 Mc/s is suitable, the 70 Mc/s band being a particularly good one. Since bursts of reflection are of short duration and low intensity, high power and good aerials and receivers are essential. It is also necessary to pre-tune the receiver accurately to the transmitter frequency so that when a burst occurs contact is established immediately.

Fade-outs and Fading

During periods of high sunspot activity two opposing effects occur in the ionosphere. As the earth comes under the influence of an active sunspot (which may recur at approximately 27-day intervals owing to the rotation of the sun), the m.u.f. and the critical frequencies increase and eventually reach peak values. At this stage the two forms of radio fade-out then often occur on frequencies

for which reflection in the ionosphere normally takes place.

The first of these is the *sudden ionosphere disturbance* (*s.i.d.*) which is characterized by the abrupt disappearance of signals for periods of a few minutes up to an hour or two, but only during daylight. These disturbances have been found to be related to chromospheric eruptions on the sun. Radiation on the lower frequencies down to about 2 Mc/s is affected to a greater extent than very high frequencies over 30 Mc/s, but very low frequencies of 10–100 kc/s undergo enhanced reflection by the D-layer.

The second type of fade-out, which is of a more serious nature, occurs under *ionosphere storm* conditions. During such a storm the ionization in the F-layer is considerably reduced and its height is subject to great variation particularly over parts of the world near the polar regions. Signal routes in southerly directions are seldom affected; in fact the m.u.f. across the equator is frequently at its highest under these conditions.

The ionosphere storm originates on the sun at the same time as the faster-moving radiations which cause the sudden ionosphere disturbances but in this case the effect is due to the arrival at the polar regions of slower-moving charged particles which take some two days to reach the earth. These ionosphere storms are accompanied by magnetic storms, and the earth's magnetic field then suffers considerable variation and auroral displays occur. Under these conditions auroral reflection is at a maximum. The onset of the ionosphere storm is generally slow, taking several hours to reach a maximum, and fade-outs last with diminishing intensity for two or three days. The higher frequencies (up to the normal m.u.f.) are most severely affected.

The *solar radiation* which is causing an s.i.d. may actually be heard on radio receivers, particularly on frequencies above 28 Mc/s, in the form of loud bursts of noise or hiss. At times this radiation is so intense that it blots out normal signals.

Because of the sun's rotation period, the peak values of the m.u.f., the sudden ionosphere disturbances and the ionosphere storms all tend to show a 27-day repetition cycle. However, many other variations are liable to occur between subsequent 27-day cycles and this period only serves as a useful guide.

Fading. When propagation takes place through the ionosphere or the troposphere, the received waves are seldom constant in intensity but are continually varying due to the changing conditions in the atmosphere. By "fading," as compared with "fade-outs" described in the preceding paragraphs, is meant the relatively rapid variations which last for perhaps a few minutes or seconds or even shorter time periods.

At any instant the fading characteristics may be different over a relatively narrow frequency band. For example, in telephony or television reception the side-bands may fade out-of-phase with the carrier and relatively to one another, thus producing bad distortion. This is known as *selective fading*.

Fading may generally be classified under one or more of the following headings: (*a*) Interference fading, (*b*) Polarization fading. (*c*) Absorption fading, (*d*) Skip fading.

Interference fading results from a condition similar to that where phase interference occurs when two or more waves from the same transmitter arrive at the receiver over paths differing slightly from one another in length.

Due to fluctuations in the ionosphere or troposphere—according to the frequency in use—the paths covered by the waves will be continually changing in length. Because of the irregularities of the transmission path, the wave finally received is really the summation of a number of waves of relatively low intensity and of random phase. Bad interference fading occurs when the ground waves and "sky" waves are of comparable amplitudes: this is, of course, an effect generally restricted to the lower frequency range. Very rapid fading, known as *flutter*, which is often experienced in long-distance reception and also frequently in local television reception, can likewise be attributed to interference effects.

Polarization fading, as its description implies, results from a continuous change in the polarization of the wave reflected from the ionosphere. These changes are in the main brought about by the effect of the earth's magnetic field on the onosphere during the reflection process.

Absorption fading is caused by variations in the degree of absorption as the wave passes through the ionosphere or troposphere, and is generally of a longer period than either interference or polarization fading. A sudden ionosphere disturbance (s.i.d.) is an extreme case of this form of energy loss.

Owing to the fact that the m.u.f. for a given path is constantly changing over short periods of time, a receiver just within the skip distance may experience *skip fading*. This will occur when the m.u.f. temporarily drops below that for the particular path and frequency in use so that the skip distance lengthens and brings the receiver within the skip zone. Such fading can be very deep and abrupt to the extent that for a time the signal completely disappears. Obviously this kind of fading is more likely to occur when the frequency in use is near the m.u.f.

A Guide to the Use of the Amateur Bands

Propagation conditions vary from one frequency band to another, and except for transmission over relatively short distances the possibilities of making contact also depend on the time of day, the season of the year, the prevailing weather and on the occurrence of sunspots. Consequently the table should be regarded only as a very rough guide.

BAND		DAY	NIGHT
160m.	1·8–2·0 Mc/s	Local contacts by ground-wave radiation up to 30 miles or so (much more over sea water). Suitable throughout the year	Up to 500 miles normally, but occasionally distances up to several thousand miles can be covered. In summer static is sometimes very troublesome.
80m.	3·5–3·8 Mc/s	Used mainly for contacts with British and Continental stations	Ranges covered are likely to be variable, but contacts over several thousand miles are possible in winter
40m.	7·0–7·1 Mc/s	Similar to characteristics of 80m. band, but the maximum ranges are often greater	
20m.	14·0–14·35 Mc/s	Best band for all-round long-distance work, but not suitable for short ranges owing to absorption of ground wave	Good for long-distance work only at certain times of the year
15m.	21·0–21·45 Mc/s	Characteristics tend to be intermediate between those of 20m. band and those of 10m. band. Often remains open for long-distance work when the 10m. band is closed	
10m.	28·0–29·7 Mc/s	At times much superior to 20m. band but markedly dependent on ionospheric conditions. Ground-wave radiation is severely attenuated	Used for local ground-wave contacts only
4m.	70·2–70·4 Mc/s	Similar to 2m. but auroral propagation is much more common. Sporadic E during summer months.	
2m.	144–146 Mc/s	Normally restricted to 60–100 miles; under abnormal meteorological conditions up to 1000 miles. Auroral reflection, sporadic E and meteor trail reflection also occur, extending range to about 1200 miles.	
70 cm.	420–450 Mc/s	Similar characteristics to 2m. band, except that topographical conditions have an even greater influence	

CHAPTER 13

H.F. AERIALS

THE aerial system is one of the most important parts of any radio station: in transmission its purpose is to draw off the maximum available r.f. power from the transmitter and to radiate that power as efficiently as possible toward a distant receiver; in reception, it should convey induced signal voltages, at maximum amplitude and with a minimum of noise, to the receiver. The difference between a bad and a good aerial can easily be equal to raising transmitter power a hundredfold. Thus it is worth weighing the cost of a better aerial against that of a higher powered transmitter. A proper understanding of the principles of aerial design is therefore fundamental to successful radio communication.

The performance of a transmitter or receiver may be measured quite easily but that of an aerial can usually be assessed only by patient communication tests. In many cases its real performance cannot be found from measurements made locally.

There is an old adage that if the r.f. power from the transmitter can be delivered successfully to the aerial, then it must radiate, and this is still true, though an important additional problem is to make the radiated power go to the right places. It will be shown later that aerials are directive devices, and that their radiation can be " focused " by combining a number of aerial wires in such a manner as to provide greater radiation in a forward direction. Such aerials are said to be *directive* and are often called *beam* aerials. They can be designed to have considerable gain over a simple aerial. However, for a given wavelength, most beam aerials occupy more space than simpler ones. Since the size of aerials is related to the wavelength in use, beam aerials are generally practicable for amateurs only when using the shorter wavelengths (higher frequencies). When space is limited to that of an average garden, useful directivity and gain can usually be obtained only from aerials operating on 14 Mc/s and higher. In the v.h.f. bands elaborate high gain aerials are possible but, for frequencies of 7 Mc/s and below, simple aerials are normally the only ones that can be used.

The directional effects and hence the gain of an aerial are the same whether it is used for transmission or reception;

thus a well designed transmitting aerial is also excellent for receiving. There is, however, a subtle difference; whereas a transmitting aerial should produce the strongest possible signal in the target area the receiving aerial must often help to separate wanted signals from extraneous noise and interference by keeping the pick-up of signals from other directions as low as possible. Since modern receivers have adequate sensitivity it may be advantageous to use an aerial with less than optimum gain but with maximum possible discrimination against unwanted signals.

FUNDAMENTAL CONCEPTS OF AERIALS

Radio Waves

Some imagination is necessary in order to form a representative picture of the structure of radio waves or the electric and magnetic fields of which they are composed. The classical method, first employed by Michael Faraday over a century ago, is one where electric and magnetic fields of action are represented by lines of force, the direction of the line being the direction of attraction, the intensity of the forces being represented by the density and formation of the lines. A line of force must either terminate on two opposite charges of electricity; for example as on the positive and negative plates of a capacitor, or must form a closed loop representing an isolated condition of electric strain in space—rather like the strain in an elastic band.

Fig. 1(a) illustrates a section of an electro-magnetic wave moving in the direction of the arrow but, in this diagram, the lines, which should really be extended indefinitely, have been cut into varying lengths to emphasize the idea of a wave. The electric field (E) is shown vertical and the wave in this case is said to be *vertically polarized*; the magnetic field (H) will then be horizontal, since the magnetic and the electric fields are always at right angles.

Since the wave originates from a localized source such as an aerial, the *wave front* of **Fig. 1(b)** is really spread over the surface of a sphere, centred on the source. At very great distances from the source the sphere would be very large and over the relatively small area of its surface occupied by a receiving aerial, the surface could be regarded as perfectly flat. At such large distances from its point of origin the wave is said to be a *plane wave*. As the wave passes any fixed point the field strength varies periodically (at the frequency of the transmitter which originated it) from a maximum positive value through zero to an equal maximum negative value.

Wavelength

The section of the wave illustrated in Fig. 1(a) is one wavelength long, and its field is repeated cyclically all along its path. It moves forward with the velocity of light, i.e.

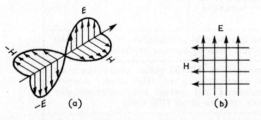

Fig. I. **Instantaneous representation of a travelling radio wave: (a) along the path of travel and (b) for the wave approaching the observer.**

300 million metres (186,000 miles) per second. If the wavelength is 1 metre then the 300 million complete oscillations will pass any point in one second. Thus, if the frequency is represented by f cycles per second and the wavelength by λ (Lambda) (in metres),

$$f\lambda = 300,000,000$$

This equation states the relationship between frequency and wavelength.

An observer facing the wave would " see " the field as shown in Fig. 1(b) which would be alternating at the frequency f. It is this alternating field that excites a receiving aerial into which it delivers some of its power. The arrows indicate the conventional directions of the electric and magnetic fields, E and H, relative to the direction of motion. If the polarity of one component along either E or H in the diagram is reversed, then the wave is receding instead of approaching the observer. The components E and H cannot be separated; together they are the wave and together they represent indestructible energy. They wax and wane together and when the energy disappears momentarily from one point, it must re-appear further along the track; in this way the wave is propagated.

Travelling and Standing Waves

The wave illustrated in Fig. 1 is unrestricted in its motion and is called a travelling wave. As long as they are confined to the vicinity of the earth all waves must, however, eventually encounter obstacles. In order to understand what happens in these circumstances, it is convenient to imagine that the obstacle is a very large sheet of metal, since metal is a good conductor of electricity and, as will be seen, an effective barrier to the wave (Fig. 2). In this case, the electric field is

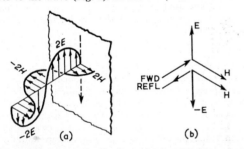

Fig. 2. Standing waves due to short circuit reflection at a metal surface, with analysis into forward and travelling wave components.

"short-circuited" by the metal and must therefore always be zero at the surface. It manifests itself in the form of a current in the sheet (shown dotted) like the current that is induced in a receiving aerial, and this current re-radiates the wave in the direction from whence it came.

In this way a wave is reflected from the metal but due to the relative directions of field and propagation, the components of forward and reflected waves appear as in Fig. 2(b). It will be seen that at the surface of the metal the two electric fields are of opposite polarity and thus cancel each other out, but the magnetic fields are additive.

If the two waves are combined the resultant wave of Fig. 2(a) is obtained in which the electric and magnetic maxima no longer coincide, but are separated by quarter wave intervals. Such a combined wave does not move, because the energy can alternate in form between electric field in one

sector and magnetic field in an adjacent one. This type of wave is called a standing wave and exists near reflecting objects comparable in size with the length of the wave. If a small receiving aerial and detector were moved outwards from the front of the reflector the output of the receiver would vary with distance and thus indicate the stationary wave pattern.

In practice radio waves more usually encounter poor conductors, such as buildings or hillsides, and in this case some of the power from the wave is propagated into or through the obstacle, the remainder being reflected. Later in this chapter, aerials will be described which incorporate conductive elements deliberately used as reflectors. It will also

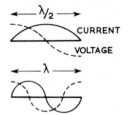

Fig. 3. Standing waves on resonant aerials, showing voltage and current variation along the wire. The upper aerial is a half wavelength long and is working at the fundamental frequency; the lower is a full-wave or second harmonic aerial.

be shown that oscillatory currents in aerials or feeders can be reflected to produce standing waves.

A travelling wave moving away into space represents a flow of energy from the source. The transmitter can be regarded as being at the centre of a large sphere, with the radiated power passing out through its surface. The larger the sphere the more thinly will it be spread, so that the further the receiver recedes from the transmitter, the smaller will be the signal extracted by means of a receiving aerial of given size from a given area of the wave front.

If an oscillatory current is passed along a wire, the electric and magnetic fields associated with it can be considered as a wave attached to the wire and travelling along it as far as it continues, and if the wire finally terminates in, say an insulator, the wave cannot proceed but is reflected. This reflection is an open-circuit reflection and the wire carries a standing-wave field complementary to a short-circuit reflection as in Fig. 2 with corresponding standing wave voltages and currents. Fig. 3 shows two typical cases where the length of the wire allows the standing wave to fit between its insulated ends. Such aerials are efficient radiators of energy and when their lengths are adjusted as shown, they are found to behave like resonant tuned circuits. If the wire is intermediate in length between two multiples of the half wavelength, it appears to be out of tune and must be resonated by adding inductance or capacitance.

Resonant Aerials

The length for true resonance is not quite an exact multiple of the half-wavelength because the effect of radiation causes a slight retardation of the wave on the wire and also because the supporting insulators may introduce a little extra capacitance at the ends. An approximate formula suitable for wire aerials is:

$$Length\ (feet) = \frac{492\ (n - 0.05)}{f}$$

where n is the number of complete half-waves in the aerial and f is the frequency in megacycles per second. More precise values are given by Fig. 43 of this chapter and Tables 3 and 5 of Chapter 14.

Radiation

A charge of electricity has associated with it an electric field extending into space, whilst a charge in motion is an electric current which has associated with it a magnetic field. The transmitter forces charges of electricity to move up and down the aerial, so that the associated oscillating electric and magnetic fields develop into a radiated wave. It must be appreciated that both are only manifestations of the same thing, hence the process is reciprocal; a passing wave can equally induce an oscillatory current in a receiving aerial.

To visualize the process of radiation from an aerial the current may be represented in terms of electric charges oscillating up and down the wire, as shown in **Fig. 4.** As the charges move outwards along the wire, the field expands as if

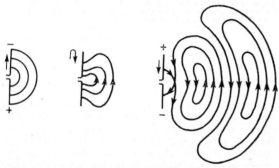

Fig. 4. Radiation from a half-wave aerial. The development of the radiated electric field is shown in stages from left to right. The magnetic field, not shown, is a set of circles centred on the wire and lying in planes perpendicular to the page.

the lines of force repelled one another. When the reflected charges are returned from the free ends of the aerial they drag the ends of the lines back with them. The more remote part of the field cannot, however, return to the wire, because it is supported by the magnetic field due to the current composed of moving charges. The E–H relationship of Fig. 1(a) must be fulfilled and as the wave-front is already moving away, it can only continue in the same direction. At the completion of one half-cycle, the reflected charges have arrived back at the centre to neutralize one another, but at the same time, the transmitter connected to the aerial is just reversing phase to start off another pair of charges, this time in opposite directions along the wire. The first set of lines of force can now " part off " and join ends, leaving loops of energy free

from the aerial, but driven away by the ever expanding field. Here two kinds of wave exist together:

(i) The standing wave field associated with the aerial and limited to the environment of the aerial;

(ii) the travelling or radiated wave which is conveyed to great distances.

The diagram is only a section and the radiation takes place in all sideways directions from the wire. Note that in directions lying near the wire itself, the lines are less closely packed. This is equivalent to saying there is less power radiated in these directions; in fact, along the direction of the wire, there is none at all. The figure-of-eight curve thus produced by a section is called a *polar diagram*. The polar diagram form of representation is more convenient for the further study of the radiating properties of aerials and is used in later sections of this chapter. An example is shown in Fig. 32.

Radiation Resistance and Aerial Impedance

Some of the power entering the aerial from the transmitter is wasted in heat, owing to the resistance of the wire or to insulator loss, but in all aerials long enough to be resonant, these losses are quite insignificant compared with the power sent away in the radiated wave. It is convenient to represent this radiated power in terms of a fictitious resistance called the *radiation resistance* of the aerial. In this way, it becomes possible to use ordinary circuit relations and say that if the radiation resistance is R and that a current I is flowing into it, the power radiated is I^2R watts.

A half-wave dipole has a radiation resistance of about 70 ohms. If it is made of highly conductive material such as copper or aluminium, the loss resistance may be less than one ohm. The conductor loss is thus relatively small and the aerial provides an efficient coupling between the transmitter and free space.

When the aerial is not a resonant length, it behaves like a resistance in series with a positive (inductive) or negative (capacitive) reactance and requires the addition of an equal but opposing reactance to bring it to resonance, so that it may be effectively supplied with power by the transmitter. The combination of resistance and reactance, which would be measured at the aerial terminals with an impedance meter, is referred to in general terms as the aerial *input impedance*. This impedance is only a pure resistance when the aerial is at one of its resonant lengths.

Fig. 5 shows, by means of equivalent circuits, how the impedance of a dipole varies according to the length in wavelength. It will be seen that the components of impedance vary over a wide range.

Instead of varying the aerial length a fixed length aerial can be used and the frequency varied. For example, if a dipole

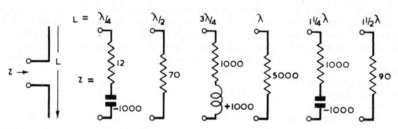

Fig. 5. Typical input impedance (Z_0) values of dipoles of various lengths. The values for $L = \lambda/2$ and $3\lambda/2$ are always approximately as shown but values for other lengths vary considerably according to the length/diameter ratio of the aerial. The values given are typical for wire h.f. aerials. Note how the reactance changes sign for each multiple of a quarter wavelength.

were 33 ft. long it would be resonant(λ/2) at 14 Mc/s, three-quarter wavelength (3λ/4) at 21 Mc/s and full wave (λ) at 28 Mc/s. At 14 Mc/s it is easy to supply power into its 70 ohm radiation resistance, but at full wave resonance at 28 Mc/s the high value of 5000 ohms presents practical difficulties. Again at 21 Mc/s where the impedance is complex and evidently high, special arrangements are necessary. These problems are discussed later in connection with tuned feeders and aerial couplers and in relation to specific aerials.

This same aerial on 7 Mc/s would only be λ/4 long, with a low resistance of 12 ohms and a high capacitive reactance. It would require a *loading coil* of 23μH inductance (1000 ohms reactance) for resonance at 7 Mc/s. Unless this loading coil were physically large it might well have appreciable loss resistance (6 ohms for example). Thus only two thirds of the power from the transmitter would reach the aerial, the remaining third being expended as heat in the coil, and the efficiency would be only 67 per cent. With 18 ohms total radiation resistance and a reactance of 1000 ohms, the Q of the circuit (ratio of reactance to resistance) would be approximately 50, which means that tuning adjustments for resonance would be critical. On 3·5 Mc/s the same aerial would have a resistance of only 3 ohms and a reactance of 2000 ohms. It would therefore be very difficult to use it efficiently as it would need re-tuning for different parts of the 3·5 Mc/s band.

Aerial Images

In considering the radiation from various types of aerials, it is necessary to include the effect of the ground, which can reflect some of the energy leaving the aerial, and make the resultant radiation pattern very different from that of an aerial in free space. The effect can be determined by treating the ground as a mirror producing an image of the true aerial, so that, in effect, there is the combined radiation of two aerials, one above the other. The diagram of **Fig. 6(a)** represents a quarter-wave vertical aerial connected to earth.

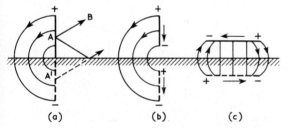

Fig. 6. Aerials and their images in the ground. (a) Quarter-wave earthed vertical (b) half-wave vertical and (c) horizontal half-wave.

Radiation from any point such as A can be received in the direction B by two paths, one direct and the other by reflection from the ground. The reflected signal appears to come from point A' on the image of the aerial. The electric field of the real aerial actually terminates on the ground and a current flows back to the base of the aerial. Alternatively the field can be considered to close on the image as illustrated.

The aerial in **Fig. 6(b)** is a complete vertical half-wave standing above the ground. The field lines between aerial and image must run between points of opposite polarity; to satisfy this requirement the upper ends of both the aerial and

image must be positive at the same time, hence the two aerials are in phase. Along the ground both signals received are in phase and therefore additive; the aerial transmits maximum energy in this direction.

In **Fig. 6(c)** the aerial is a horizontal half-wave viewed from the side, but in this case the image is in anti-phase. The two signals received along the ground are thus also in anti-phase and cancel out, leaving no resultant radiation in the horizontal plane. It will be seen later, however, that this type of aerial can radiate at angles above the horizontal. The important difference between horizontal and vertical aerials should be noted, but it must be pointed out that the ground is not a perfect conductor and is therefore not the perfect mirror assumed above, so that the distinction between vertical and horizontal reflection effects is not absolute, though quite definite.

Basic Aerial Systems

Three separate parts are involved in an aerial system: the radiator, the feed line between transmitter and radiator, and the coupling arrangements to the transmitter. Wherever possible, the aerial itself should be placed in the most advantageous position, and a feed line used to connect it to the transmitter or receiver with a minimum of loss due to resistance or radiation. In some circumstances (when space is limited or when multi-band operation is required) the feed line is omitted and the end of the aerial is brought into the station and connected directly to the apparatus.

The simplest aerials are the half-wave resonant dipole, or the multiple half-wave long wire, carrying a standing wave as in Fig. 3. Combinations of such elements are used to secure directive effects and signal strength gain, the elements being connected together in a suitable manner. Alternatively, free resonant "parasitic" radiators may be placed so as to react on the "driven" element and so force the radiation in one direction. On the lower frequency bands of 1·8–2 Mc/s and 3·5–3·8 Mc/s it is not always possible to use the full resonant length of a half-wave aerial because of limited space so it becomes necessary to bring the system to resonance by tuning it with additional inductance or capacitance. In such cases the loading circuit often becomes part of the coupling to the transmitter.

Examples of suitable arrangements are given later, but before studying them, it will be advantageous to consider the link between transmitter and aerial.

TRANSMISSION LINES

By the use of transmission lines or *feeders*, the power of the transmitter can be carried appreciable distances without much loss due to conductor resistance, insulator losses or radiation. It is thus possible to place the aerial in an advantageous position without having to suffer the effects of radiation from a *down lead*. For example, a 14 Mc/s dipole only 35 ft. long could be raised 60 ft. high and fed with power without incurring appreciable loss. If, on the other hand, the aerial wire itself were brought down from this height to the transmitter, most of the radiation would be propagated from the down-lead in a high angular direction. An arrangement of this nature would be most unsuitable for long distance communication.

There are three main types of transmission line:

   (i) The single wire feed arranged so that there is a true travelling wave on it.

(ii) The concentric line in which the outer conductor (or sheath) encloses the wave (*coaxial feeder*).

(iii) The parallel wire line with two conductors carrying equal but oppositely directed currents and voltages, i.e. balanced with respect to earth (*twin line*).

A single wire line seldom works correctly because it is very difficult to prevent it acting as a radiator instead of a pure transmission line. In the other two types, the field is confined to the immediate vicinity of the conductors and does not

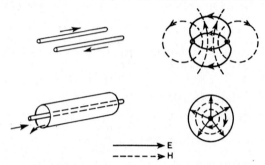

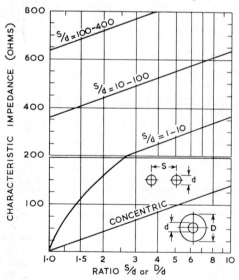

Fig. 7. Concentric and two-wire transmission lines, with cross-sections of their wave fields. The field directions correspond to waves entering the page.

radiate if proper precautions are taken. Commercially available types of feeder are dealt with in Chapter 14 (*V.H.F. Aerials*) with some emphasis on their v.h.f. applications. In this chapter the discussion is confined to the mode of working and application to frequencies below 30 Mc/s but the fundamental principles are the same.

The wave which travels on a transmission line is fundamentally the same as the free-space wave of Fig. 1 but in this case it is confined to the conductors and the field is curved about the conductors instead of being linear as in that diagram. Concentric and two-wire lines and the fields carried on them are illustrated in **Fig. 7.** In the concentric line the current passes along the centre conductor and returns along the inside of the sheath. At high frequencies the currents do not penetrate more than a few thousandths of an inch into the metal, due to skin effect; hence with any practical thickness of the sheath there is no effect on the outside. The fields are thus held inside the cable and cannot radiate.

In the twin line the two wires carry " forward and return " currents and the field is concentrated in their vicinity. When the spacing between wires is a very small fraction of the wavelength, the radiation is negligible provided the line is balanced, i.e. the currents are equal and opposite in the two parallel wires. In the h.f. range, spacings of several inches may be employed, but in the v.h.f. range small spacing is important.

Impedance Matching and Characteristic Impedance

A transmission line is used most efficiently when it carries a pure travelling wave. This is the condition that exists when the output end of the line is connected across a resistance load of the correct value; the line is then said to be *matched*. The value of this resistance in ohms corresponds to a most important property of the transmission line—its *characteristic impedance*, usually denoted by Z_0, and is equal to the voltage/current ratio—V/I—of the travelling wave on the line (or its wave equivalent E/H). When this $V/I = R$ match occurs, $R = Z_0$ and the wave cannot distinguish the resis-

tance from an extension of the line; hence all the power in the wave flows into the terminating resistance (e.g., the aerial) and none is reflected.

As a general rule, it is best to choose a line which matches the load, e.g. a 70 or 80 ohm twin line with a half-wave dipole, but when this is not possible, the line is sometimes used in a mismatched condition, or impedance transformers are used between line and load.

The characteristic impedance is determined purely by the dimensional ratios of the cross-section of the line, and not by its absolute size. A concentric line or cable with diameter ratio 2·3 : 1 and air dielectric, is always a 50 ohm line, whatever its actual diameter may be. If it is connected to an aerial of 50 ohms radiation resistance, then all the power in the line will pass into the aerial and the impedance at the sending end of the line will also appear to be 50 ohms.

Coaxial cables can conveniently be constructed with characteristic impedance values between about 50 and 120 ohms. Twin lines have higher impedances; in practice, between 80 and 600 ohms. **Fig. 8** shows the characteristic impedance of coaxial and two-wire lines in terms of the dimensional ratios, assuming air between the conductors. The formula for concentric lines of inner and outer diameters d and D respectively is:

$$Z_0 \text{ (ohms)} = 138 \, Log \, (D/d)$$

Thus if the diameter ratio D/d is 2·3 : 1 the logarithm of 2·3 is 0·362 and this, multiplied by the constant 138 gives $Z_0 = 50$ ohms. If the space between conductors is filled with insulating material with a dielectric constant (permittivity) greater than unity, the above value of Z_0 must be divided by the square root of the dielectric constant.

The usual material for insulation is polythene, which has a permittivity of 2·25. The square root of 2·25 is 1·5 so that a " solid " polythene cable has a characteristic impedance two-thirds of the value given by the formula. Many cables have a

Fig. 8. Chart giving characteristic impedances of concentric and two-wire lines in terms of their dimensional ratios, assuming air insulation. When the space around the wires is filled with insulation, the impedance given by the chart must be divided by the square-root of its dielectric constant (permittivity). The ratio of this reduction is called the velocity factor, because the wave velocity is reduced in the same proportion.

mixed air/polythene dielectric, and for these it is necessary to estimate the effect of the dielectric; this can be carried out by measuring the velocity factor as described later in this chapter.

The characteristic impedance of two-wire lines of wire diameter d and centre spacing S is given by the approximate formula

$$Z_0 \text{ (ohms)} = 276 \text{ } Log \text{ } (2S/d).$$

This formula applies to the straight parts of the lines in Fig. 8, but does not bring the impedance to zero when the conductors touch. A more precise formula is therefore used for small spacings. As with concentric lines, an allowance must be made for the effect of the insulation. A thin coat of enamel or even a p.v.c. covering will not produce any material change in lines with an impedance of 300 ohms or less, but in the moulded feeder commonly known as 80 ohm flat twin the electric field between the wires is substantially enclosed in the polythene insulator, which is thus effective in reducing the impedance to two thirds of the value given by the formula.

When an open-wire line is constructed with wooden or polythene spacers it is again difficult to estimate the effect of the insulation, but since the proportion of insulator to air is relatively small, the effect is also small. A 600 ohm line with spreaders spaced every few feet along it would normally be designed as if it were for about 625 ohms, e.g. for 16 s.w.g. wires (0.064 in. diameter) the spacing would be made 6 in. instead of 5 in. as given by the chart for 600 ohms.

A transmission line can be considered as a long ladder network of series inductances and shunt capacitances, corresponding to the inductance of the wires and the capacitance between them. It differs from conventional L/C circuits in that these properties are uniformly distributed along the line, though applications are given later where short sections of line are used instead of coil or capacitor elements. If the inductance and capacitance per unit length, say, per metre, are known, the characteristic impedance is given by:

$$Z_0 = \sqrt{L/C} \text{ (ohms)}$$

and the velocity of waves (v) on the line by:

$$v = 1 \div \sqrt{LC} \text{ metres per second}$$

The inductance and capacitance can both be determined from purely geometrical calculations on the shape of the cross-section.

Velocity Factor

The velocity of the waves on an air-spaced line can thus be calculated and will be found the same as that of waves in free space. The introduction of insulating material increases the capacitance without changing the inductance, and it will be seen (since C occurs in the denominator of both the equations already given) that insulation reduces the velocity by the same factor as it reduces the impedance. Thus the velocity in a solid polythene cable is only two-thirds of the free space velocity. This ratio 0.66 is known as the velocity factor of the cable. It varies from 0.5 for a mineral-filled line to practically unity in an air-spaced line. Semi-air-spaced lines have a factor which varies between 0.8 and 0.9 while open wire 600 ohm line may reach 0.98.

It is important to make proper allowance for this factor in some feeder applications, particularly where the feeders are used as tuning elements or interconnecting lines on aerial arrays. For example, if $v = \frac{2}{3}$, then a quarter-wave line would be physically $\frac{1}{6}$ wavelength long ($\frac{2}{3} \times \frac{1}{4} = \frac{1}{6}$).

In practice, the velocity factor v can be found by short-circuiting a length of cable with about 1 in. of wire formed into a loop and then coupling the loop to a grid dip oscillator. The *lowest* frequency at which the cable shows resonance corresponds to an *electrical* length of one quarter-wave: then

$$v = \frac{f \text{ (Mc/s)} \times Length \text{ (feet)}}{246}$$

and should have a value between 0.5 and unity.

Standing Waves

It has already been stated that when a transmission line is *terminated* by a resistance equal in value to its characteristic impedance, there is no reflection and the line carries a pure travelling wave. When the line is not correctly terminated, the voltage-to-current ratio is not the same for the load as for the line and the power fed along the line cannot all be absorbed—some of it is reflected in the form of a second travelling wave, which must return along the line. These two waves, forward and reflected, interact all along the line to set up a standing wave.

Fig. 9 illustrates these standing waves for various conditions of load. In Fig. 9(a) the end of the line is open circuit ($R =$ infinity) and no current can leave the line. The current standing wave at this point must have zero amplitude—it can be said that the forward current has turned round (and in so doing has reversed its polarity) thus cancelling itself. This is a phase reversal of current at the open circuit terminal. The current is travelling along the line, but the voltage, on the other hand, is across the line, and hence is not reversed by

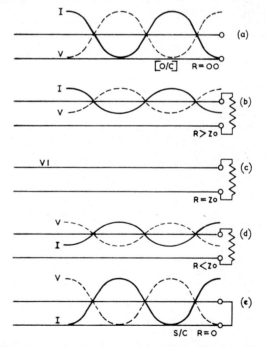

Fig. 9. Standing waves on a transmission line for various conditions of termination. (a) Open circuit (R infinite); (b) Resistance greater than Z_0; (c) Correctly terminated; (d) resistance less than Z_0; (e) Short circuit (R = 0). The curves represent amplitude variations of current *I* and voltage *V* along the line. The ratio of maximum to minimum voltage is called the voltage standing wave ratio (v.s.w.r.)

this reflection; the electric fields of the two waves add to give a double amplitude. Fig. 9(c) represents a matched line with uniform current and voltage all along its length.

At a point one electrical quarter wave from the end, the situation is very different. The forward going and reflected waves are now one half-wave apart (the journey to the end and back) which corresponds to a reversal of polarity or phase of both current and voltage. At this point, therefore, the currents add to double amplitude and the voltages cancel. In the same way, at a point one half-wave from the end of the line, the conditions are repeated; that is, the standing waves repeat regularly at half-wave intervals all along the line.

Fig. 9(e) shows a short circuit at the end of the line. The standing wave is the same as in the open circuit case, except that it is moved along to satisfy the obvious condition of zero voltage at the short circuit. It is instructive to compare this diagram with the electro-magnetic field diagram of Fig. 2.

Intermediate conditions, with R greater or less than Z_0, produce an intermediate type of standing wave pattern, as illustrated by the diagrams of Fig. 9(b) and (d); in these cases, only part of the forward wave power is reflected and the reflected wave has less amplitude than the forward wave. The pattern thus has definite maxima and minima separated by quarter-wave intervals but no defined and complete zero. The ratio of maximum to minimum voltage at the crest and trough of the standing wave, is called the *voltage standing wave ratio* (v.s.w.r., often abbreviated simply to s.w.r.), and is found to be equal to the mismatch ratio R/Z_0 when R is greater than Z_0 or Z_0/R when R is less than Z_0. Thus for a perfect match, v.s.w.r. = 1 but for a mismatch it is greater than unity, becoming infinite for open or short circuits. It should be noted that there are two ways of rating v.s.w.r. values: some workers, particularly in microwave techniques, invert the ratios so that whilst a match gives a v.s.w.r. of unity, 100 per cent mismatch gives a v.s.w.r. of zero.

Attenuation

The transmission line, even when matched, is not perfect, because some power is wasted in the resistance of the conductors and by losses in insulating materials. With the moulded twin or coaxial lines for amateur and television use, this attenuation is less than 1db per 100 ft. (when correctly matched) at frequencies below 30 Mc/s. One db loss per 100 ft. means that at the far end of the feeder the amplitude of voltage or current is just under 90 per cent of that at the input end, or the power approximately 80 per cent. A second 100 ft. extension would deliver 80 per cent of the power left at the end of the first 100 ft. or 64 per cent of the original input. For each extra 100 ft. the factor is multiplied again by 0·8 but in decibel ratios 1·0db loss is added. Open wire lines can be remarkably efficient: a 600 ohm two-wire line made from 16 s.w.g. copper wires spaced about 6 in., carefully insulated and matched, has a loss of only a few decibels *per mile* in the h.f. range.

If the line is operated with standing waves, the loss is greater than in the matched case, because increased voltages and currents are circulating on the line and the average heating of conductor and insulator is greater for the same power output. The extra loss due to standing waves increases with the v.s.w.r. but in efficient lines having a loss of not more than 1db per 100 ft. the extra loss in this length will not exceed 0·5db for v.s.w.r.'s up to 3.

An interesting point to note is that the reflected wave suffers the same attenuation as the forward wave. Thus, in a long line the standing wave ratio might be quite large at the load end, but could have become attenuated to near unity at the input end where the line would appear to be well matched. The power lost due to attenuation appears as heat and can damage the line, but any feeder considered good enough for use in an amateur station will not be overheated by the maximum authorized power, even with an immoderate v.s.w.r. A v.s.w.r. not exceeding two is satisfactory for most purposes; it should not normally exceed three because of the de-tuning effects which result when coupling to the transmitter.

Input Impedance

As an example of mismatch, consider the condition existing when a 50 ohm feeder is connected to a 500 ohm load: in such a case, only 10 per cent of the current will pass into the load, the other 90 per cent being reflected back along the line and, interacting with the forward current, produce a standing wave. This situation recurs at regular intervals along an electrical half wavelength in the line, ignoring the effects of attenuation already described. On the other hand, at the intermediate quarter-wave points it will be seen that the current and voltage amplitudes have interchanged. This means that whereas the load at the end of the line is 50×10 ohms the same load is presented as $50 \div 10$, or 5 ohms, at a point a quarter-wave removed.

This impedance inverting property of a standing wave is the basis of the *quarter-wave transformer* used for impedance matching and referred to later in this chapter. In the intermediate positions between extremes of voltage or current, the impedance is complex and appears as a combination of resistance and inductance or capacitance. For this reason the feeder exhibits tuning effects. The determination of this impedance in terms of load and line length is too complex to be described here but an example of how to assess its general form and bring it to resonance for coupling to a transmitter is given later in the section on aerials with tuned feeders. It will be realized, however, that if the load or aerial at the end of the line is not resonant, but has complex impedance, the standing wave pattern will start from an appropriate intermediate position. It will also be seen that the impedance at the sending end depends not only on the mismatch of the load, but also on the electrical length of the line in wavelengths and fractions of a wavelength.

Displaying Standing Waves

Various methods have been devised for examining the nature of the standing waves on transmission lines. The simplest, applicable to open two-wire lines, is to carry some sort of detector probe along one side and sample the voltage or current; for example, a germanium diode detector can be mounted on a pole and used to read (in association with a suitable meter) the voltage at various points along one wire. If there is enough power, say from a 100 watt amateur transmitter feeding the line, a neon lamp or stabilizer tube may be used an an indicator. This method will show the crests of the standing wave, but is not satisfactory for precise work.

For concentric lines, an instrument known as a "slotted line" or "trough line" is used. This is a section of line made to the same characteristic impedance as the feeder, but provided with a slot or open side through which a probe can be passed to sample the electric field in the line by capacitive coupling. The probe is moved along the line to examine the standing wave. The length of the line must, of course, exceed one half wavelength, and therefore the method is only practicable for very short waves.

The practical limitations to measurement of standing waves can be overcome at all frequencies by expressing the mismatch in a different way, and measuring instead what is known as the *reflection coefficient*. This parameter is, in fact, a measure of the fraction of the forward wave which has been reflected and thereby has set up a standing wave.

The reflection co-efficient is related to the mismatch ratio or s.w.r. by the expression:

$$Reflection\ co\text{-}efficient = \frac{(v.s.w.r. - 1)}{(v.s.w.r. + 1)}$$

Typical values are given in **Table 1**.

When the line is perfectly matched the reflection co-efficient is zero; with 100 per cent mismatch (open or short

TABLE I
V.S.W.R. in Terms of Reflection Coefficient

Z/Z_0 or Z_0/Z = v.s.w.r.	Reflection coefficient percentage
1·0	0
1·5	20
2	33
3	50
5	67
9	80
inf.	100

circuit) its value is unity. Direct methods of measuring reflection co-efficient are described later, and since they can be carried out with a simple Wheatstone bridge type of instrument called a reflectometer inserted into the line, they will be found a very simple aid to making matching adjustments to an aerial. All that is necessary is to make adjustments which minimize the reflected wave as indicated by the meter.

Before leaving the subject of line-impedance matching, one very important point must be emphasised: *There is nothing whatever that can be done at the sending end to remove standing waves.* They are generated at the far end of the line and can only be corrected there by correct impedance matching.

Practical Feeders

A variety of concentric and two-wire lines is commercially available, the most common being 50 ohm and 70 ohm coaxial cables with a solid or stranded inner conductor and a braided wire sheath. Two-wire lines are made with impedances of 70, 80, 150 and 300 ohms, are generally constructed in moulded polythene insulation and thus quite flexible and weatherproof. Such lines are sufficiently low loss to be suitable for amateur transmission. Their general properties are described in more detail in Chapter 14 (*V.H.F. Aerials*).

The choice of type of feeder may be governed by circumstances, but in the matter of characteristic impedance it is always best to suit the line to the aerial impedance; the use of impedance transformers at the aerial connection is always a disadvantage and may lead to practical difficulties.

For distances greater than a few wavelengths, the loss in small-size manufactured lines may be enough to warrant the

construction of an open-wire twin line. This will necessarily be of a fairly high impedance, say, 300–600 ohms. Soft-drawn enamelled instrument wire of 14–18 s.w.g. can be used, although when the line is to be strained between insulators, it is better to use hard-drawn or cadmium-copper wire. Pre-stretching to about 10 per cent extra length by means of a steady pull will appreciably harden soft-drawn copper wire and render it less liable to stretching in service.

Spacers made from ⅜ in. diameter wood dowelling or polythene rod should be fitted every few feet along the open line. Wooden spacers should be thoroughly impregnated by boiling them in wax. A small hole should be drilled in each end to take a 20 s.w.g. binding wire. A groove in the end is also a helpful aid to secure binding. It is not often practicable to thread the spacers on to the line wires themselves **(Fig. 10)**.

Moulded twin lines sometimes suffer noticeably from the effect of moisture in damp weather. This is most noticeable in the case of tuned lines, because water has a very high dielectric constant and affects the velocity factor of the line as well as its loss factor. Soot deposited on the surface will tend to retain moisture and accentuate these troubles. The remedy is to clean the line periodically and give it a dressing of silicone wax polish to repel any moisture. Tubular 300 ohm line should be sealed so that water cannot enter the interior. Although the p.v.c. outer jacket of a concentric cable is good enough to allow the cable to be buried, the open end of the cable is very vulnerable for it can " breathe in " moisture which does irreparable damage to the line. There is a variety of satisfactory sealing materials available,

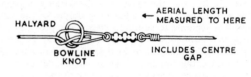
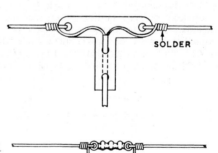
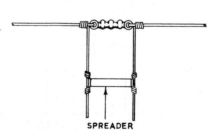

Fig. 10. Methods of making off the ends and centres of aerials. The best knot for the halyard is a bowline. The T insulator for the centre can be obtained ready made in ceramic or cut from resin board: note the method of supporting the weight of the feeder. The sketch at the lower right shows how an open wire line can be supported. Joints should be soldered and then covered with protective tape.

such as Bostick cement, Bostick sealing strip (putty) and Sylglas tape which is loaded with a silicone putty.

SIMPLE AERIALS

The Centre-fed Horizontal Wire

The wavelength to which a wire aerial tunes is approximately twice its length in metres. Hence an aerial 21 metres long (approximately 66 ft.) tunes to a wavelength of 42 metres corresponding to a frequency of 7 Mc/s. At this frequency it is a half-wave aerial, and, if fed in the centre with a balanced two-wire feeder, is called a half-wave dipole. Such an aerial would be full-wave on 14 Mc/s and three half-waves on 21 Mc/s and so on. On 3·5 Mc/s it would be a short (quarter-wave) dipole and its radiation resistance would be about 12 ohms; the wire resistance and insulator loss might contribute several ohms extra resistance, which would consume a large proportion of the transmitting power, thus preventing its useful radiation.

The 7 Mc/s half-wave dipole shown in **Fig. 11** can be fed with 70 ohm or 80 ohm twin feeder since its radiation resistance lies between 60 and 90 ohms depending on its height, the match between aerial and feeder being sufficiently accurate for all practical purposes. The feeder could be coupled to the transmitter output circuit directly by means of a two or three turn coil connected across its ends, but this is poor practice since harmonics from the transmitter are likely to be radiated. The feeder should preferably be tapped or coupled into a separate aerial tuning coil to which the transmitter is coupled via co-axial cable and link coils as shown in Fig. 11. In this way the balance of the feeder can be preserved with respect to the unbalanced output of the transmitter. The separate aerial tuning circuit also provides extra filtering of harmonics. The link coils should be tightly coupled using as many turns as possible (three or four for 7 Mc/s) until the tuning of the aerial coupler is broad, indicating efficient transference of power to the feeder.

On 14 Mc/s the same 66 ft. aerial would be extremely inefficient because the feed portion occurs between two voltage maxima. At this frequency its impedance would be 5000 ohms and the v.s.w.r. on the 80 ohm twin line 5000 ÷ 80—about 62. The line would therefore have appreciable loss. On 21 Mc/s the centre would again have a current

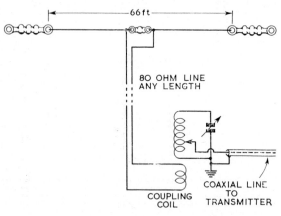

Fig. 11. Method of feeding a 7 Mc/s dipole.

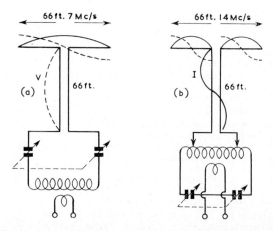

Fig. 12. Centre-fed aerials using tuned feeders. The aerial to the left is a half-wave long and has a low input impedance; the feeder is a half-wavelength long, and thus repeats the low impedance, so that series tuning could be used. On the right is a similar aerial operating at twice the frequency of the other (full wave). The input impedance is high, and the feeder one wavelength long; parallel tuning would be best. The effect of feeder length is discussed in the text, and illustrated in Fig. 13. The tuning capacitor sections should each be 50 pF maximum for 14 Mc/s and higher frequencies; proportionately larger values are needed for lower frequencies. The voltage rating of the capacitors should be the same as for those in the transmitter output tank circuit.

maximum and an impedance of about 90 ohms, which would be satisfactory for the feeder. At 28 Mc/s a high mismatch would again be presented.

The directional properties of this aerial on the various bands will be considered later; for the present a way to feed with reasonable efficiency on all the bands must be found. Obviously some compromise is needed, and three ways will now be considered—tuned feeders, methods of end-feeding the aerial, and a single wire feeder.

Tuned Feeders

The first compromise is to sacrifice the feeder match on 7 and 21 Mc/s in order to reduce the v.s.w.r. on 14 and 28 Mc/s. This can be done by using 600 ohm open wire line, which will work quite efficiently with a fairly high v.s.w.r. The impedance of 600 ohms is a mean value between say 70 ohms (on 7 Mc/s) and 5,000 ohms (on 14 Mc/s) and the v.s.w.r. will be as high as 9 on these and the other bands.

Fig. 12 shows the aerial and its feeder (also 66 ft. long) and indicates the form of the standing waves on both aerial and feeder when used on 7 and 14 Mc/s. Two different coupling circuits are shown for the transmitter, which can be regarded as alternatives to the one shown in Fig. 11.

Since the feeder is 66 ft. long, it will be a definite number of half wavelengths long on all the bands from 7 to 28 Mc/s and the input impedance will therefore be the same as the aerial impedance for each band. On 7 Mc/s, for example, the impedance is low and the *series* circuit of Fig. 12(a) would be used, the coil and tuning capacitors having about the same electrical and physical size as the transmitter tank circuit. The link coupling coil for the transmitter feeder connection should consist of three turns of insulated wire between the centre turns of the tuning coil. Alternatively the parallel tuned coupling circuit of Fig. 12(b) could be used, and the feeder tapping points set close to the centre of the coil.

Similar arrangements could also be used for 21 Mc/s with a size of coil suitable for that band. On 14 and 28 Mc/s the impedance is high, and in these cases the parallel tuning network should be used because at high impedance the taps will be at the outer ends of the coil.

If the feeder is made only 33 ft. long it will be one quarter-wavelength on 7 Mc/s, one half wavelength on 14 Mc/s, three-quarters of a wavelength on 21 Mc/s and a full wave-length (four quarter wavelengths) on 28 Mc/s. The impedance at the input to the feeder will be the same as with the 66 ft. feeder on 14 and 28 Mc/s but on 7 and 21 Mc/s where the aerial impedance is low, the odd quarter wavelength feeder will transform it to a high value on these bands also; thus, the parallel tuned coupler would be used on all bands

With the aerials described the v.s.w.r. is high and consequently the coupling circuit will carry large voltages and currents. It is essential therefore to use good quality components. The best arrangement for multi-band working is to employ a plug-in coil base with six contacts, two for the coil, two for the feeder and two for the transmitter link coil with a separate coil unit for each band. The tuning capacitor must have two sections in order to preserve feeder balance, as discussed later under aerial couplers and illustrated in Fig. 26. For 100 watts of r.f. power the feeder current may not exceed about 0·25 amp in each line when the impedance

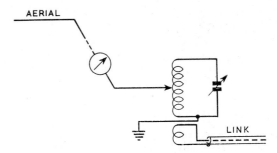

Fig. 14. Aerial coupler for end-fed aerials.

is high, but it may well exceed 1 amp for the low impedance cases, e.g. 66 ft. feeder on 7 and 21 Mc/s. This is a disadvantage in that the same r.f. ammeters cannot be used in all cases, but when the current is low and the voltage high, a small neon lamp may be used instead as a voltage indicator.

Judicious choice of feeder lengths will avoid a high voltage feed point on most bands. A suitable length may be found with the aid of **Fig. 13.** On this standing wave chart the total lengths may (if desired) include one half of the aerial so that the voltage wave illustrated starts from one aerial insulator. It will be seen that total lengths of 45 or 90 ft. bring the feeder input into the high current sections of the chart in nearly every case when using tuned feeders. It is not essential to make the aerial itself a resonant length; in fact the top can advantageously be made a little more than 66 ft. long to avoid a high voltage at the centre of the aerial on even harmonic bands.

End Feeding

The simplest way to energize an aerial is to bring one end of it into the station and connect it to earth through a tuned circuit link coupled to the transmitter.

A method used in the past was to adjust the total aerial length carefully to resonance to provide a high impedance load suitable for direct connection to the anode end of the transmitter tank circuit. Modern transmitting valves, however, require low impedance anode loads. The direct-tap method is also unsatisfactory because, first, there is no filtering of harmonics, and, second, since the aerial section nearest to the transmitter will be carrying a high r.f. voltage, there may be considerable loss of power should it have to pass through or near to surrounding structures. On the other hand, an aerial tuned to an odd number of quarter wavelengths and consequently of low input impedance, can also be inefficient as a result of the comparatively high resistance of the earth connection. It is better therefore to use an intermediate length, for example, an odd number of eighth wavelengths where the impedance will have some intermediate value and therefore a moderate current at the earth connection.

A suitable coupling circuit arrangement is illustrated in **Fig. 14.** The inductor and capacitor should be similar to those in the transmitter output tank circuit. The link coil may vary from about four turns at 3·5 Mc/s to one turn at 28 Mc/s and should be tightly coupled into the earthed end of the transmitter tank coil, the aerial tap then being adjusted for correct loading of the transmitter, with moderately broad resonance of the aerial coupler. The chart of Fig. 13 indicates whether the aerial tap should be low on the coil (low

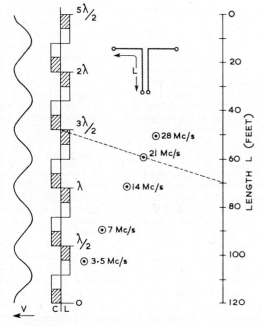

Fig. 13. Standing wave chart for tuned feeders. A line through the length L of feeder plus half-aerial, and through the frequency point will show, on the wavelength scale, the nature of the input impedance. Rectangles to the left of the line are regions of capacitive impedance, those to the right inductive. The shaded areas correspond to high impedance input (high voltage) and call for parallel-tuned couplers (Fig. 12(b)), and the blank areas to low impedances (high current) which require close taps on a parallel-tuned coupler, or a series circuit (Fig. 12(a)). The chart may also be used for feeders alone and, as coded, applies for the use of high resistance loads. When the load is lower than Z_0 the code must be reversed; the shaded areas indicate low input impedance, inductive to the left. The velocity factor of the feeder is not allowed for in the chart, and the physical length of feeder must be divided by this factor when computing length L.

impedance) or nearer the top or "hot" end (high impedance).

With a non-resonant length of aerial it may occasionally be found that, as the tap position is moved up the coil (from the "earthy" end) in order to draw more power, the coupler circuit will be thrown out of tune. This problem is considered later under "Aerial Couplers."

Earth Connections

The earth connection should preferably be taken to a copper spike or tube several feet long, or to the nearest large earthed conductor such as a water main pipe. The joint should be heavily coated with bituminous paint to avoid corrosion. *The earth connection of the electricity supply is dangerous* and may introduce noise into the receiver or be responsible for spreading interference to nearby television receivers. The transmitter earth connection should be separate from the safety earth for the equipment in the station, as it is part of the aerial system, carrying r.f. power. If the station is at the top of a building, the aerial coupler may fail to function properly on some frequencies because the earth lead is long enough to develop resonance effects. In such cases a "shortening" capacitor of 50–100 pF may be inserted into the r.f. earth lead to de-tune it. This capacitor should be an air spaced type.

The "Zepp" Aerial

If the end-fed aerial has a long vertical or semi-vertical lead much power may be wasted in useless high angle radiation, particularly at the higher frequencies. This can be partly overcome by the use of a "Zepp" feeder illustrated in **Fig. 15.**

The system is based on the concept that if the two feeder wires carry equal and opposite currents, they will not radiate. In practice it is difficult to secure this condition with the same aerial on all bands. Multiple quarter- or half-wavelength long feeder lines are unsuitable for the same reason and also because they make adjustment of the aerial coupler difficult. A length of 45 ft. (found with the aid of Fig. 13) will provide an intermediate impedance on all bands, and will work with close or medium spaced taps or series tuning on all bands except 21 Mc/s. At the latter frequency a high impedance will

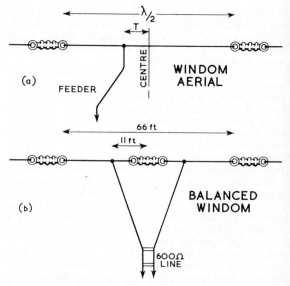

Fig. 16. (a) The Windom single wire fed aerial. (b) balanced version which minimizes feeder radiation and also works on multiple frequencies.

be presented to the feeder. Open wire 600 ohm line is preferable, because the v.s.w.r. on the line is high. The aerial should be made just over one half wavelength long at the lowest frequency to be used, say 67 ft. for frequencies from 7 Mc/s upwards (or 135 ft. if 3·5 Mc/s is to be included) and adjusted in length until the feeder currents are equal at the *lowest* frequency. If the half wavelength top cannot be erected for the lowest frequency band the free wire of the feeder (the one not connected directly to the aerial) may be disconnected at the transmitter end and the remaining wire plus the aerial used as an end-fed arrangement.

The "Windom" Aerial

When an aerial is resonant the "point impedance" (i.e., ratio of voltage to current) at any point on it is a pure resistance, varying from zero at the centre to several thousand ohms at the free end. There will therefore be an intermediate point that will match a single wire feeder, having, for example, a characteristic impedance of about 1000 ohms. If this point can be found, the radiation from the feeder will be minimized. In the original Windom **(Fig. 16(a))** the radiator is one half wavelength long, but in practice the system will work with any multiple half-wave radiator. It is a simple and attractive arrangement but requires careful adjustment to achieve best performance: the radiator must be properly resonant before the correct tapping position can be found and the feeder should hang vertically from the radiator for at least a quarter wavelength.

The correct method of adjustment is first to choose an approximate position for the tap and then insert a pair of r.f ammeters either side of the tap. Assuming the meters are alike (this may be checked by inter-changing them), they will read equal currents when the aerial has been adjusted to resonant length. The meters are then inserted in the feeder, one near the aerial and the other a quarter wavelength away and the tap moved until equal currents are again indicated.

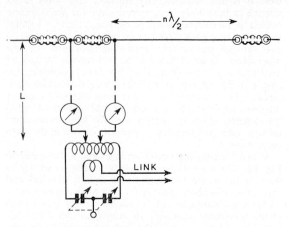

Fig. 15. The Zeppelin aerial. The length *L* of feeder is discussed in the text. Series tuning, as in Fig. 12(a), may be necessary but can usually be avoided.

TABLE 2
Single Wire Feeders

Band and Aerial	Radiator Length (feet)	Tap Distance (feet)
3·5–14 Mc/s half-wave	L = 470/f (Mc/s)	T = 66/f (Mc/s)
21–28 Mc/s half-wave	L = 460/f (Mc/s)	T = 66/f (Mc/s)
14–28 Mc/s full-wave	L = 960/f (Mc/s)	T = 170/f (Mc/s)

The values given are recommended for aerials constructed from 14 or 16 s.w.g. wire.

The dimension T in Fig. 16(a) is approximately one eighth of the half wavelength, but in practice this dimension will vary somewhat because of effects due to the environment of the aerial. **Table 2** gives typical adjustment factors. The coupling circuit at the feeder input may be similar to that described for end-fed aerials.

Although there will always be some radiation from the feeder the Windom aerial can give excellent results. Its success depends on having good conductivity soil beneath it and for this reason it is more suitable for damp locations. It is essentially a one-band aerial, but for bands other than one for which it is resonant it can be used as an end-fed aerial (aerial and feeder as one long wire). Radiation will then be partly horizontally polarized and partly vertically polarized.

The VS1AA Aerial

It will be seen from the figures of Table 2 and from the formula for half-wave aerials that a given length of wire does not resonate at true harmonic multiple frequencies. A 66 ft. wire may resonate on 7 Mc/s but would have to be nearer 68 ft. long for full-wave resonance on 14 Mc/s. At higher frequencies, as the wire accommodates more and more half-waves, this difference becomes less significant because the resonance of the aerial becomes more heavily damped by radiation. It thus becomes possible to construct a form of multi-band Windom, with the tap in an approximately correct position on all even harmonic bands. If the tap is placed one third of the way along a standing wave current loop on the lowest frequency it will always be in the same position on a current loop on all even harmonic frequencies. This system is most suitable for very long wires, the tap being about $22\frac{1}{2}$ ft. from the end for all frequencies down to 7 Mc/s, and even works quite well with long aerials on 21 Mc/s (where the " one third " rule breaks down), because the long wire places a substantial load on the end of the feeder.

The Double Windom

The VS1AA approximation has the disadvantage that there is considerable radiation from the feeder. This can be overcome by making it into the balanced system shown in **Fig. 16(b)** so that the feeder radiation is cancelled. This aerial can alternatively be regarded as a development of the centre-fed aerial with tuned feeders, the spacing of the taps helping to reduce the v.s.w.r. on the feeder. The length of the arms of the V section of the line should be at least equal to the separation between the taps, preferably more, and the overall length from one end of the aerial into the station should be chosen as for the centre-fed aerial in order to give

reasonable tuning arrangements; it may present some difficulty on 21 Mc/s because of the high standing-wave ratio.

Asymmetrical Twin Feed

It will be realized that a long-wire aerial, i.e. one which is two or more half wavelengths long, can be fed with low-impedance twin line at any current-maximum position, such as the point a quarter-wave from one end (**Fig. 17**). In such a case 70–80 ohm twin line could be used and would match the aerial well enough, though the impedance at such a point in the aerial is somewhat greater than that of a single half-wave. This could be done with a 7 Mc/s aerial, and then at 21 Mc/s the feeder would again be at a current maximum position. Other bands have an even harmonic relationship, and the feeder would be badly mismatched.

One way in which this problem has been solved is to connect the feeder into the aerial at an intermediate position at about one third of the way along the wire where the impedance is higher, and to use 300 ohm twin line. This method introduces a fresh difficulty in that, although the theoretical v.s.w.r. on the line may not be too high, the feeder is no

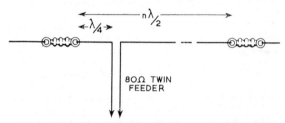

Fig. 17. Asymmetrical twin line feed for a harmonic aerial.

longer balanced because it is connected into an asymmetrical point of the aerial. The difference between the currents in the two wires of the feeder is equivalent to a single vertical radiating component, so that there is some radiation from the feeder. Nevertheless this system is an improvement over the single-wire feeder.

LOW FREQUENCY AERIALS
Marconi Type

The simple types of aerial described so far have been illustrated as horizontal aerials. On the lower frequencies, the 1·8–2·0 Mc/s and 3·5–3·8 Mc/s bands, there is often insufficient space to erect such an aerial and even if there were, it is unlikely that it would be possible to erect it sufficiently high to be really effective. In such cases some form of Marconi aerial is used. This is essentially a vertical aerial, working against an earth connection; the inverted L type is also usually considered to be a Marconi type aerial. In these aerials the image of the aerial in the ground is used to help make up the effective length to half-wave resonance.

The ideal length for a vertical aerial working against earth is one quarter-wave and since it is in effect a bisected half-wave aerial, its radiation resistance is about 35 ohms, i.e. half that of a half-wave dipole. Such a height is not usually possible, even for 3·5 Mc/s where it would be 66 ft., and hence it is necessary to use an electrically short aerial and to load it in such a way as to bring it to resonance, and if possible to increase the radiation efficiency. An aerial one tenth of a wavelength high (50 ft. for 1·8 Mc/s) has a radiation resistance of 4–5 ohms. This would not matter if the earth were a perfect conductor, but it is far from being so, and the resistance due to a most elaborate earth system, together with the loss due to the current returning through the surface, may contribute 20 ohms or more. The efficiency is thus low. At higher frequencies where vertical aerials are used for their desirable low angle radiation properties, ground plane systems can be used to reduce earth loss, but at the lower frequencies they would be too large and other methods of improving the efficiency must be sought.

It is the centre part of a tuned aerial, where the current is highest, that is responsible for most of its radiation. The ends (where voltage is high but current low) do not contribute much to the radiation, but are necessary in order to bring the aerial to resonance and build up the current at the centre. When the full resonant length cannot be erected it is necessary, in order to increase the efficiency, to load the remote end of the aerial in some way so that its electrical length is increased and so move the current maximum into the vertical part of the aerial. Another procedure is to increase the total effective length of the aerial to more than a quarter wave. This raises the impedance at the feed point, so that the power loss due to the resistance of the earth connection is relatively less.

The simplest form of loading is to add a horizontal top to make a *T* or inverted *L* aerial (**Fig. 18 (a)**) This loading should be arranged to create a current maximum in the centre of the vertical part. The distance from this point to the end of an *L* aerial is about 130 ft. for 1·8 Mc/s but somewhat less for a *T* aerial. If this cannot be done, the next alternative is to increase the loading effect of the top by making it into a cage or "flat top" of two or three wires joined in parallel; this increases the capacitance and effectively lengthens the aerial. If this procedure is not practicable, the aerial may be loaded

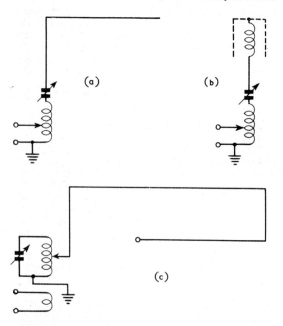

Fig. 18. Aerials for low frequency bands. (a) Quarter-wave (inverted L) aerial with series tuning. (b) End loading to raise the efficiency of a short aerial. (c) Special extended aerial with high efficiency, detailed in text. The input current in aerials (a) and (b) may be 0·5 amp. for 10 watts input; that in (c) is low, say 0·1 amp. for 10 watts

by including a length of folded or coiled wire (see **Fig. 18(b)**) near the free end of the aerial. The coil must be arranged with care, using the same size wire and avoiding sudden bends so that the standing wave starts from the far end of the aerial and not from a reflection at the coil. It may be inconvenient to support the coil in the middle of the top, but if it is to be fitted to the mast at the far end of the aerial then it must be given a capacitance "platform" to work against. This can take the form of a large can or closed screen of wire enclosing the loading coil, the far end of which is connected to it. This loading is a very noticeable help where the total space only allows the erection of a wire one eighth of a wavelength long and makes it possible to obtain useful results on the l.f. bands when the loft of a house is the only place for the aerial.

Other methods of end loading may be devised; for example, folding the aerial back on itself with spacing of, say 6 in., the aim being to bring the desired current maximum into the main part of the aerial.

Aerials for 1·8 Mc/s with relatively high input currents are preferably series-tuned, using about 250 pF capacitance with, say 30μH inductance. A suitable coil for 1·8 Mc/s could be made with 20 turns of 16 s.w.g. wire on a 3 in. diameter former, and spaced to occupy a length of 3 to 4 in. The transmitter link could be tapped across a few turns at the earthed end of the coil or the wire itself coupled to the transmitter output tank coil. About half the values given should be used for 3·5 Mc/s.

The earth system should be considered carefully, and the best possible arrangements made, including the use of buried earth wires under the aerial, wire fences and anything which will help to bring the r.f. current back to the base without travelling through soil.

To reduce the deleterious effect of an imperfect earth connection the aerial may have a total length of about $\frac{3}{8}$ or $\frac{5}{8}$ of a wavelength while still maintaining the maximum current in the vertical part. A very effective aerial is shown in **Fig. 18(c)** where the main half-wave is folded into a *U* with one leg near the ground and adjusted in length until maximum current occurs at a point half way up the righthand vertical section. The down-lead makes the total length up to about $\frac{5}{8}$ of a wavelength, so that the impedance at the feed point is a few hundred ohms and capacitive, whilst the earth current is relatively low. The coupling circuit for this aerial should be parallel tuned and use the components described for Fig. 18(b).

The 1·8 Mc/s aerials of Figs. 18(a) and (c) can also be used effectively on 3·5 Mc/s and higher frequencies, though it is difficult to predict their precise performance.

VERTICAL H.F. AERIALS

Ground-planes

At higher frequencies where a full quarter-wave can be erected the vertical aerial is used because of its attractive properties of omnidirectional low-angle radiation. Such aerials can be fed with coaxial 50 ohm cable with the sheathing joined to a good earth connection as shown in **Fig. 19(a)**. The earth resistance will, however, always be significant, causing some loss of power unless a set of 15–20 radial quarter-wave earth wires is used. One method of combatting the earth loss is to fold the radiator as in **Fig. 19(b)**. This multiplies the radiation resistance by four, making it effectively 140 ohms so that when the earth loss is added it is a

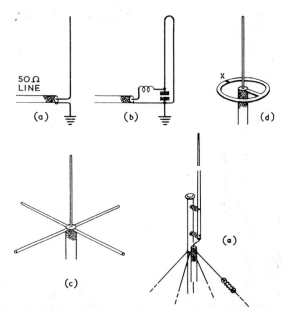

Fig. 19. Quarter wave vertical aerials. (a) Single wire using earth connection. (b) Folded wire with transformer (see text dealing with impedance matching). (c) Ground plane using artificial earth. (d) Compact ground plane. (e) Guy wires used as a ground plane. The cable size is exaggerated for clarity.

smaller proportion of the total. The total resistance of 150–200 ohms can be transformed down to match a 50 ohm or 70 ohm coaxial cable by means of a tuned transformer described later.

This folded aerial requires a support but in contrast a single rod vertical radiator can be made self supporting, so the *ground plane aerial* shown in **Fig. 19(c)** may be preferred. The inner conductor of a 50 ohm concentric line is connected to the vertical rod or wire and a set of four or more quarter-wave radials is connected to the sheath. These radials act as an artificial earth of low resistance and give the advantage that the whole aerial can be raised, so that less of its field reaches the ground and there is less obstruction of radiation by surrounding objects. The radiation resistance of a ground quarter-wave aerial is 35 ohms but that of a ground plane is less than 20 ohms, so that matching could be improved by folding it. This is usually inconvenient for a self-supporting rod aerial and it is better to raise the resistance by tilting the radials downwards. An excellent scheme is **Fig. 19(e)** where the guy wires of the mast are insulated at the correct length and used as the ground plane, four wires with a tilt of 45° giving 50 ohms aerial impedance. The tilted ground plane cannot be used to match a 70 ohm cable; if this cable must be used it may be better to make the radial earth horizontal and to fold the vertical radiator.

In some installations it may be found that the outside of the cable is " live " after it has left the ground-plane. When this occurs, it may be necessary to coil up a few feet of the cable to act as a form of choke effective on the outer surface only.

Where there is insufficient space for the radials the ground plane can be folded as in **Fig. 19(d)**. To understand how this works, imagine that a single ground radial has been provided and that after a certain distance it is split and the ends folded

into a circle. The two free ends are at the same potential and may therefore be joined together. The length of the radial part is 0.07λ and the circumference 0.43λ. This aerial is as effective as the previous one, but the tuning is somewhat more critical and the input impedance low.

IMPEDANCE MATCHING

In the section dealing with transmission lines, it was explained that the best way to use a line is in the matched condition, so that the aerial or load absorbs all the power the line supplies to it, the impedance at the sending end being the same as the characteristic impedance of the line. It was also shown that this impedance matching must be done at the load (aerial) end of the line. The various methods of matching the aerial to the line will now be discussed in rather more detail.

The problem is complicated by the need to preserve bandwidth. The aerial itself is a resonant device but is usually sufficiently broadly tuned to cover the greater part of almost any of the amateur h.f. bands, exceptions being aerials for 1·8–2 Mc/s and those which have a high gain within restricted size. A tuned line reduces bandwidth rapidly with increasing length because it is in effect a series of cascaded resonant circuits, so that even in the narrow span of an amateur band re-tuning of the coupling circuits may be necessary as the frequency is changed. Any necessary matching should therefore be carried out as near as possible to the aerial. In a similar way, a reduction of bandwidth occurs if a large ratio of impedance is to be transformed, because high ratio transformers have smaller bandwidths and greater loss. It is therefore best to use aerials and feeders with impedances as nearly alike as possible. This cannot always be done, especially if a long line is necessary, because it would then be preferable to employ a high impedance line in order to minimize losses. Another factor which must always be considered is that the feeder should not carry unintended waves, a matter discussed later under *Marconi Effect*.

Folded Dipoles and Aerial Transformers

The half-wave dipole is a balanced aerial and requires a balanced feeder. Normally this is a 70 ohm line, but it is sometimes necessary to step up the aerial input impedance to a higher value; for example, where the feeder is very long and

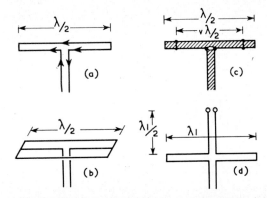

Fig. 20. Folded dipoles, including (a) simple fold; (b) three-fold; (c) folded dipole made from 300 ohm ribbon feeder with two (d) arrangement for working on half-and full-wave resonances.

300 or 600 ohm line is employed to reduce feeder loss. Another is in a beam aerial in which the dipole input impedance is too low to match 70 ohm line. A separate transformer to step the aerial impedance up to these values would reduce the bandwidth, but it has been found that by folding the aerial the step-up can be accomplished without any reduction of bandwidth. **Fig. 20(a)** shows a full-wave wire folded into a half-wave dipole. It is not a loop aerial because the two halves are only separated by a few inches.

The relative direction of currents, at current maximum, are shown by arrows in the diagram. In a straight full-wave wire they would be of opposite polarity, but folding the full-wave has " turned over " one current direction; thus the arrows in the diagram all point the same way. The folded dipole is therefore equivalent to two single-wire dipoles in parallel. The radiation resistance of the folded dipole made of the same diameter conductors is 300 ohms, which is four times that of the single wire.

One of the advantages of folding a dipole is that the bandwidth is increased because it becomes equivalent to an aerial made of a much larger diameter conductor. Such aerials have a lower Q than those made of small gauge wires. Low Q is desirable in an aerial provided it is produced by radiation load and not by conductor or insulator loss.

A folded dipole connected to a 300 ohm feeder will operate over the whole of the 14 Mc/s band with no appreciable change of impedance. For comparison a single wire dipole connected through some kind of transformer and 100 ft. of 300 ohm line might well show a 2 : 1 change of impedance over the same band.

If the aerial is made three-fold (**Fig. 20 (b)**), it is equivalent to three radiators in parallel, its radiation resistance is multiplied nine times and it would be used with a 600 ohm line.

In some multi-element arrays the radiation resistance is very low, and folding the driven element is a useful aid to correct matching since with N wires the resistance is always raised N^2 times.

The folded dipole will not normally operate on even harmonics of the frequency for which is is cut because the " folded " currents cancel each other. However, the alignment of currents is correct for the odd harmonics, so that a folded dipole for 7 Mc/s can also be used on 21 Mc/s.

A folded dipole one wavelength long can be made to radiate but only if the centre of the second conductor is broken; in such a case the input impedance is *divided* by four. The centre impedance of a full-wave dipole is 4000 to 6000 ohms; that of the folded version 1000 to 1500 ohms. **Fig. 20(d)** shows how such an aerial can be made to work at both fundamental and second harmonic frequencies by means of a length of open circuit twin line (called a *stub*) used as a " frequency switch." At the frequency at which the aerial is $\lambda/2$ long, the stub is one electrical quarter-wave long and, since its other end is open, the input end behaves as a short circuit and effectively closes the gap in the aerial. At the full-wave frequency the stub is one half-wave long and behaves as an open circuit. The stub may be made of 300 ohm twin feeder and in application to rotating beam aerials can be fixed to the mast or dropped down inside it if it is tubular.

The folded dipole can be conveniently made from 300 ohm flat twin feeder as in **Fig. 20(c)**, because the spacing is not important so long as it is a small fraction of a wavelength. Since the velocity factor of ribbon feeder is about 0·8, it is necessary to place the short circuits between the wires at this fraction of a quarter wavelength from the centre rather than at the end—e.g. 27 ft. apart in a 33 ft. long 14 Mc/s aerial.

Other ratios of transformation than four or nine can be obtained by using different conductor diameters for the elements of the radiator but these are more practicable on the higher frequencies where tubular elements can be employed. When this is done, the spacing between the conductors is important and can be varied to alter the transformation ratio. The relative size and spacings can be determined with the aid of the nomogram in **Fig. 21**.

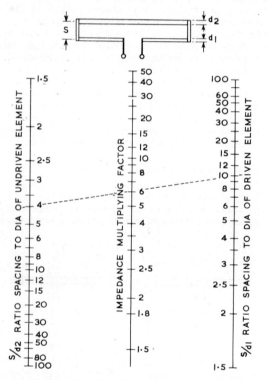

Fig. 21. **Nomogram for folded dipole calculations. The impedance multiplying factor depends on the two ratios of conductor diameter to spacing between centres, and is always 4 : 1 when the diameters are equal. A ruler laid across the scales will give pairs of spacing/diameter ratios for any required multiplier. In the example shown the driven element diameter is one-tenth of the spacing and the other element diameter one quarter of the spacing, resulting in a step up of 6 : 1. There is an unlimited number of solutions for any given ratio. The chart may also be used to find the step-up ratio of an aerial of given dimensions.**

IMPEDANCE TRANSFORMERS

The term impedance transformer has a general meaning and covers any device in which the voltage to current ratio is changed. Voltage or current is stepped up or down by the turns ratio: impedances are changed by the square of the turns ratio. At high frequencies a wide choice of types of transformer is available, usually, however, with resonant characteristics including resonant L–C circuits, coupled windings, or special arrangements of sections of transmission lines. The " turns " may not always be obvious, but all transformers have in effect a " turns ratio " and can be used for matching purposes between an aerial of one impedance and a feeder of another impedance. The output circuit of the transmitter is an example in which the 50 or 70 ohm impedance of the output line is transformed to, say, a 2000 ohm anode load required by the p.a. valve.

It has already been shown that the aerial itself may be employed as a transformer, either by folding it or by tapping along it as in the Windom. Various methods will be described for transforming externally to the aerial where for one reason or another folding or tapping the radiator is not a practicable solution. These transformers are mostly one-band devices, but in many cases it is possible to use the same aerial with its transformer on a tuned line basis on other frequencies.

It is, of course, always possible to use tuned-network transformers of coils and capacitors like the aerial coupler at the transmitter, but these are usually inconvenient and troublesome to maintain in a wire aerial and it is better to use linear transformers, i.e., those made from sections of transmission line which are lighter and more dependable when exposed to the weather. Network transformers can, however, be used at ground level as, for example, with a vertical aerial.

Quarter-wave Transformers

A typical problem is that of feeding a dipole from a transmitter some distance away where a 600 ohm open wire line would be used to minimize losses. Assuming that it is not convenient to fold the dipole to give it a radiation resistance of 600 ohms, a practicable method would be to insert a quarter-wavelength of 200 ohm line between the 70 ohm dipole and the 600 ohm main line; see **Fig. 22**. This is known as a quarter-wave transformer and its principle, illustrated in **Fig. 23**, is that its characteristic impedance is the geometric mean of the two impedances to be matched. The standing wave on the short section is used to vary the voltage/current ratio between its two ends. The relation between the three factors is

$$R_1 R_2 = Z_o^2$$

$$\text{or } Z_o = \sqrt{R_1 R_2}$$

Thus, in the example just given, $70 \times 600 = 42{,}000$ which is approximately the square of 200. The aerial must of course

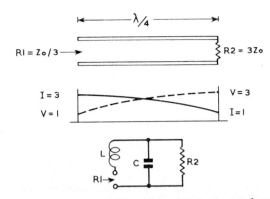

Fig. 23. Illustrating the principle of the quarter-wave transformer for the case of a 9 : 1 impedance ratio. The V/I ratio is inverted by the standing wave on the line with v.s.w.r. = 3, giving $R_1 R_2 = Z_o^2$. This corresponds to the series parallel action of a resonant circuit in which $L/C = Z_o^2$, R_2 is the parallel resistance and R_1 the equivalent series resistance.

be resonant and the velocity factor of the line should be taken into account in making the transformer. The length (in feet) of a free-space quarter-wave is

$$\frac{246}{f \text{ (Mc/s)}}.$$

The length of line required for a quarter-wave transformer is the length obtained from this expression and multiplied by the velocity factor of the line. The same transformation is obtained when the intermediate line is $\frac{3}{4}\lambda$ long, so a transformer for 7 Mc/s would also work on 21 Mc/s.

Stub Transformers

Quarter-wave resonant line transformers can be used when the impedance ratio is fairly high (e.g., greater than five-to-one) and two varieties using short- and open-circuited stubs are shown in Fig. 22(b) and 22(c) respectively. Both make use of the fact that there is a standing wave on the stubs, the main feeder being moved along the stub to a point where the

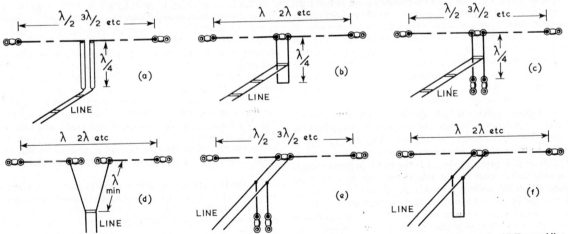

Fig. 22. Linear matching transformers. (a) Quarter-wave impedance line or " Q-Bars." (b), (c) Tapped quarter-wave stubs. (d) Tapered line. (e), (f) matching stubs. A chart for the stubs (f) is given in Chapter 14.

voltage/current ratio becomes equal to the main line impedance. They are effectively tuned resonant circuits, with the feeder tapped into them. The open stub, shown in Fig. 22(c), is employed when the feed point impedance of the aerial is too low for the line, i.e., when the overall aerial length is an odd number of half-waves, and the closed stub is used for a high impedance feed, i.e., when the aerial is a number of full waves long.

In practice the stub can be made to have the same impedance as the main line, though this is not essential. The line should be supported so that it remains at a fixed angle (preferably a right angle) to the stub. The tapping position is varied until the standing wave or the reflection coefficient on the main line is minimized. If a good match is not produced the length of the stub can be altered; should this not be successful, it is probable that the wrong type of stub is being used. It may be noted that the aerial itself need not be a resonant length, though the aerial-plus-stub must be; also, the stubs may be increased in length by one or more quarter-waves in order to bring the tap position nearer to ground level, changing from " open " to " short-circuit " or vice-versa with each quarter wavelength addition.

Tapered Lines

When the required transformer ratio is not high, for example, when an 800 ohm rhombic aerial is to be matched to a 600 or 300 ohm line, it is practicable to use the simple tapered line, shown in Fig. 22(d). At the aerial end, the spacing is correct for 800 ohms and gradually decreases to that for the lower impedance. This arrangement gradually converts the impedance from one value to the other. It is a wide-band device and, provided the taper is not less than one wavelength long, it will give a good, though not perfect, match.

For accurate matching on one band, when the impedance ratio is low, the tapped stub is no longer a quarter wave-length long because the standing wave ratio differs on opposite sides of the tap, one half being loaded and the other a free reactance.

In Figs. 22(e) and 22(f) the transformers are shown differently, the main part of the transformer being a continuation of the feed line, with the compensating stub at right angles to it. This variation does not affect the principle but is more suitable in practice and simplifies the adjustment. If the impedance ratio (i.e. the v.s.w.r.) is known, then the position and length of the compensating stub can be calculated. All that is necessary in practice is to connect the main line to the aerial and then to run a detector along the line and measure the v.s.w.r. noting the point of minimum voltage (or maximum current).

It is essential that the stub should have the same characteristic impedance as the line and it should be noted that the length includes half the shorting bar. The shorted stub is always placed on the aerial side of the voltage minimum at the distance *D* given by the chart but if this is inconvenient, an alternative point on the transmitter side may be used, though in this position an open-circuit stub is necessary. Note that the alternative stubs have complementary lengths. It is desirable but not essential that the stub be connected near the aerial though it may be convenient to work some distance from the aerial at the second or third voltage minimum. It is not necessary to have the aerial in resonance at

the feeder junction; its tuning can be completed in the resonant part of the line.

Network Transformers

At ground level, and particularly where a concentric (coaxial) feed line is used, it is often more convenient to employ a coil and capacitor network. This could be similar to any of the couplers used near the transmitter, though a simpler network is shown in **Fig. 24**. This is known as a " Green transformer " and is a heavily damped network

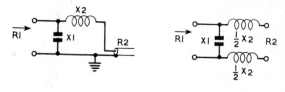

$$X1 = \mp R1 / \sqrt{R1/_{R2} - 1} \qquad X2 = \pm R2 \sqrt{R1/_{R2} - 1}$$

WITH RI GREATER THAN R2

Fig. 24. Quarterwave network transformers. Inductance and capacitance may be inter-changed, provided they have the reactance values given by the formulae for arms I and 2.

which is not critical and can often be made up from nearest available fixed values of components. A suitable protective cover for the network is a large airtight can, used upside down, with components mounted on the lid. A metalized lead-through seal from an old capacitor or transformer can be soldered into the lid for the aerial lead. A sealed r.f. connector is preferable for the cable connection. The can should have a coat of paint, and Bostick putty can be used to seal all the joints; a small bag of silica-gel may be placed in the can to guard against condensation. The components of the network should be suitable for the transmitter power; if fixed capacitors are used they should be of the foil-and-mica type.

AERIAL COUPLERS

It has been assumed in this chapter that the aerial or its feeder will not be connected direct to the transmitter output circuit because this is an obsolete practice not suited to modern conditions. The normal output from a transmitter is through a coupling network and harmonic filter into a coaxial r.f. connector. In some cases, where the aerial is already fed by coaxial lines, it can be connected directly to the transmitter output socket, but more generally it is necessary to use an intermediate coupler or transformer. Even if the line is of the same impedance as the transmitter output (say 70 ohms), it may be a balanced twin feeder and cannot therefore be connected to the unbalanced concentric transmitter output. It is therefore common practice to use an *aerial coupler* or *aerial tuning unit* (often abbreviated to a.t.u.).

The aerial coupler is sometimes built as part of the transmitter but this is not essential and it may be more convenient to extend the output cable from the transmitter to another part of the station, particularly if a change-over arrangement is required to connect the same aerial to the receiver.

The coupler may have to tune the aerial or the feeder to resonance, in addition to transforming from the one im-

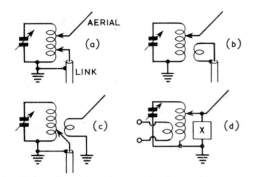

Fig. 25. Various forms of aerial coupler for end-fed aerials. The use of reactance **X** for compensation of very reactive aerials or feeder loads is discussed in the text.

pedance to another. Moreover, it may have to take a balanced input and link it to an unbalanced concentric line. The general design of the network has already been illustrated in connection with the simpler aerials and it is now necessary to consider how to choose the right one for each purpose, what value of components to use and the special requirements of balanced feeders. Series tuning was once popular for use with low impedance tuned feeders or aerials, but is a handicap if the same aerial is to be used on several bands, and can usually be avoided by compensation before transforming as described on page 370.

Unbalanced Aerials

Fig. 25 shows some variations of an aerial coupler suitable for unbalanced aerials or feeders. The general principle is that the inductance acts as a two-winding (or auto) transformer, the capacitor serving to resonate the coil to ensure a high degree of coupling, to help the network to discriminate against unwanted frequencies, and to assist in harmonic suppression. The link may have either a direct tap connection or a separate coil of a few turns interwound with the main inductance at the earthed end.

The tuning components should each have a reactance of about 500 ohms at the operating frequency. This may most conveniently be translated into practical figures by reckoning the capacitance as 1 pF per metre of wavelength, and the inductance as 0.25μH per metre. For example, at 7 Mc/s, approximately 40 pF and 12μH could be used. There is nothing critical about these values, though for a very high impedance aerial load (as may occur when using tuned feeders) it is advisable to increase the inductance and use less capacitance. Coils of about 3 in. diameter wound with 14–16 s.w.g. wire will handle the power output of a 150 watt amateur transmitter without overheating. The tuning capacitor should be of good quality, have a plate spacing of $\frac{1}{16}$ in. or more and have adequate capacitance to tune to resonance at about half its maximum value. The link coil may be self-supporting inside the end of the tuning coil or alternatively a few turns of well insulated wire supported between the turns of the tuning inductance. The link may vary from four or five turns at 3.5 Mc/s to one turn at 28 Mc/s.

The method of setting up an aerial coupler is first to reduce the link coupling or move the tapping point nearer the earthed end of the coil, and to find the resonant point of the circuit by noting its loading effect on the transmitter anode current. The aerial may next be connected or coupled in and

the circuit retuned. Less power will now be drawn, so the link coupling must be increased. The final adjustment is to bring the link to full coupling and the aerial tap or coupling as tight as consistent (high up the coil) with the transmitter still drawing maximum input power. The tuning should be very broad, so that considerable movement of the capacitor is needed to produce significant changes; this is the condition of high efficiency when the network consumes a negligible amount of power. If the aerial is coupled too tightly, it will damp the tuned circuit too much to suit the coupling of the link coil. The transmitter may then draw more anode current, but the aerial current will be less than optimum.

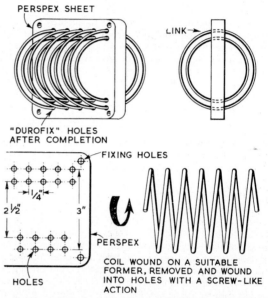

A suitable method of constructing aerial coupler coils. The coils should be $2\frac{1}{2}$ in. and 3 in. in diameter, and the turns spaced $\frac{1}{4}$ in. using 14 s.w.g. wire. If the link coil is the outer one, turns can be varied easily.

Balanced Circuits

When the aerial or the feeder is balanced it is necessary to use an aerial coupler which is also balanced, such as that shown in **Fig. 26** using a split-stator tuning capacitor. The capacitance of each half of the capacitor may be the same as

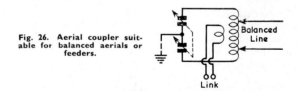

Fig. 26. Aerial coupler suitable for balanced aerials or feeders.

recommended for single-ended couplers but since the two are in series, the inductance value must be twice as big. The aerial or feeder should be tapped symmetrically about the centre of the coil with the link coil in the centre. The adjustment procedure is the same as for unbalanced lines, but in addition it is necessary to ensure that the feeder is working as a balanced system if the aerial is to operate correctly. Unbalance may be brought about by stray capacitance in the coupler.

The Marconi Effect

If the total distance from the coupler to one end of the aerial is one half wavelength, there is a tendency for the two wires of the feeder to act in parallel, and produce a *T*- aerial effect. The transmitter end of the equivalent parallel system has a high impedance to earth: thus a small stray capacitance to a live part of the network may feed considerable power into this parallel or " phantom " circuit and the feeder can of course, radiate this power. The visible effect is that the feeder wires show unequal currents or voltages. This behaviour of the feeder is often called the *Marconi Effect*.

Resonant lengths of feeder should be avoided if possible (Fig. 13) but the following points may be noted. Earthing of the frame of the split-stator capacitor usually cures the unbalance, but if this fails it may be advisable to use a separate coupling coil for the feeder (instead of tapping it on to the tuning coil) wound either over, or in the centre of, the tuning coil. The centre point of the extra coil may be earthed direct or through a 200 ohm 2 watt resistor to damp the " phantom " circuit. In any case, at the first sign of serious unbalance (e.g., unusual currents or voltages on the line) the aerial system should be inspected to locate a possible fault; the presence of excessive harmonic output from the transmitter may also be suspected as a cause of apparent unbalance.

Tuning Compensation

Coupling the aerial or feeder to the aerial tuning unit sometimes makes it impossible to adjust the circuit for reasonably high loading. This occurs with tuned feeders with a high standing wave ratio when a heavy reactance load may be presented by the line. In such cases it is better to compensate the feeder reactance separately before transforming the resistance component, using a coil or capacitor connected in parallel with the feeder (see Fig. 25(d)). If more capacitance than is available appears to be required for resonance, then capacitance loading is needed; if the converse, inductive loading is the solution. A loading component of the same value as the coil or capacitor of the tuning circuit may be tried first.

Multiband Couplers

There are many variations of the aerial couplers described. For example, a pi-network similar to those described in Chapter 6 (*H.F. Transmitters*) for transmitter output circuits is often attractive because it can be arranged to cover as many as four amateur bands with the same set of components. The couplers of Figs. 25 and 26 can usually be arranged to cover two adjacent amateur bands but where complete coverage is needed it may be necessary to make up a coil together with its link and taps as a plug-in unit for each band, though there may still be some difficulty if the capacitor has too large a minimum capacitance for 28 Mc/s or insufficient maximum capacitance for 3·5 Mc/s.

A popular multiband aerial tuning unit for 3·5–28 Mc/s is shown in **Fig. 27** and is known as a *Z-match coupler*. It is a compound network using two pairs of windings and is capable of matching the wide range of impedances which may be presented by a tuned aerial line. Coils L_1 and L_2 may each be 5 turns tightly coupled. L_3 and L_4 are 8 and 6

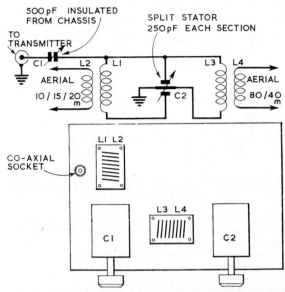

Fig. 27 (Above). Circuit diagram of the Z-match coupler. (Below) Suggested layout. C_1 is the series capacitor and C_2 the split stator capacitor in the multiband tuning circuit.

turns respectively. L_1 and L_3 may be about $2\frac{1}{2}$ in. diameter and L_2 and L_4 about 3 in. diameter (see the diagram on page 369).

The series capacitor C_1 is 500 pF maximum and it should be noted that it is " live " on both sides: the frame should be connected to the transmitter link cable and an insulated extension shaft provided. The other capacitor, C_2, is the split stator type, 250 pF per section. C_2 tunes the coupler and C_1 adjusts the load to the transmitter. A standing wave indicator (reflectometer) of the type described in Chapter 19 is an aid to tuning. C_1 and C_2 are adjusted for minimum reflection and the transmitter can then, if necessary, be trimmed for maximum output.

Where there is sufficient space it is an aid to quick band changing to set up a number of separate pre-set aerial couplers as in **Fig. 28** so that it is only necessary to change over the aerial circuit by means of clips or sockets and the link by means of coaxial connectors. The same diagram shows a change-over relay which enables the receiver to be connected to the aerial. Since the link is a low impedance

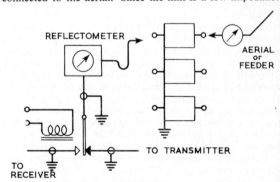

Fig. 28. Schematic diagram of aerial switchboard, with preset couplers for several bands and changeover relay for the receiver. The reflectometer indicates impedance match and power-flow

circuit, simple types of relay can be used, provided they have reasonably heavy contacts. The relay should be enclosed in a screen which is continuous with the sheath of the link cable and may be operated by the same switch which activates the transmitter.

Power Indicators

It is necessary to be cautious in interpreting the power radiated in terms of meter readings, because the current and voltage vary from point to point in an aerial system. Some suggestions as to what to expect may therefore be helpful. A 100 watt d.c. input transmitter will deliver up to 1 amp. into an 80 ohm matched line, but only about 0·35 amp. into a matched 600 ohm feeder. In both cases this can be taken to represent true power. In a tuned line, however, the current may vary over a wide range and does not reveal the real radiated power, though it still serves for indication of tuning adjustments. R.f. thermoammeters are available with maximum readings of 0·5 to 5 amp., but usually have a rather cramped and limited scale at low readings so that they cannot be used for widely differing currents. Care is necessary in cases where the current is greatly different in the same aerial for different bands, since these meters are easily damaged by overload.

When the transmitter power is very low, the current may be below the range of robust meters and a low wattage lamp is the only practicable tuning indicator. On the other hand the corresponding voltage even from a low-power transmitter is easy to indicate and **Fig. 29** shows the circuit of a simple voltage indicator, employing a germanium diode.

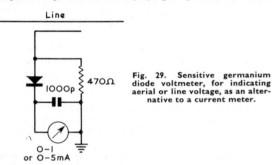

Line

Fig. 29. Sensitive germanium diode voltmeter, for indicating aerial or line voltage, as an alternative to a current meter.

1000p   470Ω

0–1 or 0–5mA

There is no need to make direct connection to the aerial line or feeder: sufficient energy can be picked up by a very small capacitance coupling, using as the capacitor an inch or so of wire fixed close to one wire of an open balanced line or inserted into a co-axial line through a slit cut in the outer sheath. The coupling wire should be held in position by adhesive tape. Sufficient coupling can usually be obtained to give several milliamperes of d.c. output: the germanium diode will pass 10 mA without damage. The meter connections can be led back to the operating position but the earth on the voltmeter should be to the aerial circuit earth or the cable sheath.

The Reflectometer S.W.R. Indicator

A number of devices have been designed which can be connected into co-axial lines to indicate separately the forward and reflected waves on a transmission line. These are much more useful than voltmeters or ammeters because the forward wave calibration can be marked to show real power

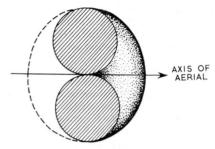

AXIS OF AERIAL

" Solid " radiation pattern of a half-wave dipole. The cut cross-section is a polar diagram in the plane of the wire (E-plane).

flow to the aerial, whilst zero reflected wave indication means that the line is matched to its load. These instruments are Wheatstone bridge arrangements, using either R–C components or coupled transmission lines. They are often referred to as s.w.r. detectors and although they can be calibrated in this way, they really measure power and reflection coefficient. It is generally necessary to reverse the R–C types to read the forward and reflected components, but the coupled line type can be arranged to avoid this. A reflectometer of the latter type is described in Chapter 19 (*Measurements*) and a typical installation is shown in Fig. 28 of this chapter, where it is included in the link cable to the aerial coupler. If the aerial is matched to a coaxial line, the reflectometer can be installed directly in the line, where it also serves as a monitor of power to the aerial.

DIRECTIVE PROPERTIES OF AERIALS

Aerials do not radiate uniformly in all directions, first because there is no radiation from the ends of a straight wire, and second because the wave reflection from the ground produces an interfering effect which may augment or reduce the direct radiation in any given direction. The effect of the ground is mostly disadvantageous, as it generally reduces low angle radiation above the horizontal, though there are cases where it can be used effectively by placing the aerial at the correct height. It also helps to produce a little useful end-fire radiation from a horizontal wire which, in free space, has none.

If there is more than one half wave in an aerial, it is found that the total radiation can be regarded as the resultant of a number of components, one from each standing wave current loop. In any given direction these components may have to travel different distances, so that they do not arrive at a distant point in the same relative phases as they had in the wire. They can, therefore, augment or oppose each other. It is, however, possible to combine a number of elementary aerials so that their radiation accumulates in some favoured direction, at the expense of radiation in other directions. This gives a much stronger signal than a single aerial would give in the required direction for the same power input.

For these reasons aerials are said to be directive and to have gain. It is usual to compare the gain of an aerial (in the direction of maximum strength) with that of a dipole energized by the same power input; the ratio is expressed in decibels. This is really a relative gain since a simple dipole does not radiate uniformly in all directions but has a slightly directive pattern and a gain of about 1·6db. Thus an aerial could be said to have a gain of 6db (relative to a dipole) or 7·6db *absolute* gain. These points are discussed in greater

371

detail in Chapter 14 (*V.H.F. Aerials*). The calculation of the gain of an aerial is difficult but that of the more conventional types of beam aerial is already known, and it is practicable for amateurs to construct beam aerials with moderate gain.

Before studying directive arrays, consideration must be given to the form of radiation pattern required by an amateur station. It is frequently desired to be able to work in any direction of the compass and this can be accomplished best by the use of a number of separate aerials. These require considerable space and more often it is necessary to use a compact rotating beam aerial. The directive pattern of such

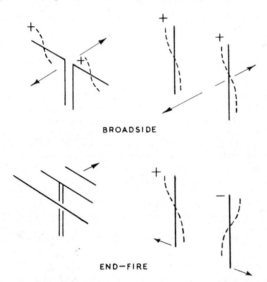

BROADSIDE

END—FIRE

Fig. 30. Horizontal (left) and vertical (right) broadside and end-fire arrays, illustrat:ng the terms. The arrows indicate directions of maximum radiation and the voltage standing waves on three of the aerials show their relative polarity or phase. The remaining aerial is a three element parasitic array and is unidirectional.

aerials not only gives gain and stronger signals, but in reception also helps to reduce interference from unwanted directions.

Beside directivity in compass direction (azimuth) it is also necessary to have the correct type of vertical section to the radiation pattern. It has been shown in Chapter 12 (*Propagation*) how short wave signals travel round the world in a number of " hops." Since each hop introduces attenuation, a minimum number is desirable. This means that for long distance work low-angle radiation is most effective and experience indicates that the maximum radiated power should leave the aerial at an angle between 5° and 15° to the ground. For shorter ranges, say from the skip distance up to 1000 miles or so, a higher angle is needed. The most useful aerial for general work is therefore one which sends most of its energy at low elevation, but leaves a little at higher angles for short range work. The vertical aerial does just this, but has no directivity in azimuth and is said to be omnidirectional. With horizontal aerials it is not usually possible (except at 21 and 28 Mc/s) to place the aerials sufficiently high to achieve very low angle radiation, and directive aerials are therefore used to force the radiation down towards the horizon.

Long wire aerials have very definite radiation patterns, as

will be seen later, but these patterns have several main beams or lobes and hence the gain is not so great as when most of the transmitter power is concentrated into one main beam. In order to achieve the latter condition, two or more elements, such as half wave dipoles, are combined in special ways and the combination is called an *array*. There are two general classes of array—the *broadside array* in which the main beam is at right angles to a plane containing the elements and the *end-fire array* in which the main beam is in the same direction as the row of elements; the two classes are illustrated in **Fig. 30.** It should be noted that the term end-fire refers to the layout of the array and not to the ends of the wires, although the term is sometimes applied to a long wire, because its direction of maximum radiation tends towards the direction of the wire.

Radiation Patterns and Polar Diagrams

In order to send the maximum signal in a given direction horizontal plane directivity is required, but to ensure that the signal " reaches out " vertical plane directivity is necessary. Each of these contributes to the total gain of the aerial. To illustrate the radiation pattern of an aerial, *polar diagrams* are used in the form of curves, the radius of which in any direction represents the relative strength of signals in that direction.

The radiation from an aerial occurs in three dimensions and therefore the radiation pattern is really a solid surface; for example, the solid pattern of a half-wave dipole on page 371. A polar diagram is any section of the solid shape and a large number of sections may be necessary to detail completely an aerial radiation pattern. In practice it is necessary to be content with two polar diagrams taken in the principal planes, usually the horizontal and vertical, and giving the two cross-sections of the main beam.

Where the polar diagram has a definite directional form, the angle between the directions where the power radiated is half the value at the point of maximum gain (−3db) is called the *beam width*. These points are marked on Fig. 41 on page 379.

To avoid confusion when discussing radiation, directions in the horizontal plane are referred to as *azimuth*: angles above the horizontal, in the vertical plane, are called *wave angles*.

It should be remembered that these radiation patterns are

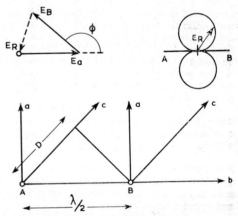

Fig. 31. Illustrating the construction of the radiation pattern of a pair of similar aerials.

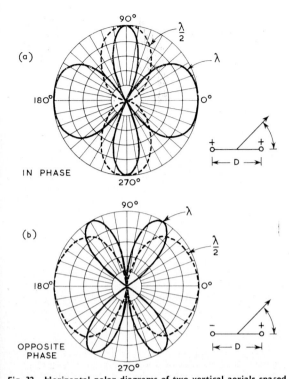

(a)

IN PHASE

(b)

OPPOSITE PHASE

Fig. 32. Horizontal polar diagrams of two vertical aerials spaced $\sqrt{2}$ and λ. The upper diagram is for aerials in phase, the lower diagram for antiphase connection. If separate feeders are used the pattern can be changed by reversing polarity of one feeder. Directions 90°, 270° are broadside: 0°, 180° end-fire. Note that the end-fire diagrams are broader than the broadside ones.

for long distances and cannot be measured locally within a distance of many wavelengths from the aerial.

Construction of Polar Diagrams

Fig. 31 is a plan of two vertical aerials A and B, spaced by one half wavelength, and carrying equal in-phase currents. A receiver at a large distance in the direction a at right angles to the line of the aerials (i.e. *broadside*) receives equally from both A and B. Since the two paths are equal the received components are in phase and directly additive, giving a relative signal strength of two units. In the direction b the signal from A travels one half-wavelength further than that from B. The two received components are therefore one half cycle different, or in antiphase, and so cancel to give zero signal. In an intermediate direction c the two paths are effectively parallel for the very distant receiver, but one component travels further by the distance D. In this case the components have a relative phase $\phi = 360\,D/\lambda$ degrees. The addition for this direction must be made *vectorially* using the " triangle of forces " also illustrated in Fig. 31 in which the two equal lines representing signal strength from A and B are set at the phase angle ϕ which corresponds to the path-difference D; the total or resultant signal is equal to the relative length of the line E_R which completes the triangle. This process could be carried out for all directions, but is tedious and it is usual therefore to convert the operations to a trigonometrical formula from which the result can be calculated more quickly. The polar diagram found in this

way is a figure-of-eight, the curve marked $\lambda/2$ in **Fig. 32(a)** If, on the other hand the two aerials had been in antiphase, the resultant signal would have been zero in the direction a and maximum in direction b and the polar diagram as in **Fig. 32(b)**

A similar procedure is used if the aerials do not carry equal currents, or if they have an arbitrary phase relations. In this case the sides of the triangle would be drawn in lengths proportional to the two aerial currents and the relative phase of these currents would be added to the angle ϕ due to path differences.

The path difference D and phase ϕ of course are proportional to the spacing between the aerials, which in the example above, was one half wavelength. If the spacing is one wavelength then the phase difference changes twice as rapidly with change of direction, and so there are twice as many maxima and minima to the pattern, giving the curves marked λ in Fig. 32. These patterns are said to have four *lobes*.

With increased spacing between the two aerials, more lobes appear, two for each half-wave of spacing, and the pattern becomes like a flower with many petals. This type of pattern is not very useful, but if the intervening space is filled with aerials spaced $\lambda/2$, one pair of lobes grows at the expense of all the others, giving a sharp main beam with a number of relatively small *minor lobes*. This is the basis of stacked beam arrays. It should be noted, however, that the beam is only developed in the plane in which the array is extended; a broadside array of aerials all in phase produces a beam which is narrow in the horizontal plane, but its vertical pattern is the same as that of a single aerial. It is therefore necessary to extend a stacked array in the vertical direction to obtain a sharp vertical pattern. In an end-fire array where the aerials are spaced and phased to give the main lobe along the line of aerials, the vertical and horizontal patterns are developed simultaneously by the single row of radiators because the array is extended simultaneously in both of these planes. The azimuth pattern of an end-fire array is always broader than that of a broadside array of the same length; this effect can be noted in the patterns of Fig. 32.

Unidirectional Patterns

The patterns so far considered are symmetrical: a somewhat different combination of aerials gives a unidirectional pattern. The two dipoles in **Fig. 33** are connected a quarter-wave apart along a common feeder, with a wave entering from the left. In the direction away to the right it does not matter whether radiation leaves via the first aerial or the second; it takes the same time to reach its destination. Thus to the right, the components of radiation are additive because

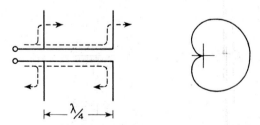

Fig. 33. Illustrating the fundamental principle of the driven reflector. The two wave components have equal path lengths in one direction, and therefore add, but in the other direction the paths differ by $\lambda/2$ and the components cancel. The polar diagram is the geometrical figure called a cardioid (heart shape).

they are in phase. This is shown by the upper set of broken lines. To the left, however, the wave from the end dipole has to travel further than that from the first dipole by a distance equal to twice the spacing between them. This extra journey is one half wavelength and hence the two components differ in phase by 180° and cancel. Because of the λ/4 spacing the currents in the two aerials have a phase difference of 90° and are said to be in *quadrature*.

This fundamental principle is often used in broadside arrays in order to make the sharp radiated beam unidirectional by placing a second set of aerials a quarter-wave behind the main set. For the same reason, long end-fire arrays are built with quarter-wave spacing and progressive 90° phasing. In practice, however, it is extremely difficult to arrange the feeder so that the dipoles have the required currents and phase, and parasitic reflectors are more often used instead, as will be described later.

Array Factor

In the discussion above, the single aerials of an array could be considered as "point sources," that is to say they could have been assumed to radiate uniformly in all directions. The diagrams in Fig. 32 are therefore correct as azimuth patterns of pairs of vertical aerials. If, however, the aerials had been horizontal along the line joining AB, then the patterns would have to be modified; in particular the end-fire radiation could not exist, because the dipoles themselves do not

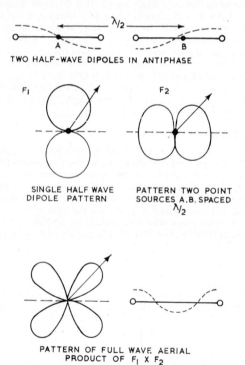

TWO HALF-WAVE DIPOLES IN ANTIPHASE

F_1 SINGLE HALF WAVE DIPOLE PATTERN

F_2 PATTERN TWO POINT SOURCES A.B. SPACED λ/2

PATTERN OF FULL WAVE AERIAL PRODUCT OF F_1 X F_2

Fig. 34. The array factor. Each dipole has a pattern like F_1. Two sources in opposite phase at A and B would have a pattern like F_2. For any direction (e.g., the arrows) the chord F_1 is multiplied by that of F_2 for the same angle. When this is done for all angles the pattern shown at the bottom is obtained for the complete aerial.

radiate that way. In such a case the final pattern is found by modifying the array pattern by that of a dipole which for practical purposes can be taken as a pair of circles. The two corresponding signal strengths of the two patterns are multiplied together for each value of ø as shown in **Fig. 34.** This is expressed symbolically as $F = F_1 \times F_2$ where F is the final pattern, F_1 that of the dipole and F_2 the array factor or pattern of the set of point sources. F_1 is unity for the azimuth pattern of vertical aerials. If each aerial were fitted with a reflector, then another multiplying factor would be included to represent the cardioid (heart shape) of Fig. 33.

The array factor depends on the spacing between the units, treating the centre of each unit as a point source. Vertical plane diagrams are found in the same way, by treating the aerial and its image in the ground as an array of two sources spaced by twice the height of the real aerial. A number of useful vertical patterns are given in **Fig. 35** from which it will be seen that choice of correct height is much more important for a single aerial than for arrays which themselves tend to radiate at low wave angles.

The fundamental difference between vertical and horizontal aerials should be clearly understood: the former can radiate a ground wave but the latter do not because of different image phases.

Effect of Soil

When considering the effect of the ground on the radiation from an aerial, the idea of an image was introduced (Fig. 6); the ground was assumed to be a perfect conductor and, therefore, a perfect reflector. The vertical plane diagrams of Fig. 35 are based on this assumption, but in practice the soil is often far from perfect, behaving rather like a clouded mirror and giving a weak image.

This has the effect that the vertical plane polar diagrams differ from the ideal diagrams for perfect reflectors. The difference is small in the case of horizontal aerials, but with vertical aerials in the h.f. range, the result is a loss of signal, particularly at low angles; for example, the vertical aerial pattern of Figs. 35(b) may become modified as indicated by the broken line patterns. The effect on a vertical aerial is not serious if the aerial can be raised, and this is one reason why ground-plane aerials are more effective than earthed quarter-wave aerials.

Sea-water and marshy ground are both quite good reflectors in the h.f. range: average soil in the British Isles may result in the loss illustrated in Fig. 35. Rocky ground locations are poor for radio communication.

Vertical Aerials

Vertical aerials are not usually made longer than a half-wave unless all the half-waves are brought into phase, because such an aerial would have a multi-lobe vertical radiation pattern. As already explained, vertical aerials are sensitive to the quality of the soil beneath them and various methods of combating earth loss have already been described (e.g. Fig. 19). Their attractiveness for low angle radiation is somewhat offset by the fact that in populated areas they may cause more interference with broadcasting services than horizontal aerials especially where a television transmission is vertically polarized. As receiving aerials, however, they are noticeably superior, because they bring in very much less ionospheric noise than horizontal aerials and, when propagation conditions are favourable, stronger signals.

Long Wire Horizontal Aerials

The basic patterns of aerials of various harmonic lengths are shown in **Fig. 36** and further information is given in **Table 3**. It will be seen that there are two lobes in the diagram for each half-wavelength of wire, and that those nearest the end-on direction are always strongest. It should be remembered that these diagrams are sections, and the reader should try to visualize the lobes as sections of cones about the aerial.

Polar diagrams represent effectively the azimuth directivity of these aerials, but their general assessment must include the effect of height, and this can be done by considering them in relation to the vertical plane diagrams of Fig. 35. There is, however, one very important feature: in conjunction with the ground these aerials produce some radiation off the ends. This may best be appreciated by holding a pencil over a mirror and looking at it from the end-on direction, when it will be seen that in this direction, for angles above the horizontal, the radiation is vertically polarized.

For a dipole one half-wavelength high, the end signal may be only 3db (one S point) less than the broadside at 30° elevation, but the effect is most useful in longer radiators where the end pattern almost fills in for elevations of 15–30°, as shown on the 2λ line in Fig. 36. In the case of a three

TABLE 3
Properties of Long Wire Radiators

Length	Angle of main lobe to wire	Gain of main lobe over half-wave dipole	Radiation resistance
1 λ	54° (90°)	0·4db	90 ohms
1½ λ	42°	1·0db	100 ohms
2 λ	36° (58°)	1·5db	110 ohms
2½ λ	33°	1·8db	115 ohms
3 λ	30° (46°)	2·3db	120 ohms
4 λ	26° (39°)	3·3db	130 ohms
5 λ	22° (35°)	4·2db	140 ohms
6 λ	20° (31°)	5·0db	147 ohms
8 λ	18° (26°)	6·4db	153 ohms
10 λ	16° (23°)	7·4db	160 ohms

The number of complete conical lobes (see Fig. 36) is equal to the number of half-waves in the aerial. The main lobe is the one nearest to the direction of the wire, and the figures in this table give its direction and gain. When a multiple full-wave aerial is centre-fed the pattern is like that of one half, but with more gain in the main lobe. The angles in brackets correspond to this case. When the aerial is terminated, or self-terminating, the radiation resistance is 30 to 50 per cent greater, and the main lobe slightly nearer to the wire.

wavelength long aerial (which would be about 100 ft. for 28 Mc/s) the end radiation at a 15° wave-angle may be much better than the broadside signal from a dipole at the same height.

The long wire aerial is the simplest form of directive aerial and is very popular because it is at the same time a good all-round aerial. Although the notch in the pattern in the

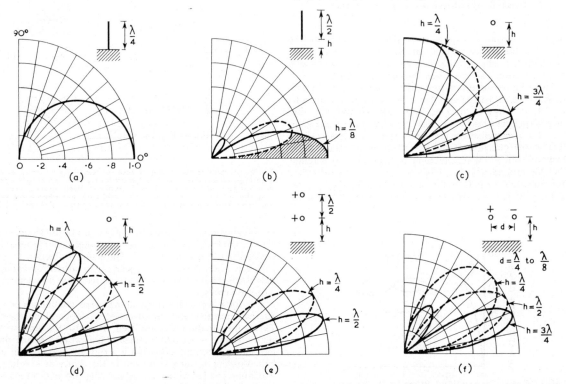

Fig. 35. Vertical plane radiation patterns. (a, b) Vertical aerials. (c, d) Horizontal dipoles and collinear arrays. (e) Broadside horizontal arrays. (f) End-fire horizontal systems—e.g. W8JK. Only half of each pattern is shown: they are symmetrical about the vertical axis, unless reflectors are also used. Diagrams (a) and (b) hold for all azimuth directions: the remainder are for broadside direction only. The beamwidth in azimuth depends on the length of the arrays, as shown in Fig. 41

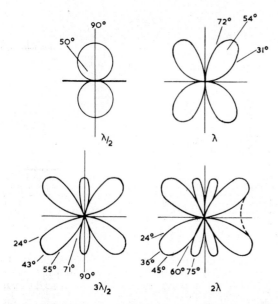

Fig. 36. Theoretical polar diagrams for wire aerials up to 2λ in length. The angles of the main lobes and crevasses are shown, also the angles at which the loss is 3 db in the main lobe. The lobes should be visualized as cones about the wire. When the aerials are horizontal, end-fire radiation can take place at useful wave angles, especially from very long wires, e.g., the broken line on the aerial. Details of long wire aerials are given in Table 3.

broadside direction is quite noticeable, in practice on the even-multiple aerials the effect of the other crevasses is not so marked, chiefly because their direction varies with wave angle, so there is always a way through for signals.

Table 3 gives important properties of wires up to 10 wavelengths long. It will be seen that a 10λ aerial has a main lobe at only 16° angle to the wire, with a gain of over 7db. Remembering that these lobes exist all round the aerial, e.g., in the vertical as well as the horizontal plane, it will be realized that in the direction of the wire there is a vertical polar diagram with a lobe maximum at 16° elevation. It is found that the ground reflection effect is small for this direction, and although the polarization is vertical, a long wire aerial gives good radiation off its end, and can be considerably

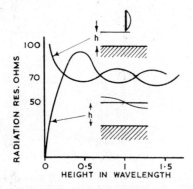

Fig. 37. Radiation resistance of half-wave horizontal and vertical dipoles as a function of height.

better than a half-wave dipole at the same height above ground. (It is this effect which sometimes causes confusion over the use of the term *end-fire* which refers to a particular type of array and not to the direction of a main lobe with respect to a wire.)

The radiation resistance figures in Table 3 are the resistance at any one current maximum, say λ/4 from the end, and are representative free space values, fluctuating somewhat with height as in **Fig. 37**. For example, the radiation resistance of a dipole is very low when it is close to the ground but rises rapidly to over 90 ohms at a height of 0·3λ, drops to about 60 ohms at 0·6λ and then settles about the free space value of 73 ohms for greater heights. The longer aerials behave in a similar way. From Table 3 it will be seen that the resistance increases steadily as the size of the radiating system increases; this is a general rule for all large directive aerial systems.

Effect of Feed Position

The general subject of how to feed energy to a long wire has already been discussed and it was indicated that it could be fed with a single wire at one end or near one end or by tuned feeders in the centre. In each case the system is in fact a

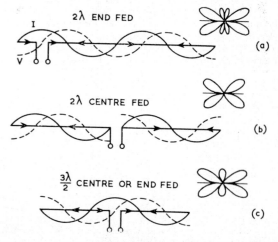

Fig. 38. Illustrating the difference between feeding at a current, or at a voltage maximum, and how centre-feed affects even- and odd-multiple half-wave aerial differently. When the feed enters a current loop the pattern is the same as with end-feed, but when a voltage loop is entered, the pattern is like that of one half only of the aerial.

multi-band aerial. A balanced line can also be used a quarter wavelength from one end but in this arrangement the aerial is essentially a one-band device. The main distinction to be considered here is whether the feed is at a current or voltage maximum, because these alternatives may give two entirely different aerials.

The long wires described above were continuous with alternate positive and negative current loops along them. This is the situation with end-feed. It is also the same with centre-feeding to an odd number of half-waves because the feed enters a current loop. But if a wire an even number of half wavelengths long is broken at the centre at a voltage maximum and fed with balanced line **(Fig. 38)** an extra phase reversal is introduced at this point, as can be seen by sketching the standing waves. Thus a centre-fed three wavelength aerial becomes an array of two 3λ/2 aerials and has a pattern

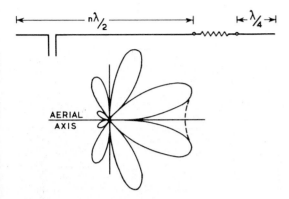

Fig. 39. A 2λ terminated aerial and its radiation pattern, showing end-fire effect. The end-to-end ratio depends on several factors, but may be 3 to 5 db for a full-wave unterminated aerial and more than 10 db for a terminated aerial. The 500 ohm terminating resistor is earthed to a λ/4 artificial earth. A multiple " earth " fan may be used to cover two or three frequency bands, These aerials do not need critical length adjustment.

which is basically that of the 3 λ/2 aerial multiplied by an array factor corresponding to the 3 λ/2 spacing between the centres of the two halves. Since this particular array factor is very nearly the same as the pattern of each half, the final diagram is very like that of a single 3 λ/2 aerial, but with emphasis on the broadside lobe. By comparison the 3λ end-fed aerial has a null in the broadside direction.

End-fire Effect

In practice a long wire fed at one end tends to radiate best from the opposite end, the pattern of a 2λ aerial tending to become like that of **Fig. 39** (these patterns are ideal patterns). This tendency is greater the longer the wire, and occurs because the lobes to the right (in Fig. 39) are due to the radiation from the forward wave along the wire, whilst those toward the left can only be due to the wave reflected from the far end. Because of loss by radiation, the reflected wave is weaker than the forward wave; thus a long wire tends to behave like a lossy transmission line. The one-way effect can be enhanced by joining the far end of the aerial to a quarter wave " artificial earth " wire through a 500 ohm (matching) resistor. This resistor must be able to absorb about 25 per cent of the transmitter power if the aerial is only 2λ long, but only about 10 per cent if it is very much longer. The power lost in this resistor is not wasted because it would all have gone in the opposite direction. Such an aerial is of course only correctly terminated on one band, though a fan of earth wires can be used, one for each band. It can be fed (for one band use) by means of an 80 ohm feeder one quarter wavelength from the free end as in Fig. 39. For multi-band working Zepp feeders at the free end may be used.

BEAM AERIALS

Directive or beam aerials may be divided into two main classes: those using arrays of half wave dipoles and those based on the known directive properties of long wires. In all cases the elements are arranged so that radiation is cumulative in the favoured direction but is minimized in other directions. The first type can be sub-divided into broadside arrays with the main beam at right angles to the plane of the

array and end-fire systems where the main beam is projected along the plane of the elements.

In broadside arrays the elements are connected together by phasing lines, so that they are all in one phase, but in the end-fire aerials the elements may be all connected to give a progressive phase change along the array (driven arrays) or there may be one driven dipole together with a number of nearly resonant free *parasitic* elements which modify the local field of the radiator so that a unidirectional end-fire pattern is produced (*parasitic arrays*). Parasitic reflectors can also be added to broadside arrays to produce a unidirectional beam instead of the fore-and-aft pattern of a single row of elements.

Although these two general classes of array are both effective in producing directivity and gain, their construction and properties are quite distinct. The arrays are resonant and interconnected by tuned lines and are therefore usually limited to one-band use, although special arrangements can be devised which will operate well on two or even three bands, at the cost of having to use tuned feeders. On the other hand their patterns are well defined and relatively free from spurious lobes; in particular the vertical and horizontal patterns of broadside arrays can be controlled separately, since they depend on the height and width respectively. In end-fire arrays this is not possible because the vertical and horizontal patterns both depend on the length. Arrays are, however, fairly complex mechanical and electrical structures and are best suited for fixed direction working; amateurs can usually only build simple arrays for h.f. work, such as the *lazy-H* or the two and three element *Yagi* arrays and although these can be made rotatable, it is in the v.h.f. field where the greatest advantage can be taken of multi-element arrays or stacks.

Long wire aerial arrays are much easier to construct and to make work, and can be erected in situations quite unsuitable for multielement arrays because they require few supports. They also have the advantage that they can be used over wide frequency ranges, say four amateur bands, though the optimum performance is limited to a 2 : 1 frequency range. Their patterns are not so well defined as those of arrays, a difference very noticeable in reception, and, like the end-fire arrays, their vertical and azimuthal patterns are determined simultaneously by the height and length. They can give a remarkable performance in the main beam direction, but tend also to radiate a good signal in all directions, which is to some extent an advantage in transmission but a disadvantage in reception. Long wire arrays do not use reflectors because they can be made unidirectional by terminating them with matching resistances.

In selecting arrangements for amateur work, first consideration should be given to acquiring a low wave-angle for improved long-distance propagation; the effective gain which can be obtained in this way is much greater than is apparent from the radiation patterns alone. The azimuthal pattern should never be too sharp for reception because the amateur requires to search. This leads to a preference for end-fire aerials; where there is space to erect them, long wire types are best because of their simplicity and effectiveness, but where space is limited two-, three- or four-element Yagis are used.

DRIVEN ARRAYS

Broadside Arrays—General

Fig. 40 gives a selection of simple broadside arrays

together with gain and average radiation resistance figures. A variety of feed connections are shown, which are interchangeable as discussed below, and it is apparent how to extend the arrays beyond the number of elements illustrated. For all these arrays the azimuth patterns can be estimated as a function of the length of the array from **Fig. 41** and the broadside vertical patterns, as a function of height from Fig. 35.

In broadside arrays, the elements are all in phase and the interconnecting *phasing lines* or stubs must be adjusted to secure this condition. The spacing between elements and between the centre of the elements need not be one half-wave, but can vary up to $\frac{3}{4}\lambda$, beyond which minor lobes in the pattern become too large to ignore. The choice of spacing is, however, in practice dependent on the type of phasing line used. The position of the feed-point depends on the input impedance required, or on the fact that some of the simpler arrays will operate on more than one band. A centre feed position should be used if possible, especially in long arrays, because power is being radiated as the currents travel along the array, and the more distant elements may not receive

their proper share. Uneven power distribution can cause the beam to broaden and " squint."

Collinear Arrays

The collinear array is the simplest method of obtaining a sharp azimuthal pattern and is simply a row of half-wave radiators strung end-to-end. To bring all elements into phase it is necessary to provide a phase reversing stub between the high voltage ends of each pair, except where the position is occupied by the feeder.

The simplest form of array is the centre-fed full-wave or *double Zepp* with a high impedance tuned line feed at the centre. In this form it can be used on other bands; when the total length is only one half-wave the impedance is between 60 and 100 ohms, but in the full-wave condition it is 5,000 ohms or more. When the frequency is raised to the value giving three half-waves the impedance is about 100 ohms, whilst at two full-waves it is about 3,000 ohms. The high impedances can be lowered to between 1,000 and 2,000 ohms by using a flat top of twin wires 2–3 ft. apart, joined in parallel, in order to improve the v.s.w.r. on a 300 ohm line;

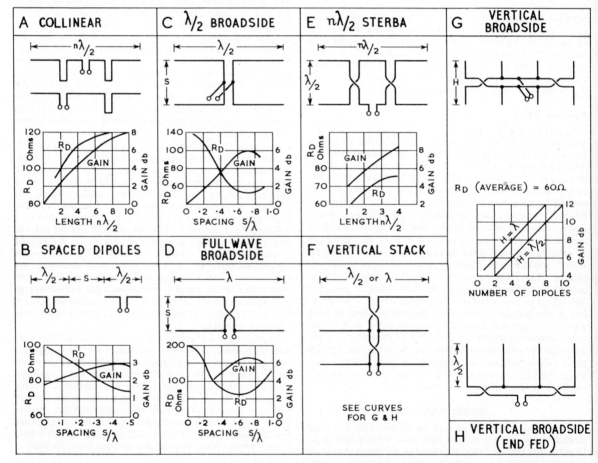

Fig. 40. Four general types of broadside array. (a) Collinear arrays. (b) End-spaced dipoles. (c, d, e) Two-tier, Sterba or Barrage arrays. (f) Pine tree or Koomans, stacked horizontal $\lambda/2$ or λ dipoles. (g,h) Vertically polarized broadside arrays. Gain figures are with reference to a free-space dipole, in terms of spacing or total length in half-waves. Resistance figures are average over the array, and are added in series or parallel according to the feed arrangements, as described in the text. Various feed positions are shown, and details given in the text. The aerial in (c) can be arranged to give a broadside beam over a 2 : 1 frequency range, e.g. 14, 21 and 28 Mc/s.

this does not alter the low impedance value. The broadside beam would only occur on the bands corresponding to half- and full-wave; on other bands the pattern would be that of the long wire type.

Tuning and Matching Collinear Arrays

In order to match a full wave aerial, a closed quarter wave stub may be added at the centre and 80 or 150 ohm twin connected into the centre of one dipole, or 300 or 600 ohm line tapped into the stub (Fig. 22(b)). The array needs tuning when a stub is used, and for this purpose the stub is made a little too long and a moving short-circuit provided. It may be possible to couple a grid dip oscillator into the bottom of the stub to find resonance. Approximate dimensions (in feet) are given by $470/f$ (Mc/s) for the radiators and $240/f$ for each leg of the stub.

The full-wave radiator can be extended to about $1\frac{1}{4}$ wavelengths (extended double Zepp) in which case the gain is increased to 3db and the v.s.w.r. reduced to about 6 on a 600 ohm line, and may be reduced further if a tuning stub, about $\frac{1}{8}$ wave long is added in parallel at the feed point. Fig. 40(b) is useful variation in which the two halves are separated, because the two equal low impedance feed lines can be connected in parallel, in or out of phase by means of a plug connector in the station, giving broadside or full-wave pattern at will. When the gap is $\lambda/2$ the pattern may be found by multiplying the λ-patterns of Fig. 32 by $sin\,\varnothing$ where $\varnothing$ is the angle to the wire (see *Array Factors*).

Longer arrays may use $\frac{1}{2}$ to $\frac{5}{8}$ wavelength elements with tuning stubs and a feed point either at the centre of one element (current maximum) or at a phase reversal point (voltage maximum). The impedance at the centre of any element rises rapidly with the number of elements but falls rapidly at the phase reversal position, the two meeting at about 1200 ohms which is the characteristic impedance of a balanced aerial. These longer aerials should be tuned up section by section as described above, the total length of wire in feet between centres of shorting bars being $950/f$ (Mc/s).

Horizontal Broadside Arrays

These aerials, consisting of two horizontal arrays one above the other, give more gain than the collinear arrays for the same number of dipoles. At low wave angles their azimuthal patterns are the same as for collinear arrays, but the vertical pattern has only one main lobe whatever the height. By comparing the pattern of Fig. 35(d) for a dipole one wavelength high with Fig. 35(e) for $h = \lambda/2$ (total height λ), it will be seen that all the energy is in the low angle lobe, and this gives greater effective gain and improvement of signal stability at long distances.

Three Band Array

The basic model using two half-wave dipoles (**Fig. 40(c)**) can be used as a broadside array over a 2 : 1 frequency band— e.g. 14, 21 and 28 Mc/s. For this purpose the vertical spacing at the lowest frequency should be $\frac{3}{8}$ of a wavelength so that at the upper frequency it will be $\frac{3}{4}$ of a wavelength. The phasing line should be 600 ohms (not crossed) with the feed point at its centre. Since it is not practicable to match over three bands it will be necessary to use tuned lines. The v.s.w.r. on 300 or 600 ohm main feeder will be between 6 and

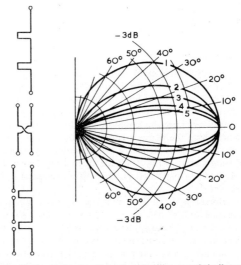

Fig. 41. Horizontal polar diagrams of collinear and similar arrays, for one to five half-waves overall length, showing half-power points (—3 db). Without a reflector the patterns are bi-directional. With a reflector, or in the case of a W8JK aerial, the patterns are only very slightly sharper, because the forward pattern of a dipole and reflector in this plane is very little different from that of a dipole, Minor lobes are not shown but should be —14 db or lower in a well adjusted array. The pattern of a 1·25λ dipole is slightly sharper than that of a full-wave dipole, but has minor lobes at —10 db level at about 60° (see Fig. 35(b)). Vertical patterns of vertically stacked dipoles are also represented by the upper half of the above curves.

10 and cannot easily be improved. There is nothing critical about any dimensions on this aerial. Methods of matching it to a line on any one frequency are considered later in this section. Arrays of four or more elements are, of course, one-band aerials.

Lazy-H and Sterba Curtain

When the array is one wavelength long it is called a *lazy-H* and the effective gain is quite high especially if the upper wire can be placed at a height of one wavelength. With the phasing line connected as in **Fig. 40(d)** it must be electrically a half wavelength long and crossed to restore phase. The impedance across the bottom end of the phasing line is then of the order of 3000 ohms and a $\lambda/4$ stub transformer would be the best matching arrangement (Fig. 22(b)). On the other hand, if it is connected as in Fig. 40(c) with a centre tap feed, there is no need to cross the line as its two branches are always in phase. This connection makes use of the quarter-wave transformer effect in the 600 ohm phase line and will reduce the feed point resistance to around 70 ohms so that a low impedance feeder can be used.

Longer arrays have, of course, sharper patterns and greater gain, generally up to 4db more than a collinear array of the same length. The loading due to radiation is also high so that a six-element array with series feed (**Fig. 40(e)**) would have effectively the input impedance of six dipoles in series, say 500 ohms, whilst an eight element array fed at the base of the centre phase line would be like four full-wave centre fed aerials in parallel, about 800 ohms. In either case, the v.s.w.r. on a 600 ohm line would be low enough without extra matching. The element length (feet) should be about

470/f (Mc/s) and the phasing line on these larger aerials may be 600 ohms open wire or 300 ohms ribbon and of resonant length.

Phasing Lines

When the phasing lines are part of a series connection (e.g. Fig. 40(d) and (e)) they must be electrically one or more complete half wavelengths long. When the length is $\lambda/2$ they must be transposed to recover the phase reversal due to the wave travelling along the length of line, but if they are one wavelength long the phase is restored and the lines are not crossed. However, if the feeder is tapped into the middle of the phasing line as in Fig. 40(c) the current divides in phase regardless of its length and no cross-over is needed in that phasing line.

The velocity factor of open wire lines is nearly unity and the length factor for a half-wave is 480-490; thus it is usually necessary to space the upper and lower rows by $\lambda/2$ in order to achieve a practical construction. When 300 ohm ribbon is used advantage can be taken of its velocity factor of 0.8 and the aerials spaced vertically by $\frac{3}{8}$ wave with an electrical half-wave of ribbon (365/f) or $\frac{3}{4}$ wave with a full-wave of ribbon. On the other hand 300 ohm ribbon is not so good for small arrays because in such applications it carries a high v.s.w.r.

Broadside Verticals and Stacks

The vertical broadside arrays are attractive because they have the low angle radiating properties of vertical aerials, but they require elaborate supports and are thus not likely to be used except on 21 or 28 Mc/s. Vertical patterns of such arrays are given in Fig. 35(a) (b), and horizontal patterns for two elements in Fig. 32. The patterns are broader than those of the equivalent collinear arrays. The half-wave dipole impedances with mutual effects tend to average 60 ohms.

The stack of horizontal dipoles is really the same aerial rotated. Its azimuth pattern is that of a single horizontal element; the vertical pattern is not illustrated, but improves on that given in Fig. 35(e), as the number of elements

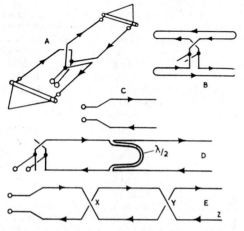

Fig. 42. Flat-top or W8JK arrays showing various methods of connecting, feeding, and matching.

increases. In these arrays advantage can be taken of the velocity factor of 80 ohm line (0.67) or 300 ohm lines (0.8) to make the phasing lines one wavelength long (uncrossed) and increase the spacing of the elements to $2/3\lambda$ or $3/4\lambda$, but the 80 ohm line should not be used with full wave dipoles because of the high v.s.w.r. it would carry.

"Flat Top" or W8JK End-fire Array

These aerials use two anti-phase radiators side by side (Fig. 42) and force the broadside radiation to low angles by cancelling the radiation in upward directions. The vertical patterns are given in Fig. 35(f). It will be seen that the wave

TABLE 4

Impedance Values for W8JK Aerials

Spacing S/λ	$L = \lambda/2$		$L = \lambda$	
	R_d	R_a	R_d	R_e
0·1	6	40,000	10	50,000
0·15	12	20,000	20	25,000
0·2	20	12,000	30	16,000
0·25	33	7,500	50	10,000
0·3	46	5,500	65	8,000
0·4	64	4,000	100	5,000
0·5	85	3,000	125	4,000

Approximate theoretical impedances in ohms at two points of a W8JK array. R_d is the impedance at the centre of any half-wave element and R_e the impedance to earth of any free end. Figures are based on an aerial characteristic impedance of 500 ohms.

angle drops as the height is raised, but the pattern does not break up at certain heights, as does that of a single wire, and so the height is not critical.

The radiators may be separated by light wooden spreaders, hanging from two supports, and the feed applied to a symmetrical point such as the exact centre of the phasing line. One side of the phasing line is always transposed, but its length is not important, except that for matching it may be convenient to have each branch a quarter wavelength long. In any case it is better to let it hang as a V so that the weight of the feeder does not pull the radiators together.

The radiators may be half wave, full wave, or extended like a collinear array. With a two or four element flat top array, the elements are half wavelength long and not critical, but in a longer array the distance between cross-over centres or between cross over centre and free end must be a resonant length. Alternatively, the phasing line can be made half-wave long (uncrossed) using 600 ohm line, and left to hang (Fig. 42(d)). The dipole lengths are slightly affected by mutual impedances: a suitable length (feet) is 460/f (Mc/s) for dipoles and 480/f for full wave aerials in these arrays.

The theoretical gain relative to a half-wave dipole is 2.5db at half-wave spacing between elements rising to nearly 4db at very small spacings. These gains are added to the collinear gain if more than two elements are used. Close spacing is attractive because apart from the higher gain the aerial is easier to support and mechanically more stable, but it will be seen from **Table 4** that radiation resistance drops to very low values at small spacings. This means large standing waves, high currents and voltages, and intense local field, which all result in power loss through conductor resistance or dielectric losses in insulators and spreaders. As a result the theoretical gain is never reached, but 3.5db can be obtained if precautions are taken.

A flat top beam comprising two half-wave dipoles spaced

TABLE 5

Input Impedances of W8JK Aerials

S/λ	$\lambda/4$ Branch Z_0	Input Impedance $\lambda/2$, 1-2-3-Fold			Fullwave Input Impedance
		1	2	3	
0·15	80	250	70	30	
	150	900	250	100	4,000
	300	—	900	400	
	600	—	—	1,600	
0·2	80	160	40	—	
	150	600	150	60	2,500
	300	—	600	250	
	600	—	—	1,000	
0·25	80	100		—	
	150	300	80	—	2,000
	300	—	300	150	
	600	—	—	600	

A few phasing-line transformer arrangements for half-wave and full-wave W8JK aerials using single or folded elements. Figures are only approximate, and are based on an aerial characteristic impedance of 500 ohms. The full wave input impedances are for single wire elements.

0·15 to 0·2λ at 14 Mc/s can be used as a full wave array of 28 Mc/s, where spacing would become 0·3 to 0·4λ and although the v.s.w.r. on the line may be high on one or more bands the aerial will at the same time perform as a beam on 21 Mc/s.

Table 4 gives dipole centre- and end-impedances for half- and full-wave arrays; it will be seen that with spacing less than 0·2λ power loss can easily occur, due to large currents in the wire and high voltages across the insulators and matching to a line may be difficult. One way to deal with the extreme impedances is to remove them by folding the radiators two or three times **(Fig. 42(b))**. This multiplies the low centre impedance by four or nine, and reduces the high impedance by the same factor. The two branch feed lines can then be used as quarter-wave transformers using suitable cable to achieve the required feed point impedance. A few examples are given in **Table 5**. An alternative method of matching using transformers in the line would be found difficult due to the high v.s.w.r.

PARASITIC ARRAYS

The broadside arrays of the previous section radiate equally fore and aft. In order to make them unidirectional, reflectors are added behind each dipole of the array. In theory, driven reflectors can raise the forward gain of an array by 3db, or that of a single dipole by 4db and at the same time produce a high front-to-back signal ratio. In practice it is very difficult to adjust arrays with driven reflectors so that the currents are equal in amplitude and 90° in phase as required by theory, because the effect of mutual impedance is to produce unequal radiation resistances in aerial and reflector.

It has been found much simpler and just as effective to use a parasitic *reflector*, which picks up some of the power of the driven dipole and re-radiates it in the required phase. At a quarter-wave spacing the coupling between aerials is however too low, and better performance is obtained by reducing the spacing and at the same time increasing the length of the reflector to make it inductive, i.e. lagging in phase: this adjusts the phase of the induced current to suit the reduced time of travel between the closer elements. The resulting array has more gain than a driven pair: at the optimum

spacing of 0·15λ the gain is 5db, and the front-to-back ratio about 12db, but the input resistance falls to 25 ohms.

The parasitic element may also be cut shorter than resonant length, so that it is capacitive or leading in phase. In this case it draws the wave forward, and at the same time cancels the radiation in the opposite direction. Such a parasitic element, called a *director*, gives a little more gain than a reflector, with a much better front-to-back ratio, especially at close spacings. It is therefore more commonly used. The optimum spacing is 0·1λ where the maximum gain is just over 5db, with the director tuned as described later. The best front-to-back ratio, 15 to 17db, occurs with a somewhat shorter director, and the gain is then slightly less. If the spacing is reduced to 0·05λ, a front-to-back ratio of over 25db can be obtained with the same gain but the aerial impedance is then very low, and fluctuates violently with movement of the conductors in the wind so that such close spacing is avoided in practice.

Adjustments in these aerials are usually made for best back-to-front ratio, because in these aerials the gain does not change very rapidly as the parasite length is adjusted, and because of the advantage of interference reduction, particularly in reception. This may be done by comparing received signals from local stations, or if the aerial can be rotated, by transmitting to or receiving from a fixed station.

A field strength indicator may help in the adjustment of these arrays, but does not give the best result, because the local field of any aerial is very different from the distant field, especially near the ground. If a field strength meter is used it should be connected to a short dipole, set up parallel to the array, at the same height and as far away as possible. An important point is that the impedance of the driven aerial changes rapidly when the parasitic element is tuned, so that the power drawn from the transmitter also varies with this tuning. Thus, unless a power-flow monitor, not an ammeter but a reflectometer (see Chapter 19—*Measurements*), is used the maximum aerial gain adjustment will not be obtained.

Two Element Arrays

The adjustment for best front-to-back ratio will give a little less than maximum gain, but once the advantage of a good ratio has been experienced in reception, it will be realized that this slight loss is well justified. It will be found that the best reflector for this aim is somewhat longer, or the best director somewhat shorter than the length giving maximum gain.

Two-element aerials of these types can be constructed for 14 Mc/s and higher frequencies, in fixed or rotating form, and as suspended wire aerials for 7 Mc/s. Rotating arrays are usually made of rigid metal tubing. When the array is fixed, for example supported between spreaders, good insulators should be used at the ends of the wires as the voltages there are relatively high, and serious loss can therefore easily occur. In the case of fixed arrays, it is convenient to be able to reverse direction, and this may be arranged by changing the parasitic element from reflector to director, using a U-section or stub in the centre which can be shorted out to change from the length of reflector to that of director. This stub can, in fact, be extended by one half or one full wavelength using 600 or 300 ohm twin line, so that the position of the shorting link can be changed at ground level without lowering the aerial.

From **Table 6,** it will be seen that 0·1λ is a good value of spacing for a combined reflector/director system; this is 7 ft. for 14 Mc/s. At this spacing the feed point impedance at the centre of the driven aerial is between 15 and 30 ohms, and the aerial is fairly sharply tuned, but can still effectively cover the 14 Mc/s band. To match this impedance to available transmission lines, a transformer is needed, and this should be introduced as near the aerial as possible in order to preserve bandwidth. The best way to do this is in the aerial itself, by using a folded radiator. A two-fold type, such as the 300 ohm ribbon folded dipole, will bring the feed impedance to a value suitable for 70–80 ohm twin feeder. When the array is rotatable and self-supporting, folding is not really practicable and open wire twin line is not suitable because it changes its characteristics as it wraps itself round the supporting mast. However, the transformers given later for

TABLE 6
Properties of Two-element Parasitic Arrays

Spacing	Reflector				Director			
s/λ	X	Gain	F/B	X	X	Gain	F/B	Rd
	ohms	db	db	ohms	ohms	db	db	ohms
0·05λ	—	—	—	—	−10	4·4	20	13
					+10	5·6	6·6	4
0·1λ	+30	5	6	16	−10	5·2	7·8	14
	+50	4	10	26	−40	4·2	17	33
0·15λ	+20	5	6	35	—	—	—	—
	+50	4	10	50	—	—	—	—

Theoretical properties of two-element parasitic arrays, which are largely realized in practice. The tuning of the parasitic element is given in terms of reactance X (see Fig. 43). Gain and front/back ratios are given in db, and feed resistance Rd in ohms. Of the two sets of figures given for each spacing, one is for maximum gain and the other maximum front/back ratio.

three-element arrays may be used, the adjustments being practically the same.

Tuning the Parasitic Elements

Formulae for element lengths are frequently quoted, but are not useful unless the diameter of the elements is also specified. What controls the performance is the reactance of the parasitic element; that is, the amount by which the element is detuned from resonance, and this, in terms of length, depends on the length/diameter ratio. **Fig. 43** shows reactance as a function of percentage change of length for various relative conductor diameters. The crossover point of the curves occurs when the radiator is a true free-space half wavelength long calculated as 492/f (ft., Mc/s). At this length the conductors all have a reactance of about + 40 ohms, and must be *end corrected* by the percentage which brings the reactance to zero to obtain resonance. For example, the correction for a relatively " fat " aerial, with L/d = 100, is 5·5 per cent so that for 28·0 Mc/s the full half-wave would be 17 ft. 6 in. and the end correction 1 ft., making the resonant length 16 ft. 6 in.

The best reflector has a positive reactance of about 40 ohms, which brings its length to almost a true half-wave, independently of diameter. For 0·1λ spacing, best director action occurs at −10 to −40 ohms reactance with a length some 5 to 10 per cent shorter than the full half wavelength. For example, at 21·0 Mc/s, λ/2 = 492/f = 23·4 ft. A 1 in. diameter half-wave radiator would have a L/d ratio of about 300, and an end-correction of −4·4 per cent, giving a resonant length of 22 ft. 4 in., whilst a director of −30 ohms reactance would be 7·4 per cent short of true half-wave, or 21 ft. 7 in.

In practice it is always advisable to find the best adjustment experimentally, using the above theory as a guide, because the environment of the aerial has some effect. The parasitic elements can be tuned first, independently of the driven element, which may then be adjusted for optimum tuning and impedance match, as described later.

Three- and Four-element Parasitic Arrays

Improved performance can be obtained by a combination of reflector and one or more directors, the usual arrangement having all the elements in one plane. Such aerials are called *Yagi* arrays, after their inventor, and give as much gain as can practically be obtained in the space they occupy. They have a relatively compact beam of radiation in the direction of the directors. There is no advantage in using more than one reflector in an in-line array, though many directors may

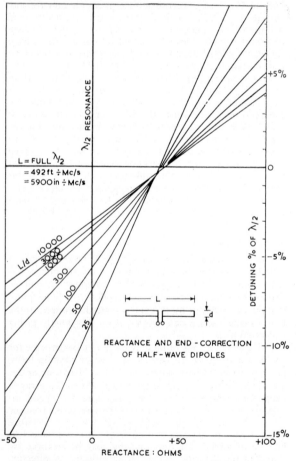

Fig. 43. Tuning and reactance chart for half-wave dipoles, as a function of the length-diameter ratio. A radiator exactly half-wave long is " over tuned " by 42 ohms, and " end correction," given as a percentage of the length, is necessary to bring it to resonance (zero reactance). The chart is useful for the construction of parasitic arrays and v.h.f. dipoles. Each I per cent. of length corresponds to 5 units in the factor 492/f or 60 in 5,900/f (f is in Mc/s).

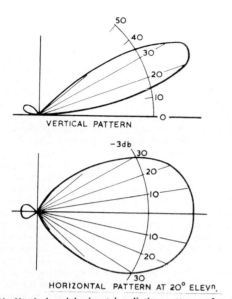

Fig. 44. Vertical and horizontal radiation patterns of a three-element Yagi array spaced 0·15 + 0·15λ, and erected at a height of one half-wavelength. These patterns, which were obtained from a scale model, do not vary much with other spacings of the elements. The vertical pattern is quite narrow compared to the free-space pattern and this is due to choice of correct height. At a height of λ the pattern is also good but at 3λ/4 an extra lobe appears in the vertical pattern. Note that the front/back ratio near the ground may be very different from that at 20° elevation.

be used with advantage. For h.f. work one, or at the most, two, directors are the limit because of the size of the array, but in the v.h.f. bands longer arrays with more than three elements may be built, and are described in Chapter 14.

The characteristics of two-element arrays can be calculated quite well, but three or more elements lead to such complexity that their analysis requires a computer. A vast amount of experiment by amateurs and others has, however, resulted in comprehensive knowledge, and an infinite variety of prescriptions for element lengths and spacings.

The vertical and horizontal radiation patterns of a three element Yagi array are given in **Fig. 44.**

The maximum theoretical gain obtainable is 7·5db for three elements and nearly 9db for four elements. These patterns have their half-power points at a beamwidth of about 55° in the *E*-plane (the plane of the elements) and 65–75° in the *H*-plane (at right angles to the elements). These high gains are, unfortunately, associated with a feed-point resistance of only a few ohms, so that in practice the loss due to conductor resistance and environment may be appreciable in proportion. In addition, the tuning is very sharp, so the array will only work usefully over a small part of, say, the 14 Mc/s band, whilst the line matching for a low v.s.w.r. is very difficult.

The power loss due to conductor resistance, or high feeder v.s.w.r., is such that these high gains are never realized in practice. It is better, therefore, to design the aerial for less gain, but better general performance. How this can be done is best seen with the aid of **Fig. 45.** This is a " contour " map of gain and impedance as a function of parasitic tuning, for a Yagi with element spacings of 0·15λ. The lower right-hand corner of the chart is clearly the region to aim for where the gain is still over 6db (or 7db for four elements) whilst the

feed resistance approaches 20 ohms. This region of the chart corresponds to rather long reflectors (+ 40 to + 50 ohms reactance) and rather shorter than optimum directors (− 30 to − 40 ohms) and also is found to be the region of best front-to-back ratio.

Although the chart is for aerials with both spacings equal to 0·15λ, the resistance and bandwidth are both somewhat improved, with the gain remaining over 6db, if the reflector spacing is raised to 0·2λ and the director spacing reduced to 0·1λ. Such an array would operate satisfactorily over at least half the 28–29·7 Mc/s band or the whole of any other band on which it could be used.

The overall array length of 0·3λ is practicable on all bands from 14 Mc/s upwards, though the 20 ft. boom required for a 14 Mc/s array is rather heavy for a rotary array, and there is a temptation to shorten it. Spacings should not be reduced below 0·1λ for both reflector and director as the tuning will again become too critical and the transmitter load unstable as the elements or the feeder move in the wind.

The optimum tunings do not vary appreciably for the different spacings, and it is therefore possible to construct a practical design chart **(Fig. 46).** An array, made with its element lengths falling in the shaded regions of the diagram, will give good performance without further adjustment. The length of the director may be decided in advance. The reflector may then be adjusted experimentally to improve the front-to-back ratio. It will be seen that the radiator is somewhat longer than a normal dipole; this is because the parasitic elements have a detuning effect on it. The addition of a second director also spaced 0·1 to 0·15λ will not materially affect the above recommendations, and can be expected to increase the gain by 1db.

The adjustment of the array can be carried out as indicated for two element arrays, using the front-to-back ratio as the

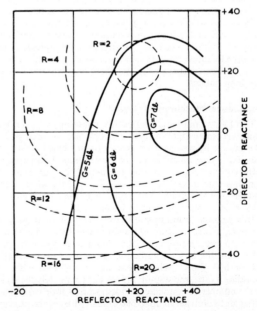

Fig. 45. Contour chart showing contours of gain (solid lines) and input resistance (broken lines) as a function of the tuning of the parasitic elements. This chart is for a spacing of 0·15λ between elements, but is also typical of arrays using 0·2 + 0·1 spacings.

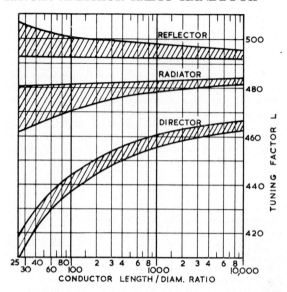

Fig. 46. Design chart for Yagi arrays, giving element lengths as a function of conductor length-to-diameter ratio. The tuning factor L is divided by the frequency in Mc/s to give the lengths in feet. These curves are for arrays of overall length 0·3λ, with reflector reactance + 40 to + 60 ohms and director —30 to —40 ohms, and give arrays of input impedance between 15 and 20 ohms. Element lengths which fall within the shaded areas will give an array which can be used without further adjustment, though the front/back ratio may be improved by adjusting the reflector.

criterion. For this purpose the elements can be made with sliding tube extensions or, alternatively, a short variable stub can be fitted at the centre. The tuning-up can be carried out without reference to impedance matching, which is always the last operation. Adjustments should be made with the array as high and as clear as possible, since tuning alters near the ground, and performance should be checked with the array in its final position. It should be emphasized that attempts to adjust for maximum gain lead inevitably into the top right-hand corner of Fig. 45 where bandwidth is low and matching difficult.

Impedance Matching of Yagis

The 15–20 ohm aerial impedance resulting from the foregoing recommendations can conveniently be matched to 80 ohm line by a single fold of the driven element. Since the impedance rises on either side of the optimum frequency, it is better not to match at this frequency, but to bring the impedance up to say, 60 ohms (v.s.w.r. = 1·3 with minimum voltage at the aerial). The aerial will then hold within a v.s.w.r. of 2 over a somewhat wider band.

It is possible to multiple-fold the driven element using, for example, a rigid central tube surrounded by a cage of wires joined to radial struts a few inches long at the free ends of the tubes. In this way the radiation resistance can be raised to 300 or 600 ohms. When there are several thin wires surrounding a tube, the step-up ratio is approximately the square of the number of conductors added, so that four wires would bring an 18 ohm aerial up to 300 ohms. Most of the examples which have been published are for maximum-gain Yagis, with a basic feed impedance of 6 to 8 ohms, and use up to nine wires. It is claimed that this multi-folding restores the

bandwidth, but this is doubtful since it is the parasitic elements which are responsible for the high Q.

It will be appreciated that two adjustments are necessary for matching to the feed line, namely, tuning and transformer ratio. Most of the known matching arrangements provide only one of these, and the operation of adjusting the length of the radiator at the same time as the transformer is tedious and difficult. The T and Gamma transformers of **Fig. 47** are in this class, and behave like two-winding transformers of such high leakage inductance that it is not possible to restore the tuning of the aerial without inserting a capacitor.

The realization of this led to the development of the *Clemens Match*, illustrated in **Fig. 48**. This arrangement is the best, and will cater for a very wide range of impedance transformations. The coaxial feeder cable is bonded to the centre " neutral " point of the aerial, and then carried along one side to a distance of 0·06λ (⅛ of the length of the aerial) where the outer conductor is bonded to the aerial and the inner conductor is joined to a tube of about one-third of the aerial diameter. The tube is spaced a few inches from the aerial and its far end is connected to the aerial through a capacitance. The spacing of the tube, varying from 0·01 to 0·02λ, adjusts the ratio, and the capacitor tunes out the transformer reactance and also helps with the tuning of the radiator. The capacitance will not exceed 50 pF at 14 Mc/s or higher frequencies. For the purpose of making adjustments, a variable capacitor may be used, being finally replaced by a high-voltage foil/mica capacitor of the required value, or by a short length of open-circuit concentric r.f. cable, reckoning 70 ohm cable as 22 pF per foot, and 50 ohm cable as 30 pF per foot. The cable can be tucked inside the transformer tubing, and should be sealed against damp, Bostick sealing strip or Sylglas tape both being very reliable for the purpose.

If balanced unscreened feeder is used with a Yagi, it is necessary to keep it away from the mast, particularly if the array is rotatable. Such a feeder is therefore troublesome, and coaxial cable is preferable. With coax it is necessary to use some method of transforming from the balanced aerial to the unbalanced line. Stub baluns (*bal*ance-to-*un*balance transformers—see Chapter 14) are used at v.h.f. but are inconvenient for h.f. work because of their length. The Clemens match of Fig. 48 solves the problem by attaching

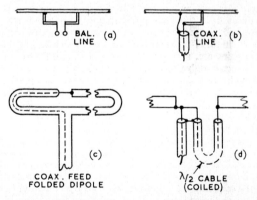

Fig. 47. Feed connections for Yagi arrays. The upper diagrams show T and gamma matching transformers for balanced and concentric lines respectively. The lower diagrams show two ways of connecting the balanced aerial into concentric (unbalanced) line. Other arrangements are shown in Fig. 48, and in Chapter 14.

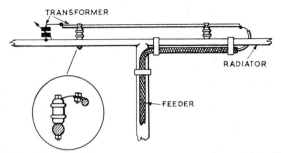

Fig. 48. The Clemens transformer, a flexible arrangement which will match a wide range of dipole impedances into a concentric 50 or 70 ohm line, and at the same time convert from balanced-to-unbalanced circuits.

the sheath to a neutral point of the system. Another method suitable for folded aerials is illustrated in Fig. 47(c). Here the whole cable is taken inside the aerial tube, or bonded along the outside, its inner and outer conductors being connected across the gap in the folded dipole. A further method is shown in Fig. 47(d) where an extra half-wave of cable is used to secure the phase split necessary for balance.

The Quad Aerial

A moderately compact directional array is the *quad aerial*, illustrated in **Fig. 49.** Compared with a three-element Yagi it has noticeably more gain, much wider bandwidth, and is

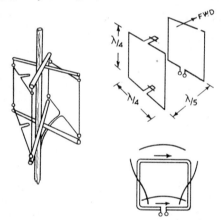

Fig. 49. The quad aerial. Diagrams showing approximate dimensions of the array, current distribution on the loops, and outline sketch of supporting structure for a rotary model. The cross arms would be set at an angle of 52° to the forward direction for $\lambda/5$ spacing of the loops, and their length would be $\lambda/3$. Bracing wires or nylon cords are advisable but are not shown in the sketch.

easier to adjust: it can be rotated in a smaller space, but it may be more difficult to produce a satisfactory construction.

The aerial is based on a quarter-wave square loop, and it will be seen from the diagram that the upper and lower sections of the radiator are in phase, but the current reverses in the side arms, so that the radiation from these is negligible. A single loop, horizontally polarized as shown, has a horizontal radiation pattern similar to that of a half-wave aerial. In the other plane the pattern is dumb-bell shaped because the two radiators are only $\lambda/4$ apart. The radiation resistance of a single loop is approximately 100 ohms, but the gain of

one loop alone is small, so that the loop by itself is not useful. With the addition of a reflector loop spaced by 0.2λ, a high front-to-back ratio is easily obtained and the gain is greater than a three element Yagi.

As with a two-element linear array, it is necessary to tune the reflector to a lower frequency and this can best be done by fitting two short tuning stubs in positions corresponding to the feed point, as shown in Fig. 49. The length of these stubs should be about 10 per cent of that of one side of the loop, using sliding shorting bars. It will be found quite easy to adjust the stubs for a front-to-back ratio of 20db or more. If this must be done with the aerial near ground it is best to make the adjustments with vertical polarization, i.e. with the array turned on its side. When the aerial is horizontally polarized, there are minor lobes of −15db amplitude at about 120° from the forward direction.

The quad aerial exhibits double tuning properties and it is possible to adjust its impedance simply by varying the size of the radiator loop. For use with 70 ohm twin feeders, the length in feet of side should be $240/f$ (Mc/s) corresponding to 16 ft. 9 in. for 14·2 Mc/s; such an array will cover the whole 14 Mc/s band. If the length factor is $250/f$ (17 ft. 6 in. for 14·2 Mc/s) the impedance rises to 150 ohms, and the bandwidth improves. A 28 Mc/s quad built to this larger scale will cover the whole band with a v.s.w.r. of not more than 1·5 on a 150 ohm twin feeder. The spacing between radiator and reflector is 0.2λ ($=200/f$ (Mc/s), measured in feet. If it is desired to match a quad to other types of feeder the radiator may be " folded "; for example, by using two turns of wire in the driven element, a nominally 70 ohm quad will match 300 ohm feeder and a 150 ohm model will match 600 ohm line. For co-axial cable, the Clemens match described on page 384 will meet all requirements.

A quad aerial is practicable for 14 Mc/s but it is, of course, a one-band aerial; however, 21 and 28 Mc/s quads can be nested inside a 14 Mc/s structure without serious interference. For a rotary array, the elements can be of wire suspended between horizontal upper and lower cross-arms, suitably braced. The cross-arms may be made of bamboo poles or fibreglass rods. If bamboo is used, it should be varnished to protect it from the weather.

The array is normally used with horizontal polarization, as illustrated, in which case the height of the centre should preferably be between $\frac{1}{2}$ and $\frac{3}{4}$ wavelength. If this is not practicable it may be better to use vertical polarization, though at some greater risk of interference to nearby sound or television receivers.

LONG WIRE BEAM AERIALS

The Vee

A long wire aerial two wavelengths long has a lobe of maximum radiation at an angle of 36° to the wire. If two such aerials are erected horizontally in the form of a *V* with an included angle of 72°, and if the phasing between them is correct, the two pairs of lobes will add fore and aft along the axis of the *V*. Remaining lobes do not act in this way, hence the *V aerial* produces one major beam along its axis, together with a rather complex pattern of minor lobes.

Fig. 50(a) illustrates the principle. If the waves on the wires were visible, they would be seen to flow in the directions of the arrows, to appear in phase from the front of the array; hence an anti-phase or balanced feed line is necessary at the apex. **Table 7** gives apex angles and gain figures for V aerials of various lengths.

The V exhibits some degree of end-fire effect and can be made unidirectional if it is terminated, for example, with the artificial earth described in connection with Fig. 39. A suitable value of resistor would be 500 ohms for each leg. The input impedance, in the resonant condition, may rise to 2000 ohms in a short V but will lie between 800 and 1000 ohms in a longer or terminated aerial and thus 600 ohm feed lines can be used. Alternatively a non-terminated V can be driven like the balanced Windom shown in Fig. 16(b).

The Rhombic

Early difficulties of terminating a wire high in the air led to the development of the rhombic aerial **(Fig. 50(b))** in which a second V is added, so that the ends can be brought together

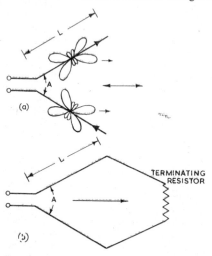

Fig. 50. V and rhombic aerials. The upper diagram shows how the main lobes of two long wire radiators are added to form the main beam. The apex angle A is given in Table 7.

and joined to a terminating resistor. The same lobe addition principle is used but there is an additional complication, because the lobes from the front and rear halves must also add in phase at the required elevation angle. This introduces an extra degree of control in the design so that considerable variation of pattern can be obtained by choosing various apex angles and heights above ground. The figures in Table 7 are average and can be varied considerably as required.

The average gain of a rhombic is 3db greater than that of a V aerial with the same legs and this is to be expected because the rhombic is twice as large.

TABLE 7
V and Rhombic Aerials

Leg Length	Angle A	Gain V Aerial	Gain Rhombic
1 λ	90	3db	6db
2 λ	72	4½db	7½db
3 λ	60	6db	9db
4 λ	50	7db	10db
5 λ	45	8db	11db
6 λ	40	9db	12db

Average design figures for V and Rhombic aerials. The angle A is the apex angle in Fig. 50.

The design of V and rhombic aerials is quite flexible and both types will work over a 2 : 1 frequency range or even more, provided the legs are at least 2λ at the lowest frequency. For such wideband use the angle is chosen to suit the length L at the mid-range frequency. Generally the beamwidth and wave angle increase at the lower frequency and decrease at the upper frequency, even though the apex angle is not ideal over the whole range.

A suitable height above ground is one wavelength, although aerials with legs as short as 2λ may produce an extra high-angle lobe at this height. A short-leg aerial may be more satisfactory at a height of $\lambda/2$ even though this raises the wave angle somewhat.

A comparison with the figures given for tuned arrays in Fig. 40 will show that, for the same total length of radiator, V and rhombic aerials give somewhat lower gain, but against this must be set the simplicity of construction, wideband properties and ease of feeding. They do require a great deal of space but where there is no room to erect the rhombic, the gain and low wave angle can, to a large extent, be obtained by placing one V over another, spaced $\lambda/2$ apart at the mean working frequency, with the lower leg not less than $\lambda/4$ high. The two feed points in this case can be joined by open wire lines. If the feed line (300 to 400 ohms) is joined to the centre point (as Fig. 40(c)) multiband operation is maintained; this, however, is practically difficult. The alternative feed, like Fig. 40(d), limits operation to one band, since the two Vs must be kept in phase with each other.

MULTIBAND AERIALS

In the average location, an amateur will not have space for many aerials, and thus the problem of making one array work usefully on more than one amateur band is an important one. Throughout this chapter, care has been taken to indicate the multiband possibilities and limitations of the various types of aerial. This section puts the question the other way round, and answers it with a few aerials designed specially to work on more than one band. The simpler aerials, such as dipoles, or long wires fed in various ways, will do this but there are always disadvantages—the radiation pattern changes, and usually there are high v.s.w.r. problems on the feeder.

Multiband Dipoles and Ground-planes

The first approach to a multiband dipole is shown in **Fig. 51(a)**. Dipoles are cut for the various bands and supported about one foot apart in the same plane, and then joined to a single 80 ohm twin line. The theory is that the aerial which is in tune at half-wave resonance takes all the power, but this simple theory ignores the coupling between the dipoles, and so the match to the line may not always be very good, and the multi-lobe patterns of the longer wires tend to appear when the shorter ones are active.

The second approach is to connect reactances into the aerial with one of two objects—(a) to cut off the aerial progressively for each frequency band, so that it is a dipole for each band, or (b) to use the reactance as a phase changer, so that at the higher frequencies the extensions behave like a collinear array. Method (a) will be described but method (b) is difficult to apply. **Fig. 51(b)** shows one way to do this, using resonant LC units (*traps*). Starting from the feeder, the radiator is cut to length for the highest frequency, say f_3. Parallel circuits, resonant at f_3 are then inserted, one for a

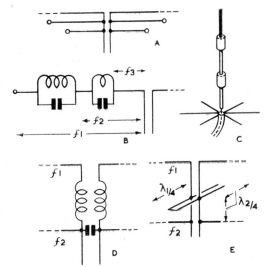

Fig. 51. Multiband arrangements. (a) Parallel dipoles. (b) Multiband dipole. (c) Ground plane equivalent of (b). (d and e) Two "frequency switch" filters for feeding two aerials over one transmission line.

TABLE 8
Characteristic and Anti-resonant Dipole Impedances

Ratio L/D	Char. Imp. Z_a	End R_e ($\lambda2$)	Centre R_C (λ)	Centre R_C (2λ)	Typical Aerial
15,000	500	4,200	5,000	3,500	66 ft. of 14 s.w.g.
10,000	480	3,800	4,600	3,200	33 ft. of 14 s.w.g.
5,000	450	3,400	4,000	2,700	16 ft. 6 in. of 14 s.w.g.
2,500	400	2,700	3,200	2,200	—
1,000	350	2,000	2,400	1,600	66 ft. 1¼ in. dia. *
500	300	1,500	1,800	1,250	33 ft. 1¼ in. dia. *
200	250	1,000	1,300	800	—
100	210	750	900	550	12½ in. by ¼ in. dia.

This table gives the quarter-wave characteristic impedance, Z_a, the end-impedance R_e of half-wave dipoles and the centre impedance R_e of full wave and 2λ aerials, in terms of conductor length/diameter (L/D) ratio. R_e is based on a radiation resistance of 60 ohms, and the full wave R_e on 100 ohm per half-wave. Values may vary by 20 per cent in practice due to environment.

does not allow for the coupling which exists between aerial sections. It is therefore advisable to adjust the aerial during construction.

When the process is applied to a ground-plane aerial, the physical construction is simpler, because the aerial can be made on a self-supporting tube. The tube can be broken and supported by rod insulated over which the coil is wound; the trap circuits can then be well protected by tape, or even encased in Fibreglass. A "whip" can be used for the top section. The ground-plane radials may not work well on all three bands, and some longer wires should be provided, if possible, for the lower frequencies.

When it is required to use two aerials on different bands with a common feeder, this can be done by inserting a low pass filter immediately after the high frequency aerial (Fig. 51(d)). The filter has a cut-off midway between the two frequencies: at this cut-off frequency the reactance of the capacitor is equal to the impedance (Z_0) of the line, whilst each inductor has half this reactance. An alternative form of filter (Fig. 51(e)) uses stubs connected a distance $\frac{1}{4}\lambda$ from the first (f_2) aerial. One stub is a $\frac{1}{2}\lambda2$ (i.e. $2\times\lambda2/4$) and is open-circuit; this therefore presents a short-circuit on to the line f_2 and thus the second stub has no effect on the first. The short circuit becomes a high impedance at the second aerial (f_1), by transformation. The second (shorted) stub tunes out the first at f_1 when the total length of the two stubs is $\frac{1}{4}\lambda1$. The length of line from the second stub to the first aerial is not important.

The G5RV 102 ft Dipole

The 102 ft. dipole has been found an excellent compromise suitable for all h.f. bands and can be fed either of the ways illustrated in Fig. 53. In the upper diagram, tuned feeders (300 to 600 ohm) are used all the way: in the lower version the high impedance feeder is 34 ft. long and is connected into a 72 ohm twin or coax line. At this junction, the aerial impedance due to standing waves is low on most bands, as can be checked with the aid of Fig. 13 for a length of 34 + 51 = 85 ft.

The aerial should be supported at the optimum height for the band which is considered most important for DX working; that is, a half or full wavelength above ground. It is perhaps better to arrange this for 14 Mc/s at which frequency the aerial is designed to present a fairly close impedance match to 72 ohm coax or twin-lead via the 34 ft. stub which, in this case, acts as a one-to-one impedance transformer.

On 1·8 Mc/s the two feeder wires at the transmitter end are connected together or the inner and outer of the coax joined

ground-plane aerial, two for a dipole, and the aerial is then extended till it resonates at f_2, the next lower frequency. The procedure is repeated for a third frequency if required. Finally the lengths of the sections are re-trimmed for each band in the same order. The ideal value of $\sqrt{L/C}$ ratio for the traps would be equal to the characteristic impedance, Z_a, of the half-aerial, which makes $2\pi fL = Z_a$, but this would cause too much shortening of the next lower frequency section of aerial, and suitable values for reactance of L and C are $\frac{1}{2}Z_a$. At half their resonant frequency the traps provide together an inductive reactance of $Z_a/3$ which is equivalent to about one-sixth of the length of the lower frequency quarter-wave. Thus for a dipole working on 14 and 7 Mc/s, with a Z_a of 500 ohms, the first section would be 16 ft. long, the coil would be approximately $2\mu H$ and the capacitance 50 pF. The residue for 14 Mc/s would then be about 10 ft. Values of Z_a are taken for the full length of the aerial from Table 8 and reactances can be translated into coils and capacitors.

A suitable coil for the above example would comprise eight turns of 16 s.w.g. wire 2 in. diameter and 2 in. long supported by polystyrene strips cemented in position. The coil should be mounted over a long insulator and the capacitor, which should be of the stacked mica type and rated at not less than 500 volts, mounted along the insulator. The whole assembly should be tuned to resonance by adjusting the coil, using a grid dip oscillator and then sealed into a polythene bag. The aerial described above will also work quite well on 21 Mc/s.

The theory of operation described is approximate, and

Fig. 52. A suitable trap design for multiband rod aerials.
(By courtesy of Mosley Electronics Ltd.)

and the top plus " feeder " used as a Marconi aerial with a series-tuned coupling circuit and a good earth connection.

On the 3·5 Mc/s band, the electrical centre of the aerial commences about 15 ft. down the open line (in other words, the middle 30 ft. of the dipole is folded up). The aerial functions as two half-waves in phase on 7 Mc/s with a portion " folded " at the centre. Although the 72 ohm feeder " sees " a somewhat reactive termination it loads satisfactorily and radiates effectively.

At 14 Mc/s the aerial functions as a three half-wavelength aerial with an effective all-round low-angle polar diagram. Since the impedance at the centre is about 100 ohms, a satisfactory match to the 72 ohm feeder is obtained via the 34 ft. of half-wave stub. By making the height a half-wave or a full-wave above ground at 14 Mc/s and then raising and lowering the aerial slightly while observing the standing wave ratio on the 72 ohm twin-lead or coax feeder by means of a s.w.r. bridge, an excellent impedance match may be obtained on this band.

On 21 Mc/s, the aerial works as a slightly extended two-wavelength system or two full waves in phase and is capable of very good results especially if tuned feeders are used to reduce loss. On 28 Mc/s it consists of two one-and-a-half wavelength in-line aerials fed in phase. Here again, results are better with a tuned feeder to minimize losses although it works satisfactorily with the 34 ft. stub and 72 ohm feeder.

When using tuned feeders, it is recommended that the feeder taps should be adjusted experimentally to obtain

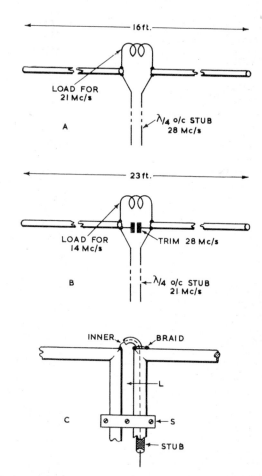

Fig. 54. Multiband parasitic elements. (a) is a director which operates on 21 and 28 Mc/s. (b) is a reflector which operates near half-wave resonance on 14 and 21 Mc/s and as a pair of reflectors on 28 Mc/s. (c) Cut-out showing how the twin support boom of the array can be used with shorting bars to provide the low frequency loading inductance, and how the stub, in this case concentric, can be stowed inside one leg of the boom.

optimum loading on each band using separate plug-in or switched coils. Connection from the a.t.u. to the transmitter should be made with 72 ohm coaxial cable in which a suitable TVI suppression (low pass) filter may be inserted.

Multiband Parasitic Arrays: Frequency Switches

The principle of a stub or network used as a frequency switch, as in Fig. 51, can be applied to parasitic arrays to enable them to work on more than one band. The range of frequency is limited to 2 : 1 because, in terms of wavelength, the spacing will change, and at only one frequency can the optimum spacing be employed. For example a spacing of $0·2\lambda$ at 28 Mc/s, which is rather higher than optimum, becomes $0·1\lambda$ at 14 Mc/s, a spacing which gives good performance but critical tuning.

Fig. 54 shows multiband elements. The radiator is made to a length suitable for one frequency, cut in the centre, and then closed by means of an open-circuit quarter wave stub. The gap is then loaded with inductance or capacitance

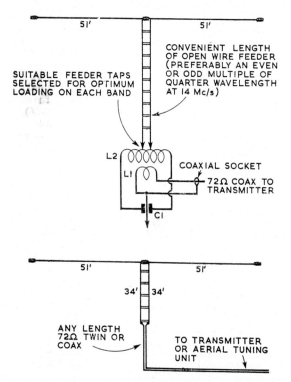

Fig. 53. Two versions of a simple but effective multiband aerial for 1·8–30 Mc/s. L_1 is the coupling coil and $C_1 L_2$ form a resonant circuit at the operating frequency.

which, together with the stub, loads the element to tune at a second frequency. At the first frequency the stub has zero impedance, and the loading reactance is therefore shorted out.

The director in Fig. 54(a) is made for 29 Mc/s with a quarter-wave stub at this frequency. The loading coil, which may be a few turns of wire about 1 in. diameter, is adjusted to give a second resonance at approximately 22 Mc/s. The tuning can be checked with a grid dip oscillator coupled to the coil or stub, but final adjustments should be made with the complete array in position. Allowing for velocity factor, the stub will be about 6 ft. 6 in. of 300 ohm twin, or 5 ft. 6 in. of 80 ohm twin feeder or concentric cable. The three-band reflector in Fig. 54(b) is adjusted to resonate, with its stub, at approximately 20 Mc/s, and loaded with a coil to work on 14 Mc/s. At 28 Mc/s the stub is longer than a quarter wave, and acts as an inductance, which is in parallel with the coil. The addition of a small capacity (a few picofarads) will produce parallel resonance with the two inductances, and can be adjusted to separate the two halves of the radiator into two separate reflectors for 28 Mc/s; it is necessary to retrim the coil for 14 Mc/s as this adjustment is made.

Fig. 54(c) shows how the loading inductance can be formed by connecting a shorting bar across a double boom which supports the array. The stub (concentric) is stowed inside one leg of the boom, with its inner and outer conductors connected across the gap in the reflector.

The Minibeam

A variety of arrays for use on more than one band, both in the h.f. and v.h.f. ranges have been developed by G. A. Bird (G4ZU), a pioneer in this field. The " Minibeam " model outlined in **Fig. 55** uses the parasitic elements shown in Fig. 54, and operates on 14, 21, and 28 Mc/s. The radiator is resonated a little below 21 Mc/s: on 14 Mc/s it acts as a short radiator, and on 28 Mc/s as a " short " full wave element. The aerial is a five-element array on 28 Mc/s, with high gain: on 21 Mc/s it is a three-element array and the gain is claimed to be a little more than for a normal Yagi, because of the extended radiator, whilst on 14 Mc/s it is a two element array with 3 to 4db gain, the director being ineffective.

The impedance of this array is very different from that of a normal three-element array, because of the untuned radiator, and the increased number of elements, and 300 ohm twin is recommended for feeding it. Adjustment follows the general lines indicated for two- and three-element arrays, but is of course more complex, as it involves three frequencies, and is mainly made to the loading devices, not the radiator. For 1 in. diameter elements, the free director resonance is about 5 per cent higher than the working frequency, the reflector about 5 per cent lower. Tuning should be carried out with the array as high as is practicable, since the elements may

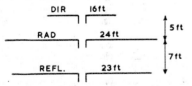

Fig. 55. The G4ZU " Minibeam " array. The radiator acts as a short dipole on 14 Mc/s, as a half-wave dipole on 21 Mc/s and as a full-wave dipole on 28 Mc/s. The aerial is equivalent to a five-element array on 28 Mc/s, a three-element array on 21 Mc/s, and a close-spaced two-element array on 14 Mc/s. The tuning of the parasitic elements is described in the text.

tune 1 per cent higher in frequency when erected than when near the ground. It is not too difficult to obtain good gain and front-to-back ratio on 21 and 28 Mc/s, but adjustment for 14 Mc/s is critical because it is a close-spaced beam on this band.

TESTING AERIALS

It is not always easy to determine whether an aerial is working at its best: its radiation pattern cannot easily be checked. Meters will show that the power is reaching the aerial, and a v.s.w.r. indicator or a reflectometer will show how well the feeder is matched. If feeder loss is suspected, then its input v.s.w.r. can be checked with the far end shorted: in this state the v.s.w.r. should be very high and a reflecto-meter should show equal currents in either direction (for example, by reversing it). But the only practicable way to assess the radiation is to compare it with another aerial for reception, using preset aerial couplers, and a change-over switch in the link circuit. It is impossible to judge an aerial by a single test because propagation conditions are so variable; the aerial should be used for a period, say several weeks, and frequently compared with its reference. Comparison tests with distant stations are not always useful, unless one knows the other operator well. The very best way to assess performance is to use the aerial and judge by the success or failure in competition with other stations.

If a two- or three-element parasitic array, erected at the correct height, shows a good front-to-back ratio under conditions of local test, then its radiation pattern is probably correct, but strange things can happen, For example there will often be periods when it seems to receive strong signals from the back, because ionospheric scattering is sending them in from an entirely different direction, or even from overhead.

CHOOSING AERIALS

This chapter has attempted to explain aerials and the principles underlying their design: a large number of aerials have been illustrated together with many accessory devices. The beginner may well be confused by the range of information, and therefore need advice on the best way to start.

The beginner is no doubt ambitious to do the things other amateurs do, but must not expect to succeed immediately. It is advisable therefore not to start off with the latest exotic " wonder-worker "; it will be found very puzzling, even if it can be made to work. Most pleasure will be obtained and more will be learnt by starting with a simple aerial which is bound to work. For instance, start with a simple one-band dipole or, if there is no space, a ground-plane on the roof, and then graduate to one of the simple multiband aerials (e.g. Figs. 16 or 51). If the dipole can be erected 40 ft. high it will be found that on 7 Mc/s the radiation angle is rather high, but it will be possible to work up to 1,000 miles or more with it, and on higher frequencies it may be possible to span the oceans.

Such aerials will be excellent during peak propagation conditions: to do better either more space or a compact beam is needed. The latter can be purchased, but much more will be learnt by building a two or three element rotating array or a " Minibeam " at home.

Those fortunate enough to be able to choose a site, should pick one with plenty of clear space, preferably on high ground.

With such a site, success comes more easily. Aerials designed for low angle projection, will increase the hours per day during which stations in, say, U.S.A. or Australia can be worked. The long wire aerials are easiest to erect, though there may be short periods when a simple aerial will be better. Ground-plane aerials give outstanding results when propagation is normal but though it will always pay to instal them solely for receiving, they may more easily cause broadcast interference than horizontal aerials. With more than one aerial, or even for multiband work, preset aerial couplers will be found a great advantage (see Fig. 28).

In order to choose and arrange the most suitable aerials it is best to make a plan of the site, showing true North, and use this in conjunction with a great circle map of the world, for example, the *Short Wave Magazine* Great Circle Map or Admiralty Chart No. 5085, obtainable from H.M.S.O. These maps, called *azimuthal projections*, show true distances and directions from London, and are suitable for use anywhere in the U.K. An example is shown in **Fig. 56**.

RECEIVING AERIALS

At the beginning of this chapter it was stated that the receiving problem is not quite the same as the transmitting one. The reciprocity theorem as applied to aerials is well founded but does not allow for interference coupled to the equivalent transmitter-receiver system. The rule concerning the use of the transmitting aerial for reception is a good one; tuned arrays, especially the unidirectional ones, can be a great help for reducing interference from directions not in the beam of the aerial. Long wire types are not so good in this respect, and often bring in more cosmic or ionospheric noise than other types: vertical aerials normally produce a much cleaner background than any others, and help to discriminate against short-range interference—say from 500 to 1000 miles, because of their selective vertical patterns. A properly constructed aerial, with a good transmission line always helps to minimize man-made interference radiated by house wiring, etc.

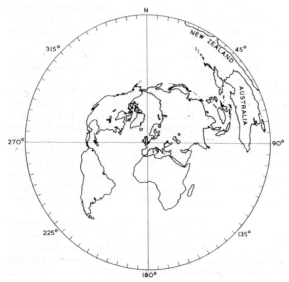

Fig. 56. A great circle map showing true direction. Such maps are used for setting out beam aerials.

It may be considered worthwhile to erect special aerials for the receiver and **Fig. 57** is an example of what can be done. A pair of ground planes are erected at a spacing of $\lambda/2$ to λ, the feeders brought in separately, and connected to the ends of a

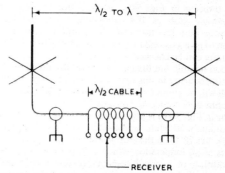

Fig. 57 Special arrangement of two ground-plane aerials providing electrical steering of the patterns given in Fig. 32. This is a great help for interference reduction in a receiver on noisy bands like 7 or 14 Mc/s, though it is not any great advantage in transmission because the patterns are very broad.

half-wave cable delay line. The delay line (which can be 24 ft. of coaxial line for 14 Mc/s) is coiled and its inner conductor brought out to switch studs at many points. When the receiver input is switched along this delay line, the horizontal patterns shown in Fig. 32 can effectively be rotated to steer the nulls against interfering stations.

INTERFERENCE

Even the best communication receiver will sometimes show signs of overloading when supplied with the full output of a very large array, such as a *V* or a rhombic. The effect is a large increase in background noise of a type which is clearly the interaction between high power stations in or near the working frequency; often a pair of stations will beat together to give an i.f. signal which does not respond to the r.f. tuning of the receiver. This is most likely to occur on the 14 and 21 Mc/s bands, and is recognized because it disappears more rapidly than the tunable signals when the gain of the receiver is gradually reduced. It really calls for preselection in front of the receiver. Since the normal outside noise level from cosmic and man-made interference overrides the internal noise of a good receiver, there is no need to give it the full output of a large aerial, and often a smaller aerial can be used.

In order to prevent interference with broadcasting, special steps are taken in the transmitter to prevent overmodulation, key clicks and harmonic output. Loose connections in and around the aerial system can undo this work and rectify the transmitter output, causing serious interference of a harmonic type. Corroded or oxidized metal contacts make rectifiers, and can act as if a diode were connected in the aerial. Offending items include poor or broken solder joints, lead-through terminals, dirty r.f. connectors in the cable system, corroded earth connections, and loose metal joints such as those in gutters or rusty wire fences. Joints in the aerial should be carefully cleaned, made tight before soldering, and arranged so that the strain on the wire does not pull on a sharp bend. The solder joint may fracture in time through vibration, and should not therefore take the strain: it should also be protected with tape, so that it does not become too dirty to re-solder. Regular inspection of the aerial system and its surroundings is necessary.

CHAPTER 14

V.H.F. AERIALS

THE range of frequencies considered in this chapter extends from 30 Mc/s to 3000 Mc/s. In accordance with the accepted terminology a distinction ought strictly to be made between the range 30–300 Mc/s which is described as *very high frequency* (*v.h.f.*) and the range 300–3000 Mc/s which is described as *ultra-high frequency* (*u.h.f.*). Over these two ranges, however, the problems of aerial design are often quite similar in character, and to avoid unnecessary repetition the term *v.h.f.* is used here to cover both of them.

Above 30 Mc/s the wavelength of the radiation becomes short enough to allow efficient aerials of comparatively small dimensions to be constructed, since the effectiveness of an aerial system generally improves when its size becomes comparable with the wavelength that is being used. A special feature of v.h.f. aerial design is the possibility of focusing the radiated energy into a beam, thereby obtaining a large effective gain in comparison with a dipole which is the standard by which most v.h.f. aerials are judged.

Power Gain and Beamwidth

A simple way to appreciate the meaning of aerial gain is as follows. Imagine the radiator to be totally enclosed in a hollow sphere, as indicated in **Fig. 1**. If the radiation is distributed uniformly over the interior surface of this sphere the radiator is said to be *isotropic*. An aerial which causes the radiation to be concentrated into any particular area of the inside surface of the sphere, and which thereby produces a greater intensity than that produced by an isotropic

ϕ = VERTICAL BEAMWIDTH (IN PLANE YZ)

θ = HORIZONTAL BEAMWIDTH (IN PLANE XZ)

A = ILLUMINATED AREA

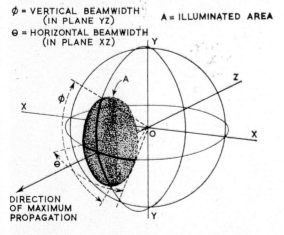

DIRECTION OF MAXIMUM PROPAGATION

$$\text{POWER GAIN} = \frac{\text{SURFACE AREA OF SPHERE}}{\text{SURFACE AREA OF "ILLUMINATED" REGION}}$$

Fig. I. Radiation from an aerial. An isotropic radiator at the point O will give uniform "illumination" over the inner surface of the sphere. A directional radiator will concentrate the energy into a beam which will illuminate only a portion of the sphere as shown shaded.

radiator fed with equal power, is said to have a *gain*. This gain is inversely proportional to the fraction of the total interior surface area which received the concentrated radiation.

The gain of an aerial is usually expressed as a power ratio, either as a multiple of so many " times " or in decibel units. For example, a power gain of 20 times could be represented as 13 dB (i.e. $10 \log_{10} 20$).

The truly isotropic radiator is a purely theoretical concept, and in practice the gain of beam aerials is usually compared

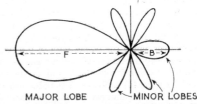

MAJOR LOBE   MINOR LOBES

Fig. 2. Typical polar diagram of a v.h.f. aerial. The front-to-back ratio is represented by *F/B*.

with the radiation from a single half-wave dipole fed with an equal amount of power. The radiation pattern of even a single half-wave dipole is markedly non-uniform, and in consequence the power gain of such an aerial compared with the hypothetical isotropic radiator is about 50 per cent (i.e. 3/2 times or 2 dB), but since the half-wave dipole is the simplest practical form of radiator it is generally acceptable as a basis of comparison.

The area of " illumination " is not sharply defined as shown by the shaded region in Fig. 1 but falls away gradually from the centre of the area. The boundaries of the illuminated area are determined by joining together all points where the radiation intensity has fallen by half (i.e. 3 dB): these are known as the *half-power points*. The gain of the aerial can then be determined by dividing the total surface area of the sphere by the illuminated area: e.g. if the total surface area were 100 sq. cm. and the illuminated area bounded by the half-power points were 20 sq. cm., the gain of the aerial would be five times or 7 dB. The radiation in any particular plane can be plotted graphically, usually in polar co-ordinates; such a plot is called a *polar diagram*. A typical polar diagram is shown in **Fig. 2.** The area of maximum radiation is called the *major lobe*. Spurious radiation is occurring in other directions and these areas, when small compared with the major lobe, are called *minor lobes*. All practical aerials exhibit such lobes and the aerial designer frequently has to compromise to obtain the optimum performance for any particular application. For example, an aerial may be designed for maximum *front-to-back ratio*; i.e. for minimum radiation in the direction opposite to the major lobe. To achieve such a condition it may be necessary to sacrifice some gain in the major lobe (or forward radiation) with a possible increase in other minor lobes (or side lobes) and thus the designer will need to consider all the implications before finalizing any particular design.

In practice the radiation from an aerial is measured in a horizontal and a vertical plane. The *beamwidth* is the angle between the two half-power points in the plane under consideration. The vertical polar diagram is greatly influenced by the height of the aerial above ground; the higher the aerial the lower will be the angle of maximum radiation, and at the same time the effects of neighbouring objects such as houses will be minimized. The important requirement is to place the aerial well clear of such objects and this frequently means as high as can be safely achieved. Any aerial which has the property of concentrating radiation into any particular direction is said to possess *directivity*.

Bandwidth

The performance of an aerial array generally depends upon the resonant properties of tuned radiators such as dipoles or other frequency sensitive elements, and therefore any statement regarding its power gain or beamwidth will be valid only over a restricted frequency band. Beyond the limits of this band the properties of an aerial system may be entirely different. Hence it is useful to define *bandwidth* as that range of frequencies over which the power gain of the aerial array does not fall by more than a certain percentage as compared with the frequency at which maximum gain is obtained (e.g. a bandwidth of 15 Mc/s for a 50 per cent reduction in power gain). Alternatively the bandwidth may be defined as the frequency band over which the standing-wave ratio of the aerial feeder does not exceed a prescribed limit (e.g. a bandwidth of 10 Mc/s for a standing-wave ratio not exceeding 2 : 1). The latter convention is the one generally used.

Capture Area or Aperture

Besides examining the action of a transmitting aerial array in concentrating the radiated power into a beam it is also helpful to examine the way in which the same aerial structure will affect the reception of an incoming signal. In this study it is convenient to introduce the concept of *capture area* or *aperture* of the aerial. This concept is frequently misunderstood, probably because it may appear to relate to the cross-sectional area of the beam (as represented by A in Fig. 1): it is in fact related to the *inverse* of the cross-sectional area of the beam inasmuch as an aerial which has a high gain usually has a sharply focused beam (i.e. one of small cross-sectional area) but at the same time the capture area of the aerial is large. The larger the capture area, the more effective is the aerial as compared with a simple dipole.

The actual size of the aerial system does not always give a reliable indication of the capture area. A high-gain array may have a capture area considerably greater than its frontal area as determined by its physical dimensions. The fundamental relationship between the capture area and the power gain of an aerial system is—

$$A = \frac{G_I . \lambda^2}{4\pi}$$

where A is the capture area and λ is the wavelength (measured in the same units as A) and G_I is the power gain relative to an isotropic radiator.

A half-wave dipole has a gain of 3/2 relative to an isotropic radiator, and therefore this formula can be modified

so as to give the capture area in terms of the gain of a half-wave dipole G_D instead of G_I simply by introducing the factor 3/2, thus—

$$A = \frac{3}{2} \times \frac{G_D . \lambda^2}{4\pi} = \frac{3 G_D . \lambda^2}{8\pi}$$

Note that for a dipole, since $G_D = 1$, the capture area is approximately $\lambda^2/8$.

This formula shows that if the wavelength is kept constant the capture area of an aerial is proportional to its gain, and therefore if an increase in gain results in a narrower beamwidth it must follow that a narrower beamwidth corresponds to a greater capture area (the term beamwidth being used here to signify both horizontal and vertical dimensions, i.e. in effect the cross-sectional area).

The formula also shows that for any given power gain the capture area is proportional to the square of the wavelength. For example, an aerial having a power gain of, say, 10 times relative to a dipole at 600 Mc/s (0·5m) would have a capture area one-sixteenth of that of an aerial having a similar power gain at 150 Mc/s (2m), and to achieve equal capture area the gain of the 600 Mc/s aerial would thus have to be 16 times greater than that of the 150 Mc/s aerial, i.e. 160 times relative to a dipole. This is unfortunate because it is the

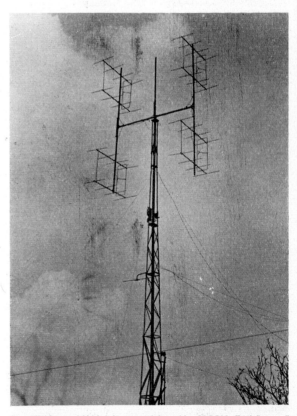

The 40 element 144 Mc/s beam aerial used by G3CCH. Each 5-over-5 slot fed Yagi is fed with 70 ohm coaxial cable which goes to a 4:1 linear matching transformer at the centre of the array and thence via 70 ohm feeder to the transmitter. The home-made tower tilts so that adjustments can be readily made to the aerial. The counterweight for the tower is approximately 200 lb. of concrete blocks.

capture area of the aerial that determines its effectiveness in absorbing the incoming radiation: it means that as the wavelength is reduced it becomes increasingly important to design the aerial to have a higher gain.

These observations apply only to signals being received or transmitted in the direction of maximum gain. For directions other than the optimum the relationships become more complex.

Multi-radiator Arrays

High-gain aerial arrays can be built up from a number of individual radiators such as half-wave dipoles. To achieve the maximum gain, the spacing of these radiators should be such that their respective capture areas just touch. Thus where the individual radiators are themselves high-gain systems, such as Yagi-arrays, the centre-to-centre spacing of each radiating system needs to be larger, since the individual capture areas are greater.

Reciprocity Theorem

The theorem of reciprocity states that any particular aerial gives the same performance either as a transmitting or as a receiving system. Practical aerial designs are therefore worked out in terms of transmission because the characteristics are more easily determined in this way, and the resulting aerials are assumed to have similar reception properties.

Angle of Radiation: Polarization

The characteristics of propagation in the v.h.f. ranges are mostly determined by the influence of the troposphere, i.e. the part of the atmosphere extending from ground level up to a few thousand feet. There is little or no ionospheric propagation on frequencies higher than about 100 Mc/s and thus any energy which is radiated at more than a few degrees above the horizontal is wasted. Similarly to transmit to a particular point it is unnecessary to radiate a broad beam in the horizontal plane. Generally, therefore, the aerial designer tries firstly to reduce the vertical beamwidth to avoid wastage of power into space and secondly to reduce the horizontal beamwidth according to the required ground coverage. However, a narrow horizontal beamwidth can be a disadvantage because stations situated off the beam may be missed when searching. Thus a compromise between gain and beamwidth has to be made.

Radio waves are constituted from electric and magnetic fields mutually at right angles and also at right angles to the direction of propagation. The ratio of the electric component E to the magnetic component H in free space ($E/H = Z$) is known as the *impedance of free space* and has a value of about 377 ohms. When the electric component is horizontal, the wave is said to be *horizontally polarized*. Such a wave is radiated from a horizontal dipole. If the electric component is vertical, as in a vertical dipole, the wave is said to be *vertically polarized*.

It has been found by experiment that in the v.h.f. range horizontally polarized waves suffer less attenuation over long distances than vertically polarized waves, and this system is therefore often preferred. It has in fact been universally adopted for amateur communication in Great Britain and many other countries. Vertically polarized waves may be more suitable for special purposes such as short-distance or mobile communication and a simple ground-plane or similar aerial can then be used, as described in Chapter 16 (*Mobile Equipment*).

Sometimes the polarization is not exclusively horizontal or vertical and the radiation is then said to be *elliptically polarized* or, in the special case where the horizontal and vertical components are equal, *circularly polarized*. The effect of the addition of two components of the same kind (i.e. electric *or* magnetic) at right angles is to create a rotating field, the direction of which depends on the relative phase of the two components. Thus the polarization of the wave will appear to have either clockwise or counter-clockwise rotation, a feature which is important in the use of helical aerials. A dipole will receive an equal pick-up from a circularly polarized wave irrespective of whether it is mounted horizontally, vertically or in an intermediate position. Horizontally or vertically polarized waves are known as *plane polarized* waves.

AERIAL FEEDERS

Before discussing aerial design it will be helpful to review the methods of conveying the power from the transmitter to the aerial. The feeder length should always be considered in terms of wavelengths rather than the actual length of the conductors. If the feeder length is short compared with the wavelength, the loss caused by its ohmic resistance and by the dielectric conductance is unimportant as also is the effect of incorrect impedance matching. However, for v.h.f. operation the aerial feeder is usually many wavelengths long, and therefore both the loss introduced and the matching of the load to the feeder are of the utmost importance.

Two types of feeder, or transmission line, are in common use, namely the *unbalanced* or *coaxial feeder* and the *balanced pair*: the latter may be either of open construction or enclosed in polythene ribbon or tubular moulding. Each type has its own particular advantages and disadvantages, and these are summarized below.

In a coaxial cable, the radio-frequency fields are contained entirely within the outer conductor and hence there should be no r.f. currents on the outside. This enables the cable to be carried in close proximity to other cables and metal objects without interaction or serious change of its cable properties which might cause reflections and thereby introduce appreciable loss. Also there is no loss by external radiation.

The open-wire or balanced feeder has a radiation-loss which is dependent upon the ratio of the spacing of the wires to the wavelength and becomes more serious as the frequency is raised. The properties can also be severely changed by the close proximity of metal objects and the accumulation of ice or water on the separating insulation, and therefore much greater care must be taken in the routing of the feeder. Difficulties are often experienced when attempting to use this type of feeder with rotatable aerial arrays. It is, for instance, quite unsatisfactory to bind a ribbon feeder directly against a metal mast. When the feeder is kept well clear of metal objects, however, the loss tends to be less than that of coaxial cable unless the frequency is so high that the radiation-loss is serious (i.e. 450 Mc/s and above).

Generally speaking, the use of open-wire feeders is restricted to bands of 144 Mc/s and below; coaxial cable is used for all frequencies up to about 3000 Mc/s. Above about 1000 Mc/s the loss in conventional types of flexible coaxial cable becomes prohibitive and rigid semi-air-spaced types of line are then used. Above 3000 Mc/s waveguides are usually necessary for feeder runs of more than a few inches.

A list of typical aerial feeder cable obtainable in Great Britain is shown in Table 1. Further information can be obtained from the various manufacturers. Complete details of r.f. cables made to Government specifications can be obtained from *Defence Specification DEF-14-A*, "*Radio Frequency Cables*" (H.M.S.O.).

In the semi-air-spaced type of coaxial cable, the centre conductor is supported either on beads or on a helical thread: in some forms a continuous filling of cellular polythene is used as the insulator. This type of cable has a lower capacity per unit length than the solid type and hence the *velocity factor* (i.e. the ratio of the wave velocity in the cable compared with that in free space) is higher, being about 0·88–0·98 for helical and bead types and about 0·8 for cellular polythene types compared with 0·66 for solid cable. The use of semi-air-spaced centre conductors allows cables to be designed with less attenuation for a given size, or with the same attenuation for a smaller size, but unfortunately the bead and helical types suffer from the disadvantage that moisture can easily enter the cable; special precautions must therefore be taken to ensure a good watertight seal at the aerial end if such cable is used. Suitable material for this purpose is *Telcompound** or *Bostik* sealing strip. Cellular polythene has non-connecting air cells distributed throughout its volume, and consequently there is no moisture ingress except at cut ends and then only for a very small distance. However, cellular polythene cables do suffer from another

* A softened polythene compound manufactured by *Telcon Plastics Division of the B.I.C.C. Group.*

disadvantage: this is that the effective dielectric constant of the cellular polythene varies according to the number and volume of the air cells per unit length which unfortunately cannot be controlled with precision during manufacture. Thus the characteristic impedance may tend to vary along a length of feeder and although this may not matter at the lower end of the v.h.f. spectrum such cable is not recommended for frequencies above about 500 Mc/s.

It is also important to exclude water even from the outer braiding of any coaxial cable. If water has once entered a cable it is impossible to dry it out, and the loss in the feeder becomes progressively higher as the copper braiding corrodes.

Open-wire Feeders

To obtain very low losses open-wire feeder line can conveniently be made from hard-drawn 16 s.w.g. copper wire

Fig. 3. Open-wire line with disc insulators. The centre portions of the insulators are removed to minimize dielectric losses.

with separating insulators placed at 12 in. intervals. The insulators should be made from polythene and be shaped in the form of a disc with the centre removed, as shown in Fig. 3. This ensures that in the places where the maximum electric stress occurs, i.e. between the conductors, the die-

TABLE I
Characteristics of Typical Radio-Frequency Feeder Cables

Type of Cable	Nominal Imped-ance Z_o(ohms)	Dimensions (in.)			Velocity Factor	Approximate Attenuation (dB per 100 ft.)				Remarks
		Centre Cond'tor	over outer sheath	over twincores		70 Mc/s	145 Mc/s	420 Mc/s	1250 Mc/s	
Standard TV feeder	75	7/·0076	0·202	—	0·67	3·5	5·1	9·2	17	—
Low-loss TV feeder (semi-air-spaced)	75	0·048	0·290	—	0·86 approx.	2·0	3·0	5·4	10	Semi-air-spaced or cellular
Flat twin	150	7/·012	—	0·18 × 0·09	0·71	2·1	3·1	5·7*	11*	* Theoretical figures, likely to be con-siderably worsened by radiation
Flat twin	300	7/·012	—	0·405 × 0·09	0·85	1·2	1·8	3·4*	6·6*	
Tubular twin ..	300	7/·012	—	0·446	0·85	1·2	1·8	3·4*	6·6*	
Uniradio 1 ..	71	0·056	0·45	—	0·67	1·4	2·2	4·5	8·5	—
Uniradio 4 ..	46	7/·032	0·405	—	0·67	1·9	2·9	5·5	10·5	—
Uniradio 6 ..	100	0·036	0·365	—	0·86	1·4	2·2	4·5	8·5	Semi-air-spaced
Uniradio 32 ..	71	0·022	0·202	—	0·67	3·5	5	10	18	—

This table is compiled from information kindly supplied by *Aerialite Ltd.*, and *B.I.C.C. Ltd.* and includes data extracted from *Defence Specification*, DEF-14-A (H.M.S.O.).

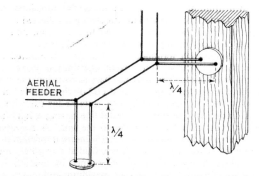

Fig. 4. Quarter-wave closed stubs are often used for supporting open-wire feeders. When used in this way they are known as " metal insulators." The inductance of the short-circuiting conductors is minimized by making them in the form of large metal plates.

lectric is air and not the solid insulating material, thus minimizing losses. To prevent excessive radiation-loss the characteristic impedance should not exceed about 300 ohms. Care must be taken to avoid sharp bends and also the close proximity of surrounding objects as already stated. The characteristic impedance of an open-twin line is given by—

$$Z_0 = 276 \log_{10} (D/d)$$

where D is the centre-to-centre spacing and d is the diameter of the wire (measured in the same units). A chart of characteristic impedance in relation to the conductor size and spacing is given on page 356.

Metal Insulators

A quarter-wave short-circuited transmission line presents a very high impedance at the open end and hence may be connected across an open-wire line without affecting the power flow in any way; such a device is called a *quarter-wave stub*. The stub so formed may conveniently be used as a support or termination for an open-wire line as shown in **Fig. 4**. Since the stub must be resonant in order to behave as an insulator it can function only over a narrow range of frequency.

Surface-Wave Transmission Lines

A type of feeder which becomes useful above about 400 Mc/s is the surface-wave transmission line. The wave is directed on to a single conductor by means of a horn: see **Fig. 5**. The dimensions of the horn are not critical but the angle should be correct, and for the best performance the sides should be several wavelengths long. The single conductor wire should be covered with a thin dielectric, preferably polythene, although enamel or even an oxidized

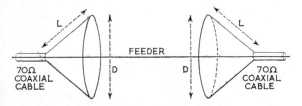

Fig. 5. Surface-wave transmission line. The outer sheathing of each length of coaxial cable is terminated by an open cone. The feeder itself should be of 10–16 s.w.g. copper wire, preferably enamelled; its length may be several hundred feet. The cone diameter D must be 0·6 L, but L itself may be of any length greater than 3λ.

covering is usually sufficient. This covering layer minimizes radiation-loss by reducing the effective diameter of the field surrounding the wire. Typical losses measured at a frequency of 3300 Mc/s (9cm) using horns 21 in. long and 13 in. in diameter and a No. 14 s.w.g. wire feeder (bare but oxidized) are about 1·35 dB per hundred feet plus about 0·4 dB per horn, making a total of just over 2 dB per hundred feet.

At 420 Mc/s the attenuation of the field 8 in. away from the feeder is about 20 dB. The feeder can therefore be run reasonably near to walls and other objects for short distances. However, if the feeder is a fairly long one it would be desirable to maintain a spacing of several feet over most of its length. Also the radius of any bends should be kept greater than about one wavelength in order to avoid losses due to the tendency of the energy to be radiated into space whenever there is a sudden change in the direction of the feeder.

Balance-to-Unbalance Transformers

In most cases the aerial requires a balanced feed with respect to ground, and therefore it is necessary to use a

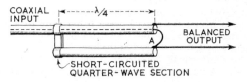

Fig. 6. Quarter-wave open balun or Pawsey stub.

device which converts the unbalanced output of a coaxial cable to a balanced output as required by the aerial. This device also prevents the wave which has been contained within the cable from tending to " spill over " the extreme end and travel back over the surface of the cable. Whenever this occurs there are two important undesired effects; firstly the re-radiated wave modifies the polar diagram of the attached aerial, and secondly the outer surface of the cable is found to have a radio-frequency voltage on it.

To prevent this, a balance-to-unbalance transformer (abbreviated to *balun*) is connected between the feeder cable

Fig. 7 (A). Coaxial-sleeve balun.

and the aerial. The most simple balun consists of a short-circuited quarter-wave section of transmission line attached to the outer-braiding of the cable, as shown in **Fig. 6**. This is often known as a *Pawsey stub*. At the point A, the quarter-wave section presents a very high impedance which prevents the wave from travelling over the surface. The performance of this device is, of course, dependent upon frequency, and its bandwidth may have to be considered in the design.

Several modifications of the simple balun are possible: for example, the single quarter-wave element may be replaced by a quarter-wave coaxial sleeve, thus reducing radiation-loss: see **Fig. 7 (A)**. To prevent the ingress of water and to improve the mechanical arrangement, the centre conductor may itself be connected to a short-circuited quarter-wave line acting as a " metallic insulator " as shown in **Fig. 7 (B)**.

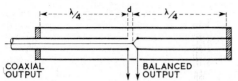

Fig. 7 (B). Totally enclosed-coaxial balun. The right-hand section acts as a " metal insulator."

The distance *d* should be kept small, and yet the capacity between the sections should also be kept small since otherwise the quarter-wave section will not be resonant at the desired frequency. A satisfactory compromise is to taper the end of the quarter-wave line, although this is by no means essential. In practice, at a frequency of 435 Mc/s about ⅛ in. is a suitable spacing. The whole balun is totally enclosed, the output being taken through two insulators mounted in the wall.

A useful variation is that shown in **Fig. 8**, which gives a 4 : 1 step-up of impedance. The half-wave loop is usually made from flexible coaxial cable, and allowance must therefore be made for the velocity factor of the cable when calculating a half-wavelength.

It may be inconvenient at frequencies above about 2000 Mc/s to mount the coaxial-sleeve balun close to a dipole radiator. In this case the sleeve can be mounted a short distance back from the end of the line.

The characteristic impedance of the balun element is not critical. A Pawsey stub may be constructed by attaching a

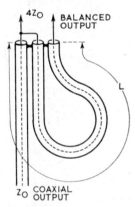

Fig. 8. Coaxial balun giving a 4 : 1 impedance step-up. The length L should be λ/2, allowing for the velocity factor of the cable. The outer braiding may be joined at the points indicated.

piece of coaxial cable one quarter-wave long (the centre conductor being unused) to the braiding of the feeder cable. The two sections should be spaced sufficiently to ensure an air dielectric between them. If the two pieces lie alongside one another the resonant length will be reduced and an inferior dielectric introduced. It is important to note that since it is the electrical characteristics of the outer surface that are being used, there is no need to allow for the velocity factor of the cable. Coaxial-sleeve baluns should have an outer-to-inner diameter ratio of between 2 : 1 and 4 : 1.

Although the type of balun illustrated in Fig. 7 (B) has a larger effective bandwidth than the other types described here, they are all suitable for the restricted frequency ranges in common use in the v.h.f. amateur bands.

IMPEDANCE MATCHING

For an aerial feeder to deliver power to the aerial with minimum loss, it is necessary for the load to behave as a pure resistance equal in value to the characteristic impedance of the line. Under these conditions no energy is reflected from the point where the feeder is joined to the aerial, and in consequence no standing waves appear on the line.

When the correct terminating resistance is connected to any feeder, the voltage and current distribution along the line will be uniform. This may be checked by using a device to explore either the magnetic field (*H*) or the electric field (*E*) along the line. One such device, suitable for use with a coaxial feeder, is a section of coaxial line having a longitudinal slot cut in the wall parallel to the line. A movable probe connected to a crystal voltmeter is inserted through the slotted wall. This samples the electric field at any point, and the standing-wave ratio may be determined by moving the probe along the line and noting the maximum and minimum readings. The distance between adjacent maxima or between adjacent minima is one half-wavelength.

The fields surrounding an open line may be explored by means of an r.f. voltmeter, but it is much more difficult to obtain precise readings than with a coaxial line because of hand-proximity effects and similar disturbances.

Another device which measures forward and reflected waves is the *reflectometer*.

The term *matching* is used to describe the procedure of suitably modifying the effective load impedance to make it behave as a resistance and to ensure that this resistance has a value equal to the characteristic impedance of the feeder used. To make a *complex* load (i.e. a load possessing both resistance and reactance) behave as a resistance, it is necessary to introduce across the load a reactance of equal value and opposite sign to that of the load, i.e. the reactance is " tuned out." A very convenient device which can theoretically give reactance values from minus infinity to plus infinity, (i.e. pure capacitance to pure inductance) is a section of transmission line either of length variable between zero and one half-wavelength having an open-circuited end or alternatively of length a little greater than one half-wavelength having a movable short-circuit capable of being adjusted over a full half-wavelength. The short-circuited stub is to be preferred since it is easier to construct.

Although there is no need to make the characteristic impedance of a stub equal to that of the transmission line, it may be desirable to do so for practical reasons.

In addition to tuning out the reactance, a match still has to be made to the transmission line. The impedance at any point along the length of a quarter-wave resonant stub varies from zero at the short-circuit to a very high impedance at the open end. If a load is connected to the open end and the

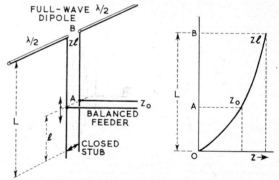

Fig. 9 (A). Stub matching applied to a full-wave dipole.

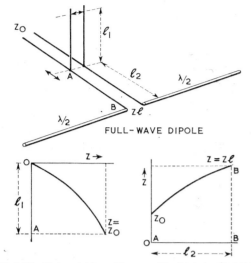

FULL-WAVE DIPOLE

Fig. 9 (B). Stub matching with a movable short-circuited stub.

until no standing waves can be detected. The feeder line is then said to be flat. However, the frequency range over which any single-stub matching device is effective is quite small, and where wideband matching is required some other matching system must be used.

Stub Tuners

On a coaxial line it is impracticable to construct a stub having an adjustable position. However, two fixed stubs spaced by a certain fraction of a wavelength can be used for matching purposes: see **Fig. 10 (A)**. The spacing usually employed is $\lambda/8$ or odd multiples thereof. With this spacing independent adjustment of the short-circuiting plungers gives a matching range from 0·5 times the characteristic impedance of the transmission line (Z_0) upwards. As the spacing is increased towards $\lambda/2$ or decreased towards zero, the matching range increases, but the adjustments then become extremely critical and the bandwidth very narrow. The theoretical limit of matching range cannot be achieved owing to the resistance of the conductors and the dielectric

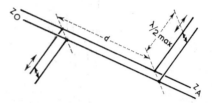

Fig. 10 (B). Two-stub open-wire tuner. With an open-wire line stubs should be mounted on opposite sides of the line as shown so as to avoid mutual coupling. The matching range can be seen from the graph in Fig. 10 (A).

power is fed into the stub at some point along its length the stub may be used as an auto-transformer to give various values of impedance, according to the position of the feed point. This is shown in **Fig. 9 (A)**. The distance L is adjusted to tune the aerial to resonance and will be one quarter-wave long if the aerial is already resonant. The distance l is adjusted to obtain a match to the line. However, it is usually more convenient to have a stub with an adjustable short-circuit which can slide along the transmission line: see **Fig. 9 (B)**.

The method of positioning the matching stub length is described in Chapter 13 (*H.F. Aerials*).

In practice matching can be achieved entirely by the " cut and try " method of adjusting the stub length and position

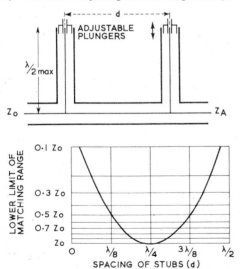

Fig. 10 (A). Two-stub coaxial tuner. The graph shows the lower limit of the matching range: the upper limit is determined by the Q of the stubs (i.e. it is dependent on the losses in the stubs). Z_0 is the characteristic impedance of the feeder.

loss; i.e. the Q is limited. To obtain the highest Q the ratio of outer-to-inner conductor diameters should be in the range 2 : 1 to 4 : 1 (as for coaxial baluns). An important mechanical detail is the provision of reliable short-circuiting plungers which will have negligible inductance and also ensure low-resistance contact. They can be constructed of short lengths of thin-walled brass tubing, their diameters being chosen to that when they are slotted and sprung they make a smooth sliding contact with both inner and outer conductors.

The two-stub tuner may be applied to open transmission

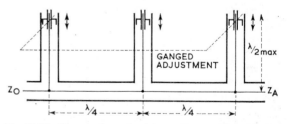

Fig. 10 (C). Three-stub tuner. This provides a greater matching range than a two-stub tuner. Z_0 is the characteristic impedance of the feeder.

lines if it is inconvenient to have a movable stub. In this case the stubs must be mounted laterally opposite to each other to prevent mutual coupling: see **Fig. 10 (B)**.

This type of tuner may, of course, be used for other purposes than to feed an aerial. For example, it will serve to match an aerial feeder into a receiver, or a transmitter into a dummy load. A greater matching range can be obtained by using a three-stub tuner, the stubs being spaced at intervals of one quarter-wavelength apart, as shown in **Fig. 10 (C)**. The first and third stubs are usually ganged together to avoid the long and tedious matching operation which becomes necessary when adjustments are made to three infinitely variable stubs.

Quarter-wave Lines

An impedance transformation can be effected by using a certain length of transmission line of a different character-istic impedance from the feeder. This may be used to match a load to a transmission line. A special condition occurs when

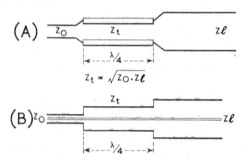

Fig. 11. Quarter-wave transformers. (A) shows a construction suitable for open-wire lines, and (B) is the corresponding method for coaxial cables. Where a solid-dielectric section is used, due allowance must be made for the velocity factor.

the length of the section of line is an odd number of quarter-wavelengths and the following formula then applies—

$$Z_t = \sqrt{Z_0 \cdot Z_l}$$

where Z_t is the characteristic impedance of the section of quarter-wave line and Z_0 and Z_l are the feeder and load impedance respectively. For example, if Z_0 is 80 ohms and Z_l is 600 ohms—

TABLE 2
Resonant Lengths of Half-wave Dipoles

$\left(\dfrac{\text{Wavelength}}{\text{Diameter}}\right)$	Value of $\left(\dfrac{\text{Dipole length}}{\text{Wavelength}}\right)$ for resonance	Feed Impedance (ohms)
50	0·458	60·5
100	0·465	61·0
200	0·471	61·6
400	0·475	63·6
1,000	0·479	65·3
4,000	0·484	67·2
10,000	0·486	68·1
100,000	0·489	69·2

The dimensions used in calculating the ratios must be in similar units (e.g. both in metres or both in centimetres).

From *Aerials for Metre and Decimetre Wavelengths* by R. A. SMITH.

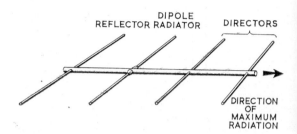

Fig. 12. Yagi array (4 elements). See Table 3 for typical dimensions

$$Z_t = \sqrt{80 \times 600} = 251 \text{ ohms}$$

This matching section is useful for transforming impedance and is called a *quarter-wave transformer*: see **Fig. 11.**

A section of tapered line can also be used to effect an impedance transformation, and an application of this principle is described later in this chapter. Again a quarter-wavelength section is only a special case, and to achieve a match in a particular installation the line lengths and the angle of taper should be varied until a perfect match is achieved. This form of matching device is often called a *delta match.*

AERIAL ARRAYS

The basic elements of v.h.f. aerial arrays are usually half-wave or full-wave dipoles, depending upon the circumstances. The characteristics of such dipoles are described in Chapter 13 (*H.F. Aerials*) and the full-wave dipole is also discussed in the following pages.

When elements are arranged together to form a beam aerial, the radiation pattern most interesting to amateurs is one having a large forward gain. However, by the study of beam-aerial polar diagrams it becomes apparent that in the course of building up a major lobe, other minor or subsidiary lobes may be created as stated previously. No purpose would be served here by discussing these minor lobes further but it is well to remember that they exist and do not necessarily imply an inferior aerial array.

Parasitic Arrays: The Yagi Array

By placing a *reflector*, usually a resonant element one half-wavelength long behind a half-wave dipole, the radiation can be concentrated within a narrower angle. By adding further elements somewhat shorter than one half-wavelength, called *directors*, at certain spacings in the forward direction, a further gain can be achieved. Any aerial array which employs elements not directly connected to the feed line, i.e. parasitic elements, is known as a *parasitic array*. If the arrangement consists of a dipole with a reflector and two or more directors it is known as a *Yagi array*: see **Fig. 12.**

When compared with other aerial systems of similar size the Yagi array is found to have the highest forward gain, and it can be constructed in a very robust form. The effect of adding the reflector and director(s) is to cause the feed impedance of the dipole to fall considerably, often to a value of about 10 ohms, and the matching is then critical and difficult to obtain. This, however, may be overcome by the use of a folded-dipole radiator. If the folded dipole has two elements of equal diameter, a 4 : 1 impedance step-up is obtained. By varying the ratio of the diameters, different impedance step-up ratios become available.

The length of the dipole or folded dipole required for resonance depends not only on the frequency but also to a lesser extent on ratio of the diameter of the element to the wavelength, the length required for resonance diminishing as the wavelength/diameter ratio is decreased: see Table 2.

The forward gain is not appreciably affected by a variation of reflector spacing over a range of $\lambda/8$ to $\lambda/4$: under these conditions the forward gain is approximately at its maximum value. However, a considerable change in feed impedance takes place when this spacing is varied and this may be used as a convenient form of adjustment. The reflector is usually $0{\cdot}5\lambda$ long although this should be reduced to about $0{\cdot}475\lambda$ for the closer spacing.

The length of the directors is usually made about $0{\cdot}43\lambda$ and the spacing approximately $0{\cdot}25\lambda$, but experiments have shown that where several directors are used, the bandwidth

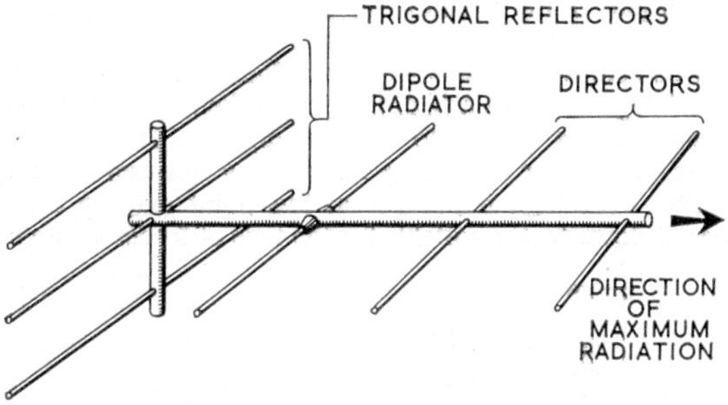

Fig. 13. Yagi array with trigonal reflectors.

can be broadened by making them progressively shorter in the pirection of radiation. The greater the number of directors, the higher the gain and the narrower the beamwidth. There is no advantage to be derived from using more reflectors spaced behind the first, but the front-to-back ratio may be improved somewhat by the use of additional reflectors as shown in **Fig. 13**. These additional reflector elements should subtend a fairly wide angle at the farthest director to be effective. In practice, a trigonal reflector element/element spacing of about $\frac{1}{4}\lambda$ is sufficient.

The gain obtainable from a Yagi array compared with a half-wave dipole is shown approximately by the empirical curve in **Fig. 14**.

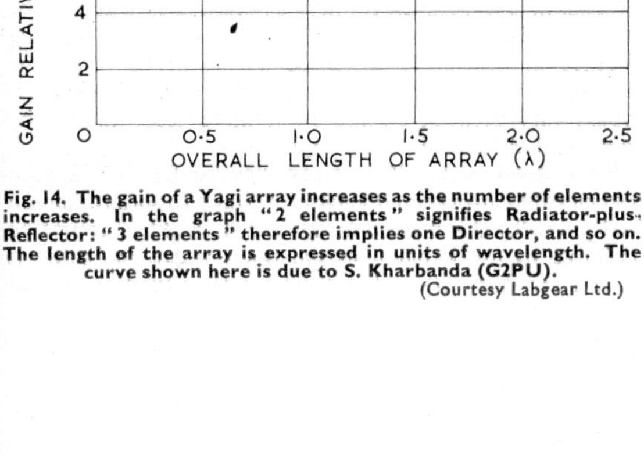

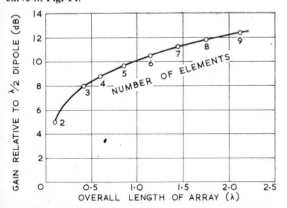

Fig. 14. The gain of a Yagi array increases as the number of elements increases. In the graph "2 elements" signifies Radiator-plus-Reflector: "3 elements" therefore implies one Director, and so on. The length of the array is expressed in units of wavelength. The curve shown here is due to S. Kharbanda (G2PU).

(Courtesy Labgear Ltd.)

The bandwidth for a standing-wave ratio less than 2:1 is about 2 per cent for close-spaced beams and about 3 per cent for wider spacing. Element lengths, particularly those of the directors, are very critical (i.e. within fractions of an inch), and ideally telescopic rods should be used to enable fine adjustments to be made. Each change of element length necessitates a readjustment of the matching either by moving the reflector or in the matching device itself.

Typical element lengths for spot frequencies in the 4m, 2m and 70cm bands are given in Table 3. The lengths are based on the assumption that the element diameter lies within the stated limits for the respective bands. Any departures from these diameter ranges will necessitate a change in the lengths of the elements; for a larger diameter the length will need to be decreased, and vice versa.

Stacked Yagi Arrays

To obtain a greater gain several Yagi arrays can be disposed horizontally or vertically or in both directions, the radiating elements being fed in phase. This is called *stacking*.

TABLE 3

Typical Dimensions of Yagi Arrays

Element	(Element length / Wavelength)	Length of Elements 70·3 Mc/s	145 Mc/s	435 Mc/s
		in.	in.	in.
Reflector	0·495	$83\frac{1}{2}$	40	$13\frac{1}{2}$
Dipole radiator	0·473	$79\frac{1}{2}$	$38\frac{1}{2}$	$12\frac{7}{8}$
Director D1	0·440	74	36	12
Director D2	0·435	$73\frac{1}{4}$	$35\frac{1}{2}$	$11\frac{7}{8}$
Director D3	0·430	$72\frac{1}{2}$	35	$11\frac{3}{4}$
Succeeding directors	0·005 successively	$71\frac{3}{4}$ etc.	$34\frac{1}{2}$ etc.	$11\frac{1}{2}$ etc.
End director	0·007 less than penultimate director	1 less	$\frac{3}{4}$ less	$\frac{3}{8}$ less

Elements	(Element spacing / Wavelength)	Spacing between Elements 70·3 Mc/s	145 Mc/s	435 Mc/s
		in.	in.	in.
Reflector/Radiator	0·125	21	$10\frac{1}{4}$	$3\frac{3}{8}$
Radiator/ Director D1	0·125	21	$10\frac{1}{4}$	$3\frac{3}{8}$
D1—D2	0·25	42	$20\frac{1}{2}$	$6\frac{3}{4}$
D2—D3, etc.	0·25	42	$20\frac{1}{2}$	$6\frac{3}{4}$

These dimensions are correct only for elements having diameters in the following ranges:

70·3 Mc/s	145 Mc/s	435 Mc/s
$\frac{1}{2}$—$\frac{3}{4}$ in.	$\frac{1}{4}$—$\frac{3}{8}$ in.	$\frac{1}{8}$—$\frac{3}{16}$ in.

The optimum stacking distance will depend on the gain of each individual Yagi array. Where the vertical and horizontal beamwidths of an individual array are approximately the same, i.e. with five or more elements, the optimum stacking distance will be approximately the same, both horizontally and vertically; this distance varies from about 0.75λ for an array of 4-element Yagis to about 2.0λ or more for 8-element Yagis. For practical reasons the spacing is usually less than optimum and there is a consequent reduction in the total gain. Theoretically, the increase in gain obtainable by stacking two identical arrays in such a way that their capture areas do not overlap is simply two times (i.e. 3 dB), but in practice this can sometimes be exceeded if there is a suitably favourable degree of coupling between the two arrays: for example, a pair of 3-element Yagi arrays could be made to yield an increase of 4.2 dB. However, the increase usually proves to be less than the theoretical 3 dB, and a figure of 2.2–2.5 dB is all that can be ordinarily expected.

The feed impedance of a stacked array theoretically is the feed impedance of an individual Yagi array divided by the total number of Yagis employed; in practice the feed impedance of stacked Yagis is slightly less than this because of interaction between each Yagi array although this reduction is not so marked at the greater spacings.

Disadvantages of Conventional Yagi Arrays

Perhaps the most important disadvantage is that the variation of the element lengths and spacings causes inter-related changes in the feed impedance of a Yagi array. To obtain the maximum possible forward gain experimentally is extremely difficult because for each change of element length it is necessary to readjust the matching either by moving the reflector or by resetting a matching device. However, a method has been devised for overcoming these practical disadvantages by the use of a radiating element in the form of a *skeleton slot*, this being far less susceptible to the changes in impedance caused by changes in the parasitic-element lengths. This development is due to B. SYKES (G2HCG).

A true slot would be a slot cut in an infinite sheet of metal, and such a slot when approximately one half-wavelength long would behave in a similar way to a dipole radiator. In contrast with a dipole, however, the polarization produced by a vertical slot is horizontal (i.e. the electric field is horizontal).

The skeleton slot was developed in the course of experiments to determine to what extent the infinite sheet of metal could be reduced before the slot aerial lost its radiating property. The limit of the reduction for satisfactory performance was found to occur when there remained approximately one half-wavelength of metal beyond the slot edges. However, further experiments showed that a thin rod bent to form a "skeleton slot" of dimensions approximately $5\lambda/8 \times 5\lambda/24$ exhibited similar properties to those of a true slot. The manner in which a skeleton slot functions can be understood by referring to the diagrams in **Fig. 15**. Consider two half-wave dipoles spaced vertically by $5\lambda/8$. Since the greater part of the radiation from each dipole takes place at the current antinode, i.e. the centre, the ends of the dipoles may be bent without serious effect. These ends may now be joined together with a high-impedance feeder, so that end-feeding can be applied to the bent dipoles. To radiate in phase, the power should be fed midway between the two dipoles. The high impedance at this point may be transformed down to one suitable for the type of feeder in use by

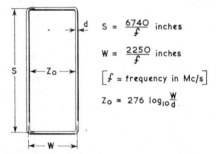

$$S = \frac{6740}{f} \text{ inches}$$

$$W = \frac{2250}{f} \text{ inches}$$

$$[f = \text{frequency in Mc/s}]$$

$$Z_0 = 276 \log_{10}\frac{W}{d}.$$

Fig. 16. Dimensional relationships of a skeleton-slot radiator. Both *S* and *W* may be varied experimentally from the values indicated by these formulae. For small variations the radiation characteristics of the slot will not change greatly, but the feed impedance will undergo appreciable change and therefore the length of the delta matching section should always be adjusted to give a perfect match to the transmission line.

means of a tapered matching-section transmission line (i.e. a delta match). Practical dimensions of skeleton-slot radiator are given in **Fig. 16**.

It is important to note that two sets of parasitic elements are required with a skeleton-slot radiator and not one set as required with a true slot. One further property of the skeleton slot is that its bandwidth is somewhat greater than a pair of stacked dipoles.

Skeleton Slot Yagi Arrays in Stack

Skeleton slot Yagi arrays may be stacked to increase the gain but the same considerations of optimum stacking distance as previously discussed apply; in this case the centre-to-centre spacing of a pair of skeleton slot Yagi arrays should vary between 1λ and 3λ or more according to the number of elements in each Yagi array.

Each skeleton-slot Yagi array may be fed by 72 ohm coaxial cable, using equal lengths of feeder to some common feed point for the stacked array, and it would of course be desirable to use a balun at the point where the cable is attached to each array. A coaxial quarter-wave transformer

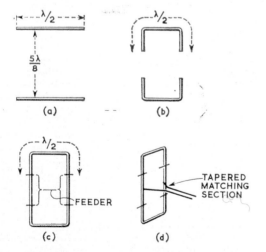

Fig. 15. Development of a skeleton-slot radiator from two half-wave dipoles spaced $5\lambda/8$ apart.

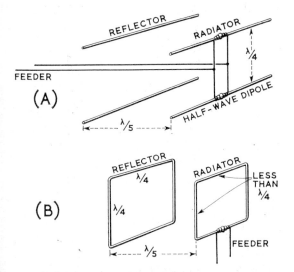

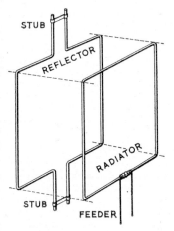

Fig. 17. Development of a bi-square aerial from a pair of dipoles and reflectors. In (A) the reflectors are λ/2 long and the dipole radiator lengths for resonance are approximately 0·48λ. In (B) the elements have been bent to form two squares, the combined reflector having sides 0·25λ long and the combined radiator having sides 0·24λ long. The two squares can be made equal in size by the method shown in Fig. 18.

can be used to transform the impedance to that of the main feeder. For example, if a pair of skeleton-slot Yagi arrays, each of 72 ohm feed impedance, are stacked, the combined impedance will be one-half of 72 ohms, i.e. 36 ohms; this may be transformed to 72 ohms by the use of a quarter-wave section of 52 ohm coaxial cable, allowance being made for its velocity factor. Larger assemblies of skeleton-slot Yagi arrays can be fed in a similar manner by joining pairs and introducing quarter-wave transformers until only one feed is needed for the whole array.

The Bi-square

Another array, developed by S. KHARBANDA (G2PU) from the "cubical-quad" aerial (page 385), is called the *bi-square*. This is related to the stacked Yagi and skeleton-slot type of aerial. Basically it comprises two stacked dipoles with reflectors, the ends of which have been bent to form two

Fig. 18. The bi-square aerial may be fitted with small stubs in the reflector element so that all the sides of both reflector and radiator can be made equal in length (approximately 0·24λ).

squares as shown in Fig. 17. For maximum forward gain the spacing between these two squares should be λ/8–λ/4: a spacing of λ/5 is frequently chosen.

As already explained the length of the dipole must be somewhat less than that of the reflector, and hence the radiating square is smaller than the reflecting square. This is inconvenient mechanically, and the size of the reflector square can be reduced by the insertion of small inductive stubs at the current antinodes as shown in Fig. 18. The use of a stub at each antinode in the reflector ensures a symmetrical polar diagram with the major lobe at right angles to the plane of the radiators unlike the conventional cubical quad in which only one stub is used. The resulting structure is very robust, and a gain of the order of 9–10 dB over a dipole is claimed for this array.

Stacked-Dipole Arrays

Both horizontal and vertical beam widths can be reduced and gain increased by building up arrays of driven dipoles. This arrangement is usually referred to merely as a *stack* or sometimes as a *bill-board* or *broadside array*. Since this type of array is constituted from a number of radiating dipoles, the feed impedance would be extremely low if the dipoles were centre-fed. However, the impedance to earth of a dipole at its end is high, the precise value depending upon the ratio of its length to diameter, and it will therefore be more convenient to use a balanced high-impedance feeder to end-feed a pair of collinear half-wave dipoles, a system called a *full-wave dipole*. The length for resonance and the feed impedance in terms of wavelength/diameter ratio is shown in Table 4.

The full-wave dipoles are usually mounted with a centre-to-centre spacing, horizontally and vertically, of one half-wavelength and are fed in phase. Typical arrangements for

TABLE 4
Resonant Lengths of Full-wave Dipoles

Wavelength / Diameter	Value of Dipole length / Wavelength for resonance	Feed Impedance (ohms)
50	0·85	500
100	0·87	900
150	0·88	1100
200	0·896	1300
300	0·906	1500
400	0·916	1700
700	0·926	2000
1,000	0·937	2400
2,000	0·945	3000
4,000	0·951	3600
10,000	0·958	4600

The dimensions used in calculating the ratios must be in similar units (e.g. both in metres or both in centimetres).

From *Aerials for Metre and Decimetre Wavelengths* by R. A. SMITH.

stacks of full-wave dipoles are shown in **Fig. 19**. Note that the feed wires between dipoles are one half-wavelength long and are crossed so that all the dipoles in each bay are fed in phase. The impedance of these phasing sections is unimportant provided that the separators, if used, are made of low-loss dielectric material and that there is sufficiently wide separation at the cross-over points to prevent unintentional contact.

To obtain the radiation pattern expected, all dipoles should be fed with equal amounts of power (as indeed would

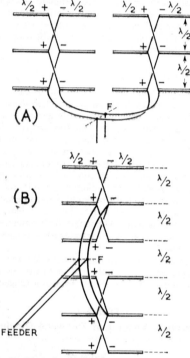

(A)

(B)

FEEDER

Fig. 19. Typical stacks of full-wave dipoles. Note that the feedpoint *F* is equidistant from each bay of dipoles. For examples of element lengths, see Table 4.

be desirable in any multi-radiator array), but this cannot be achieved in practice because the dipoles which are farthest from the feeder have a greater feeder loss than the nearest. However, by locating the main feed point as nearly symmetrically as possible these effects are minimized. Hence it would be preferable for the aerial shown at (A) in Fig. 19 to be fed in the centre of each bay of dipoles; the feeder to each bay must be connected as shown to ensure that the two bays are fed in phase. If they were fed 180° out-of-phase the resultant beam pattern would have two major side lobes and there would be very little power radiated in the desired direction. The diagram (B) in Fig. 19 shows two vertically stacked bays of full-wave dipoles fed symmetrically and in phase.

The spacing at the centre of each full-wave dipole should be sufficient to prevent a reduction of the resonant frequency by the capacity between the ends. In practice this spacing is usually about 1 in. for the 144 and 420 Mc/s bands.

Matching can be carried out by the use of movable short-circuited open-wire stubs on the feed lines. The practical

aspects of this operation are dealt with in a typical case later in this chapter.

As with the Yagi array, the gain can be increased by placing a reflector behind the radiating elements at a spacing of $0.1-0.25\lambda$, a figure of 0.125λ being frequently chosen. For the 420 Mc/s band and for higher frequencies, a plane reflector made up of 1 in. mesh wire netting stretched on a frame can be used in place of the resonant reflector at a similar spacing. The mesh of the wire should be so orientated that the interlocking twists are parallel to the dipole. The wire netting should extend at least one half-wavelength beyond the extremities of the dipoles in order to ensure a high front-to-back ratio.

The half-wave sections of the full-wave dipole should be supported at the current antinodes, i.e. at their centres, either on small insulators or in suitably drilled wooden vertical members. Supports should not be mounted parallel to the elements because of possible influence on the properties of the aerial.

The bandwidth of this type of aerial is exceptionally large and its adjustments generally are far less critical than those of Yagi arrays.

For a stack having an adequate wire-net reflector, the horizontal beamwidth θ, vertical beamwidth ϕ and power gain G (compared with an isotropic radiator) can be calculated approximately from the following formulae.

$$\theta = \frac{51\lambda}{a} \qquad \phi = \frac{51\lambda}{b} \qquad G = \frac{4\pi ab}{\lambda^2}$$

where a and b are the horizontal and vertical dimensions of the reflector respectively, both being expressed in the same units as the wavelength.

These formulae are true only for an array which is large compared with the wavelength, but are suitable as a criterion for judging aerials of any type provided the equivalent aperture or capture area is known.

Skeleton Slots in Stack

Skeleton slots can be used to replace vertically disposed pairs of half-wave dipoles. As the optimum vertical dimension for a horizontally polarized skeleton slot is approximately $5\lambda/8$, it is no longer possible to use the vertical spacings shown for full-wave stacks. The slots are mounted vertically at a centre-to-centre spacing of one wavelength and fed through a tapered matching section, as for the skeleton-slot Yagi array, and are then connected to the phasing lines. Since the spacing between feed points is one wavelength there is no phase difference and it is unnecessary to transpose the phasing wires. The tapered matching sections should be adjusted to present an impedance of N times the desired feeder-cable impedance where N is the number of skeleton slots employed. The impedance resulting from the connection of all the feed points together will then equal the cable impedance.

A broadside array of skeleton slots may be built up by adding further slots horizontally at a centre-to-centre spacing of one half-wavelength.

Disadvantage of Multi-element Arrays

As the frequency becomes higher and the wavelength becomes shorter, it is possible to construct arrays of much higher gain although, as already described, the advantage is offset by the reduction in capture area. However, if the practice already described, namely that of using many driven or parasitic elements, either in line or in stack, is adopted, the complications of feeding become increasingly greater. Also as the frequency increases, the radiation-loss from open-wire lines and from phasing and matching sections likewise increases, and it is then difficult to ensure an equal power-feed to a number of radiators. Preferably, therefore, the aerial should have a minimum number of radiating or other critical elements, such as resonant reflectors or directors. There are many aerials in this category but only those having immediate amateur application are described here.

Corner Reflector

The use of an aperiodic plane reflector spaced behind a radiating dipole has already been discussed. If this reflector is bent to form a V, as shown in **Fig. 20,** a considerably higher gain is achieved. The critical factors in the design of

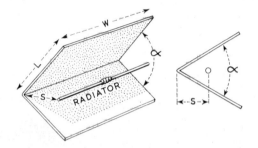

Fig. 20. Corner reflector. The half-wave dipole radiator is spaced parallel with the vertex of the reflector at a distance S. Its characteristics are shown in Figs. 21 and 22. For dimensions, see Table 5.

such an aerial array are the corner angle α and the dipole/vertex spacing S. The curves in **Fig. 21** show that as α is reduced, the gain theoretically obtainable becomes progressively greater. However, at the same time the feed impedance of the dipole radiator falls (Fig. 20) to a very low value, as can be seen from **Fig. 22:** this makes matching difficult and hence a compromise has to be reached. In practice the angle α is usually made 90° or 60°; adjustments in a 60° corner are a little more critical although the maximum obtainable gain is higher. The final matching of the radiator to the line may be carried out by adjusting the distance S, which as seen from Fig. 21 does not greatly affect the gain over a useful range of variation but causes a considerable change in radiation resistance (see Fig. 22). A two-stub tuner may also prove helpful in making final adjustments.

The length of the sides L of the reflector should exceed

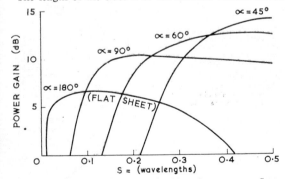

Fig. 21. Theoretical power gain obtained by using a corner reflector with a half-wave dipole radiator: see Fig. 20.

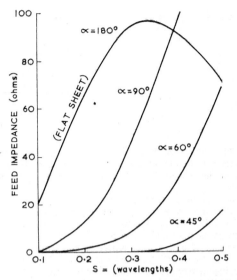

Fig. 22. Feed impedance of a half-wave dipole provided with a corner reflector: see Fig. 20.

two wavelengths to secure the characteristics indicated by Figs. 21 and 22, and the reflector width W should be greater than one wavelength for a half-wave dipole radiator. The reflecting sheet may be constructed of wire-netting as described previously or alternatively may be fabricated from metal spines arranged in a V-formation, all of them being

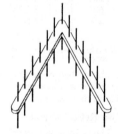

Fig. 23. The corner reflector shown in Fig. 20 can be modified by using a set of metal spines arranged in V-formation to replace the sheet-metal or wire-netting reflector.

parallel to the radiator: see **Fig. 23.** The spacing between adjacent rods should not exceed 0·1λ.

A useful approximation for the power gain G referred to a half-wave dipole is $G = 300/\alpha$, where α is the angle between the sides measured in degrees.

The maximum dipole/vertex spacing S included in the curves shown in Figs. 21 and 22 is one half-wavelength. Spacings greater than this would require rather cumbersome constructions at lower frequencies, but at the higher frequencies larger spacings become practicable, and higher gains than would be suggested by Fig. 21 can then be obtained: see Table 5. This indicates that the corner reflector can become a specially attractive proposition for the 1250 Mc/s band, but the width across the opening should be in excess of 4λ to achieve the results shown.

Trough Reflector

To reduce the overall dimensions of a large corner reflector the vertex can be cut off and replaced with a plane reflector, an arrangement known as a *trough reflector*: see

403

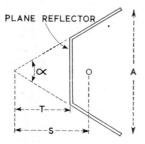

Fig. 24. Trough reflector. This is a useful modification of the corner reflector shown in Fig. 20. The vertex has been cut off and replaced by a simple plane section.

Fig. 24. Similar performance to that of the large corner reflector can thereby be achieved provided that the dimensions of the trough do not exceed the limits indicated in Table 5.

The resulting aerial has a performance very little different from the corner-reflector type and presents fewer mechanical problems since the plane centre portion is relatively easy to mount on the mast and the sides are considerably shorter.

The gain of both corner reflectors and trough reflectors may be increased still further by stacking two or more and arranging them to radiate in phase, or alternatively by adding further collinear dipoles within a wider reflector similarly fed

TABLE 5
Corner/Trough Reflector

Angle α	Value of S for maximum gain	Gain (dB)	Value of T
90°	1·5 λ	13	1λ—1·25λ
60°	1·25 λ	15	1·0λ
45°	2·0 λ	17	1·9λ

This table shows the gain obtainable for greater values of S than those covered by Fig. 21, assuming that the reflector is of adequate size.

in phase. Not more than two or three radiating units should be used since the great virtue of the simple feeder arrangement would then be lost.

The Reflex Aerial

The reflex aerial, as shown in **Fig. 25,** comprises a radiating dipole located in front of a large reflecting sheet with a grating type of structure mounted in front of and parallel to

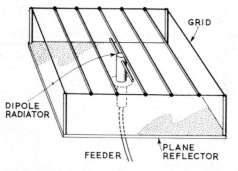

Fig. 25. Reflex aerial. Note the grid-like structure in front of the dipole radiator. The plane reflector behind the radiator may be made of sheet metal or wire netting (1 in. mesh for 420 Mc/s; ½ in. mesh for 1,250 Mc/s).

the dipole. The total gain attainable with this aerial system is about 12 db.

The dipole has a feed impedance of about 120 ohms and can be fed from a coaxial cable with, if necessary, a suitable matching device and a balun transformer. Typical dimensions for the 420 Mc/s and 1250 Mc/s bands are shown in **Fig. 26.** There is no advantage in increasing the reflector size beyond about two wavelengths square since above this size the oblique radiation from the dipole is so slight that

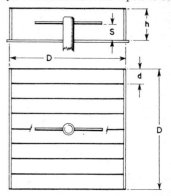

BAND	D	S	h	d	rods diam.	Dipole length	diam.
440 Mc/s	30"	7½"	12"	7½"	½"	12½"	¼"
1250 Mc/s	18"	2½"	4"	2½"	5/32"	4¼"	⅛"

Fig. 26. Typical dimensions of a reflex aerial for 420 Mc/s or 1,250 Mc/s. With these dimensions the gain should be 11–12 dB. If the size of the reflector D is increased to 2-wavelengths square, the gain rises to about 16 dB.

little further gain can be achieved. However, the gain may be increased by adding further reflex aerials either horizontally or vertically as desired and feeding them so as to radiate in phase.

The Parabolic Reflector

The principle of the parabolic reflector as used for light waves is well known. Such a reflector may be used for radio

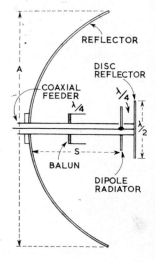

Fig. 27. Typical design for a parabolic reflector and feeder arrangement. The dipole should be at the focus of the parabola. To achieve maximum gain the distance S should be made adjustable. The coaxial-sleeve balun should be set back from the dipole.

waves, although the properties are somewhat different because the ratio of the diameter of the reflector to the wavelength is not extremely large, as it is in the case of light waves. If a radiator is placed at the focus of a paraboloid and if most of the energy is directed back into the " dish," a narrow beam will be produced. Assuming that the energy is uniformly distributed over the dish, the angular width of the beam θ will depend on the diameter of the reflector A approximately according to the formula $\theta = 60\lambda/A$, where A is expressed in wavelengths. To avoid the obvious difficulties in making a parabolic reflector from sheet metal, a skeleton form of construction of wire netting stretched over wooden ribs may be found successful for frequencies up to 1500 Mc/s but as the wavelength becomes shorter the overall surface contour of the reflector must approach that of the true paraboloid more closely.

A suitable parabolic reflector for the 1250 Mc/s and 2400 Mc/s bands may be 1–3 ft. in diameter. The radiator element is usually a half-wave dipole having a resonant reflector in the form of a disc one half-wavelength in diameter mounted one quarter-wavelength *in front* of the dipole to reflect the radiation back into the parabolic dish. The centre of the dipole should be accurately positioned at the focus of the parabola. A balun transformer of the coaxial-sleeve type may be mounted on the feed stem. A typical aerial assembly with a suitable feeder arrangement is shown in **Fig. 27**. For this system a two-stub tuner will be found particularly convenient.

The Helical Aerial

Another simple beam aerial possessing high gain and wide-band frequency characteristics simultaneously is the

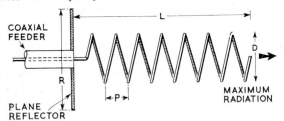

Fig. 28. The helical aerial. The plane reflector may take the form of a dart-board type of wire grid to reduce wind-resistance and weight. A gain of 12 dB is obtainable with a 7-turn helix.

helical aerial: see **Fig. 28**. When the circumference of the helix is of the order of one wavelength axial radiation occurs; i.e. the maximum field strength is found to lie along the axis of the helix. This radiation is circularly polarized, the sense of the polarization depending on whether the helix has a right- or left-hand thread.

If a pick-up dipole is used to explore the field in the direction of maximum radiation, the signal received by this dipole will show no change of amplitude as it is rotated through 360°, thus indicating true circular polarization. At any point to the side of the helix the wave will be elliptically polarized, i.e. the horizontal and vertical components will be of unequal strength.

A helix may be used to receive the circularly polarized waves radiated from a transmitting helix, but care must be taken to ensure that the receiving helix has a thread of the same sense as the radiator; if a thread of the wrong sense is used, the received signal will be very considerably weaker.

The properties of the helical aerial are determined by the diameter of the spiral D and the pitch P and depends upon

the resultant effect of the radiation taking place all along the helical conductor. The gain of the aerial depends on the number of turns in the helix. The diameter of the reflector R should be at least one half-wavelength. The diameter of the helix D should be about $\lambda/3$ and the pitch P about $\lambda/4$.

A helix of this design will have a feed impedance of about 140 ohms; this may be transformed to the feeder impedance by means of a quarter-wave transformer. A typical helical aerial having a 7-turn helix has a gain of approximately 12 dB over a 2 : 1 frequency range. However, to achieve this gain fully it is necessary to use a circularly polarized aerial (e.g. a helix of the same sense) for reception. If a plane-polarized aerial, such as a dipole, is used there will be a loss of 3 dB.

TUNING ADJUSTMENTS

To tune up any aerial system it is essential to keep it away from large objects, such as buildings, sheds and trees, and the array itself should be at least two wavelengths above the ground. It is useless to attempt any tuning indoors since the change in the surroundings will result in completely different performance when the array is taken outside.

Undoubtedly the most effective apparatus for tuning up any aerial system is a standing-wave indicator or reflectometer. If there is zero reflection from the load, the standing-wave ratio on the aerial feeder is unity. Under this condition, known as a *flat line*, the maximum power is being radiated. All aerial matching adjustments should therefore be carried out to aim at a standing-wave ratio of unity.

If suitable apparatus is not available, the next best course of action is to tune the aerial for maximum forward radiation. A convenient device for this is a field-strength meter comprising a crystal voltmeter connected to a half-wave dipole placed at least ten wavelengths from the aerial. When adjustments have resulted in a maximum reading on this voltmeter, the feed line may nevertheless not be " flat " and therefore some power will be wasted. However, if the best has been done with the resources available it is highly likely that good results will be achieved.

TYPICAL AERIALS

To illustrate the principles of construction three aerial arrays which are typical of those in use at the present time are described in detail below.

A 6-over-6 Skeleton-slot Yagi Array for the 2m Band

This array can be constructed entirely from aluminium tubing, the elements being either fitted into holes drilled in the supporting booms and secured with self-tapping screws or attached to the booms with suitable clamping devices.

With the dimensions given in **Fig. 29**, the centre frequency is 145 Mc/s and the bandwidth is approximately 7 Mc/s for a standing-wave ratio of 1·3 : 1. The beamwidth for the half-power points is 20° and the forward gain approximately 13 dB. The feed impedance is 72 ohms and good-quality 72 ohm coaxial cable should be used as the feeder. A balun has been found to have little effect on the polar diagram, but it is recommended that one should be used and may be either the Pawsey-stub or coaxial-sleeve type. For convenience in mounting this balun on the aerial mast, a short length of 72 ohm balanced-twin feeder may be used to connect the output of the balun to the feed point. To prevent the ingress of water at the top end of the coaxial cable, the whole balun

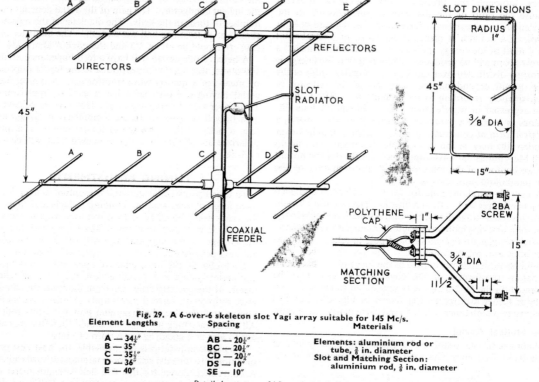

SLOT DIMENSIONS

Fig. 29. A 6-over-6 skeleton slot Yagi array suitable for 145 Mc/s.

Element Lengths	Spacing	Materials
A — 34½"	AB — 20¼"	Elements: aluminium rod or
B — 35"	BC — 20¼"	tube, ⅜ in. diameter
C — 35½"	CD — 20¼"	Slot and Matching Section:
D — 36"	DS — 10"	aluminium rod, ⅜ in. diameter
E — 40"	SE — 10"	

Details by courtesy of J-Beam Aerials Ltd.

assembly should be enclosed in polythene film.

Provided the dimensions stated are strictly adhered to, no matching adjustments will be necessary.

A Five-element Yagi Array for the 2m Band

The five-element Yagi array shown in **Fig. 30** is a typical " flat top " for v.h.f. use. With the dimensions indicated the centre frequency is 145 Mc/s.

The boom is made from wood and the elements are supported on polythene insulators mounted on wooden cross pieces. This form of construction is suitable where the workshop resources are limited and is quite as satisfactory as an all-metal construction although rather heavier.

The driven element is a folded dipole fed with 72 ohm coaxial cable through a balun of the Pawsey-stub type. This balun is constructed from brass tube, the inside diameter of which is a sliding fit over the outer covering of the coaxial

cable. The cable braiding is soldered at the aerial end of the balun to the outside of the balun tubing.

The gain of the aerial is about 9 dB, and the beamwidth is about 40° between half-power points.

A 12-element Stack for the 70cm Band

The diagram in **Fig. 31** illustrates the assembly of a twelve-element stack having a gain of 13 dB. With the dimensions indicated the centre frequency is 435 Mc/s.

The radiating elements are constructed from thin-walled ⅜ in. diameter brass tubing and the feeder and phasing wires are soldered on. The centres are supported on ½ in. polythene insulators mounted on vertical 1 in. × 1 in. wooden members. The reflecting screen is made from 1 in. mesh galvanised wire netting mounted on a framework of aluminium-alloy angle. Each bay of six full-wave dipoles is fed at the centre; the feed lines are taken straight through the

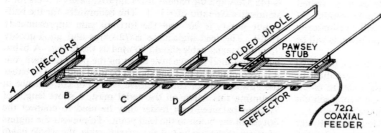

Fig. 30. A 5-element Yagi array for 145 Mc/s with a folded-dipole radiator. The gain obtainable is about 9 dB.

Element Lengths		Spacings	
A — 35"		AB — 12¼"	
B — 35½"		BC — 12¼"	
C — 36"		CD — 12¼"	
D — 38½"		DE — 20¼"	
E — 40"			

Materials

Elements: aluminium rod or tube, ¼ in. dia.
Folded dipole (D): folded part, ⅜ in. dia.
        fed part, ¼ in. dia.
        centre-to-centre spacing,
        1 in.
Balun transformer: brass tube to be a sliding
        fit over the coaxial feeder cable.

reflector, and each of these feed lines is matched to the 300 ohm open-wire feed line by a movable short-circuited stub. The two 300 ohm feeders, one from each bay, are joined to the output of a totally enclosed coaxial balun and a two-stub tuner. The aerial is fed with 72 ohm coaxial cable.

To match the aerial to the feeder, firstly one bay of the beam is disconnected and a 300 ohm 1 watt carbon resistor is substituted. The stub on this side should be set to exactly one quarter-wavelength long. The remaining bay is then matched approximately to the open-wire feed line. This may be determined by using a very low-wattage bulb (for example, 6 volt, 0·06A.), the screwed body of which is held in the hand. The presence of standing waves is then examined by observing the glow in the bulb as it is slid along the feed line with its centre connection in contact with one of the feedline conductors. The procedure is then reversed, the resistor being placed so as to represent the bay that has been matched. Both bays are then reconnected and the final matching carried out by means of the two-stub tuner using a slotted line or other matching device. If no special apparatus is available the array should be tuned for maximum gain as already described.

CHOICE OF AERIAL

The frequency ranges for which the various types of aerial described in this chapter can be recommended are shown in

TABLE 6
Recommended Frequency Ranges

Type of Aerial	70 Mc/s (4m)	144 Mc/s (2m)	420 Mc/s (70cm)	1250 Mc/s (23cm)	2400 Mc/s (12 cm)
Yagi Array	×	×	×	—	—
Stacked Array	×	×	×	—	—
Bi-Square	×	×	—	—	—
Corner/Trough	—	—	×	×	×
Reflex	—	—	×	×	×
Parabola	—	—	—	×	×
Helix	—	×	×	×	—

Table 6. The choice of an aerial for any particular band will depend upon operational requirements and upon the location, including such questions as the ease of erection and the ability to make the necessary tuning adjustments out-of-doors; moreover, wind-resistance may have to be reckoned with, especially in coastal areas.

In amateur stations it is seldom possible to predict the performance of a v.h.f. aerial with complete accuracy, and experience alone will determine the most suitable aerial for any particular location.

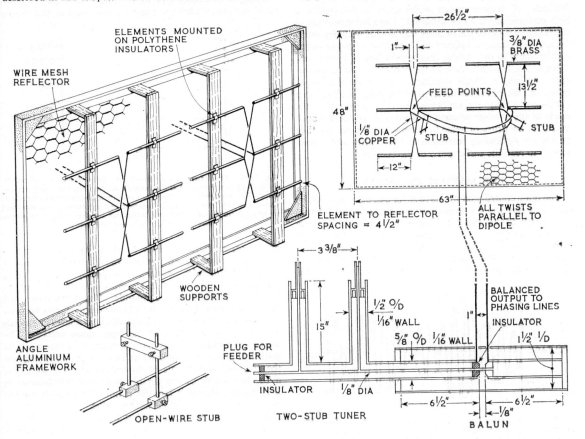

Fig. 31. A 12-element stack for 435 Mc/s, complete with two-stub tuner and enclosed coaxial balun.

CHAPTER 15

NOISE

IN every receiver there is a continuous background of noise which is present even when no signal is being received. This noise is caused partly by the valves and circuits of the receiver and partly by electrical impulses which reach the aerial from various sources; i.e. it is partly *internal* and partly *external*. In general, the more sensitive the receiver the higher the noise level, and increasing the sensitivity beyond a certain point brings no further increase in range. It is then possible to receive at adequate strength any signal not submerged in the noise, and further amplification will be of no assistance since both noise and signal will increase together. The sensitivity is then described as being *noise limited*, and this is the normal condition in modern receivers intended for weak-signal reception.

The purpose of this chapter is to discuss the characteristics of the various kinds of noise and to outline the broad principles of receiver design which must be followed if a high performance is to be achieved. Detailed treatment of special noise suppressors or noise limiters for reducing interference from ignition systems and other impulse generators will be found in the various chapters dealing with receivers.

An account is given here of the general characteristics of noise, the way it affects reception, the various sources of noise, and the principles involved in reducing its effects to a minimum. Finally the application of this knowledge to the needs of the average amateur is discussed, and it is hoped that this may prove of value to those who have not the time or are not sufficiently interested in the " whys and wherefores " to read the earlier parts of the chapter.

THE NATURE OF NOISE

The noise contributed by the receiver can be minimized by careful design, but it is important to appreciate that internal noise tends to increase with frequency whereas noise from external sources usually decreases. By careful design receiver noise can usually be made negligible compared with external noise below about 100 Mc/s. Internal noise is caused by the unavoidable random movement of electrons

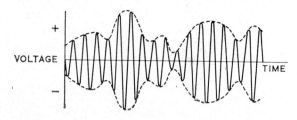

Fig. I (A). Noise waveform at the output of an i.f. amplifier. The oscillations, which are at the intermediate frequency, are approximately sinusoidal but have randomly varying amplitude.

in valves and circuits, and occasionally by avoidable defects such as dry joints in the wiring, faulty valves, and partial breakdowns of insulation. External noise can be caused by electrical machines and appliances (*man-made noise*), by atmospheric electrical discharges (*static* or *atmospherics*) and by radiations from outer space.

Most forms of electrical noise can be roughly pictured as a mixture of alternating currents of varying amplitudes and of all possible frequencies. Receivers, however, have a limited bandwidth and the observed noise level is a summation of all the components occurring within this band. As might be expected from this picture, the mean noise power is proportional to bandwidth, although at any given instant the noise amplitude can have any value depending on the extent to which the various components happen to be assisting or cancelling each other. **Fig. 1 (A)** shows a typical noise waveform such as might be produced at the output

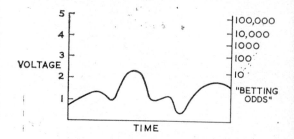

Fig. I (B). The same noise waveform after linear rectification. Note that it consists of the envelope of the original noise oscillations. The waveform as drawn has an average voltage amplitude of I volt, and the " betting odds " against any particular instantaneous amplitude being exceeded are indicated by the right-hand scale: this applies to " white noise " only.

of an intermediate-frequency amplifier by random movements of electrons in early stages; the i.f. amplifier can only transmit frequencies within its passband, and the noise applied to the detector has therefore the character of an i.f. signal of fluctuating amplitude. **Fig. 1 (B)** shows the same noise after detection by a linear rectifier; this consists of a positive (or negative) voltage which fluctuates in accordance with the amplitude of the input noise voltage. The important features of this waveform are its mean level, its statistical properties (summed up by the right-hand scale on the diagram) and its rate of fluctuation which is such that if the bandwidth of the circuits preceding the detector is B cycles per second it requires a time $1/B$ seconds for the amplitude to change significantly in value.

A steady carrier or the output from the beat-frequency oscillator when applied to the detector produces a steady d.c. output voltage V, on which the noise waveform is

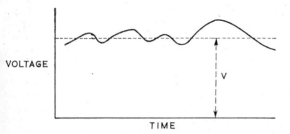

Fig. 1 (C). Output of linear detector when the input consists of a carrier (of voltage V) plus noise. Note that the average voltage remains equal to V as long as the noise peaks are less than V, i.e. as long as the noise-modulation of the carrier is less than 100 per cent.

superimposed as shown in **Fig. 1 (C)**. The noise adds or subtracts from this voltage depending on its relative phase which can have any value and, like the amplitude, tends to change from one value to another in time-intervals of the order of $1/B$ seconds. The noise fluctuations are now symmetrical in the sense that they leave the average voltage V unchanged.

One common effect of the carrier is to affect the apparent pitch of the noise; thus the waveform of Fig. 1 (B) can be thought of as being produced by noise frequencies up to a bandwidth of B cycles per second beating together, while that of Fig. 1 (C) is due (in the case of normal double sideband reception of A3 signals) to a carrier in the centre of the pass-band beating with noise frequencies out to a distance of only $B/2$ away from it on either side. This causes a lowering in

pitch of the noise at the carrier frequency and a rise in pitch when the carrier or the b.f.o. is detuned as for s.s.b. or single-signal c.w. reception. This behaviour is illustrated in **Fig. 2**. With a little practice this rise in pitch can be used as a method of setting up the b.f.o.

Frequently the presence of the carrier or the output from the b.f.o. increases the noise level, and this is commonly mistaken for noise on the carrier. The correct explanation is that when the signal level is low all detectors operate in a square-law manner, which is relatively inefficient; frequently the noise level is too low to cause the detector to operate on the linear part of its characteristic, so that the increase in noise level when the carrier is applied indicates more efficient detection and not a noisy carrier.

Noise originating externally to the receiver is often much more impulsive in character than the internal noise depicted in Fig. 1. It can have a wide variety of characteristics, which makes it difficult to discuss in general terms, but the representation of Fig. 1 can be applied to it, bearing in mind that (i) the dynamic range may be much greater and the " betting odds " of Fig. 1 (B) are not applicable, (ii) the envelope may show much slower variations, and (iii) there may be gaps in the noise waveform which can be exploited for reception particularly when, as is frequently the case in amateur working, low-grade communication is better than none.

THE EFFECT OF NOISE ON RECEPTION

The various random voltages originating in the receiver, together with certain kinds of externally-generated voltages, give rise to what is popularly known as *white noise*. It is

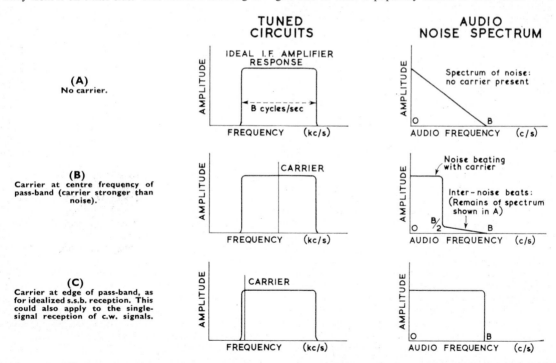

Fig. 2. Frequency characteristics of noise in various receiving conditions. When the frequency of the carrier (or the b.f.o.) is at the centre of the pass-band the noise-pitch is at its lowest, and when it is tuned to the edge of the pass-band the noise-pitch is at its highest. The bandwidth of the a.f. amplifier is assumed to be at least as great as the i.f. bandwidth (B cycles/second).

described in this way because, like white light, its energy is uniformly distributed over the relevant frequency-band. The manner in which such noise interferes with the reception of a signal is governed by certain elementary principles. Some discussion of these principles may prove interesting and helpful, although as will be seen their application to practical problems is not always straightforward.

It is useful to start by considering the nature of the signal. Any signal waveform can be considered as being built up from a succession of impulses, and it is obvious that the more rapidly the voltage constituting the signal changes, i.e. the higher the frequencies in its modulation envelope, the shorter the impulses which must be used to obtain a reasonably accurate representation of it. A c.w. signal, for example, could be built up from impulses equal in length to a Morse dot, say 0·1 second, whereas a telephony signal having frequencies up to 3 kc/s would need to be regarded as a succession of impulses not less than 1/6000 second in length. If t is the duration of an impulse, an i.f. bandwidth of $1/t$ is needed for reproducing it, i.e. 6000 cycles per second in the case of a telephony signal. The use of the term *i.f. band-width* avoids any possible confusion due to factors arising in the detection process, such as the ratio of two between the overall and i.f. noise bandwidths which is illustrated in Fig. 2 (B), but it will be shown later that such distinctions are not important during the actual reception of normal amateur signals when these are interfered with by noise only. The r.f. bandwidth is usually much greater than the i.f. bandwidth and can therefore be ignored.

The optimum bandwidth must be in the region of $1/t$, since this value allows the wanted impulse to build up almost to full amplitude and a greater bandwidth can only increase the effective amount of noise and not the signal. On the other hand, a smaller bandwidth reduces the amplitude of the signal more rapidly than that of the noise.

The noise in a bandwidth of $1/t$ also consists of impulses of duration t, but these vary in amplitude and phase in a random manner. Each impulse, before detection, normally contains a considerable number of cycles of r.f. or i.f. oscillation, like those shown in Fig. 1 (A). When a waveform is represented by impulses in this way, the phase and amplitude are regarded as being constant for the duration of any one impulse but there need not be any similarity between consecutive impulses. It will be appreciated that this is merely a convenient approximation, since in practice there is usually a smooth transition from one value to the next.

The size of any one noise impulse is a matter of chance, some values being more likely to occur than others, and Fig. 1 (B) shows the " betting odds " against any given impulse exceeding the indicated values. To see what this means in practice, consider the reception of a single Morse dot, the bandwidth being just wide enough and no more; Fig. 1 (B) shows that there is a reasonable chance of the noise amplitude reaching, say, three or four times the r.m.s. value, and unless the signal is even larger in amplitude it is likely to be mistaken for noise or vice versa. It is impossible to detect with certainty the presence of the Morse dot in these circumstances either aurally or mechanically or by any means whatsoever unless it is stronger than any likely value of the noise. In aural reception, however, with the stipulated bandwidth (about 10 c/s), the noise has a rough musical pitch similar to the wanted beat-note resulting in an unpleasant overall effect, and the discriminatory powers

of the ear are not used to best advantage. Under normal conditions it is found that the bandwidth can be extended indefinitely, and although the noise level rises the ability to copy a given weak signal through it is unaffected. This is because the ear itself, from the point of view of discrimination between signals and noise, acts as a filter having a pass-band of about 50 c/s and thus tends to determine the overall receiving bandwidth. The noise which is effective in masking a wanted 1000 c/s beat note is mainly that part of the noise spectrum between 975 and 1025 c/s, and adding noise outside these limits but between, say, 2000 and 3000 c/s has no adverse effect at normal audio levels. The usefulness of aural selectivity is not restricted to the separation of signals from noise, and most readers will be familiar with the fact that a weak Morse signal can be read in the presence of a much stronger unwanted signal when the beat notes are well separated in pitch, whereas two signals producing nearly the same heterodyne frequency are much more difficult to copy.

It has been explained above that the problem of separating weak signals from a noise background is one of deciding at each instant whether a true signal or only noise is present at the output of the receiver. This is a useful way of visualizing the basic problem, but in aural or visual reception the process is not carried out consciously and deliberately in the manner stated, and a variety of subjective or intellectual influences are usually at work. These are dependent partly on " integration " and partly on the fact that large portions of most messages are redundant so that missing words and phrases can often be filled in simply because nothing else would make sense. A missing dot in a Morse transmission may be serious if it occurs in a call-sign, but in a group of figures, known to contain no letters (e.g. a contest number or RST report), the figures can be correctly deduced by suitable reasoning even if several of the dots are missing.

Integration is the process of adding together several signal impulses to give one larger one. This is mainly the preserve of radio astronomers and radar engineers, but it also forms part of the subjective processes which are called into play while an attempt is being made to decipher a weak signal against a noise background.

Because of these and other complexities (e.g. fading) it is difficult to give any useful figures of signal-to-noise ratios required for amateur communication: more-or-less agreed figures exist for various types of commercial service, but amateur requirements tend to be both more modest and more elusive. The ability to read signals through white noise is not possessed in the same degree by all operators, but in general the human ear is a very efficient device for this purpose. When, as in amateur communication, messages are in plain language and tend to have standardized content such as RST reports, names and greetings, the aural selectivity can be supplemented by discrimination of an intellectual kind and no improvement is obtainable by the use of additional filters or other devices. It must be emphasized, however, that this applies only to white noise. It further assumes the absence of overloading in the receiver, adequate b.f.o. injection voltage at the detector and a reasonable amount of audio gain. At very high volume levels the ear has a non-linear characteristic, reception is degraded and, if the bandwidth is increased at constant gain, the noise level will be further raised and the situation will be aggravated. On the other hand, if the volume is too low, signals comparable with the noise level may not be loud enough for good intelligibility. In the case of impulsive noise (e.g. atmospherics and ignition noise) the ear can often be given considerable assistance by devices such as limiters which prevent overloading and enable a signal to be copied through gaps in the noise (see Chapters 4 and 16).

An understanding of the mechanism of detection (including the effects shown in Fig. 2 and the relatively complex phenomenon of modulation suppression) is important in the solution of many noise problems and it is also helpful, for example, in preventing the drawing of false conclusions from the way in which the amplitude and the pitch of the noise vary during the tuning-in of a signal. However, in regard to the actual copying of signals of the kinds met with in amateur radio, the problem can be very much simplified; this is because during such reception the detector is always operating *as a mixer*, i.e. there is always present a continuous signal or carrier which is strong compared with the noise, and the detector output is the beat frequency between the wanted intelligence and this strong oscillation. So long as this holds true, the detector, like any other frequency changer, is merely a device for shifting the frequency spectrum; it has no other effect on the signal or the noise, and no distinction need be made between post-detector and pre-detector selectivity, except where a factor of 2 must be introduced to allow for the superimposing of two similar sidebands in the process of detection, as indicated in Fig. 2 (B). This argument breaks down if, in a.m. reception, the carrier is not strong compared with the mean noise level, but normal speech modulation will then be unreadable in any case.

INTERNAL NOISE

Noise originating in the receiver can usually be distinguished from external noise by the fact that it persists after disconnecting the aerial, but this test can be misleading since the change in damping or tuning of the first circuit may alter the internal noise level, and it is better to make the experiment by changing over from the aerial to an equivalent dummy aerial. In the h.f. band, where external noise levels are high, this gives a simple and accurate check of the noise performance of the receiver; thus a change of 6 dB (i.e.

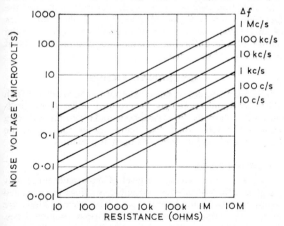

Fig. 3. Chart for determining the noise voltage developed in a resistance for a specified bandwidth Δf at room temperature 20° C.). Note that the scales are logarithmic.

a ratio of 4 : 1) in the noise level would mean that the receiver was responsible for a quarter of the total noise power, and the overall performance would be about 1 dB worse than with a perfect receiver. These figures, of course, assume linear detection and no overloading in the receiver.

Provided that no part of the internal noise is due to faulty wiring or components, it can be roughly divided into (a) thermal noise, (b) shot noise in valves, and (c) induced grid noise in valves. Whichever variety of noise is being considered, it is of practical importance only when generated in the early stages of the reciever, since noise generated later in the receiving chain is not amplified to the same extent.

Thermal Noise

The electrons in a conductor are n continuous random motion at a rate which increases with the absolute temperature (obtained in degrees Kelvin by adding 273 to the temperature in degrees Centigrade). The voltages produced by the electrons add together like other a.c. voltages, i.e. as the square root of the sum of the squares, and therefore if two similar conductors having equal resistances are joined in series the resultant noise voltage produced is $\sqrt{2}$ times that developed across either of the conductors considered singly. For any given conductor the noise voltage corresponding to a bandwidth of B cycles per second is equal to $\sqrt{(4KTBR)}$ where K is Boltzmann's constant (1.37×10^{-23} joules per deg. K), T is the absolute temperature (in deg. K) and R is the resistance of the conductor (in ohms). This relationship is plotted graphically in **Fig. 3**, but for quick reference a convenient figure to remember is 0·13 microvolts (approximately) for 1000 ohms at 1 kc/s bandwidth and at room temperature. The thermal noise generated in a tuning circuit can be calculated from the same expression if R is taken to represent the dynamic impedance: thus for a parallel resonant circuit R should be substituted by $Q\omega L$: see Chapter 1 (*Fundamentals*).

Thermal noise is seldom the most prominent form of noise. In h.f. reception it is overshadowed by noise picked up by the aerial, and in v.h.f. reception by valve noise.

The concept of noise temperature is helpful in assessing and comparing noise from all sources; thus it is now customary to express the external noise level by assigning an *equivalent temperature* to the radiation resistance of the aerial, i.e. the temperature it would be required to have if it were to produce this amount of noise merely as a consequence of thermal agitation. Similarly, valve shot noise is expressed in terms of an *equivalent* (room temperature) *noise resistance*, and induced grid noise in terms of an equivalent temperature attributed to the resistive component of the valve input impedance. The advantage of these concepts becomes apparent in dealing with *noise factor*, discussed later in this chapter.

Valve Shot Noise

This can be pictured by thinking of the anode current as being due to electrons hitting the anode like a stream of shot, or to the impact of hail against a window-pane, rather than as a continuous smooth flow. If the anode current I flows through a resistance R, the noise voltage developed is $\sqrt{(2eIBRF^2)}$ where e is the charge on an electron and F^2 is the space-charge smoothing factor. Comparison of this formula with the thermal-noise formula is the basis of the noise-diode method of measuring receiver noise performance, F^2 being unity when, as in the noise diode, all available electrons are drawn to the anode. For multi-electrode valves operating normally, F^2 is usually about 0·15 and it is convenient for comparison with aerial and thermal noise to represent the valve noise by a fictitious *equivalent noise resistance* (R_{eq}) such that a noise voltage $\sqrt{(4KTBR_{eq})}$ applied between grid and cathode would produce the equivalent fluctuation of anode current. It should be noted that the equivalent noise resistance is only a mathematical fiction and not a true resistance to which Ohm's Law could be applied.

Formulae for the calculation of the values of R_{eq} are given in Chapter 2 (*Valves*).

Induced Grid Noise

At low frequencies the voltage on the grid of a valve due to an applied signal can be considered as being constant for the complete interval of time taken for one electron to leave the cathode space charge and arrive at the anode. As the frequency is raised this state of affairs ceases to exist and in consequence a current is induced in the grid circuit giving the effect of a resistor, which decreases as the square of the frequency in shunt with the grid circuit. This resistor also appears as a generator of thermal noise at an equivalent temperature comparable with that of the valve cathode, i.e. about five times the absolute room temperature. There is partial correlation in phase between the shot noise and the induced grid noise with the result that one can be partially balanced against the other by detuning the grid circuit and thereby altering the relative phases. In general the reduction in noise is small and the two sources can be treated as independent to a first approximation, although it is often found that the signal-to-noise ratio tends to vary in an unsymmetrical way as the tuning of the input circuit is varied.

AERIAL NOISE

If a receiver is connected to a signal generator or to a dummy aerial a certain thermal noise voltage is fed into the receiver. This so-called *aerial noise* would determine the minimum usable signal level if the receiver itself generated no noise and if the real aerial produced the same noise as the dummy aerial. It has been found convenient to use the thermal noise level of the dummy aerial as a basis for the definition of *noise factor* referred to later in this chapter, because in this way the definition is directly related to the normal conditions of measurement. Unfortunately the noise levels of real and dummy aerials are usually quite different, so that both the definition and the measurements are unrelated to actuality and can be highly misleading unless the appropriate allowances are made.

When the impedance of a real aerial is measured, for example, with an impedance bridge, it is found to consist of a resistance and probably some reactance as well. The reactance can be ignored for the purpose of the present discussion since it is usually tuned out in one way or another. The resistance consists partly of radiation resistance and partly of loss resistance. The loss resistance is made up of the ohmic resistance of the aerial wire, leakage across insulators, losses in the immediate surroundings of the aerial, and also includes the resistance of the earth connection when a Marconi aerial is used; it is generally

important in the case of l.f. reception and when using indoor and frame aerials, and is one of the two factors (the other being the bandwidth) which determine the extent to which it is practicable to reduce the size of an aerial system. The loss resistance is a source of thermal noise corresponding to a temperature which is usually taken as 300° K although it can of course vary by 10 per cent or more from this figure depending on the local climatic conditions. In the higher

Typical noise diodes. Left, the CV2398 suitable for use at frequencies well above 500 Mc/s; right, the A.2087 (CV2171). Noise generators employing these valves are described in Chapter 19 (Measurements).

frequency bands the loss resistance can normally be made negligible compared with the radiation resistance, which in practical cases can be considered to have any noise temperature from less than 10°K up to thousands of millions of degrees depending on the frequency and other factors.

Radiation Resistance

There is no connection between the noise associated with the radiation resistance of an aerial and the actual physical temperature of the aerial or its surroundings, and to appreciate why this must be so it is necessary to understand the meaning of radiation resistance. When power is fed into a load, it is absorbed in the resistance of the load, and this is just as true for a transmitter feeding power into the radiation resistance of an aerial as it is for any other generator and load, but as is well known power radiated from an aerial may travel immense distances, even to outer space, before being absorbed. The radiation resistance of an aerial therefore tends to be a property of the whole of space of which the local features occupy merely a trivial part. The radiation resistance as such depends only on the fact that power is dissipated, regardless of where this takes place, but the associated thermal noise level depends on the nature of the absorbing objects and not on the actual temperature of the aerial.

EXTERNAL NOISE

The main sources of noise external to the receiver which affect communication may be grouped under three headings: (*a*) man-made, (*b*) atmospheric and (*c*) cosmic. During periods of intense solar disturbance, radio noise from the sun also tends to interfere with normal reception.

Man-made Noise

In remote rural areas, the level of man-made noise may be pleasantly low or even negligible, whereas in congested towns it may be intolerably high. The various kinds are often identifiable by reason of their time characteristics. Most of them originate in domestic electrical appliances or in industrial equipment. Common sources of this kind of noise are light switches, vacuum cleaners, refrigerator motors, advertising signs, electric shavers, electric drills, petrol engines, trolley buses and electric trains.

Intermittent clicks, such as those produced by switches and well-designed thermostats—unless very frequent—do not cause serious trouble since isolated noise impulses can only destroy occasional short elements of the signal and comparatively little of the information content is lost.

Continuous interference, such as that caused by commutators or discharge-tube lighting, is much more damaging to good communications. Such interference spreads over a very wide frequency range, although some fluorescent tubes generate a roughly tunable noise band of unstable frequency.

The type of noise associated with commutators, often known as *hash*, is only partly impulsive in character and cannot be dealt with successfully by any noise-limiting device in the receiver. The true impulse type of noise, such as ignition interference, is much easier to suppress. One of the advantages of the frequency-modulation system is that if the receiver is correctly designed and adjusted, interference from high-amplitude impulse noise is virtually eliminated, though a similar result can be achieved in the reception of a.m. signals if sufficient i.f. bandwidth and appropriate limiters are used. Individual sources of man-made noise usually have a relatively small range, and considerable improvement may be obtained by raising the aerial system as high as possible and by using a screened feeder. In the lower h.f. range, however, man-made noise from the large numbers of distant sources tends to be a limiting factor even in districts remote from centres of population.

Atmospheric Noise

The primary source of atmospheric noise (or *static*) is the ordinary lightning discharge. A typical flash has been estimated as carrying a current of 20,000 amperes. At any one time there are so many storms in progress in various parts of the world and the range of radio propagation is so great that much of the external noise which forms the background in long-distance h.f. communication must be attributed to lightning discharges in remote storms. The noise from local storms is naturally much more intense and is considerably greater on the lower radio frequencies, but of course this is only intermittent and does not require to be taken into account in the design of circuits.

A not infrequent, but usually short-lived, form of interference is due to rain static, i.e. currents induced in the aerial by electrically charged raindrops.

Cosmic (Galactic) Noise

Considerable noise radiation is received from the Milky Way and other galaxies, some of which are so remote that they are not visible even in the most powerful optical telescopes. At the wavelengths mainly used for long-distance communication, cosmic noise penetrates the ionosphere and is received at a high amplitude level. Apart from the variation with frequency, cosmic noise is similar in character to thermal noise.

TOTAL NOISE LEVEL

A general idea of the variation of atmospheric and man-made as well as cosmic noise level with frequency over the h.f. and v.h.f. bands is given in **Fig. 4**. These curves have been somewhat freely adapted from previously published data, bearing in mind the need for a simplified presentation. Below 14 Mc/s the diagram should be regarded only as a rough guide, since atmospheric and man-made noise levels are extremely variable, and the noise is generally more impulsive in character. As explained earlier, impulsive noise tends to be relatively less serious the lower the grade of communication, and for amateur purposes the *effective* lower-frequency noise levels may be lower than indicated although some slight " weighting " in this direction has taken place in the course of adapting the data.

The marked difference in atmospheric noise levels between day and night is due to the more efficient propagation at night from distance storm centres located mainly in the tropics. Above 100 Mc/s the external noise level continues to decrease, being much less than room-temperature thermal noise in the 440 Mc/s band, and frequently equivalent to only a few degrees absolute in the microwave bands.

ESTIMATION OF RECEIVER NOISE

When it is desired to measure the sensitivity of a receiver, some form of test signal is fed in through an impedance which simulates that of the aerial from which the receiver is designed to work. Such an impedance is known as a *dummy aerial* and is a source of thermal noise. If the receiver were perfect the noise at its output terminals would consist only of amplified noise from the dummy

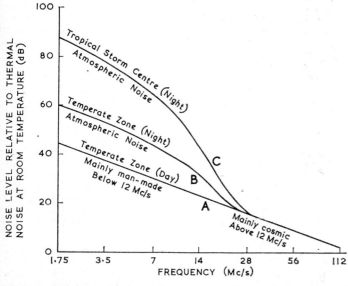

Fig. 4. Variation of external noise level with frequency. Curve A shows that during the day in temperate zones the noise is mainly man-made at frequencies above about 12 Mc/s. In these zones, atmospheric noise adds considerably to the total noise level at night (curve B). In tropical zones the atmospheric noise is relatively severe; curve C represents the worst conditions in these zones. The vertical scale indicates the number of decibels by which the noise level in a perfect receiver would increase if it were disconnected from a dummy aerial and fed from an efficient aerial of similar impedance.

413

aerial, but in practice the receiver adds a certain amount of noise as previously explained.

If the aerial noise is represented by T_a degrees (i.e. the equivalent temperature) the increase in noise due to imperfections in the receiver can be represented by T_r degrees (i.e. a rise in the equivalent temperature of the aerial). The value of T_r in comparison with T, the room temperature, is readily measurable by the noise-diode technique described in Chapter 19 (Measurements). If T_r is expressed in decibels relative to T, it can be directly compared with the noise levels indicated in Fig. 4 to find out whether it is significant in relation to the external noise level. Fig. 5 illustrates the lowest values of T_r which can be achieved without undue difficulty, as a function of frequency. As explained later, however, it is not always desirable to aim at a low value of T_r, and h.f. receivers frequently have much higher values than v.h.f. receivers.

Noise Factor

The equivalent-temperature concept of receiver noise is not yet universally adopted and the noise performance of receivers is usually specified in terms of *noise factor*. Unfortunately extreme care is required in specifying the conditions of measurement and in interpreting the figures obtained. However, if the advice offered in Chapter 19 on the subject of noise measurement is closely followed the reader is not likely to arrive at false conclusions. The method

of measurement described there is based in the definition—

$$Noise\ Factor = (T + T_r)/T$$

where T is the room temperature. This can of course be arranged in the form—

$$T_r = (Noise\ Factor - 1)T$$

to enable the noise factor as normally measured to be expressed directly as an equivalent aerial temperature. The object of good receiver design is to reduce T_r until it is negligible compared with the aerial noise temperature but not necessarily to make T_r as small as possible; any further possibility of improvement can generally be used instead to improve the receiver in other respects as discussed later, or perhaps to reduce its cost.

To reduce T_r to a negligible value, all that is necessary in principle is to step up the aerial impedance by means of a transformer to a value R_a which is large compared with the equivalent noise resistance R_{eq} of the first valve in the receiver: R_a and R_{eq} can then be thought of as two noise generators connected in series and the value of T_r/T will be equal to R_{eq}/R_a. In practice, however, the aerial impedance is shunted by other noise-generating resistances which represent losses in the input circuit and by the transit-time damping resistance associated with induced grid noise. This resistance has an equivalent temperature of $5T$ and decreases as the square of the frequency. These effects cause T_r to rise with frequency, not only because of the added noise but also because of the shunting effect which reduces aerial noise T_a relative to the valve noise which forms a major part of T_r. Since all "temperatures" have to be referred to the aerial where T_a is fixed in accordance with Figs. 4 and 5, any reduction of T_a relative to T_r is equivalent to an increase of T_r. In order to minimize this effect there is an optimum value of R_a which decreases with frequency and normally corresponds to over-coupling of the aerial into the first circuit of the receiver. This optimum value of R_a occurs because large values are heavily shunted by the transit-time damping so that as R_a is increased from zero the aerial noise voltage at the valve at first rises, as in the no-loss case, and then falls again. For the lowest noise factor, the aerial needs to be more tightly coupled than it would be for maximum gain and there is a consequent loss in r.f. selectivity. It should be remembered that R_{eq} is not an actual resistance but a designation for a noise generator; it therefore does not experience the shunting effects which R_a experiences.

Other precautions to ensure the lowest value of noise factor are to use input circuits with the highest possible inductance and Q-value, and to choose valves with low equivalent noise resistance (i.e. triodes in preference to pentodes) and high transit-time damping resistance. In r.f. or i.f. amplifiers having very great bandwidth where a low noise factor is required it is better to rely on tighter coupling to produce the necessary bandwidth than on the use of shunt resistors.

When inverse feedback is present in the input stage it usually has an equal reducing effect on the signal and on all forms of noise, and therefore does not directly affect the noise factor or the optimum design conditions, although, as in the case of the earthed-grid triode, it may produce heavy damping of the input circuit. On the other hand, the inductance of the cathode lead in a pentode causes inverse feedback which leaves partition noise unaffected and therefore degrades the noise factor.

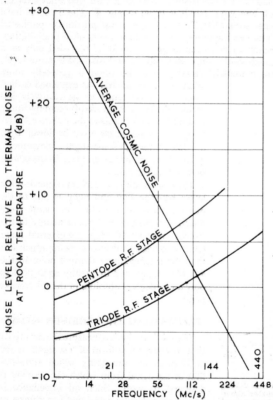

Fig. 5. Approximate relationship between aerial noise and receiver noise over the amateur frequency bands. The curves shown for pentode and triode r.f. amplifier stages represent typical good designs.

PRACTICAL ASPECTS OF NOISE

Every amateur will wish to ensure that the performance of his station is not handicapped by avoidable defects in the receiver. This situation can arise from the following causes:

(a) Gain is not sufficient to make certain that the useful sensitivity is noise-limited.

(b) Receiver contributes significantly and avoidably to the noise background level.

In the case of insufficient gain the trouble and the remedy are both obvious. Those designing their own receivers should have no difficulty in making a rough estimate, with the aid of Figs. 3 and 4 and the foregoing explanations, of the amount of r.f. and i.f. gain required to give a reasonable working level (say 1 volt) at the detector, and hence of the amount of audio gain needed to bring the rectified noise (about 0·4 volt r.m.s. assuming a diode detector with 1 volt input) up to a reasonable listening level.

Above about 100 Mc/s, low noise factor is all-important and Fig. 5 gives a guide to the performance which should be achievable by using a low-noise triode r.f. stage. On the h.f. bands it is the external noise which limits the ability of the receiver to deal with weak signals, provided of course that the aerial is a good one and that the receiver is functioning correctly. In such circumstances, if it were merely a question of ensuring an adequate signal-to-noise ratio, and if a good triode mixer is used, there would be no need for any r.f. amplifier stages and thus the risk of blocking and the production of spurious responses due to the overloading of the mixer by strong signals would be avoided. Another danger is that of an apparent increase in the noise level caused by intermodulation at the mixer between large numbers of moderately strong signals within the pass-band of the r.f. circuits. All these effects are aggravated by excessive r.f. gain and by some of the other measures which may be taken to improve the noise factor. On the other hand, if it is necessary to use an inefficient aerial, such as a wire fastened to the picture rail, or a miniature beam having appreciable loss-resistance in the elements or the feeders, the external noise level will in most cases be lower; the receiver noise must therefore be reduced in proportion and an r.f. stage will be necessary. Indoor aerials are sometimes responsible for increased pick-up of man-made noise from local sources, and in such cases this reasoning will obviously not be valid.

In defence of the standard practice of employing r.f. stages, in h.f. receivers it must be added that they provide a margin of safety against the consequences of inefficient coupling between the receiver and the aerial. Moreover the disadvantages associated with r.f. stages can often be mitigated by making sure that the r.f. gain control is not advanced beyond the point where external noise just swamps the internal noise as judged by a simple check, e.g. by disconnecting the aerial

Aural Discrimination

When the above conditions have been satisfied, discrimination between signals and noise becomes mainly a job for the ear and brain working together, and except in a few special cases very little can be done in the receiver to assist this process. If the overall bandwidth is greater than necessary, decreasing it reduces the noise level but does not make copying any easier, because it is only the noise which occupies the same acoustic band as the signal that is effective in preventing it from being copied. This argument,

however, must not be carried too far; it can, for example, be used to justify the normal practice of using bandwidths of several hundred kilocycles for the sound channel of television receivers, but it is not valid when applied to amateur v.h.f. receivers. The reason for this is that the amateur is able to make use of low signal levels, and it is possible by increasing the pre-detector bandwidth to reach a point where the noise voltage at the detector becomes comparable with the carrier voltage of, say, a just-readable telephony signal. The situation at the detector is then as depicted in Fig. 2 (C) but with the signal over-modulated by the noise, and the wanted modulation of the carrier tends to be destroyed. The effect is the same as modulation suppression, a well-known property of linear detectors whereby the presence of a strong carrier destroys the modulation of a weaker one. There is no advantage in using a square-law detector, since this also by its nature discriminates in favour of strong signals.

Effects of Overloading

Another possible cause of deterioration in the ability to copy signals through noise is overloading, particularly of the i.f. stages, by noise peaks which as shown by Fig. 1 (B) may reach several times the mean noise level and will increase in amplitude if the bandwidth is increased. If a reduction of bandwidth appears to give improved reception of weak signals, it is possible that some such effect may be taking place and the gain should be reduced.

In the case of impulsive noise like that due to ignition systems or isolated atmospherics, the dynamic range is relatively large and noise limiters are useful in the prevention of overloading, particularly if the bandwidth is large so that the impulses are not lengthened and caused to overlap—as they may be by the ear itself—before being limited. The time intervals between atmospherics are frequently long enough to enable words or syllables, or Morse characters, to be read through the gaps, and it may thus be possible to sustain low-grade communications through a relatively high noise level; in suitable circumstances this may allow some discounting of the lower-frequency noise levels plotted in Fig. 4.

Sideband Reception

In the reception of Morse and sideband signals, the voltage injected into the second detector from the beat-frequency oscillator must be large compared with the mean noise voltage, but a ratio of 8–10 times in voltage is sufficient in regard to the signal-to-noise ratio, whereas for maximum discrimination against strong signals an even higher injection level is necessary.

It is becoming common practice to employ single-sideband reception of ordinary amplitude-modulated signals in order to remove interference which may be present on one sideband. This unfortunately entails a reduction in the signal-to-noise ratio since the two sidebands of a double-sideband signal add up in phase and therefore the removal of one of them halves the signal voltage; at the same time, the noise power which accompanies the rejected sideband is eliminated. This halves the total noise power so that there is a decrease of 3 dB in the noise level to offset the decrease of 6 dB in the signal level, leaving a penalty of 3 dB. As a corollary to this, it follows that s.s.b., d.s.b. and a.m. signals should give equal signal-to-noise ratios for equal *total* sideband power.

Effects of Aerial Characteristics

The gain of an aerial, in terms of the signal-to-noise ratio, is the same as its transmitting power gain if there are no losses in the aerial and if the noise is non-directional. In relatively rare circumstances the external noise will be stronger from one direction than another, and the effective gain of the aerial will then be reduced for signals in the same direction as the noise and increased for signals in other directions. The removal of high-angle lobes should tend to reduce the external (cosmic) noise level in the 14—28 Mc/s bands. Losses in the aerial and feeder system are subtracted from the transmitting power gain but do not affect the gain in terms of the signal-to-noise ratio as long as the receiver noise can be kept well below the external noise level: thus, referring to Fig. 4, the external noise level at 14 Mc/s is 25 dB so that an aerial loss of 18 dB would still leave the external noise 7 dB above thermal noise, i.e. 6 dB above the receiver-plus-thermal noise for a noise factor of 1 dB, and the signal-to-noise ratio would be degraded only by about 1 dB compared with that for a loss-free aerial. This permits the use of much more compact aerial systems for reception than for transmission.

A very interesting point arises in the case of rhombic and certain other long-wire aerials, since the terminating resistance absorbs half the transmitter power and, of course, half the received noise power. On transmission the power which is absorbed is that which would otherwise be radiated in the backward direction, and the forward gain is unaffected. The elimination of noise from the backward direction, however, doubles the signal-to-noise ratio provided that the receiver noise level is low enough for advantage to be taken of the lower aerial noise level. Thus, in general, a terminated rhombic operating at frequencies below about 30 Mc/s has an effective gain 3 dB greater for receiving than for transmitting.

CHAPTER 16

MOBILE EQUIPMENT

THIS chapter describes a selection of portable and mobile equipment suitable for use on the h.f. bands (i.e. 1·8–30 Mc/s) and for the 144 Mc/s band. The 70 Mc/s and 420 Mc/s bands are also used for mobile work but their popularity is somewhat limited by various practical considerations. On 420 Mc/s perhaps the chief drawbacks are the specialized type of construction required and the need for high gain directive aerial systems.

Equipment intended for mobile and portable operation conforms in basic design to that used in fixed stations, but owing to the different conditions greater attention needs to be given to the physical size, robustness and reliability. In the design of mobile equipment miniaturization is essential. The apparatus must be mechanically strong, the chassis material must be stiff and heavy and all components must be securely fixed, preferably using nuts and bolts with lockwashers.

All dials and controls must be clearly marked and accessible and must be sited to allow easy operation under the various conditions which may be encountered. Provision should be made for locking variable controls to prevent any change from their correct settings due to vibration.

Wiring needs careful planning. Terminations should be firmly anchored and should not rely on the soldered joint for fixing. In oscillators and other frequency-determining circuits it is advisable to use wire not smaller in size than 16 s.w.g. In all but r.f. circuits stranded connecting wire is preferable.

Mobile equipment should have strong but resilient fixing and it is often considered an advantage to make it readily removable from the vehicle for operation from a fixed site. Generally, there is not a great deal of space available for radio equipment in the front of the modern family car and if a compact and efficient installation is desired considerable ingenuity may be required in deciding the layout and constructional details. But the most important matter affecting design is that of safety: if the station is to be operated by the driver of the vehicle, the layout and control circuits must not distract his attention from the task of controlling the car. There could be no valid defence if it were proved that an accident were due to the operation of Amateur Radio equipment by the driver of a vehicle.

NOISE SUPPRESSION

A motor vehicle generates a considerable amount of electrical noise and to permit satisfactory reception by a mobile installation it is necessary to reduce this noise to a low level. Measures which can be applied to the various parts of an automotive electrical system are outlined below. Attention is drawn to the fact that the 12 volt system of the modern car can produce far more noise than the older 6 volt system: this is one of several reasons why different vehicles may require different forms of treatment. The reduction of the noise to an acceptable level is usually the cumulative effect of attention to a number of points in the system, any one of which by itself may not appear to be a contributory cause of trouble. However, if the advice given here is followed, the noise should be reduced to such a low level that the interference which it causes to mobile operation is less than that originating in other nearby vehicles and commercial installations.

Ignition

The ignition system is responsible for a considerable amount of the electrical noise generated by a petrol-engined vehicle. The sparking plugs are sources of high-intensity noise and a suppressor comprising a 10,000 ohm resistor may be inserted in each lead immediately adjacent to the plug to reduce the interference from this source. Many modern vehicles which comply with the statutory regulations relating to the suppression of radiated noise are fitted merely with a 10,000 ohm suppressor resistor in the rotor lead of the distributor, though in some cases it may be found that the plug suppressors are unnecessary. If they are used, engine timing should be checked after installation. It is beneficial to use sheathed cable for the leads from the distributor to the sparking plugs and from the ignition coil to the rotor terminal on the distributor, the sheathing being securely bonded to the car frame. If the leads are terminated by crimped lugs the joints should be soldered to eliminate the possibility of variations in conductivity.

There are two terminals on the ignition coil and the one marked " sw " should be bypassed to the car frame through a capacitor having a capacity of 0·1-0·5μF. The normal type of suppressor capacitor is often ineffective at frequencies higher than about 3·5 Mc/s, but a capacitor of the coaxial or feed-through type (e.g. Dubilier type SBN1) will give good

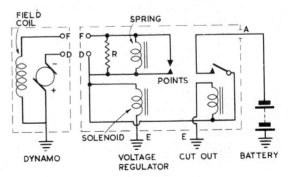

Fig. I. **The dynamo and battery charging circuit usually found in a modern car.**

suppression on all frequencies normally used in amateur mobile working.

Dynamo/regulator

To distinguish between ignition interference and charging-circuit interference, the engine should be started and run up to a fast idling speed (sufficient to generate a charging current) with the car receiver tuned to a part of the frequency band where there are no incoming signals. When the interference reaches its peak, the ignition may be switched off: if the noise is emanating from the charging circuit it will continue for a short time while the engine is running on. **Fig. 1** shows the dynamo and battery charging circuit found in most modern cars.

In the majority of cases, the dynamo whine can be eliminated by connecting a capacitance of about $0.5\mu F$ from the "D" terminal to the car frame. This may be an ordinary paper capacitor shunted with a ceramic capacitor of about $0.001\mu F$ to ensure the proper bypassing of r.f. currents. Alternatively a $0.1\mu F$ co-axial type of capacitor may be mounted on the dynamo housing and connected in series with the armature lead. In no circumstances should the field terminal "F" be bypassed in the same manner as the "D" terminal or the regulator action will be impaired and the unit damaged. If it appears beneficial to fit a suppressor to the field lead this may be done by connecting a 5 ohm carbon resistor (1 watt rating) to the "F" terminal with a ceramic capacitor of $0.001\mu F$ capacitance in series with this resistor to the frame of the vehicle.

In cases where the whine cannot be eliminated by the above measures, a trap tuned to the operating frequency may be inserted in the brush lead at the dynamo. For the 28 Mc/s band this trap should consist of 12 turns of 12 s.w.g. enamelled copper wire wound as a self-supporting coil 1 in. diameter and tuned by a 3-30 pF trimmer; this trap should be preset with the aid of a grid dip oscillator before installation.

Regulator "hash" is caused by sparking at the contact points and can usually be eliminated by connecting a bypass capacitor (0.1-$0.25\mu F$) from the terminal "A" of the regulator to earth. Here again the use of coaxial type of capacitor will ensure suppression at the higher frequencies.

Miscellaneous Sources of Noise

There are several other possible sources of noise on a vehicle but they will not necessarily require attention in every case. Certain of the gauges, and particularly the fuel gauge, may generate noise, and this can be eliminated by fitting a $0.1\mu F$ bypass capacitor.

Noise may be caused by slight vibrations and distortions of the car body itself and frequently from any movement of the exhaust pipe: the latter, if it is carried on rubber mounts, should be bonded to the car frame by heavy flexible braid. In some cars the bonnet (or hood) is not electrically bonded to the chassis and improved shielding from engine noise may be obtained by attention to this detail. Headlamp bulbs may be a source of noise when the car is in motion and all fittings should be checked to see that there is no movement or corrosion.

Noise Limiters

It is essential to include a noise limiter in any mobile receiving installation and the conventional circuits are dealt with in Chapter 4 (*H.F. Receivers*).

A unit which has been found highly effective in mobile working is the twin noise squelcher (TNS), the circuit of which is shown in **Fig. 2.** Under severe noise conditions the TNS performs better than the full-wave series limiter as far as signal-to-noise ratio and intelligibility are concerned while the squelch action eliminates the tiring background, at the same time enabling the operator to find weak signals easily. Furthermore, the twin noise squelcher does not cause

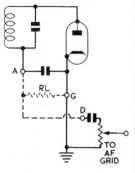

Fig. 3. Basic second detector circuit showing the connections of the twin noise squelcher. The original load resistor R_L is replaced by R_5, R_6, R_7 in Fig. 2.

distortion and may therefore well be incorporated as a permanent feature of the receiver circuit. If constructed as a separate unit, it can be built on a small chassis measuring only about $2\frac{1}{2}$ in. $\times$ $2\frac{1}{2}$ in. $\times$ 4 in.

The resistors R_5, R_6 and R_7 connected in series between the points A and G in Fig. 2 constitute the detector load, which is represented by R_L in **Fig. 3.** It should be noted that the terminal G must be separately connected to the cathode pin of the detector diode, while the leads from A and D in the unit (input and output respectively) to the associated components in the receiver must be individually shielded throughout their length.

For best results the detector should not be combined with the a.f. stage that follows it; although valves such as the 6SQ7 which combine these functions may be used they are not really satisfactory owing to leakage through the common cathode.

To adjust the TNS, the squelch control (R_3) should be advanced until all normal background noise disappears. In

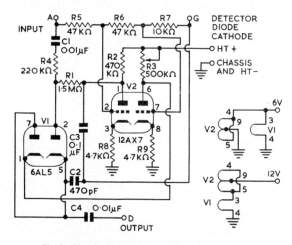

Fig. 2. Circuit diagram of the twin noise squelcher.

this condition, the squelch will automatically be triggered when a station is tuned in, so that the audio component of the signal will be heard. If the carrier is interrupted, the squelch will immediately come into operation and silence the receiver. When the squelch control is backed off to the critical setting, even a weak carrier will suffice to put the squelch out of action.

Another arrangement which incorporates an audio filter and has been found very satisfactory in mobile receivers is shown in **Fig. 4.** An EB91 is used as the combined detector and delayed a.g.c. rectifier. The delay can be varied by using other values of resistance in place of the 22 K ohms shown. Full a.g.c. voltage is available for the i.f. stages in the receiver while the potential divider comprising the 820 K and 180 K ohm resistances reduces the voltage to about one-fifth for application to the r.f. stages, in the interests of best signal to noise ratio.

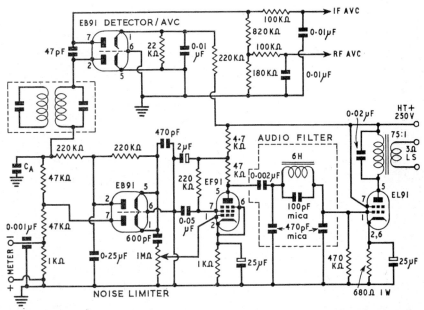

Fig. 4. Circuit diagram of noise limiter and a.f. stages for a mobile receiver. For intermediate frequencies between 450 kc/s and 2 Mc/s, the capacitor C_A should be 100pF: above 10 Mc/s the capacity should be 47pF. The two 470pF capacitors in the audio filter should be $\pm$ 2 per cent tolerance type. Variations in these values will alter the cut-off frequency as will different inductance values for the choke. The meter test point is for use when aligning the receiver.

The noise limiter, another EB91 valve, is of the shunt series type in which the series diode becomes non-conductive when a noise pulse is applied to it. Any pulses which then pass the series diode are shorted out by the shunt diode. The output from this noise limiter is somewhat low and it is therefore followed by an EF91 pentode a.f. amplifier, the output of which is fed to the grid of the EL91 output stage via an audio filter which cuts off sharply above 3 kc/s. The use of this filter reduces the random noise output very considerably and improves the intelligibility of signals without adversely affecting voice reproduction.

TEST EQUIPMENT

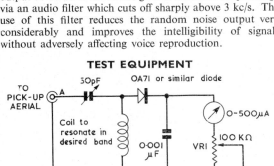

Fig. 5. Combined field-strength meter and modulation indicator.

FIELD STRENGTH METER

The most useful piece of auxiliary apparatus that can be carried in a car is a combined field strength meter and modulation indicator which can be built into a small metal box and mounted at some convenient place visible to the driver. In the circuit diagram shown in **Fig. 5** the point marked *A* should be connected to a length of coaxial cable run through the vehicle to a pick-up aerial situated near to the base of the radiator. This aerial may be about 12 in.

long and should be made of rigid wire or $\frac{1}{4}$ in. diameter aluminium tube mounted on a small stand-off insulator. The distance from the radiator may be 3-4 in. but should be adjusted to provide sufficient deflection on the meter.

The variable resistor VR_1 provides a means of adjusting the sensitivity of the meter. This is desirable since on some frequency bands the amount of pick-up may be too great. Moreover, it is usually advantageous to be able to set the meter to give an average deflection near the middle of the scale. A slight upward movement of the needle should be observed on modulation peaks.

In some vehicle installations it may be more convenient to mount the diode, choke and capacitors in a small waterproof

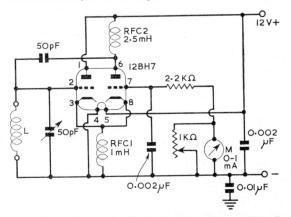

Fig. 6. Circuit diagram of a 12 volt g.d.o. for mobile use. The coils should be wound on 1 in. dia. formers: 1.8-3 Mc/s, 80 turns 30 s.w.g.; 3-6 Mc/s, 40 turns 28 s.w.g.; 10-18 Mc/s, 12 turns 20 s.w.g.; 18-32 Mc/s, 5 turns 18 s.w.g.

419

container directly under the pick-up aerial. A pair of wires should be taken to the meter and the sensitivity control VR_1 inside the vehicle. The pick-up aerial would then be connected directly to the point A. A pair of headphones can be connected in place of the meter if it is required to check the modulation.

GRID-DIP OSCILLATOR

A compact and useful accessory which is invaluable for tuning up mobile and portable equipment, and particularly for aerial adjustment, is the grid dip oscillator. A suitable circuit is shown in **Fig. 6.** This unit, which derives its power from a 12 volt car battery, is contained in a metal box 3 in. × 2 in. × 6 in. to which no direct connection is made, so that it is safe to use the g.d.o. on any car system irrespective

of whether the positive or negative terminal is earthed. It should be noted, however, that if the earthed terminal is the positive one the coils will be at the d.c. potential of the battery above earth.

The coil for the lowest frequency range (1·8-3 Mc/s) consists of 80 turns of 30 s.w.g. enamelled copper wire close wound on a 1 in. diameter former or, alternatively, a single pie section of a 2·5mH r.f. choke, suitably mounted, may be used as the coil for the 1·8-3·0 Mc/s band.

The correct method of coupling a g.d.o. to a vertical whip aerial is to insert a two turn link coil between the base of the whip and the vehicle earth, and to place the g.d.o. coil close to this link coil. A dip on the g.d.o. meter will be observed at the resonant frequency of the aerial.

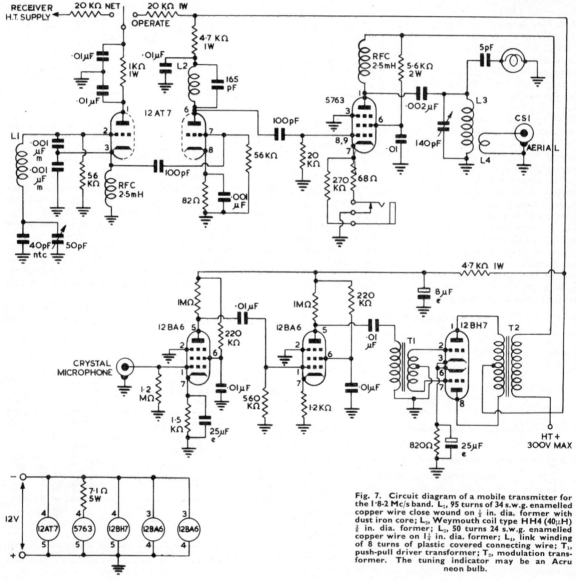

Fig. 7. Circuit diagram of a mobile transmitter for the 1·8-2 Mc/s band. L_1, 95 turns of 34 s.w.g. enamelled copper wire close wound on ½ in. dia. former with dust iron core; L_2, Weymouth coil type HH4 (40μH) ¾ in. dia. former; L_3, 50 turns 24 s.w.g. enamelled copper wire on 1¼ in. dia. former; L_4, link winding of 8 turns of plastic covered connecting wire; T_1, push-pull driver transformer; T_2, modulation transformer. The tuning indicator may be an Acru neon bulb.

Layout of the 1·8-2 Mc/s mobile transmitter within the chassis box. The transformer at the top of the picture is the modulation transformer.

H.F. MOBILE EQUIPMENT
TRANSMITTER FOR THE 1·8-2·0 MC/S BAND

The circuit diagram of a compact transmitter for 1·8-2·0 Mc/s is given in **Fig. 7.** This equipment uses a 12AT7 as a v.f.o. and buffer followed by a 5763 type power amplifier which will handle comfortably the maximum input of 10 watts permitted on the band. The speech amplifier employs two 12BA6 pentodes driving a double-triode (type 12BH7) as the modulator stage. Sufficient gain is available for a crystal microphone.

The method of construction used in the original is unorthodox in that the valves, tuning capacitors and other large components are located inside the chassis while the wiring is carried out on what is normally the top of the chassis. The whole assembly is fixed to the underside of the glove compartment by the flange. This arrangement was devised to suit a particular requirement, and a more conventional arrangement could be adopted if desired. The send-receive and aerial change-over switching will normally be effected by controls mounted on a separate panel within easy reach of the driver.

A COMPACT 28 Mc/s TRANSMITTER

The 28 Mc/s transmitter, the circuit of which is shown in **Fig. 8** incorporates provision for v.f.o. or crystal control, a.m. or c.w. operation, netting to an incoming signal, built-in relay for changing over the aerial and the power supply thus giving one-switch control, and meters for reading grid current and p.a. or modulator current.

The maximum power input to the p.a. is 15 watts (300 volts at 50 mA), and the total current consumption under modulation is approximately 120 mA at 250-300 volts, with a heater current of 1·2 amp at 12 volts. These modest requirements should present no difficulty in either mobile or portable operation.

The speech amplifier, which is designed for use with a carbon microphone, produces an output of 7 watts from the modulator with an h.t. supply of 300 volts. The 12AX7,

which is operated in class B, has a resting anode current of only 10 mA; this is invaluable in minimizing the drain on the car battery. The anode current rises to 35-40 mA on modulation peaks and the total consumption of the speech amplifier and modulator is then about 55 mA.

The v.f.o. is of orthodox design and uses an EF91. Its grid circuit is tuned to 7 Mc/s and 14 Mc/s output is obtained from the anode. A regulated supply of 150 volts is provided for the v.f.o. by a VR150/30 stabilizer tube. The normal precautions taken when constructing any v.f.o. must be observed: (a) 16 s.w.g. is desirable for connecting up, (b) the valveholder should be of the ceramic or p.t.f.e. type, (c) the tuning capacitor should have ceramic insulation, and (d) the mica and ceramic fixed capacitors should be of good quality.

For crystal controlled operation the single pole on-off switch S_1 should be left open and the grid circuit of V_1 tuned to approximately the crystal frequency. The difference in the amount of drive obtainable from the crystal and from the v.f.o. is negligible.

The second valve, a type 6AH6, doubles the frequency from 14 Mc/s to 28 Mc/s and uses a slug tuned coil in its anode circuit. The drive provided by this stage remains constant over a reasonable frequency range, but obviously if a large change is made the slug will need to be readjusted to obtain maximum output. In practice this is not a serious disadvantage since mobile operation is usually centred around one frequency in any particular locality.

If desired a type 6AK6 may be substituted for the 6AH6 with very little difference in performance. If a 6AK6 is used, a pilot lamp of 6·3V 0·3 amp rating should be connected across its heater pins to replace the 12 volt pilot lamp used in the original design. This will compensate for the heater current of the 6AH6, which is 0·45 amp compared with 0·15 amp for the 6AK6.

A 0-5 mA meter is used for measuring the grid current of the 5763 p.a. valve, which will be about 3 mA for normal telephony operation. The anode circuit of this stage utilizes a pi-network designed to match 75 ohm coaxial cable input and the usual tuning procedure for this type of circuit is applicable. The current drawn by the p.a. valve, when it is correctly loaded by an 8 ft. whip, is about 45 mA, and this is measured by a milliammeter which, by means of a d.p.d.t.

Fig. 9 An above-chassis view showing the arrangement of the larger components and valves.

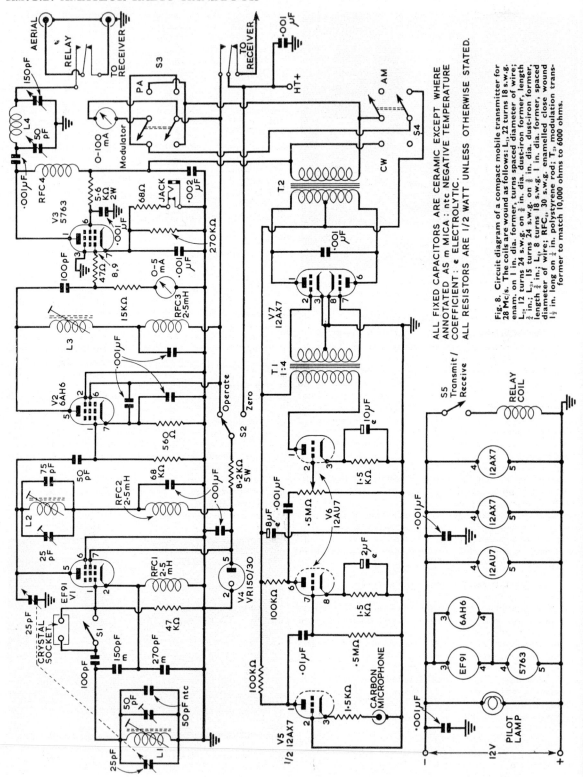

Fig. 8. Circuit diagram of a compact mobile transmitter for 28 Mc/s. The coils are wound as follows: L_1, 22 turns 18 s.w.g. enam. on 1 in. dia. former, turns spaced diameter of wire; L_2, 12 turns 24 s.w.g. on $\frac{3}{8}$ in. dia. dust-iron former, length $\frac{3}{8}$ in.; L_3, 15 turns 24 s.w.g. on $\frac{3}{8}$ in. dia. dust-iron former, length $\frac{3}{8}$ in.; L_4, 8 turns 18 s.w.g. 1 in. dia. former, spaced diameter of wire; RFC$_4$, 30 s.w.g. enamelled close wound $1\frac{1}{2}$ in. long on $\frac{1}{4}$ in. polystyrene rod; T_2, modulation transformer to match 10,000 ohms to 6000 ohms.

ALL FIXED CAPACITORS ARE CERAMIC EXCEPT WHERE ANNOTATED AS m MICA : ntc NEGATIVE TEMPERATURE COEFFICIENT : e ELECTROLYTIC. ALL RESISTORS ARE 1/2 WATT UNLESS OTHERWISE STATED.

Front panel view of the 28 Mc/s transmitter.

toggle switch, is also used to measure the modulator anode current.

Keying is effected in the cathode circuit of the 5763, while the netting switch S_2 applies h.t. to the v.f.o. only with the TRANSMIT/RECEIVE switch in the receive position so that the frequency of the transmitter can be tuned to that of an incoming signal during reception. The a.m./c.w. switch S_4 removes the h.t. from the modulator and short-circuits the secondary of the modulation transformer. The TRANSMIT/RECEIVE switch controls a d.p.c.o. 12 volt relay which, in addition to performing the function of aerial changeover, also removes the h.t. from the receiver and applies it to the transmitter. With this arrangement it is possible to use a single h.t. supply; the cables for both aerial and h.t. connections are first taken to the transmitter and thence to the receiver.

The speech-amplifier section employs one half of a 12AX7 in the first stage, the carbon microphone being connected in the cathode circuit, thus obviating the need for an energizing battery. If it is desired to use a high impedance crystal microphone the second half of the 12AX7 can be used as a voltage amplifier with appropriate changes in the circuit of the input section. Next follows a 12AU7 with the two sections in cascade and transformer-coupled to a 12AX7 which delivers sufficient power for 100 per cent anode-and-screen modulation of the 5763 p.a. valve.

This transmitter is readily adaptable to any of the other h.f. bands by substituting the correct tuned-circuit values.

The layout may be seen in Fig. 9.

CONVERTER FOR 14, 21 AND 28 MC/S

Many vehicles used for mobile operation will already be fitted with a radio receiver covering the long and medium wavebands. This converter, the circuit of which is shown in **Fig. 10**, provides reception of signals in the 14, 21 and 28 Mc/s bands with practically any type of receiver as the tunable i.f./a.f. chain. **Table 1** shows suggested tunable i.f.'s.

Only two valves are used—one as an r.f. amplifier, the other, a double triode, as a mixer and a crystal controlled local oscillator. The triode mixer section uses resistance capacity coupled output which enables any frequency band to be employed in the tunable i.f. (such as a car radio). A reduction in the value of the coupling capacitor C_{10} or the insertion of a stopper resistance will eliminate any tendency towards mixer oscillation and reduce the overall gain of the system. One section of the 6J6 (V_2) is used in an overtone oscillator circuit. Nearly all crystals operate satisfactorily in the arrangement shown, producing an output in the frequency range 10-29 Mc/s on their third or fifth overtones. Injection to the mixer section can be varied by adjusting the sense of the oscillator coil L_3 in relation to L_2 to which it should be placed parallel. The coupling can be increased by adding a small capacity between these coils but if the layout shown is

Table I

Suggested crystal frequencies and outputs for the three band converter

Band	Crystal frequency	Oscillator output	Receiver tuning
14 Mc/s	4,330 kc/s	13 Mc/s	1—1·5 Mc/s
21 Mc/s	4,000 kc/s	20 Mc/s	1—1·5 Mc/s
28—29 Mc/s	9,166 kc/s	27·5 Mc/s	0·5—1·5 Mc/s
29—30 Mc/s	5,700 kc/s	28·5 Mc/s	0·5—1·5 Mc/s
14 Mc/s	3,666 kc/s	11 Mc/s	3—6 Mc/s
21 Mc/s	5,677 kc/s	17 Mc/s	3—6 Mc/s
28 Mc/s	8,000 kc/s	24 Mc/s	3—6 Mc/s

adopted this should be unnecessary. The mixer will tend to pull the oscillator out of oscillation when its frequency approaches that of the oscillator unless an exceptionally active crystal is in use.

The converter is built into a box measuring 5 in. × 4 in. × 2 in. which should be provided with a well fitting lid so that contact is made all round with the sides of the box and

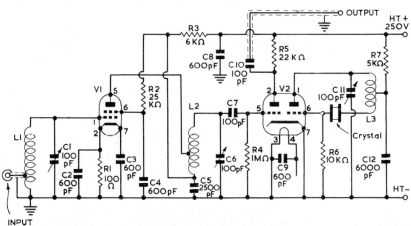

Fig. 10. Circuit diagram of the crystal controlled mobile converter. L_1, 12 turns 16 s.w.g. $\frac{3}{4}$ in. dia., $\frac{3}{4}$ in. long, tapped at $2\frac{1}{2}$ turns; L_2, 13 turns 16 s.w.g. $\frac{3}{4}$ in. dia., $\frac{3}{4}$ in. long tapped at $5\frac{1}{2}$ turns; L_3, 13 turns 16 s.w.g., $\frac{3}{4}$ in. dia., $\frac{7}{8}$ in. long, tapped at $2\frac{1}{2}$ turns. V_1, 6AK5; V_2, 6J6. Crystal, see text and Table I.

Fig. 11. Interior view of the converter for 14, 21 and 28 Mc/s.

with the screen which separates the r.f. and mixer stages. Details of the general layout may be seen in **Fig. 11.**

The earth connections from the tuning capacitors, which are mounted on the front wall of the box, are made only through their bushings and the chassis; any other form of return was found to make the r.f. amplifier unstable. The valveholder for V_1 straddles the screen to which its centre sleeve is earthed. No other leads are earthed to the screen. All bypass connections should be kept as short as possible and taken to the wall of the box immediately adjoining. Cathode bypass capacitors for the r.f. valve are placed on either side of the screen for the grid and anode circuits respectively.

After adjustment L_2 and L_3 are doped with polystyrene cement to prevent variations in inductance due to vibration. L_1 is left untreated so that it can be varied if required to suit the loading effect of the aerial in use. All the coils are self-supporting.

Power is obtained from a socket on the main receiver by means of a screened three-way cable and octal plug. The converter requires only 12-18 mA at 250 volts, depending on the activity of the crystal, and this should be within the capacity of almost any valve type car radio h.t. supply. The output from the converter is taken through a light coaxial cable, and a similar cable is used for the aerial input. Effective screening and earthing are most important in order to reduce interference from the car electrical system and to ensure stable operation.

The crystal oscillator should first be checked to verify that

it is functioning correctly. When C_{11} is varied, a symmetrical dip in the anode current (i.e. the current through R_7) should occur at the third and fifth overtones of the crystal frequency. Oscillation may, however, sustained over part of the range by ordinary feedback from L_3 through the capacity of the crystal electrodes, thus making correct adjustment of the circuit difficult. This may be remedied by moving the tap on L_3 nearer to the end of the coil connected to the crystal to reduce the feedback. The point of self-oscillation with a crystal plugged in should be about 500 kc/s less than the lowest frequency in use. Small crystals of the FT243 type which have low inter-electrode capacity make for easier circuit adjustment than those in larger holders because a greater number of turns can be used in the feedback portion of the winding without uncontrolled oscillation taking place. No trouble due to the pulling of the oscillator frequency by the mixer tuning should occur even at 29 Mc/s with an intermediate frequency of 500 kc/s.

Any receiver which has a 2 : 1 frequency range can be used as a tunable i.f. amplifier, thus providing a convenient method of tuning the three bands. The performance of the converter-receiver combination is comparable with that of many high grade communication receivers. The tuning procedure is simple and flexible, the controls merely being set to the desired band. If a weak station is heard it can be quickly " peaked up " by adjusting C_1 and C_6.

It is recommended that the position of the taps on L_1 and L_2 should be varied to suit individual requirements. Where a high gain receiver is used as the i.f. amplifier an improvement in image rejection could probably be gained by tapping the grid capacitor C_7 down to a point about two turns up from the low potential end of L_2. This is also a good way to reduce the overall gain without lowering the signal-to-noise ratio. The tap on L_1 may be placed lower down the coil if the tuning of the r.f. circuit is not sufficiently sharp as a result of heavy aerial loading.

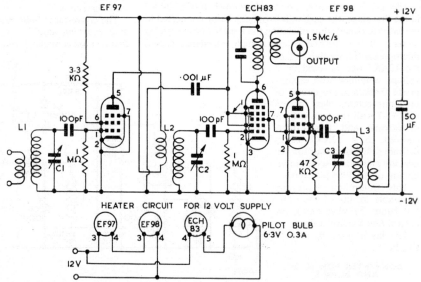

Fig. 12. Low voltage valve converter. L_1, C_1 r.f. tuned circuit, L_2, C_2 mixer tuned circuit, L_3, C_3 oscillator tuned circuit.

Fig. 13. Converter for the h.f. bands using 12 volt h.t. valves.

are conventional, while transistors are used in the modulator and the receiver i.f. and audio stages.

For a p.a. input of 20 watts an h.t. supply of 300 volts at 200 mA is required. Using a transistor d.c. converter to provide the h.t. the total power consumption is 12·6 volts

Table 2

P.A. Valve	Suggested driver	Suggested modulator	H.t. Voltage to p.a.	Power outputt (watts)
Pair 6AK5s (EF95)	6AK5	12AX7	150	1—1½
5763 (QV03—12)	EL85 or 12AT7	pair EL85 or single 6V6	300	3—4
QV04—7	EL85 or 6F17	pair EL85	300	5
QQV03—10	EL85 or 6F17	pair EL85	250	6
832A	5763	pair 6V6 or EL84s	300	10—12
QQV03—20A	5763	pair 6V6 or EL84	300	12—15

6·5—8 amp. for a.m. transmission falling to approximately 3·2 amp. on reception.

Transmitter R.F. Section

The r.f. stages of the transmitter (Fig. 15) are built on a 16 s.w.g. aluminium chassis measuring 4 in. × 10½ in. × 1½ in. and are connected to the other sections by a miniature 8-way plug and socket.

One section of a QQV03–10 double tetrode (V_1) is used as a Squier oscillator operating on the third overtone of an

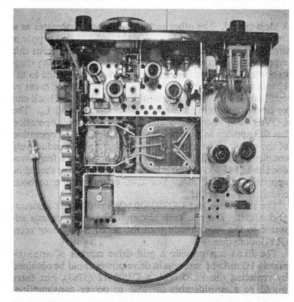

Fig. 14. In this view of the 144 Mc/s transmitter-receiver, the receiver r.f. section is at the top left with the modulator output stage below. The first four stages of the modulator are in the screened section at the rear of the main chassis. The i.f./a.f. receiver stages are on the left and the transmitter r.f. stages on the right.

The original was mounted on the steering column of the car by means of an electric conduit clamp.

LOW-VOLTAGE VALVE CONVERTER

A special series of valves has been developed for operation with an h.t. supply of only 12 volts. Their heaters are designed for a 6 volt supply and may conveniently be connected in series. A 12 volt car battery therefore provides all the power required, and the need for a vibrator unit or rotary converter or any other h.t. supply system is eliminated.

Fig. 12 shows the basic circuit of a converter suitable for use on frequencies up to 30 Mc/s and utilizing three Mullard valves types EF97, ECH83 and EF98. The ECH83 is a triode-heptode designed for use as a frequency changer, but in this circuit the triode section is not used, and a separate triode-connected EF98 is used as an oscillator. The converter is intended to feed into a car radio receiver or other suitable i.f. unit at 1·5 Mc/s. If it is desired to add an amplifier at this frequency the type EBF83 can be employed.

When the equipment is to be used in a vehicle it is important to note which pole of the battery is earthed, and if necessary suitable modifications made. Resistance-capacity filtering of the input from the car battery will generally be found to be sufficient and values of 47 ohms and 100μF are suggested.

An external view of the converter is shown in Fig. 13.

VH.F. MOBILE EQUIPMENT

The design of a v.h.f. transmitter depends mainly on the power supply unit and on the amount of current that is available from the car battery. From this starting point a suitable valve for the power amplifier should first be selected and then the best arrangement for the driver and the modulator can be devised. Typical combinations of valves for operating in the 144 Mc/s band are listed in Table 2.

TRANSMITTER-RECEIVER FOR THE 144 MC/S BAND

A compact transmitter-receiver for the 144 Mc/s band is shown in Fig. 14. The transmitter and receiver r.f. sections

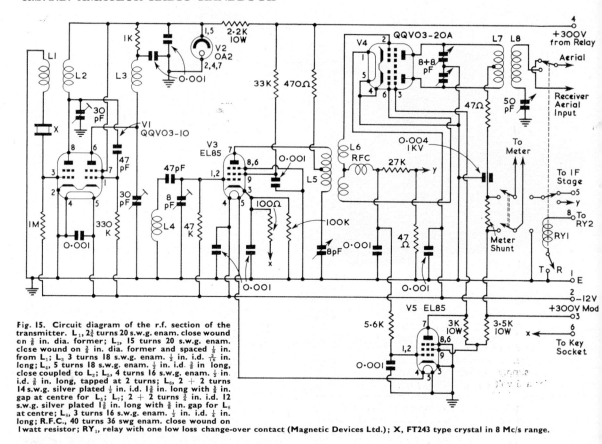

Fig. 15. Circuit diagram of the r.f. section of the transmitter. L_1, $2\frac{3}{4}$ turns 20 s.w.g. enam. close wound on $\frac{3}{8}$ in. dia. former; L_2, 15 turns 20 s.w.g. enam. close wound on $\frac{3}{8}$ in. dia. former and spaced $\frac{1}{8}$ in. from L_1; L_3 3 turns 18 s.w.g. enam. $\frac{1}{2}$ in. i.d. $\frac{3}{16}$ in. long; L_4, 5 turns 18 s.w.g. enam. $\frac{1}{2}$ in. i.d. $\frac{3}{8}$ in long, close coupled to L_3; L_5, 4 turns 18 s.w.g. enam. $\frac{1}{2}$ in. i.d. $\frac{3}{8}$ in. long, tapped at 2 turns; L_6, 2 + 2 turns 14 s.w.g. silver plated $\frac{1}{2}$ in. i.d. $1\frac{3}{4}$ in. long with $\frac{3}{8}$ in. gap at centre for L_5; L_7; 2 + 2 turns $\frac{3}{4}$ in. i.d. 12 s.w.g. silver plated $1\frac{3}{8}$ in. long with $\frac{3}{8}$ in. gap for L_8 at centre; L_8, 3 turns 16 s.w.g. enam. $\frac{1}{2}$ in. i.d. $\frac{1}{4}$ in. long; R.F.C., 40 turns 36 swg enam. close wound on I watt resistor; RY_1, relay with one low loss change-over contact (Magnetic Devices Ltd.); X, FT243 type crystal in 8 Mc/s range.

8 Mc/s crystal. The other section of the valve operates as a frequency tripler to 72 Mc/s. A stabilized 150 volt supply is used for the oscillator and the tripler is operated from this supply in order to reduce the grid drive to the following stage to a reasonable level. The grid resistors are connected to the 12 volt negative supply to provide protection in the event of oscillator failure. Adjustment of the oscillator feedback can be made by altering the spacing between L_1 and L_2. The QQV03–10 is internally neutralized for push-pull operation but this appears to have no significant effect on the operation of the circuit. The anode circuit of the tripler is inductively coupled to the grid of an EL85(V_3) operating as a frequency doubler to 144 Mc/s. The grid current of this stage should be approximately 1·2 mA. For c.w. operation the cathode circuit of V_3 is keyed.

The final stage is a QQV03–20A(V_4) with a self-resonant grid circuit. The p.a. tank circuit is above the chassis adjacent to the valve anode with the aerial changeover relay (RY_1) alongside.

The EL85 can provide a grid drive current of approximately 1·5 mA; an increase in drive power could be obtained by replacing the EL85 with a QV03–12 (5763), but there would be a considerable increase in power consumption. The EL85 has the advantage that the heater consumption is only 6·3 volts 0·2 amp. A second EL85(V_5) is used as a clamp valve for the p.a. screen grid.

A double pole change-over relay (RY_1) with one low-loss

contact set performs the aerial change-over and also switches a 1 mA meter from the receiver to the transmitter. Metering facilities are provided for the p.a. anode and grid currents during transmission. The meter operates as a signal strength indicator during reception.

The transmitter power consumption is 12·6 volts, 1·25 amp. and 300 volts at 170 mA.

Modulator

The modulator consists of a three-stage transistor amplifier, class A driver stage and class B push-pull output stage (Fig. 16). The quiescent input current is approximately 0·3 amp., rising to 2 amps, for an audio output of 12 watts.

A high input impedance is provided by the common-collector stage (TR_1). The first three stages are directly coupled and to provide d.c. stabilization the bias for the first stage is derived from the collector of TR_2.

Negative current feedback is applied to the driver stage (TR_4) by the unbypassed emitter resistor. The value of the resistor was selected to give a suitable overall gain for the particular microphone in use.

The output transistors are mounted on insulated 3 in. × 3 in. 16 s.w.g. aluminium heat sinks on either side of the driver transformer, while the other stages are mounted on a paxolin panel 4 in. × 2½ in. at the rear of the main chassis.

In order to avoid oscillation due to r.f. feedback to the modulator input the first four stages are completely screened.

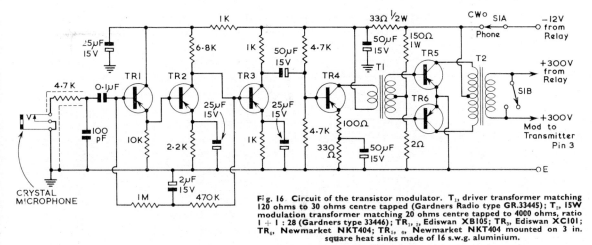

Fig. 16. Circuit of the transistor modulator. T_1, driver transformer matching 120 ohms to 30 ohms centre tapped (Gardners Radio type GR.33445); T_2, 15W modulation transformer matching 20 ohms centre tapped to 4000 ohms, ratio 1 + 1 : 28 (Gardners type 33446); $TR_{1, 2}$, Ediswan XB105; TR_3, Ediswan XC101; TR_4, Newmarket NKT404; $TR_{5, 6}$, Newmarket NKT404 mounted on 3 in. square heat sinks made of 16 s.w.g. aluminium.

particular care is necessary with the screening of the microphone input lead.

Receiver R.F. Section

This section **(Fig. 17)** of the receiver is built on a 16 s.w.g. aluminium sheet measuring 6 in. × 4 in. A simple self-excited oscillator and fixed i.f. amplifier of 5·2 Mc/s used as commercial transformers are available for this frequency.

An E88CC cascode stage (V_1) gives high r.f. gain combined with a reasonable noise factor. The aerial tapping point, grid tuning, and adjustment of the matching coil (L_2) were made to obtain optimum noise factor.

A 12AT7 (V_2) is used as the first mixer-oscillator and con-

trol of r.f. gain is obtained by varying the bias on the mixer grid. Oscillator injection is provided by a capacitance of about 2 pF connected between the oscillator anode and mixer grid. This consists of two short lengths of insulated flex twisted together and adjusted to give maximum sensitivity. Tuning of the mixer grid circuit has a small effect on oscillator frequency. The oscillator tuning capacitor (C) is mounted on top of the chassis with L_5 above it. It is a 10 + 10 pF receiver type split-stator capacitor with most of the rotor plates removed leaving only one plate per section. The 8 pF preset capacitor (mounted below the chassis) and the dimensions of L_5 can be adjusted to give suitable bandspread. To reduce oscillator drift the first mixer-oscillator is permanently connected to a 150 volt stabilized h.t. supply.

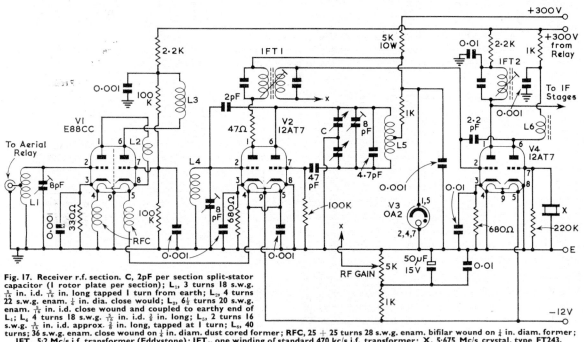

Fig. 17. Receiver r.f. section. C, 2pF per section split-stator capacitor (1 rotor plate per section); L_1, 3 turns 18 s.w.g. $\frac{5}{16}$ in. i.d. $\frac{5}{16}$ in. long tapped 1 turn from earth; L_2, 4 turns 22 s.w.g. enam. $\frac{1}{4}$ in. dia. close would; L_3, $6\frac{1}{2}$ turns 20 s.w.g. enam. $\frac{7}{16}$ in. i.d. close wound and coupled to earthy end of L_4; L_4 4 turns 18 s.w.g. $\frac{7}{16}$ in. long; L_5, 2 turns 16 s.w.g. $\frac{7}{16}$ in. i.d. approx. $\frac{3}{8}$ in. long, tapped at 1 turn; L_6, 40 turns; 36 s.w.g. enam. close wound on $\frac{1}{4}$ in. diam. dust cored former; RFC, 25 + 25 turns 28 s.w.g. enam. bifilar wound on $\frac{1}{4}$ in. diam. former; IFT$_1$, 5·2 Mc/s i.f. transformer (Eddystone); IFT$_2$, one winding of standard 470 kc/s i.f. transformer; X, 5·675 Mc/s crystal, type FT243.

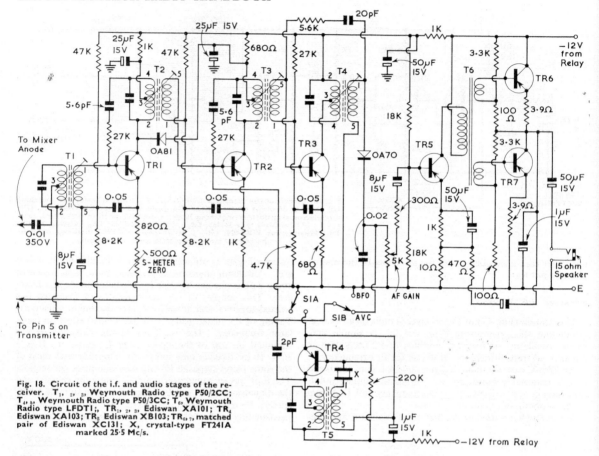

Fig. 18. Circuit of the i.f. and audio stages of the receiver. $T_{1, 2, 3}$, Weymouth Radio type P50/2CC; $T_{4, 5}$, Weymouth Radio type P50/3CC; T_6, Weymouth Radio type LFDT1; $TR_{1, 2, 3}$, Ediswan XA101; TR_4 Ediswan XA103; TR_5 Ediswan XB103; $TR_{6, 7}$, matched pair of Ediswan XC131; X, crystal-type FT241A marked 25·5 Mc/s.

The second mixer-oscillator (V_4) is another 12AT7 with which the 5·675 Mc/s crystal gives a second i.f. of 475 kc/s. The mixer output is capacity coupled to the first 475 kc/s i.f. stage.

Receiver I.F. and Audio Stages

Transistors are used in the remaining stages of the receiver, which are assembled on an 18 s.w.g. brass strip 3 in. high × 8½ in. long. The transistors and i.f. transformers are mounted along the centre of the strip and tag strips along the top and bottom. The component layout is very similar to the circuit diagram.

In order to obtain sufficient sensitivity three neutralized i.f. stages are used (Fig. 18). A.g.c. is obtained by returning the base potentiometer of TR_1 to the diode detector output. In addition, a reverse biased diode is connected to the collector of TR_1. The effect of the normal

a.g.c. is to reduce the collector current of the first stage, thus reducing the diode bias voltage. For large input signals the diode conducts, reducing the gain of the first stage and increasing

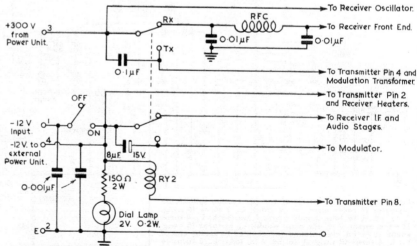

Fig. 19. Control circuits for the 144 Mc/s transmitter-receiver. The r.f. choke RFC is an Eddystone type 1010 and the relay RY_2 a model 596E8 d.p.c.o. type manufactured by Magnetic Devices Ltd.

the band-width. The 1 mA meter connected in the emitter circuit of this stage acts as a sensitive S meter while for c.w. reception a crystal controlled b.f.o. is included.

The push-pull transformerless output stage matches directly to a 15 ohm loudspeaker and provides approximately 750 mW audio output, sufficient to produce ample volume under all conditions.

Construction

The receiver and modulator are mounted on a 16 s.w.g. aluminium chassis 8 in. × 10½ in. × 1½ in. and the complete unit is enclosed in a case of perforated 18 s.w.g. sheet steel. The overall dimensions are 12½ in. × 10½ in. × 5½ in. high.

Details of additional power supply switching arrangements are given in **Fig. 19**. One set of contacts of the d.p.c.o. relay (RY₂) switches the h.t. between receiver and transmitter, while the other switches the 12 volt negative supply from the i.f. stages to the modulator. The receiver oscillator is permanently connected to the h.t. supply. The 12 volt supply for an external h.t. power unit is taken from the ON-OFF switch.

Any h.t. supply voltage in the range 200–300 volts could be used but it would be necessary to reduce the value of the stabilizer dropping resistors for voltages below 250 volts.

MOBILE AERIALS FOR THE H.F. BANDS

The success of mobile operation depends largely on the efficiency of the aerial. With the exception of the 28 Mc/s band and possibly 21 Mc/s the length of aerial which can be employed is only a small fraction of a wavelength. It is usual therefore on the lower frequencies to fit a loading coil in series with the aerial in order to make the system resonate as a quarter-wave vertical. This type of aerial, can be mounted on the front or rear bumper of a car, but better results are obtained with the aerial mounted above the boot behind the rear window or on the front wing or the bonnet. With aerials of the continuously loaded type for 21 and 28 Mc/s, it has been found that the best method of mounting is on a ski rack fitted centrally above the saloon roof.

Loading Coils

When considering the design of loading coils it is important to achieve a high Q. A separate loading coil for each band is the most efficient arrangement, although many operators have successfully worked on several bands by using tapped coils, the unused sections being short circuited. In the design of high Q coils the form of the coil (length/diameter ratio) is a primary factor, and generally it will be found that the larger the coil the higher will be the Q. The former should be made of material with good high frequency insulation, e.g. polystyrene or ceramic: wood is poor, even when completely dry. The turns of wire in a loading coil should be well spaced. It is better to use a thinner gauge of wire and space each turn than to make the coil close-wound. A coil can be more conveniently mounted on a vehicle if it has a large length/diameter ratio, and fortunately a moderate departure from the optimum form factor will not incur any noticeable loss.

In some cases, particularly on the lower frequencies, a long narrow coil will tend to radiate in addition to the whip itself. Hence the coil should be as short as possible consistent with high Q. A Q-value of at least 200 should be the aim. It must also be appreciated that the higher the Q the sharper will be the tuning of the aerial system, and this may prevent resonance over the entire band on which operation is required. This can be overcome by inserting a small series inductance which gives a coverage over the required frequency range.

Position of Loading Coil

Loading coils can be inserted into the aerial system at various points. The strength of the radiation field surrounding an aerial is proportional to the current flowing in the aerial and to the length of aerial carrying this current. A short vertical aerial will radiate best when it is arranged to carry the highest average current.

Fig. 20 shows the current distribution in four types of loaded aerials.

In (a) the feed-point impedance is high and the current flowing in the aerial is small; no radiation will take place from the screened inductance. (b) shows a similar current distribution but the energy in the coil is partially radiated; this tends to raise the radiation resistance of the aerial system slightly. In (c), a relatively high current flows in the section below the loading coil and this section therefore contributes appreciably to the total radiation from the aerial; it also raises the radiation resistance of the system. (d) shows a loading coil at the top of the aerial with a " capacity hat " to provide additional capacitance to earth. The radiation resistance is higher than in (c) and the current flowing in the total length of the radiator is increased to a maximum, thus producing the strongest external field.

However, when the loading coil is placed at the top of the aerial other factors affect the radiation efficiency and a compromise position is necessary. It will be seen that the higher a coil is placed on the aerial capacity the less will be available to resonate it to the desired frequency, and therefore the coil will become increasingly large. As the coil contains more and more wire the ohmic resistance will increase and power will be absorbed, thus decreasing the radiation efficiency. Also a coil placed high on a whip is extremely vulnerable to dirt and moisture, and mechanically is unwieldy and difficult to mount with safety.

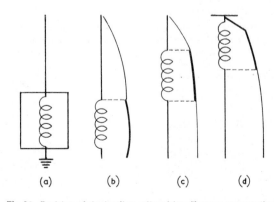

(a) (b) (c) (d)

Fig. 20. Position of the loading coil and its effect on current distribution in a whip aerial.

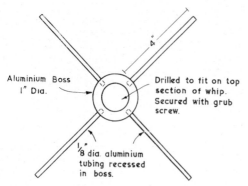

Fig. 21. A capacity hat suitable for use with vertical whip aerials.

It is obviously desirable to weatherproof the loading coil and two ways by which this may be done are:

(*a*) completely to cover the windings with adhesive p.v.c. tape which is available in widths up to 6 in.

(*b*) to apply a silicone varnish which will give a clear moisture repellant covering. Application can be by brush or by dipping the whole coil. It is recommended that three coats be applied with ample drying time between each. Proprietary brands of this type of varnish are Berger's "Hy-Meg" and Holt's "Dampstart."

Aerial for the 1·8 Mc/s Band

For portable operation it will often be possible to erect a long aerial wire and thereby achieve a reasonably high efficiency, but for mobile operation the maximum length of whip that can be considered practicable is about 8 ft.

A suitable coil for an 8 ft. centre-loaded whip consists of 145 turns of 20 s.w.g., enamelled wire close wound on a 1¾ in. diameter former. When operating from a fixed site the use of a 12 ft. whip will give better results and a loading coil consisting of 94 turns, wound as described above and inserted 4 ft. up from the bottom, will enable it to resonate over the whole of the 1·8–2·0 Mc/s band.

A small capacity hat may be constructed from 4 in. lengths of 3/16 in. o.d. aluminium tube mounted in a central boss as shown in **Fig. 21.** Its position on the upper section of the aerial can be adjusted so that the system resonates at the desired frequency.

Aerials for 3·5, 7, 14 and 21 Mc/s

For these bands, the loading coil can be inserted between the top and bottom sections, 5 ft. and 3 ft. being suggested as suitable lengths. With this arrangement the radiation resistance is increased to a reasonable figure. The dimensions given in **Table 3** serve as a guide for constructing the coils.

Table 3

Band	Inductance	Turns	Wire
3·5 Mc/s	125 μH	67	18 s.w.g.
7 Mc/s	33 μH	31	14 s.w.g.
14 Mc/s	7·6 μH	12	12 s.w.g.
21 Mc/s	1·9 μH	4	12 s.w.g.

Each coil should be wound air spaced on a ribbed former, 2½ in. in diameter, the turns being spaced by approximately

the diameter of the wire. Some final adjustment may be necessary after installation owing to differences in the method of winding, distributed capacity and other factors.

The impedance presented by this type of aerial may be 20–30 ohms. A very short length of 52 ohm coaxial cable is customarily employed to feed it, although two parallel cables to reduce the cable impedance to 26 ohms may be used to some advantage.

Aerial for 28 and 21 Mc/s

A resonant whip for the low frequency end of the 28 Mc/s band, according to calculation, should be about 8 ft. 4 in. long. However, a quarter-wave radiator of this length when working in conjunction with a car body will not operate as a true ground plane system because the electrically resonant length of the whip is altered and the aerial resonates at a higher frequency than the calculated value. To achieve resonance on the low frequency end of the band as much as 12 in. extra may be required, bringing the total length up to 9 ft. 4 in. By making the whip about 10 ft. long it can be tuned to resonance by a 250 pF variable capacitor in series with the centre conductor of the feeder at the feed point. This principle can be applied in designing a two-band aerial for 28 Mc/s and 21 Mc/s. An 11 ft. whip aerial may be resonated in the 28 Mc/s band with a series capacitor which is short circuited for the 21 Mc/s band.

Helical Aerials

At frequencies below 28 Mc/s it is impractical to use a quarter wavelength whip aerial and some form of loading must be introduced to bring the short radiator to resonance. As already stated, this is usually accomplished by a loading coil at the base or near the centre of the aerial possibly in conjunction with a capacity hat which increases the self capacitance of the whip.

An evolution of the loading coil principle is the continuously loaded, or helical whip, which is one long loading coil. These distributed load devices are usually wound on tapered fibreglass rods with a variable winding pitch. There is no

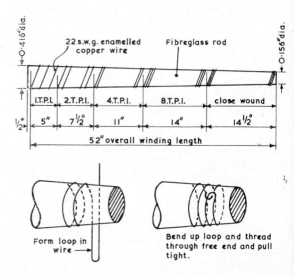

Fig. 22. Winding and mounting details for a 21 Mc/s helical whip.

simple formula for designing helical whips since there are too many variables involved.

It is sometimes inferred that it is unimportant if a mobile aerial is poorly matched to its feeder because the loss due to standing waves in the very short line used in most mobile installations is insignificant. Whilst this is true, there may be difficulty in loading the p.a. to the correct value if a bad match exists.

Experience has shown that a distributed load aerial generally has a higher radiation resistance, or impedance, than a quarter wavelength whip for the same frequency. The helical whip for the 21 Mc/s band, shown diagrammatically in **Fig. 22**, has an impedance of 67 ohms when mounted centrally on the roof of an average size family saloon.

This aerial is wound on a $52\frac{1}{2}$ in., tapered fibreglass fishing rod purchased from a fishing tackle supply store. Approximately seven-eighths of a wavelength of 22 s.w.g. enamel covered wire is required. The rod is first marked off in sections as shown, each such section then being further subdivided by pencil marks so that the wire can be wound on evenly. The end of each section should be securely taped during winding in case the rod is dropped. The method of mechanically fixing the aerial to the car is left to the individual constructor.

To bring the aerial to resonance, disconnect the feeder and place a one turn link between the bottom of the whip and the earthed car body. Loosely couple a g.d.o. to find the resonant frequency. This will probably be lower than 21 Mc/s, so remove two or three turns from the top, re-tape and check the resonant frequency again, repeating the procedure until the desired frequency is obtained. Most g.d.o.'s are not too accurate and it is advisable to check the exact frequency against a calibrated receiver.

When correctly tuned, the top winding can be finished off as shown in Fig. 22 and the whole aerial given a coat or two of varnish. An ideal product for this purpose is Holt's " Dampstart " which is applied by an aerosol spray.

Checks with a commercial s.w.r. bridge indicated an s.w.r. of 1·4 to 1 at the extreme edges of the 21 Mc/s band, with a minimum of 1·3 to 1 near the centre.

There is obviously considerable scope for further experiments with this type of aerial. For instance, for the lower frequencies, when the radiation resistance can be expected to be lower than for the design described, the feedline could be tapped up the winding to reduce the s.w.r. as much as possible. Capacity hats could be tried in order to reduce the amount of wire and hence the loss due to the r.f. resistance of the winding.

Tuning the Aerial

Any of the mobile whip aerials described above can be tuned by either (*a*) the field-strength method, i.e. comparing measurements of radiated power at a distance of at least several wavelengths, or (*b*) coupling a grid dip oscillator to a two-turn link coil inserted between the base of the aerial and the nearest earth point on the car body. If the latter method is used it should be remembered that when the aerial is connected to the feeder there will be a mismatch which will slightly alter the resonance frequency of the system owing to the introduction of a reactive component.

MOBILE AERIALS FOR THE V.H.F. BANDS

The directional properties of certain v.h.f. aerials which are commonly considered to be advantageous in fixed stations and in portable stations operating at a fixed site are undesirable in mobile operation. The problem is made more difficult by the fact that all v.h.f. fixed stations in Great Britain use horizontal polarization. In practice, the effects of cross polarization, when simple vertical aerials are used by a mobile station, are often decreased due to changes in the polarization of the signals as they are bounced back and forth between buildings and hills.

Another important question is the type of feeder to use. An aerial system which requires a high impedance feeder (e.g. 300 ohms or higher) would give unexpectedly poor results owing to the influence of the car body on the characteristics of the feeder cable. It is therefore usual to select a design in which the feeder is of the low impedance type (i.e. less than about 120 ohms). Coaxial cable is always preferred.

Quarter-wave Whip

The simplest form of v.h.f. aerial for mobile operation is a quarter-wave whip or ground plane aerial and the ideal position for it is in the centre of the car roof. One of the obvious advantages of a quarter-wave aerial is of course the small length of the radiating element—only about 19 in. for the 144 Mc/s band. For such an aerial the feed-point impedance is about 40 ohms.

As there are almost certain to be objections to drilling a hole in the car roof to carry the insulated bushing and for earthing the outer conductor of the coaxial feeder cable, it will be found satisfactory to mount a quarter-wave whip elsewhere on the vehicle using the body as a " ground plane," but the aerial may then show directional characteristics.

From good sites ranges of up to 35 miles are possible with this simple aerial. It is worth remembering that many telescopic car radio aerials reduce to 19 in.

Simple Dipole for 144 Mc/s

An effective mobile aerial for 144 Mc/s is the horizontal dipole which can be constructed as shown in **Fig. 23**. A length of 75 ohm coaxial cable is threaded through the dural tube and the centre and outer conductors of the cable are soldered to the inner ends of the dipole. The space between the elements at the centre should be about $\frac{1}{4}$ in. Weather protection for the connection is provided by filling the inspection hole with wax or some other suitable material such as Telcompound. The dipole should be mounted a half-wavelength above the roof of the vehicle.

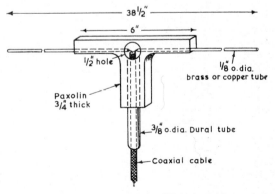

Fig. 23. Simple half-wave dipole for 144 Mc/s mobile operation.

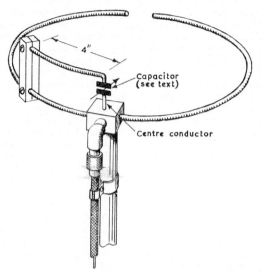

Fig. 24. Construction of a 144 Mc/s halo aerial.

Halo Aerial

The halo is the most commonly used type of mobile v.h.f. aerial and has an almost omni-directional polar diagram with horizontal polarization. For 144 Mc/s, a dipole 38 in. in length and made of brass or copper rod is bent into an open circle of about 1 ft. diameter and mounted horizontally at least 24 in. above the car roof. This aerial can be fed with a gamma match, the matching section being connected 4 in. from the centre of the aerial and a 50 pF air-spaced trimmer capacity connected as shown in **Fig. 24.** The gamma match should be adjusted to give a minimum standing wave ratio.

POWER SUPPLIES

Until recently conversion of low voltage to the higher voltage required by valved equipment was usually accomplished by vibrators or rotary converters. These mechanical

systems have several drawbacks in that they require continuous maintenance with respect to contacts, brushes and bearings, are susceptible to shock and vibration and have problems of ventilation. An additional disadvantage is that the make and break nature of the interruption of the d.c. current made by both of these systems produces electrical interference which is sometimes difficult to eliminate.

The use of transistors as the switching elements removes the above drawbacks and the efficiency rises to 80–90 per cent, in comparison to the usual 65 per cent of the vibrator power supply and the somewhat lower figure (about 40 per cent) of the rotary converter which takes a high starting current. The transistor d.c. converter is compact and robust and because of the elimination of mechanical friction and metal fatigue, the life expectancy is greatly increased and is limited only to that of the components. The transistors are used as switching elements to interrupt the d.c. current in a circuit which consists of a self oscillating system providing both the switching signal and primary power to the load.

An essential requirement for operating power transistors at their maximum ratings is an adequate heat sink and due allowance for this must be made when determining the physical layout of the converter. Aluminium, at least $\frac{1}{16}$ in. thick, has a much lower thermal resistance than steel and the radiation efficiency as a heat sink can be considerably increased by the application of a coat of matt black paint on the external surface. It should be noted that where the transistors are mounted directly on to the heat sinks without the use of mica washers, the sinks must be isolated from the main chassis.

Fig. 25 is the circuit of a typical transistor d.c. converter suitable for amateur mobile or portable use. The frequency of oscillation is approximately 200 c/s and the two biasing resistors are included to ensure that the oscillation is self starting under load. The $25\mu F$ capacitor is intended to limit the voltage spikes representing switching transients which appear on the leading edge of the emitter-to-collector waveform. Conventional metal rectifier units can be used in a bridge circuit, but increased efficiency and reduced size and weight will result from the employment of silicon diodes which, in this instance, should have a peak inverse voltage rating of at least 400. The $0 \cdot 1\mu F$ capacitor and 1K ohm resistor in series across the secondary of the transformer form a transient limiting circuit for the protection of the silicon diodes.

A steady output of at least 30 watts can be obtained from a pair of Newmarket NKT404 transistors when mounted on a heat sink of 50 sq. in. of 16 s.w.g. aluminium which must be sited so that the junction temperature does not exceed the maximum rating figure of 75°C.

It is strongly recommended that the fuses shown in the input and output circuits should be incorporated as the transistors can easily be damaged or destroyed.

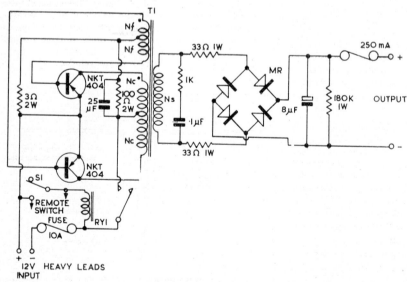

Fig. 25. Transistor d.c.-to-d.c. power supply.

CHAPTER 17

POWER SUPPLIES

AN essentially pure direct current high tension supply is required to prevent serious hum in the output of receivers, speech amplifiers, modulators and transmitters. In addition direct current is required for the operation of many types of relays and also for the grid bias voltages used in transmitters and modulators.

The cathodes of most modern low power valves are indirectly heated and may be supplied with either alternating current (a.c.) or direct current (d.c.). Exceptions to this are low level audio amplifying stages and variable frequency oscillators, where it may be essential to operate the heaters from direct current to ensure a hum-free output. The larger types of r.f. power amplifier and modulator valves are directly heated but their filaments may be supplied from a.c. or d.c., when used at the high signal levels found in p.a. and modulator stages.

When alternating current supply mains are available, as is the case with most fixed stations, the high voltage, heater and bias supplies are most conveniently obtained by means of a combination of transformer, rectifier and filter system, the valve heaters or filaments being supplied from a separate heater transformer, or from additional low voltage windings on the transformer feeding the rectifier. Separate transformers for heater and bias voltages are usually employed in very high voltage power units because of the simplification of control and protection circuitry which results.

Having produced the required voltages, means are required for controlling them, either directly by switching, or remotely by means of contactors or relays. These may be associated with pilot lamps showing which parts of the circuit are live. Fuses or overload cutouts are also necessary to protect the rectifier and other vulnerable components in the event of overload or component breakdown. The control and overload circuitry may be designed to meet the requirements of the individual constructor but it is essential that due regard be paid to the necessity of removing all voltages rapidly in the event of overload or other emergency.

RECTIFIER CIRCUITS

A rectifier in one of its several forms is necessary when a.c. is to be converted to d.c. The rectifier functions by virtue of its property of unilateral conduction, i.e. it passes current only when the applied voltage has the correct polarity to bias it to a low resistance condition. When the polarity of the input voltage is reversed the rectifier exhibits a very high resistance, approaching infinity in the case of a thermionic rectifier, and current cannot flow. At the present time both valve and semiconductor rectifiers are used in amateur practice, each with particular advantages in its own field.

Fig. 1 shows three types of rectifier circuit which cover most of the applications in amateur equipment, together with curves indicating the shape of the current wave delivered

by the rectifier in a resistive load. The output current is seen to be unidirectional but pulsating in character and may be shown to consist of a d.c. component plus an a.c. component. The a.c. component is composed of the fundamental and harmonics of the supply frequency, the fundamental being predominant in the half-wave circuit and the second harmonic in the full-wave circuit. This a.c. component is termed *ripple* and may be removed or greatly attenuated to any desired degree by the filter which follows the rectifier.

The half-wave circuit (**Fig. 1 (a)**) is best suited to low current applications such as grid bias supplies and the e.h.t. supply for cathode ray tubes. When used to supply appreciable current of the order of tens of milliamperes and higher, the half-wave circuit has disadvantages in that the ripple content is high, necessitating a large filter; in addition the d.c. load current flows through the secondary winding of the transformer feeding the rectifier, and saturates the core which

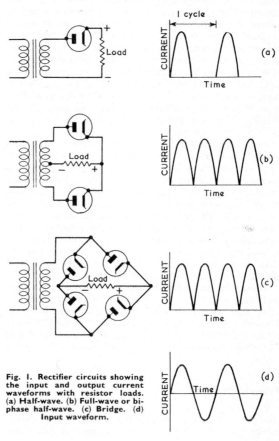

Fig. I. Rectifier circuits showing the input and output current waveforms with resistor loads. (a) Half-wave. (b) Full-wave or bi-phase half-wave. (c) Bridge. (d) Input waveform.

TABLE I
Single Phase Rectifiers

	Half-wave	Full-wave or biphase half-wave	Full-wave bridge
Circuit	Fig. 1 (a)	Fig. 1 (b)	Fig. 1 (c)
Number of rectifiers	1	2	4
Current per rectifier — mean — peak inductive load — peak resistive — r.m.s.	$1.0 I_{dc}$ — $3.14 I_{dc}$ $2.22 I_{dc}$	$0.5 I_{dc}$ $1.0 I_{dc}$ $1.57 I_{dc}$ $1.11 I_{dc}$	$0.5 I_{dc}$ $1.0 I_{dc}$ $1.0 I_{dc}$ $0.707 I_{dc}$
Peak inverse voltage across rectifier	$3.14 V_{dc}$ $2.83 V_{dc}$	$3.14 V_{dc}$ $2.83 V_{in}$	$1.57 V_{dc}$ $1.41 V_{in}$
R.m.s. secondary voltage R.m.s. Current	$2.22 V_{dc}$ $1.0 I_{dc}$	$1.11 V_{dc}*$ $0.707 I_{dc}$	$1.11 V_{dc}$ $1.0 I_{dc}$

V_{dc} = output voltage I_{dc} = output current V_{in} = input a.c. voltage
* Each half of the h.t. winding.

gives rise to low transformer efficiency. The regulation or variation of output voltage with load current is also poor.

The full-wave circuit (**Fig. 1 (b)**), also known more correctly as the bi-phase half-wave circuit, is the most commonly used rectifier circuit suitable for voltages up to about 1500 volts and currents of the order of 1 ampere. A centre tapped winding is used to supply the rectifiers and must provide twice the a.c. voltage applied to each rectifier. The load is connected between the centre tap of the transformer and the output terminals of the rectifiers which are connected together. Each rectifier conducts during the time when the voltage applied to its input is positive with respect to the centre tap, i.e. on alternate half cycles and contributes one half of the total load current. The d.c. component of the load current flows through each half of the transformer secondary in such a direction as to cancel the d.c. magnetization of the core, enabling a smaller and more efficient transformer to be used than is possible in a half wave circuit providing the same output.

The bridge circuit (**Fig. 1 (c)**) is to be preferred when output voltages in excess of about 1500 volts are required, as the *peak inverse voltage* across each rectifier in the circuit is halved compared with the bi-phase circuit for the same output voltage. (The peak inverse voltage is the voltage which appears across the rectifier when it is not conducting). During each half cycle of the input voltage two of the rectifiers, in Fig. 1 (c), are conducting and supply half of the total load current. The d.c. magnetisation of the transformer core is thus effectively cancelled as the d.c. component of the load current flows through the h.t. secondary winding in opposite directions during each half cycle.

Three separate heater windings must be used when valve rectifiers are employed in the bridge circuit since only two of the four valves have their cathodes at the same potential. However, the circuit is more economical as far as the size of the h.t. transformer is concerned and a superior degree of voltage regulation is obtained relative to the bi-phase circuit.

Types of Rectifier

Both semiconductor and valve rectifiers may be used in the circuits described in the previous section. Semiconductor rectifiers have the advantage of low voltage drop and of not requiring heater power, but are more susceptible to break-down when misused, particularly in respect of excessive operating temperature and peak inverse voltage. Generally speaking the semiconductor rectifier is preferred for use in low voltage high current supplies where the bridge connection is normally employed and in e.h.t. supplies, particularly when one of the various types of voltage multiplication circuits described later in the chapter is employed. In passing it may be noted that the terminal of a semiconductor diode corresponding to the cathode of a thermionic diode is marked + or carries a red colour indication.

The valve rectifier is manufactured in a great variety of types and ratings suitable for almost any application in amateur equipment. They may be divided into two types—high vacuum and gas or mercury vapour filled, each having its particular field of usefulness.

The high vacuum rectifier is available in both half-wave and full-wave types, the latter consisting of two diodes in the same envelope with a common cathode and heater assembly. The indirectly heated type of low-power rectifier is preferred in current practice although the earlier directly heated types are still used. The indirectly heated type warms up at sensibly the same rate as the other indirectly heated valves in an equipment and so avoids the application of high no-load h.t. line voltages to the circuit. Some types of indirectly heated rectifiers will withstand heater to cathode voltages of up to 650 volts peak and are provided with 6·3 volt heaters, thus permitting the use of the same heater winding for all valves, e.g. in a receiver or test equipment. The vacuum rectifier is characterized by a relatively high internal resistance between anode and cathode which renders it less susceptible to damage from temporary overload. The maximum d.c. load current available from the larger type of full wave rectifier is 250 mA, and the maximum a.c. input voltage to each anode is 600-1000 volts dependent upon the type of filter circuit employed. The two anodes of a full wave rectifier may be paralleled via current equalizing resistors of 50–100 ohms if higher current output is required. Two such valves used in the full-wave circuit will provide twice the output current of one valve, with some improvement in regulation.

Gas-filled or mercury vapour rectifiers are used when the current and voltage requirements are in excess of the ratings of high vacuum types. They are normally directly heated half-wave types so that two valves are required in the full-wave circuit. Both gas-filled and mercury vapour rectifiers have a low internal voltage drop of 10–20 volts independent of load current. In the case of mercury vapour types there are certain operating limitations which must be observed, i.e. the h.t. voltage must not be applied until all the liquid mercury within the bulb has been vaporized by pre-heating the filament and the bulb temperature must be kept within prescribed limits set by the manufacturer. Non-observance of these points entails premature failure of the rectifier. Gas-filled types are less critical in operation but the filament must be allowed to reach its normal operating temperature before applying h.t.

Rectifier Ratings

Valve and semiconductor rectifiers are subject to limitations in respect of peak inverse voltage and peak current handling capability, both when delivering power to a load and when switching on. In this connection it should be noted that when h.t. voltage is applied to a rectifier (assuming the cathode is at normal operating temperature in the case of a valve) having a capacitor input filter, the capacitor when uncharged presents virtually a short circuit to the rectifier. Under these conditions a very large current flows, only limited by the internal impedance of the transformer and the rectifier itself, until the capacitor is charged. In order to ensure that an acceptable life is obtained from the rectifier the manufacturers provide recommendations in respect of the minimum value of series impedance which should be present to limit this surge current to a safe value. This information is often presented in the form of rating charts, from which suitable operating conditions may be selected with a minimum of calculation. A study of the manufacturers' data on maximum ratings will be well repaid in long life when the rectifier is correctly chosen and its associated circuitry so designed that none of the ratings are exceeded.

Operation of Rectifiers

It is important to ensure that the filament or heater of the valve rectifier is operated at the correct voltage, measured at the valve pins. Reduced life expectancy and performance will occur if the heater or filament is under-run. The larger types of valve rectifier take considerable heater or filament current and an adequate gauge of wire should be used when wiring up the valveholder. The choice of valveholder is also important as in many instances each electrode of the valve is at a high potential to earth. Ceramic valveholders spaced away from the chassis if necessary are recommended for high voltage rectifiers operating at 500 volts or more.

It is desirable to mount rectifier valves, either vacuum or mercury vapour and gas filled types, in the vertical position, with base downwards, to assist ventilation and avoid short circuits due to a sagging filament touching the anode, particularly when low impedance directly heated rectifiers are employed.

When mercury vapour rectifiers are first put into service or after a prolonged period of storage, they should be operated at normal filament voltage for at least 30 minutes prior to applying the anode voltage. This is to ensure that any liquid mercury which has become attached to the filament is evaporated, as otherwise arc-back may occur with consequent damage to the filament and its oxide coating. After the valve has been put into operation, a heater warm up time of 30–60 seconds will be adequate before anode voltage is applied. The use of a thermal delay switch to delay application of the h.t. voltage to the rectifier valves until the heaters have warmed up is recommended. A typical circuit employing a thermal delay switch for this purpose is shown in Fig. 16, on page 444.

SMOOTHING CIRCUITS

The pulsating d.c. from the rectifier circuits illustrated in **Fig. 1** is not sufficiently constant in amplitude to be used to operate equipment directly and means must be provided to smooth out the variations. This function is carried out by means of a combination of series inductors or resistors and parallel capacitors termed a filter or smoothing circuit. As described earlier, the output from the rectifier consists of d.c. plus a superimposed a.c. component and expressed in its simplest terms the action of the filter is to separate one from the other and allow the d.c. to pass to the load while the a.c. is bypassed and confined to the filter circuit. Apart from its basic purpose of separating the a.c. and d.c. components of the rectifier output, the filter has a profound effect upon the operation of the rectifier itself and the d.c. voltage output, the voltage regulation of the supply and the maximum load current which can be safely drawn depend to a large extent upon the design of the filter.

Power supply filters fall into two classifications. depending upon whether the first component of the filter network is a capacitor or an inductor (choke). Capacitor input filters

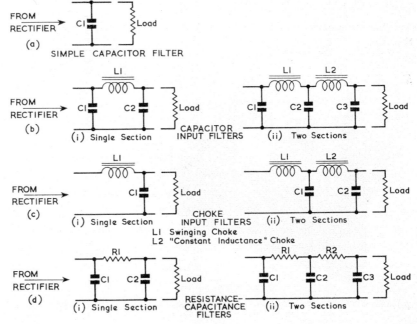

Fig. 2. Typical filter circuits. (a) Simple capacitor filter. (b) Capacitor input filters. (c) Choke input filters. (d) Resistance capacitance filters.

SIMPLE CAPACITOR FILTER

CAPACITOR INPUT FILTERS
(i) Single Section   (ii) Two Sections

CHOKE INPUT FILTERS
(i) Single Section   (ii) Two Sections
L1 Swinging Choke
L2 "Constant Inductance" Choke

RESISTANCE-CAPACITANCE FILTERS
(i) Single Section   (ii) Two Sections

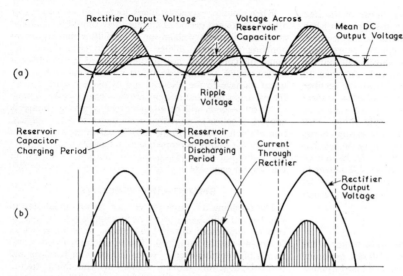

(a)

(b)

Fig. 3. Curves illustrating the output voltage and current waveforms from a full-wave rectifier with capacitor input filter. The shaded portions in (a) represent periods during which the rectifier input voltage exceeds the voltage across the reservoir capacitor causing charging current to flow into it from the rectifier

are characterized by a relatively high d.c. output voltage for a given a.c. input voltage to the rectifier, but the regulation is poor and the rectifier is called upon to handle higher peak voltages and currents than when choke input is used. A choke input filter provides much better regulation when properly designed but the d.c. output voltage is lower. The resistance-capacitance filter is a variant of the capacitor input filter where resistors replace the inductors. The use of this type of filter is normally confined to low current applications because of the relatively high voltage drop across the series resistors. Typical filter circuit configurations are shown in **Fig. 2.**

The Capacitor Input Filter

The simplest form of capacitor input filter is illustrated in Fig. 2(a) and consists of a single capacitor C_1 placed in parallel with the output of the rectifier and the load resistance R_1. During the periods in which the rectifier is conducting C_1 charges up to nearly the peak value of the a.c. voltage

A typical 1250 volt 250mA power unit employing mercury vapour rectifiers and a single section choke input filter.

applied to the rectifier, and if no load current were drawn the voltage on C_1 would remain constant. When a load is placed across the capacitor, it discharges into the load and the voltage across it falls until the arrival of the next pulse of current from the rectifier which recharges the capacitor to its original voltage. This process is repetitive and the resulting waveform of the output voltage is as shown in **Fig. 3(a)** for a full-wave rectifier. Thus the capacitor C_1 acts as a reservoir of charge which is depleted by the load and replenished by the rectifier during the period when the rectifier output voltage exceeds the capacitor voltage Fig. 3(b). C_1 is therefore known as the *reservoir capacitor*.

The current which flows into C_1 from the rectifier is very large and limited only by the internal resistance of the rectifier and the total effective resistance of the transformer windings. In order not to exceed the maximum surge current rating of the rectifier it may be necessary in practical circuits to increase the effective resistance of the transformer by inserting additional resistance between the transformer and the anode or anodes of the rectifier. The total source resistance as seen by the reservoir capacitor will determine how closely the capacitor voltage will approach the peak value of the a.c. voltage during the charging period, i.e. the lower the source resistance the more closely the two voltages will approach each other. When a load is connected the capacitor voltage falls between pulses of charging current, the amount by which it falls being determined by the load resistance. A decrease in the load resistance causes a greater fall in voltage. The amplitude of the variation in capacitor voltage or *ripple voltage* which varies about a mean value corresponding to the d.c. output voltage, is therefore determined by the load resistance, and to a lesser extent by the source resistance. A graph showing approximate values of ripple voltage expressed as a percentage of the d.c. output voltage plotted against load resistance is shown in **Fig. 4** for three typical values of reservoir capacitor.

A reservoir capacitor of 16 μF represents the maximum value which should normally be used with a full wave rectifier and 32 μF for a half-wave circuit. Increasing these values will produce relatively small improvements in voltage regulation and ripple but are undesirable because of the increased surge current through the rectifier and also because of increased ripple current through the reservoir capacitor. The amount of ripple current flowing is of great importance when an electrolytic capacitor is used as a reservoir, and too high a value of ripple current will lead to overheating and breakdown of the capacitor. A typical value of maximum permissible ripple current is 260 mA for a 16 μF 450 volt working electrolytic of plain foil construction and 122 mA for an etched foil type. Provided that a d.c. load current of not more than 120 mA is taken when a plain foil type is used and 70 mA in the case of etched foil types, there is little danger of exceeding the maximum ripple currents stated.

The d.c. working voltage of the reservoir capacitor whether electrolytic or paper should be at least equal to the peak value of the a.c. applied to the rectifier, i.e. $\sqrt{2}$ times the transformer h.t. secondary voltage in half-wave and bridge circuits and $\sqrt{2}$ times the half secondary voltage in the biphase circuit. The peak inverse voltage which the rectifier

must withstand approaches $2\sqrt{2}$ times the a.c. voltage at light loads in the half-wave and biphase circuits and $\sqrt{2}$ times the a.c. voltage in the bridge circuit. **Table 1** summarizes the voltage and current relationships existing in the circuits of Fig. 1.

Choke Input Filters

The choke input filter is used when good regulation of the output voltage is important as for example in the h.t. supply for a class AB2 modulator stage, where the maximum load current may be 4–5 times the minimum. The output voltage obtained is somewhat lower than when a capacitor input filter is used and allowance must be made for this when selecting a suitable h.t. transformer.

Full-wave rectifier circuits are normally used with choke input filters as the output voltage would be inconveniently low if the half-wave circuit is used. Neglecting the voltage drop in the choke and rectifier, the mean d.c. output voltage of a choke input filter fed by a full-wave rectifier is 0·9 times the applied a.c. voltage. The choke input filter is illustrated in Fig 2 (c) and consists of an iron cored inductor L_1 in series with the load and a capacitor C_1 across the load. The action of the inductor L_1 is to attempt to maintain a constant flow of current through the rectifier throughout the a.c. cycle. If the inductance of L_1 were infinite the current would be constant, but in practice this cannot be achieved, and some variation of current does occur and appears as ripple, but provided the peak-to-peak amplitude of the variation does not exceed the d.c. load current satisfactory constant current operation will be obtained. The minimum value of inductance required to do this is called the *critical inductance*, L_C. Assuming the source resistance as seen by the rectifier is small compared with the load resistance R_L (d.c. output voltage/d.c. output current), then L_C in Henrys is given by the following equation:

$$L_c = R_L/940 \text{ for a 50 c/s supply.}$$

It will be seen from the equation for critical inductance that the value of L_C becomes lower as the load current is increased. This permits the use of a swinging choke for L_1 with considerable economy in cost over that of an ordinary "constant inductance" choke. The inductance of a swinging choke is high at low currents falling off to perhaps 20-25 per cent of its low current value as the current flowing is increased to its maximum rating. This characteristic permits the use of a smaller and less expensive component, a typical specification of which would be 25 Henries at 50 mA, falling to 5 Henries at 250 mA.

If the minimum inductance is insufficient the filter will function as a capacitor input filter with its attendant rise in

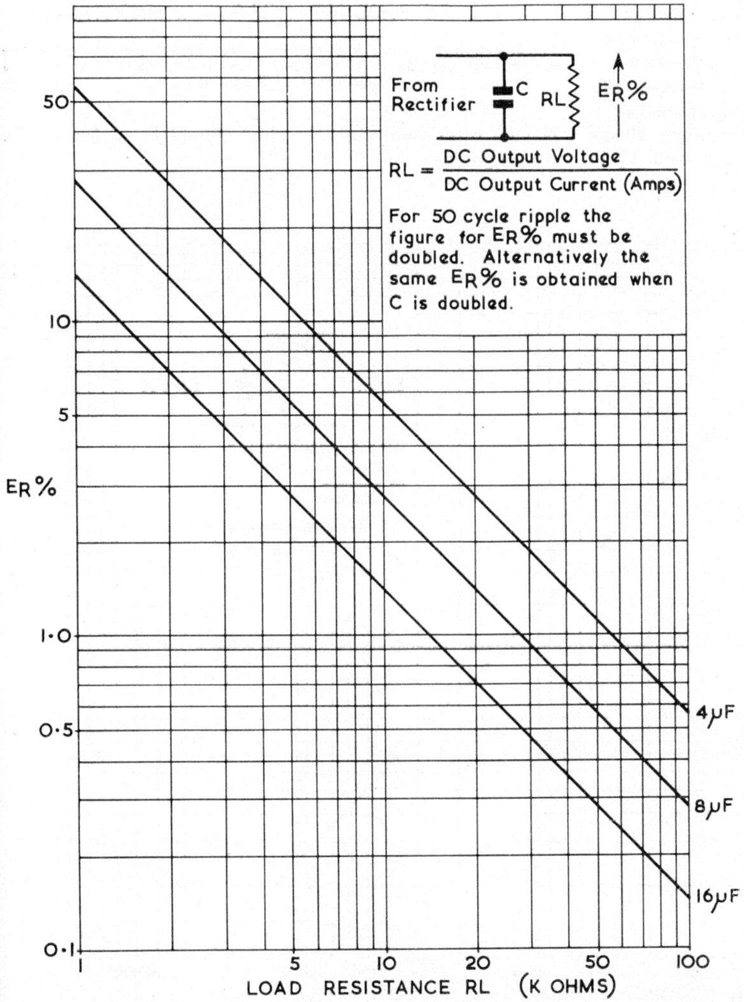

Fig. 4. Curves showing 100 c/s ripple component as a percentage of the d.c. output voltage across a reservoir capacitor.

output voltage at light loads. At light loads, i.e. high values of R_L, the value of L_C required for proper operation would be inconveniently high, and it is usual to connect an artificial load or bleeder resistance across the output of the supply to ensure that sufficient current is drawn at all times to enable a reasonable value of L_C to be used. If the value of L_C has already been determined by available components, then the approximate value of bleeder current required (i.e. maximum value of R_L permissible) is given by the following expression:

$$Bleeder\ current\ in\ milliamperes = \frac{D.C.\ output\ voltage}{L_{MAX}\ (in\ Henrys)}$$

where L_{MAX} = maximum inductance of the swinging choke.

Further attenuation of the ripple component is achieved by the parallel capacitor C_1 and the overall reduction of ripple by a choke input filter is relatively high compared with the capacitor input filter of Fig. 2 (a). A graph showing the relation between percentage ripple and the product L_1C_1 in henries and microfarads is shown in **Fig. 5.** Values of L_1 and C_1 which lead to conditions approaching series resonance at the ripple frequency should be avoided as the ripple voltage would build up to high values, which apart from defeating the object of the filter, may cause excessive rectifier peak currents and unduly high peak inverse voltages. The product of L_1 and C_1 producing resonance is 2·53 assuming 100 c/s ripple and 10·12 assuming 50 c/s ripple, and the product of C_1 in microfarads and L_1 in

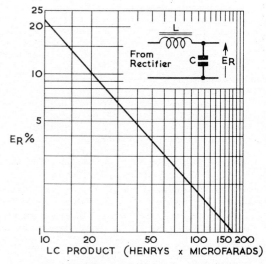

Fig. 5. Graph showing 100 c/s ripple voltage E_R as a percentage of the d.c. output voltage at the output of a choke input filter plotted against the LC product.

henries (maximum current value) should be at least twice these figures.

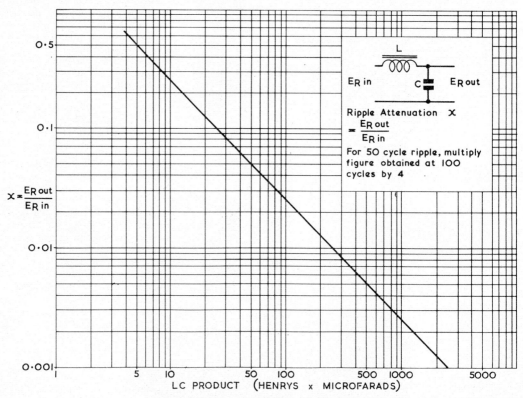

Fig. 6. Ripple attenuation of LC filter sections at 100 c/s.'

The simple capacitor input and choke input filters described will not reduce the ripple voltage to a low enough value for use in power units supplying the low level stages of transmitters and receivers and further LC filter sections will be required as shown in Fig. 2 (b) and 2 (c). The ripple attenuation produced by a single section of given LC product is given in **Fig. 6.**

As a guide to the number of filter sections needed the following permissible ripple percentages may be quoted for various types of load:

C.w. transmitters	5 per cent
Telephony transmitters	1 per cent
Class B modulators	0·25 per cent
V.F.O.'s, speech amplifiers and	
receivers, s.s.b. generators	0·01 per cent

For most purposes one additional section will be adequate behind a choke input filter, and one or two sections, depending upon the required ripple attenuation, behind a simple capacitor input filter. The capacitors used in the additional sections should have a working voltage at least equal to, and preferably greater than, the peak a.c. voltage. The chokes should be constant inductance types rated to provide the required inductance at the maximum current taken by the load.

Resistance Capacitance Filters

The substitution of resistors for inductors in the filter sections following the reservoir capacitor provides an economical and space saving method of ripple attenuation when the regulation of the supply is not important and the relatively high voltage drop across the series resistors can be tolerated. The ripple attenuation x (where $x = $ output/input ripple) plotted against the values of RC from 10^2 to 10^6 is shown in **Fig. 7** where RC is the product of series resistance in ohms and parallel capacitance in microfarads. The same requirements regarding the capacitor working voltage apply as when LC sections are used. It is also necessary to ensure that the series resistors are of adequate power handling capacity to avoid overheating. The required value of dissipation in watts may be computed from the usual formula $W = I^2R$ where I is in amperes and R in ohms, and the voltage drop from the formula $V = IR$ using the same units. To reduce the voltage drop, the highest practicable values of C should be used. This will also be advantageous in providing a low impedance path to audio frequencies, so reducing the possibility of low frequency instability when this smoothing system is used in conjunction with multistage audio frequency amplifiers.

SELECTION OF A SUITABLE TRANSFORMER

The transformer secondary voltage required for a given d.c. output voltage is best obtained from the manufacturers' characteristic curves for the rectifier to be used. Due allowance should be made for the voltage drop in the filter chokes, and also for the fall in transformer output voltage when current is drawn. A fall in transformer output voltage of

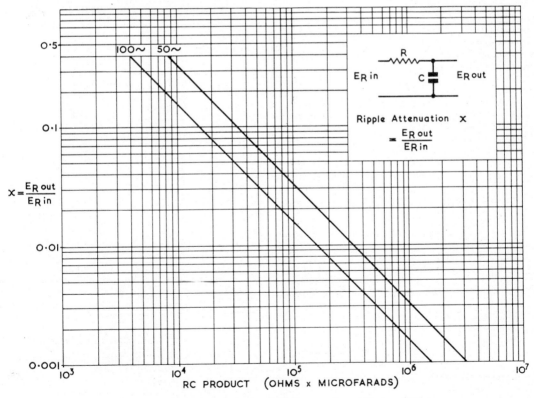

Fig. 7. Ripple attentuation of RC filters sections at 50 c/s and 100 c/s.

from 5 to 10 per cent of the open circuit voltage may be expected at full load. In most instances a commercially manufactured transformer will be employed in amateur equipment and it will be necessary to specify the maximum d.c. load current and type of rectifier circuit to be used when ordering an h.t. transformer.

The source resistance presented to a rectifier is determined by the winding resistance of the h.t. transformer plus any additional resistance inserted to bring the value up to the minimum required by the operating conditions of the rectifier. The effective transformer winding resistance is given by the following equation:

Effective winding resistance $= N^2Rp + Rs$ ohms

where $N =$ transformer turns ratio primary to secondary and *Rp* and *Rs* are the d.c. resistances of the primary and secondary windings. When the transformer feeds a biphase rectifier, the turns ratio from primary to half h.t. secondary should be taken and also the resistance of half the total h.t. secondary winding.

Heater windings should be adequately rated for the total heater current to be drawn. Any deficiencies in this respect will give rise to excessive voltage drop in the transformer windings causing overheating and insufficient heater voltage to the valves themselves. When a heater winding is used to supply valves in a circuit susceptible to hum pickup it may be desirable to use a centre tapped heater winding, the centre tap being earthed and the heater wiring carried out in twisted pair. Transformers having heater windings should have an adequate number of tappings on the primary to enable the heater voltage to be adjusted to its correct value with changes in the supply voltage. The mains voltage is normally held to within 10 per cent of its declared value in U.K. and therefore taps at 200, 220 and 240 volts are desirable.

Valves taking a heavy heater current are usually supplied from a separate heater transformer mounted near the valve-holder to avoid the necessity of running excessively heavy heater leads.

The provision of an earthed electrostatic shield between the primary and other windings of mains transformers is recommended. Apart from its basic function of reducing the interwinding capacitance, the shield provides an added factor of safety in the event of breakdown between high voltage windings and the primary of the transformer. Reduction of the interwinding capacitance results in less mains-borne noise being coupled into the equipment via the power supply.

POTENTIAL DIVIDERS AND SERIES DROPPING RESISTORS

Voltages of lower value than that provided by the power supply may be obtained by the use of a potential divider which is a form of potentiometer where the tapping points on the resistance are fixed or adjustable instead of being continuously variable. As many tapping points as desired may be used to give various voltages, but each additional point from which current is taken will affect the voltage at each of the other tapping points. The extent to which the output voltage varies depends upon the current taken from each point and the resistance between the tapping points. The lower the total divider resistance, the better will be the voltage regulation at the tapping points.

By the application of Ohm's Law, it is a relatively simple matter to calculate the resistances of each section of the potential divider network, provided the voltage and current

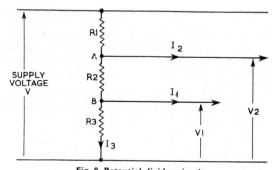

Fig. 8. Potential divider circuit.

taken at each tapping point is known. **Fig. 8** shows a typical arrangement with two tapping points at *A* and *B*, providing voltages V_1 and V_2 at currents I_1 and I_2. The resistor R_3 acts as a bleeder and determines the minimum current I_3 flowing through the divider network when the loads at *A* and *B* are removed. A suitable value for I_3 would be 10 per cent of the total load, this being a suitable compromise between the degree of voltage regulation obtained and the wastage of current through the divider chain. Having fixed a value for I_3 the procedure is as follows:

Calculate $R_3 = V_1/I_3$

Calculate $R_2 = (V_2 - V_1) / (I_1 + I_3)$

Calculate $R_1 = (V - V_2) / (I_1 + I_2 + I_3)$

where $V =$ supply voltage and all currents are in amperes.

The wattage rating of the resistors may be calculated from the usual formulae, $W = VI = V^2/R = I^2R$, V, I, and R being in volts, amperes and ohms respectively.

In order to utilize the current in I_3, which is otherwise wasted, it may be convenient to insert a relay or pilot lamp in series with R_1, adjusting the value of the latter appropriately. The relay will operate when the supply voltage is applied and its contacts used to operate other circuits as required. The insulation of the relay should be adequate for the functions its contacts are required to perform.

Where only one reduced voltage is required at constant current, a simple series resistance may be used the value of which can be calculated as follows:

$$\text{Required series resistance in ohms} = \frac{\text{Voltage dropped across resistor}}{\text{Current taken by load in amperes}}$$

In many instances it will be found necessary to decouple the load side of the resistor with a suitable capacitor to avoid instability due to the high source impedance presented by the series resistor. Decoupling may also be required at the tapping points of the voltage divider. A capacitor of at least 2 μF will be required to decouple audio frequencies and 0·1 μF for radio frequencies.

VOLTAGE STABILIZATION

Certain types of circuit require a source of stabilized voltage for their correct operation. Examples of such circuits are local oscillators and *Q* multipliers in receivers and variable frequency oscillators in transmitters. A stabilized grid bias supply is also desirable for the correct operation of class AB2 and class B amplifiers used in modulators and s.s.b. transmitters. Changes in frequency or operating conditions due to variations in mains voltage and load variations may be eliminated or greatly reduced by the use of voltage stabilization circuits.

A moderate degree of stabilization is obtained by the use of one or more cold cathode stabilizer valves (described in Chapter 2—*Valves*). These will reduce voltage variations to within 2–3 per cent of the nominal stabilized voltage but the output voltage and load current variation is controlled by the type of valve employed and cannot be varied. A much closer degree of stabilization is obtained by means of a hard valve stabilizer circuit employing high vacuum valves in addition to one or more cold cathode stabilizers used as voltage references. A very low output impedance may be obtained by suitable circuit design and the output voltage is variable manually over a wide range if required. These advantages are gained at the expense of considerable complexity of circuit and number of components required and are only justified when a high degree of stabilization is necessary.

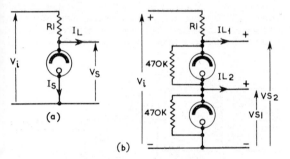

Fig. 9. Gas-filled voltage stabilizer circuits. (a) Simple voltage stabilizer arrangement. (b) Two or more stabilizer tubes in series to provide increased values of regulated voltage.

Cold Cathode Stabilizer Circuits

The basic circuit of a cold cathode stabilizer is very simple, consisting of a resistor in series with the tube, the two being shunted across the unstabilized supply. The stabilized voltage is taken from the junction of the series resistor and anode of the tube, thus the circuit resembles a potential divider. The value of the series resistor is determined by the characteristics of the tube and the stabilized supply voltage. The characteristics of the cold cathode voltage stabilizer are such that it will maintain a nominally constant voltage between its anode and cathode over a specified range of current through the valve, typically 5 to 40 mA. The value of the series resistor must theoretically be selected to maintain the current through the valve within the specified minimum and maximum values under all conditions of operation. In practice it is found that any one value of resistor may not satisfy all the circuit conditions and a compromise is made, the value of series resistor being chosen, so that the current through the valve does not exceed the specified maximum when no current is being drawn by the load circuit (**Fig. 9 (a)**). The use of voltage stabilizers having a separate striking electrode will assist in ensuring that the stabilizer strikes when the load circuit is drawing current. The striking electrode is connected to the unstabilized supply via a 270K ohms resistor.

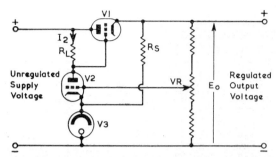

Fig. 10. Basic circuit of series valve voltage stabilizer. R_L, anode load; R_S, series voltage dropping resistor for V_3. V_1, series valve; V_2, d.c. coupled voltage amplifier; V_3, reference voltage source (gas-filled stabilizer or reference tube); VR, output voltage control.

The value of R_1 is given by the following expression:

$$R_1 = \frac{V_{i\,max} - V_s}{I_{s\,max}}$$

where $V_{i\,max}$ is the maximum value of the unstabilized supply voltage, V_s is the nominal stabilized voltage and I_s is the maximum permissible stabilizer current in amperes. The maximum variation of load current I_L should not be greater than $(I_{smax} - I_{smin})$, and should preferably be rather less to allow for variations in the unstabilized voltage.

The value of the unstabilized voltage must be at least 30–40 per cent greater than the stabilized voltage to ensure that the valve will strike when first switched on. Two or more stabilizers of similar current rating may be connected in series with a common limiting resistor to produce higher values of stabilized voltage as shown in Fig. 9 (b). The unstabilized supply voltage should be at least equal to the sum of the *striking* voltages of each valve in the chain to ensure that they will conduct when the supply is first switched on. The shunt resistors shown in Fig. 9 (b) will assist in initial striking of the stabilizers and should not be omitted. Current may be drawn from intermediate stabilizers if desired but the total load should not exceed $(I_{s\,max} - I_{s\,min})$.

The connection of voltage stabilizer valves in parallel to increase the permissible load current is not recommended,

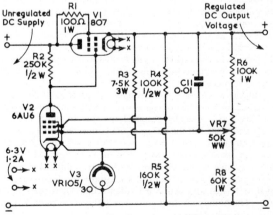

Fig. 11. Typical series valve voltage stabilizer circuit.

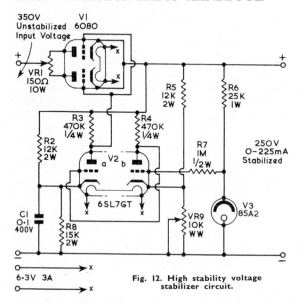

350V
Unstabilized
Input Voltage

VI
6080

VRI
150Ω
10W

R5
12K
2W

R6
25K
1W

R3
470K
1/4W

R4
470K
1/4W

R2
12K
2W

R7
1M
1/2W

250V
0-225mA
Stabilized

a V2 b

6SL7GT

V3
85A2

C1
0·1
400V

R8
15K
2W

VR9
10K
WW

6·3V 3A

Fig. 12. High stability voltage
stabilizer circuit.

as one tube will strike, lowering the available striking voltage on the other valves which will remain inoperative.

Voltage stabilizer tubes are polarised, i.e. they have a preferred direction of conduction and their stabilizing properties will be impaired if the rated maximum inverse voltage is exceeded.

Hard Valve Stabilizer Circuits

The basic circuit of the series valve stabilizer is shown in **Fig. 10.** The valve V_1 functions as a variable resistor whose value is varied by a change in grid bias voltage. When the output voltage E_0 tends to decrease, the grid voltage of V_2 becomes less positive. The cathode of V_2 is maintained at a constant potential above earth and positive with respect to its grid by the gas-filled stabilizer V_3. Reducing the positive grid voltage on V_2 is therefore equivalent to increasing the net negative grid to cathode voltage and the anode current I_2 will decrease taking the anode of V_2 more positive. Since the grid of V_1 is d.c. coupled to the anode of V_2, this will reduce the effective negative bias on the grid of V_1 and its anode to cathode voltage will decrease, tending to restore the output voltage E_0 to its original value. An increase in E_0 will produce the reverse effect. The circuit may be considered as a d.c. amplifier with negative voltage feedback. By the application of sufficient feedback the output impedance may be made very low, approaching zero and even negative values.

The valve used at V_1 should have a high mutual conductance and a low anode resistance to minimize the voltage drop. Suitable types specially designed for this function are the 12E1 and 6080, but the 807 or 6L6G connected as triodes are satisfactory. A typical practical circuit is shown in **Fig. 11.** The heaters of the 6AU6 and 807 should be supplied from a well insulated heater winding. With an unstabilized input of 600 volts, the output voltage is constant for load currents of 0 to 40 mA and within 0·5 volt for load currents of 0–70 mA. The nominal output voltage is 300 volts variable over a small range by VR_7.

A slightly more elaborate circuit with improved performance using double triodes type 6080 and 6SL7GT is shown in **Fig. 12.** A variation of less than 0·2 volts is obtained about a nominal output voltage of 250 volts when the load current is varied from 0 to 225 mA. The nominal unstabilized input voltage is 350 volts.

GRID BIAS SUPPLIES

Operating and protective grid bias for class C and modulator stages is conveniently obtained from a small power supply shunted with a heavy bleeder resistor to minimize the variation of output voltage when grid current flows. The standing current through the bleeder resistor should be at least five times, and preferably ten times, the total grid current flowing. One or more variable tapping points on the bleeder resistor will enable the bias voltage to be adjusted to any desired value—**Fig. 13 (a)**.

A gas filled stabilizer and limiting resistor may be substituted for the bleeder resistor to improve the regulation of the bias supply—see **Fig. 13 (b)**. The series resistor should be adjusted so that the stabilizer draws its rated minimum current when no grid current is present. The flow of grid current will increase the current through the stabilizer and the total grid current of all stages connected to the supply should be limited to a value not greater than the maximum

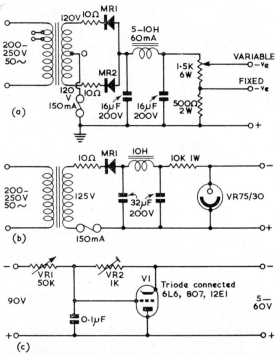

Fig. 13. Typical bias supply circuits. (a) Supply providing a fixed bias voltage of —30 volts and a variable bias of —30 to —120 volts. Grid current should not exceed 10–15 mA with this circuit if the regulation is important. MR_1, MR_2, may be two type RM1, FST1/4 or equivalent. (b) 75 volt grid bias supply with VR75/30 stabilizer to improve regulation. Grid current of up to 30-35mA may be drawn. MR_1 may be type RM1, FST1/4 or equivalent. (c) Simple shunt stabilizing circuit providing variable regulated bias voltage. Grid current of up to 10-15 mA may be drawn. The output voltage is held within 5 volts over the range 30–60 volts.

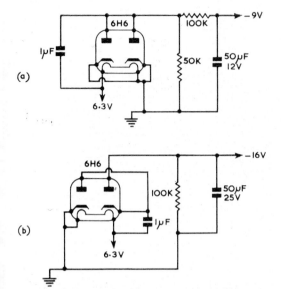

Fig. 14. Low voltage bias supplies deriving their input voltages from the heater line in the equipment. These circuits are not suitable for use when appreciable grid current is to be drawn.

permissible stabilizer current. When used in conjunction with class C amplifiers the output voltage of the supply is adjusted to provide approximately cut-off bias, the difference between operating bias and cut-off bias being provided by the flow of grid current through the appropriate value of grid leak.

Fig. 13 (c) shows a simple shunt stabilizer circuit which may be used to hold the grid bias voltage constant within a few volts with quite large variations of grid current. The circuit functions as a cathode follower and has a low output impedance of the order of 100 ohms. Referring to the circuit of Fig. 13(c) the output voltage is set by VR_1 and VR_2 is used to set the minimum grid bias on V_1. A parasitic suppressor may be necessary at the grid of V_1 as the circuit may oscillate at v.h.f. with low values of grid bias on V_1.

Two simple circuits for obtaining low values of bias voltage from the heater line are shown in **Fig. 14 (a)** and **(b)**. The 6AL5, EB91 or other miniature double diodes may be used if desired. The circuit of Fig. 14 (a) is useful in receivers to supply bias for gain control in r.f., i.f. and a.f. stages and the voltage doubling circuit of Fig. 14 (b) for a.f. output stages which do not draw grid current.

VOLTAGE MULTIPLIER CIRCUITS

The voltage multiplier is a form of rectifier circuit where the output voltage may be two or more times that obtained from the conventional half-wave or full-wave rectifier with capacitor input when supplied with the same a.c. input voltage. A combination of rectifiers and capacitors is used such that the capacitors are charged in parallel via the rectifiers and then discharged in series, the rectifiers acting as switches in addition to their normal function. The regulation of these circuits is poor as a result of this mode of operation, but they are quite satisfactory for use in circuits where the current taken does not vary greatly.

Half-wave and full-wave voltage doubler circuits are illustrated in **Fig. 15 (a)** and **(b)**. The full-wave circuit has better

regulation but has the disadvantage of not having a common input and output terminal. As in all full-wave circuits, the ripple component is at twice the supply frequency and is therefore easier to remove. At zero load, the output voltage is very nearly twice the peak value of the input a.c. voltage but falls rapidly to a value approximately twice the R.M.S. input voltage when appreciable current is drawn. The regulation may be improved by increasing the size of the capacitors, but care should be taken to ensure that the peak current ratings of the rectifiers are not exceeded. Semiconductor rectifiers are more convenient for use in these circuits although valve rectifiers may be used if desired.

Voltage tripler and quadrupler circuits are illustrated in Fig. 15 (c) and (d). The tripler is a form of half-wave circuit where the output of a half-wave doubler is added to a normal half-wave rectifier. The quadrupler circuit is also known as the Cockcroft-Walton multiplier and if required, additional stages may be added to provide higher output voltages.

When used to provide appreciable currents (up to 50–60 mA) the capacitors shown in the circuits of Fig. 15 (a), (b) and (c) should be at least 8 μF and preferably 16 μF, to provide reasonable regulation of the output voltage. Lower values (0·1 to 0·5 μF) will be satisfactory when the load is not more than 1–2 mA as in e.h.t. supplies. The polarity of the output voltage may be reversed in all of the circuits shown by reversing the connections to each rectifier.

CONSTRUCTION OF POWER SUPPLIES

The layout and construction of power supplies is by no means critical but there are certain design features which if adhered to will assist materially in producing a reliable and safe unit.

The conventional four-sided chassis with or without a front panel has the merit of being readily made up or purchased, and in conjunction with through-chassis mounting components produces a layout where the greater part of the high voltage and mains wiring may be underneath the chassis. A perforated metal cover overall will ensure

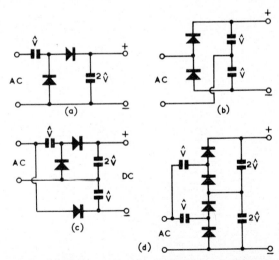

Fig. 15. Voltage multiplier circuits. (a) Half-wave voltage doubler. (b) Full-wave voltage doubler. (c) Voltage tripler. (d) Voltage quadrupler. $\hat{V}$ — the peak value of the a.c. input voltage. The working voltages of the capacitors should not be less than the values shown.

that exposed high voltage terminals are out of immediate reach.

Input and output connections are preferably made with shielded plugs and sockets, male chassis connectors being used for mains input and female chassis connectors for output. The rear side member of the chassis is convenient for mounting these components. Three pole mains input connectors should always be used when the power supply is built as a separate unit, the third pole of the connector being taken to chassis so that the metalwork is earthed via the three core mains cable. When the power unit chassis forms part of a rack or cabinet of equipment, each chassis should be bonded together independently of any other connections and earthed, either to the mains earth as above or to a separate properly constructed earth connection. A water pipe must not be used because it is now common practice to use plastic pipe.

Double pole mains switches should be used and wired in next to the mains input so that the unit may be isolated completely when changing fuses and making circuit adjustments. When the power unit chassis is to be enclosed in a cabinet or rack, adequate ventilation of heat producing components is essential. Valve rectifiers should be mounted towards the rear edge of the chassis to allow free circulation of air. Semiconductor rectifiers with fins must always be mounted with the fins vertical and preferably over a rectangular hole in the chassis. The more recently introduced wire ended silicon rectifiers are conveniently wired to tag strips and interconnections made between the tags to produce bridge, biphase or other circuits as required.

Paper capacitors are preferable to electrolytic types where reliability is of primary importance but tend to be expensive when high values and working voltages are called for. It is possible to use electrolytic capacitors by connecting units

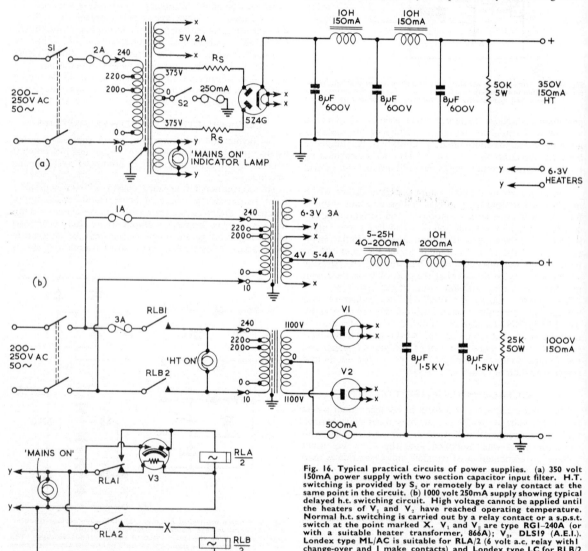

Fig. 16. Typical practical circuits of power supplies. (a) 350 volt 150mA power supply with two section capacitor input filter. H.T. switching is provided by S_2 or remotely by a relay contact at the same point in the circuit. (b) 1000 volt 250mA supply showing typical delayed h.t. switching circuit. High voltage cannot be applied until the heaters of V_1 and V_2 have reached operating temperature. Normal h.t. switching is carried out by a relay contact or a s.p.s.t. switch at the point marked X. V_1 and V_2 are type RG1–240A (or with a suitable heater transformer, 866A); V_3, DLS19 (A.E.I.). Londex type ML/AC is suitable for RLA/2 (6 volt a.c. relay with1 change-over and 1 make contacts) and Londex type LC for RLB/2 (6 volt a.c. contactor with 2 heavy duty make contacts).

A low power h.t. and heater supply unit. Note the recessed mains
input connector on the right drop of the chassis.

of similar capacitance and working voltage in series to
produce a capacitor of twice the working voltage and half the
capacitance of one unit provided that voltage equalizing
resistors of 50–100K ohms are connected across each
capacitor. The outer can of the capacitor which is at high
potential will be at a potential of several hundred volts above
chassis and should therefore be adequately insulated.

When multiple unit electrolytic capacitors are used it
should be noted that one unit is often specially processed
for use as a reservoir capacitor and care should be taken
to ensure that the correct unit is used in this position. Plain

foil electrolytics are recommended rather than etched foil
types as although somewhat larger physically, they provide
a greater factor of safety in respect of working voltage and
ripple current. It should not be assumed that the outer
case of metal cased electrolytics is isolated from the electrodes
and when used in grid bias supplies or other circuits where
the negative terminal is above chassis potential, the metal
case should be insulated by means of p.v.c. or polythene sheet
wrapped around it, if this is not already provided by the
manufacturer.

A bleeder resistor should always be used across the output
of a power supply as it provides a means of discharging the
capacitors when the equipment is switched off. The resistor
used should be of adequate wattage rating, as an open-
circuit bleeder is a hazard to safety. A 60 mA pilot lamp
placed in series with the low potential end of the bleeder
resistor will provide an indication of bleeder continuity
and also act as an " HT ON " indicator. Alternatively the
bleeder may form the series resistor for an h.t. voltmeter.
A 5 mA meter movement may be rescaled for this purpose
and will provide a useful indication apart from its safety
function.

Fuses should not be omitted from power supplies where
necessary as it is false economy to lose a rectifier or transformer as a result of omitting a fuse. The practical power
supply circuits illustrated in **Fig. 16** show the points where
fuses are most usefully employed. Where large transformers
having low resistance primary windings are employed it may
be found that the primary fuse blows on switching on due
to the high initial surge current; this may be eliminated by
the use of a current sensitive resistor (Brimistor or Varistor)
in series with the primary winding. The Brimistor or Varistor
has a high initial resistance which falls rapidly as it warms
up to a value of a few ohms and may be left permanently in
circuit. Similarly a Brimistor may be connected in the h.t.
winding centre-tap or between the rectifier and the reservoir
capacitor to prevent the h.t. fuse blowing at switch-on.
Used in this way the Brimistor will also delay the application
of h.t. voltage to the remainder of the circuit when a directly
heated rectifier or semiconductor rectifier is employed.

CHAPTER 18

INTERFERENCE

IN addition to the carrier frequency and the sidebands necessary to convey intelligence in the form of code, telephony, etc., a transmitter may radiate unnecessary frequencies due to distortion of the modulation, harmonics of the carrier frequency or parasitic oscillations. Any of these radiated frequencies, necessary or otherwise, may cause interference in various ways, namely—

  (a) to reception of other amateur transmissions,

  (b) to television reception (TVI),

  (c) to sound broadcast reception (BCI),

  (d) to protected services.

  (e) to other services.

Interference to other services is relatively unimportant only because it is rarely encountered, but when such services operate in a shared band the amateur operator, to comply with the terms of his licence, may have to close down or change frequency at the request of the other station or temporarily cease transmitting.

Official reports show that radio amateurs are responsible for only a very small fraction of the total interference to television and broadcast reception. In some cases in which amateurs are involved the interference is due to bad design, maladjustment or careless operation of the transmitter. In other instances interference can be traced to poor installation or inadequate design of the domestic receiver. Occasionally it may be found that a " perfect " transmitter interferes with a " perfect " receiver and in such instances the trouble may be attributed to external cross-modulation effects or the radiation of harmonics produced by contact rectification in metal objects in the immediate vicinity. Lastly, a swamp signal on the fundamental frequency due to close proximity may blanket the domestic installation.

TRANSMITTER CONSIDERATIONS

In general it must be expected that telephony transmissions are more likely to cause interference than telegraphy transmissions and that the interference whenever it does occur is likely to be more troublesome. This does not mean that the problems of preventing a c.w. transmitter from causing unnecessary interference are trivial but that the telephony operator should understand that he is trying to meet a more stringent set of requirements. The following paragraphs deal first with the special problems relating to telephony and telegraphy and next with questions common to both systems such as the prevention of parasitic oscillation and the elimination of harmonics.

Telephony

In view of the congested state of the radio frequency spectrum the International Amateur Radio Union (Region 1) has recommended that, irrespective of the modulation system in use, the maximum modulation frequency should be 4 kc/s, while the International Telecommunications Union supports 3 kc/s. This upper frequency limit is a reasonable compromise between bandwidth and speech quality. Since most audio-frequency amplifiers have a frequency range exceeding the I.A.R.U. recommendation positive steps should be taken to restrict the bandwidth by incorporating some form of low-pass filter. Resistance-capacity networks are worthwhile but much more effective filtering can be obtained by using the inductance-capacity type of filter.

Low-pass filters can be installed in the low-level stages of the modulator although if this arrangement is adopted any harmonic distortion occurring in the modulator output stage will be unaffected by the filter and thus the transmitted bandwidth will be greater than that desired. It is therefore strongly recommended that the low-pass filter be fitted between the modulator and the modulated radio-frequency amplifier.

Even when the frequency response of the modulator has been restricted, the transmitted bandwidth may be much greater than necessary because of bad design or incorrect adjustment of the r.f. section of the transmitter. The major troubles are due to a shifting carrier frequency, non-linearity (distortion) and over-modulation.

A carrier frequency which changes when the transmitter is amplitude-modulated can cause a most annoying form of interference to stations working on adjacent channels. The frequency shift is caused by the feedback of r.f. energy from the modulated stage into the oscillator. This can occur as a result of poor screening, lack of neutralization or bad layout, and the effect is most marked on the lower frequency bands where the oscillator and the power amplifier are often operated on the same frequency (i.e. when there are no frequency-multiplying stages). In severe cases the carrier may shift several kilocycles from the no-signal frequency and the receiver then has to be tuned to the setting where the carrier happens to be during actual speech transmission thus giving the appearance of asymmetrical tuning. In milder cases the tuning may appear to be normal but any heterodyne interference which may be present cannot be properly rejected at the receiver because the heterodyne note is not constant in frequency.

Appreciable non-linearity is inherent in all efficiency-modulation systems especially when a modulation depth approaching 100 per cent is attempted. Anode modulation, which is relatively distortion-free and does not require critical adjustment, is therefore to be recommended whenever interference is likely to be a problem.

Where the anode modulation system is used for modulating a tetrode or a pentode, it is essential to modulate the screen as well as the anode. Failure to do this will result in severe distortion, probably indicated by so-called downward modulation and the consequent radiation of "splatter." In this respect a common source of trouble is the use of too large a screen bypass capacitance in which case the higher modulation frequencies are prevented from modulating the screen grid. This results in downward modulation of high notes although when a constant tone of low pitch is directed into the microphone the modulation may appear to be quite normal. A somewhat similar effect can be caused when the cathode bias resistor of the modulated r.f. stage is inadequately bypassed for audio frequencies. In this case, however, it is the low frequencies which may be distorted.

Over-modulation is probably the most common fault in telephony operation and the resulting interference can be very severe, often being audible on frequencies more than 100 kc/s away on either side of the carrier frequency. The depth of modulation is preferably checked by using a cathode ray tube monitor but, failing this, the p.a. anode current will serve as a useful guide: during a transmission that is free from splatter it should not vary by more than about 5 per cent. Most cases of over-modulation are due to carelessness, and some form of automatic limiting device such as volume compression or speech clipping is desirable. The latter system is the more popular one amongst amateurs as it gives a greater increase in the effective " voice power " of the transmitter. When speech clipping is used it is essential to install a good low-pass filter after the clipping circuit. preferably between the modulator and the modulated stage, Examples of suitable circuits and filters are given in Chapter 9 (*Modulation*).

Narrow-band frequency modulation is an alternative system which is sometimes used with great success where all attempts to eliminate TVI and BCI appear to fail. Its principles and application are described in Chapter 11 (*Frequency Modulation*).

Telegraphy

Although it may appear that interference problems arising from the use of amplitude modulation could be altogether avoided by reverting to c.w. telegraphy, it should not be forgotten that keying is in itself a form of modulation and many of the difficulties encountered in the use of telephony may still have to be faced. In the conventional method of keying a transmitter the carrier is amplitude-modulated 100 per cent, and the rate at which the carrier

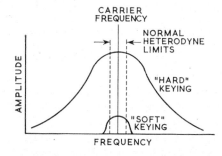

Fig. I. The sidebands produced by key-clicks from a badly adjusted transmitter may extend over a wide frequency range on either side of the carrier. With a "soft" keying characteristic the interference from these sidebands should be negligible.

level rises and falls during the keying determines the character of the keying sidebands and therefore the amount of interference likely to be caused to other stations. If the keying arrangement is such as to give a "soft" characteristic the carrier level does not change very rapidly and the sidebands may be negligible. On the other hand a "hard" keying characteristic means that the changes in carrier level are quite abrupt and the resultant sidebands may spread to frequencies far removed from the carrier frequency. Fig. 1 gives an impression of how the interference due to key-clicks depends on the keying characteristics.

Another aspect of interference from a telegraphy transmitter is the variation of carrier frequency generally known as *chirp*, which although being confined within perhaps 200–300 cycles of the proper carrier frequency, may have disastrous effects on a transmission occupying an adjacent channel. Chirp is analogous to the frequency shift which may occur in a telephony transmitter and often arises from the same causes. It is unlikely to occur in a well designed transmitter provided that there is a suitable buffer stage between the keyed stage and the v.f.o.

These questions are not examined in detail here as they are better considered in relation to the general subject of keying which is discussed fully in Chapter 8 (*Keying & Break-in*).

Parasitic Oscillations

Parasitic oscillations in radio transmitters can be responsible for distortion, low efficiency, and instability and can cause interference to other services. The oscillations can be divided into three groups depending on whether their frequency is (*a*) much lower than that of the carrier, (*b*) approximately equal to the carrier frequency or (*c*) much higher than the carrier frequency.

Low-frequency oscillations are usually recognised by the fact that the transmitter radiates a number of frequencies on each side of the carrier at a spacing of some tens or hundreds of kilocycles. This is because the carrier is modulated by the parasitic oscillation and the spurious frequencies are the sidebands spaced at intervals equal to the oscillation frequency. The most common cause of l.f. oscillations is the use of r.f. chokes in the anode and grid circuits of an r.f. amplifier such that, in conjunction with the capacities present, a tuned-anode/tuned-grid type of oscillator circuit is formed. The normal neutralizing circuits are quite ineffective at the parasitic frequency but the trouble may be cured either by tuning the grid choke to a higher frequency than that of the anode choke (in which case the t.a.t.g. circuit cannot oscillate) or, preferably, by avoiding the use of a grid choke altogether. In most tetrode power amplifiers a grid choke is quite unnecessary if relatively high values of grid resistor are used. The extra r.f. loss which may, in certain circuits, result from the omission of the grid choke is not usually serious. If, in a telephony transmitter, the trouble cannot be attributed to r.f. chokes the fault is most likely due to oscillation at a supersonic frequency in the modulator.

A parasitic oscillation on or near the carrier frequency is caused by r.f. feedback in one of the r.f. amplifier stages (usually the power amplifier) and is due to lack of neutralization, poor screening or bad layout. The oscillation may not be present while the carrier remains unmodulated and may only occur when the drive is removed from the amplifier (e.g. when the driver stage is keyed). In these circumstances, when the key is up, an unstable carrier may be radiated in another part of or even outside the band in use. Unless the transmitter has been carefully checked for oscillations during its initial tests this state of affairs may persist for some time as it is difficult for a receiving operator to identify and associate an unstable spacer with any particular station. Sometimes these oscillations (together with l.f. and more especially h.f. oscillations) occur only during certain parts of the modulation envelope thus giving rise to disconnected "monkey chatter" on telephony and to violent key-clicks on telegraphy. Once it is determined that oscillations are present the cure is usually obvious. Overrunning and excessive h.t. is another cause of these difficulties, particularly when using tetrodes and pentodes.

V.h.f. parasitic oscillations are almost always due to an unfortunate choice of layout and they may occur in r.f. amplifiers or in modulator stages. The oscillations, which are usually generated by a form of t.a.t.g. circuit*, can be cured by fitting grid-stopper resistances. These may be shunted by v.h.f. chokes to prevent power loss and overheating at the carrier frequency in the case of r.f. stages and to avoid distortion in the case of a.f. stages which are driven into grid current. If it is impracticable to use grid stoppers in v.h.f. transmitters because of the consequent power loss, the layout must be changed with a view to making the parasite-generator circuits such that the anode circuit resonates at a lower frequency than the grid circuit. Sometimes a v.h.f. parasitic can be eliminated by connecting a capacitance of about 30 pF from grid to earth or from anode to earth in the suspected amplifier, although of course capacitances of this order are not permissible in r.f. stages operating on frequencies higher than about 28 Mc/s.

An essential procedure in the testing of a new transmitter is the running of the power amplifier without drive and with the maximum possible safe anode current. Under these conditions the anode and grid tuning should be varied on all bands to ensure that no parasitic oscillations are being generated. The presence of parasitics may be indicated by sudden changes in the anode current when the tuning controls are varied, by the existence of grid current or by the lighting of a neon lamp held close to the anode circuit. A transmitter should never be connected to an aerial until it has satisfactorily passed this test. While testing, a suitable load or dummy aerial may be coupled to the output tank circuit.

Harmonics

Perhaps the most common form of interference caused by amateurs is that due to the radiation from the transmitter of harmonics which happen to fall in the wavebands allocated to the television service. Harmonic radiation also causes interference to amateurs working on higher frequency bands and to other services using frequencies which are not in the amateur bands but which are harmonically related to a lower frequency amateur band. The responsibility for curing this type of interference rests with the amateur concerned, and hence the suppression of harmonics is a vitally important factor in the design of a transmitter.

The majority of amateur transmitters incorporate at least one stage operating in class C and must therefore

* T. a. t. g. (tuned anode tuned grid) or t. p. t. g. (tuned plate tuned grid) circuit.

be expected to produce quite strong harmonics. The conventional output stage itself, operating in class C, must be suspected of contributing largely to the harmonic radiation from the transmitter since it is working at the highest power level and has nothing but the output coupling arrangements to separate it from the aerial. However, it should not be assumed that the p.a. stage is the only likely source of harmonic generation. The advent of s.s.b. and the efficiency of modern output tetrodes and pentodes permits operating the final amplifier under other than class C conditions with a view to reducing harmonics.

Care should always be taken to ensure that a class C output stage is not driven any harder than is necessary to maintain maximum output or in the case of a telephony transmitter to maintain linear modulation. Excessive drive will not only increase the harmonic output but in a tetrode or pentode power amplifier may even reduce the output of the fundamental. Some method of controlling the drive power is therefore desirable (especially in multi-band transmitters) and a convenient way of achieving this is to vary the screen potential in the driver stage.

One of the ways in which the radiation of harmonics can be avoided is to design the transmitter so that all stages, including the oscillator, operate at the output frequency. This may require more skill and attention to detail than the popular practice of deliberately generating harmonics in the early stages of the transmitter so as to permit the oscillator to operate at a relatively low frequency where stability is easier to achieve. One suitable type of oscillator for use at the carrier frequency (i.e. without relying on frequency multiplication) is the Tesla oscillator, described in detail in Chapter 6 (*H.F. Transmitters*). Such an oscillator may be followed by a number of amplifying stages all working at the same frequency and all designed to produce the minimum amount of harmonics. Another satisfactory method of minimizing harmonic generation and radiation is to use a mixer master oscillator system to generate the desired final frequency which can then be amplified, preferably by a linear amplifier. A system of this kind may be worth considering where the suppression of harmonics generated in a frequency-multiplying type of transmitter proves too difficult.

Tank Circuit Design. In a class C amplifier the anode current flows in a constant succession of pulses and its waveform is therefore markedly non-sinusoidal. This means that it unavoidably contains a number of unwanted harmonics in addition to the fundamental component. Fortunately a certain amount of filtering is provided by the tuned anode tank circuit which presents a high impedance at the fundamental frequency and a low impedance at all other frequencies including the harmonics. Whatever harmonic currents may be present are bypassed to earth through the shunt capacitance in the tank circuit, and in order to ensure a low reactance in this path it is important to make the connections from the anode to the tuning capacitor and thence to earth as short as possible.

Some tank circuit arrangements may prove rather ineffective in reducing the harmonic amplitude in the output unless suitable precautions are taken. A typical example is that of a push-pull output circuit in which the split-stator tuning condenser has its rotor connected to earth and the coil centre-tap is connected to the h.t. line through an r.f. choke: see **Fig. 2.** This arrangement is normally used to provide a better circuit balance and a low-impedance path to earth for harmonic frequencies. The even-harmonic frequencies present at the valve anodes are in phase with each other and therefore cancel as far as inductive coupling is concerned. However, it will be seen that the entire tank coil is "live" at even-harmonic frequencies owing to the presence of the r.f. choke, and hence these frequencies may be transferred by unintentional capacitive coupling to the output feeder. Unwanted capacitive coupling can be minimized by making an earth connection to the coupling coil. Transmitters designed to produce a minimum amount of harmonic radiation should have an unbalanced coupling coil feeding into a coaxial output feeder since this arrangement simplifies the screening problem. The coil itself should always be coupled to the "earthy" part of the main tank coil.

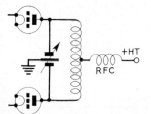

Fig. 2. A push-pull anode tank circuit of this form may be responsible for troublesome even-harmonic radiation.

In addition, the use of a *Faraday screen* between the tank coil and the output coupling coil is preferable, since this will serve to eliminate the capacitive coupling without affecting the inductive coupling. This is desirable because the higher-order harmonics which are to be suppressed will be more readily passed by any stray capacitive coupling, and this point should be borne in mind when determining the layout. The Faraday screen, in its most simple form, shown in **Fig. 3(A)**, consists of a number of closely spaced insulated parallel wires joined together at one end and connected to earth (or any other convenient fixed potential). For use between concentric coils it can be given a cylindrical shape, as shown in **Fig. 3(B)**. Where the output coupling coil consists of merely one or two turns the principle of the shielded loop illustrated in **Fig. 4** is often used.

Pi-networks. If the p.a. stage is of the single-ended switched-band type the most satisfactory output circuit is that using a pi-network: see **Fig. 5**. When used correctly this circuit gives very good discrimination against harmonics owing to the frequency-dependent action of the

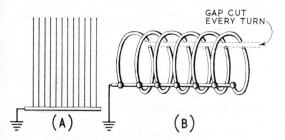

Fig. 3. Faraday screens. The wires must be insulated from each other to prevent the formation of closed loops which would act as inductive shields. The flat screen (A) can be used between coils which are arranged end-to-end. The cylindrical screen (B) is intended for use with concentric coils: it can be made by winding a single-layer coil of suitable diameter, connecting all the turns together along one side and cutting a gap along the other side.

potential divider formed by L_1 and C_2. The improvement as compared with a simple tuned circuit is a factor of 4 for the second harmonic, 9 for the third harmonic and n^2 for

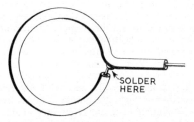

Fig. 4. Shielded link coil made from coaxial cable. The outer braiding is left in position but does not form a closed loop. The inner conductor is soldered to the outer braiding at the point shown. The construction is not suitable for coils of more than a few turns.

the nth harmonic. To obtain the best results from the circuit it should be properly designed to transform the transmitter load impedance (usually less than 100 ohms) to a value suitable for correct operation of the p.a. valve. Design charts are given on page 188. While the pi-network tank circuit is better than a simple tuned circuit in attenuating frequencies *higher* than that to which it is tuned it is less effective in attenuating *lower* frequencies. A power amplifier

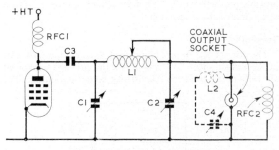

Fig. 5. Pi-network output circuit.
C1, 250 pF tuning capacitor; C2, 0·0015 μF loading capacitor; C3, 0·001 μF blocking capacitor; C4, 50 pF trimmer; L1, tapped inductance; L2 to resonate with C4 for reducing a specific harmonic; RFC1 anode choke; RFC2, safety choke. The choke RFC2, serves to prevent the appearance of high voltage from the h.t. supply on the output feeder cable in the event of a failure of the blocking condenser C3. It is not essential if the cable has a low-resistance d.c. path to earth at the far end.

using a pi-network circuit should therefore be driven by a buffer amplifier rather than by a frequency multiplier, since in the latter case strong low-frequency signals (often erroneously called sub-harmonics) may be radiated.

As with other forms of tank circuit, the pi-network should be connected to the aerial via a suitable aerial tuning unit.

Harmonic Traps and Filters. In spite of the use of a correctly designed tank circuit and coupling system, it is sometimes found that the harmonic radiation is still sufficient to interfere with local receivers. In this event, a series-tuned trap adjusted to resonate at the offending harmonic frequency should be connected across the transmitter output socket as shown at L_2C_4 in Fig. 5. This trap circuit should be tuned for minimum output at the harmonic frequency, using an insulated trimming tool inserted through a hole in the transmitter screening. When the harmonic to be rejected lies in the television band the component values will be such as to leave the fundamental operation

449

of the transmitter unaffected while the trimmer is being adjusted. Parallel-tuned circuits used as harmonic traps in the anode lead of the p.a. valve are not recommended since they may give rise to parasitic oscillations. Tuned traps may need readjustment whenever the transmitter frequency is varied, and for this purpose it is helpful to incorporate a harmonic-indicating device in the transmitter.

Further attenuation of harmonics may be achieved by fitting a low pass filter between the transmitter and aerial coupler. To avoid interference to television reception such a filter would normally pass all frequencies up to 30 Mc/s and have a high attenuation at higher frequencies. Examples of suitable filter are given later in this chapter, and here it is only necessary to stress that if optimum performance is to be obtained the filter must be designed for, and terminated by, the correct load impedance. In general, the proper adjustment of the aerial coupler can only be achieved by using a v.s.w.r. bridge (see Chapter 19— *Measurements*.)

It is sometimes found that a low pass filter does not reduce the harmonic radiation; on the contrary the interference may be worse. This condition can occur when harmonic radiation takes place directly from the transmitter wiring. Such radiation may be reduced by operating all the frequency-multiplying stages at the lowest possible power level, but the most reliable cure is to screen every part of the transmitter.

Screening

The correct use of screening plays a very important part in the reduction of TVI but unless the principles involved are fully understood the results may be disappointing. The

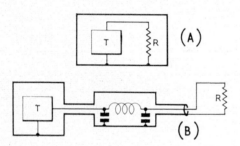

Fig. 6. The perfect shielding shown at A prevents any radiation from the transmitter or its load. In the arrangement B a low-pass filter is inserted in the line between the transmitter and its load to eliminate harmonics while permitting the radiation of the fundamental.

basic principle can be explained with the aid of the simplified arrangement shown in **Fig. 6(A)**. A transmitter T is enclosed with its load resistance R in a perfect screening box. Because the screening is perfect there will be no detectable radiation outside. For the sake of simplicity, it is assumed that the transmitter derives its power from batteries also contained within the box so that there can be no question of radiation from any power supply lines. The problem is to allow the transmitter to radiate its energy outside the box but only at the proper frequency: any other frequencies such as those which could cause TVI must be prevented from leaving the box. **Fig. 6(B)** shows how this can be achieved. Here the transmitter is connected to an external load by screened cable (with its associated plugs and sockets) and a screened

lowpass filter. The load receives r.f. power from the transmitter at the wanted frequency while the filter stops the transmission of any r.f. energy whose frequency may lie within the television bands. It is important to note that the screening must be continuous to ensure that the only way out of the box is through the filter.

Although the arrangement of Fig. 6(B) enables a carrier to be radiated without harmonics there still remain the practical problems of making connections to a modulator or a keying circuit and also of connecting a mains supply to feed a power unit instead of the internal battery. These

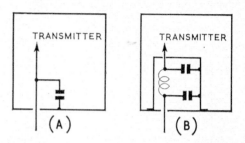

Fig. 7. Methods of preventing the escape of r.f. energy along the supply leads feeding a screened transmitter. The pi-filter shown at B is usually more effective than the simple bypass condenser A.

various problems are really one, i.e. that of taking connections into or out of the box and at the same time preventing r.f. energy from escaping out of the box along the lead. To do this it must be made impossible for any r.f. potential difference to exist between the leads and the outside of the box. **Fig. 7** shows two convenient methods. The capacitance values are not critical and usually lie between 500pF and 1000pF; such values are large enough for adequate bypassing at television frequencies and yet have negligible effect on the supply carried by the lead. The capacitors should preferably be of the feedthrough or mica-disc type because these have exceptional low series inductance. When other types of condensers are used the connecting leads must be kept as short as possible: a typical arrangement is shown in **Fig. 8**. It will be noted that the portion of the lead *inside* the box is shown as being screened. The use of screening is strongly recommended on all internal leads which are not normally carrying r.f. currents. In such screened leads the insulating material need not be of a low-loss type since any r.f. loss will help to attenuate any r.f. currents which might be present.

The choke shown at (B) in Fig. 7 may be made by winding approximately one-quarter wavelength (at the frequency to

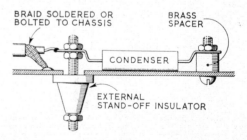

Fig. 8. An effective method of using a standard moulded-case mica condenser for bypassing a power-supply lead entering a screened cabinet.

be attenuated) of suitable wire on a former about $\frac{3}{8}$ in. diameter. It is well to bear in mind that r.f. chokes often have series resonances and may therefore offer negligible impedance at certain frequencies. These frequencies are not readily predictable but they can be changed by altering the number of turns in the coil or the spacing between the turns. A grid dip oscillator is useful in detecting such resonances.

Where the power supply unit is remote from the transmitter chassis some difficulty may be encountered in constructing an effective r.f. filter for the heater supply leads owing to the relatively heavy currents and the consequent large amount of space occupied by the chokes. This may be avoided by mounting the heater transformer directly on the transmitter chassis, as near as possible to the valve sockets, and the r.f. chokes for the heater supply can then be inserted in the primary circuit instead of the secondary.

The effectiveness of lead filters may be checked by coupling a receiver fitted with a signal-strength meter to the lead in question. The receiver should be of the straight (t.r.f.) type to avoid spurious responses, the degree of amplification depending on the sensitivity required. In some cases a simple crystal set may be sufficient.

The screening box itself should preferably be made from sheet brass or aluminium, although when ventilation has to be provided it may be satisfactory to use perforated or expanded metal sheet. Fine-mesh woven wire gauze will give good results but its performance may deteriorate with time owing to the development of high-resistance contacts at the intersections of the wires. There should not be less than $\frac{1}{2}$ in. overlap at every joint, and bolted joints should have bolts not more than 3 in. apart. It is not always essential to screen meter holes, but when necessary the meters can be mounted in screened enclosures (with the leads by-passed to the enclosure), or alternatively the meters may be viewed through metal gauze.

Screened transmitters built according to the principles described and used in conjunction with a screened low-pass filter will give a substantially harmonic-free output irrespective of the transmitter circuit details and of the amount of harmonic energy produced in the various stages. The principles are particularly easy to apply to self-contained equipment such as a " table-top " transmitter.

RECEIVER CONSIDERATIONS

The majority of interference problems occurring in receivers can perhaps be analysed in terms of selectivity of the various tuned circuits, although sometimes the source of trouble can be traced to other parts of the receiver such as the a.f. amplifier or the power supply. In general, they may be grouped under one or more of the following headings:

(a) Adjacent-channel selectivity.

(b) Spurious responses in superheterodyne receivers.

(c) Cross-modulation.

(d) Rectification in a.f. stages.

(e) Mains-borne interference.

Adjacent-channel Selectivity

The overall selectivity of the receiver determines its ability to reject transmissions occurring on adjacent channels. As the channel spacing varies according to the class of service so likewise does the receiver bandwidth. Typical bandwidths

vary from a few megacycles in television receivers to a few hundred cycles in receivers for hand-keyed telegraphy reception. In some types of receiver the bandwidth is variable. Because television receivers have the greatest bandwidth they are the most susceptible to interference from spurious signals radiated by transmitters whose fundamental output is in another part of the frequency spectrum.

Spurious Responses in Superheterodyne Receivers

Interference effects in a superheterodyne receiver can be of several different forms including interference by image signals, the break-through of signals on or near the intermediate frequency, and various beats produced by harmonics of the signal or of the local oscillator.

Images. If the local oscillator in a superheterodyne receiver has a frequency f_0 and if the intermediate frequency is f_i, the receiver will produce an output when the incoming signal has a frequency of either $f_0 + f_i$ or $f_0 - f_i$. If as in most receivers the oscillator frequency is designed to be higher than that of the wanted signal, the unwanted or " image " signal will be on a frequency $f_0 + f_i$. The only possible means of preventing interference by an image signal is to provide sufficient selectivity ahead of the mixer stage.

" Half-image " Frequency. It is possible for signals on frequencies of $f_0 + \frac{1}{2}f_i$ and $f_0 - \frac{1}{2}f_i$ to produce at the mixer anode a frequency of $\frac{1}{2}f_i$ together with its harmonics. The second harmonic of this frequency is of course f_i and interference may therefore occur. It should be noted that $f_0 - \frac{1}{2}f_i$ is relatively close to the wanted frequency of $f_0 - f_i$ and that the pre-mixer selectivity which is adequate for image-frequency rejection will not necessarily preclude this form of interference. Fortunately this effect is only likely to be encountered when the interfering signal is exceptionally strong since the output of such harmonics from the mixer is quite low.

Intermediate-frequency Breakthrough. This type of interference is due to the reception of a transmission occurring on or near the intermediate frequency of the receiver. It is usually due to insufficient selectivity ahead of the mixer stage but in rare cases it may result from direct pick-up in the i.f. amplifier wiring. Most communications receivers have adequate pre-mixer selectivity to avoid this breakthrough effect and some broadcast receivers have a built-in i.f. trap to reject stations working near the intermediate frequency (usually 465 kc/s). A number of television receivers have no i.f. traps and are rather susceptible to i.f. breakthrough.

Harmonic Beats. Interference may be caused by any signal whose fundamental or harmonics can beat with the receiver's local r.f. oscillator or with any of its harmonics and thereby produce the intermediate frequency. The effect can be minimized by reducing the harmonic output of the local oscillator, but in the case of interference from an amateur transmitter it is usually easier to prevent the interfering signals from reaching the receiver input by installing a suitable filter at the input to the receiver.

Cross-modulation

Cross-modulation occurs when two signals are applied to a non-linear device such as a badly adjusted or overloaded valve amplifier and results in each signal being modulated by the other. The effect used to be very marked when

451

sharp cut-off screen grid and pentode valve were in common use as r.f. amplifiers but it has ceased to be important in normal reception since the advent of the variable-μ valve with its gradual change of slope. However, when the interfering signal is very strong cross-modulation will occur even with variable-μ valves and, because the modulation from the interfering signal is impressed on the wanted signal, no amount of selectivity in the stages following the one at which the effect was produced will remove the interference.

Ideally all the selectivity should be achieved ahead of the first valve in the receiver so that cross-modulation cannot occur. As this is impossible it is common practice in communications receivers to incorporate the most selective circuit, usually a crystal filter, immediately after the mixer valve and care is taken that the r.f. stages have only enough gain to obtain a reasonable signal-to-noise ratio. This ensures a low signal level at the mixer grid and hence minimizes cross-modulation.

The effect is only likely to occur when the interfering signal is very strong and it usually shows itself as a speech background to the wanted signal. When the interfering station is using telegraphy the strength of the wanted signal may vary in synchronism with the keying. In both cases no trace of the interfering signal will be heard if the wanted signal ceases.

While not strictly a cross-modulation effect, it is appropriate to mention here a property of most a.m. detectors which allows a strong signal to demodulate a weaker one. If the interfering signal is sufficiently strong at the detector stage the wanted signal may completely vanish leaving only the interference. This effect is variously known as *wipe-out*, *blanketing* or *overloading* and usually occurs only in receivers having very poor selectivity.

Rectification in A.f. Stages

Appreciable r.f. energy from a strong local transmitter can be picked up directly by the a.f. stages of a receiver; rectification may then occur owing to non-linearity in the amplifier characteristics and interference will result. The interference may be in the form of speech or, in the case of telegraphy interference, fluctuating output. The effect is not restricted to radio receivers and it may be observed in public-address equipment, gramophone amplifiers, electronic organs and deaf aids. It is sometimes experienced in ordinary G.P.O. telephones and when this occurs the G.P.O. will undertake to suppress it.

The r.f. energy may enter the equipment from the aerial or along the leads or microphone cables or may even be picked up by the internal wiring. The trouble can usually be cured by fitting a small bypass condenser (100–500 pF) between the grid of the offending stage and earth. Often a grid stopper will suffice, the resistance in conjunction with the input capacity of the valve then forming an r.f. attenuator. The component values are normally found by trial-and-error.

It has been found that such troubles in a.f. amplifiers may be cured by connecting bypass capacitors of 0.01 μF from the heater leads to the chassis. Also it is sometimes worth while to connect an r.f. bypass condenser across a cathode bias resistance which although it may already be bypassed for a.f. currents by a large condenser is not effectively bypassed for r.f. currents owing to the appreciable

self-inductance of the a.f. shunt condenser. A suitable value would be about 0.001 μF.

If 1·8 Mc/s and 3·5 Mc/s transmissions are picked up by the video stages of a television receiver interference to the picture will be caused without any necessity for rectification. The problem may be difficult to solve because installing r.f. bypass capacitors will completely upset the performance of the receiver. It is fortunate that this effect is rarely encountered since the only satisfactory cure is to improve the screening in the receiver.

Direct pick-up on the c.r.t. grid and the use of unscreened leads from the vision output to the c.r.t. may also be the cause of interference.

Mains-borne Interference

Even when the transmitter is fitted with a mains filter a nearby receiver may suffer from mains-borne interference owing to r.f. energy being induced in the house wiring from the transmitting aerial. A cure can usually be effected by fitting condensers (of the order of 0·005 μF) from each mains lead to the receiver chassis although a more elaborate filter on the lines of Fig. 17 might be necessary in stubborn cases. In general the receiver should have a good short earth connection but the effect of removing the earth lead should not be overlooked since in some instances this may be found to reduce the interference.

Mains-borne interference is seldom very troublesome but a.c./d.c. receivers are more susceptible than purely a.c. types. If the latter have a mains transformer with a screened primary winding there should be little or no r.f. energy entering the receiver circuits: even when the screen is omitted the capacity of the transformer winding to earth is often sufficient to prevent interference which may be carried by the mains.

It is important that the chassis should be connected to the neutral line.

Amateur Station Receivers

An unskilled operator may have some difficulty in deciding whether interference is due to inadequate selectivity or to a "broad" transmission. If the receiver can be detuned some 10 kc/s from a strong telephony signal without greatly impairing the quality of the speech, the selectivity can be considered poor: if the speech is received as "splatter," the transmission is at fault.

Image interference is usually no problem when using the more elaborate type of communications receiver having two r.f. stages although it is frequently troublesome at 14 Mc/s and higher in the simpler receivers. The interference can be reduced by connecting a parallel LC circuit, tuned so as to reject the image signal, close to the aerial terminal of the receiver. Image rejection can be improved in the design stage by choosing a relatively high value (e.g. 1·6 Mc/s) for the intermediate frequency since this increases the frequency difference between the signal and image frequencies. The adjacent-channel selectivity of a normal i.f. amplifier operating at 1·6 Mc/s is not very good and it has become popular to use a double-superheterodyne circuit with a second i.f. of about 100 kc/s with which it is comparatively easy to obtain a high degree of selectivity. In such an arrangement, of course, the selectivity is concentrated at the back end of the receiver thus leaving the front end wide open for cross-modulation to occur. This can be avoided by fitting a 1·6 Mc/s crystal filter immediately after the mixer but a high degree of stability in the second oscillator would then become necessary. If the station is situated close to other amateur stations it might be preferable to use a single-i.f. type of receiver having two r.f. stages and an i.f. amplifier operating at about 465 kc/s.

A further improvement in selectivity can be achieved by using the transmitting aerial for reception rather than the nondescript piece of wire that is so often relied upon, since

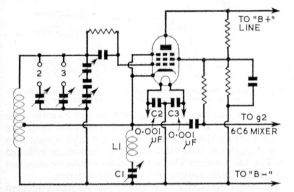

Fig. 9. Modification of the oscillator circuit in an HRO receiver to suppress the third harmonic when operating in the 14 Mc/s band. C1, 30 pF air trimmer; C2, C3, 0·001 μF mica (connected directly to valve socket); L1, 20 turns No. 22 s.w.g. enamelled copper wire close-wound on $\frac{7}{16}$ in. diameter former. Winding length $\frac{13}{16}$ in.

most transmitting aerials have fairly sharp resonance characteristics.

Severe cross-modulation may appear as a result of "improving" the front end of a receiver by changing the first r.f. stage from the original variable-μ valve to a sharp cut-off type in order to increase the signal-to-noise ratio. While this may improve the performance on the higher frequency bands it will be at the expense of cross-modulation trouble on the lower frequency bands where local stations radiate extremely powerful ground waves.

Communications receivers, in common with other short-wave receivers, can cause TVI by the radiation of harmonics of the local oscillator. Such harmonics can be detected by coupling a sensitive indicating absorption wavemeter to the oscillator coil or wiring. For example, interference to television on Channel 1 may be caused by an HRO receiver due to third-harmonic radiation when operating on the 14 Mc/s band. This interference can be eliminated by bypassing the heater pins of the oscillator valve to earth and connecting a series-tuned circuit between its cathode and earth as shown at L_1C_1 in **Fig. 9.** The trimmer C_1 is adjusted for minimum third-harmonic output.

Broadcast Receivers

Modern broadcast receivers are of the superheterodyne type and rarely suffer interference from amateur transmitters on the score of poor adjacent-channel selectivity. On the other hand, because they usually have only one tuned circuit at the signal frequency they are rather susceptible to interference due to spurious responses. Receivers having an intermediate frequency of 465 kc/s have an image response in the 1·8–2·0 Mc/s amateur band when tuned to frequencies between 870 and 1,070 kc/s. As amateur stations operating on this band radiate extremely strong

local ground waves it is hardly surprising that interference can be caused not only by image response but also by harmonic beats and cross-modulation

The interference can nearly always be cured by installing a suitable filter between the aerial and the receiver. A single r.f. choke in series with the aerial and mounted close to the aerial terminal may prove successful in mild cases. A tuned wave-trap is often satisfactory but it is not recommended for general use because it will require re-tuning whenever the transmitter frequency is changed appreciably. The most satisfactory device is a conventional low-pass filter.

Filters for use with broadcast receivers are commonly designed for a terminating impedance of 400 ohms, and an example is given later in this chapter. The filter should preferably be screened and it should be fitted as close as possible to the aerial and earth terminals of the receiver to avoid pick-up of the unwanted signal after the filter.

If filtering the input to the receiver proves unsuccessful, the interference is due to r.f. pick-up either by the mains or by the a.f. stages.

Telegraphy interference from m.f. coast stations may be experienced in broadcast receivers having no i.f. trap, and widespread interference has been traced to v.h.f. parasitic oscillations generated in the a.f. stages of broadcast receivers or in gramophone amplifiers. Neither of these effects really concerns the amateur but it is possible that initially he may be blamed for them. It is in cases like these that the value of a well-kept log book becomes unquestionable.

Television Receivers

After harmonic radiation, perhaps the most common form of interference to television receivers by local amateur transmitters is cross-modulation or blanketing due to the presence of a strong unintentional signal at the input

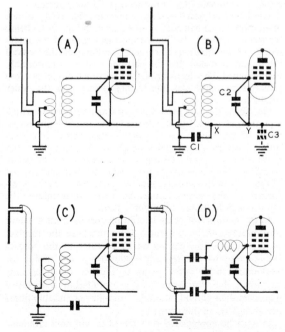

Fig. 10. Aerial coupling arrangements in television receivers.

terminals. Where a high outdoor television aerial is installed it behaves as an excellent Marconi type of vertical receiving aerial for signals on the lower frequency amateur bands. If the aerial system were balanced, as shown in **Fig. 10(A)**, any pick-up on the feeder from a local transmitter would be the same in each wire and would be self-cancelling at the centre-tapped input coil of the receiver. Thus in spite of heavy interfering currents flowing in the feeder and earth lead reception would be free from all interference except for the slight amount picked up by the dipole itself.

The receiver chassis is usually connected either directly or, in the case of a.c./d.c. sets, through a condenser to the earth terminal, and this can give rise to interference even with a perfectly balanced aerial system as a result of earth currents flowing in the chassis or the wiring. An example of such a possibility is illustrated in **Fig. 10(B)**: here C_1 is the condenser connecting the chassis to earth, C_2 is the tuning condenser (often merely the valve input capacity) and C_3 is the capacity of the chassis and mains lead to earth. Some of the interfering current induced in the aerial will flow directly to earth and some will flow to earth through C_1 and C_3, the proportions depending on the relative impedances of the two paths to earth. If C_1 is connected as shown to the point X an interfering current flows in the input circuit between the points X and Y, and since there may be appreciable reactance between X and Y an interfering voltage can reach the grid of the valve. The interference may be reduced if C_1 is connected to the point Y instead of X. Chassis currents can also cause trouble in other ways. The situation is greatly eased if C_1 is connected to earth through an entirely separate path such as the earth wire of a three-core mains lead. In this case the only interfering current in the chassis will be that flowing through the very small capacitance between the aerial and the grid coil and this could be eliminated by introducing a Faraday screen.

The balanced aerial system shown in Fig. 10(A) is not often used, the unbalanced system shown in **Fig. 10(C)** being far more common. In this arrangement most of the interfering current flows in the outer sheathing of the coaxial cable, and provided that the earthing system is reasonably well designed the selectivity of the first tuned circuit is often sufficient to reject the interference present on the inner conductor.

Fig. 10(D) shows a particularly bad arrangement in which a pi-network is used to match the feeder to the input impedance of the valve. As explained earlier, this circuit gives little protection against signals on a lower frequency than that to which it is tuned. Owing to the absence of inductive coupling, it is impossible to keep the interfering currents out of the receiver by the use of separate earth leads. If the interference is very severe it may be necessary to rebuild the input circuit in more conventional form.

In the majority of cases interfering signals from amateur transmitters can be prevented from reaching the receiver by installing a suitable wave-trap or filter in the coaxial feeder close to the receiver. Wave-traps are useful for exploratory work when trying to identify the interfering frequency, but for a permanent installation a screened high-pass filter should be used. Examples of suitable filters are given later in this chapter.

It must be appreciated that the filter will only attenuate interfering signals present on the inner conductor of the

coaxial cable. If the effect of the filter is not as good as was expected the residual interference is probably caused by currents on the outer conductor affecting the receiver in a manner similar to that indicated in Fig. 10(B). In such circumstances the interference may be appreciably reduced by ensuring that the current induced in the outer conductor can reach earth without passing through the receiver

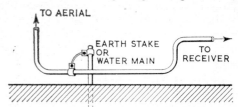

Fig. 11. By-passing interference currents on a TV coaxial feeder cable to earth before they enter the receiver.

wiring, for example by running the cable past an earth stake or the point at which the water main enters the house and there earthing the outer conductor. The cable should then run along the ground until it reaches the receiver, as indicated in **Fig. 11.** *Caution:* The earthed outer conductor must not come into direct contact with the receiver chassis.

In some early receivers the intermediate frequency adopted was near the 14 Mc/s amateur band. A frequency of this order was chosen in order to reduce internal beats or "birdies" without any consideration being given to the possibility of interference from amateur transmitters. This unwise choice has lead to many cases of i.f. break-through, the majority of which could easily have been cured by fitting i.f. traps or high-pass filters. When i.f. interference cannot be cured by external filtering the trouble is probably due to pick-up in the wiring and this may necessitate major changes in the receiver. In general the amateur is advised not to undertake such work. A satisfactory solution in a case of this type can only be assured by the close collaboration between the amateur, the complainant, the G.P.O. and representatives of the receiver manufacturer. Fortunately such severe cases are rare and i.f. break-through is now of minor importance as a result of the general adoption of a high intermediate frequency and the inclusion of i.f. filters.

Most of the interference to television is picked by the aerial but occasionally it is brought in along the mains. Mains-borne interference can be identified by removing the aerial from the receiver, turning up the contrast control and then noting whether or not there are signs of interference to sound or vision. If interference is present, it is either being picked up in the set wiring or, far more likely, mains-borne. If the latter, it can often be cured by fitting r.f. chokes in the mains leads close to the receiver. These chokes must of course be capable of carrying the receiver mains current (large transmitting-type chokes are generally suitable) and they should be mounted in a well-earthed screening box. The earthing is important not only for the effective suppression of the interference but also in the interests of safety. Raising the impedance of the mains leads may cure interference which is not mains-borne by reducing the stray "aerial" currents in the receiver wiring as described above.

CONTACT RECTIFICATION

Any substantial lengths or areas of metal which make partial contact with each other will, by virtue of the existence of oxides and other substances associated with tarnishing, behave like an aerial system having a detector somewhere along its length. If two signals are present simultaneously in this system, cross-modulation may occur and the wanted signal, modulated by the unwanted signal, may re-radiate from the metalwork and be picked up by a local receiving aerial. Even if no cross-modulation takes place, harmonics of the signals present may be generated as a consequence of the non-linear behaviour of the partial contact and these may again be radiated and cause interference. In the event of cross-modulation no amount of selectivity at the receiver can reduce the interference, and in the event of harmonic generation nothing can be done at the transmitter to cure the trouble.

Common causes of the effect are rusty joints in gutters, drain pipes, gas pipes, electrical conduit, etc. Unless the effect is only slight, the source may often be located by the use of a battery-operated portable receiver having two r.f. stages tuned to the offending harmonic frequency and having a tuned loop aerial. The transmitter should be modulated and operated at full power while the receiver is moved round the neighbourhood exploring for points of origin as indicated by maximum receiver output. The tuned loop aerial will be found to be directional enough to locate faulty joints in hidden conductors in walls and under floors.

Even when the source has been identified it may be difficult to effect a cure since the faulty joint may be inaccessible or may be on the property of a third party. If the joint is accessible, the trouble can easily be eliminated by improving the electrical contact, but if it is not little can be done unless the receiving aerial can be oriented so as to minimize the interference.

CURING TVI

There are three categories of TVI in which the amateur may be involved:

A. Harmonic, parasitic or spurious radiation from the transmitter and/or its aerial system.

B. Response by the television receiver to signals outside its proper passband.

C. Cross-modulation or the generation of harmonics caused by contact-rectification in non-linear elements in the vicinity of the transmitter.

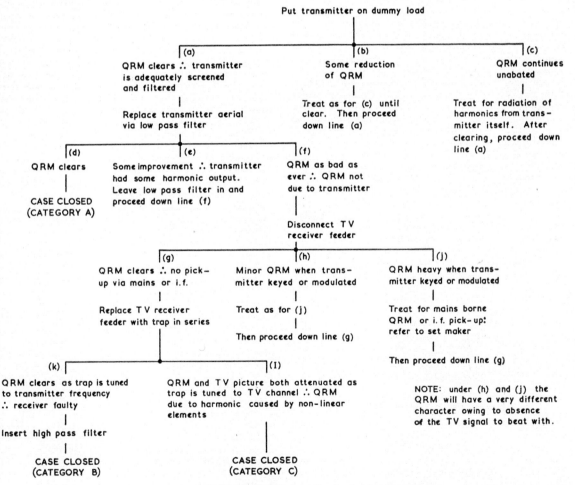

Chart devised by **G2IG** for the rapid diagnosis of television interference.

Cases in Category *A* must obviously be treated at the transmitter and the amateur cannot escape responsibility. Those in Category *B* can only be cured at the receiver, and in general the G.P.O. is sympathetic towards the principle that the amateur is not to blame. In Category *C* neither the transmitting amateur nor the receiver owner is to blame except insofar as either of them may have somewhere about his property metalwork which, owing to corrosion or the manner of its assembly, is causing trouble. A corroded receiving aerial of course comes into this category and the owner has the cure within his own province. In some cases it may be desirable to resite the receiving and transmitting aerials, bearing in mind the "second comer" policy adopted by the P.O.

Before TVI can be cured the nature of the trouble must be correctly diagnosed. The chart shown here sets out a logical series of tests which will enable this to be done expeditiously. Once the cause is known the cure should follow the lines already described.

Although the cure may be simple from a technical point of view its accomplishment may present numerous difficulties. A great deal of tact is called for on the part of the amateur and it is important to remember that the complainant is seldom technically minded and, having spent a considerable sum of money on his receiving equipment, he feels, rightly or wrongly, that he is entitled to interference-free reception. The amateur should never become embroiled in an argument on "rights"; if the complainant appears unreasonable he should be referred to the G.P.O. and the amateur himself should also contact the local Radio Branch of the G.P.O. stating the facts of the case as completely as possible. The local G.P.O. engineers are usually very co-operative and possess test equipment not always available to the amateur. Nevertheless they are often extremely busy and their assistance should not be requested unless it is absolutely necessary.

It is not to be expected that each amateur should have full facilities for dealing with all TVI problems, and here the value of co-operative effort becomes apparent. All well-organised radio groups and clubs should have a small nucleus of members who can form a TVI committee. The committee as a whole should be reasonably well skilled in the diagnosis of TVI and should have available, as club property, test equipment such as high-pass and low-pass filters, wave-traps, coaxial couplers and adaptors. If an old t.r.f. television receiver can be acquired or borrowed it will be found invaluable in checking interference to B.B.C. transmissions as convincing demonstrations can be given in the complainant's house when the trouble is due to spurious responses in a superheterodyne receiver. The services and facilities of the TVI committee should preferably be available to *all* local amateurs whether club members or not because a badly handled case of TVI directs public opinion against Amateur Radio as a whole.

WAVE TRAPS AND FILTERS

A wave-trap comprises a resonant circuit so connected in a system that currents of a certain frequency are severely attenuated. It may be designed to have either a very high impedance (a parallel-tuned or rejector circuit) or a very low impedance (a series-tuned or acceptor circuit) at the specified frequency. An example of the use of a parallel-tuned circuit is the i.f. trap in a broadcast receiver. Here the voltage from the aerial is applied to the trap in series with the receiver input circuit. Since the impedance of the tuned trap circuit is very much higher than that of the receiver input circuit the interfering voltage is much reduced.

Parallel-tuned circuits are a powerful tool in identifying interfering frequencies. A shielded trap having a set of plug-in coils can be inserted into the coaxial feeder of a television receiver and tuned to the point at which the interference is reduced, thus indicating the offending frequency. Such a trap may be calibrated either by means of a grid-dip oscillator or by connecting it in series with the input of a calibrated communications receiver, the latter method having the advantage that the calibration can be carried out with the shielding *in situ*. A tuning capacitor of not less than 150 pF is recommended in order that a reasonable frequency range can be covered.

Series-resonant circuits are often connected in shunt with other circuits (as, for example, a coaxial feeder) to produce a short-circuit at a given frequency. A series-resonant circuit can be simulated by an open-ended feeder one electrical quarter wavelength long. In practice, the physical length is shorter than this depending upon the velocity factor of the feeder used. This figure is given by the cable manufacturer; in the case of solid polythene it is 0·66 and hence the feeder should be 0·66 times one quarter wavelength long. Open-ended quarter-wave stubs are often used on transmitter feeders to short-circuit unwanted harmonics (the "quarter-wave" relating of course to the unwanted frequency), but unless the unwanted frequency is quite high a cheaper and neater method is to use coils and condensers.

For the best performance from parallel-tuned or series-tuned traps the coils should have the highest possible *Q*. Unfortunately this means that the trap will be highly selective and hence traps are rarely used to protect receivers from interference by amateur transmitters because they are effective at only one frequency. High-pass or low-pass filters are generally preferred because they are more convenient and more widely applicable.

Wave-trap components are usually of the variable type and therefore the correct setting can be obtained by trial-and-error, whereas filter components (other than those used in "brute-force" filters) are fixed at values determined by the design formulae. Usually the values should be within 5 per cent of the calculated values, and to this end condensers may be purchased with the correct value or, if a suitable measuring bridge is available, they can be made up of series and parallel combinations.

For correct operation within the specified pass-band the filter must be properly terminated and this condition is achieved in transmitter filters by using a coupling unit as already described. In a television receiving installation the filter-terminating impedance is equal to the input impedance of the receiver which should already have been adjusted by the manufacturer to be about 80 ohms. In a broadcast receiver the input impedance is usually unknown but filters for these receivers are generally based on an impedance of 400 ohms and a 400-ohm resistance is often included in the filter. The attenuation of a filter in its stop-band is not greatly affected by a mis-match at the output terminals. In the case of *m*-derived filters incorporating parallel-resonant or series resonant circuits it is more important that these circuits should be tuned to the correct frequency

Low pass (left) and high pass filters

than that the actual values of *L* and *C* should be correct. The resonant frequencies can be checked with the aid of a grid-dip oscillator.

Filters for r.f. use should always be enclosed in screening boxes fitted with suitable screened connectors. Failure to ensure good bonding between the box and the outer conductor of a coaxial cable may ruin the effectiveness of the filter. It is advantageous to divide the box into compartments because ideally there should be no coupling between the various inductances.

The effectiveness of r.f. high-pass and low-pass filters can easily be checked by using a communications receiver and a television receiver, and since the input impedance of both types of receiver is usually about 80 ohms the tests are likely to be quite realistic. The communications receiver should be arranged for a coaxial cable input by suitable connection to the earthing link and it is worthwhile, although not essential, to fit a coaxial input socket. If the receiver is well shielded there should be negligible pick-up when the aerial is disconnected, which is of course a desirable condition for filter testing.

When testing a low-pass filter for use with a transmitter it should be inserted into the coaxial cable feeding the communications receiver. Within the pass-band of the filter there should be little or no effect on the strength of incoming signals. To test the effectiveness in the stop-band the filter may be inserted into the feeder of the television receiver: it should be found that the television signals are greatly attenuated or even totally suppressed. With a high-pass filter for use with a television receiver there should be no reduction in signal strength when so used, but when the filter is inserted into the feeder of the communications receiver all signals should be greatly attenuated. The reduction in S-meter reading with a given signal when the filter is inserted may be taken as a rough measure of the filter attenuation.

In a properly constructed amateur transmitter the harmonic component should be at least 40db down on the fundamental. (This figure relates to the effective radiated power at the transmitter output terminals.) On no account should the power of the harmonics radiated from the chassis or connecting leads exceed that measured at the aerial terminals. Sub-harmonics from early stages of the transmitter are included in this test.

Practical High and Low Pass Filters

Transmission line filters described here will be found satisfactory in primary TV service areas but may not have sufficient harmonic attenuation for use in localities of poor signal strength. In the latter case a more elaborate filter is necessary such as that described later in this chapter. One important consideration is the effective impedance presented to the filter at the harmonic frequency but the filters described here can be adjusted to provide the optimum performance in any particular application. Only very elementary hand tools are required to build these filters and most of the materials are cheaply obtainable. Provided reasonable care and attention is paid to the winding details for the inductors and to the location of the components, the results attained should be equal to if not better than those achieved with the prototypes.

The photograph at the top of the page shows examples of simple low pass (left) and high pass (right) types.

The filters employ *m* derived end sections in conjunction with *m* derived *T* centre sections. Individual component values have been determined to allow the mean band of high attenuation between 32 and 38 Mc/s (the standard i.f. range for television receivers manufactured in the United Kingdom) to be adjusted by approximately ± 10 per cent.

The input and output characteristic impedance is centred on 75 ohms. This facilitates the use of co-axial cable and connectors which, in conjunction with a good earth system, should ensure effective screening of the "filtered" lead-through and thereby optimum performance.

The low pass filter is for transmitter r.f. output circuits using co-axial 75 ohm cable. The high attenuation mean band is 32 Mc/s to 38 Mc/s adjustable ± 10 per cent. The cut-off frequency is 32 Mc/s ± 10 per cent. It employs five inductors, three capacitor combinations, two co-axial connectors and a tag strip mounted in a tinned-iron box.

The high pass filter is for television co-axial aerial feeder circuits of 75 ohm characteristic impedance. The high attenuation mean band is 32 to 38 Mc/s adjustable ± 10 per cent. The cut-off frequency is 38 Mc/s ±10 per cent. It employs five capacitor combinations, three inductors, two co-axial connectors and a tag strip mounted in a tinned-iron box.

In order to simplify the construction as much as possible, neither filter has internal screening between its various branches. Even so, their effectiveness is quite impressive in a correctly matched system, and they should give a good account of themselves in operation.

Fig. 12 shows the circuits of both types. As long as there are no abnormal standing-waves or excessive transmitter harmonics on any part of the feeder system, the components specified for the low pass filter are adequate for h.f. transmitters with d.c. inputs up to 150 watts.

In view of the need to obtain positive contact particularly in the screen and earthed side of the filter network as well as to ensure that in use there can be no possibility of contact rectification occurring, tin-plate (tinned iron) is far superior to aluminium for the box. Tin-plate of 20/22 gauge lends itself to bending and soldering as well as affording reasonably effective shielding.

To allow adequate separation between the inductors in each branch of the filter and the minimum of interaction in the absence of internal screening, the box should be made at least 4 in. long, 3 in. wide and 2 in. deep. Suitable tinned-iron boxes may well be obtained from retail shops. **Fig. 13** shows the general arrangements for making them up.

After marking out and either drilling or punching all the holes in the flat pieces of metal, the box can be bent into shape. To facilitate this, a block of wood, preferably a hard variety cut to the internal dimensions of the box, will be found most useful. To make the lid a good fit it should be formed in position on the box with the block of wood inside. Self-tapping P.K. screws can be used to fix the lid to the box, or alternatively it may be fixed with a number of spot solder joints, but not until the unit has been checked and aligned. The seams of the box should be soldered with a hot iron. Care in carrying out this operation should result in a smooth and mechanically sound joint which will make the box extremely rigid. The 20/22 gauge tinned-iron sheet for the box is generally available from ironmongers.

Other materials required in constructing each filter are two co-axial sockets, 6 B.A. nuts and bolts, a small stand-off insulator or tag strip, self-tapping screws, insulated sleeving, tinned copper wire, a reel of 18 s.w.g. enamelled wire and strips of rubber, Perspex or wood for the underside of the box.

Assembling

Before construction commences, the inductors, capacitors, co-axial sockets and the tag strip should all be tinned. When this has been done the following assembly procedure will be found a useful guide:

(i) Fix the ceramic variable capacitors in position as indicated in Fig. 13, using 6 B.A. nuts and bolts. (The heads of the bolts should be on the underside of the box.)

Coil Table

In both low and high pass filters all inductors are wound with 18 s.w.g. enamelled copper wire on a ⅜ in. mandrel (former).

Low Pass Filter

L1 (two required). Total length of wire including leads 13½ in. 9 turns close wound, opened to 11/16 in. winding length (Inductance 0·4 µH).

L2 (two required). Total length of wire including leads 9¾ in. 6 turns close wound, opened to 7/16 in. winding length (Inductance 0·225 µH).

L3 (one required). Total length of wire including leads 8½ in. 5 turns close wound, opened to 7/16 in. winding length (Inductance 0·2 µH).

High Pass Filter

L4 (two required). Total length of wire including leads 14¾ in. 10 turns close wound, opened to 11/16 in. winding length (Inductance 0·49 µH).

L5 (one required). Total length of wire including leads 9¾ in. 6 turns close wound, opened to ½ in. winding length (Inductance 0·24 µH).

Capacitor Table

Low Pass Filter

C1 (two required). Total capacitance 52pF maximum made up of a 5–35pF ceramic variable in parallel with 17pF fixed.

C2 (one required). Total capacitance 85pF maximum made up of 5–35pF ceramic variable in parallel with a 50pF fixed.

Although ceramic variable capacitors are suggested above on the grounds of economy, air spaced variables are to be preferred for use in filters for transmitters in the high power class. Other combinations of variable and fixed capacity may be used provided the total meets the specification. At least 20pF variable capacity should be allowed.

High Pass Filter

C3 (two required). Total capacitance 65pF maximum made up of a 5–35pF ceramic variable in parallel with 30pF fixed.

C4 (two required). Total capacitance 83pF comprising close tolerance capacitors of 33pF and 50pF in parallel.

C5 (one required). Total capacitance 103pF maximum made up of a 5–35pF ceramic variable in parallel with 68pF fixed.

(ii) Fit the co-axial sockets and tag strip.

(iii) Add the fixed capacitors in parallel with the variables, at the same time securely soldering the earthy ends to the tin box using the shortest possible leads.

(iv) The three series inductors (L1, L3 or L4, L5) should then be connected between the free ends of the capacitors and the co-axial connectors or tag strip points. Note that the centre inductors should be fixed at right angles to the two end inductors.

(v) Finally, depending on whether the filter is low or high pass, the in-line inductors (L2) or capacitors (C4) may be soldered into position.

This completes the construction but in order to ensure that the screw heads on the underside of the box do not damage any surface on which the unit may be placed it is as well to affix small pieces of rubber, Perspex or wood strips to the bottom.

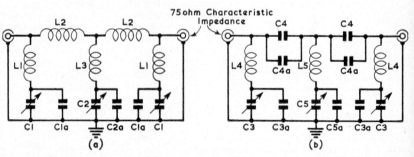

Fig. 12 (a) Low pass filter. (b) High pass filter. The fixed capacitors, marked "a" indicate that the capacitor is in fact made up of fixed and variable capacitors as indicated in the Table.

Checking and Adjusting

Before attempting to make any tuning adjustments on the filters it is as well to test for continuity, open-circuits or short circuits using Figs. 12 (a) and (b) for reference.

With a grid-dip oscillator which covers 30 Mc/s to 40 Mc/s (preferably calibrated at least at each Megacycle) adjustment of the filter may be carried out using the simple test circuit shown in **Fig. 14.**

The alignment procedure for each type of filter is as follows *Low Pass Filter.* With the test oscillator set at 30 Mc/s adjust the link coupling to give about 300 microamps deflection on the meter with the filter out of circuit. Set the oscillator to 32 Mc/s and connect up the filter as shown in Fig. 14. Tune each C_1 until the meter reading just begins to fall. By doing this a number of times and by swinging the oscillator from 30 Mc/s to 40 Mc/s in the process, the function of the filter will become apparent. When this has been done, the meter should read about 300 microamps below 32 Mc/s, but above this frequency the reading will fall rapidly.

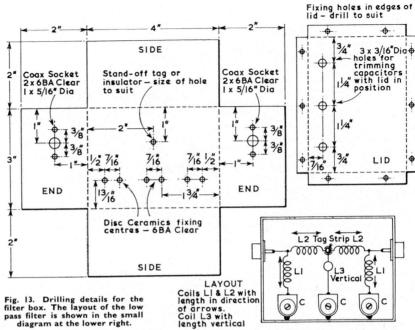

Fig. 13. Drilling details for the filter box. The layout of the low pass filter is shown in the small diagram at the lower right.

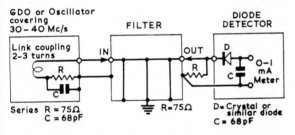

Fig. 14. Arrangement of test equipment for filter alignment.

Between 36 and 38 Mc/s there may be a small peak but this can be eliminated by adjusting C_2. Repeating the test is good practice and helps to achieve optimum results as well as demonstrating in a practical way the filter characteristics.

If each C_1 is tuned at 35 Mc/s instead of 32 Mc/s the filter will provide fairly high attenuation extending over television Channel 1.

High Pass Filter. In this case the test oscillator should be set at 40 Mc/s and the coupling adjusted to give about 300 microamps deflection on the meter with the filter out of circuit. Set the oscillator to 38 Mc/s and connect the filter according to Fig. 14. Now tune each C_3 until the meter reading just begins to fall. Continue to do this a number of times and swing the oscillator from 30 Mc/s to 40 Mc/s in the process. The action of the filter should show that above 38 Mc/s the meter reads about 300 microamps while below 38 Mc/s its value falls rapidly. There may be a small

peak at approximately 32 Mc/s but by tuning C_5 it can be completely eliminated. The same remarks on repeating the test apply. If each C_3 is adjusted at 36 Mc/s instead of 38 Mc/s the filter will show fairly high attenuation extending down to 28 Mc/s, which is useful in the case of 10m operation.

Low pass Filter of High Attenuation

A low-pass filter designed to be used with a transmitter working into an 80-ohm load is shown in **Fig. 15.** The series-resonant sections L_1C_1 and L_5C_4 are tuned to 42 Mc/s and C_1 and C_4 may, if desired, be made adjustable

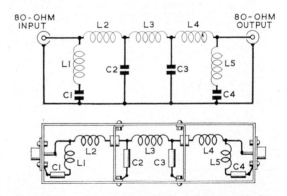

Fig. 15. Circuit and layout of a four-section low-pass filter suitable for use with any transmitter on all bands 1·8–30 Mc/s. It is designed for insertion in an 80-ohm coaxial feeder. C1, C4 — 36 pF mica, 750 V d.c. working (5% tolerance). C2, C3 — 120 pF mica, 750 V d.v. working (5% tolerance). L1, L5 — 0·36 μH: 7 turns, winding length 1 in. L2, L4 — 0·59 μH: 10 turns, winding length 1 in. L3 — 0·73 μH: 12 turns, winding length 1⁷⁄₁₆ in. All coils are of No. 16 s.w.g. copper wire, ½ in. internal diameter self-supporting, with a connecting lead 1 in. long at each end.

459

to ensure this condition. The working voltages of the condensers should be at least 750 volts so as to provide a reasonable factor of safety during the initial adjustment of the aerial coupling unit, but in many cases a lower voltage rating may be found practicable. As previously described, the coupler must be properly adjusted if optimum performance is to be obtained from the filter. When correctly terminated a filter of this type has an attenuation characteristic which should give adequate harmonic suppression in all locations.

Filter for Broadcast Receiver

A filter circuit suitable for protecting a broadcast receiver from transmitters working on the lower frequency bands is shown in **Fig. 16.** The theoretically correct capacitance values are given but in practice good results will be obtained by choosing the nearest standard values. If the inductances L_1, L_2 and L_3 are provided with adjustable iron cores they can be set so that the resonant frequencies of L_1C_1 and L_3C_5

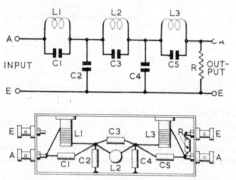

Fig. 16. Circuit and layout of a low-pass filter suitable for use with a medium-wave broadcast receiver.

		Calculated values	Suggested nominal values
C1, C5	... ...	327 pF	330 pF
C2, C4	... ...	357 pF	360 pF
C3	... ...	26·2 pF	27 pF

L1, L3 — 21·45 µH: 50 turns No. 32 s.w.g. enamelled copper wire on Aladdin former, type F804, with dust-iron core.
L2 — 71·7 µH: 90 turns No. 38 s.w.g. enamelled copper wire on Aladdin former, type F804, with dust-iron core.
R — 400ohm, ¼ W (10% tolerance).

are each 1·9 Mc/s and the resonant frequency of L_2C_3 is

3·65 Mc/s. Since few broadcast receivers have a coaxial input socket this particular filter is provided with terminal connections, and it cannot be overstressed that the leads between the filter and the receiver must be as short as possible.

Mains Filters

The usual type of r.f. mains filter is not designed to work into a specific load resistance and the component values used in them are not critical. A typical arrangement is shown in **Fig. 17.** For use with a receiver the coils may be made by winding 100–200 turns of 18 s.w.g. enamelled wire on a ½-inch diameter former while the condensers may have a capacitance of 0·0005–0·005 µF: they should have a mica dielectric and for a 240-volt supply their voltage rating should be at least 750 volts. If the performance is not entirely satisfactory an improvement may be obtained by removing the earth connections from the condensers: this is especially worth trying when the earth lead is a long one. In some cases the chokes alone will suffice.

If the receiver has a three-core mains cable it may be necessary to fit a choke in the earth wire and rely on a

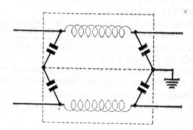

Fig. 17. A typical r.f. filter for insertion in mains supply leads. See text for details.

separate earth for the aerial system. Commercial suppressors are available for installing in mains leads and these are often very effective. A suppressor suitable for protection on medium and short waves should be chosen where the problem is to reduce TVI from amateur transmissions. Filters should always be installed as close to the receiver as possible so as to minimise the risk of pick-up on the leads following the filter.

CHAPTER 19

MEASUREMENTS

CORRECT operation of radio equipment involves measurements to ensure optimum performance, to comply with the terms of the amateur transmitting licence and to avoid interference to other users. The purpose of these measurements is to give the operator information regarding the condition under which his equipment is functioning. Basically, they are concerned with voltage, current and frequency. For example, in even the simplest transmitter it is necessary to know the grid drive to the various stages (current measurements), the input power to the p.a. (current and voltage measurements) and the frequency of the radiated signal.

While it is possible to make do with only one or two simple items of test gear, it is the purpose of this chapter to describe a range of equipment which will be found of value in both transmitting and receiving stations.

D.C. MEASUREMENTS

The basis of most instruments for the measurement of voltage, current and resistance is the *moving coil meter* in which the coil of wire, generally wound on a rectangular former, is mounted on pivots in the field of a permanent magnet (**Fig. 1**). The coil experiences a torque proportional to (i) the current flowing through it and (ii) the strength of the field of the permanent magnet. Current is fed to the coil through two hairsprings mounted near to each end of the spindle. These springs also serve to return the pointer to the zero position (on the left hand side of its travel in standard meters) when the current ceases to flow. Provision for adjusting the position of the pointer is made by a *zero adjuster* accessible from the front of the instrument.

Since the movement of the coil and its associated pointer is proportional to the field of the magnet and that of the current being measured, the scale is linear. A minor disadvantage is that the instrument can only be used on d.c., but it can be adapted to measure a.c. with a suitable rectifier.

It is usual to damp the coil system (i.e. prevent it swinging freely after a change of current), a common method being to wind the coil on an aluminium former which then acts as a

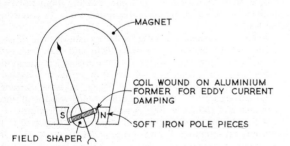

Fig. I. Construction of the moving coil meter.

short circuited single turn coil in which the eddy currents serve to oppose the movement. The degree of eddy current damping is also dependent on the external resistance across the terminals of the moving coil and is greatest when the resistance is low. It is a wise precaution to protect sensitive instruments not in use by short circuiting the terminals.

When a moving coil meter is used for measuring current it is called an *ammeter, milliammeter* or *microammeter* depending on its full scale deflection (f.s.d.). A *d.c. voltmeter* is a milliammeter or microammeter equipped with a voltage dropping (series) resistor.

Milliammeters

Milliammeters and microammeters are commonly manufactured with basic full scale deflections of $0-50\mu A$, $0-100\mu A$, $0-500\mu A$, $0-1mA$, $0-5mA$ and $0-10mA$. For higher current

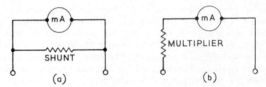

Fig. 2. Extending the range of the m.c. meter. (a) To read higher current with a parallel shunt. (b) To measure voltage with a series resistor or multiplier.

ranges, a *shunt* resistor is connected across the meter (**Fig. 2(a)**). The value of the shunt may be obtained from the formula

$$R_s = \frac{Rm}{n-1}$$

where R_s is the resistance of the shunt, R_m is the resistance of the meter and n is the scale multiplying factor.

For example, if a milliammeter of 10 ohms resistance and a f.s.d. of 1mA is to be used to measure 100mA, a shunt must be provided to carry the excess current, that is, 100–1 milliamperes (= 99mA). Thus the required resistance of the shunt is

$$R_s = \frac{10}{100-1} = \frac{10}{99} = 0{\cdot}101 \text{ ohm.}$$

When m.c. meters are used in circuits where high voltages are present (i.e., in p.a. anode circuits) care must be taken to avoid accidental electric shock from the zero adjuster which may be live. If the instrument is the flush type the front of the meter may be covered with a piece of clear plastic about $\frac{1}{16}$in. thick.

Voltmeters

A milliammeter may be used to read d.c. voltages by connecting a resistor, termed a *multiplier*, in series with it

(Fig. 2 (b)). The value of the multiplier depends on the f.s.d. of the meter and may be calculated from Ohm's Law.

For low voltage ranges, the value of the multiplier can be obtained from

$$R_S = R_M \left(\frac{V}{V_M} - 1 \right)$$

where R_S is the resistance of the multiplier, R_M the resistance of the meter, V is the required voltage and V_M the voltage across the meter (this can be determined by applying Ohm's Law to the resistance of the meter and current flowing through it). In practice, however, the resistance of the meter can be ignored and the formula simplified to

$$R_S = \frac{1000 \, V}{I}$$

where V is the desired voltage range and I is the f.s.d. of the meter in milliamps.

For example, a 0–5mA meter is to be used as the basis of a voltmeter to read 100V. Then

$$R_S = \frac{1000 \times 100}{5} = 20{,}000 \text{ ohms}$$

It is usual to describe the sensitivity of a voltmeter in ohms per volt; in the example considered above, the meter reading 100 volts for a full scale deflection of 5mA would be said to have a sensitivity of 200 ohms per volt. In practice, such a sensitivity is too low for accurate measurements in radio and electronic equipment due to the current drawn and a more sensitive meter would therefore be chosen as the basis of the instrument. The lowest sensitivity which can be considered satisfactory for amateur purposes is 1000 ohms per volt (requiring a 0–1mA meter) but sensitivities of 5000, 10,000 and 20,000 ohms per volt are common for accurate work.

The accuracy of a voltmeter depends largely on the accuracy of the multipliers. Precision resistors are the most suitable but rather costly and may be replaced in home-built gear by 1 per cent close tolerance carbon resistors of adequate

The Taylor Model 127A multimeter with a sensitivity of 20,000 ohms per volt. The instrument has 20 ranges and measures resistance up to 20 Megohms.
(Photo by courtesy of Taylor Electrical Instruments Ltd.).

power rating. Alternatively, some dealers may be persuaded to select suitable values from normal stock.

Measurement of Resistance

The measurement of resistance is based on Ohm's Law, two common arrangements being shown in **Fig. 3** (a) and (b).

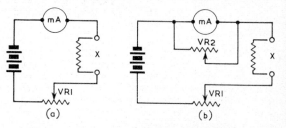

Fig. 3(a). Measurement of resistance with a simple ohmmeter. In (b) VR₂ is to adjust the sensitivity of the meter to compensate for a drop in battery voltage. In both circuits VR₁ is for setting the meter to full scale deflection with the terminals X short circuited.

It will be seen that each circuit comprises a battery in a series with a milliammeter, a resistor VR_1 and an unknown resistor X. In practice, the terminals across which X is connected are first short circuited and VR_1 adjusted until the meter reads full scale. When the resistor X is connected across the terminals, the meter reading will fall; calibration can therefore be carried out by connecting a number of resistors of known value across the terminals in turn and

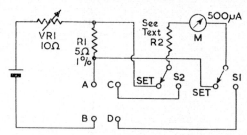

Fig. 4. Circuit of the direct reading low resistance ohmmeter. R₂ should be a high stability resistor of 1 per cent tolerance and ½ watt rating. R₄ should be 1000 ohms less the internal resistance of the meter. The terminals A and B should be insulated and have large contact areas.

marking the scale accordingly. Alternatively, a graph relating meter current and resistance can be prepared.

An instrument designed for resistance measurements is termed an *ohmmeter* and may have several ranges.

The resistance ranges in multimeters are based on these simple circuits but are not very accurate below about 5 ohms. Such inaccuracy is partly due to the resistance in the connecting leads.

A circuit arrangement suitable for measuring low resistances and differentiating between them and short circuits is shown in **Fig. 4**. The instrument measures resistance up to 5 ohms by comparing the voltage drop across a standard resistor and the unknown resistor when the same current flows through both. By selecting a 5 ohms resistor as the standard and using a 0–500 μA meter as a 0–0·5 voltmeter, it is possible to use the calibrated scale, each 100μA (0·1V) division representing 1 ohm. The leads from A and B terminate in strong crocodile clips and those from C and D in sharp test prods.

The method of operation is as follows. With the meter switch at SET and the variable resistor VR$_1$ at maximum, the unknown resistor R$_2$ is connected across terminals A and B. VR$_1$ is then adjusted so that the meter reads full scale. The switch is next moved to the READ position, the meter then indicating the resistance of R$_2$ directly.

An example of the use of the instrument is illustrated in **Fig. 5** where the resistance between a solder tag and chassis is to be found. Terminal A is connected to the chassis and B to the wire to the tag at any point; terminals C and D are connected to the chassis as near to the joint as possible.

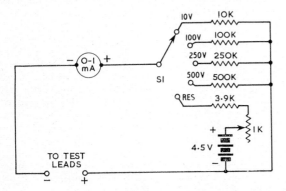

Fig. 5. Use of the low resistance ohmmeter of Fig. 4.

In this way, the same current flows through the standard resistor (R$_1$) as through the joint and the resistance of the connecting leads to A and B does not affect the reading.

Multirange Meters

A number of shunts and multipliers selected by a switch can be used in association with a single basic meter to form a multirange instrument (often known as a *multimeter*) measuring current and voltage. Meters of this type, adapted to measure resistance as well as a.c. and d.c. voltage and current are available from a number of manufacturers at prices dependent largely on the size of the meter scale and the sensitivity of the movement. Kits are also available.

A unit of this type for d.c. only can be easily home constructed and a simple circuit for use with a 0–1mA meter is shown in **Fig. 6**. The meter and other components may be fitted into a small box, preferably insulated. A resistance range is included and while of limited application for measuring resistors, will be found useful as a continuity tester when servicing equipment. A simple instrument of this type will find many applications around the amateur station and is

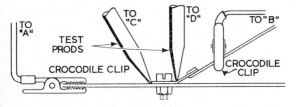

Fig. 6. Simple multimeter for reading voltage and continuity.

The Avo Multiminor test instrument which uses a printed circuit.
(Photo by courtesy of Avo Ltd.).

well worth constructing even if a high grade commercial multimeter is available.

A.C. AND R.F. MEASUREMENTS

The moving coil meter can be adapted to measure a.c. by the addition of a suitable rectifier such as the *copper oxide* type. Such a meter will read a.c. of audio frequencies, indicating the average value or 0·636 of the peak value of a

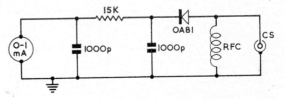

Fig. 7. Simple r.f. voltmeter.

sine wave. With a crystal rectifier, useful indications can be obtained up to v.h.f. A typical circuit is shown in **Fig. 7**.

In conjunction with a *thermo-couple*, a moving coil instrument can be used to read alternating currents of both audio and radio frequencies. The thermo-couple is a junction of two dissimilar metals which, when heated, produces a d.c. voltage. The junction is heated by the current to be measured passing through a "heater" to which it is attached. A disadvantage of the arrangement is that low current readings are rather severely compressed and it is necessary therefore to have several instruments if widely different currents are to be measured.

The *hot wire ammeter* is also designed to make use of the heating effect of a current through a wire. In this case, the wire is supported at both ends and kept under tension by a fibre attached to its centre and loaded by a spring. The current through the wire causes heating and expansion to take place so that a spindle, round which the fibre is wound, moves a pointer across a scale. The heating effect is independent of the type of current and both a.c. and d.c. may therefore be measured. Despite its simplicity, the instrument is now rarely used as it is rather innaccurate.

The *moving iron meter* is useful for measurements on a.c. circuits (40–60 c/s) where the current taken is unimportant. In these instruments fixed iron and moving iron elements are mounted in the magnetic field at the centre of a coil through which the current to be measured is passing. Under these conditions, a mutual repulsion exists between the two parts, the moving iron being deflected, thus indicating on a scale the current measured.

The deflection obtained is approximately proportional to the square of the current or voltage measured (i.e., it is a square law instrument). The scale divisions are thus close together at the low end of the scale and opened out at the higher. This means that accurate readings cannot be taken at the low end but the open scale at the top is sometimes useful. For example, a moving iron meter with a full scale deflection of 250 volts would be excellent for reading small changes of voltage on a nominally 240 volt mains supply but would be useless for measuring voltages below about 50.

VALVE VOLTMETERS

Even in its simplest form, the valve voltmeter is of great value in amateur stations, especially those in which experimental work is the main interest. One of its most useful applications is the direct measurement of voltage across the grid resistor of any stage drawing grid current, which makes it unnecessary to provide jacks, meters or their associated decoupling components in the grid return circuit. Due to its high input resistance, it enables potentials of a fraction of a volt and upwards to be measured with little or no disturbance to the circuit to which it is connected. By the addition of a simple probe, r.f. voltages may be measured as easily as d.c.

In addition to its high input resistance, the valve voltmeter has the advantage that large deflections may be obtained on a relatively insensitive meter movement. It is also much less susceptible to damage by a heavy overload than a sensitive voltmeter of the normal type.

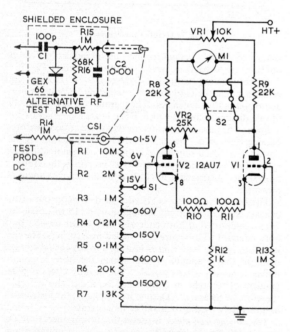

Fig. 8. Simplified valve voltmeter. The meter M_1 (0-500 μA f.s.d.) should be calibrated 0-1·5 and 0-6 volts. R_1-R_7 should be 1 per cent tolerance type and S_1 should have ceramic insulation.

SIMPLE VALVE VOLTMETER

Fig. 8 shows the circuit of a simple but reliable instrument. In some aspects the design is not ideal, but it will be found adequate for the demands which most amateurs are likely to make upon it. On the credit side, it will work from almost any receiver or low-voltage transmitter power supply, because it is not unduly sensitive to variations in h.t. voltage.

Layout is not critical, although it is advisable to use a ceramic or p.t.f.e. valveholder because of the high resistance in the grid circuit at the lower voltage ranges. For the same reason, a ceramic switch wafer is most suitable for the range switch S_1 which should naturally be mounted on the front panel, as should VR_1, the zero-adjusting control. S_2 is provided so that the polarity of the micro-ammeter M_1 may be reversed, thereby allowing both positive and negative voltages to be read directly. This control is useful rather than essential, and if it is included it should be fitted on the front panel. VR_2 is used to adjust the calibration of the instrument. Normally it can be set initially and then ignored, so it may be mounted anywhere on the chassis and should, for convenience, have a slotted spindle.

Adjustment is extremely simple. The instrument should be allowed to warm up for ten or fifteen minutes, and then VR_1 should be adjusted for zero deflection of the meter. While this is being done, it is desirable to short the tip of the d.c. test probe to the chassis. It will be noticed that unless the prod is earthed, the meter needle will tend to stray a little on the two lower voltage ranges. This is a natural effect with most valve voltmeters and need cause no misgivings. (The resistance of many of the circuits to which the instrument is likely to be connected will be low enough to nullify all tendency to error under practical working conditions.) A 1·5 volt dry cell of proven accuracy should then be placed across the input. With the range switch set to the 1·5 V range and S_2 at the correct polarity, VR_2 should be adjusted until the meter reads 1·5 V. As a final check, the polarity of both the battery and S_2 should be reversed and the reading noted. If it is unchanged, all is well. If not, the valve is out of balance and should be changed. A very small amount of unbalance may of course be tolerated, but that is a matter for each individual constructor to decide for himself. It is wise to age the valve by running it for 24 hours or so before carrying out final calibration.

The probes are more or less self-explanatory, Quarter-inch flexible coaxial cable makes good test leads, and although R_{14} may be a little difficult to attach securely to the inner conductor, it should not be omitted, because it serves to isolate the circuit under measurement from the self-capacitance of the test lead. This enables d.c. to be measured in the presence of r.f. without upsetting the r.f. operation of the circuit. The alternative test probe allows r.f. to be measured in the presence of d.c. The germanium diode should be tested for high reverse resistance, otherwise misleading results may be obtained. C_1 should be capable of withstanding the highest d.c. voltage which it is likely to meet. R_{15}, C_2 play no part in the operation of the probe; they are merely a low-pass filter to prevent r.f. leaking back into the valve voltmeter itself.

In operation, a valve voltmeter behaves just like a more conventional instrument. It is, however, desirable to check the zero-adjustment before making a measurement, as this is liable to fluctuate slightly.

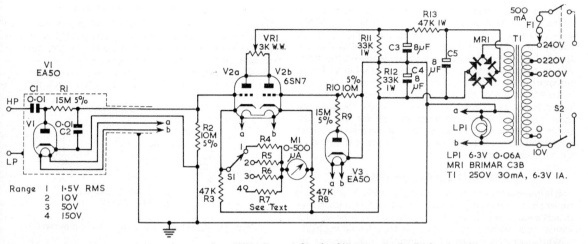

Fig. 9. A.c. valve voltmeter. C_1 is a mica capacitor, 500V wkg. and C_2 mica 350V wkg. R_1, R_2, R_9, R_{10} should be $\frac{1}{2}$ watt high stability resistors 5 per cent tolerance; R_3, R_8, should be $\frac{1}{2}$ watt 10 per cent tolerance. The value of R_4 is 200 ohms less the resistance of the meter M_1. R_5, 7K ohms; R_6, 39K ohms; R_7, 119K ohms; R_4, R_5, R_6, R_7 are $\frac{1}{4}$ watt rating, R_{11}, R_{12}, 1 watt 10 per cent tolerance and R_{13} 1 watt 20 per cent tolerance.

A.C. VALVE VOLTMETER

The circuit of a more sophisticated valve voltmeter suitable for measuring audio and radio frequency voltages up to at least 50 Mc/s and providing useful indications at 150 Mc/s is shown in **Fig. 9.** It is based on a design evolved by S. W. Amos of the B.B.C.

The circuit consists of a diode detector producing a d.c. output voltage proportional to the peak value of the applied

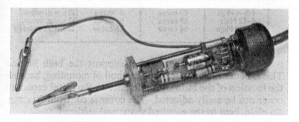

Fig. 10. Construction of the probe for use with the a.c. valve voltmeter.

alternating voltage, followed by a differential d.c. amplifier using a double triode. Considerable d.c. negative feedback is applied to each triode which serves to linearize the input/output characteristic of the amplifier, and also improves the zero stability. Further improvement of zero stability is obtained by applying the output of a second diode to the other input of the differential amplifier. This type of amplifier responds to the difference between the potentials applied to its two inputs, thus provided similar diodes are used at V_1 and V_3, changes in the contact potential of the diodes will not vary the zero setting appreciably.

The diode V_1 and its associated components R_1, C_1 and C_2 are built in the form of a shielded probe which is applied to the circuit under test when measurements are to be made. The input resistance of the probe is 3–4 Megohms and the input capacitance approximately 8pF. The input capacitance would be reduced further by dispensing with the earthed shield but this would render the probe very sensitive to stray pickup, particularly when the instrument is used on its lowest

range. An illustration of the probe is shown in **Fig. 10.** Connection of the probe to the remainder of the circuit is made by a four-way screened lead terminated in a four-pin valve base which fits a standard four-pin valveholder on the panel.

In use the high and low potential terminals of the probe are short-circuited and the meter set to zero by means of the potentiometer VR_1 with the range switch S_1 at Range 1. The terminals are then separated and the high potential terminal applied to the point at which measurements are to be made, the low potential terminal being connected to chassis or earth. The instrument should be allowed to warm-up for five minutes or so before setting the zero.

Calibration may be carried out at 50 c/s, but care should be taken to ensure that the applied voltage is sinusoidal as rectifier voltmeters are calibrated to read the R.M.S. value

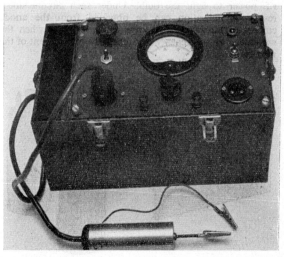

Fig. 11. External appearance of the a.c. valve voltmeter.

465

of a sine wave voltage. Exact adjustment of the full scale deflection for each range is achieved by variation of the appropriate meter series resistances R_4, R_5, R_6 and R_7 by adding an additional resistor in series or parallel with the specified resistor. At least two separate scales on the meter will be required as the 1·5 volt range is non-linear due to curvature of the diode characteristics at low input voltages.

An illustration of the complete instrument in its case is shown in **Fig. 11.** The additional switch below the potentiometer knob and the pair of terminals near the front of the panel visible in Fig. 11 were fitted to isolate the meter circuit and are not required when the instrument is used as an a.c. valve voltmeter.

FREQUENCY MEASUREMENT

It is important to know the frequency to which a receiver is tuned and the frequency of a signal radiated by a transmitter; in particular, it is necessary to be quite sure that the signal is within the amateur band in which operation is taking place.

With a crystal controlled transmitter this presents no great difficulty because the frequency will be almost entirely dependent on the crystal. A new crystal is normally sold with a certificate of frequency but if using second-hand or government surplus crystals it is advisable to check their frequencies.

The Absorption Wavemeter

Knowing the crystal frequency, however, is not in itself sufficient because there is the possibility that the final output from the transmitter may be on the wrong harmonic of that frequency. To ensure that this is not so, it is necessary to use an absorption wavemeter such as that shown in **Fig. 12.** With the wavemeter resonated to the circuit to which it is coupled some energy is absorbed from that circuit. If the wavemeter is held close enough the r.f. current induced into it will be sufficient to light the bulb. Thus, provided that the wavemeter has been previously calibrated, it is only a matter of tuning for a resonance indication on the bulb and reading off the frequency.

A low power stage may not be capable of providing enough r.f. power to light the bulb. Under such circumstances resonance indication can be obtained from the anode current of the low power stage which will rise when the wavemeter absorbs energy or a dip in the grid current of the next stage.

Fig. 12. View of the wavemeter of Fig. 13 showing the scale, cursor resonance indicator lamp and spare coils.

ABSORPTION WAVEMETER FOR 1·5–30 Mc/s

The circuit of a simple absorption wavemeter for 1·5–30 Mc/s is shown in **Fig. 13.** It will be seen that the wavemeter frame is connected to one side of the tuning coil, coupling coil, and tuning capacitor. An ordinary 6 V. 0·3 A. bulb is used to indicate resonance. A lower consumption bulb would provide a more accurate indication, but the type

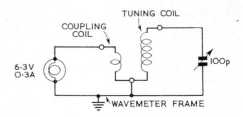

Fig. 13. Absorption wavemeter for 1·8–30 Mc/s.

specified is more robust and will withstand greater overloads, while showing a sufficiently sharp resonance point for all practical purposes.

The tuning capacitor is mounted directly on the front panel, while the tuning coil holder (an octal valve socket) is off-mounted from the front panel by the use of two tapped aluminium distance pieces. Two stiff lengths of copper

TABLE I

Range	Tuning Coil	Coupling Coil	Wire
1·5–4 Mc/s	80 turns	6 turns	32 s.w.g. enam.
4–12 Mc/s	29 turns	3 turns	22 s.w.g. enam.
12–30 Mc/s	6½ turns	2½ turns	22 s.w.g. enam.

wire attached to the coil socket support the bulb holder. This is better than a more rigid method of mounting, because the location of the bulb with reference to the metal capacitor cover can be easily adjusted. The cover is cut from 20 s.w.g. tin plate, bent to the required shape and soldered.

The coil formers are made from octal valve bases, force-fitted into a bakelized paper tube 2½ in. long by 1⅛ in. diameter (internal diameter ⅞ in.). After fitting, the tube and base should be cemented together.

The coils should be wound in accordance with the data given in **Table 1.** The construction is illustrated in **Fig. 14.**

Calibration

Calibration may be carried out with the aid of an oscillator or a calibrated receiver. As most amateur stations have an accurately calibrated communications receiver, this method will be described.

With the receiver switched on and the aerial connected, a signal is tuned in at the low frequency end of the band to be calibrated. A coupling coil consisting of a few turns of sufficient diameter to slide over the wavemeter tuning coil is connected to the aerial. The S meter reading should be observed while the wavemeter is slowly tuned: at one point the reading will drop, indicating that signal frequency energy is being absorbed. This point can now be marked on the prepared dial of the wavemeter. The receiver is then tuned

Fig. 14. Internal construction of the absorption wavemeter.

to the next signal higher in frequency, and the process is repeated until finally the whole dial is calibrated.

Some receivers are not fitted with an S meter, in which case the b.f.o. should be switched on, an a.c. rectifier type voltmeter being connected to the phones terminals of the set. A signal is then tuned in until the beat note provides a convenient reading on the voltmeter. As before, the wavemeter (coupled to the receiver aerial) should be tuned slowly until a dip occurs in the reading, indicating a calibration point.

When calibration has been completed, the dial may be removed and permanently marked with Indian ink, after which it should be replaced and covered with a protective sheet of $\frac{1}{16}$ in. Perspex, held at the corners by 6 B.A. screws tapped into the front panel. Perspex of the same thickness is also used for the dial cursor, a central hairline being engraved on it with a stylus.

The size of the front panel is $2\frac{1}{2} \times 3\frac{1}{2}$ in., and the capacitor cover box is $2\frac{1}{8} \times 2\frac{1}{8} \times 3\frac{1}{4}$ in. The resonance indicator bulb is pushed through a hole drilled in the top of the cover, and is protected from shock by a rubber grommet.

For checking any apparatus which has a power output of a $\frac{1}{2}$ watt or more, the bulb will indicate resonance quite satisfactorily, but where the output is low, as in the local oscillator circuit of a receiver, a meter inserted in the grid-leak earth return will dip as the wavemeter is tuned through resonance. Alternatively, a milliammeter may be inserted in the anode circuit of the local oscillator valve, and this will given an increased reading as the wavemeter is tuned through resonance.

SIMPLE ABSORPTION WAVEMETER FOR 65-230 MC/S

Finding the amateur band is perhaps the biggest problem to overcome when starting work on v.h.f. The absorption wavemeter, the circuit of which is shown in **Fig. 15,** is an

easily built unit covering 65 to 230 Mc/s and can therefore be used to check frequencies in Band 2 (F.m. broadcasting) and Band 3 (Television) in addition to 70 and 144 Mc/s stages in amateur v.h.f. transmitters.

Construction is straightforward and all the components, apart from the meter are mounted on a Perspex plate measuring $7\frac{1}{2}$ in. by 3 in. by $\frac{1}{8}$ in. Details of the tuned circuit are shown in **Fig. 16(a)** and should be closely followed. The layout of the other components is not critical provided they are kept away from the inductance loop. To prevent damage to the crystal when soldering, a heat shunt should be used.

For accurate calibration a signal generator would be required but provided the inductance loop is carefully constructed and the knob and scale are non-metallic, dial markings can be determined from **Fig. 16 (b).** These should be accurate enough for most purposes.

In operation, the unit should be loosely coupled to the

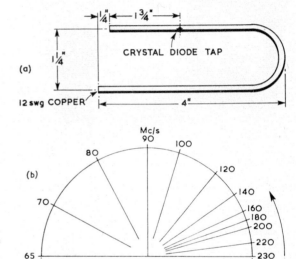

Fig. 16 (a) Details of the inductance loop made of 12 s.w.g. copper wire. The dimensions should be closely followed if the calibration of (b) is to be used. (b) Dial calibration. The calibration points relative to the base line (anti-clockwise) are; 230 Mc/s–0°: 220 Mc/s–8°: 200 Mc/s–16°: 180 Mc/s–20°: 160 Mc/s–25°: 140 Mc/s–35°: 120 Mc/s–50°: 100 Mc/s–73°: 90 Mc/s–90°: 80 Mc/s–118°: 70 Mc/s–152°: 65 Mc/s–180°.

tuned circuit under test and the capacitor then tuned until the meter indicates resonance. For low power oscillators a more sensitive meter should be used if available.

The wavemeter can also be used to make adjustments to v.h.f. aerial arrays. A single turn coil should be loosely coupled to the wavemeter loop and connected via a low impedance feeder to a dipole directed towards the aerial under test.

The appearance of the wavemeter with its associated indicating meter can be seen in **Fig. 17.**

Lecher Wires

Above about 100 Mc/s it is practicable to measure directly the wavelength at which a transmitter or oscillator is operating by using *Lecher wires* which comprise a pair of taut parallel wires, spaced an inch or so apart to form an

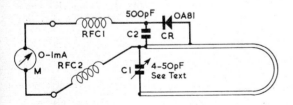

Fig. 15. Circuit diagram of the v.h.f. wavemeter. C₁ (4–50 pF) is a type C.804 manufactured by Jackson Bros. M₁ should have a f.s.d. of 1–2 mA. RFC₍₁₂₎, 80 turns s.w.g. enamelled wire wound on $\frac{1}{4}$ watt resistor of 1K ohms or more and wax dipped.

open wire transmission line, and a bridge to short circuit the wires. The latter device can be moved along the line as required.

For transmitter frequency measurement one end of the line is loosely coupled by a loop to the p.a. circuit. Starting near the coupling loop end of the line, the bridge is slowly moved towards the open end of the line until a point of maximum current in the bridge is found; this will be indicated by a deflection on the anode current meter, or by observing when a flash lamp and loop loosely coupled to the p.a. coil passes through a minimum in brightness. This position should be carefully noted and the bridge then moved

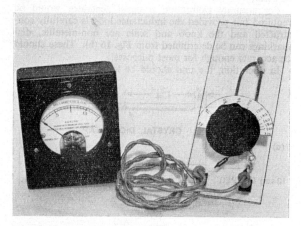

Fig. 17. V.h.f. absorption wavemeter with its indicating meter

further along the line until the next similar position is found. The distance between the two points will be one-half of the wavelength at which the transmitter is oscillating.

Application of the formula

$$Frequency\ Mc/s = \frac{15,000}{Distance\ between\ bridge\ positions\ in\ cm.}$$

will enable the frequency of the oscillation to be determined. For example if the distance between the two bridge positions is found to be 100 cm, then by substituting in the formula,

$$Frequency = \frac{15,000}{100}\ Mc/s\ =\ 150\ Mc/s.$$

For the most sensitive condition of adjustment, the Lecher

wires and the bulb and loop should be very loosely coupled to the tank circuit. This is especially important when measuring the frequency of a self-excited oscillator whose frequency may be altered if the coupling is too tight. Although the accuracy of frequency measurement by this method is not very high the method is of great use to the amateur as the only instrument required is a good ruler, preferably a metre rule. The longer the Lecher wires and the further the two minima are from the coupling loop end, the more accurate will be the reading. An accuracy of 0·1 per cent can be attained with care.

Crystal Calibrator

When using a variable frequency oscillator the absorption wavemeter is invaluable for checking that circuits are tuned to the correct harmonics but it is not capable of giving a sufficiently accurate reading of the actual frequency. It is essential therefore to compare the transmitter against a more accurate frequency standard and the obvious choice is a crystal-controlled oscillator.

CALIBRATION UNIT FOR A V.F.O.

A simple way of adding a crystal-controlled calibrating unit to a v.f.o. is shown in **Fig. 18**. The triode section of V_1 is used for the crystal oscillator. The crystal behaves rather like a parallel tuned circuit and, when L_1, C_3 is resonated to approximately the crystal frequency, the feedback *via* the anode-grid capacitance causes oscillation. Grid 3 of the hexode (or mixer) section of V_1 receives an r.f. voltage from this oscillator *via* the internal connection to the triode grid while grid 1 receives another r.f. voltage from the v.f.o. or, preferably, from the anode of a buffer stage following the v.f.o. Since grid 1 controls the electron flow of the entire hexode section, the alternating anode current due to the r.f. voltage on grid 3 will be modulated by that on grid 1. The alternating voltage appearing across R_3 will consequently contain not only the two original frequencies, but the sum frequency and the difference frequency.

It is the difference frequency which is important because when this is reduced to zero the v.f.o. must be tuned to the crystal frequency. Thus V_2 is added to amplify the difference or beat, frequency as it is called, so that it can be heard in a pair of headphones. The two original radio frequencies and the sum frequency will, of course, be inaudible but C_6 is included to suppress them so that they do not overload V_2.

Assuming that the v.f.o. tunes from 3·5 to 3·8 Mc/s,

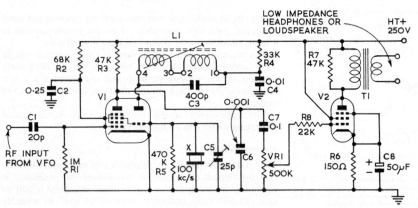

Fig. 18. Simple crystal calibrator for addition to a v.f.o. The inductance L_1 is an Osmor type OA9. If necessary, the inductance can be increased slightly by squeezing the windings closer together. Final adjustment of the inductance may be made by varying the position of the core. R_8 (22 K ohms ¼ watt) is wired direct to the valveholder for V_2 to act as a parasitic stopper. T_1 is a small pentode output transformer. The crystal X is a 100 kc/s unit and details of the circuit should be given when ordering.

suppose for a moment that the crystal oscillator operates at 3·5 Mc/s. This would permit tuning the v.f.o. accurately to that frequency by tuning for a zero-frequency beat note in the headphones. As the v.f.o. approaches the crystal frequency a beat note whose pitch becomes lower as the difference between the two frequencies becomes less will be heard. As rotation of the v.f.o. tuning capacitor in the same direction continues there would be a momentary silence as it passes through the crystal frequency and then the beat note would start to rise in pitch again. Because of the deficiencies of normal headphones it may not be possible to hear a beat note lower than about 200 c/s and zero beat must be taken as being roughly in the centre of the silent zone. This may at first seem rather inaccurate but it must be remembered that even if the tuning were as much as 200 c/s out in 3·5 Mc/s this would only amount to an error of 0·006 per cent.

Now if, as has just been supposed, the crystal frequency were 3·5 Mc/s, this would give only one check point which is not really sufficient. A selection of crystals could be used but this would be rather expensive. A more economical method is to have the crystal oscillator on 100 kc/s. It will then give harmonics at 3·5, 3·6, 3·7 and 3·8 Mc/s etc., thus providing many check frequencies with only one crystal. These harmonics, and the beat notes they produce, will be rather weak, but the circuit gives sufficient amplification for them to be easily audible on headphones, or even on a loudspeaker.

There will, in fact, be some other audible beats as well. When the v.f.o. is tuned to 3·55 Mc/s for example, its second harmonic (7·1 Mc/s) will produce a beat with the 71st harmonic of 100 kc/s. Other beats will be similarly produced at 3·65 and 3·75 Mc/s. These three intermediate beats will be easily distinguishable from the main ones by their relative weakness. Still fainter beats may be heard at 3·533, 3·567, 3·633, 3·667, 3·733 and 3·767 Mc/s, these being caused by the third harmonic of the v.f.o. beating with harmonics of 100 kc/s.

When using the 100 kc/s crystal oscillator for the initial calibration of the v.f.o. care must be taken that the lowest v.f.o. frequency is really 3·5 Mc/s and not 3·4 or 3·6 Mc/s. The accuracy of the average absorption wavemeter is not adequate to make such a distinction and an additional check should be made by tuning in the v.f.o. on an accurately calibrated receiver. When doing this care must be taken not to feed too strong a signal into the receiver as this might sometimes lead to an erroneous result by cross modulation.

Although it has been assumed above that the v.f.o. output would be on the 3·5 Mc/s band the circuit of Fig. 18 could be applied to a v.f.o. operating in any other band. With the v.f.o. output in the 1·8 Mc/s band, for example, the crystal would give three main check points at 1·8, 1·9 and 2·0 Mc/s, together with additional check points at 1·85, 1·95, and possibly at 1·833, 1·867, 1·933 and 1·967 Mc/s.

It is possible to check the calibration of a v.f.o. against a crystal oscillator by using a receiver. The latter is tuned to the required harmonic of the oscillator and the v.f.o. coupled into the receiver input and tuned for zero beat. It is an unfortunate characteristic of a superheterodyne receiver, however, that a strong signal can be received at several spurious tuning points and it is not always obvious which signals are true harmonics of 100 kc/s and which are spurious. There are consequently possibilities for errors and the use of this method is not recommended.

The Jasonkit Crystal Calibrator type CC10 giving outputs at 10 kc/s 100 kc/s, 1 Mc/s and 10 Mc/s.
(Photo by courtesy of Jason Electronic Designs Ltd.).

Checking the 100 kc/s Oscillator

In the British Isles an accurate 200 kc/s frequency standard is available in the form of the B.B.C. long wave Light Programme transmissions. These are very convenient for checking the frequency of the 100 kc/s crystal oscillator, as a receiver can be tuned to 200 kc/s and, by suitably coupling the aerial wire to the crystal oscillator, an audible beat obtained between the second harmonic of the latter and the B.B.C. station.

Although the oscillator frequency will be primarily determined by the crystal it will be possible to effect a very fine control by means of the preset capacitor C_5. Provided that the crystal has been purchased as being suitable for this type of circuit it will be possible by means of this capacitor to adjust the frequency to within 1 c/s of 100 kc/s. A 1 c/s beat note itself is, of course, inaudible but its effect on speech or music—a slow repetitive rise and fall in amplitude—is by no means inaudible.

Heterodyne Frequency Meters

Many amateurs do not have a crystal calibrator built in as an integral part of their transmitters but have what is usually called a heterodyne frequency meter as a separate instrument. This normally consists of an accurately calibrated v.f.o. complete with a crystal calibrator similar to that which has been described here. With some instruments the calibrated oscillator must be compared with the transmitter v.f.o. using a receiver. Others have facilities for accepting a small r.f. voltage from the transmitter, the comparison being effected by producing a beat note between the two frequencies within the instrument itself. Many amateurs use an excellent American instrument of the latter type, the BC221, which is obtainable on the government surplus market from time to time.

AMATEUR BANDS FREQUENCY METER

The circuit of a home-built heterodyne frequency meter is shown in **Fig. 19**. It achieves a high degree of accuracy by using a 100 kc/s crystal sub-standard to check a variable oscillator by interpolating between successive harmonics of the crystal in the ranges covered. The crystal itself may be compared with standard frequency transmissions such as those from MSF at Rugby (operated by the Post Office for the National Physical Laboratory), WWV (the National Bureau of Standards transmitter in the United States) or certain B.B.C. stations of which the Light Programme transmitter on 200 kc/s is probably the most convenient.

To obtain as open a scale as possible provision is made for the coverage of the amateur bands only in two ranges: 1·75 to 2 Mc/s, the second harmonic of which includes the 3·5 to 3·8 Mc/s allocation, and 7 to 7·5 Mc/s. On the second range the fundamental, second, third and fourth harmonics serve for measurement in the 7, 14, 21 and 28 Mc/s bands.

The output of the frequency meter is taken from a low impedance point and fed directly into the receiver via a length of coaxial cable thus preventing to a large extent the radiation of oscillator harmonics on television frequencies. A simple attenuator enables the output from the instrument to be controlled over a wide range. Either a c.w. or m.c.w. signal is available.

The addition of a further oscillator in the circuit provides a stable source of oscillations at approximately 1 Mc/s for

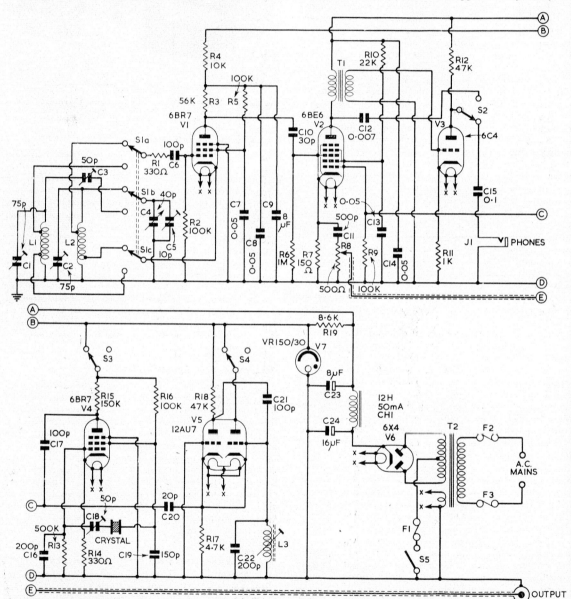

Fig. 19 Circuit diagram of the amateur bands heterodyne frequency meter. L₁, 16 turns 24 s.w.g. 1 in. dia., ¾ in. long, cathode tap 2 turns, grid tap 11 turns from earthy end: L₂, 67 turns 26 s w.g. enam. 1 in. dia. 1¼ in. long, cathode tap 5 turns, grid tap 41 turns from earthy end: L₃, Osmor type QO5. The h t line marked B should be decoupled to earth with a 0·05μF capacitor The range switch S1 is shown in the Range 1 position T₂ should be 250-0-250v 60mA, 6·3v 3A.

aid in the preliminary calibration of the meter or for rapid checking of an uncalibrated receiver.

The variable capacitor C_{18} in series with the 100 kc/s crystal is for setting its frequency against a standard frequency transmission, and is mounted on the chassis inside the case. If it is desired to control the frequency of the crystal to very fine limits it is suggested that either C_{18} be mounted on the rear drop of the chassis and a hole cut in the back of the cabinet for access or a small additional 10pF variable capacitor be similarly mounted and connected in parallel with it.

The purposes of V_2 is to make audible, and V_3 to amplify, the beats between the crystal oscillator harmonics and the variable oscillator when checking the calibration of the latter throughout its ranges or to detect the beat note between an external oscillator and the variable oscillator as is necessary when measuring the frequency of a transmitter. The output from V_2 is taken across its unbypassed cathode resistor by way of an ordinary 500–1000 ohm carbon track potentiometer. This gives a good measure of control of the signal fed to the receiver and, as the source is of low impedance, the loss in the coaxial lead is small. To avoid loading the receiver input circuit excessively, as well as to minimize radiation of the frequency meter harmonics from the aerial, it is recommended that a carbon resistor of 1000 ohms or so be connected between the centre conductor of the coaxial line and the aerial terminal of the receiver.

It is often difficult to pick out a frequency meter signal from other strong carriers on a band and it is a definite advantage, therefore, to be able to modulate the local signal if required. In this design modulation is introduced by employing V_3 as an a.f. oscillator in conjunction with the coupling transformer between its grid and the anode of V_2. The switch, S_2, cuts the headphone jack out of circuit when modulation is applied.

Good mechanical stability is an essential feature of a frequency meter which is to have any pretence to accuracy. The dimensions of the chassis are 14 in. × 7 in. × 3 in. deep; and the general layout is shown in **Fig. 20.**

All connections are carried out in "push-back" wire and extensive use is made of tie points for mounting the smaller parts to prevent vibration.

No matter how well made a frequency meter may be it is next to useless without a dial which can be read clearly to the necessary degree of accuracy. To this end a Muirhead component similar to that used on the National HRO receiver is used. This dial provides 500 divisions approximately ¼ in. apart with an effective scale length of 12 ft. 6 in.; it is to all intents and purposes free from backlash.

Alignment

Connect a coaxial lead between the frequency meter and a receiver tuned to the 1·8 Mc/s band and check that harmonics of the crystal are audible. If nothing is heard first make sure that C_{18} is not set to too low a capacity. Then, with the bandswitch on Range 1 and a pair of high resistance 'phones plugged into the frequency meter, make sure that V_1 is oscillating by noting the beats between the variable and the crystal oscillators as the tuning is varied. Adjust C_2 so that 2 Mc/s is reached at around 490 degrees on the dial and coincides with one of the crystal harmonics. The ZERO SET capacitor, C_5, should be at half capacity. Three crystal harmonics lower should bring the variable

oscillator to 1·7 Mc/s and this should be checked on the receiver. If the calibration of the receiver is not known to within 100 kc/s the 2 Mc/s point will have to be found with the aid of the 1 Mc/s oscillator.

Switch next to Range 2 and locate 7 Mc/s on the receiver by reference to the amateur band; with the tuning dial at about 20 degrees and C_3 at about 75 per cent of its maximum capacity, set the variable oscillator to this point by adjustment of C_1. To cover the 28 Mc/s band fully the variable oscillator must tune to 7·5 Mc/s and this should occur at about 490 degrees on the dial. Some juggling with the capacities of C_2 and C_3 will be called for before the required range " fits " the dial, the operation being similar to ganging a receiver. C_1 is adjusted at the *high* frequency end and C_3 at the *low*.

Calibration

First, the crystal oscillator should be checked against one of the standard frequency transmissions, MSF on 5 Mc/s being convenient. At the same time the 1 Mc/s oscillator can be adjusted, its tuning range (by variation of the iron core of L_3) being insufficient for a mistake to be made on the fifth harmonic. Should the receiver cover only the amateur bands the accuracy of the crystal may be checked by

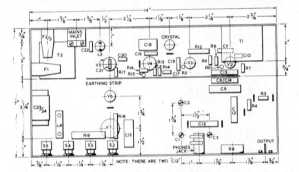

Fig. 20. Layout of the principal components beneath the chassis of the heterodyne frequency meter.

reference to the 200 kc/s Light Programme transmitter on a broadcast receiver, C_{18} being carefully adjusted until the quality of speech and music are barely affected.

On Range 1 note the dial readings for zero beat for 1·7, 1·8, 1·9 and 2 Mc/s and either draw a graph or record them in a book.

Calibration of Range 2 should be carried out in a similar manner between 7 and 7·5 Mc/s and will be possible to at least the 50 kc/s points without difficulty. Interpolation between these points may be considered to be linear for most purposes but if the user wishes to ascertain the 25 kc/s positions exactly the receiver should be tuned to the 28 to 29·7 Mc/s band where the variable oscillator appears to tune four times as fast as on the fundamental and therefore each coincidence between the oscillator and the 100 kc/s points will represent a movement of 25 kc/s at the fundamental frequency.

It will be found that some slight changes take place from time to time in the frequency of the variable oscillator and these should be corrected before readings are taken by setting the dial for the previously ascertained reading for the 100 kc/s point nearest to the frequency it is required to measure and setting the oscillator stage (V_1) accurately to zero beat by means of capacitor C_5.

471

The tuning rate on Range 1, assuming coverage from 1·7 to 3 Mc/s, is 1¼ divisions per kc/s and on the 28 Mc/s band nearly 4 kc/s per division. On the latter range, if full coverage to 29·7 Mc/s is not required, the tuning rate may be considerably improved by setting C_3 for greater bandspread.

If a modulated note cannot be obtained the connections to either the primary or secondary of T_1 should be reversed. The modulation frequency depends largely upon the capacity of C_{12}. The 0·007μF used in the original model was obtained by series connection of 0·05 and 0·01μF capacitors, but this would not be necessary if a satisfactory note were forthcoming with the aid of a single component. T_1 is not critical and almost any transformer with a ratio of between 3·5 and 5 to 1 should be satisfactory. A change from these ratios would almost certainly require a different value of C_{12}.

Use

To measure the frequency of an external oscillator a short wire probe may be necessary and should be plugged

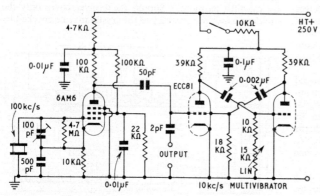

Fig. 21. Crystal calibrator giving frequency markers every 100 and 10 kc/s provided the multivibrator circuit is correctly adjusted.

into either the end of the coaxial cable or the output socket so that the incoming signal can be heterodyned by the variable oscillator. The latter is corrected, if necessary, at the nearest crystal harmonic to the unknown frequency but when actually taking a reading both the crystal and 1 Mc/s oscillators should be off.

10/100 KC/S CRYSTAL CALIBRATOR

One of the simplest frequency standards for use in the amateur station is a 100 kc/s crystal oscillator, particularly if it is employed in conjunction with a multivibrator to provide calibration markers every 10 kc/s. The circuit diagram of an easily built unit of this type is shown in **Fig. 21.** Accuracy is assured by the use of the 100pF capacitor in parallel with the crystal which permits the second harmonic of the oscillator frequency to be adjusted precisely to the frequency of the B.B.C. Light Programme on 200 kc/s.

TRANSISTOR 1 MC/S CRYSTAL MARKER

A crystal controlled oscillator providing signals every megacycle to well above 30 Mc/s is shown in **Fig. 22** and comprises a single transistor, a 1 Mc/s crystal and a few small components. Its frequency can be checked by comparison with the 5 Mc/s transmissions from MSF or WWV.

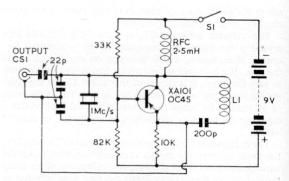

Fig. 22. Transistor 1 Mc/s crystal oscillator. The capacitors should all be silvered mica type. L_1 is 80 turns 32 s.w.g. pile wound on a ¼ in. diameter former.

BAND EDGE MARKER FOR 144 MC/S

Although many heterodyne frequency meters will provide harmonics in the 144 Mc/s band, the output is generally extremely low and considerable confusion can arise from multiple beats due to the harmonics of the crystal oscillator in the converter and the variable oscillator in the main receiver. Various methods can be employed to increase the level of harmonics but the requirements for a self-contained device producing excellent signals in the band are so simple it is more satisfactory to build a special unit. The circuit of a suitable arrangement producing signals at 144, 145 and 146 Mc/s is shown in **Fig. 23.**

An Ediswan XA101 r.f. transistor is employed as a 1 Mc/s crystal controlled oscillator using the crystal in a parallel mode of oscillation between the collector and the base, similar to the Pierce oscillator used in valve circuitry. The bias on the base, and thus the output, is varied by the potentiometer VR_1 which tends to vary the frequency about 500 c/s at 145 Mc/s. It could be omitted if the device were to be used only as a marker: the 33 K ohms resistor R_3 could then be

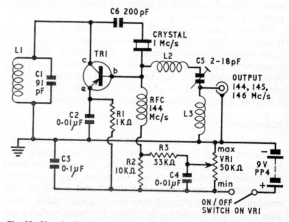

Fig. 23. Circuit diagram of the transistorized band edge and centre marker for the 144 Mc/s band. The transistor may be any type capable of oscillating at 1 Mc/s such as the XA101, OC44 or OC45. The coils are constructed as follows; L_1, 120 turns 30 s.w.g. pile wound on ¼ in. dia. slug tuned former (1 Mc/s): L_2, 5¾ turns 18 s.w.g. tinned copper ⅜ in. dia. ⅝ in. long, self supporting: L_3, 20 s.w.g. brass strip 3¼ in. long by ¾ in. wide, suitably bent to fit into the container; RFC, 19 in. 26 s.w.g. ⅛ in. dia. 1¼ in. long.

taken direct to chassis and C_4 omitted. Harmonics are generated by the diode action between the base and emitter of the XA101 and the required 144 Mc/s content is selected by the network L_2, C_5 and L_3. Any transistor capable of oscillating at 1 Mc/s will be found suitable.

L_3 is a strip line made of 20 s.w.g. brass $3\frac{1}{4}$ in. × $\frac{3}{8}$ in. and has sufficient inductance at 144 Mc/s to match into a 80 ohm line. The circuit is a derivation of the pi-network using a low value of inductance in lieu of a large value of capacitance at the output end. At 144 Mc/s it is difficult to obtain a non-inductive capacitance, whereas a low inductance can easily be made from brass or copper strip. A further advantage is that the strip is virtually a short circuit at lower frequencies and gives far more attenuation of the fundamental and low order harmonics than would a normal parallel tuned circuit and output coupling loop. The layout is shown in **Fig. 24.**

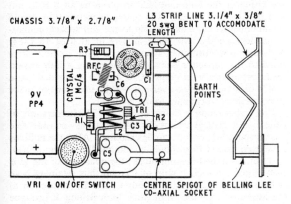

Fig. 24. Layout of components in the 144 Mc/s band edge marker and construction of the strip line L_3.

Grid Dip Oscillators

Another type of frequency measuring device which is extremely useful is the grid dip oscillator. This is really nothing more than a calibrated oscillator which can be tuned over a wide range of frequencies and which has a moving coil meter indicating the grid current. If it is coupled to an external tuned circuit the grid current meter will dip when the oscillator is tuned to the reasonant frequency of that circuit because the circuit will absorb energy from the oscillator,

thus reducing the amount of r.f. feedback to the grid and, in consequence, reducing the grid current.

Since the grid dip oscillator provides its own r.f. energy it does not require the circuit being checked to be energized. It is therefore useful for checking the resonant frequency of tuned circuits, r.f. chokes and aerial systems. The g.d.o. is also useful as an absorption wavemeter, signal monitor or simple signal generator.

The circuit of a typical instrument covering the frequency range 400 kc/s to 195 Mc/s is shown in **Fig. 25.**

On ranges above 1·5 Mc/s, V_1 functions as a Colpitts oscillator; when this is coupled to an external circuit of the same frequency, some of the energy is absorbed and there is a sharp fall in grid current. The calibration of the grid meter scale is immaterial as no actual readings are required, the meter merely showing that a *change* in current has occurred. Below 1·5 Mc/s, the high *LC* ratio at the high end of each range would tend to cause unstable oscillation. L_1 and L_2 are therefore tapped to change the circuit to that of a Hartley oscillator. In the prototype, both coils were tapped at the centre; if it is found that the amplitude of oscillation is too high the tap may be moved nearer the grid end of the coils.

When the oscillator is used as a signal generator, audio voltages can be injected at socket J_1, in series with the meter, to provide a modulated test signal, the modulation frequency being entirely dependent on that of the a.f. source. The same jack is used as the headphone connector when the instrument is employed as an absorption wavemeter or monitor, or as a reacting detector for the identification of spurious signals, etc.

The power supplies for the oscillator are derived from a conventional full-wave rectifier arrangement. The valve used, however, is a type 6AL5 which is quite capable of passing the current required, yet small enough to permit the complete power unit to be fitted inside the oscillator case. H.T. is controlled by switch S_2.

Construction

As can be seen from the photograph, the complete instrument, including power supply and indicating meter, fits into a convenient probelike case measuring 9 in. × 3 in. × 3 in. This case is made in two parts; the front panel and ends are shaped from a $3\frac{3}{4}$ in. strip of 16 s.w.g. aluminium, and the

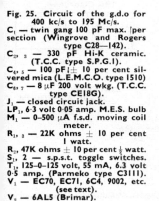

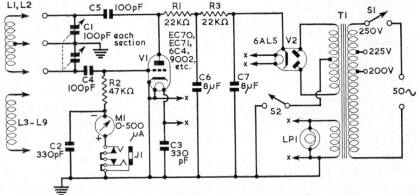

Fig. 25. Circuit of the g.d.o for 400 kc/s to 195 Mc/s.

C_1 — twin gang 100 pF max. [per section (Wingrove and Rogers type C28—142).
$C_{2,3}$ — 330 pF Hi-K ceramic. (T.C.C. type S.P.G.I).
$C_{4,5}$ — 100 pF ± 10 per cent silvered mica (L.E.M.C.O. type 1510).
$C_{6,7}$ — 8 μF 200 volt wkg. (T.C.C. type CE18G).
J_1 — closed circuit jack.
LP_1, 6·3 volt 0·05 amp. M.E.S. bulb
M_1 — 0–500 μA f.s.d. moving coil meter.
$R_{1,3}$ — 22K ohms ± 10 per cent 1 watt.
R_2, 47K ohms ± 10 per cent ¼ watt.
$S_{1,2}$ — s.p.s.t. toggle switches.
T_1, 125–0–125 volt, 55 mA, 6·3 volt 0·5 amp. (Parmeko type C3111).
V_1 — EC70, EC71, 6C4, 9002, etc. (see text).
V_2 — 6AL5 (Brimar).

three remaining sides from a single sheet of the same material. A $\frac{3}{8}$ in. lip is left around each edge of the first piece to provide a base to which the sides can be screwed when the instrument is complete. The layout is shown in **Fig. 26.**

The mains transformer occupying a cube with approximately $2\frac{1}{2}$ in. sides, is mounted at one end of the case. On the end wall next to the transformer are the a.c. and h.t. toggle switches and a small grommeted hole for the mains input lead. Next to the transformer comes the 500 μA indicating meter. Using an average meter of not more than about $1\frac{1}{2}$ in. depth, there is sufficient room to mount the power unit components behind it. A Paxolin panel is used to support the resistors and capacitors, while a small aluminium bracket holds the horizontally-mounted rectifier valve.

On the opposite end wall of the case, a $1\frac{1}{2}$ in. diameter hole is cut for the coil holder. This is a 2 in. square of Perspex with three 3mm sockets (Belling & Lee type L1317) mounted

Fig. 26. Internal layout of the components in the g.d.o.

across the middle at $\frac{7}{16}$ in. centres. The holder is fitted over the inside of the hole and held in place by an 8 B.A. nut and bolt in each corner. The tuning capacitor (C_1) should be mounted as close as possible to the coil socket, connections between the two being in wire of at least 16 s.w.g. Although not absolutely necessary, a slow motion drive fitted to the capacitor helps to make tuning a little easier. In the prototype, V_1 is a type EC70, but if it is intended to use a 6C4 or similar plug-in valve it will be necessary to make some mechanical changes to the layout.

Coil construction is shown in **Fig. 27.** The holders are, of course, not critical except for plug spacing—considerable " constructor's licence " can be exercised. After the bobbins have been wound they should be mounted in a $\frac{5}{8}$ in. $\times$ 1 in. $\times$ $1\frac{1}{2}$ in. U-shaped Paxolin block; the open end of the U is then closed by a small strip of Paxolin thus retaining both bobbin and core in position. For L_1 and L_2 connection to the oscillator is by means of three 3mm Belling & Lee type OZ plugs mounted on a small Paxolin strip at $\frac{7}{16}$ in. centres; L_3 requires only two plugs, these being mounted at $\frac{7}{8}$ in. centres. In each case, the shanks of the plugs are cut off to a length of $\frac{1}{4}$ in. and recessed into the strip, the leads from the

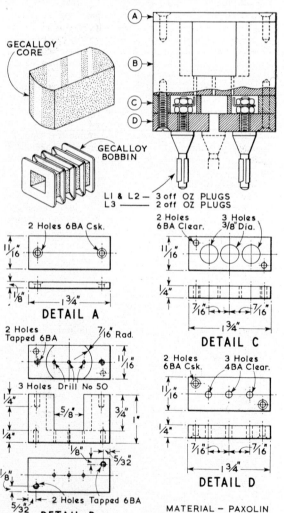

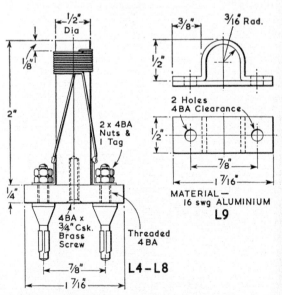

Fig. 27. Construction of the coils. The Gecalloy bobbins are type 15 and the cores type 15 grade ME material. Winding details are given in Table 2. A coat of polystyrene cement should be applied to the joining faces before they are screwed together.

coil going to the appropriate plug via small holes drilled through the block. The mounting strip can then be screwed to the bottom edge of the block with 8 B.A. countersunk screws at the corners.

In case of difficulty, the cores and formers specified for L_1, L_2 and L_3 may be obtained from Salford Instruments, Ltd., Components Group, Times Mill, Heywood, Lancashire.

Calibration

The dial is directly calibrated and is made from a 3 in. square of white ivorine sheet. Using Indian ink, five circles, about ¼ in. apart are drawn around the dial; each circle is then divided into two halves, one half being used for the calibration of each coil.

On the lower frequency ranges, calibration can be carried out with the aid of a crystal calibrator and a receiver. With the receiver b.f.o. switched on, C_1 is adjusted for resonance at 1 Mc/s and 100 kc/s intervals throughout each range. In the absence of a v.h.f. signal generator or a general coverage v.h.f. receiver, Lecher lines may be used for calibration above 30 Mc/s.

When sufficient points have been noted, a circular piece of clear Perspex with a fine black hair-line engraved along one diameter is locked on to the capacitor tuning knob to provide a cursor. This transparent dial should be just large enough to cover the entire area of the outer-most circle; it will then give some measure of protection to the markings.

Finally, all the coils should be given a liberal coat of coil cement. An alternative arrangement for L_4 to L_8 is to gently warm a plastic sleeve of suitable diameter and carefully slide it over the windings; when it cools, the sleeve will shrink and hold the windings in position. (In the prototype the sleeves were cut from a length of 9/16 in. diameter transparent p.v.c. tubing.) Polystyrene cement is available from Woolworths.

Using the G.d.o.

Determination of the Resonant Frequency of a Tuned Circuit. The resonant frequency of a tuned circuit is found by placing the g.d.o. coil close to that of the circuit and tuning C_1 for resonance. No power should be applied to the circuit under test and the coupling should be as loose as possible consistent with a reasonable dip being obtained on the indicating meter. The size of the dip is proportional to the Q of the circuit under test, a circuit having a high Q producing a more pronounced dip than one having only a low or moderate Q.

Absorption Wavemeter. By switching off the h.t. and coupling the g.d.o. in the usual manner, the instrument may be used as an absorption wavemeter. In this case power has to be applied to the circuit under test. Resonance is detected by a deflection on the g.d.o. meter due to rectified r.f. It should be noted that an absorption wavemeter will respond to harmonics if harmonic power is present and the wavemeter is tuned to the frequency of the harmonic.

Capacitance and Inductance. Obviously, if an instrument has the ability to measure the frequency of a tuned circuit, it can also be used for the determination of capacitance and inductance. To measure capacitance, a close tolerance capacitor (C_s) is first connected in parallel with a coil (any coil will do, providing it will resonate at a frequency within the range of the g.d.o.). This circuit is coupled to the oscillator and its frequency (F_1 Mc/s) noted. The unknown capacitor (C_x) is then connected in place of C_s and the resonant frequency again determined. If this is now F_2 Mc/s, the unknown capacitance is given by:

$$C_x = \frac{F_1^2 \, C_s}{F_2^2} \text{ pF}$$

Similarly, inductances may be measured by connecting the unknown coil in parallel with a known capacitance and applying the formula

$$L = \frac{25,300}{CF_2}$$

where L is in μH, C is in pF and F_2 is the resonant frequency expressed in Mc/s.

Signal Generator. For receiver testing the g.d.o. may be used to provide unmodulated c.w. signals by tuning the oscillator to the required frequency and placing it close to the aerial terminal of the receiver. The amplitude of the signal may be controlled by adjusting the distance between the g.d.o. coil and the aerial terminal.

A.f. signals can be injected at the jack socket on the g.d.o. to provide a modulated test signal, the modulation depth being dependent on the level of the modulation voltage, 5 volts being adequate. A d.c. return path must be provided for V_1.

C.W. and Phone Monitor. By connecting a pair of headphones to J_1, the instrument may be used as a c.w. monitor. It should be tuned to the transmitter frequency and the distance between the oscillator and transmitter adjusted for optimum signal strength. To monitor telephony transmissions the h.t. is switched off by means of S_2.

Checking Crystals. It is possible to check the activity and frequency of oscillation of a crystal by inserting it in the coil socket of the g.d.o. and setting the frequency dial to

TABLE 2

Coil	Range	Inductance	Winding
L_1	400–750 kc/s	2·7 mH	305 t., 36 s.w.g. d.s.c. (see text)
L_2	750–1500 kc/s	770 μH	163 t. 36 s.w.g. d.s.c. (see text)
L_3	1·5–3 Mc/s	214 μH	85·5 t., 36 s.w.g. d.s.c.
L_4	3–6 Mc/s	50·5 μH	120 t., 36 s.w.g. d.s.c.
L_5	6–12 Mc/s	13·0 μH	40 t., 36 s.w.g. d.s.c.
L_6	12–25 Mc/s	3·35 μH	14 t., 36 s.w.g. d.s.c.
L_7	24–50 Mc/s	0·875 μH	6·25 t., 24 s.w.g. d.s.c.
L_8	45–100 Mc/s	0·25 μH	2·25 t., 24 s.w.g. d.s.c.
L_9	90–195 Mc/s	0·05 μH	See Fig. 27

The complete g.d.o. in its case.

maximum (i.e., minimum tuning capacitance). The meter reading will vary in accordance with the activity of the crystal and the frequency may be checked by locating the oscillation on a calibrated receiver. Generally speaking, this procedure may only be applied to fundamental mode crystals.

STANDARD FREQUENCY SERVICES IN THE UNITED KINGDOM

MSF 2·5, 5 and 10 Mc/s

The MSF service of high frequency transmissions is designed to provide a frequency and time reference receivable on at least one of three frequencies throughout the United Kingdom. In practice the service area of the transmissions extends to a radius of 1000-1500 km. from Rugby and thus covers also a large part of western Europe. The h.f. transmissions radiated simultaneously on 2·5, 5 and 10 Mc/s are continuous during the 24 hours except for an interruption of five minutes from minute 15 to minute 20 in each hour. All transmissions are modulated with 1 c/s pulses for a total of 35 minutes in each hour, the pulses consisting of 5 cycles of 1000 c/s tone while the minute signals

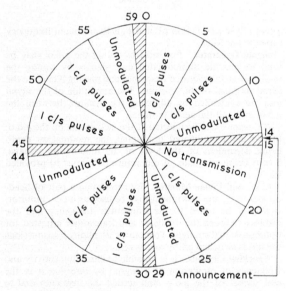

are lengthened to 100 cycles of tone. The periods of 1000 c/s modulation previously broadcast have been replaced by periods of 1 c/s pulses following a recommendation by the C.C.I.R. The carrier and modulation frequencies are all derived from a single crystal oscillator which is regulated to ± five parts in 10^9 and calibrated with an accuracy of ± two parts in 10^{10} in terms of the caesium resonator at the National Physical Laboratory.

Except in a small region adjacent to Rugby where the ground wave predominates, the h.f. signals are received after reflection in the ionosphere. Variations in ionospheric conditions cause fluctuations in the received carrier frequencies which may amount to several parts in 10^7. This limitation on the accuracy of the signals can be overcome by making use of the low and very low frequency transmissions from Rugby.

MSF 60 kc/s and GBR 16 kc/s

MSF 60 kc/s is transmitted for one hour each day at 14.29-15.30 UT and it follows the same modulation programme as the h.f. transmissions. The carrier power is 10 kW and the phase stability of the received signal in the United Kingdom is about 0·1 microsecond thus allowing a comparison accuracy of at least one part in 10^{10} in the period of the transmission. The deviation of the carrier frequency relative to the N.P.L. caesium resonator is measured each day to an accuracy of two parts in 10^{10} and the results are published monthly in *Electronic Technology* (U.T. = G.M.T.).

The MSF oscillator, in addition to controlling the l.f. and h.f. transmissions, is also used to generate the carrier frequency of the v.l.f. telegraphy transmitter GBR on 16 kc/s. This has an effective power of about 400 kW and, generally, is in use for about 22 hours per day, the maintenance period being 13.00-15.00 UT. The phase stability of the received signal is of the order of 1 microsecond thus providing a frequency reference usable to about one part in 10^{10} in a period of a few hours.

Droitwich 200 kc/s

This station which carries the Light Programme transmission of the B.B.C. and some foreign language broadcasts operates for about 18 hours per day. The radiated power is approximately 270 kW by day and 400 kW after sunset and a satisfactory signal is received throughout the British Isles.

The controlling crystal is allowed to drift over a range of about five parts in 10^8 before being reset to the initial value. The phase of the received carrier is stable to better than 0·1 microsecond but the short period instability of the crystal drive does not permit frequency comparisons to better than one part in 10^9 except over a strictly defined time interval. The deviation of the carrier frequency is measured at 10.30 UT each week-day at the N.P.L. with respect to the caesium resonator and the values published monthly in *Electronic Technology* to an accuracy of one part in 10^9.

SIGNAL GENERATORS

In setting up and testing radio and electronic equipment it is frequently necessary to have an a.f. or r.f. signal of suitable frequency. A.f. oscillators are used in the testing of speech amplifiers and modulators and in setting up single sideband transmitters while r.f. signal generators are of great value in the alignment of communication receivers and converters.

SIMPLE A.F. OSCILLATOR

An audio oscillator for amateur use need not be very complicated and in fact the essential part of the circuit to be described consists simply of two equal *RC* time constants, one in parallel and one in series, which are connected to a regenerative system in which the gain and phase relationship will sustain oscillation at a frequency which depends solely on the *RC* values.

In the circuit shown in **Fig. 28** the twin triode oscillator (V_1) feeds a cathode follower (V_2) so that it remains unaffected by the load into which it works. The switch $S_{1a,b}$ provides six ranges covering 32 c/s to 33 kc/s.

The frequency can be readily calculated from $f = \dfrac{1}{2\pi RC}$

where R is the value to which one section of the twin potentiometer VR_1, VR_2, has been adjusted and C is the capacity of

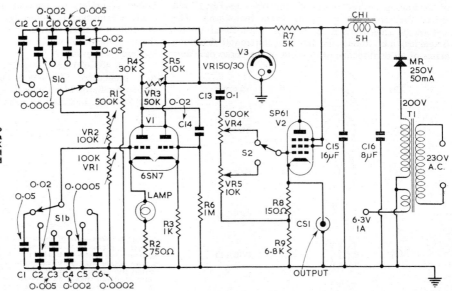

Fig. 28. Circuit of the audio oscillator. VR₁ and VR₂ are a twin potentiometer, 100 K ohms each section. The metal rectifier MR₁ should be rated for 250 volts 60 mA.

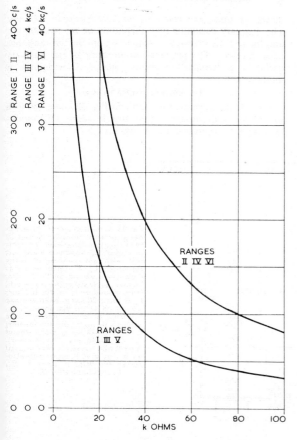

Fig. 29. Frequency v. resistance curve for the circuit and values of Fig. 28.

the respective range capacitor. For this relationship to hold, the R and C values in each section should be within $\pm$ 1 per cent of each other.

Each section of the potentiometer VR_1, VR_2 is 100,000 ohms. Other values can be used, e.g., 50,000 ohms, in which case all the associated capacity values should be doubled, or 200,000 ohms with all the capacity values halved. Beyond these extremes, the R/C ratios become rather big in one case and small in the other, and oscillation is erratic at the ends of each range.

The lamp in the cathode circuit of V_1 is a 230 volt type of 5 to 15 watts consumption. The resistance of the lamp varies with the thermal effect of the current flowing through it and keeps the amplitude of oscillation reasonably constant independent of the frequency. The filament does not glow but its operation can be verified by watching the a.f. voltage across it on an oscilloscope. The thermal lag of a few seconds can be observed and the lamp therefore requires to accommodate itself after a frequency change has been made.

The variable resistor VR_3 is a regeneration control and has a marked effect on the distortion present. If VR_3 is at its maximum value the output is more or less distorted at all frequencies. Its resistance should be reduced until the circuit just oscillates satisfactorily on all ranges. Oscilloscope traces of the output look clean with the exception of those on the lowest ranges which may still have a flattened crest. This can be remedied by shunting C_7 to earth with a 500,000 ohm resistor R_1.

The maximum audio voltage available is about 7 volts R.M.S. For many purposes, lower voltages are required and VR_5 in conjunction with S_2 permits the output to be adjusted from 0 to 150 mV.

Fig. 29 shows the frequency versus resistance curves of the circuit described. It is clear that 10 octaves can be covered without the cramped part of each range being used by working from 100,000 ohms to 20,000 ohms.

Lissajous figures are often suggested as the best means

of calibrating an instrument of the type described, and indeed they are excellent for the lower frequencies. The method of using them is as follows. With 50 c/s (mains frequency) a.c. voltage fed into the horizontal deflecting plates of an oscilloscope, the output of the audio oscillator

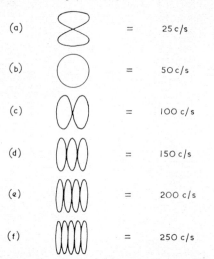

(a)		=	25 c/s	
(b)		=	50 c/s	
(c)		=	100 c/s	
(d)		=	150 c/s	
(e)		=	200 c/s	
(f)		=	250 c/s	

Fig. 30. Calibration of an audio oscillator by means of Lissajous' figures.

should be applied to the vertical plates and the tuning control adjusted until the pattern of **Fig. 30(a)** appears on the screen. The oscillator frequency is then 25 c/s and the scale may be appropriately marked. The tuning control may then be rotated until the pattern of **Fig. 30(b)** appears, which indicates a frequency of 50 c/s. Similarly, the calibration points relating to the range 100–250 c/s may be fixed by reference to the patterns shown; finally the whole scale may be cali-

brated accurately by interpolation. There are of course many intermediate Lissajous figures which may be obtained in addition to those shown. Readers who wish to work out the frequencies for which these apply may do so from the method given in **Fig. 31**.

Above 400–600 c/s calibration against the mains ceases to be practicable. One way to go on from there is to use a second oscillator which may be set to an intermediate point (say 200 c/s) and used to calibrate the first oscillator by

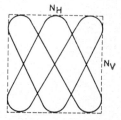

Fig. 31 If a sine-wave of unknown frequency is fed to the horizontal deflecting plates of an oscilloscope, and a signal from a calibrated source is fed to the vertical plates, a stationary pattern such as that shown above may be obtained by adjusting the frequency of the calibrated source. The number of loops in both horizontal and vertical planes should be counted, and the unknown frequency may then be calculated from the following equation; Unknown frequency = NV/NH × frequency of calibrated source. In the diagram, the unknown frequency is $\frac{2}{3}$ of the calibrating frequency.

means of Lissajous figures up to approximately 1000 c/s. The auxiliary oscillator may thereupon be set to 1000 c/s, and the process repeated in sequence until the full range has been covered. The principal requirement of the auxiliary oscillator is frequency stability; purity of waveform is unimportant.

R.F. SIGNAL GENERATOR

The r.f. signal generator shown in **Fig. 32** covers 80 kc/s to 56 Mc/s and employs a transitron oscillator (V_1) modulated by a conventional a.f. oscillator (V_2).

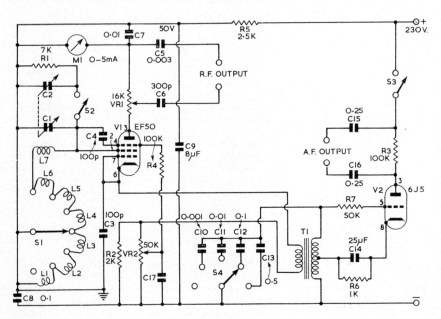

Fig. 32. Circuit of a transitron signal generator covering 80 kc/s–56 Mc/s. L_1, two long wave b.c. coils in series; L_2, medium wave b.c. coil with one quarter of turns removed; L_3, 23 turns 40 s.w.g. d.c.c. close wound on 1¼ in. dia. former; L_4, 17 turns 24 s.w.g. enam. close wound on 1¼ in. dia. former; L_5, 8 turns 20 s.w.g. enamel close wound on 1¼ in. dia. former; L_6, 7 turns 20 s.w.g. enam. close wound ⅜ in. inside dia. (no former) L_7, 7 turns 20 s.w.g. close wound $\frac{5}{16}$ in. inside dia. (no former). A 6·8 K ohms resistor may be used for R_1 and a 10 K ohms potentiometer for VR_1 if desired. C_{17} should be 0·001μF.

Approximately 3–4 mA anode current and 6–8mA screen current is drawn by V_1, the sum of the two being practically constant for any setting of VR_2. The value of R_5 depends on the h.t. supply and should be arranged to produce 50 volts at the point indicated. Construction is simplified if this 50 volt rail is earthed instead of the negative as is usual practice.

The seven range coil assembly consists of inductances in series which are tapped by S_1. One end of the highest frequency coil, L_7, should be mounted directly on the screen grid pin of the valveholder, the switch being arranged close to it. Winding of the coils should commence from the L_7 end to make sure that there are no gaps. Some experiment may be necessary with the number of turns.

A 500pF twin gang capacitor with ceramic insulation is used for C_1, C_2. The C_1 section is reduced to approximately 100pF by removing vanes; it is used on Ranges 4 to 7. For Ranges 1 to 3, C_2 is switched in parallel with C_1 by means of S_2.

The frequency ranges covered by the capacitors suggested and the coils specified, are as follows: *Range 1*, 80 to 220 kc/s; *Range 2*, 210 to 760 kc/s; *Range 3*, 660 to 2700 kc/s; *Range 4*, 2·6 to 6·5 Mc/s; *Range 5*, 5·6 to 15·8 Mc/s; *Range 6*, 14 to 29 Mc/s; *Range 7*, 24 to 56 Mc/s.

Attenuation of the r.f. output is provided by VR_1, a non-inductive carbon type potentiometer. The arrangement is unorthodox but it does provide an easy means of attenuating the output. Modulation is by cathode injection, the audio oscillator V_2 providing four fixed tones selected by S_4.

Screening of the entire unit, including the power pack, is desirable in order to avoid signal leakage. The tuning dial should be fitted with a vernier so that it may be read to one-tenth of a degree.

Calibration can be carried out with the aid of a frequency meter or by listening on a receiver for beats with known broadcast stations and short-wave stations.

MEASUREMENT OF NOISE FACTOR AND EQUIVALENT NOISE TEMPERATURE

The importance of evaluating the noise performance of a receiver in relation to the noise produced in the other parts of a communication system has already been discussed in Chapter 15. The purpose of this section is to describe the principles and practice involved in the construction of noise generators, and the method of using a thermionic diode noise generator to determine the noise factor of a receiver. In addition, details are given of a germanium diode noise source which, while not suitable for absolute measurement of noise factor, is convenient to use when making adjustments to the input circuits of a receiver to determine whether any improvement in noise factor has been achieved.

The anode current of a diode contains noise components due to shot effect, and the frequency spectrum covered by the noise output is exceedingly wide, from zero up to the kilomegacycle region and so may be used as a source of noise signal at any frequency within this range. When the diode is operated under temperature limited conditions, i.e. the emission is controlled only by cathode temperature and not by anode to cathode potential, the noise power output may be shown to be directly proportional to anode current. Thus by varying the filament current, and hence its temperature, a close control of noise power output may be achieved.

The germanium diode generates considerable noise power when a current of a few milliamperes is passed through it in the reverse conduction (high resistance) direction. It has been found that low turnover voltage diodes produce the greatest noise output. Unfortunately the law relating diode current to noise output varies for each diode so that a germanium diode source requires calibration by a thermionic generator if it is to be used for absolute measurements.

Design Considerations

The noise output of the generator is developed across a load resistor equal in value to the source resistance from which the receiver under test is designed to operate. The anode resistance and output capacitance of the noise diode appear in shunt with the load resistor and care must be taken in the practical layout to keep the r.f. connections as short as possible to reduce the stray capacitance to a minimum. At the higher frequencies it is desirable to tune out the stray capacitance by means of shunt inductance if the greatest accuracy is required. This problem arises because the value of the load resistor appears in the formula used to calculate the noise factor and any shunt capacitance will lower the effective value of the load to an extent directly proportional to the frequency of measurement. The anode resistance of the diode will be much higher than the load resistor as the diode is operated with sufficiently high anode voltage to give anode current saturation and the resistive component of the shunt impedance may be neglected for all practical purposes. The d.c. anode supply to the diode must be fed in via r.f. chokes to ensure that all the noise generated is passed to the load resistor. It is not necessary for very elaborate smoothing to be used as the anode current will be independent of anode voltage variations under saturation conditions. A suitable noise diode is the A.2087(CV2171) made by M-O Valve Co. Ltd. This is a B7G based valve with a short mount, which minimises the lead inductance associated with the valve itself. An h.t. supply of 100–150 volts at 20 mA is required together with a filament supply capable of varying the applied voltage up to a maximum of 4·4 volts. The tungsten filament takes 0.64 amp at the maximum filament voltage. The anode current of the CV2171 should not be allowed to exceed 20 mA.

For use at 450 Mc/s, the M-O.V. CV2398 is preferable, although the CV2171 is satisfactory at this frequency. The CV2398 is a noval based flying lead valve, requiring an unscreened p.t.f.e. lead mounting. A suitable component is made by McMurdo Instruments Ltd., under the code FB9A/F. The CV2398 has a tungsten filament rated at 6·0 volts, 1·15 amps and requires an h.t. supply of 100—150 volts at 45 mA maximum. An illustration of noise diodes type CV2171 and CV2398 appears in Chapter 15.

VALVE-TYPE NOISE GENERATORS

For ease of operation it is desirable to use coarse and fine variable reistors for the filament supply so that the noise diode anode current may be set accurately to any required value. For complete versatility, the noise generator should be capable of operating in an unbalanced or balanced condition in order to cater for both types of receiver input circuit. The simplest method of doing this is to provide two noise diode circuits fed from a common power unit, the noise diode being plugged into the appropriate valveholder as required. Suitable circuit arrangements are shown in

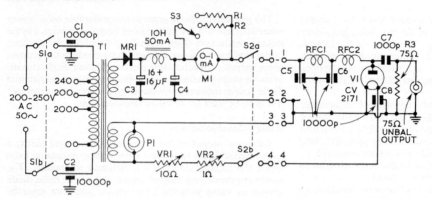

Fig. 33. Noise generator using CV2171, suitable for unbalanced input. C_1, C_2, C_5, C_6, C_8, are 10,000 pF lead-through capacitors. C_7, 1000 pF tubular ceramic; VR_1, 10 ohm 5 per cent wire wound linear (Reliance type TW); VR_2, 1 ohm 10 per cent wire wound linear (Reliance type TW); R_3, 75 ohm 5 per cent coaxial resistor (Welwyn type DSR/4/1); T_1, 125 V 50 mA, 4·5 V 1A; S_{1a}, b, S_{2a}, b, d.p.st. toggle; S_3, s.p. three way wafer; RFC_1, 2, 50 turns 30 s.w.g. close wound on $\frac{3}{8}$ in. former; MR_1, S.T.C. type C2H.

Figs. 33 and **34.** The meter M_1 has three ranges, 1, 5 and 25 mA f.s.d., obtained by switching in appropriate shunts across the basic 0–1 mA meter. The maximum values of noise factor which may be measured on each range are shown in **Table 3.** When measurements at 75 ohms only are required then a 0–5 mA meter shunted to read 25 mA will be adequate.

The figures given in Table 3 are calculated by substitution in the formula $F(db) = 10\ log_{10}\ 20\ IR$, where R is the source resistance in ohms, and I is in amperes.

At frequencies up to 150 Mc/s it is permissible to connect the noise generator to the receiver by a short coaxial or

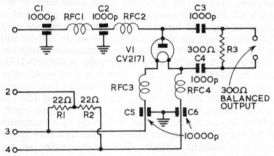

Fig. 34. Noise diode circuit suitable for balanced input. C_1, C_2, 1000 pF ceramic lead-through capacitors; C_3, C_4, 1000 pF tubular ceramic; C_5, C_6, 10,000 pF ceramic lead-through; R_1, R_2, 22 ohm $\frac{1}{2}$ watt; R_3, 300 ohm 5 per cent (Erie type 5B); RFC_1, RFC_2, 50 turns 30 s.w.g. close wound on $\frac{3}{8}$ in. dia. former; RFC_3, RFC_4, 36 turns 18 s.w.g. self-supporting $\frac{1}{2}$ in. internal diameter.

balanced line but for the highest possible accuracy of measurement at 450 Mc/s the noise diode and its associated r.f. circuit should be constructed in the form of a probe, which can be connected directly to the input of the receiver under test.

The load resistor used should be of a type having minimum

TABLE 3

Meter F.s.d.	Noise Factor	
	75 ohms	300 ohms
1 mA	1·76 db	7·78 db
5 mA	8·75 db	14·77 db
25 mA	15·74 db	21·76 db

associated series inductance and parallel capacitance, and a coaxial resistor is recommended, such as the type DSR/4/1 made by the Welwyn Resistor Company in various values and tolerances. For this application a tolerance of ± 5 per cent will be adequate. The coaxial resistor is formed in the shape of a thin disc of ceramic coated with resistive material. Electrical connections are made to the centre and circumference of the disc by silver plated metal contacts. The method of mounting the resistor is shown in the illustration of the germanium diode noise generator (Fig. 36).

When shunt inductance compensation is used, the inductance is adjusted to resonance with the stray capacitance at the frequency of test as indicated by a rise in the noise output of the generator. Strictly speaking inductance compensation is accurate at one frequency only, but the resulting error in calculated noise factor is negligible over the frequency bands of interest to the amateur. A practical point to observe when using a noise diode is to permit anode current to flow for the minimum time possible when making measurements as the expected life of a valve of this type does not exceed a few hundred hours and is much less if the filament voltage is maintained at the maximum value for long periods.

GERMANIUM DIODE NOISE GENERATOR

An illustration of a germanium diode noise generator is shown in **Fig. 36** and the circuit is given in **Fig. 35.** The construction is quite straightforward and follows the

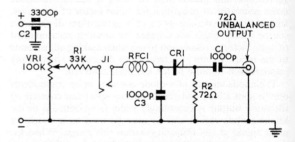

Fig. 35. Circuit of a germanium diode noise generator. C_1, C_2, 1000 pF tubular ceramic; C_2, 3300 pF lead-through; CR_1, GD8 or equivalent; R_1, 33 K ohm $\frac{1}{4}$ watt; R_2, 72 ohm 5 per cent coaxial resistor (Welwyn type DSR/4/1); VR_1, 100 K linear wire wound potentiometer (Colvern); RFC_1, 25 turns 22 s.w.g. enam. air wound $\frac{1}{4}$ in. i.d. The germanium diode CR_1 should be the low reverse voltage type.

principles outlined for valve diode generators. The generator requires 100 volts at 5 mA which may be obtained from any convenient supply. In use a 0–5 mA meter is plugged into the jack to measure the crystal current. With some germanium diodes it may be found that the noise output first increases and then falls off before rising again with increase of crystal current. This departure from linearity will not be a disadvantage as the germanium diode noise generator is used principally for qualitative assessment of receiver performance.

Method of Using the Noise Generator to measure the Noise Factor of a Receiver

It is essential, when a noise factor measurement is to be made, to ensure that the measuring system is linear, as the definition of noise factor is based upon this assumption. The receiver under test may be assumed to be linear for this purpose if doubling the input power produces a corresponding doubling of the output power. This relation may not hold over a wide range of signal levels and settings of the receiver gain controls, but provided that the measurement is

Fig. 36. A view inside the germanium diode type noise generator of Fig. 35.

carried out at signal levels and gain settings at which the receiver is known to be linear then the conditions imposed by the definition of noise factor which follows will be satisfied. The *noise factor* of a linear receiver, or any other four terminal network having its input terminals connected to an impedance of stated value and temperature, is the number of times by which an addition to the noise power available from this impedance must exceed the thermal noise at signal frequency in order to double the noise power available from the output terminals of the network, provided that all sources of noise give the same frequency spectrum at the output terminals.

Two methods of using the noise generator to measure the noise factor of a receiver will be described. The first is a simple method, involving one measurement only of noise diode anode current while the other involves three such measurements and a little more calculation, but has the advantage of incorporating a linearity check.

Both methods require some form of power measuring device which is connected to the receiver at a suitable point to measure the a.f. noise output. In the event that an a.f. output meter is not available, a low range a.c. volt meter may be connected across the primary of the receiver output transformer. Alternatively an 0–100 μA d.c. meter may be placed in series with the earthy end of the detector diode load. A fairly heavily damped meter will assist in reducing the fluctuations observed when reading noise output. It should be remembered that power is proportional to voltage or current squared so that to double the power output when reading in microamperes or volts the meter reading should increase by a factor of $\sqrt{2}$.

In the first method of measuring the noise factor the noise

generator is connected to the input terminals of the receiver but not switched on. The i.f. and a.f. gain controls are adjusted to give a convenient reading on the output meter. If a d.c. microammeter in the detector diode load is being used, the a.f. gain control is ignored and the i.f. gain control adjusted to give a reading of 20–40 μA. The noise diode is then switched on and the anode current increased until the receiver power output is doubled. The noise factor of the

receiver in decibels is given by $F\,db = 10\,log_{10}\,\dfrac{20\,IR}{1000}$ where

I is the noise diode current in milliamperes and R is the value of the noise generator source impedance.

The procedure described above is only valid if the receiver is known to be linear over the range of input levels involved in making the measurement. If there is any doubt then the three measurement method should be used as follows:

With the noise generator connected but not switched on the receiver gain is adjusted to give a convenient meter reading, P_1, due to its own noise. The noise generator is then switched on and the noise diode anode current adjusted to give a considerable increase in receiver noise power output, but not enough to cause saturation. Let this output power be P_2 and the noise diode anode current required to produce it I_1. The gain is now reduced appreciably, and the noise diode currents I_2 (usually made equal to I_1 by suitable adjustment of the gain control) and I_3 required to give the original output readings P_1 and P_2 are determined, and the three values of I substituted in the following formula:

$$F\,(db) = 10\,log_{10}\,\frac{20\,I_1\,I_2\,R}{I_3 - I_2 - I_1}$$

where R is the noise generator load impedance and I_1, I_2 and I_3 are in milliamperes. It should be noted that if $I_1 + I_2$ is nearly equal to I_3, a small error in readings gives a large error in F, and this condition should be avoided by making P_2/P_1 as large as possible.

The equivalent noise temperature of the receiver is given by $T_r = (F-1)T_0$ where F is the numerical value of noise factor and T_0 is the equivalent noise temperature of the load resistor, which may be assumed to be 290° K. The numerical value of the noise factor F is a ratio and not the figure given in db quoted in the valve makers' data. In order to substitute for F in the equation for equivalent noise temperature, it is necessary to take the antilogarithm of the quoted noise factor in db divided by 10, i.e. numerical

value $=$ antilog $\dfrac{F\,(db)}{10}$.

Using the Germanium Diode Noise Generator

The germanium diode noise generator cannot be used to measure the absolute value of noise factor as already stated but it is very useful as a means of assessing improvements to receiver aerial coupling circuits and r.f. stages. When used in this manner the generator is connected to the receiver and the increase in noise output produced when the generator is turned on is recorded. Next the desired modification is made and the procedure repeated. If after the modification less diode current is required to produce the same increase in noise output from the receiver, then it can be assumed that an improvement in noise factor has resulted. The converse is also true.

481

Noise Generation above 500 Mc/s

Current practice at frequencies in excess of 500 Mc/s is to use an Argon-filled fluorescent discharge tube as a noise source, the noise power being extracted by an external coupled helix terminated at one end by a load resistor equal to the required source impedance, while the other end is connected to the receiver under test by a short coaxial cable of suitable impedance. When the tube is conducting, it generates noise at an equivalent noise temperature of 10,100° K, i.e. approx. 15·5db excess noise power, which is fixed by the type of tube. In use a variable attenuator is employed at i.f. to reduce the gain of the receiver under test until the noise power output of the receiver is the same with the fluorescent noise source switched on as when switched off. The value of the noise factor F in db using a fluorescent noise source is given by

$$F(db) = 10 \log_{10} (C - 1) \left(\frac{P_{ON}}{P_{OFF}} - 1 \right)$$

where $C =$ the ratio of the noise temperatures of the source when switched on and switched off, and P_{ON}/P_{OFF} is the loss inserted by the attenuator to maintain the receiver noise output constant. Corrections are applied which allow for the incomplete coupling of the fluorescent tube to the helix and also for the mismatch introduced by the tube and helix in the extinguished condition. If the receiver has an appreciable response at the image frequency a further correction is necessary. This last correction will apply to the measurement of noise factor by any form of noise generator and amounts to as much as 3db if the image response is equal to the required response.

AERIAL AND FEEDER MEASUREMENTS

Radio frequency ammeters and voltmeters do not reveal the true power unless the line in which they are connected is correctly matched, but they may always be used as a means of tuning up the transmitter and the aerial coupler. The *reflectometer* is, however, an instrument which can distinguish between the forward and reflected waves in a standing-wave system, and can therefore be used to indicate a true match of impedance; because only the forward wave is radiated, such an instrument can be calibrated to read true power flow into the aerial.

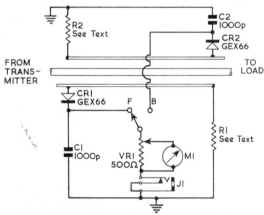

Fig. 37. Circuit arrangement of a reflectometer for the h.f. amateur bands.

Reflectometers are Wheatstone-bridge arrangements, balanced to indicate flow in one direction only along a line. Several varieties have been described in radio publications in which the bridge comprises physical components built into the concentric line, but these require careful construction for successful results. That described here uses the properties of coupled transmission lines, and two arms of the bridge are formed by the electric (capacitive) and magnetic (inductive) couplings. The coaxial line impedance and a balancing resistor in the reflectometer make up the remainder of the bridge.

H.F. REFLECTOMETER

The reflectometer is essentially simple in principle and in construction. **Fig. 37** shows the main conductor of a coaxial line, and coupled to it are two secondary lines, each fitted with a diode detector and a terminating resistance. The forward wave from transmitter to aerial can only induce a wave flowing in the opposite direction on the secondary line. This is a fundamental property of coupled lines. The lower

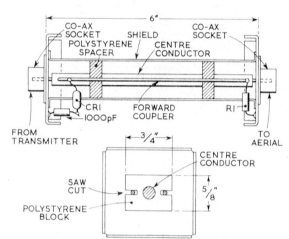

Fig. 38. Practical details of a reflectometer for the 14, 21 and 28 Mc/s amateur bands. For 3·5–28 Mc/s the length should be 12 in.

line detector CR_1 therefore receives a voltage proportional to the amplitude of the forward wave, the flow from transmitter to aerial. In the upper line the induced wave travels towards R_2, and if this also matches its line, the induced wave is absorbed and nothing reaches detector CR_2. On the other hand, if the aerial is not matched to its line, then it will reflect power back to the transmitter: the forward diode CR_1 now shows total power going to the aerial and the backward diode CR_2 the reflected portion.

Fig. 38 illustrates a construction suitable for insertion in a coaxial line using coaxial connectors. Only the essential dimensions are given. The concentric line is converted to a parallel plate line, comprising a ¼ in. conductor between two "earth" strips ¾ in. wide and ⅝ in. apart which are bolted to the two end plates holding the connectors. The secondary lines, made of 16 s.w.g. wire, are supported in sawcuts in two polystyrene blocks, and the diodes and resistors are soldered to these lines. The complete instrument is boxed in by a metal wrapping screen over its end plates.

The impedance of the strip line is 50 ohms, but it may also

be used in 70 ohm circuits because R_1 and R_2 can be varied to adjust the balance of the equivalent bridge circuits. These resistors may be of $\frac{1}{2}$ watt rating but must be carbon and not wirewound. The value is 150 ohms for a 50 ohm reflectometer, and 100 ohms for 70 ohm use. The indicating meter is connected across a potentiometer VR_1 which adjusts the sensitivity. This meter may be 0–1 mA f.s.d. for 50 watts on 14, 21 and 28 Mc/s, but for lower frequencies a more sensitive meter may be needed, since the output of the coupling lines is proportional to frequency; alternatively, the instrument may be made twice as long as suggested in Fig. 38 to double its sensitivity. Small wire-ended germanium diodes (e.g. GEX66) are suitable detectors.

It is necessary to balance the coupling lines, and this is done by moving them parallel to the main line to make a small adjustment to their characteristic impedance. For this purpose it is necessary to terminate the aerial socket in a pure resistance equal to the line characteristic impedance but unless high-power accurate r.f. loads are available this adjustment must be done at low power, in which case the meter is not sensitive enough. The procedure then is to replace the meter by a pair of headphones and use some audio modulation on the transmitter or its low power driver, using very low output coupling and a 1 or 2 watt carbon resistor as a standard load of value equal to the coaxial line impedance. With this arrangement the backward-wave line is adjusted for zero output and then the instrument is reversed and the forward line set up. The adjustment should bring the secondary lines to about $\frac{1}{4}$ in. from the main conductor. It has been found that an improved balance is obtained if the diode is connected about $\frac{1}{2}$ in. from the end of its line to form a small end-capacitance. The balancing adjustment should always be made at the highest frequency at which the reflectometer is to be used, because there the errors are most important, and it is also most sensitive there. When the adjustments are finished the wires can be cemented in position.

In use, the potentiometer VR_1 is set for full-scale meter reading when switched to FORWARD; the meter will indicate reflection coefficient when changed to the backward position. If there is a reasonable resistance, say at least 1000 ohms, between the meter and the diode, the latter will give fairly linear meter readings, proportional to reflection amplitude, but with no damping it is nearer to square-law and reads proportional to power.

The reflection coefficient K is the best matching parameter to use, since it is zero when the line is matched, but if it is preferred to work in terms of v.s.w.r. the meter can be calibrated by means of the formula:

$$V.s.w.r. = \frac{1+K}{1-K}$$

from which some values are given in Table 1 on page 359.

The reflectometer can be used " in the field " as a very helpful aid to aerial matching operations, but its normal use is in the station, either in the aerial feeder or in the link line between transmitter and aerial coupler (see Chapter 13— *H. F. Aerials*, Fig. 28)). Where two or more aerials are used on one band it is a big advantage to have each aerial matched into the line (either directly or via an aerial coupler) because then the transmitter can be adjusted for a matched line load, and change of aerial can be made instantly as required. A good match is indicated by zero or very low reflection when the meter is switched to the backward diode (CR_2) . When

the reflection is zero, the forward detector indicates true power flow to the aerial and can obviously be used for transmitter adjustment and as a permanent monitor. For a.m. phone work side tone may be obtained by plugging headphones into J_1.

A rough power calibration of the forward detector can be made by using a 25 or 100 watt lamp as a load on the aerial coupler, and matching its brilliance with a similar lamp supplied with mains power. The r.f. lamp is tapped into the aerial coupler as if it were the aerial and adjustments made until it matches the link line. This procedure needs patience because the lamp resistance changes rapidly with power input. The reference lamp is connected with meters to read the current through it and the voltage across it, and is supplied from a suitable source of power with a variable resistance in series with the matching lamp. The two lamps should, of course, be of the same type.

It should be remembered that when the diodes are passing rectified current they are also generating harmonics and may therefore cause some degree of TVI. For this reason the complete instrument should be properly screened in a closed metal box and if the meter is detached, its leads should be screened and decoupled. A choke or single section TVI filter between the switch and potentiometer will help prevent harmonic generation and radiation.

This meter has been described in some detail because it is so exceptionally useful that once it is installed it is difficult to imagine how adjustments could be made without it. Reflectometers can also be designed to couple into two-wire lines, but require much more skill in design and use, because they are more sensitive to spurious effects such as stray capacitance couplings or unbalance currents on the line. The instrument illustrated in Fig. 38 will perform quite well at 145 Mc/s.

FIELD STRENGTH METER

A field strength meter is a useful tool for use in adjusting aerial systems and as a visual indication of a signal being radiated. As may be seen from **Fig. 39**, it comprises a tuned circuit, switched for the required bands, and a crystal rectifier feeding a single stage transistor d.c. amplifier. The signal level is indicated on a 0–1 mA meter. The instrument should be constructed in a metal box, its pick-up aerial being connected via a suitable insulated terminal.

To avoid obtaining confusing results, a field strength meter should be situated several wavelengths away from an aerial under adjustment.

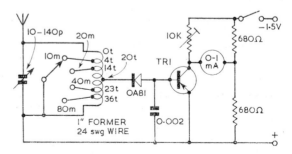

Fig. 43. Simple field strength meter for 10–80 metres. **TR₁** may be any general purpose transistor. A short rod aerial should be used (3–6 ft.).

CATHODE RAY OSCILLOSCOPES

The oscilloscope is one of the most versatile instruments an amateur can possess and permits the visual display of a.f. and r.f. signals. It is particularly useful for monitoring phone transmissions.

Commercial instruments are often unnecessarily elaborate for amateur purposes but it is perfectly feasible to build simple units at home.

The heart of the oscilloscope is the cathode ray tube, the operation of which is described in Chapter 2. If it is desired to examine a waveform, the input is connected to the vertical plates while a sweep or time base circuit is connected to the horizontal deflection plates. For many applications it is sufficient to derive the sweep voltage from the a.c. mains.

By using readily available and inexpensive tubes, an instrument designed expressly for 'phone monitoring may be constructed quite cheaply. Of the government surplus tubes the 3BP1 has features which make it perhaps the most suitable. Its screen is large enough to give an unambiguous picture, and although it is a short and handy tube, it has a reasonably high deflection sensitivity so that a high input is not required. This obviates the need for deflection amplifiers in monitor service. A number of tubes of this type have been tested and all were found to have the electron guns so well centred that the spot appeared in the centre of the screen without the assistance of a shift-control network. This simplifies construction and reduces cost. The anode voltage requirements are modest; many tubes will give a quite well focused spot at voltages as low as 400–500, and nearly all will work excellently at 700 volts and above.

For transmission monitoring it is sufficient to provide a heater supply only, because the existing power supply for the transmitter final will almost invariably be capable of providing the few milliamperes drawn by the cathode ray tube and its control network. It is unfortunate that external fields are liable to cause trouble unless the final anode and the deflector plates of the tube are operated at earth potential. It is therefore highly desirable to provide the few components needed to furnish a negative h.t. supply for the tube's cathode.

MONITORING DISPLAY UNIT

The circuit of a cathode ray oscilloscope embodying the foregoing principles is given in **Fig. 40.** This, though deliberately modest, is adequate for setting up s.s.b. transmitters and monitoring a.m. transmitters. The lead from the heater of V_1 may be connected to either end of the high-voltage secondary of the p.a. power supply transformer, and after smoothing in the RC filter comprised of C_5, R_8 and C_4, a negative d.c. output of almost 1·4 times the R.M.S. half-secondary voltage will be provided for the cathode-ray tube. Due to the negligible current drain, RC filtering is adequate. Brilliance of the pattern is controlled by VR_3, and focus by VR_2. It should be noted that a high-intensity spot must not be permitted to remain stationary on the screen for any length of time, otherwise it will leave a permanent blemish on the fluorescent phosphor. Horizontal sweep is taken from the 50 c/s a.c. mains. It is therefore necessary to make sure that C_1 is connected to the live side of the mains supply. If no sweep is obtained on switching on, it is clear that C_1 is connected to the neutral lead, and the fault should be rectified either by transferring it to the other side of the heater transformer primary or by

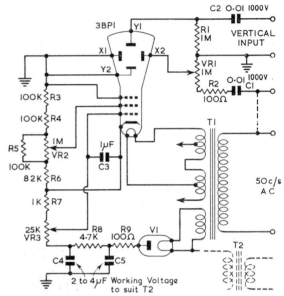

Fig. 40. Oscilloscope display unit for monitoring telephony transmissions. T_1 must be adequately insulated for the voltage in use. T_2 is the existing p.a. power supply transformer (see text). V_1 may be a U27 or other suitable rectifier.

reversing the mains plug in its socket. A 50 c/s sweep causes some distortion of the display, but this may be kept within reasonable limits by using a high sweep amplitude so that only the centre portion of the sweep appears on the screen. The resulting trace is linear enough for most monitoring work. The sweep amplitude may be reduced by VR_1, but this control should be set at maximum when monitoring is being carried out.

If other work is contemplated, it is worth including some form of linear horizontal sweep. The Miller-transitron oscillator, shown in its most elementary form in **Fig. 41**, has much to commend it. Any sharp cut-off pentode may be used in this circuit, so long as it has its suppressor grid brought out to a separate pin. As the valve requires only a few milliamperes of h.t. at 200–300 volts, it will probably be possible to " borrow " the necessary supply from an existing power-pack. If the linear sweep of Fig. 41 is preferred to the 50 c/s mains sweep, C_1 in Fig. 40 should be disconnected from the primary of the heater transformer and connected to the anode of the oscillator valve.

The small $\frac{1}{10}$th watt resistors R_2 and R_9 are the only

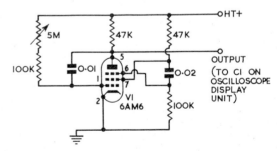

Fig. 41. Miller-transitron sawtooth time base generator for use with the oscilloscope of Fig. 44.

components which remain to be explained. They are included merely to act as fuses in the event of other components breaking down.

This simple display unit can be employed for monitoring a.m. transmissions using the method described, with illustrations of typical patterns, in Chapter 9 (*Modulation*). Connections for envelope and trapezoidal patterns are shown in **Fig. 42.**

Calculation of modulation depth using the trapezoidal

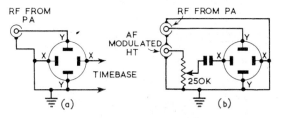

Fig. 42(a). **Oscilloscope connections for envelope pattern. (b) Connections for trapezoidal pattern.**

method is possible by measuring the sides of the trapezium and using the abac of **Fig. 43.** A disadvantage of the trapezoidal method is the necessity to tap off from the secondary of the modulation transformer an audio signal for the *X* (horizontal) plates. However, this can be overcome by building a small tuned circuit and demodulator unit (**Fig. 44**) which can be connected to the output of the transmitter to provide the necessary audio signal. The unit should be made up on a small sub-chassis and fitted as near to the holder of the cathode ray tube as possible. If the signal is fed to the *X* amplifier input the trapezoidal display will be obtained.

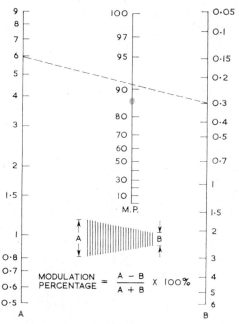

Fig. 43. **Abac for the calculation of modulation depth from the trapezoidal pattern. The dotted line illustrates an example in which the large side (A) is 6 units long and the shorter one (B) 3 units indicating a depth of modulation of just over 90 per cent.**

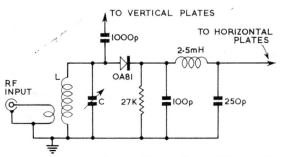

Fig. 44. **Demodulator unit to provide an audio signal for connection to the X plates of the oscilloscope in the trapezoidal method of measuring modulation depth**

When it is fed to the sync. terminal on an oscilloscope such as the Heathkit OS–1 the waveform pattern will be shown.

S.s.b. transmissions may be conveniently checked by the 45° method which calls for the application of similar

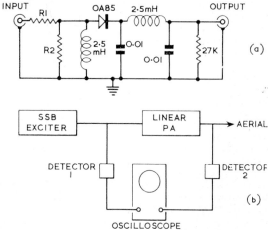

Fig. 45. **(a) Demodulator unit. (b) Circuit arrangement for checking s.s.b. transmissions by the 45° method.**

voltages from the input and output of the linear amplifier. This necessitates the use of two detectors, as shown in **Fig. 45**; the resistors R_1 and R_2 should be adjusted so that the voltage output from each is similar. The interpretation

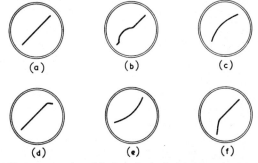

Fig. 46. **Interpretation of displays obtained with the arrangement of Fig. 45. (a) Linear condition. (b) Incorrect grid circuit loading. (c) Incorrect bias. (d) Amplifier overloaded. (e) Insufficient standing current in amplifier. (f) Pattern obtained from speech input to a correctly adjusted linear amplifier.**

485

of the various displays obtained when a sinusoidal tone is fed into the s.s.b. transmitter is shown in **Fig. 46.**

BUILT-IN MODULATION MONITOR

Availability of the 1CP1 c.r. tube makes it possible to build a monitor into a transmitter, the display screen taking its place on the front panel with the grid and anode current meters. A suitable circuit, provided by Electronic Tubes Ltd., is shown in **Fig. 47.** It comprises a small cathode ray tube, a time base generator and a phase splitting X amplifier. This type of monitor may be used to display the modulation envelope or the modulation trapezium, the display being selected by means of S_1.

While the Y deflection of the tube is simplified in this case by the fact that the tube is designed for asymmetric Y deflection, the X deflection will still require symmetrical deflection. (Asymmetric X deflection could be used, directly from the time base, but would probably introduce trapezium distortion on the display. This could be misleading when displaying the modulation trapezium.) For this purpose the phase splitting amplifier V_2 is introduced. This amplifier also serves the purpose of amplifying the modulating waveform—which may be taken at a low level—when the trapezium is to be displayed.

The time-base generator V_1 is a transitron-Miller circuit which in spite of its simplicity, provides a linear waveform. Synchronization of the time base sweep may be effected by applying a small amount of the audio to be displayed through a small capacitance to the suppressor grid of the pentode, provided that the time-base repetition rate and the modulating frequency are not very greatly different.

The cathode ray tube 1CP1 operates from a 500 volt supply and, therefore, requires an extra 150 volts in addition to the 350V h.t. line. The arrangement shown in **Fig. 48** is a simple and inexpensive means of obtaining this voltage. Operation of the tube is simplified by the use of automatic biasing in place of the usual brilliance control and by the fact that the tube is designed to focus automatically.

If the monitor is to be used in an s.s.b. transmitter, the circuit can be further simplified by omission of the time-base generator.

SERVICING OSCILLOSCOPE

The circuit diagram of a complete oscilloscope employing a $2\frac{3}{4}$ in. tube type 3AFP1 is shown in **Fig. 49.** This instrument, the Heathkit Model OS–1, has X and Y amplifiers and a Miller transistron time-base generator covering 15 c/s to

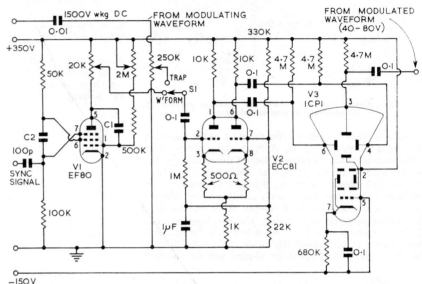

Fig. 47. Modulation monitor employing a ICP1 tube. The unit is suitable for building into a transmitter. The time base speed depends on the value of C_1 which may be 300pF (1·2–6 kc/s), 1000pF (400 c/s to 2 kc/s) or 3000pF (120 c/s to 600 c/s). C_2 should be five times the value of C_1.

150 kc/s. The frequency response of the X amplifier is $\pm$ 3db from 150 c/s to 500 kc/s and the Y amplifier within $\pm$ 3db from 10 c/s to 1·5 Mc/s and within $\pm$ 3db from 10 c/s to 2·5 Mc/s. It is thus suitable for all the work likely in the amateur station—waveform investigation, testing audio

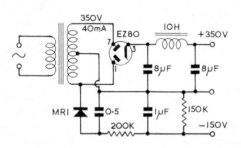

Fig. 48. Power supply for the modulation monitor of Fig. 47.

The Heathkit Model OS–1 oscilloscope. The complete circuit diagram is shown in Fig. 49.

486

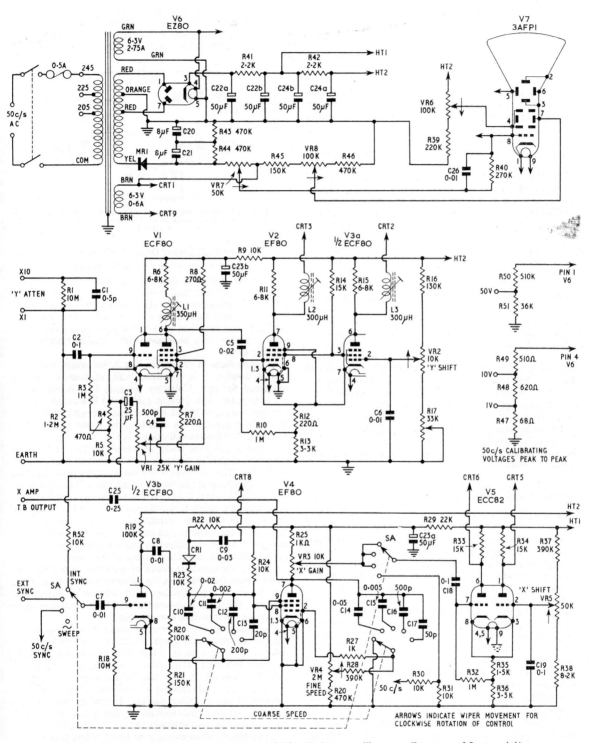

Fig. 49. Circuit diagram of the Heathkit Model OS-1 cathode ray oscilloscope. (*By courtesy of Daystrom Ltd.*)

amplifiers and servicing communication and television receivers.

Two input sockets for the Y amplifier are provided, one being direct, the other introducing an attentuation of 10 : 1. The first section of V_1 is a cathode follower, gain being controlled by VR_1 (Y GAIN). Vertical positioning of the tube trace is provided by VR_2.

V_{3b} is used as a sync. amplifier, the valve operating with zero bias and producing at its anode an amplified and limited signal of the sync. input. This output is positive going and is fed to the suppressor grid of the time-base generator V_4. Three methods of synchronisation may be used: internal, external or 50 c/s. Internal synchronisation is obtained from the cathode of V_1 through an isolating resistor R_{52}.

Coarse frequency control of the time base (V_4) is provided by the switch S_B and fine speed control by VR_4. Output from the anode of V_4 is taken through an isolating capacitor to the X AMP socket on the front panel so that while the time base is operating a saw tooth waveform is available at this point. One of the positions of S_B allows the time base to be switched off and an external signal or time base fed into X amp socket. Amplitude of the signal is variable by means of VR_3. Output from VR_3 (X GAIN) is fed to V_5 connected as a cathode coupled pair. Horizontal positioning of the trace is adjusted by VR_5 (X SHIFT). A 50 c/s sinusoidal time base is provided by a position on switch S_A which switches out the time base and connects V_5 to a source of 50 c/s. Calibration voltages of 1, 10 and 50 volts peak-to-peak at 50 c/s are available from sockets on the front panel.

E.h.t. supplies for the tube are derived from a resistor chain across the supply from the rectifier MR1 (type K8/40 selenium). The maximum voltage fed to pin 8 via VR_7 is— 700 volts. VR_6 is a spot shape or astigmatism control and is adjusted in conjunction with VR_7 (BRILLIANCE) and VR_8 (FOCUS) to produce a well-defined trace. Flyback suppression is achieved by taking a negative pulse from the screen of V_4. This pulse is limited by CR_1 and the resulting flat topped waveform fed to the grid of the tube to blank the retrace or flyback of the time-base sweep.

MODULATION MONITOR FOR USE WITH A RECEIVER

The circuit of a modulation indicator for use with a receiver is shown in **Fig. 50.** L_1 and L_2 are the coils of an i.f. transformer of the same frequency as the receiver intermediate frequency. The signal is fed through a small capacitor connected to the final i.f. valve via coaxial cable to point A, and to Y_1 via the 0.005 μF capacitor. With S_1 in position 1, the signal is fed inductively to the X plate, with 90° phase shift, thus creating a circular trace on every carrier tuned in. Depth of modulation is shown by the extent to which the circular trace is thickened inwards and outwards, full modulation being shown as a disc. Overmodulation will produce overbrilliance at the centre due to overlapping.

When an a.c. source is connected to position 2 of S_1, and with the switch in this position, the envelope trace for modulation results.

On setting up the monitor, a strong steady carrier should be accurately tuned in, and the 100 pF trimmers adjusted for the best circular trace, although it may be found that the trace is rather elliptical, The cores of the i.f. transformer should be initially withdrawn sufficiently for the tuning to be carried out with the 100 pF trimmers only. The 0.005 μF

capacitors should be rated to suit the tube voltages and the a.c. supply at position 2 of the switch. For safe working, if d.c. voltages only are shown on capacitors, this figure should be divided by 3 to obtain the safe a.c. working voltage.

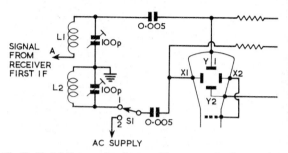

Fig. 50. Modulation monitor for use with a communications receiver L_1 **and** L_2 **are the windings of an i.f. transformer of appropriate frequency.**

MISCELLANEOUS TEST GEAR
P-N-P AND N-P-N TRANSISTOR TESTER

A test set providing quick and accurate direct measurement of current gain and collector leakage current of p-n-p and n-p-n transistors under static, grounded emitter conditions is a useful tool in the modern radio workshop. The unit described here will also give a good indication of the state of diodes when compared with a similar type in good working order.

A simple form of protection is included which will guard against damage if a transistor with an internal short is connected for test. Collector leakage, I'_{co}, is read on a 0–1 mA meter. The current gain (*beta*) is arranged in two switched ranges: 0–100 at 100 μA base current and 0–250 at 40 μA base current. On *beta* test, the meter is shunted to read 10 mA full-scale deflection (f.s.d.).

Testing a transistor under grounded emitter conditions is somewhat similar to testing a valve for mutual conductance, the emitter, base and collector of the transistor corresponding to the cathode, grid and anode of the valve. The base is the controlling element; if there is a small change in base current there will be a much larger change in the collector current. The grounded emitter current gain, termed *beta* or α' is the ratio of the collector and base currents, and the measurement of it is here simplified by using a defined base current and indicating the collector current on the meter.

Fig. 51 is the complete circuit of the tester. A 0–1 milliammeter is used for indicating the collector leakage current and was chosen as a good compromise between sensitivity and expense. The meter is shunted to read 10 mA full scale when measuring the transistor current gain.

The operation is as follows: connect a transistor to the appropriate terminals, close switch S_1 and read off the collector leakage current. (The value of this will normally be under 100 μA.) Next close switch S_2, allowing a base current of 100 μA to flow, and then read off the collector current. A full scale reading will indicate a gain of 100 (the ratio of 10 mA collector current, divided by 100 μA base current). An OC71 for example may give 5 mA, thus indicating a gain of 50, and similarly for other transistors.

To enable n-p-n transistors to be tested, a four-pole changeover switch is used to reverse the battery and meter connections. Some transistors such as the OC44 and the V6/8R have a high gain and a small allowable dissipation. R_2, in conjunction with R_1 (68 K and 43 K ohms respectively), limits the base current to 40 μA. In this position, full scale deflection of the meter indicates a gain of 250 (10 mA collector current divided by the 40 μA base current is equivalent to a gain of 250). The purpose of R_3 (4·3 K ohms) is to limit the meter to full scale deflection should a transistor with an internal short be connected. In this case, the push switch

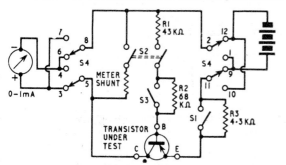

Fig. 51. Complete circuit diagram of the transistor tester.

must *not* be pressed, thus avoiding meter overload, and the faulty item should be discarded.

Some readers building this tester may wish to use a meter which they have on hand. In such cases the required shunt-resistor can be calculated from the formula on page 461. With a 0–1 mA meter the scale multiplying factor is 10. With a 250 μA meter it would be 40.

The limiting resistor R_3 should be changed to 8·2 K ohms if a 0–500 μA meter is used and to 15–18 K ohms with a 0–250 μA movement.

The layout is shown in **Fig. 52,** the components used fitting comfortably into an Eddystone diecast box.

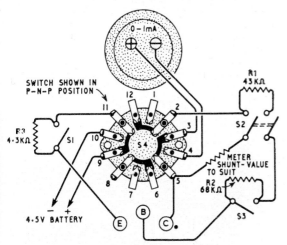

Fig. 52. The layout viewed from the rear of the diecast box.

The switch wafer is wired as shown in **Fig. 53** but on the under side for neatness. The contacts should be of the non-shorting type; that is, break before make.

R_1 and R_2 are standard value ¼-watt resistors of close tolerance and high stability. If another type of resistor is used, any small variation from the values quoted should be toward a lower resistance, certainly not a higher. The meter shunt resistor must be selected carefully if accuracy of measurement is to be obtained. The meter and its shunt should be compared with an instrument of known accuracy before fitting into the tester.

Operation

Transistor Test. Open both toggle switches, set switch S_4 to the *p-n-p* position. In the first instance only, use a voltmeter to check that the collector terminal is negative with respect to the emitter terminal. This being so, connect a *p-n-p* transistor, such as an OC44 or OC71. If the meter reads full scale, an internal short is indicated and the transistor is unserviceable. If the meter is not indicating full scale deflection, press the button and read off the collector leakage current directly on the 0–1 mA scale. As transistors of the germanium type are very temperature conscious, an abnormally high leakage, perhaps double the normal, will be

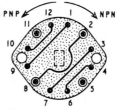

Fig. 53. Wiring of the wafer switch.

indicated if the transistor is handled for too long with warm hands especially near a fire or a hot radiator. The transistor should be at normal room temperature when tested.

Next close switch S_2 and read off the current gain on the 0–250 scale. If the gain is under 100, close switch S_3 and read on the 0–100 scale. It is quite normal for the transistor gain to be a little higher (or lower in some cases) on the 0–100 scale due to operation on a different part of its characteristic curve. (This curve is not quite linear.)

For *n-p-n* transistors, set switch S_4 to the *n-p-n* position and carry out the testing procedure as above.

Diode Testing. With switch S_4 in the *p-n-p* position and switch S_2 open, connect the cathode (bar and red end) of the diode to the collector terminal and the anode to the emitter terminal. The meter should give a full scale deflection, indicating a low forward resistance. Move switch S_4 to the *n-p-n* position (this reverses the voltage on the diode) and the meter should drop to zero, indicating a high back resistance. As this is only a simple check, and not a measurement, it may be advisable to compare the results with a diode of the same type which is known to function correctly. In this test, the push button S_1 is not used.

CHAPTER 20

OPERATING TECHNIQUE AND STATION LAYOUT

THE basic principles for attaining a good operating technique are equally applicable to both morse and telephony operation, and can be summarised quite briefly—judgment and courtesy.

Attaining a Standard

While studying to pass the Morse test the newly licensed amateur will probably have spent a considerable time listening on the various amateur bands and will have noticed the widely differing standards of operating technique to be heard. The good operator is not necessarily the man who can send fast, but the man whose sending is easy to read. Automatic Morse, derived from an automatic keyer which delivers perfectly formed characters, is the easiest to read, and therefore the amateur should always strive to send Morse that sounds as if it were being transmitted by an automatic sender. The ability to listen to one's own transmission is essential if a good style is to be achieved and maintained: this practice is sometimes known as *side-tone*.

Similarly, in voice operation care should be taken to speak as clearly as possible; this includes speaking slowly and choosing simple " basic " words when the other operator is obviously not fluent in the language being used.

An amateur should never send c.w. at a faster rate than he knows he can send perfectly, because a very quick deterioration results from even slightly exceeding his maximum speed capability. The best speed is the maximum speed at which the other operator can receive the whole of the message being transmitted. It is generally a good principle to send at the speed used by the station being worked.

DX Operating

When trying to work DX stations the amateur should maintain a close watching brief over the band. He will usually find it preferable to call specific stations rather than to rely on CQ calls, but if he decides to make a CQ call he should first listen on the particular frequency to ensure that it is clear of interference and that by sending out a call on it he will not be interfering with any other transmission.

CQ calls should be short and frequently interspersed with the call-sign. The following example may be taken as the approximate optimum length of a CQ call:

cq cq cq de g2xyz g2xyz cq cq cq de g2xyz g2xyz cq cq cq de g2xyz g2xyz ar k

If, after the first CQ call, no station is heard replying, another CQ may be transmitted, but the procedure of first listening on the frequency to ensure freedom from interference should again be followed. It is better to make several short CQ calls with listening periods in between than

one over-long call, for not only is the risk of interference thereby diminished but the chances of effecting a contact are considerably increased. Many possible contacts have been lost because the other station tired of listening to a seemingly never ending CQ call and listened instead for a station the length of whose call did not require so much patience.

Similarly, when answering a CQ call, the length of the transmission should be kept to a minimum and interspersed with frequent listening periods.

When a rare DX station is heard there will usually be a number of other stations who are also eager to get into contact with him. Obviously the station with the most effective transmitter and aerial system stands a good chance of being heard by the DX station by virtue of his stronger-than-average signal, but medium-powered stations using quite simple aerial systems, and in the hands of really first-class operators, can often outwit the higher-powered stations whose operators are not quite so accomplished. In fact the method to be followed when a number of stations are calling a DX station depends to a certain extent on the signal being radiated, and the less potent the signal the greater is the need for highly skilled operating. The operator of a high-power station with a high-gain beam can often raise a wanted station by the mere fact that his signal is stronger than the others, and he can call the station on whatever frequency he chooses with a reasonable chance of his call being heard. However, very few amateurs are in this happy position and they must plan their approach more carefully.

The first thing to do is to listen for any indication from the DX station regarding the part of the band he will be searching

Many amateurs favour the console type of operating position. This neat arrangement is at G2HKU.

for calls: he may say that he will tune from a certain frequency upwards, or on so many kilocycles either side of his frequency.

In c.w. operation this indication takes the form " U 10 " (meaning *Transmit on 10 kc/s higher than this frequency*) or "L 10" (if the frequency is to be 10 kc/s lower) or one of the following forms:

QLM I will listen from the low-frequency end of the band up to the middle.

QML . . . . . middle down to the low-frequency end.

QHM . . . . . high-frequency end down to the middle.

QMH . . . . . middle up to the high-frequency end.

If he makes no such indication it is a good idea to give him a short call a few kilocycles off his frequency (so that no interference will ensue), and to keep repeating this call until an answer is received or until he commences a contact with another station. Assuming that a contact with another station is commenced, the next step is to try to hear the station being worked. Then move to the same frequency and give the rare station a short call immediately after the current contact is completed. This may well prove effective as he will obviously have his receiver tuned to the frequency on which the other station was transmitting. If the other station cannot be heard the only alternative is to try short calls at different spots slightly off the frequency each time a contact is completed. By listening to the DX station it is often possible to get some idea of which part of the band he is listening on even if it is not possible to hear any of the stations being worked. To raise a station in the face of strong competition is much more satisfying than to have raised him knowing that no other station was calling: it is a tribute not only to the efficiency of the equipment but also to the competence of the operator.

In no circumstances should a station be called until his current contact is completed, for not only will this fail in its purpose, but will cause confusion and will earn the offending caller the reputation of being a bad operator.

If a rare station is worked on his own frequency it is only common courtesy to move the v.f.o. off that frequency when the contact has been completed so that the channel may remain clear for others.

Advice on the use of the amateur bands will be found in Chapter 12 (*Propagation*).

Helpfulness

A good operator will always be helpful, not only to the newcomer but to any amateur who is in need of co-operation in order to carry out tests on his transmitter or aerials in order to bring them up to the desired performance. In the same way it would be a friendly gesture to inform any operator, whose signals are defective, that his transmission is not as it should be (and possibly violating the licence conditions) and at the same time to offer reports on any adjustments that may appear necessary to cure the faulty transmission.

A good operator will also always give an honest and useful report to the stations he works. He should endeavour to give the sort of reports that he himself would appreciate, remembering that signal strength is not the sole criterion of a good transmission and that the bandwidth occupied by a telephony signal or the keying waveshape of a morse signal is even more important than its strength.

Codes and Abbreviations

A great deal of information can be transmitted in a short time by Morse, even at moderately slow speeds, by operators who make full use of the various codes and abbreviations. The Q code and the RST code are international, but there are also a number of abbreviations which are extremely useful although they have not been internationally defined and vary in use from station to station. Telephony operators also make use of a number of these abbreviations, but a good telephony operator will generally use the proper word when he knows that it will be understood.

Originally the only code used for reporting on signals was in regard to strength: the loudness was graded in rather arbitrary units in the scale R1–R9. Later when interference became an important factor it was necessary to describe the readability of the signal, since under heavy interference even a strong signal might be only partly readable. Accordingly the strength was indicated by the scale QSA1–QSA5 and at the same time the readability was denoted by the scale QRK1–QRK9. This system was found to be not

Morse Code and Sound Equivalents			
A	di-dah	S	di-di-dit
B	dah-di-di-dit	T	dah
C	dah-di-dah-dit	U	di-di-dah
D	dah-di-dit	V	di-di-di-dah
E	dit	W	di-dah-dah
F	di-di-dah-dit	X	dah-di-di-dah
G	dah-dah-dit	Y	dah-di-dah-dah
H	di-di-di-dit	Z	dah-dah-di-dit
I	di-dit	1	di-dah-dah-dah-dah
J	di-dah-dah-dah	2	di-di-dah-dah-dah
K	dah-di-dah	3	di-di-di-dah-dah
L	di-dah-di-dit	4	di-di-di-di-dah
M	dah-dah	5	di-di-di-di-dit
N	dah-dit	6	dah-di-di-di-dit
O	dah-dah-dah	7	dah-dah-di-di-dit
P	di-dah-dah-dit	8	dah-dah-dah-di-dit
Q	dah-dah-di-dah	9	dah-dah-dah-dah-dit
R	di-dah-dit	0	dah-dah-dah-dah-dah

(0 is sometimes sent as one long dah)

Punctuation
Frequently employed in Amateur Radio

Question Mark	di-di-dah-dah-di-dit
Full Stop	di-dah-di-dah-di-dah
Comma*	dah-dah-di-di-dah-dah

* Often used to indicate exclamation mark.

Procedure Signals

Stroke	dah-di-di-dah-dit
Break sign (=)	dah-di-di-di-dah
End of Message (+ or $\overline{AR}$)	di-dah-di-dah-dit
End of Work ($\overline{VA}$)	di-di-di-dah-di-dah
Wait ($\overline{AS}$)	di-dah-di-di-dit
Preliminary call ($\overline{CT}$)	dah-di-dah-di-dah
Error	di-di-di-di-di-di-dit
Invitation to transmit (K)	dah-di-dah
$\overline{KN}$	dah-di-dah-dah-dit

★   ★   ★

One dah should be equal to three di's (dit's).

The space between parts of the same letter should be equal to one di (dit).

The space between two letters should be equal to three di's (dit's).

The space between two words should be equal to from five to seven di's (dit's).

491

altogether free from confused interpretation, and eventually, when increasing attention was being paid to the tone of c.w. telegraphic signals, another code was evolved. This was the R.S.T. code, indicating *Readability* (1–5), *Strength* (1–9) and *Tone* (1–9). It is now in universal use by c.w. operators and seems to serve most requirements satisfactorily.

Of special importance to good operating is the correct use of the abbreviations used at the end of transmissions and contacts. A proper understanding of these abbreviations is necessary in order to avoid the confusion that can be caused by other stations calling before a contact has been completed. The four terminations of a transmission are $\overline{AR}$, K, $\overline{KN}$ and $\overline{SK}$. $\overline{AR}$ is generally used at the end of a CQ and invites stations to call. K indicates the end of a transmission but not the end of a contact; it does not preclude the possibility of another station joining the contact. $\overline{KN}$ is sent at the end of a transmission to a nominated station and indicates that other stations should not call. $\overline{SK}$ is sent at the end of a contact and implies that the station is prepared to receive other calls. If on the completion of a contact he is going to close down his station he should send $\overline{SK}$ CL.

If a station wants another contact after one has just been finished he should not send QRZ? (which should only be used when a station has been heard calling, but whose identification has not been established) but should first check the frequency and then transmit a CQ call.

THE RST CODE

Readability

R1 Unreadable.
R2 Barely readable, occasional words distinguishable.
R3 Readable with considerable difficulty.
R4 Readable with practically no difficulty.
R5 Perfectly readable.

Strength

S1 Faint signals, barely perceptible.
S2 Very weak signals.
S3 Weak signals.
S4 Fair signals.
S5 Fairly good signals.
S6 Good signals.
S7 Moderately strong signals.
S8 Strong signals.
S9 Extremely strong signals.

Tone

T1 Extremely rough hissing note.
T2 Very rough a.c. note, no trace of musicality.
T3 Rough, low-pitched a.c. note, slightly musical.
T4 Rather rough a.c. note, moderately musical.
T5 Musically modulated note.
T6 Modulated note, slight trace of whistle.
T7 Near d.c. note, smooth ripple.
T8 Good d.c. note, just a trace of ripple.
T9 Purest d.c. note.

An "X" is added after the appropriate T number if the transmission appears to be crystal controlled.

Phonetic Alphabet

A	Alfa	N	November
B	Bravo	O	Oscar
C	Charlie	P	Papa
D	Delta	Q	Quebec
E	Echo	R	Romeo
F	Foxtrot	S	Sierra
G	Golf	T	Tango
H	Hotel	U	Uniform
I	India	V	Victor
J	Juliet	W	Whiskey
K	Kilo	X	X-ray
L	Lima	Y	Yankee
M	Mike	Z	Zulu

Note.—Amateurs are not restricted to any particular phonetic letters. They should, however, be conversant with the above which are now regularized for world-wide use. (I.T.U. Regulations, Geneva, 1959).

When operating on telephony care should be taken to ensure that transmissions are kept short and that the station call sign is given at frequent intervals: this is obligatory under the terms of the transmitting licence. Telephony operators should avoid the use of facetious or misleading phonetic words when spelling out proper nouns.

Keeping a Log

The Post Office transmitting licence stipulates that every amateur must keep an accurate log book containing details of all transmissions emanating from his station. Such details must include the date and time of commencement of all transmissions, the frequency used, and the call-signs and times of starting and finishing contacts with other stations. These entries, which must be made in a properly bound book (not a loose-leaf book), should always state the time in G.M.T.

Suitable log books complying with all these requirements are readily available, and may be purchased through R.S.G.B. Headquarters.

Power

The Post Office transmitting licence stipulates the maximum power input permissible on the various amateur bands. On the majority of bands this is 150 watts. Ideally, the maximum power that should be used is the lowest that will ensure satisfactory reception by the other station, and except where the transmitter is designed only for low power it is desirable to have some easy means for reducing power whenever conditions permit. This helps to reduce any interference caused to other stations.

STATION LAYOUT

Before commencing to build even the first piece of equipment it is desirable to have some idea of the ultimate layout of the completed station, for the physical size of the various units will, to some extent, depend on whether a table-top, bureau-bookcase, cupboard, rack-and-panel or console assembly will be used, and this in turn will depend on the amount of space that can be devoted to the station.

Choosing a Site

Amateur stations have been set up in many different places in and around the home, the location chosen depending on domestic circumstances, the accommodation available and the operator's ambitions. Ideally the best arrangement is for an entire room to be devoted to the station, and the small bedroom that is generally found in the average three- or four-bedroomed house is the obvious choice. Not only does such accommodation provide the maximum comfort and quietness for operating, but also affords complete safety from danger to other members of the family. However, there are other quite suitable places in the home.

Very efficient installations have been set up in the cupboard under the staircase, built into a bureau or cupboard in a downstairs room, or in a shed in the garden. All these places suffer from some drawback that does not exist for the lucky person who can devote a whole room to his station. The site under the staircase will inevitably be small, dark and difficult to ventilate, and the station in the downstairs room shared with other members of the family will often be noisy, while the shed in the garden may be too cold and damp in winter and too hot in summer, besides being less accessible. The choice must be made by each individual, preferably in consultation with the rest of the family, after weighing up the pros and cons of each possible alternative.

Presuming that a separate room is available, even if it contains a bed and other furniture, the aim must be to arrange the equipment in such a way that operating, even

An excellent example of the table-top station—this is G4ZU.

over long periods, is a pleasure and so that the maximum efficiency is obtained.

Arranging the Equipment

Two typical arrangements of the basic equipment that goes to make up the average station are shown in **Fig. 1** but there are, of course, many other ways of assembling the various items. It should, however, be borne in mind that the focal point of the station is the receiving position. One important feature of this is the operator's chair, which should be as comfortable as possible, and from the operating position all the main controls should be within easy reach and all meters clearly in view.

The position of the transmitter should be such that the connection of aerial feeders can be made without introducing too many bends, and that in the case of tuned feeders they should be spaced as far as possible from all solid objects.

The morse key is normally on the right-hand side of the desk or table but some operators have their own special preferences. Whatever position is chosen it should be the one that affords the greatest comfort during periods of sustained operation.

For telephony working the microphone can be located in any convenient position on the desk. Some amateurs like to mount it on an adjustable floor stand.

A good flat surface with an area large enough to accommodate the key, microphone, log, scribbling pad and large ashtray is essential for comfortable operating.

Station Wiring

The care that has gone into the construction of the individual items of equipment should be continued when linking them up. Connecting cables should be short and concealed wherever possible. It is a good idea to use connecting leads of different colours, since not only does this facilitate rapid servicing but it is also a useful safety precaution. Another point that should be watched where several plugs and sockets are used for carrying different voltages on one chassis is never to use identical components, because it is easy to make a mistake and put the wrong plug into the socket. Here again colour coding of the leads is helpful.

The methodical amateur will not need to be told that circuit diagrams of the station equipment should always be readily available, as it is an obvious aid to rapid and efficient

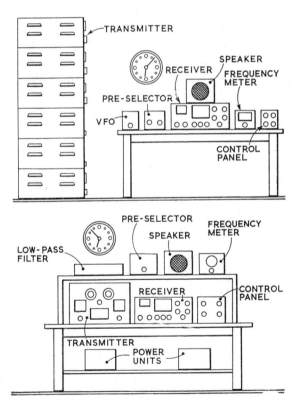

Fig. 1. Two alternative arrangements for an amateur station comprising approximately the same equipment. In the assembly where a rack and panel transmitter is used, the v.f.o. is placed on the operating table for convenience, while space is found in the transmitter rack for the low pass filter and sundry small power supplies. In the table-top arrangement the v.f.o. is an integral part of the transmitter.

servicing. Diagrams of all the interconnecting wiring will also be found invaluable.

Insurance

While every amateur will strive to build and maintain his station so that it is completely safe both for himself and for anyone else, there is always the possibility that an accident may occur. A visitor may accidentally receive a severe electric shock, or a mast may fall causing personal injury to a neighbour or damage to his property. Such an occurrence can result in legal action and the awarding of very heavy damages against the person held responsible for the accident. This risk can be insured against, either by an extension to the existing householder's comprehensive policy or by taking out a separate public liability policy if only a fire insurance policy is held. The annual premium will only be a matter of shillings.

Switching Systems

The minimum number of switches should be used to change the equipment from the *send* to the *receive* position, and this is best achieved by the use of relays so that at least single-switch operation is possible. Most communications receivers have a send-receive switch, and there are often terminals at the rear of the chassis, which had a d.c. voltage across them in the *receive* position, suitable for operating a relay. With the switch in the *receive* position and the relay wired up as shown in **Fig. 2,** there will be a voltage on the relay, and this will open-circuit the high-tension leads to the transmitter and modulator and to the aerial change-over relay (if this is wired so that in the *rest* position the aerial is connected to the receiver). When the switch is in the *send* position the relay closes the circuits switching on the transmitter and modulator and energising the aerial relay so that the aerial is connected to the transmitter. A relay suitable for carrying out these functions will draw only a small current, and even if terminals are not provided on the receiver it is a very simple matter to bring a suitable voltage out from the receiver.

If the position where the transmitter is keyed is such that a high voltage is likely to be produced across the terminals of the key a relay should be used. In any case a keying relay

is desirable where the leads from the keyed circuit to the key itself are of any appreciable length.

Break-in keying and voice-operated transmitter control are additional refinements.

SAFETY PRECAUTIONS

Safety is of paramount importance. Every precaution should be taken to ensure that the equipment is perfectly safe, not only for the operator himself but also for the other members of the household. Double-pole switches should

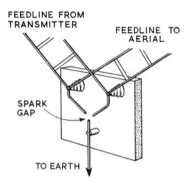

Fig. 3. Lightning Arrester. This arrangement is suitable for all types of twin-feeder systems. The mounting board should be of fireproof insulating material provided that the spacing between the feeder and earth gaps is considerably smaller than the distance between the feeder gaps and the metal plate.

be used for all mains circuits, and interconnected switches should be fitted so that no part of the equipment can have high voltages applied until the valve heaters and low-power stages have first been switched on. This precaution may not only save the life of the operator but it also protects the transmitter against damage.

The whole station should be controlled by a master switch located in a prominent position and all members of the household should be instructed to switch it to the OFF position in case of emergency.

All aerials should be safeguarded against lightning, either by manual switching to a good earth when the station is not

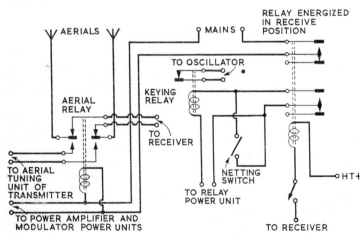

Fig. 2. A method of obtaining single switch control of the station. All relays are shown in the normal " receive " position. The driver stages may also be switched on and off with the power-amplifier and modulator h.t. supplies by using an additional pair of contacts on the receiver-controlled relay. Provided that suitable relays are chosen, the keying and aerial change-over relays may be energised from the same power supply, but where open-wire feeders are switched a mains-energised relay will probably be found more suitable.

being used or by the fitting of lightning arresters. The construction of a suitable spark-gap arrester is illustrated in **Fig. 3.**

Another often overlooked precaution concerns the rating of the mains supply to the station. A 150 watt amateur station fully equipped with ancillary apparatus can draw quite a heavy current from the mains, and before assembling or operating the station it is essential to calculate the current that will be drawn and to ascertain that the existing wiring will carry this current without being overloaded.

Every amateur soon learns to pay healthy respect to h.t. supplies of 350 volts or more and soon develops a sound safety discipline. He is usually well aware of the possible danger. But the Achilles' heel of many amateur stations and workshops, too often forgotten or disregarded, is the " live " (or more correctly the " line ") lead of the mains supply.

Every year there are over 100 fatalities from electric shock in the U.K. alone, the vast majority from 240 volt supplies. Indeed, there is some evidence to show that because of the different physiological effects, those who find themselves across voltages greater than 1,000 volts have a better chance of recovery than those subjected to severe medium voltage shocks. Even the 32 volt mains supplies in some American farm areas have been known to prove lethal. As the jingle says, " It's volts that jolts, but mils that kills."

Clearly, the real danger from mains supplies is where either the skin resistance is lowered by dampness or perspiration, or where the victim firmly grips an extensive area of " live " metal while in good contact with earth. It is against this second possibility that particular care is necessary in amateur stations.

One hazard is equipment with a mains-connected chassis used under conditions for which it was not intended. *All* modern British television sets and a fair proportion of domestic radio receivers fall into this category: not only all the " a.c./d.c." sets but also—and this is not always appreciated—a goodly proportion of " a.c. only " models. These sets are usually built strictly to comply with the British Standards safety specification (B.S.415) which, among many other precautions, lays down that it should be impossible for a " little finger " to touch any part of the chassis and also insists on double-pole on-off switches. But old radio sets, particularly pre-war models, often do not comply with B.S.415, or may have damaged " card backs " or be used with exposed control spindles of grub screws. If there is any such equipment around *your* shack make sure by checking with a neon bulb, that the exposed parts are not " live " with the on/off switch in both positions (remember that a single-pole switch in a neutral lead will leave the chassis " live " with the set off even if the chassis is connected to " neutral " when the set is on). After checking, fit a *non-reversible* mains plug. It is also well worth while to ensure that all three-pin mains sockets in the shack (and in the house generally) are wired correctly: unfortunately many sockets in our homes are wrongly wired. A three-pin *socket* with the thick " earth " socket on top should have the " neutral " socket on the bottom left, and the " line " socket (i.e., the live one) on the bottom right—these directions are when looking into the socket and must be reversed when looking at the back of a socket for wiring. Correct colour coding of leads in the U.K. is: " *line*," red; " *neutral*," black; " *earth*" brown or green: see **Fig. 4.** The use of modern 13 amp fused plugs is recommended.

An even greater hazard, because seldom anticipated, can arise under " fault conditions " on equipment fitted with a double wound (i.e. isolating) mains transformer, as used in the vast majority of amateur receivers and transmitters. It is by no means unknown for the primary winding to short-circuit to the screening plate between primary and secondary, the core or to one of the secondary windings, so that the chassis of the equipment becomes " live." Such equipment will often continue to operate quite normally and can thus represent a real danger over a considerable period. The best safeguard against this is to ensure that the shield between the primary and the other windings, the core and the chassis are all effectively earthed. The earth connection *must* be of sufficiently low resistance to cause the supply fuses (which should always be the minimum amperage practicable) to blow. It is no use having a 50 ohm resistance to earth and a 10 amp fuse—if this is the case the size of the electricity bills may be surprising, but the hazard is quite likely to remain undetected.

Another potential danger is the electric tool which has faulted and which has a " live " outer casing. This can happen, for example, with soldering irons and power drills. The modern domestic drill of reputable make is designed with this danger very much in mind but even so it should be remembered that in industry it is often recommended that such tools should be used only in " earth free " areas—which is very far from being the case in the average amateur shack. Keep a careful eye on the state of all flex cords and investigate immediately if any " tingles " are noticed when using power tools.

Many amateurs fit extra sockets in their stations and the control arrangements may call for quite a lot of semi-

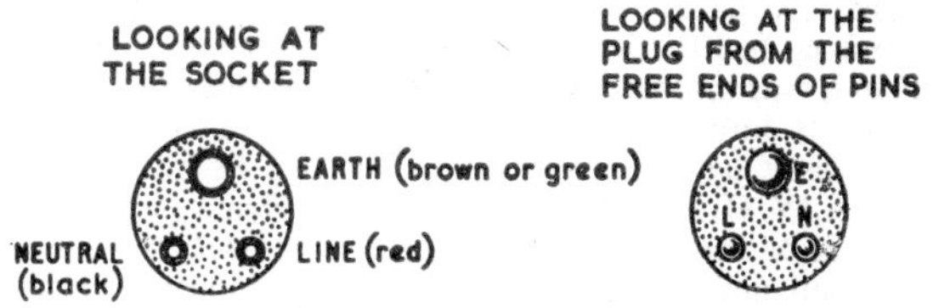

Fig. 4. The correct wiring for three-pin plugs and sockets. To test that a socket is correctly wired, a lamp should light if connected between "L" and "N" or "L" and "E" but not when connected between "N" and "E." A neon bulb will glow when touched against "L."

permanent a.c. wiring and switching. These should always conform with the high standards laid down in the I.E.E. Wiring Regulations (13th edition). These are rather formidable reading for the non-professional but a number of books giving sound advice on modern wiring practice, based on the I.E.E. recommendations, have been published and can often be obtained from local libraries. (For example, *Modern Wiring Practice* by W. E. Steward (Newnes)). If in any doubt get expert advice.

CHAPTER 21

THE R.S.G.B. AND THE RADIO AMATEUR

THE chief objects for which the Radio Society of Great Britain is established are to promote the general advancement of the science and practice of Amateur Radio communication and to encourage the exchange of information and ideas amongst its members. The Society holds meetings for reading and discussing papers bearing on the science of radio, it promotes exhibitions of radio apparatus and it publishes literature bearing on the activities of members including a monthly magazine, the R.S.G.B. BULLETIN.

The Society aims to promote interest in the art of sending and receiving messages to and from Amateur Radio stations of which there are more than 250,000 throughout the world.

History

The Society was founded in 1913, as the London Wireless Club, by a small group of enthusiasts who were interested in the then new science of wireless communication and who were anxious to co-operate with one another in their experiments. One of the Founder Members was Mr. Rene Klein who was in 1961 still living in the house at Hampstead, London, in which the inaugural meeting was held on July 5, 1913. The first few meetings of the London Wireless Club were held at an address in Hatton Garden, London, on premises rented from Gamages of Holborn. Shortly afterwards the name was changed to the Wireless Society of London. In 1922 the Society assumed its present title and in 1926 it was incorporated under the Companies Act.

It was during that era that men famous in wireless circles such as Guglielmo Marconi, Campbell Swinton, Oliver Lodge, W. H. Eccles, Ambrose Fleming, Henry Jackson, and Erskine Murray became actively associated with the Society. Marconi and Fleming were elected Honorary Members; others mentioned occupied the Presidential Chair. These great scientists helped to lay the foundation upon which later generations of members have built up a nation-wide organization.

The period 1921-26 witnessed epoch-making discoveries by amateurs who demonstrated that wavelengths below 100 metres were capable of being used for world-wide communication. The Society played a prominent part in these pioneer achievements and did much to encourage development, by organizing in collaboration with the American Radio Relay League, the first trans-Atlantic tests. In more recent years members of the Society have played an important part in the development of the metre and centimetre wavelengths.

Prior to the 1939-45 war the Society co-operated with the Admiralty and Air Ministry in the formation and organization of the Royal Naval Volunteer (Wireless) Reserve and Royal Air Force Civilian Wireless Reserve. At the outbreak of hostilities many hundreds of members joined the fighting Services, and by reason of their expert radio knowledge were able, with little special training, to undertake duties of great importance.

Following the disastrous floods of January and February, 1953, the Society set up the Radio Amateur Emergency Network which today works in collaboration with the British Red Cross Society, the St. John Ambulance Brigade and the Police.

During the International Geophysical Year (July 1957-December 1958) the Society operated a high power 144 Mc/s beacon station under the call-sign GB3IGY. Transmissions from this station provided valuable data. Many members of the Society took part in I.G.Y. observations, the results of which were passed on to the appropriate scientific bodies.

During 1959 many Society members engaged in a special programme known as International Geophysical Co-operation.

In December 1960 a new beacon transmitter using the call-sign GB3VHF was brought into operation at Wrotham, Kent, by arrangement with the British Broadcasting Corporation. The aerial for GB3VHF is situated high on the B.B.C.'s mast.

Liaison with the G.P.O.

The General Post Office is the licence-issuing authority for the United Kingdom and all licences are issued in the name of H.M. Postmaster General.

From the earliest days of its existence the Society has acted as spokesman for the radio amateurs of the United Kingdom whenever matters affecting their welfare have been under discussion in official circles.

The decision of the Council in September 1939 that the Society should continue to function during the war years meant that when hostilities ceased the R.S.G.B. was in a position to negotiate immediately for the restoration of amateur transmitting facilities. The first post-war licences were in fact issued only a few months after the war had finished. The terms and conditions under which such licences were issued were considerably more favourable than was the case before the war.

Even more liberal licence conditions came into force during 1954. These new conditions allow amateurs to operate portable and/or mobile equipment anywhere in the United Kingdom. As the result of negotiations between the Society and the Post Office, United Kingdom amateurs are now permitted to transmit television, slow scan television and facsimile; to use frequency modulation on all amateur bands; to operate from aboard ship on certain frequencies, and to use RTTY (radio teleprinting).

The Society maintains day-to-day liaison with the Radio Services Department of the G.P.O. with the result that action can often be taken promptly on matters of special importance.

The Society publishes each year an up-to-date directory of the names and addresses of those who hold U.K. amateur transmitting licences. The accuracy of the directory is assured as the result of a decision by the Post Office to allow the Society to make full use of the Official Call-Sign Record. The *R.S.G.B. Amateur Radio Call Book* is published annually, usually in November.

International Co-operation

The Society is a Founder Member of the International Amateur Radio Union and contributes financially to the Region I Division of the I.A.R.U. which embraces most of the I.A.R.U. National Societies in Europe and Africa.

As a Member of the I.A.R.U., the R.S.G.B. has the right to nominate observers to attend International Telecommunication Union Conferences. The R.S.G.B. was represented at the Madrid (1932), Cairo (1938), Atlantic City (1947) and Geneva (1959) Conferences and at the VIIth Plenary Assembly of the International Radio Consultative Committee (London 1953).

Demands upon the frequency spectrum make it increasingly necessary for the Amateur Radio movement to be represented adequately at I.T.U. Conferences; it is at such conferences that world frequency allocation tables are negotiated.

Membership

During recent years the membership of the Society has increased considerably. From a pre-war figure of about 3,500 the number on the register had increased to about 11,000 by the end of 1961. Of this number about 7,000 held a transmitting licence issued by the P.M.G., while another 1,000 held transmitting licences issued by an overseas administration. The remaining members were either enthusiastic short-wave listeners or aspiring to obtain a licence.

Members who do not hold a transmitting licence are issued with a number for identification purposes. Those resident in the British Isles receive British Receiving Station (B.R.S.) numbers. Short wave listeners resident within the British Commonwealth receive B.C.R.S. numbers while those who live outside the Commonwealth receive F.R.S. (Foreign Receiving Stations) numbers. Associates receive an A number.

Membership Conditions

Candidates to be eligible as Corporate Members must be actively engaged in radio research experimentation or communication.

Prospective members under 21 years of age who do not fulfil the foregoing condition but who are interested in radio are eligible for election as Associates but they may not vote upon any matter affecting the management of the Society. Associates do not receive individual notices of meetings. On reaching 21 years of age Associates are required to apply for transfer to the Corporate grade if desirous of retaining membership of the Society. The holder of permission from any official National authority to install, maintain and operate an Amateur Radio transmitting station is not eligible for election as an Associate and if such permission is granted to an Associate he must at once apply for transfer to the Corporate grade.

Every candidate for election as a member shall be proposed by two Corporate members having personal knowledge of him, but if the candidate is not acquainted with Corporate members who will propose him, two references in writing from persons of standing should be submitted, though the Council may, in their discretion, waive this requirement.

Readers who wish to apply for membership are invited to write to the General Secretary, Radio Society of Great Britain, 28 Little Russell Street, London, W.C.1 for the appropriate form. When completed this should be returned to the Society together with a remittance for the initial subscription.

Applications for membership are placed before the Council at its monthly meetings which generally take place during the second or third week of the month. A membership certificate and copy of the current R.S.G.B. BULLETIN are dispatched to new members shortly after their election. Members also receive a lapel badge.

Amateur Radio is the only hobby governed by international treaty. This picture was taken at the Geneva Conference in 1959, at which R.S.G.B representatives were present.

R.S.G.B. AMATEUR RADIO HANDBOOK

Subscription Rates

The current annual subscription rates are as follows:

Home Corporate members	..	..	£1 10s. 0d.
Overseas Corporate members ..	..	..	£1 8s. 0d.
Associates	.. ..	..	15s. 0d.

Subscriptions are due annually on the first day of the month in which a member was elected.

At any time after being a Corporate member for five consecutive years a member may, subject to the approval of the Council, commute all future annual subscriptions by a payment of £20.

Every member admitted into the Society is liable for the payment of his subscription until his name has been removed from the register or, having previously paid all arrears, he has signified to the Secretary in writing his desire to resign.

Privileges of Membership

Membership of the Society carries with it many privileges including participation in field day events, contests, rallies, local meetings and the like.

R.S.G.B. Bulletin

Without doubt the Society's Journal—known as the R.S.G.B. BULLETIN—offers the most important privilege of membership. From its inception in July 1925 the BULLETIN has aimed to provide up-to-date news on every important phase of Amateur Radio activity, and for more than 36 years it has been one of the principle sources of information for amateur enthusiasts in the United Kingdom and abroad. Some of its features have been running for more than 20 years.

The R.S.G.B. BULLETIN is the oldest and most respected British magazine devoted entirely to Amateur Radio and the high standard of its technical and constructional articles has made it internationally recognized as an authoritative source of information.

The BULLETIN has no commercial connection of any other kind other than the friendly relationship which exists with advertisers.

No attempt is made to boost circulation by placing the BULLETIN on bookstalls; it is, and has been from its inception, a private journal for members and it is in being chiefly for keeping them abreast on all matters of general interest. It is neither highbrow nor lowbrow but attempts to please all by pursuing a sound general policy aimed at meeting the wishes of the majority of members.

Articles regularly include descriptions of transmitters, receivers, aerial systems, test and measuring gear, v.h.f., u.h.f. and transistor equipment, new products: in fact, all the information the amateur, whether newcomer or veteran, needs to know.

The Month on the Air and *Four Metres and Down* features provide running commentaries on all matters of interest to those working on the DX and v.h.f./u.h.f. bands. *Technical Topics* is a bi-monthly survey of the latest ideas and circuits.

The BULLETIN is printed on good quality paper and is sent post free to members on or about the 15th of each month. Each issue is well illustrated by diagrams and photographs.

Small advertisements which are published at low rates, enable members to sell and exchange apparatus to advantage. The main advertising pages contain announcements by leading manufacturers.

Readers who wish to examine a recent issue of the BULLETIN may do so by forwarding a remittance for 2s. 6d. to the Society.

R.S.G.B. QSL Bureau

Many years ago the Society realized that a useful service would be rendered to members if their QSL cards addressed to amateurs in other parts of the country or abroad could be collected at one central point and dispatched in batches at regular intervals. Without such a service the active amateur would be compelled to send each card separately at a considerable annual cost. Fortunately National Amateur Radio societies in other parts of the world realized the value of establishing similar QSL Bureaux in their respective countries with the result that today practically every National Society is in a position to accept and dispatch cards in bulk. In many countries a charge is made for the service but the R.S.G.B. has adhered to a policy of offering this service free as a privilege of membership.

A leaflet giving full details of the R.S.G.B. free QSL service is sent to all members on election. Non-members may obtain a copy by sending a stamped and addressed envelope to Society Headquarters.

Contests and Field Days

Society contests and field days are organized with a view to encouraging interest in some definite direction. This is particularly the case with v.h.f. and u.h.f. contests.

National Field Day and Direction Finding events attract much interest each year as do the B.E.R.U. and Telephony Contests. Specialized contests are arranged for Top Band enthusiasts and for those who enjoy low power work.

Valuable trophies are awarded to the winners of the various events while certificates of merit are sent to those who occupy prominent positions in the tables of results.

Log forms for use when submitting entries for R.S.G.B.

RADIO SOCIETY OF GREAT BRITAIN

This is to Certify that

has been elected a Corporate Member of this Society

DATE   PRESIDENT

All new members receive a handsome certificate upon election.

The Empire DX Certificate is the premier DX award of the R.S.G.B. Each certificate is hand printed on vellum. To obtain one, you must prove contact with 50 call areas in the British Commonwealth on 14 Mc/s, and 50 call areas on any other bands.

contests are available from Headquarters by sending a large stamped addressed envelope.

Achievement Certificates

The Society issues a number of certificates in recognition of the achievements of its members in the field of Amateur Radio.

The Empire DX Certificate, introduced by the Society in 1947, is regarded as the world's premier operating award. Each certificate is hand-produced on vellum and a special lapel badge is issued to those who qualify.

Although the W.B.E. (Worked British Empire), B.E.R.T.A. (British Empire Radio Transmission Award) and H.B.E. (Heard British Empire) were introduced more than 20 years ago they have lost none of their popularity.

The DX Listeners' Century Award is available to short wave listeners who have received signals from amateur stations in 100 or more countries.

The " Four Metres and Down " certificates are intended to mark successful v.h.f. and u.h.f. achievements and are available in eight categories.

A copy of the rules governing the award of all R.S.G.B. certificates can be obtained upon application to Society Headquarters.

Slow Morse Transmissions

The Society sponsors the transmission by amateurs throughout the British Isles of Morse practice lessons intended for beginners. The times and frequencies of these transmissions appear regularly in the R.S.G.B. BULLETIN.

Slow Morse practices are also given at meetings organized by various local R.S.G.B. groups and by societies affiliated to the R.S.G.B. These practices alternate with technical instruction designed to provide information for those who aspire to obtain an amateur licence.

THE R.S.G.B. AND THE RADIO AMATEUR

Technical Lectures

Technical lectures are delivered at meetings of the Society held at the Institution of Electrical Engineers, London, and at many local meetings. A list of forthcoming events appears in each issue of the R.S.G.B. BULLETIN.

R.S.G.B. News Bulletin

In order to provide members with topical information, the Society is permitted by the Post Office to broadcast a news bulletin every Sunday morning. The bulletin is transmitted by authorized members under the Society's special call-sign, GB2RS, on about 3,600 kc/s and on frequencies in the 145 Mc/s band.

Organisation

The affairs of the Society are governed by a Council of 18 Corporate members, six of whom are known as Zonal Representatives. Council members serve for a period of three years and are eligible for re-election. The Council meets at least once a month at Society Headquarters.

The day-to-day administration of the Society is undertaken by the General Secretary (who also acts as Editor of the R.S.G.B. BULLETIN and other Society publications) and the Headquarters staff.

In order to expedite the business of the Society the Council constitutes each year a number of Committees. The Committees deal in detail with various aspects of the Society's work and it is their duty to submit recommendations affecting policy to the Council.

In order to provide a link between Headquarters and the home membership a scheme of representation is in operation. The British Isles is divided into 17 Regions each under an elected Regional Representative. County and Town Representatives contribute to the three-tiered form of representation.

Official Regional Meetings are held every few years in each Region while local meetings are held at frequent intervals in towns and cities throughout the country.

Radio Exhibitions

The R.S.G.B. Radio Hobbies Exhibition is held annually in November, usually at the Royal Horticultural Society's Hall in London. Examples of modern amateur and commercially built equipment are on display at the Exhibition which attracts very large attendances.

The Society also participates in the annual National Radio and Television Show organized by Radio Industry Exhibitions Ltd. The Society's stand attracts much attention and provides a meeting place for amateurs who visit the exhibition.

R.S.G.B. Headquarters

The Headquarters of the Society are located at 28 Little Russell Street, London, W.C.1, which is within one minute of the British Museum, and only a few minutes from Holborn and Tottenham Court Road Underground Stations. Several bus routes pass within 50 yards.

Technical publications and other material may be purchased during normal office hours (Monday to Friday, 9.30 a.m. to 5 p.m.).

CHAPTER 22

GENERAL DATA

Bias Resistor

The value of the resistance to be connected in the cathode lead for developing the required bias is—

$$R_c = \frac{E_c}{I_c} \times 1{,}000 \text{ ohms}$$

where E_c = bias voltage required (volts)
I_c = total cathode current (mA)

Capacitance

The capacitance of a parallel-plate capacitor is—

$$C = \frac{0 \cdot 224 \ KA}{d} \text{ picofarads}$$

where K = dielectric constant (air = $1 \cdot 0$)
A = area of dielectric (sq. in.)
d = thickness of dielectric (in.)
If A is expressed in sq. cm. and d in cm.,

$$C = \frac{0 \cdot 0885 \ KA}{d} \text{ picofarads}$$

For multi-plate capacitors, multiply by the number of dielectric thicknesses.

Capacitance of a coaxial cylinder—

$$C = \frac{0 \cdot 242}{\log_{10} \dfrac{r1}{r2}} \text{ picofarads per cm. length}$$

$r1$ = radius of outer cylinder, $r2$ = radius of inner cylinder.

Capacitors in Series or Parallel

The effective capacitance of a number of condensers in *series* is—

$$C = \frac{1}{\dfrac{1}{C_1} + \dfrac{1}{C_2} + \dfrac{1}{C_3} + \text{etc.}}$$

The effective capacitance of a number of condensers in *parallel* is—

$$C = C_1 + C_2 + C_3 + \text{etc.}$$

Characteristic Impedance

The characteristic impedance Z_0 of a feeder or transmission line depends on its cross-sectional dimensions.
(i) Open-wire line:

$$Z_0 = 276 \log_{10} \frac{2 \ D}{d} \text{ ohms}$$

where D = centre-to-centre spacing of wires (in.)
d = wire diameter (in.)
(ii) Coaxial line:

$$Z_0 = \frac{138}{\sqrt{K}} \log_{10} \frac{d_o}{d_i}$$

where K = dielectric constant of insulation between the conductors (e.g. $2 \cdot 3$ for polythene, $1 \cdot 0$ for air)
d_o = inside diameter of outer conductor (in.)
d_i = diameter of inner conductor (in.)

Decibel

The decibel is the unit commonly used for expressing the relationship between two power levels (or between two voltages or two currents). A *decibel* (dB) is one-tenth of a *bel* (B). The number of decibels representing the ratio of two power levels P_1 and P_2 is ten times the common logarithm of the power ratio: thus—

$$\text{the } ratio \ N = 10 \log_{10} \frac{P_2}{P_1} \text{ decibels}$$

If it is required to express *voltage* (or *current*) ratios in this way, they must relate to similar impedance values; i.e. the two different voltages must appear across equal impedances (or the two different currents must flow through equal impedances). Under such conditions the *power* ratio is proportional to the square of the *voltage* (or the *current*) ratio, and hence—

$$N = 20 \log_{10} \frac{V_2}{V_1} \text{ decibels} \qquad N = 20 \log_{10} \frac{I_2}{I_1} \text{ decibels}$$

Dynamic Resistance

In a parallel-tuned circuit at resonance the dynamic resistance is—

$$R_D = \frac{L}{Cr} = Q\omega L = \frac{Q}{\omega C} \text{ ohms}$$

where L = inductance (henrys)
C = capacitance (farads)
r = effective series resistance (ohms)
Q = Q-value of coil
ω = $2\pi \times$ frequency (cycles/sec.)

Frequency—Wavelength—Velocity

The velocity of propagation of a wave is—

$$v = f\lambda \text{ centimetres per second}$$

where f = frequency (cycles per second)
λ = wavelength (centimetres)

For electromagnetic waves in free space the velocity of propagation v is approximately 3×10^{10} cm./sec., and if f is expressed in kilocycles per second and λ in metres—

$$f = \frac{300,000}{\lambda} \text{ kilocycles per second}$$

$$\lambda = \frac{300,000}{f} \text{ metres}$$

Impedance

The impedance of a circuit comprising inductance, capacitance and resistance in series is—

$$Z = \sqrt{R^2 + \left(\omega L - \frac{1}{\omega C} \right)^2}$$

where R = resistance (ohms)
$\omega = 2\pi \times$ frequency (c/s)
L = inductance (henrys)
C = capacitance (farads)

Inductance of a Single-Layer Coil

For coils of ordinary proportions, the inductance is given approximately by—

$$L = \frac{a^2 n^2}{5 (3a + 9b)} \text{ microhenrys} \qquad = \frac{r^2 n^2}{9r + 10l}$$

where a = diameter of coil (in.) r = radius of coil
n = number of turns l = length of coil
b = length of coil (in.)
By rearranging the formula—

$$n = \frac{1}{a} \sqrt{5 L (3a + 9b)}$$

Slug Tuning. The variation in inductance obtainable with adjustable slugs depends on the winding length and the size and composition of the core and no universal correction factor can be given. For coils wound on *Aladdin* type F804 formers and having a winding length of 0·3–0·8 in. a dust-iron core will *increase* the inductance to about twice the air-core value: a brass core will *reduce* the inductance to a minimum of about 0·8 times the air-core value.

Inductances in Series or Parallel

The total effective value of a number of inductances connected in *series* (assuming that there is no mutual coupling) is given by—

$$L = L_1 + L_2 + L_3 + \text{ etc.}$$

If they are connected in *parallel*, the total effective value is—

$$L = \frac{1}{\frac{1}{L_1} + \frac{1}{L_2} + \frac{1}{L_3} + \text{ etc.}}$$

When there is mutual coupling M, the total effective value of two inductances connected in series is—

$$L = L_1 + L_2 + 2 M \text{ (windings aiding)}$$
$$\text{or } L = L_1 + L_2 - 2 M \text{ (windings opposing)}$$

Neon Stabilizer Dropper Resistance

The resistance to be connected in series with a neon stabilizer tube is—

$$R = \frac{E_s - E_r}{I} \times 1,000 \text{ ohms}$$

where E_s = unregulated h.t. supply voltage (volts)
E_r = regulated h.t. supply voltage (volts)
I = maximum permissible current in regulator tube (milliamperes)

Ohm's Law

For a unidirectional current of constant magnitude flowing in a metallic conductor—

$$I = \frac{E}{R} \qquad\qquad E = I R \qquad\qquad R = \frac{E}{I}$$

where I = current (amperes)
E = voltage (volts)
R = resistance (ohms)

Power

In a d.c. circuit the power developed is given by—

$$W = E I = \frac{E^2}{R} = I^2 R \text{ watts}$$

where E = voltage (volts)
I = current (amperes)
R = resistance (ohms)

Q

The Q-value of an inductance is given by—

$$Q = \frac{\omega L}{R}$$

where $\omega = 2\pi \times$ frequency (cycles/sec.)
L = inductance (henrys)
R = effective resistance (ohms)

Reactance

The reactance of an inductance and a capacitance respectively is given by—

$$X_L = \omega L \text{ ohms} \qquad\qquad X_C = \frac{1}{\omega C} \text{ ohms}$$

where $\omega = 2\pi \times$ frequency (cycles/sec.)
L = inductance (henrys)
C = capacitance (farads)
The total reactance of an inductance and a capacitance in series is $X_L - X_C$.

Resistances in Series or Parallel

The effective value of several resistances connected in series is—

$$R = R_1 + R_2 + R_3 + \text{ etc.}$$

When several resistances are connected in parallel the effective total resistance is—

$$R = \cfrac{1}{\cfrac{1}{R_1} + \cfrac{1}{R_2} + \cfrac{1}{R_3} + \text{etc.}}$$

Resonance

The resonant frequency of a tuned circuit is given by—

$$f = \frac{1}{2\pi\sqrt{LC}} \text{ cycles per second}$$

where L = inductance (henrys)
C = capacitance (farads)
If L is in microhenrys (μH) and C is in picofarads (pF = $\mu\mu$F), this formula becomes—

$$f = \frac{10^6}{2\pi\sqrt{LC}} \text{ kilocycles per second}$$

The basic formula can be rearranged thus:

$$L = \frac{1}{4\pi^2 f^2 C} \text{ henrys} \qquad C = \frac{1}{4\pi^2 f^2 L} \text{ farads}$$

Since $2\pi f$ is commonly represented by ω, these expressions can be written as—

$$L = \frac{1}{\omega^2 C} \text{ henrys} \qquad C = \frac{1}{\omega^2 L} \text{ farads}$$

Time Constant

For a combination of inductance and resistance in series the time constant (i.e. the time required for the current to reach $1/\epsilon$ or 63 per cent of its final value) is given by—

$$t = \frac{L}{R} \text{ seconds}$$

where L = inductance (henrys)
R = resistance (ohms)
For a combination of capacitance and resistance in series the time constant (i.e. the time required for the voltage across the capacitance to reach $1/\epsilon$ or 63 per cent of its final value) is given by—

$$t = CR \text{ seconds}$$

where C = capacitance (farads)
R = resistance (ohms)

Transformer Ratios

The ratio of a transformer refers to the ratio of the number of turns in one winding to the number of turns in the other winding. To avoid confusion it is always desirable to state in which sense the ratio is being expressed: e.g. the "primary-to-secondary" ratio n_p/n_s. The turns ratio is related to the impedance ratio thus—

$$\frac{n_p}{n_s} = \sqrt{\frac{Z_p}{Z_s}}$$

where n_p = number of primary turns
n_s = number of secondary turns
Z_p = impedance of primary circuit (ohms)
Z_s = impedance of secondary circuit (ohms)

CONNECTIONS FOR WODEN TYPES U.M.1, U.M.2, U.M.3 & U.M.4 MODULATION TRANSFORMERS

PRIMARY CONNECTIONS FOR MODULATING VALVES				Join 9 and 10 conn. to 7 and 12	Join 9 and 10 conn. to 8 and 12	Join 9 and 10 conn. to 8 and 11	Join 8 and 9 conn. to 7 and 12	Join 7 and 9 conn. to 10 and 12	Join 8 and 9 conn. to 10 and 11	Join 3 and 4 conn. to 1 and 6	Join 3 and 4 conn. to 2 and 6	Join 2 and 3 conn. to 1 and 6	Join 3 and 4 conn. to 2 and 5	Join 1 and 3 conn. to 4 and 6 conn. to 1 and 4	Join 7 and 11 conn. to 7 and 8	Join 1 and 5 conn. to 2 and 6 conn. to 1 and 2
A to A Imp. Ohms	A	CT	A													
2000	2	3– 4	5	8600	6350	4300	3620	2150	1070	—	—	—	—	—	200	—
2000	1	2– 5	6	15700	11400	7900	6650	3920	1950	—	—	—	—	—	350	—
3000	2	3– 4	5	13000	9400	6500	5500	3240	1620	—	—	—	—	—	300	—
3000	1	2– 5	6	23500	17000	11800	10000	5900	2950	—	—	—	—	—	520	—
3800	2	3– 4	5	16400	12000	8200	7000	4100	2050	—	—	—	—	—	380	—
3800	1	2– 5	6	29800	21500	15000	12600	7500	3740	—	—	—	—	—	660	—
4000	2	3– 4	5	17400	12500	8650	7300	4300	2160	—	—	—	—	—	400	—
4000	8	9–10	11	—	—	—	—	—	—	5500	3450	2850	1850	1380	—	250
5000	2	3– 4	5	21600	15700	10800	9150	5400	2700	—	—	—	—	—	500	—
5000	8	9–10	11	—	—	—	—	—	—	7000	4300	3500	2300	1730	—	300
6000	1	3– 4	6	8600	6350	4300	3620	2140	1070	—	—	—	—	—	200	—
6000	8	9–10	11	—	—	—	—	—	—	8300	5150	4250	2750	2180	—	370
6600	1	3– 4	6	9500	7000	4750	4000	2350	1180	—	—	—	—	—	220	—
6600	8	9–10	11	—	—	—	—	—	—	9100	5650	4660	3000	2400	—	405
7000	1	3– 4	6	10000	7300	5050	4280	2500	1250	—	—	—	—	—	230	—
7000	8	9–10	11	—	—	—	—	—	—	9700	6000	5000	3200	2400	—	430
8000	1	3– 4	6	12000	8400	5800	4900	2900	1440	—	—	—	—	—	270	—
8000	8	9–10	11	—	—	—	—	—	—	11000	6900	5650	3700	2760	—	500
9000	1	3– 4	6	13000	9400	6500	5500	3200	1620	—	—	—	—	—	300	—
9000	8	9–10	11	—	—	—	—	—	—	12500	7750	6300	4150	3100	—	550
9000	7	9–10	12	—	—	—	—	—	—	6200	3900	3200	2050	1550	—	275
10000	1	3– 4	6	14400	10500	7200	6100	3600	1800	—	—	—	—	—	330	—
10000	8	9–10	11	—	—	—	—	—	—	14000	8600	7100	4600	3450	—	600
10000	7	9–10	12	—	—	—	—	—	—	6900	4300	3500	2300	1740	—	310
12000	1	3– 4	6	17400	12500	8700	7250	4320	2150	—	—	—	—	—	400	—
12000	7	9–10	12	—	—	—	—	—	—	8300	5150	4250	2750	2070	—	370
14000	7	9–10	12	—	—	—	—	—	—	9700	6000	4900	3200	2440	—	430
16000	7	9–10	12	—	—	—	—	—	—	11000	6900	4600	3700	2789	—	500
18000	7	9–10	12	—	—	—	—	—	—	12500	7750	6300	4150	3140	—	550

UNITED KINGDOM TELEVISION CHANNELS

Channel	Station	Frequency in Mc/s Vision	Frequency in Mc/s Sound	E.R.P. in kW Vision	E.R.P. in kW Sound	Aerial Polarization
1	Crystal Palace	45·0	41·5	200	50	V
	Divis	45·0	41·5	12	3	H
2	Holme Moss	51·75	48·25	100	20	V
	North Hessary Tor	51·75	48·25	15	3	V
	Truleigh Hill and Dover	51·75	48·25	1·5	1	V
	Londonderry	51·75	48·25	1	0·2	H
	Rosemarkie	51·75	48·25	12	3	V
3	Kirk O'Shotts	56·75	53·25	100	20	V
	Norwich	56·75	53·25	15	3	H
	Rowridge	56·75	53·35	12	3	V
	Blaen Plwyf	56·75	53·25	2	0·5	H
4	Sutton Coldfield	61·75	58·25	100	20	V
	Sandal	61·75	58·25	20	5	H
	Meldrum	61·75	58·25	12	3	H
	Folkestone and Les Platons	61·75	58·25	1	0·2	H
5	Wenvoe	66·75	63·25	100	24	V
	Pontop Pike	66·75	63·25	12	2·5	H
	Douglas	66·75	63·25	2	8·5	V
	Orkneys	66·75	63·25	1	0·2	V
6		179·75	176·25			
7		184·75	181·25			
8	Lichfield	189·75	186·25	120	30	V
	Newcastle	189·75	186·25	100	20	H
9	Winterhill	194·75	191·25	200	40	V
	Croydon	194·75	191·25	200	30	V
10	Blackhill	199·75	196·25	300	50	V
	Emley Moor	199·75	196·25	200	40	V
	St. Hillary Down	199·75	196·25	200	40	V
11	Ipswich	204·75	201·25	200	40	H
	Isle of Wight	204·75	201·25	100	20	V
12		209·75	206·25			
13		214·75	211·25			

All stations employ asymmetric sideband operation (+ 1·25 — 3·25 Mc/s).

UNITED KINGDOM V.H.F. (F.M.) BROADCAST CHANNELS

Station	Frequency in Mc/s Home	Frequency in Mc/s Light	Frequency in Mc/s Third	E.R.P in kW
North Hessary Tor ...	92·5	88·1	90·3	60
Sutton Coldfield ...	92·7	88·3	90·5	120
Pontop Pike	92·9	88·5	90·7	60
Blaen Plwyf	93·1	88·7	90·9	60
Meldrum	93·1	88·7	90·9	60
Wrotham	93·5	89·1	91·3	120
Holme Moss	93·7	89·3	91·5	120
Norwich	94·1	89·7	91·9	120
Divis	94·5	90·1	92·3	60
Rowridge	92·9	88·5	90·7	60
Kirk O'Shotts ...	94·3	89·9	92·1	120
Sandal	{92·5 / 94·7}	88·1	90·3	120
Wenvoe	{94·3 / 92·1}	89·9	96·8	120
North Wales	94·0	89·6	91·8	7
Douglas	92·8	89·9	90·6	3
Orkney	93·7	89·3	91·5	6

COMPARISON OF CENTIGRADE AND FAHRENHEIT THERMOMETER SCALES

Centigrade	Fahrenheit	Centigrade	Fahrenheit
− 50	− 58	+ 80	+ 176
− 45	− 49	+ 85	+ 185
− 40	− 40	+ 90	+ 194
− 35	− 31	+ 95	+ 203
− 30	− 22	+ 100	+ 212
− 25	− 13	+ 105	+ 221
− 20	− 4	+ 110	+ 230
− 15	+ 5	+ 115	+ 239
− 10	+ 14	+ 120	+ 248
− 5	+ 23	+ 125	+ 257
0	+ 32	+ 130	+ 266
+ 5	+ 41	+ 135	+ 275
+ 10	+ 50	+ 140	+ 284
+ 15	+ 59	+ 145	+ 293
+ 20	+ 68	+ 150	+ 302
+ 25	+ 77	+ 155	+ 311
+ 30	+ 86	+ 160	+ 320
+ 35	+ 95	+ 165	+ 329
+ 40	+ 104	+ 170	+ 338
+ 45	+ 113	+ 175	+ 347
+ 50	+ 122	+ 180	+ 356
+ 55	+ 131	+ 185	+ 365
+ 60	+ 140	+ 190	+ 374
+ 65	+ 149	+ 195	+ 383
+ 70	+ 158	+ 200	+ 392
+ 75	+ 167		

STANDARD WIRE TABLE

S.w.g.	Diameter (inches)	Current* at 1000A/in.²	Fusing current	Resistance ohms† 1,000 yd.	Turns per inch† Single cotton	Double cotton	Single silk	Double silk	Enamel	Nearest American wire gauge	Weight yards/lb.
12	0·104	8·5	—	2·83	—	8·48	—	—	9·26	10	10
14	0·08	5·03	—	4·78	—	10·7	—	—	12·1	12	17
16	0·064	3·217	166	7·46	14·1	13·3	15	14·7	14·8	14	27
18	0·048	1·81	107	13·27	18·3	17·3	20	19·6	19·7	16	48
20	0·036	1·02	69·9	23·6	24·1	21·7	26·3	25·3	26·1	19	85
22	0·028	0·61	48	39	29·8	26·3	33·3	31·8	33·3	21	140
24	0·022	0·38	33·4	63·2	37	31·3	42·1	40	41·1	23	227
26	0·018	0·254	24·7	94·3	43·5	35·7	50·6	47·6	50·6	25	340
28	0·0148	0·17	18·4	139·5	50·5	40·2	60·4	56·2	61·4	27	503
30	0·0124	0·12	14·1	199·0	57·5	44·7	72	67·1	73·3	28	716
32	0·0108	0·09	11·5	262	63·5	50·5	81·3	75·2	83	29	944
34	0·0092	0·07	—	361	70·5	54·9	93·4	85·5	98	31	1,300
36	0·0076	0·05	6·79	529	86·2	64·1	110	102	116	32	1,905
38	0·006	0·03	—	849	100	71·4	133	121	143	34	3,060
40	0·0048	0·018	3·41	1326	112·5	78·1	159	142	180	36	4,775
42	0·004	0·0126	—	1910	—	—	192	161	217	38	6,880
44	0·0032	0·008	—	2985	—	—	227	185	270	40	10,750
46	0·0024	0·0045	—	5307	—	—	278	217	357	—	—

Notes (*) Current loading may be used up to 2000A/in.²
(†) Some small variations depending on makers.

REACTANCE AND RESONANCE CHART

AUDIO FREQUENCY

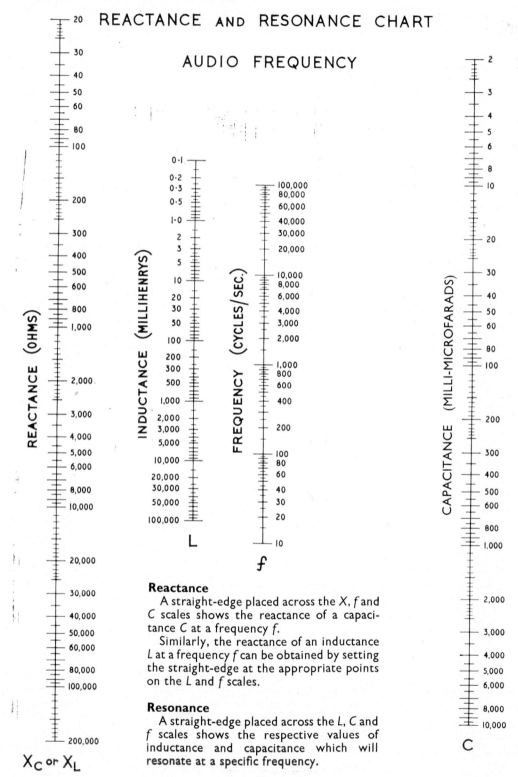

REACTANCE (OHMS)

INDUCTANCE (MILLIHENRYS)

L

FREQUENCY (CYCLES/SEC.)

ƒ

CAPACITANCE (MILLI-MICROFARADS)

X_C or X_L

C

Reactance
A straight-edge placed across the X, ƒ and C scales shows the reactance of a capacitance C at a frequency ƒ.
Similarly, the reactance of an inductance L at a frequency ƒ can be obtained by setting the straight-edge at the appropriate points on the L and ƒ scales.

Resonance
A straight-edge placed across the L, C and ƒ scales shows the respective values of inductance and capacitance which will resonate at a specific frequency.

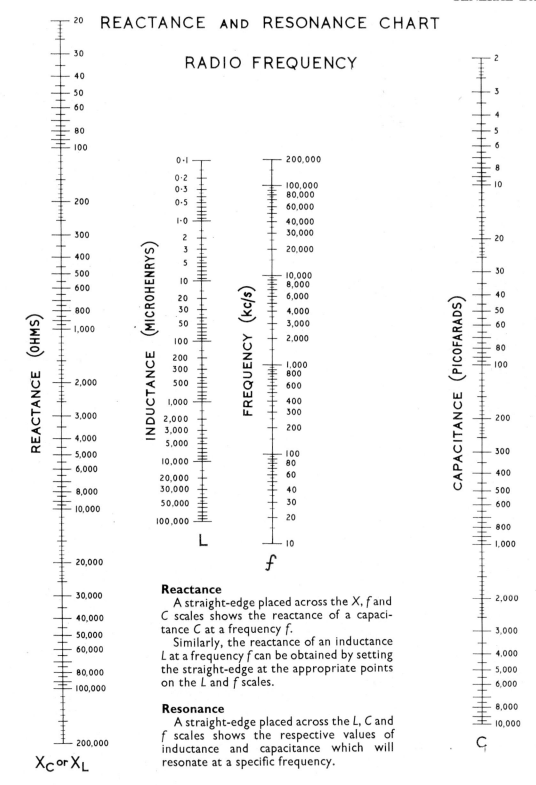

REACTANCE AND RESONANCE CHART

RADIO FREQUENCY

REACTANCE (OHMS)

X_C or X_L

INDUCTANCE (MICROHENRYS)

L

FREQUENCY (kc/s)

f

CAPACITANCE (PICOFARADS)

C

Reactance
A straight-edge placed across the X, f and C scales shows the reactance of a capacitance C at a frequency f.

Similarly, the reactance of an inductance L at a frequency f can be obtained by setting the straight-edge at the appropriate points on the L and f scales.

Resonance
A straight-edge placed across the L, C and f scales shows the respective values of inductance and capacitance which will resonate at a specific frequency.

GREEK ALPHABET

Capital letters	Small letters	Greek name	English equivalent
A	α	*Alpha*	a
B	β	*Beta*	b
Γ	γ	*Gamma*	g
Δ	δ	*Delta*	d
E	ε	*Epsilon*	e
Z	ζ	*Zeta*	z
H	η	*Eta*	é
Θ	θ	*Theta*	th
I	ι	*Iota*	i
K	κ	*Kappa*	k
Λ	λ	*Lambda*	l
M	μ	*Mu*	m
N	ν	*Nu*	n
Ξ	ξ	*Xi*	x
O	o	*Omicron*	ö
Π	π	*Pi*	p
P	ρ	*Rho*	r
Σ	ς	*Sigma*	s
T	τ	*Tau*	t
Υ	υ	*Upsilon*	u
Φ	φ	*Phi*	ph
X	χ	*Chi*	ch
Ψ	ψ	*Psi*	ps
Ω	ω	*Omega*	ō

COMPARATIVE RESISTANCES

Material	Relative resistance
Copper	1·0
German Silver	11·7—18·5
Eureka	29·3
Nichrome	55
Silver	0·94
Aluminium	1·6
Brass	4·4
Nickel	4·3
Iron	6·1

VALVE SOCKET FIXING

Socket Type	Socket Hole Diam. (A)	Fixing Hole Centres (B)	Fixing Hole Size (C)
B4 and B5	1¼	1½	$\frac{5}{32}$ (No. 24 drill)
UX4 and UX5	1¼	1½	$\frac{5}{32}$ (No. 24 drill)
B7G	$\frac{5}{8}$	$\frac{7}{8}$	$\frac{1}{8}$ (No. 32 drill)
B8 (Octal and Loctal) ...	1$\frac{1}{8}$	1¼	$\frac{5}{32}$ (No. 24 drill)
B9A (Noval)	$\frac{3}{4}$	1¼	$\frac{1}{8}$ (No. 32 drill)
B9G	1½	1$\frac{13}{16}$	$\frac{5}{32}$ (No. 24 drill)

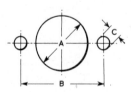

BANDS AVAILABLE

AMATEUR (SOUND) AND (SOUND MOBILE) LICENCES

Note No.	Frequency Bands (in Mc/s)	Classes of Emission	Maximum D.C. Input Power
1	1·8 — 2		10 watts
2	3·5 — 3·8		
—	7·0 — 7·10		
—	14·0 — 14·35		150 watts
—	21·0 — 21·45		
—	28·0 — 29·7		
3	70·2 — 70·4	A1, A2, A3, A3A, F1, F2 and F3	50 watts
1 and 4	144 — 145		
—	145 — 146		
1	420 — 450		
1	1215 — 1325		150 watts
1	2300 — 2450		
1	3400 — 3475		
1	5650 — 5850		
1	10000 — 10500		
1	21000 — 22000		
1	2350 — 2400		25 watts mean power and 2·5 kilowatts peak power.
1	5700 — 5800	P1D, P2D, P2E, P3D and P3E	
1	10050 — 10450		
—	21150 — 21850		

Notes

1. This band is allocated to stations in the Amateur Service on a secondary basis on condition that they shall not cause interference to other services.
2. This band is shared by other services.
3. This band is available to amateurs until further notice provided that frequencies between 70·2—70·3 Mc/s inclusive may not be used on the North West side of the line Firth of Lorne to the Moray Firth.
4. The following spot aeronautical frequencies must be avoided: 144·0, 144·09, 144·18, 144·27, 144·36, 144·45, 144·54, 144·63, 144·72, 144·81 and 144·9 Mc/s.
5. The symbols used to designate the classes of emission have the meanings assigned to them in the Telecommunication Convention.

AMATEUR (TELEVISION) LICENCE

Frequency Bands (in Mc/s)	Classes of Emission (see A below)	Maximum D.C. Input Power (see B below)
*425 — 445		
*1225 — 1290		
*2300 — 2450	A1, A2, A3, A5, F1, F2, F3 and F5	150 watts
*5650 — 5850		
*10000 — 10500		
21000 — 22000		

Notes

* This band is allocated to stations in the Amateur Service on a secondary basis on condition that they shall not cause interference to other services.

A. The symbols used to designate the classes of emission have the meanings assigned to them in the Telecommunication Convention.

B. D.C. input power is the total direct current power input to the anode circuit of the valve(s) energizing the aerial in the fully modulated condition, e.g. peak white in an amplitude modulated positive modulation system.

USEFUL TWIST DRILL SIZES

Twist Drill No.	¼" 0·250"	1 0·228"	9 0·196"	17 0·173"	24 0·152"	32 0·116"	43 0·089"	50 0·070"
Clearance for woodscrew No.	14	12	10	8	6	4	2	0
Clearance for B.A.	0	1	2	3	4	6	8	10
Tapping size for B.A.	—	—	0	1	2	4	6	8

WINDING COILS ON STANDARD FORMERS

Coil formers of the Aladdin type are widely used in modern radio equipment. There is however, always the problem of calculating the number of turns required. For this reason two charts have been prepared by J. Greenwell (G3AEZ) to enable the amateur to calculate quickly and easily the necessary winding data.

Use of Chart I

The use of **Chart I** on page 508 is best illustrated by describing a typical calculation.

Example: It is required to wind a coil on an Aladdin type F804 former which will resonate at 7 Mc/s with a 50pF capacitor.

The method is as follows:

1. Draw a straight line through 50 pF (axis *A*) and 7 Mc/s (axis *B*).
2. Project the line to cut axis *C* and read off the required inductance, which in this case is 10·3μH.
3. Draw a horizontal line through 10·3μH on axis *D* and a vertical line through a reasonable winding length (say 0·5 in.) and determine the most suitable wire gauge to use, i.e., 32 s.w.g.
4. From the 32 s.w.g. curve determine the exact winding length to give an inductance of 10·3μH, i.e., 0·48 in.

The coil required will therefore be close wound with 32 s.w.g. enamelled copper wire and 0·48 in. long.

If desired, the number of turns may be calculated using wire tables (such as **Table I**) from which it will be found that the turns per inch for 32 s.w.g. enamelled copper wire is 83. Hence, a winding 0·48 in. long will consist of (83 × 0·48) = 40 turns.

Table I

The following table, prepared from information provided by the London Electric Wire Company, shows the minimum turns per in. for enamelled copper wire of the gauges most commonly used by amateurs.

Gauge	Turns	Gauge	Turns
20 s.w.g.	26 t.p.i.	32 s.w.g.	82·6 t.p.i.
22 s.w.g.	33 t.p.i.	34 s.w.g.	96·2 t.p.i.
24 s.w.g.	41·5 t.p.i.	36 s.w.g.	116·3 t.p.i.
26 s.w.g.	50·3 t.p.i.	38 s.w.g.	144·9 t.p.i.
28 s.w.g.	61 t.p.i.	30 s.w.g.	178·6 t.p.i.
30 s.w.g.	72·5 t.p.i.	42 s.w.g.	212 t.p.i.

For coils of low inductance, i.e., less than 1μH, it is advisable to space wind rather than close wind with a heavy gauge wire. Curves are, therefore, given in Chart I for pitches of 10, 15 and 20 turns per inch using 26 s.w.g. enamelled copper wire. Other gauges may be used, however, without introducing significant errors.

The values shown in Chart I for Aladdin F804 formers have been calculated for formers without cores. The variation in inductance obtainable with dust-iron or brass cores depends on the winding length and composition of the core material and no simple correction factor may be quoted. However, experiments show that for coils between 0·3 and 0·8 in. long a dust-ron core will give a maximum possible inductance of about twice the " core-less " inductance and a brass core a minimum possible inductance of about 0·8 times the " core-less " inductance. These factors should be borne in mind when designing variable inductances from the charts.

Chart for 0·3 in. Diameter Formers

The inductance required is found from **Chart I** in the same way as for Aladdin F804 formers and the winding details determined from Chart II.

Measurements show that the effect of a screening can on the average coil wound on 0·3 in. diameter formers is to reduce the inductance by about 5 per cent.

When designing very low inductance coils, an allowance of approximately 0·15μH should be made for the leads.

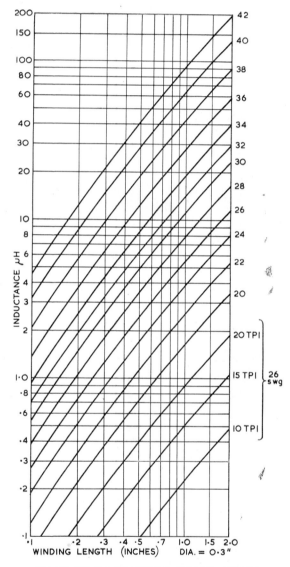

Chart II. Winding data for 0·3 in. diameter coil forms

AUDIO FREQUENCY STANDARD

A piano can be used as an accurate standard of audio frequency. The standard pitch is based on A = 440 cycles per second.

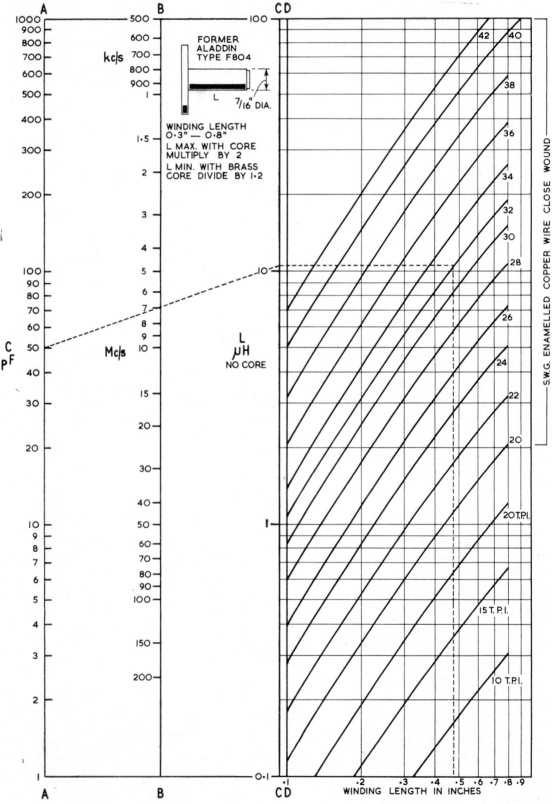

Chart 1 The calculation of inductance required and winding data for Aladdin type F804 coil formers. The dashed lines refer to the worked example.

ADVERTISEMENT SECTION

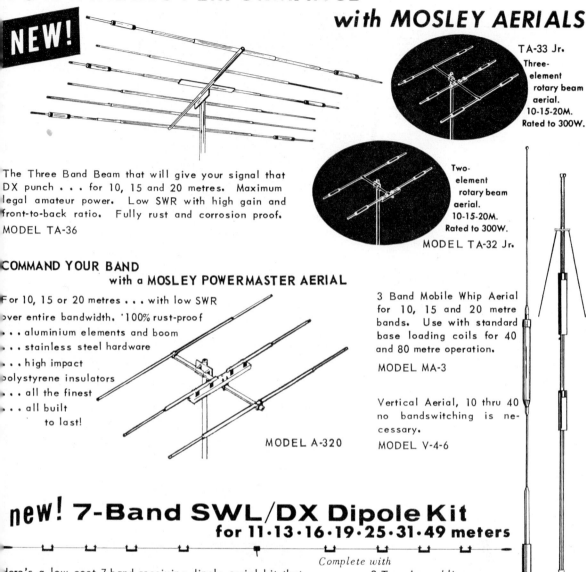

whenever

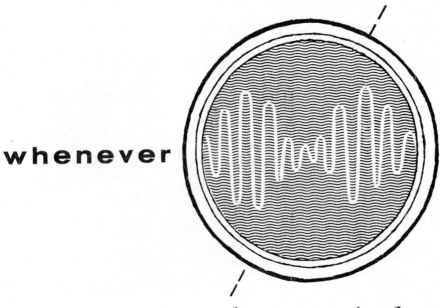

peak performance is the aim . . .

. . . Brimar valves are today's first choice, in every sphere of electronics. Whether the need is for a sub-miniature valve for service in a guided missile — or a pentode for use in a straightforward amplifier — precision-made Brimar valves promise optimum results *always*. Brimar's name for peak performance is well recognised by Britain's leading manufacturers. And this same performance makes Brimar valves first choice for replacement purposes too.

better make it

Brimar Commercial Division

THORN—AEI RADIO VALVES & TUBES LIMITED, ROCHESTER, KENT.   TEL: CHATHAM 44411

512

B·B·C MONITORING SERVICE

uses the BRT.400

BBC's monitoring station at Crowsley Park, near Reading

BRT.400K receiver

The BRT.400 general-purpose communication receiver is widely used by the British Broadcasting Corporation to monitor programmes from all over the world. Outstanding features of this receiver are its simplicity of operation, extreme sensitivity to weak signals and reliability of performance.

513

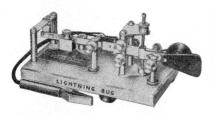

Bring out the best
in your equipment

with a *Grampian* DP4

The Grampian DP4 provides the Radio Amateur with a really sensitive dynamic microphone that will give improved performance out of all proportion to its modest cost. With a uniform frequency range of 50 c/s.—15,000 c/s., it satisfies the most exacting user.

Ideal too, for every method of recording, public address call systems, etc.

Grampian DP4/L (low impedance) microphone complete with connector and 18 ft. screened lead. **£8. 0. 0.** *Medium and high impedance models* **£9. 0. 0.**

A complete range of stands, swivel holders and other accessories is available.

GRAMPIAN REPRODUCERS LTD
Hanworth Trading Estate, Feltham, Middlesex
FELtham 2657

Grampian SOUND EQUIPMENT

Highest quality kit-sets at lowest possible cost

THE British-made range of world-famous HEATHKIT equipment now comprises over 45 models. Their reliability, excellent performance, low price and easy assembly, make them the choice of all those who demand the best.

★ *Amateur Gear*

↗ *Test Instruments*

↗ *Radio*

↗ *Tape Equipment*

↗ *Hi-Fi*

↗ *Cabinets*

A SELECTION FROM OUR MODELS OF SPECIAL INTEREST TO AMATEURS

SINGLE SIDEBAND ADAPTER

Model SB-10U

SB-10U

May be used with most A.M. transmitters. Less than 3w R.F. input power required for 10w output. Operation on 80, 40, 20, 15 and 10m bands on U.S.B., L.S.B. or D.S.B.

AMATEUR TRANSMITTER

Model DX-40U

DX-40U

From 80–10m Power input 75w. C.W., 60w peak controlled carrier phone. Output 40w to aerial. Provision for V.F.O.

GRID-DIP METER

Model GD-1U

GD-1U

Functions as oscillator or absorption wave meter. With plug-in coils for continuous frequency coverage from 1·8 Mc/s to 250 Mc/s.

TRANSISTORISED VERSION Model XGD-1

Similar to GD-1U. Fully transistorised with a frequency range of 1·8 to 45 Mc/s.

AMATEUR TRANSMITTER

Model DX-100U

DX-100U

The world's most popular amateur transmitter. Covers all amateur bands from 160 to 10 metres. Self-contained, with Power Supply, Modulator and V.F.O. 150 watts D.C. input.

VARIABLE FREQUENCY OSCILLATOR

Model VF-1U

VF-1U

Calibrated 160–10m. Fundamentals on 160 and 40 m. **Ideal for our DX-40U and similar transmitters.**

THE "MOHICAN" RECEIVER

Model GC-1U

GC-1U

10 transistors. 4 piezoelectric transfilters. To overcome the problems of alignment, etc., the R.F. "front end" is supplied as a pre-assembled and prealigned unit.

Our comprehensive catalogue and detailed information on any model will be gladly sent free of charge and without obligation, on request.

DAYSTROM LTD.
Dept. R.B.A. GLOUCESTER, England

A member of the Daystrom Group, manufacturers of

THE LARGEST SELLING ELECTRONIC KIT-SETS IN THE WORLD

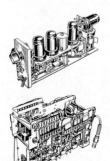

Put Cinch into Circuit
for easy assembly

Every component in the famous CINCH range is precision made for a lifetime of reliable service, and designed for fast, easy assembly. For positive connections at low cost— choose CINCH components.

The CINCH range includes:—
Audio Plugs and Sockets, Barrier Terminal Strips, Valveholders, Multi-Way Connectors, Printed Circuit Components.

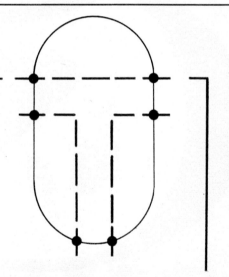

THE MODERN BOOK COMPANY

SHORT WAVE RECEIVERS FOR THE BEGINNER. A Data Pub.: 6/-. *Postage 6d.*

HANDBOOK FOR RADIO OPERATORS. GPO. Working Installations. H.M.S.O. 6/-. *Postage 9d.*

RADIO AMATEUR'S HANDBOOK by A.R.R.L. 1961 edition. 32/6. *Postage 2/-.*

SINGLE SIDEBAND FOR THE RADIO AMATEUR. A.R.R.L. 14/-. *Postage 1/-.*

THE MOBILE MANUAL FOR RADIO AMATEURS. A.R.R.L. 24/-. *Postage 1/-.*

WORLD RADIO TV HANDBOOK, 1961. 16/6. *Postage 1/-.*

VALVE AND TELETUBE MANUAL. No. 8 by Brimar. 6/-. *Postage 9d.*

RADIO VALVE DATA. 7th ed. Compiled by "WW" 6/-. *Postage 9d.*

PRINCIPLES OF SEMICONDUCTORS by M. G. Scroggie. 21/-. *Postage 1/-.*

A TO Z IN AUDIO by G. A. Briggs. 15/6. *Postage 9d.*

RADIO AMATEURS' EXAMINATION MANUAL by R.S.G.B. Pub.: 5/-. *Postage 6d.*

BASIC ELECTRONICS. 6 Parts. 66/-. *Postage 1/6.*

TELECOMMUNICATIONS. Principles and Practice by W. T. Perkins. 21/-. *Postage 9d.*

MODEL RADIO-CONTROL by E. L. Safford. 21/-. *Postage 9d.*

ELEMENTARY TELECOMMUNICATIONS EXAMINATION GUIDE by W. T. Perkins. 17/6. *Postage 9d.*

TELEVISION ENGINEERS' POCKET BOOK by J. P. Hawker. 12/6. *Postage 6d,*

BASIC MATHEMATICS FOR RADIO AND ELECTRONICS by F. M. Colebrook & J. W. Head. 17/6. *Postage 1/-.*

REFERENCE MANUAL OF TRANSISTOR CIRCUITS by Mullard. 12/6. *Postage 1/-.*

TELEVISION SERVICING HANDBOOK by G. W. King. 30/-. *Postage 1/3.*

THE ALL IN ONE TAPE RECORDER BOOK by J. M. Lloyd. 12/-. *Postage 9d.*

WE ARE THE LARGEST STOCKISTS OF BRITISH AND AMERICAN ELECTRONIC BOOKS IN THIS COUNTRY

19-21 PRAED STREET, LONDON, W.2

PAD 4185   Open 6 days 9 a.m. to 6 p.m.   Nearest Station Edgware Road   PAD 2926

526

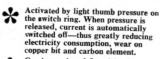

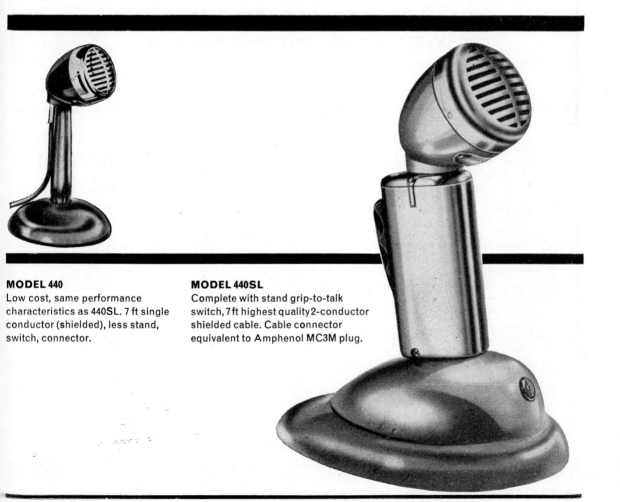

  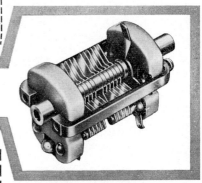

INDEX TO ADVERTISERS

	PAGE		PAGE
Brimar	512	Light Soldering Developments Ltd.	522
British Institute of Engineering Technology ..	530	Lustraphone Ltd.	523
British National Radio School	526	Modern Book Company	525
British Tungsram Radio Works Ltd.	530	Mosley Electronics Ltd.	511
S. G. Brown Ltd.	510	Oliver & Randall Ltd.	528
Carr Fastener Co. Ltd.	521	Olivers Socket Screws Ltd.	526
Daystrom Ltd.	517	E. J. Philpotts Metalworks Ltd.	527
Denco (Clacton) Ltd.	524	The Quartz Crystal Co. Ltd.	526
Electronic & Mechanical Engineering Co. Ltd. ..	527	Jas. Scott	514
Electroniques (Felixstowe) Ltd.	525	" Short Wave Magazine "	518
Enthoven Solders Ltd.	528	Shure Electronics Ltd.	529
General Electric Co. Ltd.	513	Tottenham Radio Valve Co. Ltd.	522
Grampian Reproducers Ltd	516	The Vibroplex Co. Inc.	515
Henry's Radio Ltd.	520	Webb's Radio	519
Jackson Brothers (London) Ltd.	531	Chas. H. Young Ltd.	528

R.S.G.B. Publications

A GUIDE TO AMATEUR RADIO—Ninth Edition.

Provides the newcomer to Amateur Radio with all the basic information he requires on receivers, transmitters and aerials. Also explains how to obtain an amateur transmitting licence. **Price 3/6** (By Post 4/-)

COMMUNICATION RECEIVERS

Brings together in one cover a series of articles originally published in the R.S.G.B. BULLETIN. Consideration is given to the basic requirements, circuit details and component selection. A design for a high performance communication receiver for the amateur is included.

Price 2/6 (By Post 3/-)

THE MORSE CODE FOR RADIO AMATEURS—Second Edition

A carefully graded selection of exercises designed to make learning the Morse Code as simple as possible. **Price 1/6** (By Post 1/9)

THE RADIO AMATEURS' EXAMINATION MANUAL

Designed for those studying for the Radio Amateurs' Examination. Chapters on Licence Requirements and Conditions, Interference, Receivers, Circuits, Calculations, Aerials and Propagation. Covers the syllabus of the City and Guilds of London Institute's Examination.

Price 5/- (By Post 5/6)

R.S.G.B. AMATEUR RADIO CALL BOOK—1962 Edition

The most accurate and comprehensive list of Amateur Radio fixed and mobile stations in the United Kingdom. Also lists stations in the Republic of Ireland. **Price 4/6** (By Post 5/-)

SERVICE VALVE EQUIVALENTS—Second Edition

Contains the commercial equivalents of all the CV numbered valves, cathode ray tubes and semiconductors useful to the amateur. Also lists British Army, Royal Navy, Royal Air Force and U.S. Signal Corps valves. Pocket size. **Price 2/-** (By Post 2/6)

Obtainable from leading booksellers or direct from:

RADIO SOCIETY OF GREAT BRITAIN

28 Little Russell Street, London, W.C.1

Radio Society of Great Britain

(INCORPORATED 1926)

Patron: H.R.H. THE PRINCE PHILIP, DUKE OF EDINBURGH, K.G.

Application for Corporate Membership

To the Secretary,
Radio Society of Great Britain,
New Ruskin House, Little Russell Street,
London, W.C.I.

I hereby apply for election as a Corporate Member of the Society and enclose herewith a remittance for the appropriate amount of my first annual subscription.

I agree that in the event of my election I will abide by and observe the Rules, Regulations and Articles of Association of the Society and that in the event of my resignation from the Society given under my hand in writing, I shall after payment of all arrears which may be due by me at that period, be free from this obligation. I further agree to observe strictly the terms of any licence issued to me by the responsible authorities to operate transmitting or receiving apparatus.

Signed..

PERSONAL DETAILS TO BE COMPLETED BY THE APPLICANT

Surname (BLOCK LETTERS) ....

Christian Names in full (BLOCK LETTERS)..

Address for all correspondence (BLOCK LETTERS) ....

....

Nationality.. Age (if under 21)..

Current Call-sign (if any)..

Details of previous membership (if any)..

DETAILS TO BE COMPLETED BY THE TWO PROPOSERS

I wish to propose..for Corporate Membership.

Proposer's Name (BLOCK LETTERS)..

Address (BLOCK LETTERS) ....

Call-sign (or B.R.S. No.)..

Signed..

I wish to propose..for Corporate Membership.

Proposer's Name (BLOCK LETTERS)..

Address (BLOCK LETTERS) ....

Call-sign (or B.R.S. No.)..

Signed..

FOR OFFICE USE ONLY

Approved by Council ....

B.R.S. Number Issued.. First Subscription paid..

If the applicant is not acquainted with two Corporate Members willing to propose him for election he may submit two suitable references in writing from persons of standing.

THE APPROPRIATE SUBSCRIPTION SHOULD BE REMITTED WITH THE APPLICATION FORM—see page 498.

Index

A

Abacs
  For determining grid tank circuit capacitance .. 183
  For determining anode tank circuit capacitance .. 184
A.C. (Alternating current) 20
  Frequency of 21
  R.M.S. 21
  Resistance 45
Acceptor Circuit 23
Accumulator 10
Acoustics, Basic Principles of 263
Adjacent Channel Selectivity 451
Adler Tubes 62
Aerials, H.F. 29, 352, 391
  Aerial Couplers 368
  Array Factor 374
  Asymmetrical Twin Feed 363
  Attenuation 358
  Beam Aerials 377
  Beamwidth 372
  Broadside Array 372, 377
  Broadside Vertical 380
  Centre-fed Wire 360
  Characteristic Impedance 356
  Clemens Match 384
  Collinear Array 378
  Dipole, Multiband 386
  Directive Properties 371
  Earth Connections 362
  End-fed Wire 361
  End-fire Array 372, 380
  End-fire Effect 377
  Feeding Long Wires 376
  Folded Dipole 365, 366
  Gamma Match 384
  Ground-plane 364
  Half-wave Dipoles .. 355, 360, 382, 398
  Hertzian Aerial 29
  Images 355
  Impedance Matching 356, 365
  Impedance Transformers 366
  Input Impedance 354
  Lazy H 379
  Long Wire Horizontal 375
  Marconi 29, 363, 370
  Measuring Devices 482
  Minibeam 389
  Multiband Couplers 370
  Network Transformers 368
  Parasitic Arrays 377, 381, 382, 388
  Phasing Lines 380
  Polar Diagram 354, 372
  Power Indicators 371

Quad 385
Quarter-wave Transformers 367
Radiation Patterns 372
Radiation Resistance 354
Receiving Aerials 390
Reflection Coefficient 359
Reflectometer S.W.R. Indicator 371, 482
Resonant Aerials 353
Rhombic Aerial 386
Soil, Effect of 374
Sterba Curtain 379
Stub Transformers 367
Tapered Lines 368
Three-band Array 379
Three and Four Element Parasitic Arrays 382
T-Match 384
Transmission Lines and Feeders 355, 359
Tuned Feeders 360
Two Element Array 381
Windom Aerial 362, 363
W8JK End-fire Array 380
Vee Aerial 385
Vertical 364, 374
Voltage Standing Wave Ratio 358
VS1AA 363
Yagi 382, 384
Zepp Aerial 362
Z Match Coupler 370
Aerials, Mobile 429, 430, 431, 432
Aerials, V.H.F. 391
  Angle of Radiation, Polarization 393
  Arrays 398
  Bi-square, The 401
  Bandwidth 392
  Beamwidth 392
  Choice of 407
  Corner Reflector 403
  Feeders for 393, 394
  Front-to-back Ratio 391
  Full-wave Dipoles 401
  Half-wave Dipole, Resonant Length of .. 398
  Impedance Matching 396
  Metal Insulators 395
  Multi-radiator Arrays 393
  Noise 412
  Parabolic Reflector 404
  Reciprocity Theorem 393
  Reflex 404
  Stack for 70 cm, 12 element 406
  Stacked Dipole 401
  Stub Matching 396
  Surface Wave Transmission Curves .. 395
  Trough Reflectors 403
  Yagi Arrays 398, 399, 400, 405

Amateur Bands, A Guide to the 351
Ampere 11
Amplification 31
   Linear, Theory of 316
Amplification Factor 45
   Inner 45
   Outer 45
Amplifiers
   Beam Parametric 62
   Class A, AB, B .. 49, 265, 271, 272, 318, 319, 321
   Class C 176
   Grounded Grid 130
   High Power for 70 cm 240
   I.F., Transistorized for 470 kc/s 74
   Linear .. 318, 319, 320, 321, 322, 325, 326, 327, 328, 330
   Low Power Tripler for 70 cm 232, 234
   Medium Power for 144 Mc/s 230
   Neutralized 50
   Parallel 49
   Parametric 150
   Paraphase 53
   Power 176, 212
   Power Ratings of R.F. Amplifiers 190
   Push-pull 49, 129, 267
   Push-pull Transistorized 72
   R.F. Amplifier, Cascode 129
   R.F. Amplifiers for V.H.F. Receiver .. 128, 152
   R.F. Amplifier for 430 Mc/s 150
   R.F. Power 36
   Series Cascode or Driven Grounded Grid 130
   Speech Amplifiers 265, 270
   Tetrode and Pentode Amplifiers 178
   Transformer Coupled 267
   Triode, R.F. 177
   Valves commonly used in Amplifiers 271
   Voltage Amplifiers 266
   Wallman Cascode 129
Amplitude of A.C. 21
Amplitude Modulation 37, 254
Anode 41
   Anode Bend Detectors 56
   Dissipation 45
   Efficiency and Power Output 190
   Feed, Parallel 174
   Follower 53, 269
   Neutralization 178
   Tank Circuits 184
Aperture or Capture Area 392
Array Factor 374
A T-cut Crystals 33
Atmospheric Noise 413
Atoms 9
Audio Filter 96
Audio Frequencies 96
   A.f. Stages 96
   Reactance and Resonance Charts 504
Aural Discrimination 415
Auroral Reflection 349
Automatic Gain Control Circuit 94
Automatic Gain Control Circuit, Transistorized .. 74

B

Balanced Stages, Twin Pi-network Coupler for .. 188
Balance to Unbalanced Transformer (Balun) 395
   Co-axial Balun 396
Bandpass Filters, Crystal 89
Beam Aerials 377
Beam Tetrodes 43
Beam Parametric Amplifiers 62
Beamwidth 372, 392
Beat Frequency Oscillator (B.F.O.) 93
Bias
   Cathode 42, 181
   Fixed 180
   Grid 42, 180
   Grid Drive Requirements 182
   Grid Resistance 180
   Grid Supplies 442
   Resistor 500
Blanketing.. 453
Break-in 247, 250
Brimistor 445
Broadcast Channels, V.H.F. 503
Broadcast Interference 454
Broadside array 372, 377
Broadside Vertical 380

C

Capacitance 14, 500
   Valve input 46
Capacitors (Condensers) 14, 15, 16
   Air-dielectric 15
   Anode tank, Abac for determining 184
   Ceramic 15
   Coupling 172
   Disc type 217
   Electrolytic 15
   Feed-through 15
   Fixed 16
   Grid Tank, Abac for determining 183
   Mica 15
   Parallel, Capacitors in 16
   Padding 103, 500
   Paper 15
   Ratings of 191
   Reactance of 22
   Series, Capacitors in 16, 500
   Split-stator 16
   Trimmer 103
Carbon Microphone 264
Cathode 41
   Bias 42, 181
   Coupled Phase Splitter 54
   Follower 52, 269
   Interface Impedance 48
   Modulation 260
Cathode Ray Tubes 62
   Oscilloscopes 484, 488
Cell 10
   Primary 10
   Secondary 10
Characteristic Curves 43
Characteristic Impedance 500
Characteristics, Transistor 66

Characteristics of Quartz Crystals 160
Chirp 447
    Causes of 247
    Keying 247, 447
Chokes, R.F. 174
Circuit Noise of V.H.F. Receiver 122
Circuit Q 166
Clamp Valve 182
Clapp Oscillator 70, 169, 194
Class A Operation 48
Class AB1 .. .. 49, 318
Class AB2 .. .. 49, 319, 321
Class B 49, 177
Class C 50, 176
Class C Output Stage 448
Clemens Match 384
Clippers
    Low Level 279
    High Level 280
Clipping, Speech 278, 277
Co-axial
    Balun 396
    Cables 394
    Cavity 144
    Circuits 215
Codes and Abbreviations 491
Coils (Inductance) 491
    Coils and Wavechanging 100
    Dust Iron Core 19
    Ferrites 19
    L.F. and R.F. 19
    Loading Coils for Mobile Aerials 429
    Winding, Guide to 101
Collinear Arrays 378
Colpitts Oscillator 165, 168
Conductance 12
    Conversion 48
    Mutual 45
Conductors 9
Configuration 65, 66
    Common Base 65
    Common Collector 66
    Common Emitter 66
    Transistor 65
Constant, Dielectric 14
Contact Potential 48
Contact Rectification 454
Continuous Commercial Service Rating .. 190
Conversion Conductance or Gain 48
Converters.. 132, 134, 136, 138, 143, 153, 154, 423, 425
Cosmic (Galactic) Noise 413
Coulomb 11
Coupler
    Aerial 368
    Interstage Pi-network 175
    Multiband 370
    Practical Wideband Coupler for Transmitter .. 193
    Z Match 370
Coupling
    Aerial 186
    Bandpass 173
    Capacitive 172
    Circuits for Transistor Stages 68
    Critical 173

    Inductive 26, 172
    Inter-stage 172
    Interstage Pi-network 175
    Link 173
Critical Frequency 346
Critical Wave Angle 346
Cross-modulation 452
Crystals
    Adjusting Frequencies 311
    AT-cut 33
    Filter, Using the Single Crystal 105
    FT241 Crystals.. .. .. .. 90, 308
    Surplus, Suitable for Sideband Filters .. 308
Crystal Oscillators 34, 159, 160, 161, 162, 163, 164, 205, 210
Current 27
    Calculation of Bleeder Current 438
    Magnetizing 27

D

D Layer 344
Decibel 500
Detectors 92
    Anode Bend 56
    Diode 55, 92
    Infinite Impedance 56, 93
    Leaky Grid 55
    Product or Heterodyne 93, 331
    Ratio 340
    Regenerative 77, 92
    Super-regenerative 78
    Synchronous 334
Dielectric Constants 14
Diodes 30, 41, 75
    Crystal 63
    Discriminator 340
    Germanium 63
    Junction 64
    Noise 55
    Point-contact 64
    Power 75
    Tunnel 76, 150
    Variable Capacity 76
    Zener 76
    Frequency Changer 57
Dipole
    Full-wave 401
    Half-wave 398
    Multiband 386
    Stacked 401
Directive Properties of Aerials 371
Dissipation
    Anode 45
    Grid 46
    Screen 46
Discriminator 338
    Diodes 340
    Double Tuned Circuit 339
    Foster-Seeley 340
Double Beam Tube 62
Double Sideband 333
Doubler. Push-pull 175
Drive Power 182
    Grid 51, 182
Driver 274

Dust Iron-core Coils 19
DX Operating 490
Dynamic Resistance 25, 500
Dynamotors 10

E

E Layer 344
Earphone 18
Efficiency, Power Output and Anode 190
Electromagnetism 28
    Deflection 62
    Induction 18
    Spectrum 28
Electron 9
Electron Coupled Oscillator 167
Electron Multipliers 59
Electrostatic Focusing 62
Emission
    Primary 47
    Secondary 48
End-fire Array 372, 380
End-fire Effect 377
Equivalent Noise Resistance 46
External Noise 412

F

F Layer 344
Fading and Fadeouts 29, 350
    Absorption 351
    Interference 350
    Ionosperic Storm 350
    Polarization 351
    Selective 350
    Skip 351
    Solar Radiation 351
Faraday Screen 449
Feedback 32, 72
    Negative 32, 72, 269
    Positive 32
Feed, Parallel Anode 174
Feeders and Feed Systems 393
    Characteristics of Typical R.F. Feeder Cables .. 394
    Long Wire 376
    Open Wire 394
Ferrite Bead 186
Ferrites 19
Field Strength 343
    Meter for Measuring 419, 483
Filters, Crystal 88
    Bandpass 89
Filter, System for Sideband Attenuation 307
    Half-lattice 89, 307
    High Frequency 90
    Using the Single 105
Filters 282
    Audio Filter, Low Pass 282, 283, 306
    Audio Frequency 96, 282, 283
    Bridge T. 91
    Capacitor Input 436
    Capacitor Reservoir 436
    Ceramic 91
    Choke Input 437
    Low and High-Pass Filters 446, 457, 458
    Mains 460

Mechanical 90, 299
Power Supplies, Filters for 435
Radio Frequency for Heater Supply 451
Resistance Capacitive 439
Ripple Attenuation, LC and RC Filters 438
Fixed Bias 180
Followers
    Anode 269
    Cathode.. 269
Franklin Oscillator 170
Frequency Modulation (F.M.) 38, 335
    Alignment of F.M. Receivers 340
    Deviation Ratio 335
    Diode Discriminator 340
    Double Tuned Discriminator 339
    F.M. Detector 339
    F.M. Discriminator 338
    F.M. Limiters 339
    F.M. Reception 338
    F.M. Transmitters 336
    Foster-Seeley Discriminator 340
    Modulation Index 335
    Narrow Band F.M. 336
    Principles 335
    Ratio Detector 340
Frequency and Wavelength 28, 500
    Crystal, Varying the Frequency of 163
    Frequency Changers, Diode 57
    Frequency Changers, Multi-grid 58
    Frequency Changers, Pentode 58
    Frequency Changers, Transistorized 73
    Frequency Changers, Triode 57
    Modulation 38
    Modulator, A Simple 338
Frequency Multipliers .. 56, 57, 159, 175, 176, 212
Front-to-back Ratio 391

G

Gain Control Circuit, Automatic Transistorized .. 74
Gamma Match 384
Gated Beam Valves 44
Germanium Crystal Diodes 34, 63
Greek Alphabet 506
Grids 42
    Bias 42, 180, 442
    Capacitance 183
    Dissipation 46
    Driving Power 51, 182
    Grounded 51
    Keying 249
    Leak Detectors 55
    Neutralization 179
    Noise, Induced Grid 47
    Resistance Bias 181
    Tank Circuits, Abac for determining 183
Grounded Grid 51
Ground Wave Propagation 345

H

Half-lattice Crystal Filter 89, 307
Half-wave Dipole, Resonant Lengths of 398
Half-wave Dipole, Tuning and Reactance Chart for .. 382
Harmonic Beats 451

Harmonic Content 49, 448
Harmonic Traps and Filters 449
Hartley Oscillator 126, 165, 168
Helical Aerial 405
Hertzian Aerial 29
Hexode 58
H.F. Aerials 352
H.F. Receivers 77
H.F. Transmitters 159
Hiss and Hum 47

I

Image 451
  Image response 40
  Interference 40
Impedance 23, 28, 45
  Characteristic 500
  Input 46
  Load 45
  Matching 396
Induced Grid Noise 412
Inductance 18, 19
  Mutual 18
  Parallel and Series 20, 501
  Self 18
  Single Layer Coil 501
  Slug Tuning 20
Inductive Coupling 26, 172
Inductive Reactance 22
Infinite Impedance Detector 56
Insulators 9
Interference
  BCI 453
  Contact Rectification 454
  Cross-modulation and Blanketing 451, 453
  I.F. Breakthrough 447
  Keying 447
  Mains Borne 452, 460
  Second Channel or Image Response 40
  Telegraphy 447
  Television 446
  Transmitter Considerations 446, 453
Insurance 494
Intermediate Frequency 451
  Break-through 451
  Choice of I.F. for H.F. Receivers 86
  Regeneration in H.F. Receivers 88
  Selectivity 87
  Transistorized I.F. Amplifier for 470 kc/s 74
Intermittent Commercial and Amateur Service Rating 190
Interstage Pi-network Coupling 175
Ionosphere 344
  Absorption 347
  Propagation 345
  Scatter 349
  Storms 350

J

Johnson Noise 47

K

Keying and Break-in 247
  Filter circuit 249
  Key Clicks and Chirp 247

Keyers Electronic 252
Keying 247
  Cathode.. 248
  Characteristics 247
  Envelopes 247
  Grid Block 249, 449
  H.T. Supply 248
  Methods 248
  Monitors 253
  Power transformer 248
  Relays 248
  Screen Grid 249
  Suppressor Grid 249
Klystrons 61

L

Lazy H and Sterba Curtain 379
Leakage Current, Collector 67
Lecher Lines 467
Lightning Arrester 494
Linear Tuned Circuits 214
Link Coupling 173
Link Neutralization 179
Load Lines 46
Log Keeping 492
Long Wire Horizontal Aerials 375
Low Frequency Oscillations 448
Low Frequency Parasitics 185
Low Pass Filters 459, 460
Lowest Usable High Frequency (L.U.H.F.) 347

M

Magnetrons 61
Magnets
  Electromagnets.. 17
  Permanent 16
Magnetizing Current 27
Magnification Factor (Q) 24
Man-made Noise 412
Masers 150
Maximum Usable Frequency (M.U.F.) 345
Measurements 461
  Absorption Wavemeter 466, 467
  Audio Frequency Oscillator 476
  Band Edge Marker for 144 Mc/s 472
  Cathode Ray Oscilloscope 484
  Crystal Calibrator 468, 472
  Field Strength Meter 419, 483
  Frequency Meter for Amateur Bands 469
  Germanium Diode Noise Generator 489
  Grid Dip Oscillator 419, 473
  Hot-wire Ammeter 463
  Milliammeter 461
  Modulation Monitor, Built-in 486
  Modulation Monitor for Receiver 488
  Monitoring Display Unit 484
  Moving Coil Meters 463
  Moving Iron Meters 463
  Multirange Meter 463
  Ohmmeter 462
  Oscilloscopes, Servicing 486
  Reflectometer, H. F. 482
  R.F. Signal Generator 478

S-meter 95
Thermocouple 463
Valve Noise Generator 479
Valve Voltmeter 464, 465
Voltmeter 461, 463
Wavemeter 466
Metal Insulators 395
Meteor-trail Scatter 350
Microphones 263
Basic Acoustical Principles 263
Capacitor 265
Carbon 264
Crystal 265
Moving Coil 264
Ribbon 265
Transistor Pre-amplifier for 71
Transverse-current 264
Velocity 263
Voltage Output of 265
Miller Effect 46
Minibeam Aerial 389
Mixers 39, 83, 146, 150, 171
Mobile Equipment 417
Aerials for 1·8-28 Mc/s 429, 430
Capacity Hat 430
Converter for 14, 21 and 28 Mc/s 423
Converter, Low Voltage Valve 425
Dipole for 144 Mc/s 431
Halo Aerial 432
Helical Aerials 430
Ignition Interference 417
Loading Coils 429
Noise Limiters 418, 419
Noise Suppression 417
Power Supplies 432
Test Equipment for Mobile Use 419
Transmitter for 1·8-2 Mc/s 421
Transmitter for 28 Mc/s 421
Transmitter-Receiver for 144 Mc/s 425
Modulation 285, 288, 484, 486, 488
Amplitude 254, 256
Anode 38, 256, 258
Cathode.. 260
Choke 257
Clamp 259
Depth 254, 286
Downward 288
Efficiency Systems 258
Frequency 38, 335
Grid 258, 260
Linearity 255
Low Level 262
Monitors 285, 288, 484, 486, 488
Negative Cycle Loading 282
Oscilloscope Patterns 287
Over-modulation 447
Power 255
Screen Grid 259
Series Gate 257, 261
Suppressor Grid 260
Transformer 257, 274, 502
Trapezoidal Pattern Abac 485
Modulators 289, 290, 291
Balanced 294

Beginners' Low Power 289
Design and Construction 272, 275, 276
Diode 298
Driver Stage of 274
Frequency Range 274
High Power 291
Narrow Band Frequency Modulator 337
Simple Frequency Modulator 338
Stage 270
Valves, Typical 273
Variable Reactance Valve 336
Morse Code and Sound Equivalents 491
Multiple Valves 58
Multiband Aerials 386
Multiband Tank Circuits.. 187
Multipliers, Frequency 57, 59, 175, 176
Multiplier (Meter) 461
Muting, Receiver 120, 250
Mutual Conductance 45

N

Narrow Band Frequency Modulator (N.B.F.M.) .. 337
Negative Cycle Loading 282
Negative Feedback 32, 72, 269
Neon Stabilizer Dropper Resistance 501
Neutralized Amplifiers 50
Neutralization 178, 180, 218
Anode 178
Grid 179
Link 179
Push-pull 180
Series-capacitance 179
Noise 408
Aerial Noise 412
Atmospheric 413
Aural Discrimination 415
Cosmic (Galactic) 413
Diodes 55
Effects of Aerial Characteristics on Noise 416
Equivalent 411
Factor, Noise 121, 414
Induced Grid 412
Internal and External 411, 412
Limiters 97, 418, 419
Man-made 412
Nature of 408
Noise Resistance 58, 411
Practical Aspects 415
Radiation Resistance 412
Receiver, Effect of Noise on 409
Suppression 417
Thermal.. 411
Valve Shot Noise 411
White Noise 409
Nuvistors 61, 141, 152

O

Ohms Law.. .. .. 11, 12, 501
Operation 180, 490
Breakin 250
Parallel 178
Push-pull 178
Optimum Load 46
Oscillations, parasitic 185, 447, 448
Low Frequency 447

Oscillators
  Audio, Transistorized   70
  Audio Frequency Oscillator   476
  B.F.O.   93
  Butler Overtone 128, 163, 211
  Carrier Injection   93
  Carrier Insertion Oscillator, Crystal Controlled   ..   332
  Clapp 70, 169
  Colpitts 126, 165, 168
  Crystal 127, 159, 160, 163, 164, 210
  Dollar, Robert   211
  Electron Coupled   167
  Franklin   170
  Grid Dip 420, 473-475
  Harmonic Crystal   163
  Hartley 126, 165, 168
  Kalitron for 144 Mc/s 125, 244
  Mixer Oscillators   171
  Overtone Oscillators 128, 163, 210
  Pierce-Colpitts   161
  Squier 163, 211
  Tesla (Vackar)   169
  Tritet   162
  Variable Frequency 164, 165, 167, 205
Output Power and Anode Efficiency   190
Overmodulation   448

P

Padding Capacitor   103
Parabolic Reflectors   404
Paraphase Amplifier 53, 268
Paraphase Circuits   268
Parallel Amplifiers   49
Parallel Anode Feed   174
Parallel Tuned Circuits   456
Parasitic Arrays 377, 381, 382
Parasitic Oscillations 185, 449
Parasitics
  Ferrite Bead Suppressors   186
  Identification   186
  Low Frequency   185
  V.H.F.   185
Pawsey Stub   395
Peak Inverse Voltage (P.I.V.)   434
Pentagrid   58
Pentode   43
  Amplifier   178
  Frequency Changer   57
P.E.P. (Peak Envelope Power) 209, 294, 321
Phase Difference (A.C.)   21
Phase Inversion   53
Phase-splitter Circuit 53, 268
  Cathode Coupled   268
  Split Load   268
Phasing Lines   380
Pi-network   449
  Coupler   187
  Interstage Coupler   175
  R.F. Choke   207
  Twin Coupler for Balanced Stages   188
Piezoelectric Effect   32
Polar Diagram 354, 372, 391
Polarization   343
  Angle of Radiation   393

Positive Feedback   32
Potentiometer 13, 440
Power   501
Power Amplifiers 36, 176, 189, 230
Power Drive   182
Power Indicators for H.F. Aerials   371
Power Output 46, 190
Power Ratings   190
Power Supplies   433
  Construction of 443, 444
  Transformer Power, Selection of   439
Pre-amplifier 141, 142, 151
Primary Cell   10
Primary Emission   47
Propagation 29, 342
  Auroral Reflection   349
  Critical Frequency   346
  Critical Wave Angle   346
  D Layer   344
  E Layer   344
  F_1 and F_2 Layers   344
  Ground Waves   345
  Ionosphere   345
  Ionospheric Absorption   347
  Lowest Usable High Frequency (L.U.H.F.)   ..   347
  Maximum Usable Frequency (M.U.F.)   ..   347
  Meteor Trail Scatter   350
  Modes of   343
  Refraction   344
  Scatter   349
  Skip Distance   346
  Sporadic E 344, 347
  Sunspots   344
  Tropospheric   348
  Tropospheric Scatter   349
Push-pull
  Amplifier, R.f.   49
  Doubler   175

Q

Q 26, 178, 501
Q Break, High   147
Q Multiplier 91, 112
Quad Aerial   385
Quartz Crystals   32
  AT-cut Crystal   33
  Characteristics of   160
Quarter-wave Lines   398
Quarter-wave Stubs   456

R

R (Resistance) 11, 25, 462
Radio Frequency (R.F.)
  Amplifiers 150, 177, 178, 190
  Chokes or Coils 19, 174, 207
  Reactance and Resonance Chart   505
Radio Waves 344, 352
Radiation Patterns 342, 372
Radiation Resistance   412
Ratings, Capacitor   191
Ratio, Turns   27
Reactance, Capacitive 22, 501
Reactance, Inductive   22
Receivers, H. F.   77
  Advanced Receiver with Tunable I.f.   115

Aerial Coupling in TV Receivers	455
A.F. Stages	96
Alignment	119
Amateur Station	452
Audio Filters	96
Automatic Gain Control	94
Bandpass Crystal Filter	89
Bandwidth	79
Basic Types of	77
Bridge T Filters	91
B.F.O.	93
Carrier Injection Oscillator	93
Ceramic Filters	91
Choice of i.f.	86
Construction	99
Considerations	451
Coil Winding, Guide to	101
Coils and Wavechanging	100
Cross-modulation and Blocking	81
Crystal Filters 88, 89, 90, 105, 307, 332
Diode Detector	92
Double Conversion 86, 113
FT241 Crystals	90
Half-lattice Filters	89
H.F. Oscillators	83
Input Limiter	252
I.F. Amplification	85
I.F. Regeneration	88
I.F. Selectivity	87
Infinite Impedance Detector	93
Maintenance and Fault Finding	106
Mechanical Filters	90
Mixer	83
Muting 120, 250
Noise Limiters 97, 418, 419
Operating	104
Permeability Tuning	101
Power Supplies	98
Product or Heterodyne Detector	93
Q Multiplier 91, 112
Re-alignment	107
Regenerative Detector 77, 92
R.F. Amplifiers	81
Selectivity	79
Sensitivity	79
Shape Factor	80
Sideband, Selectable 78, 106
Signal-to-noise Ratio	79
Smooth Regeneration	104
Spurious Responses 80, 103
Stability	80
Standby Switching	99
Superhet 38, 40, 78, 102, 110
Super-regenerative Detector	78
T.R.F. 77, 108
Tuning Mechanisms	101
Tuning Rate	80
Receivers, V.H.F./U.H.F.	121
Cascode Crystal Controlled Converter for 144 Mc/s	136
Choice of First I.f. 123, 147
Circuit Noise	122
Co-axial Cavities	144
Converters 132, 134, 136, 138, 143, 153, 156
Crystal Oscillator Multiplier Chains	149
Front-end Stages	121
High Q Break	147
Local Oscillator	124
Low Noise Crystal Controlled Converter for 144 Mc/s	134
Masers	150
Mixers 146, 150
Noise Factor	121
Nuvistor Preamplifier	141
Oscillators 125, 126, 127, 148
R.F. Amplifiers	128
R.F. Amplifier, Cascode	129
R.F. Amplifier, Push-pull	129
R.S.G.B. 144 Mc/s Converter	132
Simple 420 Mc/s Converter	153
Transistorized 144 Mc/s Converter	138
Trough Lines	145
Tuned Circuits	144
Valves for V.H.F. Receivers	131
Wallman Cascode Amplifier	129
70 Mc/s Converter	143
420 Mc/s Converter using Cavities	154
1296 Mc/s Converter	156
Receiving Aerials	390
Rectifiers 54, 433, 434
Rectification 31, 433, 452
Reflectometer S.W.R. Indicator 371, 482
Reflex Aerial	404
Refraction of Radio Waves	344
Regeneration	
Detector 77, 92
I.f. Regeneration	88
Smooth	104
Rejector Circuit	24
Resistance-Capacity Coupled Amplifier ..	51
Resistors 13, 102
Bias	500
Comparative Resistances	506
Dropper, Neon Stabilizer	501
Parallel and Series	13
Potential Dividers and Series Dropping ..	440
Series and Parallel	501
Shunt (Meters)	461
Stopper	185
Resonance 23, 502
Curve	25
Rhombic aerial	386
Rhumbatrons	61
Ripple Voltage	436
Root Mean Square (R.M.S.)	21
R.S.G.B.	
Achievement Certificates	499
Bulletin	498
Contests and Field Days	498
Exhibitions	499
G.P.O. Liaison	496
Headquarters	499
History	496
I.A.R.U.	497
Membership	497
News Bulletin	499
Organization	499
QSL Bureau	498
Slow Morse Transmissions	499
Technical Lectures	499

S

S Meters 95
Safety Precautions 494
Screening 450
Screen Dissipation 46
Screen Voltage Supply 191
Second Channel Interference 40
Secondary Cell 10
Selectivity 25
Semiconductors 63
   Crystal Diodes 34, 63, 75
   Junction Diode 64
   Point Contact Diode 64
   Power Diode 75
   Transistors 34, 63, 65
Series Capacitance Neutralization 179
Series and Parallel
   Capacitors 16
   Inductors 20
   Resistors 13
Series Resonance Circuits 456
Series Tuned Trap 449
Shot Noise 46
Sideband, Double 333
Sideband Reception 415
Sideband, Single 293
   Attenuation, Sideband 300
   Audio Filter, Low Pass 306
   Balanced Modulators .. 295, 296, 297, 298, 299, 300
   Carrier Suppression 294
   Communications Efficiency of 294
   Crystal Frequencies 308, 311
   Exciters .. 303, 304, 306, 309, 311, 313, 316
   Frequency Conversion 314
   Generation, Third Method of 312
   Linear Amplification 316
   Linear Amplifiers 317-328
   Linear Amplifiers, Alignment of 328
   Phaseshift Networks, Audio 302
   Phaseshift Networks, Dome 302
   Phaseshift Networks, R.F. 301
   Phaseshift Networks, S.S.B. Junior 302
   Phasing System of Sideband Attenuation .. 301
   Reception of S.s.b. 330, 331
   Two Tone Test 329
   Valves 318
   Voice Control 311
Skin Distance 346
Skin Effect 12
Slug Tuning 20
Smoothing Circuits 435
Soil, Effect of 374
Solar Radiation 350
Solenoid 17
Space Charge 41
Specific Resistance (Resistivity) 11, 12
Spectrum, Electromagnetic 28
Speech Amplifiers 265, 270
Speech Clipping and Filtering 277, 278
Speech Clipping and Volume Compression .. 277
Split-load Phase Inverter 53, 268
Sporadic E Layer Ionization 344, 347
Spurious Responses 103, 451
Squier Overtone Oscillator 163, 211

Standard Frequency Services in the U.K. 476
Standard Wire Table 503
Standing Wave 353, 357
Station Layout 492
Station Wiring 493
Sterba Curtain 379
Stopper Resistances 185
Stub Aerial Matching 396
Stub Tuners 397
Sunspots 344
Surface Wave 395
Susceptance 22
Switching
   Aerial 251
   Standby 99, 251
   Systems 494
Symbols for Electrical Quantities 11

T

T Match 384
Tank Circuit 184
   Anode 184
   Design 182, 184, 212, 214, 215, 216, 448
   Grid 182
   Multiband 187
Tapered Lines 368
Telephony, Adjusting and Monitoring 285
Television Channels 503
Television Receivers, Aerial Coupling Circuits .. 454
Temperature Effects on V.F.O. 165
Tesla (Vackar) Oscillator 169, 170
Tetrode 43
   R.F. Amplifier 178
Three Band Arrays 379, 382
Time Constant 502
Transformers 439
   Ratio 502
Transistors 34, 63, 65
   Common-base Configuration 65
   Common-collector Configuration 66
   Common-emitter Configuration 66
   Junctions, Small-signal Low Frequency Characteristics
     of 66
   Point Contact 65
   V.H.F. 76
Transistor I.F. Amplifier, Neutralized 69, 74
Transistor R.F. Stages 69
Transistor Tester 488
Transistorized Equipment
   Audio Oscillator 70
   Automatic Gain Control Circuit 74
   Clapp Oscillator 70
   Converter for 144 Mc/s 138
   Crystal Marker 472
   Frequency Changer Unit for 1·8-2 Mc/s .. 73
   Microphone Pre-amplifiers 71
   Modulator 427
   Power Output Stages 71
   Precautions when Servicing 70
   Tuner Unit 73
Transmission Line Resonators, Design of 215
Transmitters 35, 159, 210
   Adjustment and Monitoring of Telephony .. 285
   Crystal Oscillators 159, 160, 161

Circuit *Q* 166
Designs 193, 218, 421
Double Sideband 333
Five-band 150 watt 199
Frequency Multiplication 159
Loading Effects 166
Low Power C.w./Phone Transmitter for 1·8/3·5 Mc/s 203
Low Power for 144 Mc/s 227
Metering 193
Mobile for 1·8-2 Mc/s.. 421
Parallel Anode Feed 174
Ratings of 209
R.F. Chokes 174
Simple Phone and C.w. Transmitter for 144 Mc/s.. 222
Three-band 25 watt Output Transmitter for 3·5, 7 and
    14 Mc/s 195
Transmitter with Break-in Facilities for 14, 21 and
    28 Mc/s 205
Tripler for 23 cm 242
15 watt Phone Transmitter for 144 Mc/s .. 225
70 cm Transmitter 231
50 watt Phone and C.W. Transmitter for 70 Mc/s .. 219
Traps 450
Travelling-wave 353
Travelling-wave Valve 61
Triode Amplifier 36, 177
Triode Frequency Changer 57
Triodes 31, 42
Tropospheric Propagation 344, 348
Tropospheric Scatter 344, 349
Trough Line for U.H.F. Receiver 145
Trough Reflector 403
Tuned Feeders 360
Tuned Linear Circuits 214
Tuned R.f. Receiver (T.R.F.) 77
Tuning
    Mechanisms 101
    Permeability 101
Tuning Indicators ("Magic Eye") 59
Turns Ratio 27
TVI, Curing 455
Twin Pi-network Coupler for Balanced Stages 188
Twist-drill Sizes 506
Two-element array 381

U

Ultra-linear Operation 50
Units and Symbols 11

V

Valves 41
    Adler 62
    Beam Deflection 297, 315
    Beam Tetrode 43
    Clamp 182
    Diodes 41, 30
    Disc Seal 60
    Double Beam 62
    Frame Grid 60
    Gated Beam 44
    Hexode 58
    Klystrons 61
    Magnetron 61
    Mixer 39
    Multiple 58

Noise Diode 55
Nuvistor 61
Pentagrid 58
Pentode 43
Rhumbatrons 61
Tetrode 43
Transmitting 60, 213
Travelling-wave 61
Triode 30, 42
Variable-μ valves 45
V.H.F. Valves 131, 152
Valve Socket Fixing 506
Variable Frequency Oscillators (V.F.O.)
    Calibrator Unit 468
    Circuits 167
    Clapp Oscillator, Transistor 70
    Crystal Oscillator, Mixer Type 205
    Designs Recommendations 167
    Electron-coupled 167
    Kalitron 244
    Simple Two-valve Clapp Unit 194
    Temperature Effects 165
    V.F.O. for 144 Mc/s 244
Variable-μ Valves 45
Variable-reactance valve modulator 336
Variometer 20
Varistor 445
Vee Aerial 20
Velocity Microphone 263
Vertical Aerials 374
V.H.F. Aerials 391
V.H.F. Dummy Load for 245
V.H.F. Parasitics 185
V.H.F. Power Amplifiers 212, 230
V.H.F. Receivers 121
V.H.F. Transmitters 210
V.H.F. Tuned Circuits 212
Volt 11
Voltage
    Amplifier 51, 266
    Gain 45
    Multiplier Circuit 443
    Reference Tubes 59
    Stabilizers 59, 440, 442
    Supply 191
    Volume Compression 277, 280

W

Watt 12
Wavelength and Frequency 28, 342, 500
Wavetraps and Filters 456
Wideband Coupler 193, 194
Windom Aerial 362

Y

Yagi Aerial 382, 398
    Five element for 2m 406
    Impedance matching of 384
    Six-over-six skeleton slot for 2m 405
    Skeleton Slot 400
    Typical dimensions for 399

Z

Z Match 370
Zepp Aerial 362